ADVANCES IN ROCK MECHANICS

Volume II, Part A

Reports of Current Research

PROGRÈS EN MÉCANIQUE DES ROCHES

Volume II, Tome A

Les Recherches Actuelle

FORTSCHRITTE IN DER FELSMECHANIK

Band II, Teil A

Berichte Derzeitige Forschung

Proceedings of the Third Congress of the International Society for Rock Mechanics

Comptes Rendu du Troisième Congrès de la Société Internationale de Mécanique des Roches

Sitzungsberichte des Dritten Kongresses der Internationalen Gesellschaft für Felsmechanik

Themes 1–2

Thèmes 1–2

Themen 1–2

Denver, Colorado
September 1–7, 1974

Denver, Colorado
Septembre 1–7, 1974

Denver, Colorado
September 1–7, 1974

U.S. National Committee for Rock Mechanics
National Research Council
National Academy of Sciences / National Academy of Engineering

NATIONAL ACADEMY OF SCIENCES
Washington, D.C. 1974

PUBLISHER'S NOTE

To expedite the appearance of this manuscript in book form, the text has been reproduced directly from the authors' typescript. Use of this format eliminates the considerable time and expense required for detailed text editing and composition in print—processes that sometimes act to delay or prevent publication of significant manuscripts whose specialized nature or currency of content demand prompt publication.

Readers will find the text edited to a satisfactory level of completeness and comprehensibility, although no special effort has been made to achieve the standard of editorial consistency in minor detail that is typical of typeset books issued under our imprint.

National Academy of Sciences
Printing and Publishing Office

International Standard Book Number 0-309-02246-0
Library of Congress Catalog Card Number 74-12773

Available from
Printing and Publishing Office
National Academy of Sciences
2101 Constitution Avenue, N.W.
Washington, D.C. 20418 USA

Printed in the United States of America

FOREWORD

The Council of the International Society for Rock Mechanics, at its meeting during the Second International Congress on Rock Mechanics, held in Belgrade, Yugoslavia, in September 1970, accepted the invitation of the United States National Academy of Sciences and National Academy of Engineering to hold the Third International Congress on Rock Mechanics in the United States. The Congress will convene in Denver, Colorado, September 1-7, 1974, with the U.S. National Committee for Rock Mechanics serving as host committee. The U.S. National Committee's plans for the Congress were reviewed and approved by the ISRM Council at its meeting in October 1971 at Nancy, France.

The objective of the Third Congress is to ascertain on an international scale the advances in rock mechanics during the years since the Second ISRM Congress and to indicate directions for further effort. The success of the Congress depends in large measure upon the extent to which international communication and oral discussion of recent developments in rock mechanics can be stimulated during the one-week meeting. To this end, the Organizing Committee has solicited the help of nearly 30 outstanding authorities from around the world in preparing comprehensive reports on "Recent Advances in Rock Mechanics" for the five major subdivisions of the field that were chosen as themes for the Congress. The state-of-the-art in each theme is covered in a major report be the General Reporter for that theme, followed by four or five supplementary reports by the theme Panelists. These reports are being published as Volume I of the Congress Proceedings.

Volume II of the Proceedings contains approximately 230 papers submitted from all parts of the world. As with Volume I, because of the large amount of material, Volume II is being published in two separately bound parts of approximately equal size. Part A contains the individual papers for Themes 1-2 and Part B contains those for Themes 3-5. In accordance with ISRM statutes, the National Groups within each member country selected the papers for the Congress Proceedings. Papers of authors from countries that do not have National Groups were screened by the Organizing Committee. To keep the size and cost of the proceedings within reasonable bounds, the Organizing Committee suggested national quotas based on the number of papers in the field of rock mechanics published by workers of each country during the past seven years. The quotas were offered as guidelines only, and the Chairmen of the National Groups were invited to submit all papers with significant new findings.

The papers in Volume II have been assembled, first, by the five major themes of the Congress; then, within each theme, by categories that unite papers of similar concepts, methodologies, or applications; and finally, within each category, alphabetically by senior author. There are a total of 24 categories distributed among the five themes as follows:

Theme 1 - Physical Properties of Intact Rock and Rock Masses

(A) Rock Classification and Engineering Application in Relation to Rock Properties, (B) Static or Quasi-Static Deformation and Strength Tests, (C) Shear Testing, (D) Time-Dependent Deformation in Relation to Rock Strength, (E) Cyclic Loading and Fatigue, (F) Dynamic Strength and Elastic Properties and Wave Propagation, and (G) Measuring Devices.

Theme 2 - Tectonophysics

(A) Laboratory Tests and Rock Properties, (B) State of Stress, (C) Geologic Structures and Tectonic Models, and (D) Fluid Flow Effects.

Theme 3 - Surface Workings

(A) Testing and Improvement of Foundation Rock Properties, (B) Slope Stability Analysis and Case Studies, (C) Rock Slides, and (D) Dam Foundation Analysis and Case Studies.

Theme 4 - Underground Openings

(A) Stability of Openings, (B) Subsidence and Other Surface Effects of Underground Extraction, (C) Design of Roof Support and Tunnel Lining, (D) Ground Reinforcement and Grouting, and (E) Case Studies of Tunnels and Mines.

Theme 5 - Fragmentation Systems

(A) Explosive Fragmentation, (B) Mechanical Fragmentation, (C) Novel Fragmentation Methods, and (D) Effect of Rock Properties on Fragmentation.

The Organizing Committee has made every effort to place each paper in the most appropriate category. Where known, the author's desires as to theme assignment have been followed, under the constraint of achieving a reasonably balanced distribution of papers among the themes.

Together, Volumes I and II of the Proceedings serve as a comprehensive statement of current worldwide thinking in rock mechanics. They are being published in advance of the Congress so that participants can arrive fully prepared for discussions. Summaries of papers from Volume II, selected by the General Reporter and Panelists for each theme, will be presented by the authors at Discussion Sessions of the Congress following the Plenary Session for the theme. Special efforts will be made to develop effective international communication through simultaneous translation in the official ISRM languages. Discussions from the floor and other events of the Congress will be recorded and summarized in Volume III of the Proceedings, to be published following the Congress.

It is the hope of the Organizing Committee that its efforts will result in a Congress that will be remembered as a major milestone in the process of fully establishing sound principles of rock mechanics, from which solutions to important practical problems can be derived. The Committee is sincerely grateful to the authors and to many other colleagues in the United States and abroad who, already engaged full-time in other duties, have selflessly devoted many hours to the tasks of writing, translating, and assembling for publication all of the material in these volumes. On behalf of everyone associated with rock mechanics we offer them our sincere thanks.

Thomas C. Atchison

Publications Chairman, Third ISRM Congress

Charles Fairhurst

Chairman, U.S. National Committee for Rock Mechanics, and Program Chairman, Third ISRM Congress

George B. Wallace

Chairman, Organizing Committee, Third ISRM Congress

AVANT PROPOS

Lors de la réunion qu'il a tenue, en septembre, à l'occasion du Deuxième Congres de mécanique des roches, à Belgrade, en Yougoslavie, le Conseil de la Société internationale de mécanique des roches a accepté, comme l'y invitaient la National Academy of Sciences et la National Academy of Engineering des Etats-Unis, de tenir le Troisième Congrès international de mécanique des roches dans ce pays. Le Congrès aura donc lieu à Denver, Etat du Colorado, du ler au 7 septembre 1974; le comité hôte sera le Comité national de mécanique des roches des Etats-Unis. Le Conseil de la SIMR a étudié et approuvé les projets du Comité national des Etats-Unis lors de la réunion qu'il a tenue en octobre 1971 à Nancy, en France.

Le Troisième Congrès se donne pour objectif de faire le point, sur le plan international, des progrès réalisés par la mécanique des roches depuis le Deuxième Congrès de la SIMR et d'indiquer les directions dans lesquelles de nouveaux efforts pourraient être entrepris. La réussite du Congrès dépend, dans une large mesure, des présentations et des échanges de vues qui peuvent avoir lieu, au cours d'une semaine, au sujet des progrès récents de la mécanique des roches. A cette fin, le Comité d'organisation a demandé à une trentaine de spécialistes éminents du monde entier de préparer des rapports détaillés sur le "Progrès récents de la mécanique des roches" dans l'optique des cinq grandes sub-divisions qui ont été retenues comme thèmes du Congrès. Le rapporteur général présente un exposé d'ensemble faisant le point de la situation au sujet de chaque thème; ces exposes sont completes par quatre ou cinq rapports supplémentaires des membres du panel. Tous ces textes sont réunis dans le Volume I des comptes-rendus.

Le Volume II des comptes-rendus contient environ 230 communications soumises par des spécialistes du monde entier. Comme dans le cas du Volume I, la richesse des matériaux publiés exige que le Volume II soit publié en deux tomes de dimensions analogues. Le tome A contient les communications se rapportant aux thèmes 1 et 2, tandis que le tome B renferme les communications qui ont trait aux thèmes 3, 4 et 5. Afin de maintenir le volume et le coût des publications dans des limites raisonnables, le Comité d'organisation a proposé des contingents nationaux qui ont été établis en fonction du nombre d'articles publiés au cours des sept dernières années par les spécialistes de chaque pays. Ces contingents ont été fixés uniquement à titre d'indication; en effet, les Présidents des groupes nationaux ont été invités à soumettre toutes les communications qui présentaient d'importants faits nouveaux.

Les communications du Volume II ont été groupées, d'abord, en fonction des cinq grands thèmes du Congrès puis, dans le cadre de chaque thème, par catégories qui réunissent les présentations qui portent sur des principes, méthodes ou applications analogues; dans le cadre de chaque catégorie, les communications sont présentées par ordre alphabétique d'auteurs. Au total, les cinq thèmes comportent les 24 catégories suivantes:

Thème 1 - Propriétés physiques de la roche intacte et des massifs rocheux

(A) Classement et utilisation technique des roches à la lumière de leurs propriétés; (B) Déformation statique ou quasi-statique et essais de résistance; (C) Essai de cisaillement; (D) La déformation sous le temps en fonction de la résistance des roches; (E) Renversement de charge et d'endurance; (F) Résistance dynamique, propriétés élastiques et propagation d'ondes; et (G) Appareils de mesure.

Thème 2 - Tectonophysique

(A) Essais en laboratoire et propriétés des roches; (B) Etat de contrainte; (C) Structures géologiques et modèles tectoniques; et (D) Effets de l'écoulement du liquide.

Thème 3 - Travaux de surface

(A) Essais et amélioration des propriétés de la roche de fondation; (B) Analyse de la stabilité du talus et études de cas; (C) Glissements de roches; et (D) Analyse des fondations de barrages et études de cas.

Thème 4 - Percées souterraines

(A) Stabilité des percées; (B) Effets d'affaissement et autres effets de surface imputables à l'extraction souterraine; (C) Tracé du soutient de la toiture et du revêtement du tunnel; (D) Renforcement du sol et colmatages; et (E) Etudes de cas relatives aux tunnels et aux mines.

Thème 5 - Systèmes de comminution

(A) Comminution par explosifs; (B) Comminution mécanique; (C) Nouvelles méthodes de comminution; (D) Effet des propriétés des roches sur la comminution.

Le Comité d'organisation a fait de son mieux pour ranger les communications dans la catégorie qui leur correspond. Lorsque les auteurs en ont exprimé le desir, leur communication a été rangée dans telle ou telle catégorie, à condition bien entendu qu'on puisse équilibrer raisonnablement la repartition des présentations entre les divers thèmes.

L'ensemble que constituent les Volumes I et II des comptes-rendus est un exposé detaille de la situation actuelle de la mécanique des roches. Ces ouvrages sont publiés avant le Congrès, de façon à permettre aux participants de se préparer pour les discussions. Dans le cadre de chaque thème, le Rapporteur général et les panélistes demanderont aux auteurs de certaines communications du Volume II d'en présenter un résumé durant les séances de discussions qui suivront la séance plénière consacrée au thème. Grâce a l'interprétation simultanée, un effort tout particulier a été fait pour assurer les bonnes communications internationales. Les questions posées en cours de séance, ainsi que les réponses qui leur seront faites, seront enregistrées et résumées dans un Volume III, publié après le Congrès.

Le Comité d'organisation espère que ses efforts permettront de marquer d'une pierre blanche le Congrès de Denver, dans la longue route qui conduit à la definition de principes solides de mécanique des roches, permettant a leur tour d'arriver à la solution d'importants problèmes d'ordre pratique. Le Comité remercie sincèrement les auteurs et de nombreux autres collègues des Etats-Unis et d'ailleurs qui, malgré leurs multiples occupations, ont sans compter consacré de longues heures à la rédaction, a la traduction et au collationnement de ces volumes. Nous leur offrons nos remerciements les plus sincères au nom de tous ceux qui s'interessent à la mécanique des roches.

Thomas C. Atchison

Président, responsable des publications,
Troisième Congrès de la SIMR

Charles Fairhurst

Président du Comité national U.S. de la mécanique des roches et Président du Comité du programme,
Troisième Congrès de la SIMR

George B. Wallace

Président du Comité d'organisation,
Troisième Congrès de la SIMR

VORWORT

Während des im September 1970 in Belgrad, Jugoslawien stattgefundenen Zweiten Internationalen Kongresses für Gebirgsmechanik akzeptierten die Mitglieder der Internationalen Gesellschaft für Gebirgsmechanik die von der Nationalen Wissenschaftsakademie und der Nationalen Ingenieursakademie der Vereinigten Staaten ausgesprochene Einladung, einen Dritten Internationalen Kongress für Gebirgsmechanik in den Vereinigten Staaten zu halten. Der Kongress wird vom 1.-7. September 1974 in Denver, Colorado einberufen, und zwar wird das U.S. Nationalkomitee für Gebirgsmechanik als Gastkomitee fungieren. Die Pläne des U.S. Nationalkomitees wurden von den ISRM-Mitgliedern anlässlich der im Oktober 1971 in Nancy, Frankreich stattgefundenen Versammlung überprüft und genehmigt.

Das Ziel des Dritten Kongresses ist, nach einem internationalen Massstab die in den seit dem Zweiten ISRM Kongress vergangenen Jahren gemachten Fortschritte auf dem Gebiet der Gebirgsmechanik zu ermitteln und Richtlinien für weitere Bemühungen zu geben. Der Erfolg des Kongresses hängt in grossem Masse davon ab, bis zu welchem Grad während der einwöchigen Zusammenkunft die internationalen Verbindungen und die mündlichen Diskussionen angeregt werden können. Bis zu diesem Zeitpunkt hat das Organisationskomitee nahezu 30 aussenstehende Autoritäten rund um die Welt um Hilfe ersucht, umfassende Berichte für "Moderne Fortschritte der Gebirgsmechanik" für die fünf auf dem Kongress zu behandelnden Themen vorzubereiten. Die in den einzelnen Themen zum Ausdruck gebrachten neuesten Kenntnisse auf dem Gebiet der Gebirgsmechanik wurden von dem Hauptberichterstatter im Hauptbericht ausführlich behandelt. Es folgen vier oder fünf Ergänzungsberichte der Diskussionsteilnehmer. Diese Berichte werden aufgrund von Kongress-Verhandlungen in Band I veröffentlicht.

Der Band II enthält ca. 230 Artikel, die aus allen Teilen der Welt eingereicht wurden. Aufgrund des so umfangreichen Materials wird Band II in zwei separaten Teilen - wie Band I - herausgegeben. Der Teil A enthält die individuellen Artikel für die Themen 1 und 2, und Teil B wird die der Themen 3 bis einschliesslich 5 umfassen.

Alle für den Kongress bestimmten Artikel wurden in Ubereinstimmung mit den ISRM-Satzungen von den Nationalgruppen eines jeden Mitglieds-Landes ausgewählt. Artikel von Autoren, deren Länder keine Nationalgruppe haben, wurden von dem Organisationskomitee bestimmt.

Um die Ausweitung und Kosten der Verhandlungen in angemessenem Rahmen zu halten, wurden von dem Organisationskomitee Nationalquoten vorgeschlagen, die auf allen veröffentlichten Artikeln auf dem Gebiete der Gebirgsmechanik eines jeden Landes innerhalb der letzten sieben Jahre basieren. Diese Quoten wurden nur als Richtlinie offeriert, und die Vorsitzenden der Nationalgruppen wurden gebeten, alle Artikel mit bezeichnenden neuen Erkenntnissen einzureichen.

Alle Artikel im Band II wurden zuerst unter die fünf Hauptthemen des Kongresses zusammengestellt; weiterhin wurden diese innerhalb eines Themas wiederum in die entsprechende Kategorie, welcher die einzelnen Artikel ähnlich sind im Konzept, der Methode und den Anwendungen, unterteilt. Und zum Schluss folgt innerhalb einer jeden Kategorie die alphabetische Unterteilung der Senior-Autoren. Innerhalb der fünf Themen sind insgesamt folgende 24 Kategorien zusammengestellt worden:

Thema 1 - Physikalische Eigenschaften des intakten Felsens und der Felsmassen

(A) Klassifizierung des Felsens und technische Anwendungen in Verbindung mit den Felseigenschaften; (B) Feststehende oder quasi-feststehende Deformierungen und Stärkeversuche; (C) Scherversuche; (D) Zeitabhängige Deformierungen in Verbindung mit der Felsstärke; (E) Zyklische Belastung und Erschöpfung; (F) Dynamische Stärke, elastische Eigenschaften und Wellenverbreitung und (G) Messungsgeräte.

Thema 2 - Tektonophysiks

(A) Laboratoriumsversuche und Felseigenschaften; (B) Spannungszustand; (C) Geologische Strukturen und tektonische Modelle und (D) Flüssigkeitsströmungseffekt.

Thema 3 - Ubertagebau

(A) Versuche und Fortschritte der Grundfelseigenschaften; (B) Stabilitätsanalysen von Neigungen und Fachstudien; (C) Felsgleitungen und (D) Analysen über Dammfundamente und Fachstudien.

Thema 4 - Untertagebau

(A) Stabilität der Öffnungen; (B) Bodensenkungs- und andere Oberflächeneffekte der Untertagebauextraktionen; (C) Entwurf der Dachunterstützung und der Tunnelausmauerung; (D) Untergrundverstärkung und Mörtelausfüllung und (E) Fachstudien über Tunnels und Bergwerksbauten.

Thema 5 - Gesteinszerkleinerung

(A) Explosive Gesteinszerkleinerung; (B) Mechanische Gesteinszerkleinerung; (C) Neueste Gesteinszerkleinerungsmethode und (D) Effekte der Felseigenschaften anlässlich der Gesteinszerkleinerung.

Das Organisationskomitee hat sich den grössten Bemühungen unterzogen, jeden Artikel in die am besten infrage kommende Kategorie einzustufen. Die von den Autoren ausgesprochenen Wünsche wurden berücksichtigt unter der Bedingung, dass einer einigermassen gut balanzierten Zusammenstellung der Artikel innerhalb der Themen nichts im Wege stand.

Zusammengefasst werden die Bände I und II einen umfassenden Überblick der zur Zeit herrschenden weltweiten Auffassung bezüglich der Gebirgsmechanik geben. Diese Bände werden aus dem Grunde vor Eröffnung des Kongresses publiziert, damit alle Teilnehmer bereits gut vorbereitet zu den Diskussionen erscheinen können.

Die von dem Hauptberichterstatter sowie den Referanten der einzelnen Themen auserwählten Zusammenfassungen der Artikel aus dem Band II werden von den Autoren während der Diskussionssitzung repräsentiert werden, die im Anschluss an die Plenarsitzungen stattfinden werden. Damit diese Diskussionen früchtetragend verlaufen, wird man sich besonderen Bemühungen unterziehen, die offiziellen ISRM-Sprachen gleichzeitig, d.h., sofort während der Verhandlungen zu übersetzen. Sitzungsdiskussionen sowie andere von Interesse anbelangte Begebenheiten werden aufgenommen und in einem Band III zusammengefasst. Die Veröffentlichung dieses Bandes wird nach Beendigung des Kongresses erfolgen.

Das Organisationskomitee hofft, dass die oben erwähnten Arrangements an einen Kongress erinnern werden, der mit den Grundstein zur Weiterentwicklung des Verfahrens von unberührten Grundbestandteilen in der Gebirgsmechanik gelegt hat und dass von den in der Praxis auftretenden Schwierigkeiten ein Nutzen gezogen werden kann.

Das Komitee möchte allen Berichterstattern sowie vielen anderen Kollegen sowohl aus den Vereinigten Staaten als auch aus dem Ausland, die, obwohl bereits anderweitig vollauf beschäftigt sind, in grosser Selbstaufopferung mit dem Schreiben, Übersetzen und der Zusammenstellung des gesamten Materials für die Publikation dieser Bände mitgewirkt haben, seinen verbindlichsten Dank aussprechen. Ebenso wird allen anderen Mitarbeitern, die mit der Gebirgsmechanik verbunden sind, herzlichst gedankt.

Thomas C. Atchison

Redaktionsvorsitzender des Dritten Kongresses der IGFM

Carles Fairhurst

Vorsitzender des Nationalkomitees für Felsmechanik in U.S.A. und Programmvorsitzender des Dritten Kongresses der IGFM

George B. Wallace

Vorsitzender des Organisationskomitees des Dritten Kongresses der IGFM

A NOTE OF APPRECIATION

A special expression of appreciation is extended to the United States Bureau of Mines, the major sponsor of the Congress. The Bureau has given very generously of the time and effort of its staff at all levels of the organizational and preparatory activities of the Congress, and has provided a very substantial proportion of the Congress funding.

REMERCIMENTS

On remercie particulièrement le Bureau des Mines des États Unis, qui est le garant principal du Congrès. A chaque niveau de l'organisation et du préparation du Congrès, les membres du Bureau ont contribué très généreusement de leur temps et de leurs efforts, et le Bureau a contribué largement au fonds du Congrès.

ANERKENNUNG

Ganz besonderer Dank sei dem Hauptförderer des Kongresses, United States Bureau of Mines, gewidmet. Das U.S. Bureau of Mines war sehr grosszügig, Personal zur Verfügung zu stellen, welches an der Vorbereitung des Kongresses mitgewirkt hat. Zusätzlich hat das Bureau of Mines dem Kongress einen grossen Teil der Unterstützungsgelder anhand gegeben.

ORGANIZATION OF THE THIRD ISRM CONGRESS
DIE ORGANISATION DES DRITTEN KONGRESSES DER IGFM
ORGANISATION DU TROISIÈME CONGRÈS DE LA SIMR

U.S. ORGANIZING COMMITTEE
COMITÉ D'ORGANISATION AMÉRICAIN
U.S. ORGANISATIONSKOMITEE

Chairman, George B. Wallace
Vice Chairman, William R. Judd
Program, Charles Fairhurst
Publications, Thomas C. Atchison
Field Trips, Richard E. Goodman
Activities, Louis A. Panek
Translations, Kenneth S. Lane
Secretary, Albert N. Bove

TECHNICAL PROGRAM COMMITTEE
COMITÉ DU PROGRAMME TECHNIQUE
TECHNISCHES PROGRAMMKOMITEE

Theme 1 F.D. Patton, Chairman; K.S. Lane, W.R. Wawersik
Theme 2 C.B. Raleigh, Chairman; W.F. Brace, J.W. Handin
Theme 3 D.L. Misterek, Chairman; R.E. Goodman, L.B. Underwood
Theme 4 L.A. Panek, Chairman; J.F.T. Agapito, H.D. Dahl, T.A. Lang
Theme 5 D.E. Fogelson, Chairman; P.F. Gnirk, W.C. Maurer

GENERAL REPORTERS
RAPPORTEURS GÉNÉRAUX
GENERAL-BERICHTERSTATTER

Theme 1 J. Bernaix (France)
Theme 2 A. Nur (U.S.A.)
Theme 3 E. Hoek (U.K.) and P. Londe (France)
Theme 4 M.D.G. Salamon (R.S.A.)
Theme 5 C.H. Johansson (Sweden)

U.S. NATIONAL COMMITTEE FOR ROCK MECHANICS
COMITÉ NATIONAL DE LA MÉCANIQUE DES ROCHES DES ÉTATS-UNIS
NATIONALE KOMITEE FUR FELSMECHANIK IN DEN U.S.

Charles Fairhurst, *Chairman*
George B. Wallace, *Vice Chairman*
Jose F.T. Agapito
William F. Brace
Wayne S. Brown
George B. Clark
Robert A. Cunningham
Edward J. Deklotz
Hugh C. Heard
Earl R. Hoskins
William N. Lucke
Dewayne L. Misterek
C. Barry Raleigh
Robert E. Riecker
Gerald B. Rupert
David T. Snow
Harry Sutcliffe
Albert N. Bove, *Executive Secretary*

ISRM ADVISORY COMMITTEE
COMITÉ CONSEIL DE LA SIMR
IGFM BERATENDES KOMITEE

President, ISRM, Leonard A. Obert
Secretary-General, Ricardo Oliveira
Vice Pres., Asia — B. Aisenstein
Vice Pres., Europe — B. Kujundzic
Vice Pres., North America — D.F. Coates
Vice Pres., South America — Victor de Mello
Vice Pres., Africa — Eng. A. Chaoui
Vice Pres., Australasia — A.J. Hargraves

CONTENTS
TABLE DES MATIÈRES
INHALTSVERZEICHNIS

Author and Country Auteur et Terre Autor und Land	Title Titre Titel

B. STATE OF STRESS

B. ÉTAT DE CONTRAINTE

Author and Country Auteur et Terre Autor und Land	Title Titre Titel

D. FLUID FLOW EFFECTS

D. EFFETS DE L'ECOULEMENT DU LIQUIDE

Author and Country Auteur et Terre Autor und Land	Title Titre Titel

THEME 1

PHYSICAL PROPERTIES OF INTACT ROCK AND ROCK MASSES

THÈME 1

PROPRIÉTÉS PHYSIQUES DE LA ROCHE INTACTE ET DES MASSIFS ROCHEUX

THEMA 1

PHYSIKALISCHE EIGENSCHAFTEN DES INTAKTEN FELSENS UND DER FELSMASSEN

THEME 1

THÈME 1

THEMA 1

A

Rock Classification and Engineering Applications in Relation to Rock Properties

A

Classement et utilisation technique des roches à la lumière de leurs propriétés

A

Klassifizierung des Felsens und technische Anwendungen in Verbindung mit den Felseigenschaften

PLANUNG UND BERECHNUNG GROSSER FELSBAUTEN UNTER BERÜCKSICHTIGUNG FELSMECHANISCHER KONTROLLMÖGLICHKEITEN

PLANNING AND DESIGN OF LARGE ROCK CONSTRUCTION PROJECTS AS AFFECTED BY ROCK MECHANICS OBSERVATION METHODS

ÉTUDE ET CALCUL DES GRANDES CONSTRUCTIONS EN ROCHES TENANT COMPTE DES POSSIBILITÉS DE CONTRÔLE PAR LA MÉCANIQUE DES ROCHES

K.-H. ABRAHAM A. PAHL

West Germany

Zusammenfassung

Die Planung großer Kavernen, Baugruben und Böschungen im Fels muß sich wesentlich auf die felsmechanischen Eigenschaften des Gebirgskörpers stützen. Es wird untersucht, welche Eigenschaften und Gebirgskennziffern qualitative oder quantitative Aussagekraft für die Planung und Berechnung haben.

Die Bedeutung der felsmechanischen Voruntersuchung für die Planung und die statische Beurteilung sowie die Notwendigkeit einer Bauwerksüberwachung wird an Beispielen erläutert.

Summary

Planning of large caverns, excavations and sloped cuts in rock must essentially take into account the rock-mechanics properties of the mass. The authors deal with the question of what properties and characteristics of the mass permit qualitative and quantitative conclusions to be drawn for purposes of planning and design.

The importance of preliminary rock-mechanics investigations for planning and stress assessment and the necessity of in-progress and post-construction surveillance are explained by way of examples.

Résumé

L'étude de grandes salles souterraines, fouilles et talus réalisés dans le rocher doit essentiellement s'appuyer sur les propriétés mécaniques des terrains. On recherche les propriétés et coefficients du terrain qui sont quantitativement et qualitativement déterminants pour l'étude et le calcul.

L'importance de l'analyse préliminaire sur le plan de la mécanique des roches pour l'étude, l'appréciation en matière de statique et la nécessité d'une surveillance de l'ouvrage est exposée à l'appui de quelques exemples.

Auf die Planung eines Felsbauwerkes hat das umgebende Gebirge als eigentlicher Baustoff einen überragenden Einfluß. Da unsere Fels-Hohlräume fast immer in einem inhomogenen anisotropen Medium hergestellt werden müssen, sind dessen Eigenschaften für den Ausbruch, die dauerhafte Sicherung und die Kosten entscheidend.

So kann es zweckmäßig sein, die Bauwerksachse nach den gemessenen Hauptspannungsrichtungen auszurichten, um die Kosten für Ausbruch und Sicherung zu senken. Dies bedeutet allerdings für die Planung Änderungen bei den zu- und abführenden Bauten, wie Zufahrtsstollen, Ableitungen o.ä. Meist ist ein Kompromiß zwischen der Zweckbestimmung des Bauwerkes und den gebirgsmechanischen Möglichkeiten zu suchen.

Die geologische Entwicklung des Gebirges hat im allgemeinen zu zahlreichen Trennflächen geführt, die das mechanische Verhalten des Gebirgskörpers beeinflussen, wie Schichtung, Klüfte und Störungen. Deshalb muß untersucht werden, welche Trennflächen bzw. welcher Durchtrennungsgrad Verformungen bestimmter Ausmaße zuläßt. Darüber liegen einige Erfahrungen vor, die sich ganz grob unter Zugrundelegung gleicher petrographischer Ausbildung vielleicht folgendermaßen zusammenfassen lassen:

Massiges, trennflächenfreies Gebirge und intaktes Gebirge mit Trennflächen zeigen geringe Verformungen. Wesentlich größere Verformungen zeigt dagegen das stark gestörte - verruschelte - Gebirge mit dicht liegenden Trennflächen.

Dazu ein Beispiel aus dem Bergbau mit allgemeiner Beobachtung der Verformungen (Abb.1). Im Zuge von Untersuchungsarbeiten im Siegerland - Wieder Spateisensteinbezirk wurde eine Strecke im generellen Gebirgsstreichen geplant und mit Rücksicht auf parallel dazu verlaufende Störungszonen mehrmals im Streichen abgewinkelt. Das Gebirge bestand aus Tonschiefern mit wechselndem Sandanteil und einzelnen Grauwackenlagen bzw. -bänken. In den Störungszonen war das Gebirge sehr stark tektonisch beansprucht und drückte trotz Stahlbogenausbau in die Strecke, so daß zeitweise nachgearbeitet werden mußte. In den dazwischenliegenden Gebirgsteilen blieb die Strecke meistens ohne Ausbau frei von Nachbruch und sichtbaren Verformungen, obgleich das Gebirge auch hier nicht ganz ungestört und von Trennflächen durchzogen war. Diese Streckenführung zeigt deutlich die Berücksichtigung der strukturabhängigen Verformungen.

Bei der Wahl der Querschnittsform ist das Verhältnis von Vertikal- zu Horizontaldruck, wie auch der Stich der Ausrundungen maßgebend für Sicherungsaufwand und Bauablauf. Die Planung nimmt hinsichtlich der Anordnung der Einbauten Rücksicht auf die gebirgsmechanischen Gegebenheiten. Sie muß dabei abwägen, welche Kosten durch die Herstellung des Hohlraumes durch ungünstigere Anordnung der Einbauten anzusetzen sind.

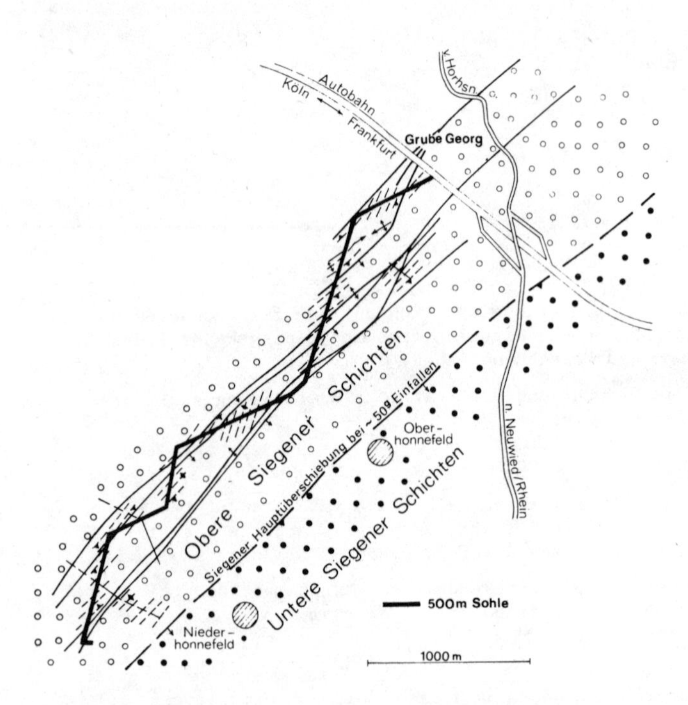

Abb.1: Abgewinkelte Streckenführung in Tonschiefern mit einzelnen Grauwackenlagen unter Vermeidung von parallel laufenden Störungen

The zigzag layout of this penstock in shaly clay with individual graywacke layers avoids parallel faults.

Tracé en ligne brisée de la galerie dans le schiste argileux avec quelques lits de grauwacke pour éviter un tracé parallèle aux remaniements.

Dem Planer von Felsbauwerken steht auf der einen Seite die ingenieurgeologisch-tektonische Beschreibung und Darstellung des Gebirges, auf der anderen Seite die felsmechanisch zahlenmäßige Erfassung von Gebirgseigenschaften und -verhalten in Form von Kennziffern zur Verfügung.

Beides in Einklang zu bringen, bereitet heute bisweilen noch Schwierigkeiten. Im allgemeinen gelingen zusammenfassende Aussagen über einen Gebirgsabschnitt sehr gut, wenn felsmechanische Untersuchungsergebnisse auf der Grundlage intensiver ingenieurgeologischer Aufnahmen eine breite Anwendungsbasis finden. Schwierigkeiten bereitet dagegen oft noch die detaillierte Aussage über den Einfluß der tektonischen Struktur und der Zeit auf das Verformungsverhalten von Felsbauwerken.

Die Gebirgskörper, in denen wir unsere Bauwerke ausführen, haben in den meisten Fällen schon erhebliche Verformungen erlitten. Das sind vor allem langzeitige Vorgänge, die mit der Gebirgsbildung begannen.

Auf die intensive Beanspruchung reagierten die Schichten im allgemeinen zuerst durch Biegefaltung und schließlich durch Ausbildung neuer Trenn- und Bewegungsflächen. An Störungen konnten sich Gebirgsteile weiter gegeneinander verschieben. Der Faltungsdruck kann nach dem seinerzeit herrschenden Überlagerungsdruck grob geschätzt werden.

Relikte dieser Verformungsvorgänge sind die inneren Spannungen der Gebirgskörper, von denen noch heute Spannungsumlagerungen und Entspannungen im Zuge von Auffahrungsarbeiten erwartet werden können. Mehr kurzzeitige Verformungen des Gebirgskörpers werden durch die Wasserführung, durch Erdfälle oder auch durch Erdbeben hervorgerufen. Hierzu gehören auch Nachbrüche von ehemaligen Grubenbauten, die in unmittelbarer Nähe neuer Felshohlbauten liegen. Einen kurzzeitigen Verformungsvorgang ruft die Sprengerschütterung hervor. Ein großer Anteil der Verformungen geht auf die Auflockerung durch Verwitterung zurück.

Die Zeitdauer der Verformungsvorgänge reicht also von wenigen Sekunden bei der Sprengauflockerung bis zu Millionen Jahren bei epirogenetischen Krustenbewegungen. Es ist schwierig, hier exakte Zeitgrenzen zu ziehen, weil manche Vorgänge sich auch überschneiden können. So können Einzelvorgänge der Gebirgsbildung sehr kurzzeitig ablaufen, wie es manche Erdbeben zeigen.

Kurzzeitige Verformungen von einer Dauer bis zu einigen Monaten können schon während der Vor- und Bauarbeiten erfaßt und berücksichtigt werden. Dazu gehören insbesondere die Beobachtungen und Messungen der Auflockerung, die sich nach der Auffahrung eines Felshohlraumes einstellt.

Weitaus schwieriger ist die Erfassung langzeitiger Verformungen, die sich über Jahre hinweg erstrecken. Hier ist es schon schwierig, die Tendenz während der Bauzeit zu bestimmen. Spannungsumlagerungen können durch die Auffahrung einer ganzen Reihe benachbarter Felshohlräume ausgelöst werden.

Deshalb ist es oft nicht möglich und vor allem nicht wirtschaftlich, allen nur eventuell auftretenden langzeitigen Gebirgsverformungen durch einen von vornherein entsprechend stark bemessenen Ausbau zu begegnen. Vielmehr sollte versucht werden, den Ausbau möglichst so zu gestalten, daß er die Belastungen aufnehmen kann, die bei den Untersuchungen vor und während der Bauzeit erkannt wurden. Durch zusätzliche langzeitige Messungen über Jahre hinweg, sind Ausbau und Gebirge kontrollierbar und im Falle einer Überbelastung muß dann, vielleicht nur in einzelnen Abschnitten, eine Verstärkung in Kauf genommen werden.

Im Rahmen der Vorarbeiten sind ingenieurgeologische Untersuchungen, wie petrographische Auswertungen, Angaben über Trennflächengefüge, Störungen, Kluftrichtung, -abstände, -weite und -füllung sowie deren Oberflächenbeschaffenheit und Durchtrennungsgrad zu fordern. Hinzu kommen Klüftigkeitsziffer =

($= \frac{\text{Anzahl}}{\text{pro m}}$) und Wasserdurchlässigkeit, zu erwartende Auflockerung, Verwitterungseinflüsse, Gebirgswasserdruck, -strömung und chemische Zusammensetzung.

Diese Angaben sind überwiegend qualitativ zu werten und bilden die Grundlage für die Wahl des statischen Modells.

Außerdem sind felsmechanische Kennziffern zu ermitteln, wie für Gebirgsfestigkeiten, tektonische Spannungen, Seitendruckverhältnis, Reibungswinkel und Kohäsion auf den Kluftflächen bzw. innerhalb der Störungen, Verformungsmoduln des Gebirges und des vorgesehenen Ausbaus. Alle diese Angaben sind aber stark abhängig von der Größe des untersuchten Bereiches und der gewählten Meßmethode. Hinzu kommt noch die Zeitabhängigkeit einiger Kennziffern.

Es ist nun Aufgabe des Felsmechanikers, gemeinsam mit dem planenden Ingenieur eine Auswahl aus der Vielzahl von gemessenen Werten für die statische Berechnung zu treffen.

Dabei ist es aber fast nie möglich, nur die ungünstigsten Werte anzusetzen, da sie meist unwirtschaftliche Dimensionen des Ausbaus ergeben würden. Vielmehr kommt es auf eine wirklichkeitsnahe Bewertung der Kennwerte und Auswahl der für das Tragverhalten des Gebirges wesentlichen Trennflächen an.

Natürlich wird man die Berechnung mit unterschiedlichen Werten mehrfach wiederholen. Aber die Zahl der Rechengänge hat ihre Grenzen in der Zahl der erforderlichen Rechenoperationen und deren Dauer.

Für eine statische Untersuchung stehen heute zahlreiche Rechenmodelle und -programme zur Verfügung, die weitgehend Struktur und Eigenschaften des umgebenden Gebirges zu erfassen versuchen.

Es ist aber wesentlich beim Abschätzen der Kennwerte die voraussichtlichen Auswirkungen auf Modellannahme und Rechenergebnis zu kennen.

So sind für die Modellauswahl von Bedeutung: die Form des Querschnitts, seine Dimensionen, der einzubeziehende Gebirgsbereich, Zahl, Anordnung und Verlauf der Trennflächen und ein etwaiger Ausbauwiderstand sowie die Frage der zwei- oder dreidimensionalen Betrachtung.

Für die Dimensionen ist außer der Zweckbestimmung des Bauwerkes die Größe des Verhältnisses von Vertikal- zu Seitendruck maßgebend. Dieses ist aber besonders schwierig beim in-situ-Versuch zu ermitteln. Hier sind Überlegungen einer möglichen früheren Überdekkungshöhe und evtl. Entspannungsmöglichkeiten in geologischen Zeiträumen anzustellen.

Die Seitendruckziffer (λ) kann durch Überbohrversuch und Messung der Entspannung vor Beginn der Baumaßnahmen bzw. während der Auffahrung eines Felshohlraumes durch rechtzeitig eingesetzte Meßgeräte bestimmt werden.

Der Überbohrversuch liefert den gewünschten Kennwert im allgemeinen nur für einen sehr kleinen Gebirgsabschnitt und es muß aufgrund einer ingenieurgeologischen Spezialkartierung geprüft werden, ob oder unter welchem Vorbehalt dieser Gebirgsabschnitt repräsentativ für den größeren Planungsbereich ist.

Am Beispiel des Pumpspeicherwerkes Waldeck II zeigte sich eine relativ gute Übereinstimmung der Ergebnisse von nachträglich durchgeführten Überbohrversuchen mit dem Ergebnis der Gesamtverformung der Kaverne.

Meist wird in gestörtem Gebirge nur eine Wahl zwischen min 2o % und max loo % des Überdeckungsgewichtes bleiben; der geringe Seitendruckanteil wird nur in geschlossenem bankigen Gebirge mit hoher Scherfestigkeit, der höhere bei stärker gestörtem Gebirge infrage kommen. In der Berechnung ist meist erst eine merkbare Änderung der Ergebnisse festzustellen, wenn λ um lo % oder mehr verändert wird. In der Regel wird man sich mit je einem Rechenlauf begnügen, wenn λ um 2o % vom Firstdruck variiert wird.

Unter der Voraussetzung, daß es die Planung zuläßt, kann eine Anpassung der Querschnittsdimensionen an das Verhältnis von First- zu Seitendruck eine deutliche Verminderung des Sicherungsaufwandes zur Folge haben.

Eine niedrige Seitendruckziffer erlaubt vertikale oder wenig gekrümmte Ulmen. Falls aber von Seiten der Planung vertikale Ulmen bei hohem Seitendruckverhältnis gefordert werden, bedeutet dies tiefe Auflockerungsbereiche in den Ulmen. Die Sekundärspannungen und der Sicherungsaufwand steigen stark an, wodurch Kosten und Bauzeit beeinflußt werden.

Die für die meisten Berechnungsverfahren geforderte Kenntnis der Primärspannungen ist wegen der Schwierigkeiten, die nur örtlich gültigen Messungen auf den Großraum zu beziehen und wegen der Fehlerquellen beim Meßvorgang schwer erfüllbar. Man versucht durch eine Vielzahl von Messungen das Abschätzen zu erleichtern, aber mitunter wird dadurch die Streuung noch größer. Dann kann man nur noch vom derzeitigen Überlagerungsdruck ausgehen.

Ferner ist die Auswahl der in das statische Modell einzubeziehenden Trennflächen von Bedeutung. Ist das umgebende Gebirge von einigen Störungen durchzogen, deren Zerrüttungszone einen deutlich abweichenden V-Modul besitzt, müssen sie Berücksichtigung finden; weitgehend verfestigte Störungen sind als Sollbruchflächen zu betrachten. Ebenso müssen ausgeprägte Klüfte behandelt werden, wenn ihr Durchtrennungsgrad auf eine Länge von etwa 2D von der Leibung aus gesehen mehr als 7o % beträgt. Dabei muß ihre Neigung größer als der Reibungswinkel der Füllung bzw. zwischen den Flächen sein.

Im geschieferten Material werden Reibung und Kohäsion je nach Spannungsrichtung stark voneinander abweichen. Diese Werte sollten im Modell wenigstens in der Richtung parallel zur Schieferung Berücksichtigung finden. Sobald ein örtlicher Bruch erfolgt, wird meist die Kohäsion nahezu verschwinden, dafür aber der Reibungswinkel wegen der nur selten glatten Oberfläche der Bruchflächen ansteigen, so daß der Ausgangswert wieder erreicht wird. Für eine erneute Berechnung sind erst Annahmen von mehr als $\pm 5^{o}$ von Interesse.

Eine hohe Klüftigkeitsziffer oder zerbrochenes wieder verfugtes Gebirge verhält sich großräumig trotz niedriger V-Moduln wie ein homogenes Material. Hier sollte man wenigstens die Obergrenze der gemessenen V-Moduln ansetzen. Es ist zu erwarten, daß gleich nach dem Ausbruch größere Verformungen einsetzen, die bis zum Einbau der Sicherung bereits im Abklingen sind.

Die V-Modul-Werte sind im Hinblick auf die Berechnung nur bei Abweichungen von mehr als 2o ooo kp/cm^2 in den betrachteten Querschnittsbereichen von Bedeutung. Dabei ist zu bemerken, daß höhere Werte, mit denen operiert werden muß, größere Intervalle erfordern, ehe sie merklichen Einfluß auf die Berechnung nehmen.

Oft werden Kriecheigenschaften des Gebirges meßtechnisch nicht erfaßt. Trotzdem sollte geprüft werden, ob sie in der Berechnung Eingang finden müssen. Dies wird der Fall sein, wenn Trennflächen zum Hohlraum hin geneigt und der Reibungswinkel bei geringer Kohäsion ähnlich dem Winkel des Einfallens ist.

Einige Rechenmodelle erlauben auch die Berücksichtigung der bereits eingetretenen Kriechverformungen zum Zeitpunkt des Einbaus. Um aber diese Einflüsse einsetzen zu können, muß der Zeiteinfluß schon bei einem Probeausbruch beobachtet werden und der Bauablauf zeitlich bekannt sein. Häufig wird man Annahmen zu machen haben.

Ebenso ist auch das Eintreten von Sekundärspannungen weniger von den Bewegungen auf Trennflächen während des Umlagerungsvorganges als von der "Bauweise", also dem Zeitraum zwischen Ausbruch und Wirkungsbeginn der Sicherung abhängig. Es sollten auch hierfür Erfahrungswerte bekannt sein, die aus Messungen während Probeausbrüchen gewonnen wurden. Dieser Einfluß wird umso größer sein, je häufiger Umlagerungen durch Ausbrucharbeiten in der Nähe des Hohlraumes erzwungen werden.

Die Planung sollte anstreben, daß nach Möglichkeit die Abstände zwischen Hohlräumen mehr als 3x Hohlraumbreite betragen und der Ausbruchvorgang möglichst nur einmal die tragende Gebirgsschale erschüttert. Dies kann durch Vollausbruch mit gebirgsschonendem Schießen oder bei Teilausbruch mit nachfolgendem Strossenabbau geschehen. Bei letzterem muß allerdings alles getan werden, damit Setzungen der Kalottensicherung vermieden werden. Sprengstoffaufwand und Abschlagtiefe sowie Sprengbild sind auf diese Forderung abzustimmen.

Bei allen Baumaßnahmen ist zu berücksichtigen, daß man in einem vorgespannten Medium arbeitet. Kerbspannungen in der tragenden Schale sind also zu vermeiden. Darum haben Ausrundungen auch in Bauzuständen einen günstigen Einfluß auf das Tragverhalten des Gebirges. Sie sollten schon in der Ausschreibung gefordert werden. Ebenso muß eine kurzfristig wirksame Sicherung verlangt werden, um die Sekundärspannungen zu verringern. Diese aber beeinflußt die Bauzeit und die Kosten.

Bei der Festlegung des Ausbauwiderstandes, der in die Berechnung Eingang findet, kommen in der Regel nur Werte zwischen o,5 und 3 kp/cm^2 in Betracht. Ein Ausbauwiderstand unter o,5 kp/cm^2 ist im allgemeinen felsmechanisch nur ungenügend wirksam, während Ausbauwiderstände über 3 kp/cm^2 wirtschaftlich kaum tragbar sind. Als 1. Schätzung sollte man mit 1 kp/cm^2 beginnen. Der Einfluß des Ausbauwiderstandes in der Berechnung ist ziemlich gering, so daß eine Veränderung für den nächsten Lauf nicht weniger als o,5 kp/cm^2 betragen sollte.

Der im Rechenmodell einzubeziehende Bereich braucht nicht größer als 1,o - 1,5 B bzw. H von der Ausbruchleibung zu sein. Der von der Theorie meist geforderte Bereich von 5 (B+H) wirkt sich i.a. auf die Baupraxis nicht aus, d.h. die Verformungen in größerer Teufe sind so gering, daß sie für das Bauwerk keine Bedeutung mehr haben.

Beim Berechnungsansatz sollte man sich stets vor Augen halten, daß die gemessenen Werte nur an einer Meßstelle korrekt ermittelt sind, aber das Verhalten des betrachteten Großraumes davon stark abweichen kann. Man darf nicht nur die Meßwerte sehen, sondern sie im Blick auf den untersuchten Großraum zu interpretieren suchen.

Auch die Entscheidung, ob nach der Finite-Element-Methode, mit Gitterstabsystemen oder nach der Differenzenmethode o.ä. gerechnet werden soll, ist keine prinzipielle Entscheidung, sondern vielmehr subjektiv. Ebenso ob zweidimensionale oder dreidimensionale Betrachtung angewandt werden soll, ist mehr eine Frage der zur Verfügung stehenden Computer-Leistung als der Genauigkeit. Denn so lange es nicht möglich ist, einen Großraum vor der Auffahrung sowohl im Ganzen als auch in Teilabschnitten meßtechnisch zu erfassen und sein Verhalten während und nach dem Ausbruch vorauszusagen, so lange kann die Berechnung trotz Exaktheit und Einarbeitung aller theoretischen Überlegungen in das Rechenmodell nicht der Wirklichkeit entsprechen. Sie kann also nur eine Abschätzung der Spannungen und Verformungen bringen, ohne einen Sicherheitsgrad festzustellen.

Diese Abschätzung bedarf unbedingt der Bestätigung durch Messungen am Bauwerk während und nach dem Vortrieb. Erst die Bauwerksbeobachtung entscheidet letztlich, ob Voruntersuchung, Planung, Berechnung und Bemessung den Weg eingeschlagen haben, der das Bauwerk langfristig funktionssicher macht. Die Standsicherheit wird dabei durch abklingende Deformationswerte ersetzt, die beweisen, daß die Umlagerungen beendet sind und ein Gleichgewicht der Kräfte eingetreten ist.

Wenn aber der Deformationsverlauf die Werte der Berechnung rasch erreicht und zu übersteigen droht - wobei die Zeit eine wichtige Rolle spielt - ist offensichtlich die exakte Berechnung mit einer Kombination zu günstiger Meßwerte oder unter Berücksichtigung eines nicht realistischen Modells durchgeführt worden.

Von der Planung sind daher stets zusätzlich mögliche Sicherungen vorzusehen und bereitzustellen.

Da sich Spannungen am Bauwerk während des Bauablaufes nur schwer messen lassen, muß man vor allem die Deformationen messen. Dazu gehören Konvergenz- und Extensometermessungen, die so früh wie möglich beginnen sollten, um wenigstens einen Teil der Anfangsverformungen erfassen zu können. Vor allem sollten die Verformungen, die sich nach dem Abwandern der mittragenden Ortsbrust einstellen, kontrolliert werden.

Noch wertvoller ist es, mit den Deformationsmessungen schon vor dem Einsetzen der Umlagerung im Gebirge zu beginnen. Dies kann durch Einbau von Meßgeräten in vorausgehenden Bohrlöchern geschehen, die während des Vortriebs und weiterem Bauablauf bis zur Konsolidierung beobachtet werden.

Aufgrund solcher Ablesungen ist erkennbar, ob

der Ausbauwiderstand genügt,
die Bauweise und -betrieb geändert werden müssen,
die Ankerlängen ausreichen,
die Einbauten (z.B. Panzerung) einbetoniert werden dürfen und
der Sohlschluß beschleunigt werden muß.

Die Bauwerksbeobachtung muß schon bei der Planung für die Bauausführung vorgesehen werden. Als Richtwert sollten 3 - 5 % der Summe für Ausbruch und Sicherung angesetzt werden, wobei die Schwankungsbreite der Kosten überwiegend vom Gebirgsverhalten, aber auch von Umfang und Sorgfalt der Voruntersuchungen abhängig ist. Nachstehend soll der Einfluß der felsmechanischen Untersuchungen und der Bauwerksbeobachtung auf Planung und Ausführung an zwei Beispielen gezeigt werden:

Pumpspeicherwerk Rönkhausen

Die annähernd hufeisenförmige Baugrube von 4o m Tiefe erhielt aufgrund der Voruntersuchungen im unteren Teil eine Böschungsneigung von 6o°, im oberen 45°, wobei alle 6 - 8 m eine 1 m breite Berme angeordnet wurde. Bei einer zulässigen Setzung von 2 cm durfte eine Bodenpressung von 2o kp/cm² auftreten. Die statische Berechnung ergab jedoch eine fast doppelt so hohe Kantenpressung. Deshalb war eine Vergrößerung der Aufstandsfläche notwendig, die eine Änderung der Böschungsneigung im unteren Bereich auf 9o° auf 6,5o m Höhe zur Folge hatte. Hierdurch ergab sich eine unmittelbare Rutschgefahr größerer Gesteinspartien, während in einem anderen Teil die Gefahr des Hangschubes bestand. Aufgrund der ingenieurgeologischen Verhältnisse wurde eine Felsverankerung eingeplant.

Im Bereich der West- und Nordwand streichen die Schichten des Grauwackensandsteins spitzwinklig zur Böschung und fallen mit 32° zur Baugrube ein. Die Schichtflächen sind überwiegend eben und glatt,außerdem treten häufig Tonschieferlagen mit weichplastischen Lettenzonen auf. Sie bildeten Gleitflächen für die bei einem ermittelten Gleitwinkel von 22° - 25° eine unmittelbare Rutschgefahr bestand. Bei einem geforderten Sicherheitsbeiwert von 1,1 wurde eine Verankerung gewählt, die 115 Anker zu je 3o Mp Gebrauchslast notwendig machte.

An der Ost- und Südwand der Baugrube lagen etwas günstigere Bedingungen vor, weil die Schichtung gegen die Böschung einfiel. Trotzdem bestand wegen der gegebenen starken Teilbeweglichkeit des stark geklüfteten Gebirges die Gefahr des Hangschubes. Da keine ausgeprägte Gleitfläche erkennbar war, wurde aufgrund von Erfahrungen bei anderen Bauvorhaben im Rheinischen Schiefergebirge eine Rutschzone angenommen,die über einer 35° geneigten Fläche vom Fußpunkt der Baugrube aus anzusetzen war. Die Sicherung erfolgte mit 18,5 m langen Ankern, deren Verankerungsstrecke im nicht mehr rutschgefährdeten Gebirgsbereich lag.Der Winkel für diese Anker wurde unter Berücksichtigung von Lagerung und Schieferung mit 5° - 1o° zur Horizontalen nach unten geneigt festgelegt.

Die Anker von 3o Mp Gebrauchslast wurden wegen der Labilität und fortgeschrittenen Auflockerung nur mit 1o Mp vorgespannt (Abb.2).

Mit Rücksicht auf die Schwierigkeiten einer wirklichkeitsnahen Abschätzung wurde zur Sicherung der Mannschaften in der Baugrube eine Meßanlage mit einer Genauigkeit von o,5 mm vorgesehen.

Die angeschlossene Warnanlage war auf Bewegungen größer als 1o mm eingestellt. Zur Abklärung der Lage der Bewegungsflächen wurden die Festpunkte der Extensometer in 3, 9 und 3o m Tiefe angeordnet. Die Stangenextensometer von 3o m Länge wurden in 4 Meßquerschnitten eingebaut und elektrisch außerhalb der Baugrube gemessen. Die Ablesungen erfolgten täglich 3 x und wurden 1 x durch mechanische Ablesung überprüft. Die Bewegungen lagen an 2 Meßstellen zwischen 1,o und 1,5 mm. Am 3.Meßpunkt waren in 2o Tagen über 2 mm erreicht, sie stiegen während des fortschreitenden Ausbruchs auf 4 mm an.

Pumpspeicherwerk Waldeck II

Im folgenden soll die Zusammenarbeit von Ingenieurgeologie, Geomechanik und Planung am Projekt des PSW Waldeck II (1969-1973) erläutert werden. Es sollte ein Hohlraum für 2 Maschinensätze von je 23o MW, ein Schachtwasserschloß von 23,5 Ø und 5o m Höhe im östlichen Teil des Rheinischen Schiefergebirges hergestellt werden. Das Gebirge besteht aus einer Wechsellagerung von sandgebänderten Schiefertonen und konglomeratischen Grauwacke-Sandsteinen. Die Voruntersuchungen ergaben nach Auffahren von 13oo m Probestollen, 2 Probekavernen und 14oo m Bohrung die günstigste Lage der Kavernenachse und Höhenlage der Maschinensätze sowie die Anordnung des Wasserschlosses des Zufahrtsstollens und der Zu- und Abführung der Triebwasserleitung zur Kaverne.

In den aufgefahrenen Versuchsstollen und Kavernen wurden eine Reihe von felsmechanischen Versuchen in situ ausgeführt.

Bei der stark wechselnden Lagerung von Gestein verschiedener Härte von jeweils wenigen cm Dicke mit zahlreichen Trennflächen und unterschiedlichen Durchtrennungsgraden, traten Schwankungsbreiten von 2o % - 5o % der verschiedenen Kennziffern auf. (Abb.3)

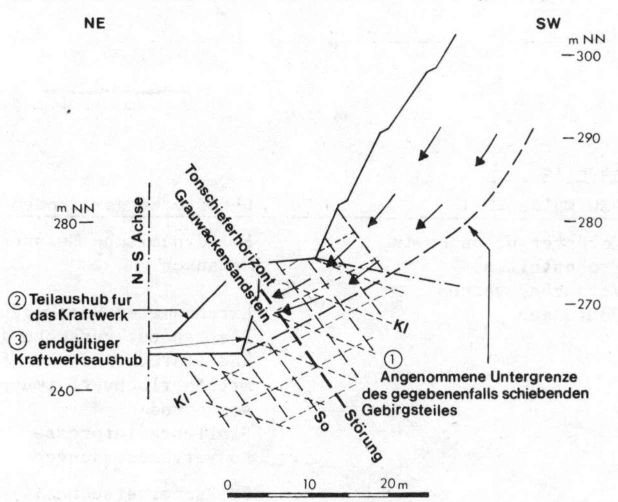

Abb.2: Baugeologischer Schnitt mit Verankerungsmaßnahmen der Süd- und Ostseite

— — — Anker, Anchors, Boulons d'ancrage

So — — — Schichtung, Strata, Couches

Kl - - - - - Klüftung, Joints, Diaclases

1. Teilaushub für das Kraftwerk
2. endgültiger Kraftwerksaushub
3. vorgesehene Kranbahnfundamente

Engineering geological cross-section with the anchoring scheme used on the south and east sides

1. Assumed lower boundary of the potentially sliding mass
2. Partial excavation for the pumped-storage station
3. Final excavation for the pumped-storage station

Coupe géologique avec ancrage des faces sud et est

1. Limite inférieure admise de la partie du terrain exerçant éventuellement une pous
2. Déblai partiel pour la centrale
3. Déblai définitif pour la centrale

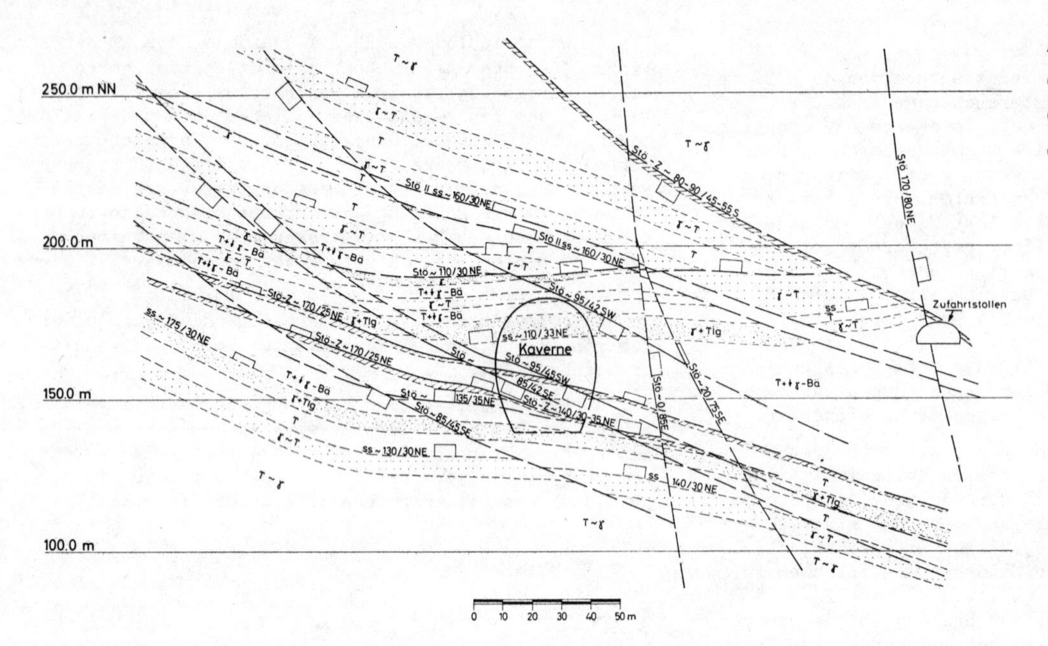

Abb.3:
Geologischer Querschnitt
Geological cross-section
Coupe géologique

Tabelle 1

PSW Waldeck II	Untersuchungsmethoden	Zweck-Kennzifferbestimmung
Voruntersuchungen in Probestollen, Versuchskavernen Bohrungen	Felsdynamische Messungen Meßanker	Auswahl der Druckstollentrasse, Auflockerungszone, Spannungsverteilung Kontrolle der Ankervorspannkraft
	Extensometer Messungen Plattendruckversuche (9) Radialdruckversuche (6) mit Bohrlochverformungssonde und Stollenradialpresse Konvergenzmessungen	Elastizitätsmodul Verformungsmodul Zeit-Verformungsverhalten, Seitendruckziffer
	Großscherversuche (4) Probenuntersuchungen im Labor	Reibungswinkel, Kohäsion Gesteinskennziffern (Druckfestigkeit, Trockenraumgewicht)
Messungen während der Bauausführung	Verformungsmessungen Einfach- und Mehrfachextensometer, IDI-Meßketten, Kontrollen der Ankervorspannung Felsdynamische Kontrollmessungen	Kontrolle der Standsicherheit der verschiedenen Bauabschnitte
Messungen nach Fertigstellung	Verformungsmessungen, Kontrollen der Ankervorspannung, Messungen des Gebirgswasserdruckes	Langzeitkontrolle der Standsicherheit

Die Planung der Maschinenkaverne für das Pumpspeicherwerk Waldeck II konnte die Gebirgseigenschaften und speziell das Verformungsverhalten der anstehenden Schiefer und Grauwacken zugrunde legen, das im Zuge der Auffahrung einer Versuchskaverne von etwa 11 m Höhe, 9 m Breite und 15 m Länge untersucht worden war. Hier konnten Verformungsmessungen nach jedem Abschlag vorgenommen werden. Während die ingenieurgeologische Spezialkartierung eine deutliche 3-Gliederung zeigt, spiegelt sich diese deutliche tektonische Gliederung in den Meßergebnissen nicht wider. Eine wichtige Feststellung wurde aus dem zeitlichen Verformungsverhalten gewonnen: Die Verformungen klangen schon wenige Tage nach Beendigung der Auffahrungsarbeiten ab. Für die Planung ergab sich daraus der Hinweis auf die zu erwartende Höhe der Strossenabschnitte und den zeitlichen Ablauf der Sicherungsarbeiten.

Auch aus den Ergebnissen von Belastungsversuchen ließen sich Hinweise auf den Einfluß der tektonischen Kleinstrukturen auf das Verformungsverhalten ziehen. In dem gleichen Gebirge wie oben beschrieben wiesen die Verformungen bei einem Radialbelastungsversuch darauf hin, daß sich insbesondere jede petrographisch anders ausgebildete Schicht durch bestimmte Verformungen hervorhebt und dadurch die tektonischen Einflüsse überprägt werden.

Tabelle 2 Felsmechanische Grundlagen-Kennziffern (vereinfachte Übersicht)

Verformungsmodul kp/cm^2	Schieferton mit Sandbändern Schieferton mit Grauwacke in Wechsellagerung Grauwacke	2o ooo 4o ooo 45 ooo - loo ooo
Auflockerungszone	Große Meßkaverne 1 - 1,5 m	Probestollen o,5 m
Seitendruckziffer	λ = o,4	
Reibungswinkel	schichtparallel ϕ = 2o°	senkrecht zur Schichtung ϕ = 37°
Kohäsion	c = 1,5 kp/cm^2	c = 15 kp/cm^2
Gesteinsdruckfestigkeit	Schieferton 5oo kp/cm^2	Grauwacke 8oo kp/cm^2
Trockenraumgewicht	2,63 Mp/m^3	

Eine Reihe von Plattendruckversuchen bestätigte ebenfalls, daß in einer Wechsellagerung von Schiefern mit Grauwacken die tektonische Struktur, insbesondere Klüftung, Lage der Schichtung zur Belastungsrichtung und schwach ausgebildete Störungen nur untergeordneten Einfluß haben. Diese Erfahrungen konnten für die statischen Berechnungen und Modelle herangezogen werden, in denen die Verformungsmoduln für größere Gebirgsabschnitte eingesetzt und nur einzelne Störungen berücksichtigt wurden.

Großscherversuche ergaben eine klare Abhängigkeit des Reibungswinkels (ϕ) und der Kohäsion (c) von der Richtung der Scherkraft zur Schichtung.

Von jedem Versuchsort wurden ingenieurgeologische Aufnahmen erstellt, die einen Vergleich mit den im Großraum angetroffenen Partien möglich machten, so daß die Versuchsergebnisse übertragbar wurden. Danach konnte der jeweilige Ausbauwiderstand verändert werden.

Für die statische Berechnung mußten aber Vereinfachungen eingeführt werden. Die Untersuchungen waren zweidimensional, da das Tragverhalten in Richtung parallel zur Bauwerksachse als unbedeutend angesehen wurde. (Abb.4)

Da Zweifel an der Seitendruckziffer von etwa o,4 auftraten - es waren in einer Großlochbohrung viel höhere Werte gemessen worden -, wurden zusätzlich spannungsoptische Versuche mit verschiedenen Seitendruckziffern ausgeführt. Bei diesen Modellen wurden unterschiedliche E-Moduln in 3 Bereichen eines Querschnitts, Störungen mit kleinerem E-Modul und einige Klüfte mit hohem Durchtrennungsgrad und verringerter Reibung in den Berührungsflächen berücksichtigt. Sie wurden mit steigenden Seitendruckverhältnissen λ bis 2,5 belastet und nach Messung der Verformungen bis zur Bruchlast gebracht (Abb.5). Gleichzeitig sollte damit geprüft werden, ob der Stich der Ulmen-Wölbung ausreichend war. Diese Ausrundungen waren anfangs von der Planung nicht vorgesehen gewesen, um Ausbruch zu sparen. Aufgrund der statischen Berechnung und danach wieder bei den spannungsoptischen Versuchen zeigte sich, daß bei vertikalen Ulmen Zugzonen auftraten, die eine Auflockerung nach sich zogen (Abb.6). Die Tiefanker mußten deutlich vermehrt und verlängert werden. Bei der gewölbten Ulme hingegen war erkennbar, daß die Verformungen nach etwa 17 - 2o m von der Ausbruchleibung entfernt weitgehend abgeklungen waren. Auch konnte man aus der Spannungsoptik erkennen, daß sich eine Vergrößerung der Kavernenbreite günstig auf

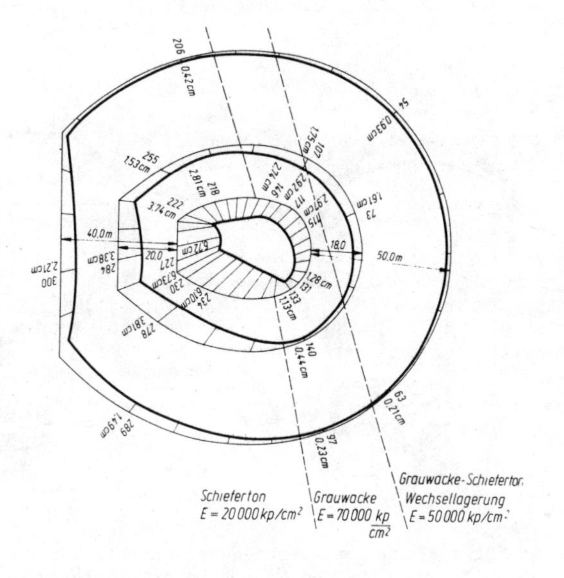

Abb.4: Rechnerische Deformationswerte in 18 und 3o m Entfernung vom Ausbruchrand nach der FE-Methode (nach Zienkiewicz)

Deformations at 18 m and 3o m from the excavation boundary as calculated by the finite-element method (according to Zienkiewicz)

Déformations calculées par la méthode des éléments finis (selon Zienkiewicz) à 18 et 3o m du bord de creusement

die Spannungen um den Hohlraum herum auswirkte. Die zulässigen Scherfestigkeiten wurden trotz relativ hoher Spannungen nicht annähernd erreicht.

Nachteilig wirkte sich aber aus, daß die Pumpenkugelschieber, die im Querschnitt seitlich angeordnet waren, eine Verschlechterung des Bildes der Spannungstrajektorien ergab, da die Querschnittsellipse unten eine breite Aufstandsfläche erhalten mußte. Schließlich gelang es der Planung unter Mitwirkung der Maschinenfirma den UW-seitigen Kugelschieber unter den Maschinensatz zu legen. Dadurch wurde zwar die Kaverne um 7 m höher, aber die elliptische Form bedeutend günstiger (Abb.7).

Wichtig war auch die Verhinderung von Kerbspannungen in der im Endzustand tragenden Hülle. Um das Gebirge

Abb.5: Spannungsoptisches Modell mit Berücksichtigung mechanisch wirksamer Klüfte und Störungen sowie mehrere Versuche mit steigenden Seitendruckziffern (nach Rescher)

Photoelastic model taking into account mechanically effective joints and faults; several tests with rising lateral-pressure coefficients (according to Rescher)

Maquette photo-élastique tenant compte des diaclases et remaniements mécaniquement actifs ainsi que de plusieurs essais avec des coefficients croissants de pression latérale (selon Rescher)

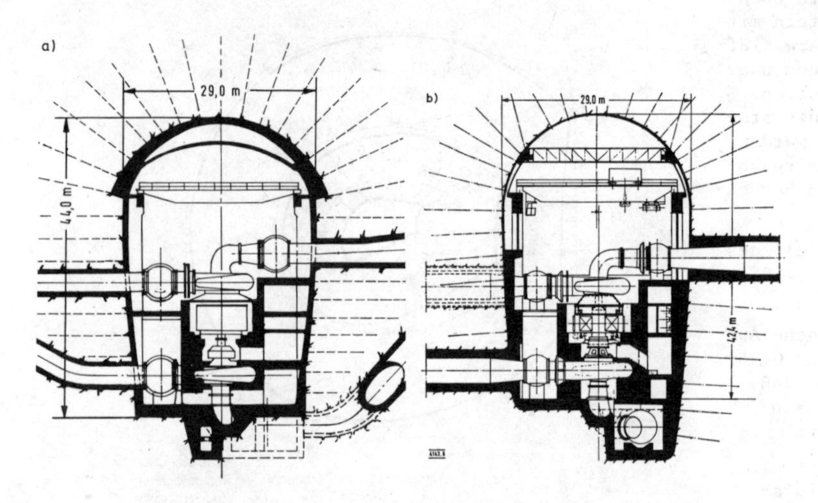

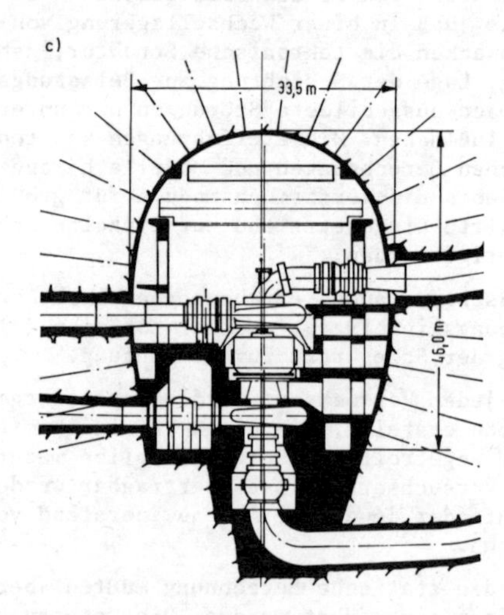

Abb.6: Entwicklung der Kavernenquerschnittsform von 33,5o m Breite und 46 m Höhe mit fast geraden Ulmen und Ankersicherung ohne starre Auskleidung (nach Siemens)

Development planned cavern cross-section of 33,4o m width and 46 m height with nearly straight sidewalls and anchor securing scheme rather than rigid lining (according to Siemens)

Développement de section prévue de salle souterraine de 33,5o m de large et de 46 m de haut avec des murs presque droits et ancrage sans revêtement rigide (selon Siemens)

Abb.7: Querschnitt der Maschinen-Kaverne (nach Siemens)

Finally cross-section of the machine hall cavern (according to Siemens)

Definitif coupe de la salle souterraine des machines (selon Siemens)

keinen Zugspannungen auszusetzen, wurde die geeignete Form vor allem für den Ausbruch im Firstbereich und in Zwischenbauzuständen spannungsoptisch ermittelt.

Mit Rücksicht auf die tiefe Lage der Kaverne für die Zufahrt enthielt die Planung zunächst einen großen Trafostollen und einen Transportstollen, um die 44o Mp-Trafos nahezu horizontal einfahren zu können, während die Maschinenteile mit Hilfe eines Übergabekrans vom Stollen in die Kaverne herabgelassen werden sollten.

Da der große Trafo-Stollenquerschnitt parallel zur Kavernenachse neben und über der Kaverne verlief, mußte mit steigenden Umlagerungsdrücken und Entfestigung des tragenden Kavernenbereichs gerechnet werden. Man ordnete daher unter Wegfall des großen Stollens und Änderung der Zufahrtsstollentrasse den Standort der Trafos in der Verlängerung der Kaverne an. Dies beeinflußte zwar stark die Anordnung der Betriebsräume, Warte usw., aber die Sicherheit des Bauwerkes nahm zu.

Mit Rücksicht auf die Annahmen der Statik, als Kontrolle für das gebirgsschonende Sprengen und zur Prüfung der Ankerlängen, die im deformationsfreien Tiefenbereich ihre Verankerung haben sollten, wurde eine Bauwerksbeobachtung beschlossen (Abb.8). Diese bestand aus Meßketten mit induktiven Deformationsindikatoren, Extensometern und Kontrollen der Ulmen mit dem Pilotfernrohr.

Eine Meßkette wurde vor Ausbruchsbeginn in ein 6o m langes Bohrloch 2 m über der Kavernenfirste von einer Nische des Probestollens aus eingebaut und ermöglichte die Beobachtung der Gebirgsverformung während und nach dem Ausbau (Abb.9). Außerdem wurde die stabilisierende Wirkung des Ankereinbaus, der Zeitpunkt der Beruhigung des Gebirges und schließlich auch die Sicherheit der Mannschaft kontrolliert. An Stellen mit Störungen oder durchziehenden Klüften mit hohem Durchtrennungsgrad wurden gleich nach dem Abschlag 7 m lange Stabextensometer mit einfacher Noniusablesung gesetzt, um möglichst frühzeitig die Tendenz der Deformation zu erfassen. Außerdem erfolgte frühzeitig das Setzen der 35 und 4o m langen Einfach- und Mehrfachextensometer (Abb.1o).

Diese erlaubten zusammen mit den Spannkraftmessungen an den Ankern eine Beurteilung des Gebirgsverhaltens, der Dauer der Umlagerungen, der ausreichenden Ankerlänge und des Ausbauwiderstandes. Die Überwachung erfolgte in kurzen Zeitabständen beim Durchgang des Strossenabbaus und Auffahrung der Abgänge der OW-und UW-Verteilleitungen.

Die Messungen der Meßkette im First ergab mit einer Ausnahme keine Verformung größer als 2o mm. Die Extensometermessungen der Ulmen kamen schon nach

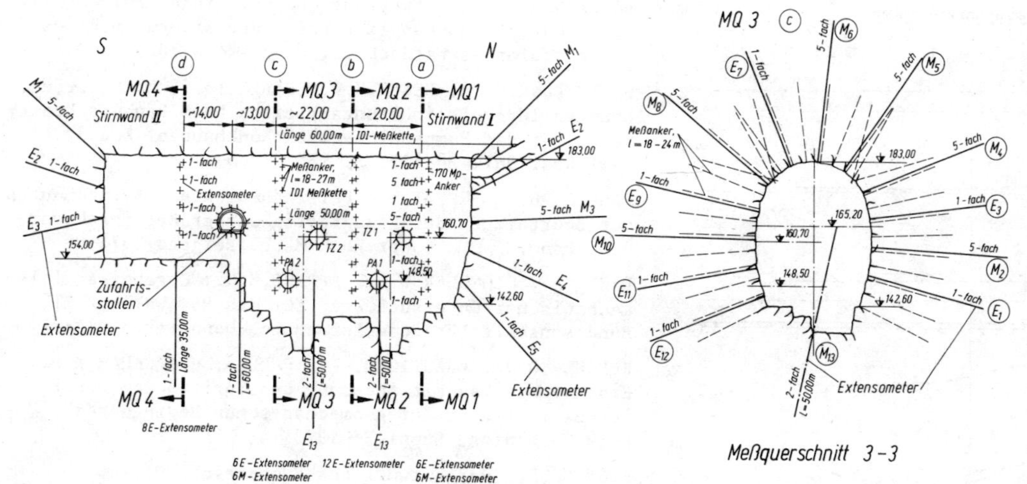

Abb.8:

Meßanlage zur Bauwerksüberwachung mit 48 Extensometern 35-4o m lg.; 2 induktiven Deformationsmeßketten von 6o u. 5o m Länge und 96 Ankerkraftmeßdosen

Project surveillance system comprising 48 extensometer of 35-4o m length,2 inductive deformation measuring cascades of 6o m and 5o m length, and 96 anchor load cells

Equipement de mesure pour la surveillance de l'ouvrage: 48 extensomètres de 35 à 4o m de long, 2 chaînes de mesure de 6o et 5o m de long constituées par des indicateurs de déformation inductifs; 96 celleles dynamométriques d'ancrage.

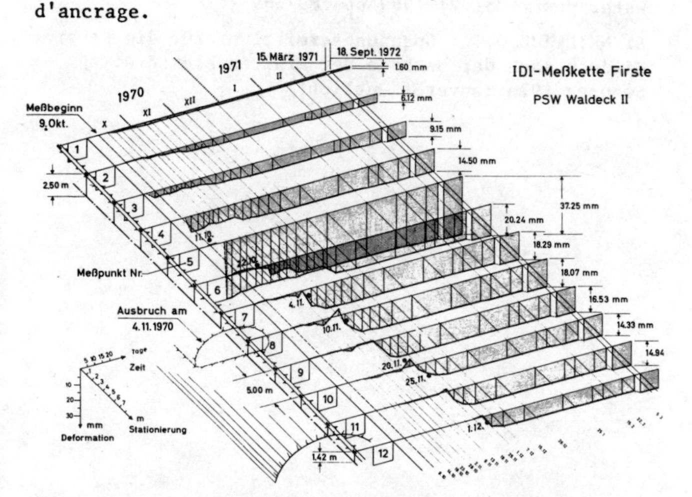

Abb.9: Deformationsverlauf der IDI-Meßkette vor, während und nach Firstaufbruch und nachfolgendem Strossenabbau

Deformations measured with the IDI cascade before and during excavation of the cavern crown and during subsequent enlargement

Evolution des déformations de la chaîne de mesure IDI,avant,pendant et après le creusement du toit et l'abattage par bancs qui lui fait suite

8-1o Wochen so weit zur Ruhe, daß danach nur noch 1/1o oder 1/1oo mm beobachtet werden konnte (Abb.11).

Die Verformungen erfolgten überwiegend im 1o m-Bereich von der Kavernenleibung aus gerechnet. Bei 25 m waren die Verformungen überall abgeklungen. Im Ulmenbereich blieben die Verformungen unter 7 mm. Die gemittelte Kurve aller Extensometer-Ablesungen der UW-Seite zeigte, daß weiter als 1o m von der Ulme entfernt nur noch 2o% der Verformungen auftreten,während die statischen Untersuchungen noch Verformungen bei 19 m Tiefe und Gesamtwerte bis zu 9 cm voraussagten (Abb.12).

Die Bauwerksbeobachtung erlaubte nicht nur einen zügigen Ablauf der Bauarbeiten,sondern machte überhaupt

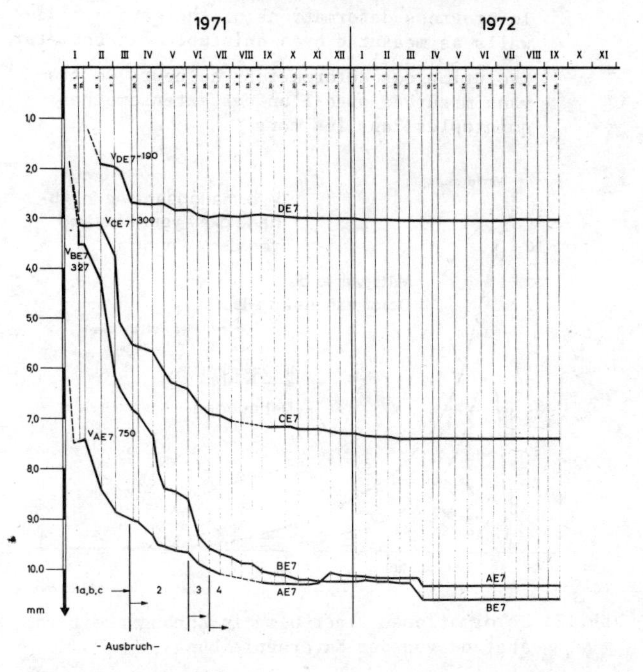

Abb.1o: Deformationsverlauf an vier Extensometern in der Kavernenfirste

Deformations measured by four extensometers in the cavern crown

Evolution des déformations mesurées avec quatre extensomètres dans le toit de la salle souterraine

erst die Herstellung einer so großen Kaverne mit 139o m^2 Querschnitt in einem aus Sedimentgesteinen aufgebauten Gebirge möglich.

Die Kosten für den umbauten Raum betrugen für Ausbruch und Sicherung,Baustelleneinrichtung und Wasserhaltung 16o,-- DM/m^3,die Kosten für die Meßanlage beliefen sich auf ca. 7,-- DM/m^3.

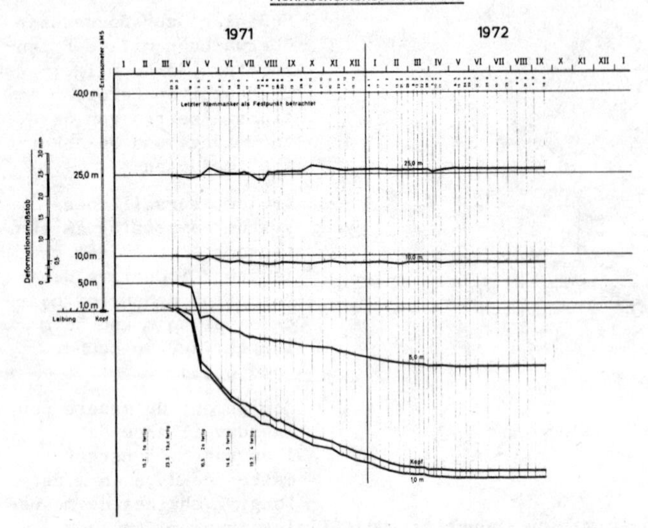

Abb.11: Deformationsverlauf an einem Fünffachextensometer der Ulmen während des Bauablaufs

In-progress deformations of the cavern sidewalls as measured by a quintuple extensometer

Evolution des déformations au cours de travaux mesurées avec l'un des extensomètres quintuples dans les murs

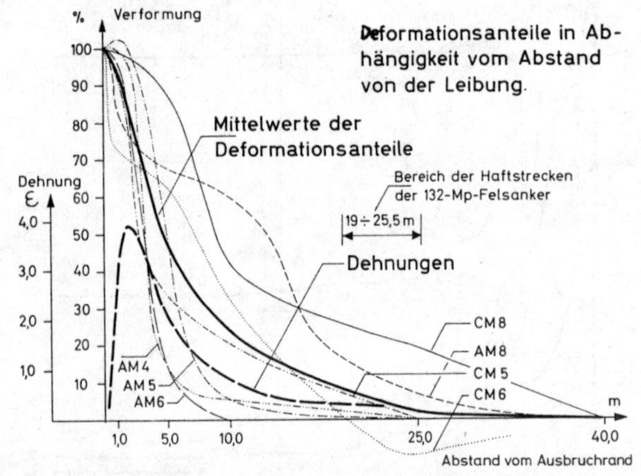

Abb.12: Deformationen einer Ulme in Abhängigkeit vom Abstand von der Kavernenleibung

Deformation versus distance from cavern sidewall

Déformations d'un mur en fonction de la distance à l'intrados

Schrifttum

ABRAHAM,K.H.: "Stand der Kavernenbautechnik für Pumpspeicherwerke in Mitteleuropa". Wasserwirtschaft 62. Jg.(1972) S. lo3 - 11o

ABRAHAM,K.H. u.PORZIG,R.: "Die Felsanker des Pumpspeicherwerkes Waldeck II". Baumaschine u.Bautechnik 1973, H. 6 u. 7

BARTH,St.: Felsmechanische Probleme beim Entwurf der Kaverne des Pumpspeicherwerkes Waldeck II. Die Bautechnik 49(1972), S. 73 - 83

BRÄUTIGAM,F.: Hauptbericht über die ingenieurgeologischen Untersuchungen im Bereich der Kaverne und des Wasserschlosses Waldeck II. Olpe, 3o.6.7o

HEITFELD,K.H. u. HESSE,K.H.: Baugeologische Untersuchungen für Felssicherungsarbeiten beim Bau des Kraftwerks für das Pumpspeicherwerk Rönkhausen. Z.d.dt. geol.Ges.1967, Bd.119, S. 285 - 3o5

PAHL,A. u. ALBRECHT,H.: Felsmechanische Untersuchungen zur Beurteilung der Standfestigkeit großer Felskavernen. Proc.2. Int. Congr.Rock Mech.,Belgrad 197o

PAHL, A., GLÖGGLER,W. u. SPRADO,K.H.: Ergebnisse felsmechanischer Untersuchungen für das PSW Waldeck II. Bundesanstalt für Bodenforschung, Hannover, 197o/71

RESCHER,O.J., BRÄUTIGAM, F., PAHL,A. u.ABRAHAM,K.H.: "Ein Kavernenbau mit Ankerung und Spritzbeton unter Berücksichtigung der geomechanischen Bedingungen". Rock Mechanics, Suppl.2, 1973

RICHTER,E.: Der Entwurf des Pumpspeicherwerkes Waldeck II. Elektrizitätswirtschaft 1972, H.6

THOMANN, G.: The Rönkhausen Pumped-Storage Project. Water Power Vol.21 1969 pp 289-269

ZIENKIEWICZ,O.C.: Spannungsermittlung für die Kaverne Waldeck nach der Methode der Finiten Elemente. Swansea 197o (unveröffentlicht)

ROCK MASS INVESTIGATION IN DEPTH: RELIABILITY OF DIFFERENT METHODS FOR DRILL HOLE INVESTIGATIONS

EXAMENES EN PROFONDEUR DE LA MASSE ROCHEUSE: L'EXACTITUDE DES DIFFÉRENTES MÉTHODES POUR L'EXAMEN

TIEFUNTERSUCHUNGEN IM GEBIRGE: ZUVERLÄSSIGKEIT DER VERSCHIEDENEN METHODEN FÜR BOHRLOCHUNTERSUCHUNGEN

Magnus BERGMANN

M.Sc. Civil Engineering, Hagconsult AG.
Stockholm,Sweden

SUMMARY. Without exception some form of rock investigation forms the basis for the projecting work in a rock excavation operation. Such investigations, which may take a great variety of forms, are in turn based on information about the rock and rock mass which is obtained by different investigation methods. The reliability of this information is of decisive importance for the rock mechanical analyses and judgments which are founded on it.
This paper characterizes five investigation methods: core drilling, investigative percussion drilling, a method for integral sampling of rock and rock masses, TV examination of the drill hole, and water pressure testing, with a view to the information which can be communicated by each method. An evaluation of the reliability of the information gained is outlined and commented upon.
The results should make it easier to optimize the role of investigations in the projecting work for rock excavation.

RÉSUMÉ. Sans exception, un examen de la roche sert come point de départ pour le travail de projection qui précède toute oevre de génie civil qui comporte creusement de roche. De tels examens, qui peuvent se réaliser dans un grand nombre de formes, se basent à leur tour sur des renseignements sur la roche et sur la masse rocheuse obtenus par diverses méthodes d'examen. L'exactitude de ces renseignements preliminaires est d'une importance décisive pour les analyses et les évaluations de la mécanique de roche qui s'y basent.
Dans cet article cinq méthodes d'examen se caractérisent -- le carottage, le forage avec marteau perforateur, une méthode de sondage intégral des massifs rocheux, l'examen par télévision dans le trou de forage, et des essais avec de l'eau sous pression -- en ce qui concerne leur aptitude de communiquer des renseignements sur la roche et sur la masse rocheuse. Une évluation comparative de l'exactitude de ces renseignements est présentée et commentée.
Les résultats doivent faciliter l'optimasation du rôle de l'examen dans le travail de projection pour les ouvres de génie civil en roche dure.

ZUSAMMANFASSUNG. Als Grund der Projektierung einer Anlage im Gebirge liegt fasst ohne Ausnahme eine Untersuchung des Gebirges. Derartige Untersuchungen, die stark variierende Ausführungsformen aufweisen können, sind ihrerseits basiert auf Information über Gestein und Gebirge, erhalten durch verschiedene Voruntersuchungsmethoden. Die Zuverlässigkeit dieser Information ist von entscheidender Bedeutung für die darauf begründeten, bergmechanischen Analysen und Beurteilungen.
In vorliegendem Aufsatz werden fünf Untersuchungsmethoden - Kernbohrung, schlagende Sondierungsbohrung, eine Methode zur Entnahme vollständiger Gebirgsproben, TV-Inspektion innerhalb Bohrlöcher und Wasserdrucksprüfung - hinsichtlich der mit einschlägiger Methode erfassungsbaren Information von Gestein und Felsmasse. Eine Auswertung von Zuverlässigkeit dieser Information wird vorgelegt und kommentiert.
Die Resultate solle die Optimierung des Untersuchungseinsatz bei Projektierungen von Gebirgsanlagen erleichtern.

INTRODUCTION.

The execution of a rock excavation operation of any size is in practice always preceded by a thorough investigation, within the limits imposed by know-how and resources. The conclusions based on the results of this preparatory rock mass investigation are intended for the project engineer and should, among other functions, serve as a basis for his evaluations and efforts to get the rock excavation operation on the most favorable technical and economical footing. It is then extremely important that the information furnished by the rock mass investigation is both the data needed by the recipient to carry out his work in the best way, and that this information is founded on reliable observations on the rock types and the rock mass.

The reliability of this information is very difficult to judge on an objective basis since there are numerous subjective stages and steps before the material of the investigation is communicated in the form of a report. But one thing is undeniable: the reliability of the conclusions presented is never greater than the reliability of the basic material, or, to go a step further, the reliability of the investigation methods which have been employed.

Since rigorous demands for information reliability generally entail high investigation costs, an analysis should be made for each individual project to determine the quality level which is desirable and economically justifiable in the investigation. Such a decision does, however, presuppose a system for comparative evaluations of the information content of the different investigation methods. The objective of the research project reported in this paper was, against this background, to compare, specify and characterize the possibilities of various investigation methods to communicate reliable information about rock types and rock masses.

FORMULATION OF THE PROBLEM

In the project work of a rock excavation operation there is a continuous need for technical information about the properties of the rock mass, all the way from the earliest preprojecting stage to the execution of the job. In the course of the project work there arise both general and detailed practical rock construction problems which vary with the nature of the installation and the basic geological conditions of the area.

The projecting engineer (and later the contractor as well), whose job it is to solve these practical problems, has access to the conclusions of the rock investigation as his main source of technical data and information. This information will form the basis of the analyses, calculations and judgments which follow. It is then obviously of the greatest importance that the information of the rock investigation is formulated in such a way that it is meaningful and of practical use to the projecting engineer.

Of even greater importance perhaps in solving these problems is, however, the reliability and relevance of the basic material from the rock investigation. On what practical investigations are the conclusions based? What are the inherent uncertainties in the information about the rock types and rock mass which are directly accountable to the method employed? Just how was the investigation carried out? The answers to these questions are decisive for the accuracy or reliability of the solid geometrical model of the rock mass, including the variations in types of rock, the systems of fissures and discontinuities, on which the subsequent analyses and calculations will be founded.

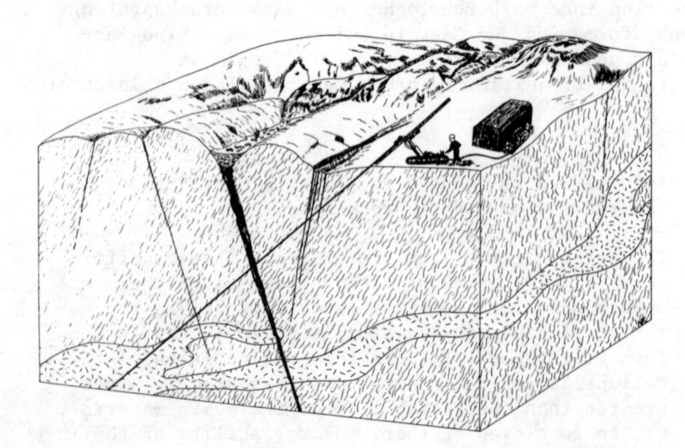

Fig. 2. On the basis of surface observations the drill holes are positioned and directed for the investigation in depth.

INFORMATION CONTENT IN ROCK MASS INVESTIGATIONS

A rock mass investigation can naturally vary in scale depending on the nature and scope of project, but the course of the investigation is always guided by the sequence of projecting work and can at least for an underground project be generalized to the principles shown in the block diagram of Figure 1.

The fundamental operation, and the one which determines the continued investigation, are the geological investigations which are carried out from the surface. The results of these investigations, often completed by seismic investigations, form the basis on which the subsequent in-depth investigations are set up (Fig. 2). Here becomes evident the need of complementary rock mass investigations in depth, i.e. the scope and the design of complementary drillhole investigations, in order to clarify the solid geometrical build up of the rock mass.

The purpose of the in-depth investigations is to provide detailed information on rock conditions, everything from the characteristics of the types of rock to the tectonical macro-structures of the rock mass.

Each phase of these investigations entails that greater and greater volumes of rock are taken into consideration, as various technical and geological parameters are evaluated and, preferably, quantified in order to be employed in and for rock mechanical analyses and judgments.

Even if all parameters should, in principle, always be considered, the primary need for parameters varies above all with the scope and nature of the project the geological formations present, and previous experience of the rock in the area. Decisive for the possibility of interpreting the various parameters and for the reliability of this interpretation are the capacity of the investigation methods employed to communicate the desired information and the nature of this information.

METHODS OF INVESTIGATION

The currently available methods of investigaion can be listed in the following main groups:

1. Methods practised - and/or measuring and registration carried out - from the ground and rock surface. This group, which includes geological mapping, seismic and aerial interpretations, serves, as noted earlier, as the base of reference for succeeding drill hole investigations. This group will not, however, be treated at greater length in this paper.

2. Drilling methods or methods for excavating a hole while collecting samples or data on the rock.

3. Methods for investigating or evaluating the rock mass from the completed drill hole.

Referring to groups 2 and 3 above, it is important to note that the corresponding methods of investigation give information only about the rock near the drill hole, which imphasizes the previously mentioned need for geological input data.

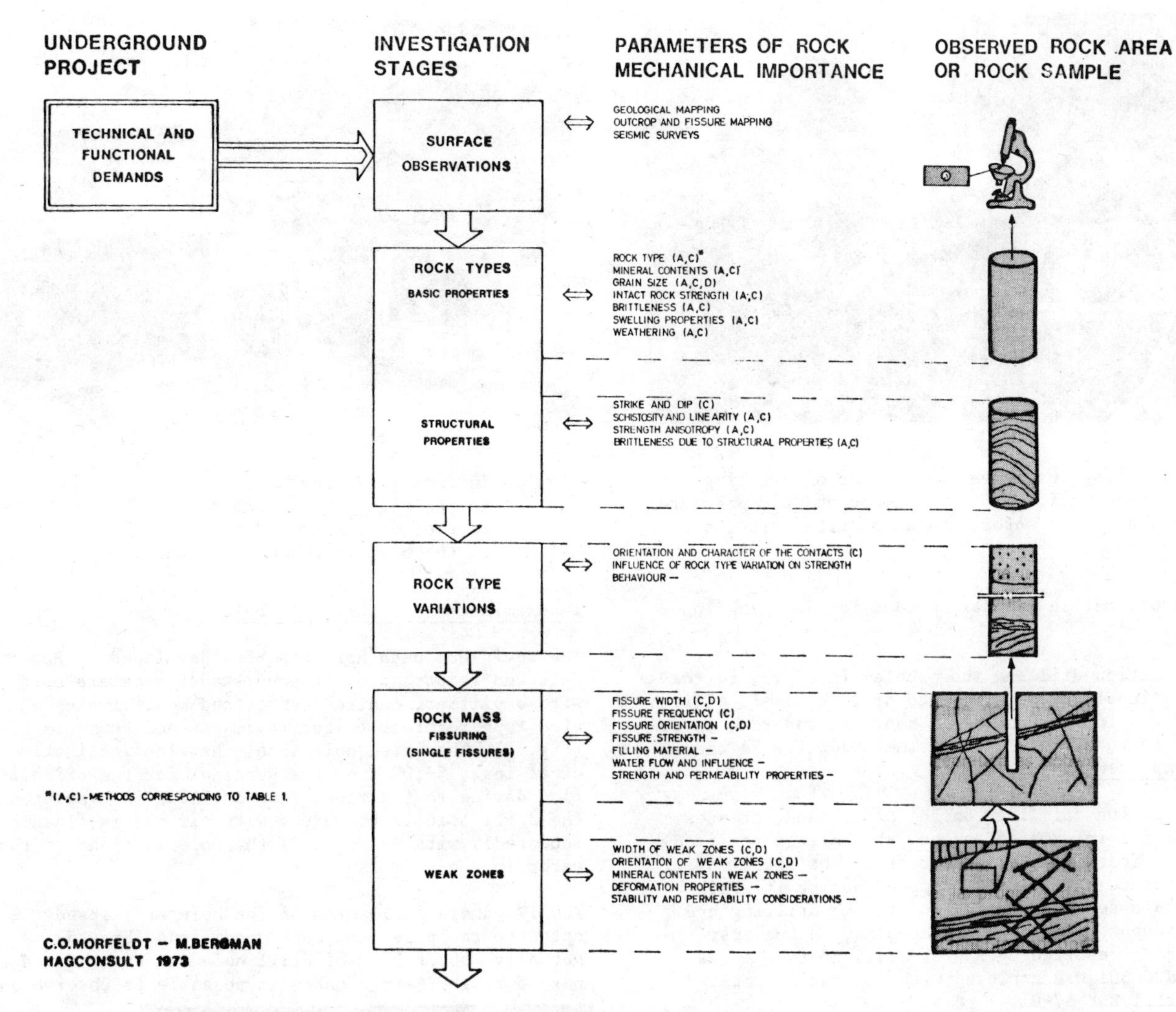

Fig. 1. Block diagram illustrating the scope of a rock mass investigation.

In the project under discussion it was decided to study in detail three methods from category 2 and two methods form category 3, as follows:

2.A Core drilling
.B Investigative percussion drilling
.C Integral sampling (as described in the following)
.D TV examination of the hole
.E Water pressure testing.

As a first stage these methods were subjected to a detailed analyses and discussion with reference to the character of the information which they provided. These analyses were then projected against a number of completed rock mass investigations where the various investigation methods had been used and where it had been possible at a later date to establish the accurace of the prognoses made (Morfeldt, et al, 1973). At present, as a second phase in this research project, specially designed full-scale tests are being made where these methods, under careful scrutiny, are compared with each other and with the above mentioned analyses. The method for integral sampling of rock and rock masses has, however, only been studied during a visit to Laboratório Nacional de Engenharia Civil (LNEC) in Lisbon.

Here follows a brief description of each method as practised in these tests. For more detailed descriptions we refer to Morfeldt, et al, 1973.

Core drilling

Core drilling has been carried out with a 56 mm diamond bit, giving a 42 mm core, 3 m long core barrels, of the double core barrel type, and water flushing. The core drill employed was of type Atlas Copco Craelius D750. The drilling work, which was down to depths of 60 m, was followed at all times by a geologist who, in addition to the logbook of the drilling foreman, made his own notes on the flushing water discoloration, feeding and penetration rate variations, and mapped the cores as they were recovered.

Investigative percussion drilling

Investigation drilling with heavy chain-fed rock drills is a rather new concept in drilling technology and poses problems of quite a different nature

Fig. 3. During investigative percussion drilling, rate of penetration, rotation speed and air pressure on the chain feed motor were automatically registered by a recorder.

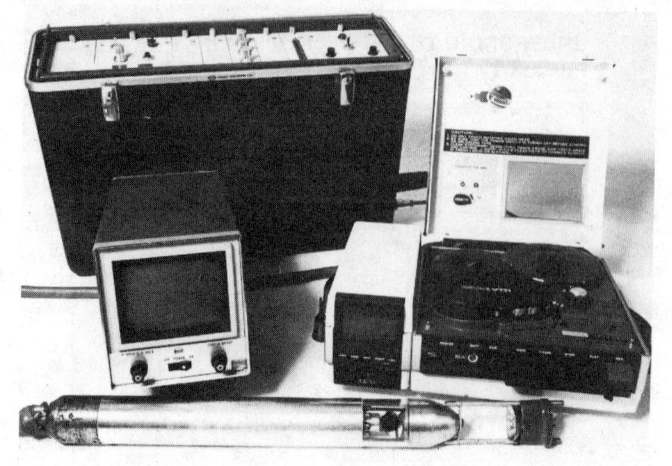

Fig. 4. In front: TV-camera
To the right: Tape recorder
To the left: Extra TV-monitor
In the background: Control unit.

than those met in ordinary production drilling in mining.

In production drilling the problem faced is, in the most rational way possible, to drill holes in a given rock formation through soil, boulders and rock in order to introduce explosives. The objective is then the completed blast hole.

Investigation drilling, on the other hand, creates demands for information on how the hole is realized. Here the focal point of interest is the actual drilling sequence and all that happens during it. This requires a sensitive attention to the drilling and a continuous record of what happens. In the tests here being reported a crawler drill of type Atlas Copco ROC 601 was employed with separately rotated rock drill BBE 57-01.

The drilling was performed by 64 mm cemented carbide tipped drill bits, 10' 1 1/2" extension rods, and water flushing. Drill holes were down to depths of 60 m, running parallel to the holes made with core drilling as mentioned above. During drilling, rate of penetration, rotation speed, and air pressure on the chain feed motor were automatically registered by a recorder (Fig. 3).

Integral sampling

This method, which was developed at LNEC in Lisbon (Rocha, 1971) consists essentially of obtaining a core sample from the rock mass after it has been reinforced with a bar, which assures the integrity of the entire sampled material. The method can be applied along the full length of a drill hole or only in the zones where conditions in the rock mass or the requirements of the structure to be built make its use advisable. In principle a core with a small diameter (36 mm) is first drilled out over a length of 1,5 m, then a steel bar of the same size is grouted in place in the hole. After this operation the reinforced rock and steel are drilled out with a larger coring bit (normally 76 or 86 mm). According to reports, samples have been taken at depths down to 60 m.

TV examination of the drill hole

The equipment used here has been developed by Hagconsult and is portable. It consists of a camera unit with amplifier, control center and monitor plus a vieo tape recorder to record images and comments (Fig. 4). The drill hole should have an inclination of at least 5-10° from the vertical for the orientation device to function. When drilling is completed, the drill hole is blown out with air and is flushed repeatedly with water until the hole is clean or the water in the hole is clear.

The TV camera is lowered in the hole at a speed adapted to the prevalent rock conditions (Fig. 5). Normally, about 20 m of drill hole can be examined per hour. The method makes it possible to observe and

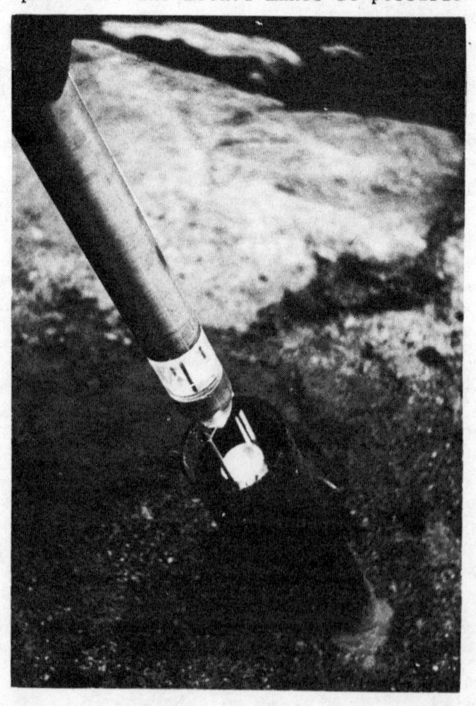

Fig. 5. The TV camera being lowered into the drill hole.

study carefully the rock mass and such variations in it as fissures, fissured and crush zones and certain variations in the type of rock. A record is kept during the examination. Sections of interest according to the criteria above are recorded on the tape, accompanied by an oral commentary on the depth from the surface, geological observations and so on. See further Lundström, 1973.

Water pressure testings

Testing the water pressure or measuring water loss in the drill hole is a method of determining the permeability of the rock mass.

A water line is connected to the hole where the water pressure is to be tested, with a seal between the walls of the hole and the end of the line. The volume of water which can be forced into the rock at a given water pressure gives a measurement of how closed or open the rock is. When processing the data obtained, corrections are made for flow losses in the lines, the ground water pressure and so on.

RELIABILITY

It can be established as a general truth for all the investigation methods that the quality of the information obtained is wholly dependent on the skill and exactitude of the field personnel. The method most reliable in practise can yield completely erroneous results if administered by unexperienced personnel. A presupposition for the various methods characterized in the following is that well-experienced personnel is engaged.

A further basic condition is that a detailed geological mapping of outcroppings and fissures has preceded and initiated each investigation and that data from this is available when evaluating the respective method of investigation.

From Table 1 can be concluded the possibility and capacity of the investigation methods to communicate information on different parameters of rock types and rock masses. To serve as a basis for discussions about suitable investigation methods at different stages and under variable conditions, the technical parameters are completed in Fig. 1, with the most reliable method (A-E) for achieving a good result.

Below follows a verbal characterization of the different methods, corresponding to Table 1.

Characteristics of core drilling

If well cared-for, modern equipment is used, operated by skilled and experienced personel, core drilling provides quite complete material for study in the form of cores and the drilling logbook. The evaluation of the material will in certain vital sections be impaired by subjective views, so that it should be carried out by an experienced specialist in order to increase prognosis accuracy. The core makes it possible to make laboratory measurements of the various material properties of the rock types.

Determination of the rock types deep in the rock mass, their structural characteristics and boundaries is normally possible with satisfactory accuracy with core drilling. The loss of cores, however, excludes

Parameters \ Investigation method	Core drilling A	Percussive investigationdrilling B	Integral sampling C	TV examination (incl. investigation drilling) D	Water pressure testing E
ROCK TYPE — Characteristics of rock types					
Mineral content incl. binder if present	3	2	3	2	0
Grain size	3	0	3	3	0
Structural characteristics	3	0	3	2	0
Strike and dip	2	0	3	2	0
Mechanical properties	3	1	3	0	0
ROCK MASS — Fissuring (individual fissures)					
Fissure frequency (presence)	2	1	3	2	1
Fissure widths	0	0	3	3	1
Filling material in fissures	1	0	2	0	0
Degree of filling in fissures	0	0	2	2	0
Orientation of fissures	1	0	3	3	0
Weak zones					
Presence	2	2	3	3	1
Width of weak zones	2	1	3	3	1
Mineral content in weak zones	2	0	2	1	0
Orientation of weak zones	1	0	3	3	0
State of stress	0	0	0	0	0
Permeability	0	0	0	0	2
3 = Complete, unambiguous information 2 = Good but not unambiguous information 1 = Some information difficult to interpret 0 = No information	Core drilling may entail a risk of underrate the properties of the rock mass because of fissures caused by drilling.	Percussive investigation drilling in itself gives a very limited picture of the rock mass. It does indicate suspicious levels for a subsequent TV examination.	Seen in overall terms, this method gives very good information about the rock mass. A prerequisite however is that the walls of the first small diameter core-drilled hole do not collapse.	TV examination presupposes that the hole is intact so that the camera can be lowered. The method may entail a certain risk of overrating the rock mass since closed fissures are not evident.	Since water pressure tests are always carried out in conjunction with drilling, the information thus gained is often a valuable complement in evaluations.

Tabel 1. The possibility for various investigation methods to communicate reliable information about rock types and rock masses.

the possibility of such direct assessments.

An evaluation of the macrostructures of the rock mass with point of departure in the drilled-out cores and attendant drilling logbook is a very complicated task, with many ambiguities. Certain information on the general structure of the rock can be obtained but a detailed mapping of weak zones of rock, of special interest for the projecting work, is accompanied by uncertainties, which are above all due to the difficulty in such zones of reconstructing core losses, secondary fissures and primary fissures. In addition, core drilling has the weakness that the width of fissures crossing the drill hole and the direction of the fissure planes cannot be determined under normal conditions.

Characteristics of percussion drilling

The results of investigative percussion drilling are unavoidably conditioned by subjective judgment, which naturally entails a high degree of uncertainty in the conclusions. The greater the experience and exactitude of the operator and interpreter, the greater the accuracy in the prognosis.

Assessments of the rock types deep in the rock mass are made very uncertain in percussive investigation drilling. The prerequisite for making a very rough evaluation of this type is that flushing is continuous and satisfactory so that cuttings can be continually recovered for analysis. No theoretical model for assessing the types of rock for field use has been developed for use with investigative percussion drilling in non-homogeneous rock masses.

Investigative percussion drilling does provide certain indirect information on the deep structure of the rock mass. This information is in the form of indications that the drilling sequence has been affected on certain levels by structurally determined strength variations in the rocks, lack of homogeneity in the rock mass, or by variations in the performance of the machine plant. The localization of weak points and zones which is possible with this method is however of great importance as complementary information to that provided by other methods.

Characteristics of the method for integral sampling

By means of this method it is possible to obtain samples localized in space, representative of all of the features of the rock mass, such as joints, faults and other fractures and especially their infillings. In addition, the samples can be tested with a view to determining the properties, particularly the mechanical ones, of the rock mass.

Scrutiny of the samples makes it possible to get an overall view of the actual conditions inside the rock mass.

Characteristics of TV examination of the drill hole

TV examination, combined with the results of outcropping and fissure mapping plus percussive or core drilling, gives a qualitatively relatively complete material for study in the form of the recorded comments and video tapes. Evaluation is however always subjective and requires an experienced specialist, if satisfactory prognosis accuracy is to be obtained. There is however the advantage that problematic points and zones can be recorded on the tape, which makes it possible for other experts to participate in the evaluation.

The possibilities of determining the types of rock in the depths of the rock mass and their boundaries are dependent to a great extent on the knowledge of the rock mass which has been obtained by other investigations, e.g. geological surface mapping. It is normally the case that types of rock which differ appreciably as concerns structural features, grain size and reproduction in black-&-white can be determined, if the types of rock prevalent in the area are known. The mechanical properties of the rocks can, however, not be established, so that samples for such investigations must be taken in conjuction with drilling.

With TV examination it is possible to evaluate the structure of the rock mass in almost undisturbed rock. The information obtained on fissures very nearly corresponds to actual conditions. The method makes it possible to localize the fissures of the rock mass, the fissure widths, the fissure plane and other discontinuities. Certain "healed" fissures may occasionally be difficult to identify.

Characteristics of water pressure testings

It can be claimed in principle that measurements of water losses give an indication of the permeability of the rock mass and of the degree of openness of certain fissure systems. There are several external factors which can affect the results of water pressure tests and produce erroneous or difficulty interpreted data. For example, leakage may occur between the sleeve and the rock wall, and not always be discovered. In addition, the water pressure may produce an increase in the ground water counter-pressure which is often difficult to evaluate. The increases in water flow and pressure also disturb the rock mass and this naturally affects the measured water losses.

CONCLUDING REMARKS

In the evaluation of the information content of drill hole investigation methods which has been reported here, it was noted that the various methods have greatly differing basic abilities to communicate reliable information on the rock types and the rock mass. In addition, they cover differing areas as concerns the character of the information which can be communicated.

It is, however, generally true that careful geological surface mapping is a prerequisite for carrying out a meaningful evaluation of drill hole investigations with reference to establishing the solid geometrical construction of the rock mass.

Different projects and different geological formations require access to different primary technical and geological parameters. Against this background, it is advisable in projecting work to exploit or combine the investigation methods which have the prerequisites to communicate as reliable information as possible about the parameters which can be expected to be meaninful. The above outlined evaluation system should facilitate such an optimization of the investigation work in individual projects.

ACKNOWLEDGEMENTS

The research project described in this paper is carried out by Hagconsult AB and is financed through grant from the Swedish Council for Building Research.

REFERENCES

Lundström L. Inspection of Drillholes by means of a TV-camera. ISRM, Stuttgart 1972.

Morfeldt, C-O; Bergman, M; Lundström, L; Bergundersökningar. Kvalitetsvärdering av undersökningsmetoder. (Rock mass investigations. Evaluation of methods.) The Swedish Council for Building Research. Report R34:1973. English summary and captions.

Rocha, M; A method of integral sampling of rock masses. Rock Mechanics, Vol. II/1-1971.
Rocha, M; Barosso, M; Some applications of the new integral sampling method in rock masses. Laboratorio Nacional de Engenharia Civil, Memoria 397, Lisbon, 1971.

SOME CRITICAL CONSIDERATIONS ON THE DEFORMATION AND FAILURE OF ROCK SAMPLES IN THE LABORATORY

CONSIDERATIONS CRITIQUES SUR LA DÉFORMATION ET LA RUPTURE DES ÉCHANTILLONS DE ROCHE EN LABORATOIRE

BETRACHTUNGEN ÜBER DAS VERFORMUNGS- UND BRUCHVERHALTEN VON FELSPROBEN

Paolo BERTACCHI Engineer, Hydraulic and Structural Center, ENEL

Armando SAMPAOLO Geologist, Hydraulic and Structural Center, ENEL

Milano, Italy

SUMMARY. Taking the opportunity from geomechanical laboratory research on different rocks, some critical considerations are advanced as to how far test results accord with the parameters being sought; separate consideration is given to: - deformation behaviour under compression stress, giving characteristic examples and indicating some anomalies; - failure behaviour under compression and tension stresses, emphasizing the considerable divergence between failure modes and the scheme generally assumed in evaluating the results; - shear behaviour, describing the type of test performed, its value and the results obtained. It is constantly emphasized that the more the sample behaviour and test results depart from the theoretical pattern, the more the material is characterized by discontinuity and anisotropy. Lastly, it is recommended that a careful critical study be made in order to suit the test and interpretation of the results to the actual geomechanical characteristics of the sample.

SOMMAIRE. Des recherches géomécaniques de laboratoire sur des roches de différente nature nous ont fourni l'idée de faire quelques considérations critiques sur la correspondance entre les résultats des essais et les paramètres qu'on entend rechercher; on examine séparemment les questions suivantes: - comportement de déformation à la compression, en mentionnant des exemples caractéristiques et en signalant des anomalies; - comportement à la rupture à la compression et à la traction, en mettant en évidence des différences sensibles entre les modalités de rupture et le schéma usuellement adopté pour l'évaluation des résultats; - comportement au cisaillement, en traitant du type d'essai réalisé ainsi que des résultats obtenus. On met en évidence constamment que plus le matériau est caractérisé par des discontinuités et anisotropies, plus le comportement de l'échantillon et les résultats de l'essai même s'éloignent du schéma théorique. Pour conclure, on recommande un examen critique attentif en vue de rendre l'essai et l'interprétation des résultats aptes à fournir les caractéristiques géomécaniques réelles de l'échantillon.

ZUSAMMENFASSUNG. Es wird hier Anlass von geomechanischen Laboratoriumsversuchen genommen über Felsmassen verschiedener Art, um einige kritischen Betrachtungen über der Beziehung zwischen den Versuchsergebnissen und den zu suchenden Parametern anzustellen; es werden einzeln geprüft: - Druck-Verformungsverhalten, mit Aufstellung einiger bezeichnenden Beispiele und Unregelmässigkeiten; - Druck-und Zug-Bruchverhalten, mit besonderer Rücksicht auf bedeutenden Abweichungen zwischen den Bruchbedingungen und zur Ergebnisauswertung üblich angenommenen Schema; - Scherverhalten mit Beschreibung des realisierten Versuchstypes und der erreichten Ergebnisse. Es wird fortwährend unterstrichen, dass sich das Probenverhalten und die Versuch sergebnisse desto vom theoretischen Schema abweichen, je mehr das Material durch Unterbrechungen und Anisotropien gekenzeichnet ist. Man empfehlt, zum Schluss eine aufmerksame kritische Prüfung vorzunehmen, um den Versuch und die Ergebnisauffassung den reellen geomechanischen Eigenschaften anzupassen.

1 - INTRODUCTION

Laboratory testing on rock samples in connection with the design of major civil engineering projects is often considered from two opposite points of view, both of them questionable: scepticism, due to the difficulty of testing samples that actually represent the rock in situ; full confidence to obtain condition characteristics that exactly accord with the static scheme and the mathematical model, within whose framework the designer wish to work.

The extreme variability of the nature of the rock makes testing a delicate process and imposes the following conditions: - knowledge of sampling methods and of sample representativeness; - complete mineralogical and structural analysis to establish the specific characteristics of the lithotype being considered; - constant reference to those characteristics, as

well as to actual conditions in which the rock will have to work, in preparing the sample, in assembling the instruments and in carrying out the test;
- careful comparison of deformation and failure behaviour, with the theoretical conditions on which the test is based. Close co-operation between geologist and engineer is therefore essential at all the stages, viz. sampling, test and interpretation of the results.

This paper aims at emphasizing some deductions based on the experience gained in the course of extensive geomechanical investigations carried out on different types of rock involved in the construction of hydroelectric projects. Experimental research was performed at the Niguarda (Milan) Laboratory of the Hydraulic and Structural Research Centre of ENEL (Italian State Electricity Board) on behalf of the Project Design Centres of the same Board, which are concerned with the construction of major civil engineering works.

The types of rock herein referred to are:
- Biotitic granite of holocrystalline texture, sometimes porphyritic due to coarse orthoclase crystalline elements and porphyry, at the Taloro (Sardinia) underground power station.
- Anatexitic gneiss (biotitic anatexites, biotitic gneiss and embrechite), locally with a pronounced structure, at the Entracque (Piedmont) underground power station.
- Clhoritic micaceous schistose gneiss and anatexitic gneiss, at the Chiotas (Piedmont) dam foundation.
- Micaschist and schistose gneiss with quartzose feldspathic lenticles, at the S. Fiorano (Lombardy) underground power station.
- Marl and microcrystalline marlaceous limestone of marked and frequent bedding, at the Pelos (Venetia) underground power station.

Except for the first, the aforesaid lithotypes are characterized by anisotropy and more or less marked discontinuity. Lastly, it should be mentioned that the results and graphs referred to hereafter are, in each specific case, those that best illustrate the considerations contained in this paper, and should not be taken as generally valid data for that particular rock.

2 - DEFORMABILITY

In order to predict settlement after excavations, or foundation settlement due to applied load the designer asks the laboratory to let him know the elastic characteristics of the rock, often expressed in terms of Young's modulus E and Poisson's ratio ν. Thus the deformation mode of the rock is assumed to be linear, in the same way as may reasonably be assumed with a construction material, such as concrete. This behaviour, however, may only in exceptional cases be found in rock material.

On the contrary, both in-situ load tests on rock masses, and on rock samples in the laboratory, show that deformation behaviour is generally far from being linear; indeed, the more it deviates from the behaviour typical of artificial construction materials the more the rock formation deviates from the ideal pattern of continuity, homogeneity and isotropy. At ENEL's laboratory, deformability tests are carried out by applying loads by means of hydraulic testing machines and measuring deformations (axial ε_a and diametral ε_d) by means of electric strain gauges or by inductive transducers. The recording of data is made for a great number of load values, in order to obtain stress-strain curves as far as possible complete, representing the actual characteristics of the sample deformability.

Thus, it is possible to have pairs of values of $E_{tg} = \dfrac{\Delta\ \sigma}{\Delta\ \varepsilon_a}$, $\nu_{tg} = \dfrac{\Delta\ \varepsilon_d}{\Delta\ \varepsilon_a}$ for any level of stress that has to be taken into account in the calculation. These "tangent" values are more actual than the corresponding "secant" values (E_{sec}, ν_{sec}), to which reference is often made in practice, evaluated by taking into account the overall stress and deformation starting from a state of no-load.

In the case of rock that may be considered practically isotropic, it is noted that deformation measurements are independent on the positioning of the strain gauges around the sample. On the contrary, in the more frequent case of rock of anisotropic behaviour, the deformation recorded depends closely on the position of the strain gauge; fig. 1 shows the considerable differences of recorded deformations on a highly anisotropic rock sample, depending on the positioning of strain gauges.

Of the various lithotypes examined, the micaschist showed an abnormal behaviour, which occurred systematically in a large number of samples: thus, as the stress increased, the diametral deformations ε'_d, ε''_d measured in orthogonal positions, over a wide initial part of the total applied load, showed contraction rather than dilatation, with consequent negative value of ν (Fig. 2).

This is certainly associated with the presence of strata of material of varying deformability and the

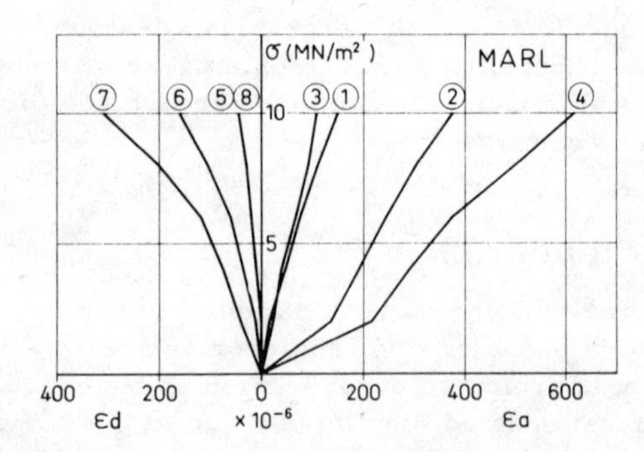

Fig. 1 - Influence of strain gauge positioning around the sample upon deformation measurement.

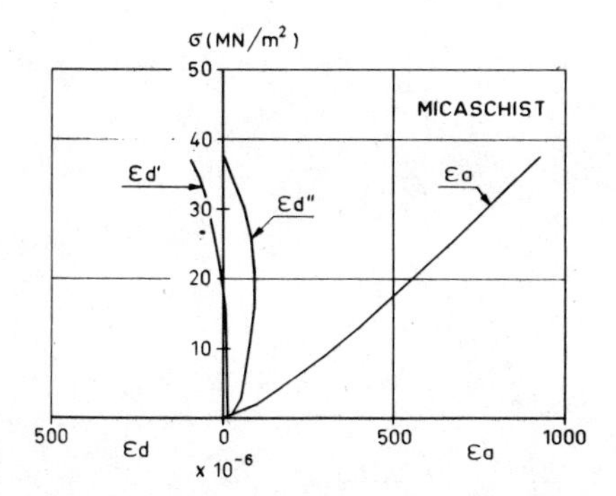

Fig. 2 - Anomalies of diametral deformation of a micaschist.

extent of this anomaly is associated with the angle formed by the strata with the load axis.

The deformation behaviour of rock material varies considerably, depending on the nature and formation of the tested rock; fig. 3 gives the stress-strain diagrams, typical of some rocks tested in ENEL's laboratory. As regards the axial deformation only, four fundamental types of behaviour may be identified: - elastic, almost linear for granite; - plasto-elastic for gneiss; - elasto-plastic for marl; -prevalently plastic for micaschist. Classification on the basis of diametral deformations, which are more sensitive to load variations, is more difficult.

Fig. 4 shows the curves of E_{tg}, E_{sec} and ν_{tg}, ν_{sec} values as a function of loads, referring to the aforesaid four types. First of all, it may be noted that the curves of "tangent" values give a more direct interpretation of the deformation behaviour of the sample, and that the more they deviate from the curves of the corresponding "secant" values, the less linear is that behaviour. This applies particularly to Poisson's ratio.

Laboratory deformability tests may, moreover, be discussed for the relatively short time taken over the test. Sometimes a marked influence of load increase velocity on the deformation may be noted: this may affect the evaluation of the parameters to be determined; it is therefore advisable, after load application, to wait for the deformation to settle down. Fig. 5 gives, as an example, the deformation versus time curves observed in two different rocks at constant load: with a normal settlement (Curve A) for gneiss, and a very slow settlement (Curve B) for a micaschist.

Sonic velocity measurements are held to be valid method for qualitatively characterizing a given type of rock, though not for obtaining values of elastic modulus. Systematic comparison between in-situ sonic logs and laboratory velocity measurement on rock samples is certainly useful for quantitative evaluation of the degree of soundness of in-situ rock.

A type of test which, in our opinion, may be of some interest consists in measuring the propagation velocity of a longitudinal sonic wave (V l) along the axis of a sample, subjected to compression, by means of small piezoelectric transducers, placed, with elastic suspension, in the loading plates. As is known, the velocity V l tends to increase with increasing in the compression load: it has been noted that, given the

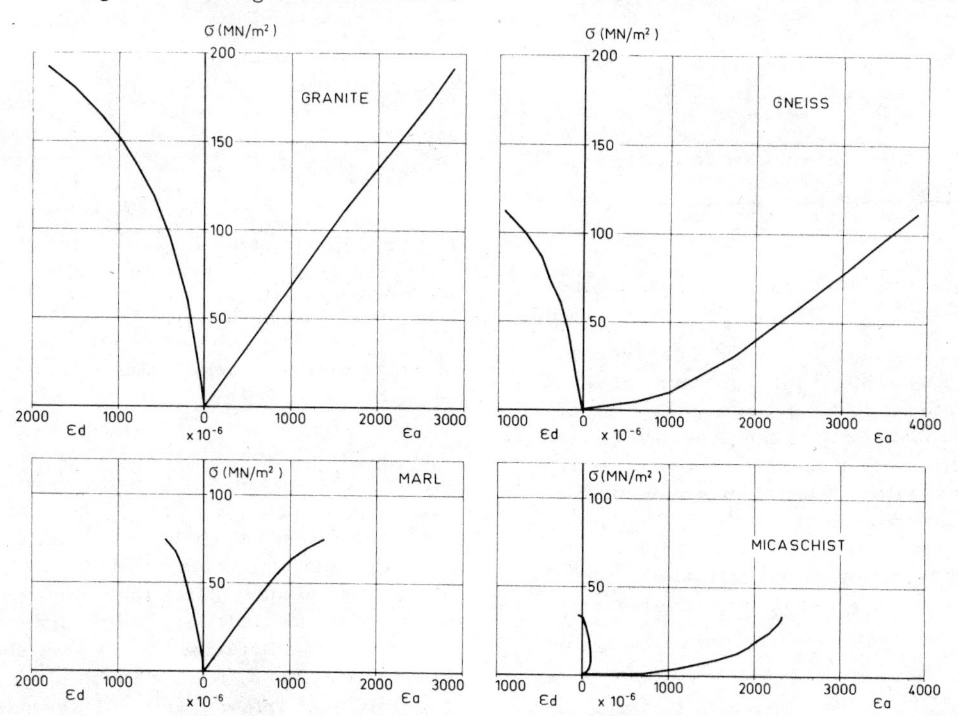

Fig. 3 - Deformation behaviour of four typical rocks.

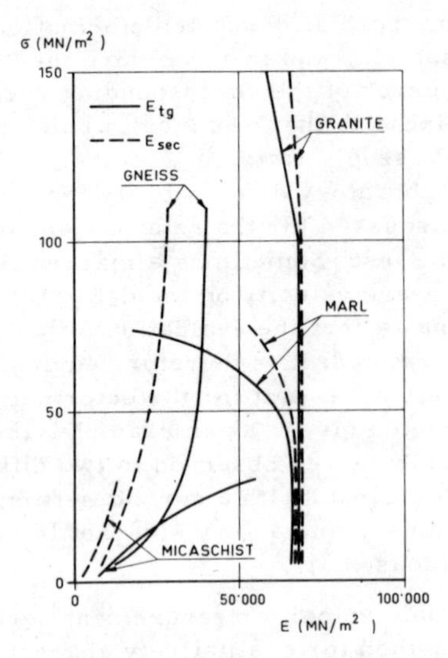

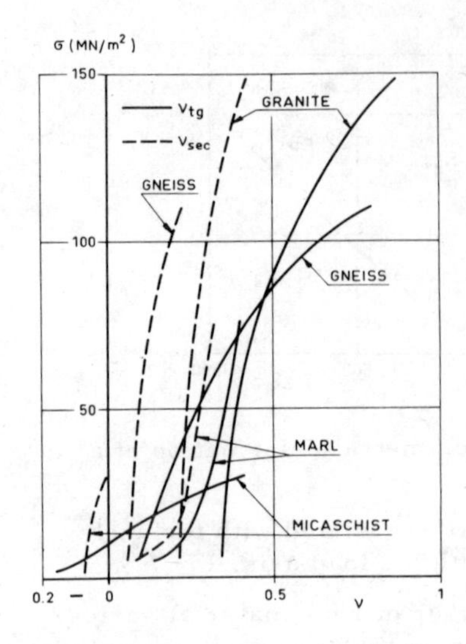

Fig. 4 - Young's moduli and Poisson's ratios, tangent and secant, referred to four typical rocks.

same type of rock, the lower was the initial value of V l (Fig. 6) the more marked is the increase in propagation velocity. Velocity in the samples, as the load increases, tends towards a limit value which is assumed to represent the wave velocity, once total

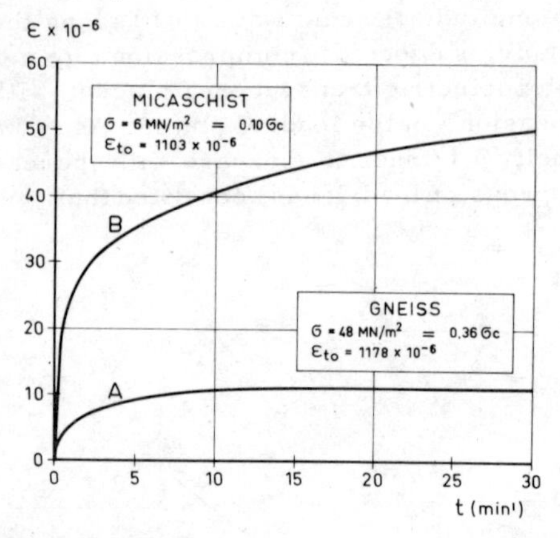

Fig. 5 - Deformation curves versus time at constant load.

rock compaction has been achieved. The highest velocities often found by sonic logging in sound rock masses compared to those that can be measured on cored samples, are probably due to the presence of stress in the rock in situ, which makes it more compact. It is believed that after a sufficient experience, overall indications may be obtained on the stress condition of the rock masses, by comparing the propagation velocity measured in situ with that obtained in the laboratory with different mono- and triaxial load values.

3 - FAILURE

As is known, the uniaxial compressive test gives the strength value of a material, as the ratio between the load (N) and the area (A) of the sample cross section. For rock samples of sufficient continuity, homogeneity and isotropy this method is certainly valid and leads to consistent statistical values. However, as

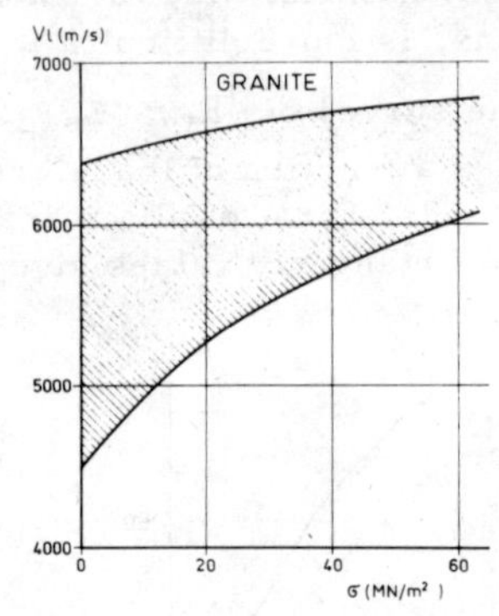

Fig. 6 - Range of sonic wave velocity on a granite versus axial load.

regards rocks that, for their texture, deviate from the ideal scheme, the value of compressive strength taken as the N/A ratio has to be interpreted on the basis of actual failure modes observed during test. Indeed, when a sample of anisotropic rock is subjected to uniaxial compression test, failure frequently occurs in accordance with natural surfaces, so as to show typical shear failure. These natural surfaces include the trend of the crystalline texture, the alternation of different mineral layers and the presence of fracture planes. Often there are several groups of preferential surfaces, having different directions, each being characterized by its own shearing strength. In all these cases, failure takes place in accordance with the most unfavourable surface, depending on the dip angle it forms in respect of the sample axis;

sometimes the failure occurs following a combination of surfaces, each close to the limit condition. Thus, a considerable dispersion of results is obtained, if they are evaluated as a whole. A more realistic analysis consists in grouping the values obtained for every sample in accordance with the failure type. It will generally be necessary to plan for an investigation of three-dimensional type, designed to provide the complete distribution of the strength, the values being given for any direction whatever. In the simpler cases, as, for instance, for transversally isotropic rock, a two-dimensional research may be sufficient.

The values for two series of compression strength tests, obtained on a fairly isotropic granite, and on a transversally isotropic marl, are given, as an example, hereunder:

- Granite - No. 29 σ_c MN/m^2 159 S.D.% 17
- Marl - No. 36 σ_c MN/m^2 61.5 S.D.% 48

Fig. 7 shows, for the same marl, the mean behaviour of σ_c as a function of the angle α, formed by the load axis and the dip direction of bedding.

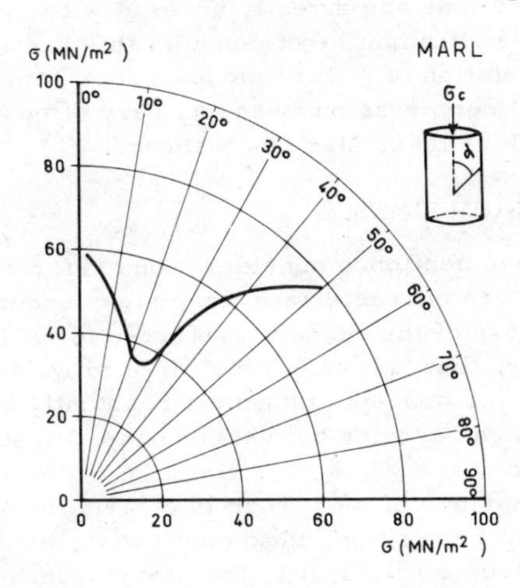

Fig. 7 - Compressive strength of a marl as a function of the α angle.

The so called "Brasilian" test is sometimes required to determine the tensile strength.
In rock mechanics this test is fairly significant for continuous and isotropic rocks, provided the tensile failure takes place on the diametral plane itself. If the abovesaid rock conditions are lacking, the distribution of stresses in the diametral section of the sample is quite different from that of a simple tension. Failure occurs outside the diametral plane, with extreme variability in tensile strength values. Examples of "Brasilian" test results on isotropic materials and on highly anisotropic material are given in the following table:

Granite	No. 17	σ_t MN/m^2 8	S.D.% 18
Micaschist: schistosity in respect of load:			
a) parallel	No. 13	σ_t MN/m^2 1.2	S.D.% 31
b) different dip	No. 33	σ_t MN/m^2 3.1	S.D.% 46

While, for the granite, the results are fully acceptable, for the micaschist, particularly for type b) samples, the deviation of the results and the type of failure rob the test of any confidence.

4 - SHEAR BEHAVIOUR

A rock mass may often be represented as an ensemble of blocks, separated by groups of discontinuity, differently dipping. For the stability analysis it is essential to know the characteristics of shear strength and friction along these discontinuities. It is therefore necessary to carry out suitable tests separately on each typical discontinuity group characterizing the rock in question. These are schistosity planes, beddings, joints, faults, etc. Each of these discontinuities forms an existing or potential shear plane. The test has to be performed in such a way that the tangential stress plane coincides with the discontinuity to be tested; it is therefore an imposed shear surface test. Having to work on these different groups, and under different conditions of normal load, and having, obviously, to perform an adequate repetition of each test, the resulting number of tests is rather high, and this is only possible in a laboratory. However, it is essential that at least some typical situations be checked by means of in-situ tests on blocks of suitable size.

ENEL's laboratory has available a shear testing apparatus that makes it possible to work on sample sections up to 100 cm^2, however positioned, enclosed in a suitable matrix, with normal and tangential load up to 5 x 10^5 N. The shearing box is equipped with transducers, sited in such a way as to measure the sample deformation, in both tangential and normal directions; deformations γ are plotted directly as a function of tangential stress τ. Fig. 8 shows some diagrams τ / γ, representative of the main types of rock behaviour most frequently encountered in the laboratory shear tests (diagrams A relative to samples of schistose gneiss; diagrams B, to stratified marl samples). Curves 1 refer to intact samples, without preferential shearing planes; curves 2 refer to intact samples, loaded at a preferential shearing plane (schistosity plane in A_2, bedding plane in B_2); curves 3 refer to shearing tests along the already existing separation planes.
In both the first two cases a "peak" is noted, (much marked obviously in the case 1) which represents the initial shear strength τ_t; a decreasing more or less quick is then noted, towards the residual strength τ_r. In the case 3 the "peak" disappears and is replaced by a slight convexity of the curve: the values τ_t and τ_r practically coincide.

The mineralogical nature and the structure of the rock affect mainly the initial values τ and γ and secondarily the residual values and behaviour of the

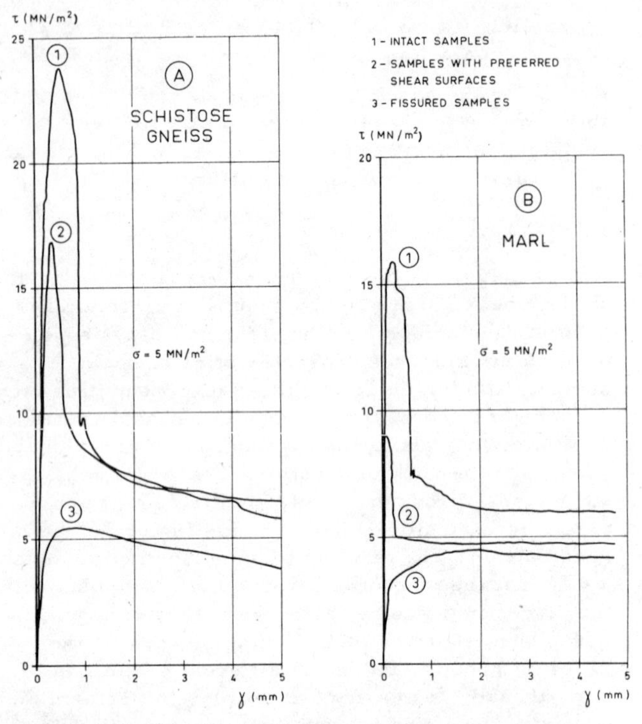

Fig. 8 - Shear behaviour of two rocks on samples having three different conditions of the shear plane.

curves. The value of the residual friction τ_r is depending especially on the geometric shape of the shearing surface (degree of roughness), on the presence of minerals of lamellar texture (mica or chlorite), on the degree of weathering of the mineralogical elements, and lastly, in the case of preexisting fissures, on the nature of filling material.

As already said, for a given shear surface, it is necessary to perform tests using different values of σ. The following three diagrams (Fig. 9) show the results obtained with a series of tests made on the

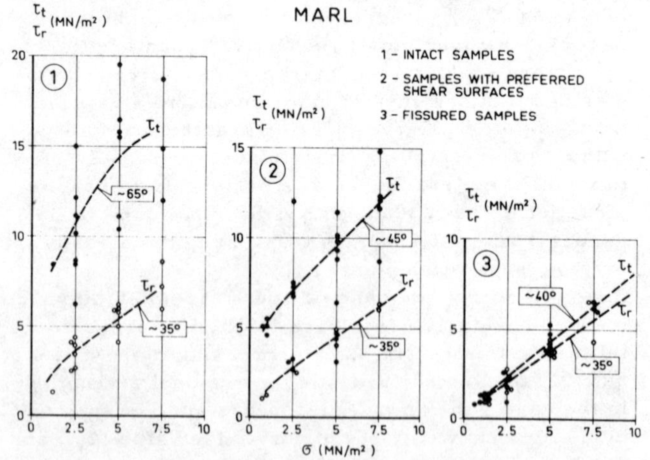

Fig. 9 - Diagrams of initial (τ_t) and residual (τ_r) shear strength versus normal stress (σ) on a marl.

same stratified marl, referred to in Fig. 9B, on intact samples (1), on samples having a preferential shear plane (2), and on already fractured samples (3). The results of separate tests are grouped and interpreted by two curves, the highest of which $\tau_t - \sigma$ shows the mean strength characteristics related to "peak", and the lowest $\tau_r - \sigma$, the mean residual strength characteristics. τ_t values have a marked dispersion in the case 1: the curve that interprets its behaviour is valid purely from a qualitative point of view. The curve $\tau_t - \sigma$ has a higher meaning in the cases 2 and 3. In the latter the curves $\tau_t - \sigma$ and $\tau_r - \sigma$ virtually coincide. It may be noted, for this lithological type, the substantial invariability of residual strength for shearing on surfaces, no matter how they have been caused.

To conclude, to characterize a particular type of rock, it is felt very useful to have available an extensive experimental documentation on the parameters relating to shear, in accordance with the different groups of potential or actual shearing surfaces. Knowledge of curves $\tau - \sigma$ depending on the possible shearing directions are directly necessary to the design; moreover it might be of considerable use in rational interpretation of failure mode of rock sample under uniaxial compression when, as very often happens, this failure takes place as a shear.

5 - CONCLUSIONS

The aforementioned considerations refer only to some more characteristic examples encountered in the course of the research referred to. It is thought, however, that they may well serve to re-emphasize some basic concepts that must constantly be borne in mind when carrying out geomechanical testing in the laboratory.

The behaviour of most rock is clearly far from theoretical schemes applied to continuous, homogeneous and isotropic solids; it is therefore necessary to make a continuous and critical study of the choice of the sample, of test and measurement methods and of the process of deformation and failure.

Often the results show that the behaviour of the sample differs entirely from the forecasts. It is then essential to discuss and, if necessary, to reject the test, rather than compel it to fit into a predetermined theoretical scheme. In some cases, it will be necessary to change the type and method of the test, to make it as far as possible suitable for obtaining the parameter required, taking into account the specific characteristics of the rock in question.

GEOMECHANICS CLASSIFICATION OF ROCK MASSES AND ITS APPLICATION IN TUNNELING

CLASSIFICATION GÉOMÉCANIQUE DES MASSES ROCHEUSES ET SON APPLICATION POUR LE PERCEMENT DES TUNNELS

GEOMECHANISCHE GEBIRGSKLASSIFIZIERUNG UND IHRE ANWENDUNG IM TUNNELBAU

Z.T. BIENIAWSKI
Head of Geomechanics Division
Council for Scientific and Industrial Research
Pretoria, South Africa

SUMMARY. An engineering classification of jointed rock masses, termed the Geomechanics Classification, is proposed. It is based on six parameters: the uniaxial compressive strength of the rock material, drill core quality RQD, spacing, orientation and condition of joints, and ground water inflow. Importance ratings are allocated to each parameter and total ratings for rock mass classes are specified. The meaning of each rock mass class is given in terms of an unsupported span and its stand-up time. The potential of the Geomechanics Classification is demonstrated by applying it to a selection of primary support for tunnels in rock.

RESUME. Une classification pour l'ingénieur, des masses de roches fracturées, appelée Classification Géomécanique, est proposée. Elle dépend de six paramètres: La résistance à la compression simple, la qualité des carottes de sondage obtenues (valeur RQD), espacement, orientation et état des fissures, et les venues d'eau souterraines. On définie des valeurs relatives pour chaque paramètre et des valeurs totales pour la masse rocheuse. La signification de chaque classification rocheuse est donnée en termes de portée non supportée et de son temps de stabilité. En l'appliquant on montre le potentiel de la Classification Géomécanique pour determiner le soutènement primaire en tunnels, creusés en matière rocheuse.

ZUSAMMENFASSUNG. Eine für den Ingenieur bestimmte Klassifizierung für klüftiges Gebirge, geomechanische Gebirgsklassifizierung genannt, wird vorgeschlagen. Sie gründet sich auf sechs Parameter: Die einachsige Gesteinsdruckfestigkeit, die Qualität der gewonnenen Bohrkerne (RQD- Wert), den Kluftabstand, die Kluftstellung und den Zustand der Klüfte, sowie auf den Grundwasserzufluss. Jeder Parameter wird nach seiner relativen Wichtigkeit bewertet und die Gesamtbewertung des Gebirges wird definiert. Die Bedeutung der einzelnen Gebirgsklassen ist in den Begriffen der Stützweite und der Standzeit ausgedrückt. Die Möglichkeiten der geomechanischen Gebirgsklassifizierung werden beschrieben, um sie zur Bestimmung von Stützmassnahmen (Aussengewölbe) von Tunnels in Fels heranziehen zu können.

INTRODUCTION

Practical experience still plays today a major part in the design and construction of structures built in rock. The reason for this situation is that although rock mechanics has made much progress, particularly in the last ten years, there is still a lack of understanding of many phenomena associated with this field. Due to the highly complex nature of rock masses, it is not surprising that the relationships governing their behaviour are not yet fully established.

With reference to tunnelling, the present state of the art was best summarised by a statement made at the First North American Rapid Excavation and Tunnelling Conference (Wickham, et al, 1972):

"Predicting support requirements for tunnels has, for many years, been based on observation, experience and personal judgment of those involved in tunnel construction. Barring an unforeseen breakthrough in geophysical techniques for making tunnel site investigations, the prediction of support requirements for future tunnels will require the same approach."

Under such conditions, an assessment of rock masses based on a classification system is believed to be of great value if it can be related to the solution of specific engineering problems.

It is the purpose of this paper to introduce a rock mass classification which can estimate the necessary support measures needed in tunnel construction .

CLASSIFICATION AND TUNNELLING

A classification system for rock masses is essential to ensure understanding and communication among those concerned with a given tunnelling project, such as the Owner, the Engineer, the Contractor, the rock mechanics engineer and the engineering geologist. A classification system is also important in designing the route and tunnel cross-sections, drawing up preliminary cost estimates, determining the construction time, tendering, choosing the methods of excavation and primary support and evaluating experiences obtained during construction.

In general, a rock mass classification has the following purposes in a tunnelling application:

1. To divide a particular rock mass into groups of similar behaviour;
2. To provide a basis for understanding the characteristics of each group;
3. To yield quantitative data for the design of tunnel support;
4. To provide a common basis for communication.

These aims should be fulfilled by ensuring that a classification system has the following attributes:

(a) is simple, easily remembered and understandable;
(b) each term is clear and the terminology used is widely acceptable;
(c) only the most significant properties of rock masses are included;
(d) is based on measurable parameters which can be determined by relevant tests quickly and cheaply in the field;
(e) it is based on a rating system which can weigh the relative importance of classification parameters;
(f) is general enough so that the same rock will possess the same classification, regardless how it is being used (e.g. for tunnel roof stability as well as for excavation purposes).

The need for a suitable classification in the field of rock mechanics has long been recognised and, in fact, numerous proposals have been made. Nevertheless, although some of the existing classifications have a considerable potential none is fully satisfactory in terms of the above pre-requisites.

For example, many classifications are based on rock material characteristics only and are not functional enough. Others have disadvantages of a different type. The Terzaghi classification (1946) while dominant in the USA for many years and excellent for the purpose for which it was evolved, is basically applicable to tunnels with steel supports and is not suitable for modern tunnelling methods using shotcrete and rockbolts. It provides no quantitative information on the properties of rock masses. The Lauffer classification (1958) was a considerable step forward in the art of tunnelling since it introduced the concept of an active unsupported rock span and the corresponding stand-up time, both of which are very relevant parameters for determination of the type and amount of primary support in tunnels. The disadvantage of this classification is that these two parameters are difficult to establish and much is demanded of practical experience. The Deere classification (1970) relating the rock quality designation (RQD) to tunnel support is simple and practical but the RQD method disregards the influence of joint orientations, continuity and gouge materials which are of great importance in many cases.

STRUCTURAL REGIONS IN ROCK MASSES

A rock mass (also referred to as the "rock system" or the "rock body") consists of blocks of rock material (also referred to as "the intact rock element") which are separated by various types of discontinuities such as joints, faults, bedding planes, etc. In considering a classification of such a heterogeneous and anisotropic assemblage, it is necessary and convenient to distinguish a number of structural regions in a rock mass, each region having certain uniform features and similar characteristics. Although rock masses are discontinuous in nature, they may nevertheless be uniform in regions when, for example, the type of rock or the joint spacings are the same throughout the structural region. For such a region only one type of support will be needed and it will not be economical to change it until the rock mass conditions change distinctly, i.e. a new structural region can be distinguished. Generally, the boundaries of structural regions, to be determined by an engineering geologist, coincide with major geological features such as faults, dykes, shear zones, etc.

Once structural regions have been defined, a rock mass classification should be applied to each region.

PARAMETERS FOR CLASSIFICATION

Much of the problem in proposing a classification system is to select a set of parameters of greatest significance. It is believed that there is no single parameter or index which can fully and quantitatively describe a jointed rock mass for tunnelling purposes. Various factors have different significance and only if taken together can they describe satisfactorily a rock mass. Although the significance of some factors may be different in different cases, e.g. in roof stability and in blastability or drillability, certain parameters are related to one another and can be used in different applications.

A detailed study of this problem (Bieniawski, 1973) revealed that, for practical applications, the following six parameters are most significant in the behaviour of rock masses:

1. Uniaxial compressive strength of rock material;
2. Drill core quality RQD;
3. Spacing of joints;
4. Orientation of joints;
5. Condition of joints;
6. Ground water inflow.

All of these classification parameters can be measured in the field and they can also be grouped in accordance with already widely accepted divisions.

The uniaxial compressive strength of intact rock material is included for a number of reasons. If the discontinuities are widely spaced and the rock material is weak, the rock material properties will influence the behaviour of the rock mass. Under the same confining pressure, the strength of rock material constitutes the highest strength limit of the rock mass. The rock material is important if the joints are not continuous or if the use of tunnelling machines is contemplated. Finally, a sample of the rock material represents sometimes a small scale model of the rock mass since they have both been subjected to the same geological processes.

The determination of the uniaxial compressive strength of rock materials is a simple process for which standard techniques are available. Since, however, usual laboratory tests require careful specimen preparation and elaborate testing apparatus, it is recommended that the strength of rock materials be determined in the field from the point-load strength index. This involves testing on site of unprepared rock cores using simple portable equipment. Figure 1 shows that in this test a piece of drill core fails as a result of fracture across its diameter. The point-load strength index is calculated as the ratio of the applied load to the square of core diameter. The results given in Figure 1 show that a close correlation exists between the uniaxial compressive strength and the point-load strength index. Table 1 lists the corresponding strength ranges for strength classification of rock materials, after Deere modified to SI units. Note that σ_c = 1 MPa is considered as the lowest strength limit for rock materials.

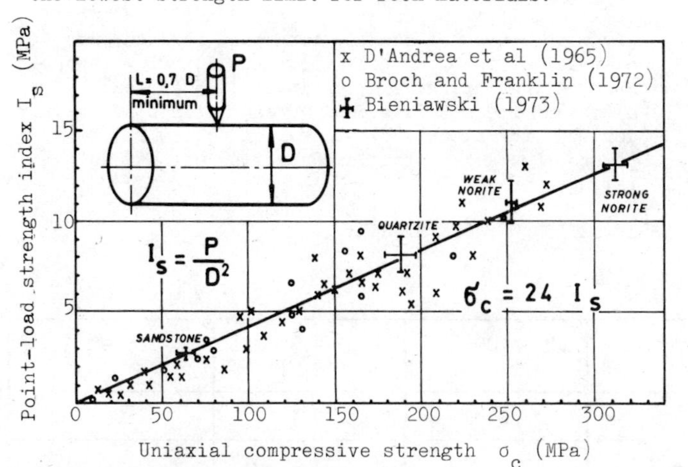

Fig. 1 Relationship between index I_s and strength σ_c for NX core (54 mm diameter).

TABLE 1 : STRENGTH CLASSIFICATION FOR ROCK MATERIALS

Description	Uniaxial compressive strength, MPa	Point-load strength index, MPa
Very high strength	> 200	> 8
High strength	100 - 200	4 - 8
Medium strength	50 - 100	2 - 4
Low strength	25 - 50	1 - 2
Very low strength	1 - 25	< 1

Rock quality designation (RQD) is a measure of drill core quality as obtained from boreholes but it is a more general measure than fracture frequency since it is based indirectly on both the degree of fracturing and the amount of weathering in the rock mass. The RQD is a quantitative index based on a modified core recovery procedure which incorporates only those pieces of hard, sound core which are 100 mm or greater in length. Shorter lengths of core are ignored as they are considered to be due to close shearing, jointing or weathering in the rock mass.

Since only hard, sound core is included in RQD determination, this means that rock core which is highly weathered receives zero RQD. For this purpose "highly weathered rock" means that weathering extends throughout the rock mass. The rock material is partly friable, has no lustre and all material except quartz is discoloured or stained. Highly weathered rock can be excavated with a geologist's pick.

For RQD determination, the core should be at least 50 mm in diameter and double tube N size core barrels (75 mm O.D.) with non-rotating inner barrels are recommended.

With the aid of RQD it is not normally possible to assess the spacing of joints from a single set of borehole cores. The RQD also disregards the influence of joint tightness, orientation, continuity and gouge material. Consequently while it seems an essential parameter (it was found useful by Deere et al, 1970, in classifying rock masses for selection of temporary tunnel support systems) it is not the only parameter for the full description of a rock mass.

Spacing and orientations of joints are of paramount importance for the stability of structures in jointed rock masses. The presence of joints reduces the strength of a rock mass and the joint spacing as well as their dip and strike govern the degree of such reduction. For example, a rock material with a high strength but intensely jointed will yield a weak rock mass. The data on spacing of joints must be obtained from a joint survey, for each joint set, and not from borehole logs. Table 2 gives the generally accepted joint spacing divisions, after Deere. It should be noted that in a rock mass there is usually more than one set of joints. Thus, in Table 1 the term "blocky" applies to the case of three joint sets, while for two joint sets the term "columnar" is suggested and in the case of one set of joints the term "tabular" may be suitable.

The term joint means all discontinuities which may be technically joints, faults, bedding planes or other surfaces of weakness. The spacing of joints means the mean distance apart of the planes of weakness in the rock mass in the direction perpendicular to the joint planes.

TABLE 2 : CLASSIFICATION OF JOINTS BASED ON SPACING

Description	Spacing of joints	Rock mass designation
Very wide	> 3 m	Solid
Wide	1 - 3 m	Massive
Moderately close	0,3 - 1 m	Blocky/seamy
Close	50 - 300 mm	Fractured
Very close	< 50 mm	Crushed

Condition of joints includes separation of joints (distance between joint surfaces), continuity and roughness of joints as well as gouge material. Tight joints with rough surfaces and no gouge have a high strength. On the other hand, open continuous joints will facilitate unrestricted inflow of ground water. The continuity of joints influences the extent to which the rock material and the joints separately affect the behaviour of the rock mass. A joint is continuous if its length is greater than the diameter of the tunnel. A joint may be continuous with or without containing any gouge, i.e. the material occurring on the joint surfaces. If gouge is present its type, thickness, consistency and continuity should be described.

Ground water is known to have an important effect on the behaviour of jointed rock masses. In the case of tunnels, the rate of inflow of ground water in litres per minute was shown to be the governing factor (Wickham, et al, 1972). This can be estabilished in exploration adits, pilot headings or in the actual tunnels under construction.

The classification parameters discussed above are to be provided by the engineering geologist from his measurements conducted in the field. One complete set of data is needed for each structural region as encountered along the tunnel route. While the data required are the minimum needed for an initial design of a tunnel, the geologist should supply any additional information which he considers useful and relevant.

THE GEOMECHANICS CLASSIFICATION

A rock mass classification, incorporating the parameters discussed above and termed the Geomechanics Classification, is proposed in Table 3. This classification satisfies the requirements stated earlier and combines the best features of existing classifications.

A number of observations should be made with respect to Table 3. It will be noted that rock parameters and rock masses are grouped into five classes. This is considered sufficient to provide for meaningful discrimination in all the parameters. More classes could be difficult to work with while fewer classes may not offer sufficiently clear distinctions.

In applying various parameters to a rock mass classification, it is necessary to note that different parameters are not equally important for the overall classification of a rock mass. Accordingly, importance ratings are also given in Table 3 for each parameter and its subdivisions. These ratings are partly derived from a study by Wickham et al, 1972. Two points should be noted in connection with these ratings.

TABLE 3 : GEOMECHANICS CLASSIFICATION OF ROCK MASSES

A. CLASSIFICATION PARAMETERS AND THEIR RATINGS

	Parameter					
1	Uniaxial compressive strength of intact rock	> 200 MPa	100 - 200 MPa	50 - 100 MPa	25 - 50 MPa	< 25 MPa
	Rating	10	5	2	1	0
2	Drill core quality RQD	90% - 100%	75% - 90%	50% - 75%	25% - 50%	< 25% or highly weathered
	Rating	20	17	14	8	3
3	Spacing of joints	> 3 m	1 - 3 m	0,3 - 1 m	50 - 300 mm	< 50 mm
	Rating	30	25	20	10	5
4	Strike and dip orientations of joints	Very favourable	Favourable	Fair	Unfavourable	Very unfavourable
	Rating	15	13	10	6	3
5	Condition of joints	Very tight: separation < 0,1 mm Not continuous		Tight: < 1 mm and continuous No gouge	Open: 1 - 5 mm Continuous Gouge < 5 mm	Open > 5 mm Continuous Gouge > 5 mm
	Rating	15		10	5	0
6	Ground water inflow (per 10 m of tunnel length)	N o n e		< 25 litres/min	25 - 125 litres/min	> 125 litres/min
	Rating	10		8	5	2

B. ROCK MASS CLASSES AND THEIR RATINGS

Class No.	I	II	III	IV	V
Description of class	Very good rock	Good rock	Fair rock	Poor rock	Very poor rock
Total rating	100 ← 90	90 ← 70	70 ← 50	50 ← 25	< 25

C. MEANING OF ROCK MASS CLASSES IN TUNNELLING

Class No.	I	II	III	IV	V
Unsupported span	5 m	4 m	3 m	1,5 m	0,5 m
Average stand-up time	10 years	6 months	1 week	5 hours	10 minutes

Firstly, the ratings given for joint spacings apply to rock masses having three sets of joints. Thus, when only one or two sets of joints are present, a conservative assessment is obtained. Secondly, some difficulties may be experienced in deciding whether strike and dip orientations are favourable or not in a given tunnel. For this purpose, reference should be made to Table 4 which is based on a detailed study (Wickham, et al, 1972) of this aspect.

TABLE 4 : THE EFFECT OF JOINT STRIKE AND DIP ORIENTATIONS IN TUNNELLING

Strike perpendicular to tunnel axis				Strike parallel to tunnel axis	
Drive with dip		Drive against dip			
Dip 45°-90°	Dip 20°-45°	Dip 45°-90°	Dip 20°-45°	Dip 45°-90°	Dip 20°-45°
Very favourable	Favourable	Fair	Unfavourable	Very unfavourable	Fair
Dip 0° - 20° : Unfavourable, irrespective of strike					

Once the importance ratings of the classification parameters are established, the ratings for all the individual parameters are added giving the total rating for the rock mass, i.e. its structural region under consideration. Note that the higher the total rating, the better the rock mass conditions.

Section B of Table 3 gives the total ratings for the five rock mass classes together with their descriptions.

As explained earlier, any rock mass classification must be related to specific engineering problems and hence the Geomechanics Classification should also have a practical meaning for tunnel design and construction.

The meaning of each rock mass class for tunnelling purposes is given in Section C of Table 3. This is done by specifying for each rock mass class an active unsupported span and the stand-up time that this span takes to failure. An active unsupported span is the width of the tunnel or the distance from support to the face if this is less than the width of the tunnel. This idea was first provided by Lauffer in 1958 but his original classification has since been modified many times. In the case of the Geomechanics Classification, the full relationship between the unsupported span and the stand-up time is given in Figure 2 while Section C of Table 3 gives the average data. It must be emphasized that since Figure 2 is derived from practical experience, some provision should be made to check on this relationship in the exploration test adits or, as will be discussed later, during the tunnel construction.

It will be seen from Figure 2 that a span of 2 m will stand unsupported for over one month in a rock of Class III ("fair rock") but only for a few days in a rock mass of Class IV ("poor rock"). Longer stand-up time in these rock mass classes can only be achieved once suitable support measures are introduced.

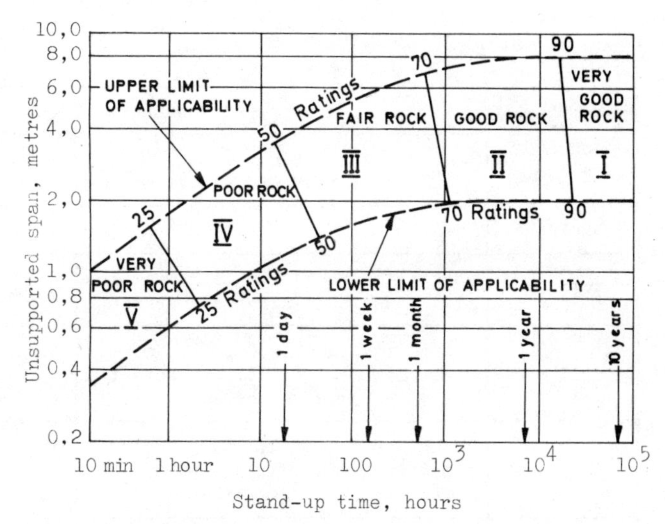

Fig. 2 Geomechanics classification for tunnelling. (Modified after Lauffer, 1958)

These measures will constitute the primary support (otherwise known as the temporary support) and they will aim at ensuring tunnel stability until the secondary support (or the permanent support, e.g. the concrete lining) is installed. They depend on such factors as the depth below surface (field stresses), tunnel size and shape and methods of excavation.

The primary support measures are given in Table 5 for shallow tunnels 5 m to 12 m in diameter driven by drilling and blasting. Three alternative methods of support are presented. This table, again compiled from experience, represents the modern technological practice in Europe, the U.S.A. and South Africa.

It should be emphasized that although the support measures listed in Table 5 are given for primary (temporary) support they will probably be able to carry all the load ever acting on the tunnel. After all, modern supports do not deteriorate easily and the traditional concept of the temporary or permanent support is losing its meaning.

As a consequence, the tunnels are overdesigned since the primary support is probably too strong. However, since our knowledge of tunnel engineering is far from complete, a radical departure from the customary methods of design may not be justified.

A solution to this problem is to conduct certain field measurements in the tunnel during its construction. This is also desirable since the information provided in Figure 2 and in Table 5 is based on experience which may not necessarily be fully applicable to all tunnels. Hence, on the basis of appropriate field measurements, the initial design may be adjusted during construction to conform with the behaviour of the rock mass. The measurements can also indicate to which extent the thickness of the final lining may be reduced. The most common field measurements are: precise levelling, convergence measurements across the tunnel cross-sections, borehole extensometer measurements around the tunnel circumference and pressure measurements in the lining and at the rock/concrete interface.

TABLE 5 : GUIDE FOR SELECTION OF PRIMARY SUPPORT IN 5 m to 12 m DIAMETER TUNNELS AT SHALLOW DEPTH

Rock mass class	Alternative support systems for drilling and blasting construction		
	Mainly ROCKBOLTS*	Mainly SHOTCRETE	Mainly STEEL RIBS
I	GENERALLY NO SUPPORT IS REQUIRED		
II	Rockbolts spaced 1,5 to 2,0 m plus occasional wire mesh in crown	Shotcrete 50 mm in crown	Uneconomic
III	Rockbolts spaced 1,0 to 1,5 m plus wire mesh and 30 mm shotcrete in crown where required	Shotcrete 100 mm in crown and 50 mm in sides plus occasional wire mesh and rockbolts where required	Light sets spaced 1,5 m to 2 m
IV	Rockbolts spaced 0,5 to 1,0 m plus wire mesh and 30 - 50 mm shotcrete in crown and sides	Shotcrete 150 mm in crown and 100 mm in sides plus wire mesh and rockbolts, 3 m long spaced 1,5 m	Medium sets spaced 0,7 m to 1,5 m plus 50 mm shotcrete in crown
V	Not recommended	Shotcrete 200 mm in crown and 150 mm in sides plus wire mesh, rockbolts and light steel sets. Close invert.	Heavy sets spaced 0,7 m with lagging. Shotcrete 75 mm as soon as possible.

* Resin bonded bolts 20 mm diameter, length $\frac{1}{2}$ tunnel width.

A CASE STUDY

Recently, a certain unsupported section of a road tunnel in South Africa collapsed providing information on the unsupported span and the stand-up time. It was decided to cross-check the Geomechanics Classification with this information.

The tunnel in question involved a heading, about 5 m in width and the same in height, being driven in slightly weathered quartzite. This heading was unsupported and its roof fell down over the full span after 5 months. The heading constituted one structural region in the tunnel for which the following input data were determined (where applicable the average ratings are given with individual values in brackets):

Parameter	Value		Rating
Uniaxial compressive strength	153 MPa		5
Core quality RQD	90 - 94%		20
Spacing of joints	Set 1: 0,3 - 1 m	(20)	22
	Set 2: 0,3 -0,6 m	(20)	
	Set 3: 2 m	(25)	
Orientations of joints	Set 1: Horizontal	(6)	8
	Set 2: Vertical; parallel to tunnel axis	(3)	
	Set 3: Vertical; perpendicular to tunnel axis	(15)	
Condition of joints	Separation < 1 mm Continuous joints		10
Ground water inflow	None		10
	TOTAL		75

From Table 3, a rating of 75 classifies this rock mass as "good rock". This rating falls in the first quarter of Class II which ranges from 70 to 90. From Figure 2, the expected stand-up time is determined for rating 75 and an unsupported span of 5 m (the width of the pilot tunnel). This leads to the stand-up time of about 1600 hours (67 days). In the actual case the rock stood unsupported for 5 months which indicates the conservative nature of the Geomechanics Classification. From Table 5, the pilot tunnel in question should have been supported (within two months) with 2,5 m long rockbolts, spaced at 1,5 m with occasional wire mesh placed in the crown to prevent isolated rockfalls.

--oOo---

The Geomechanics Classification has been successfully applied for some time for classification of rock masses in civil engineering and in mining situations. It was found that geologists had no difficulties in determining the input parameters needed for this classification and that if a few engineers classified independently they would arrive at the same classification of a given rock mass.

REFERENCES

Bieniawski, Z.T. Engineering classification of jointed rock masses. Trans. S. Afr. Instn Civil Engrs, 1973, in press.

Deere, D.U., Peck, R.B., Parker, H.W. and Monsees, J.E. Design of tunnel support systems. Highway Research Record, No. 339, 1970, pp. 26-33.

Lauffer, H. Gebirgsklassifizierung für den Stollenbau. Geologie und Bauwesen, vol. 24, 1958, pp. 46-51.

Terzaghi, K. Rock defects and loads on tunnel supports. Rock Tunnelling with Steel Supports, eds. Proctor and White, Commercial Shearing Co., Youngstown, 1946, pp 15-99.

Wickham, G.E., Tiedemann, H.R. and Skinner, E.H. Support determinations based on geological predictions. Proc. First North American Tunnelling Conference, AIME, New York, 1972, pp. 43-64.

THE INFLUENCE OF WATER ON SOME ROCK PROPERTIES

L'INFLUENCE DE L'EAU SUR QUELQUES PROPRIÉTÉS DE ROCHES

DER EINFLUSS VON WASSER AUS EINIGEN FELSEIGENSCHAFTEN

E. BROCH

Senior Lecturer in Engineering Geology

The Norwegian Institute of Technology, Trondheim

Trondheim, Norway

Summary.

Cores of strong rocks with low porosity were tested under variable degrees of water saturation. The rate of loss of water from fully saturated cores stored in a laboratory environment is demonstrated (fig. 1). The P-wave velocity increases with increasing water saturation and is very sensible to small changes in water content near full saturation (fig. 2). The point load strength decreases with increasing water content. Anisotropic rocks are especially sensible to changes in water contents below 25% (fig. 3). The reduction in uniaxial compressive strength is of the same nature as for point load strength, but normally greater. Reduction in strength of rocks under triaxial compression caused by water saturation may be due both to reduction in surface energy and to reduction in internal friction (fig. 4 and 5).

---o0o---

Zusammenfassung.

Kerne von starkem Fels mit kleiner Porosität wurden unter variablen Wassersättigungsgraden untersucht. Die Verdunstungszeit von vollgesättigten, freistehenden Kernen in einem Laboratorium ist demonstriert (Fig. 1). Die Primärwellengeschwindigkeit wird mit höherem Sättigungsgrad grösser und ist für kleine Änderungen im Wassergehalt in der Nähe von 100% sehr empfindlich (Fig. 2). Die Punktlastfestigkeit wird mit höherem Sättigungsgrad kleiner. Anisotropen Felsen sind für Änderungen im Wassergehalt unter 25% besonders empfindlich (Fig. 3). Die Reduktion in einachsiger Druckfestigkeit ist von der selben Natur als für die Punktlastfestigkeit, aber normalerweiser grösser. Die Festigkeitsreduktion vom Fels unter dreiachsigem Druck verursacht von Wassersättigung, kann sowohl von Reduktion in Oberflächenenergie als von Reduktion im Reibungswert schuldig sein (Fig. 4 und 5).

---o0o---

Résumé.

Cylindres de roches fortes durs de porosité faible ont été testés sous degrés variables de saturation d'eau. La quantité de perte d'eau sur des cylindres complètement saturés conservés dans les environments d'un laboratoire est démonstrée (fig. 1). La vélocité des vagues primaires augmente avec l'augmentation de la saturation d'eau, et elle est très sensitive aux petits changements du contenu d'eau près de saturation complète (fig. 2). La résistance a l'essai ponctuel est plus petit quand on fait plus petit le contenu de l'eau. De roches anisotropics sont éspécialement sensitives aux changements du contenu d'eau sous 25% (fig. 3). La réduction dans la résistance à la compression est de la même nature que pour la resistance a l'essai ponctuel, mais normalement plus grande. La réduction dans la résistance des roches sous compression triaxiale causée par la saturation puisse être caussée et par la réduction de l'énergie superficielle et par la reduction dans la friction internale (fig. 4 et 5).

---o0o---

INTRODUCTION.

With few exceptions rocks in situ are fully saturated by water, or have at least a high water content. In spite of this, testing of rocks in the laboratory is often performed on dry specimens or specimens with uncontrolled water content. This change of environmental condition may greatly influence the results from a number of tests as reported by different authors.

This paper deals with the influence water may have on the results from some important standard tests. The tested rocks are all from Norway and are crystalline and of Precambrian or Paleozoic age. They are thus very old. According to the classification diagram presented by Franklin et al. (1971) they can all be described as having very high or extremely high strength. The porosity is low, varying between 0,3 and 1,2%.

From large rock pieces cores with a diameter of 32 mm were drilled and the ends were cut and carefully ground. Both relatively isotropic and clearly anisotropic rocks were tested. For the latter, cores were drilled both parallel and normal to the shistosity or foliation planes.

To obtain fully water satured cores, the specimens were first oven dried for 2 days at a temperature of 105°C and then slowly cooled (12 hours) in an absolutely dry exicator. The remaining air in cracks and pores was evacuated for three hours before distilled water was carefully added under low pressure, 20 mm Hg. When no air bubbles were observed, the pressure was slowly raised to one atmosphere, and the cores were kept submerged for 15 hours.

The water content of the cores was kept under close control during the different tests, partly by covering them with a very thin layer of selfsticking polyethylene. Fully saturated and uncovered cores of three different rock types were placed in a normal laboratory environment, temperature 20 - 22° centigrade and a relative humidity of 60 - 65%, to investigate the rate of the loss of water. As figure 1 shows 25% of the water was lost after only 10 minutes. After 1 hour the water content was down to approximately 50%, after 1 day (24 hours) between 18 and 40% of the water was left and after 1 month 2 - 6% water was left under these conditions. This clearly demonstrates that great care should be taken when rock specimens are stored prior to testing even in a laboratory environment.

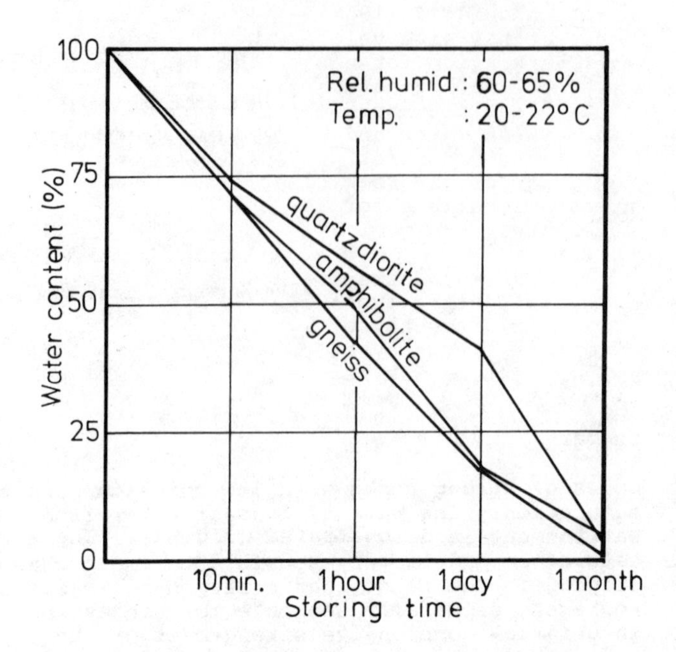

Figure 1 - Water content in rock cores as a function of storing time in a laboratory environment with relative humidity of 60 - 65% and temperature of 20 - 22°C.

P-WAVE VELOCITY.

P-wave velocity, or the velocity of longitudinal shock waves, measured on cores are widely used as a physical index for rock. The great advantages of the test is that it is easy and quick to perform and that it is nondestructive, which means that on the same specimens it can be combined with destructive tests, as for instance the point load test. By measuring P-wave velocities on cores drilled both parallel and normal to the foliation in anisotropic rocks, a reliable index for the maximum physical anisotropy of the rock can be obtained.

Although it is a well known fact that fully saturated rock specimens show a higher P-wave velocity than dry specimens, very little has been reported on how the velocity varies with the degree of saturation and how different rocks react on saturation.

Wyllie et al. (1956) found that there was a rapid increase in P-wave velocity with an increase in water saturation from 70 to 100% for three different sandstones with a very high porosity (16,3 - 21,7 and 29,9%). Below a water saturation of 70% the changes in velocity were practically negligible.

Dortman and Magid (1968) explained the increase in P-wave velocity with increasing water saturation for rocks with low porosity, by the much greater difference in volume elasticity between air and minerals than between water and minerals. Air in microcracks and pores will disturb the elasticity of the rock. Water saturation is more favourable for the transmission of shock waves.

For the present tests a "Dawe Ultrasonic Materials Tester; type UCT2, 1822" with a transducer frequency of 100 KHz and pulse repetition frequency of 50 Hz was used. Travelling time was recorded with an accuracy of ± 0,1 millisecond, and length of the cores measured to an accuracy of ± 0,1 mm.

The results are presented in figure 2 where P-wave velocity is plotted against water saturation. Cores drilled parallel to the foliation are marked || and cores normal to the foliation ⊥ . The curves clearly demonstrate the rapid increase in velocity as the saturation is approaching 100%. Keeping in mind from figure 1 that water saturation for rock cores is reduced to approcimately 75% after only 10 minutes in a normal laboratory environment, one will appreciate the need for a strict and controlled testing procedure.

It is evident from figure 2 that rocks with low P-wave velocities when dry show a greater increase in velocities when saturated, than do high velocity rocks. The curves also show that variations in P-wave velocities between rocks of different types are far greater for dry specimens than for fully saturated specimens. This implies that the degree of P-wave velocity anisotropy is reduced when rocks are saturated by water.

It is interesting to see how two gabbros which can hardly be differentiated by macroscopic examination show two very different curves in the diagramme. From examination of thin sections of the two rocks with a microscope, gabbro B seems to be slightly finer grained, but clearly with less microcracking of the pyroxenes.

The marble has an almost constant increase in P-wave velocity as the saturation increases. This rock further shows the greatest increase from dry to fully saturated, i.e. more than 100%. This may be due to a slight dissolving of calsium carbonate by the water which would increase the size of small cracks and pores. This would allow more water to enter the rock, which again should give possibilities for higher P-wave velocity.

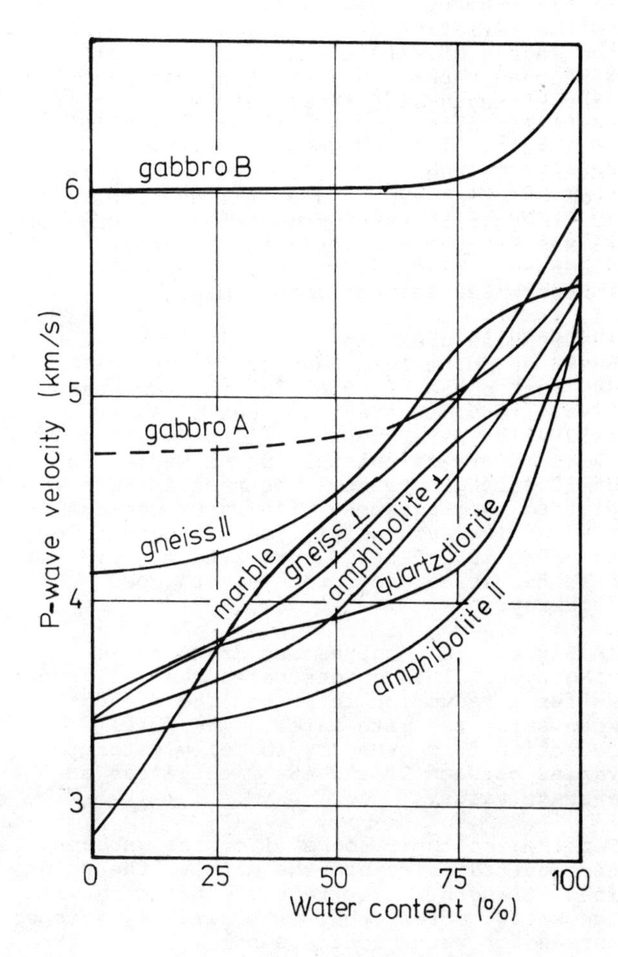

Figure 2 - P-wave velocity as a function of the water content in rock cores.

POINT LOAD STRENGTH.

In document No. 1 from the I.S.R.M.'s "Commission on Standardization of Laboratory and Field Tests", dated October 1972, a method for determining the point load strength index is suggested. The test is intended as a method for measuring the strength of rock specimens in the field, and uses portable equipment. In recent years there has also been an increasing interest for using this test in the laboratory.

The point load strength test is described in detail by the author, Broch (1971) and Broch and Franklin (1972). This includes a brief description of observed strength reduction from oven dry to fully saturated specimens of three different rocks; a granite with 0,0% porosity, a weak sandstone with 12,5% porosity and a strong sandstone with 1,6% porosity. The strength reductions were 13,3%, 33,0% and 22,0% respectively.

So far however, nothing has been published on the variation of point load strength with the degree of saturation. In the last mentioned paper the assumption was made that "the strength difference between fully and partially saturated specimens is likely to be small". This assumption was based on results Colback and Wiid (1965) had presented from uniaxial compressive strength tests on specimens with varying degree of saturation. It was further suggested that standard strength - classification tests should employ water-saturated specimens.

The results presented in this paper are based on point load testing of approximately 300 rock cores of 80 mm length. For each rock 6 to 9 different degrees of water saturation were chosen. All strength indexes were calculated as the median value of 12 strength tests. The results were plotted in diagrammes with water content in % as abcissa and point load strength index as ordinate. Fitting curves to the plotted results was an easy process with good accuracy.

In figure 3 all curves are drawn on to one diagramme. This demonstrates that all rocks suffer a reduction in point load strength when saturated with water. The total reduction from oven dry to fully saturated varies between 20 and 45% with 34% as an average value.

For the isotropic rocks, i.e. the gabbros, the quartzdiorite and the marble, the point load strength varies fairly constantly with the water content, but with slightly steeper curves for water contents below 50%. For gabbro B the variation is very nearly linear. This rock has a low porosity; only 0,30%, but in spite of this suffers a total strength reduction of 33%.

For the anisotropic rocks, i.e. the gneiss and the amphibolite, the greater part of the strength reduction occurs before the water content has reached approximately 25%. For higher water contents the strength reduction is low, and the strength varies fairly constantly with the water content. This seems to be valid for cores drilled both parallel and normal to the foliation.

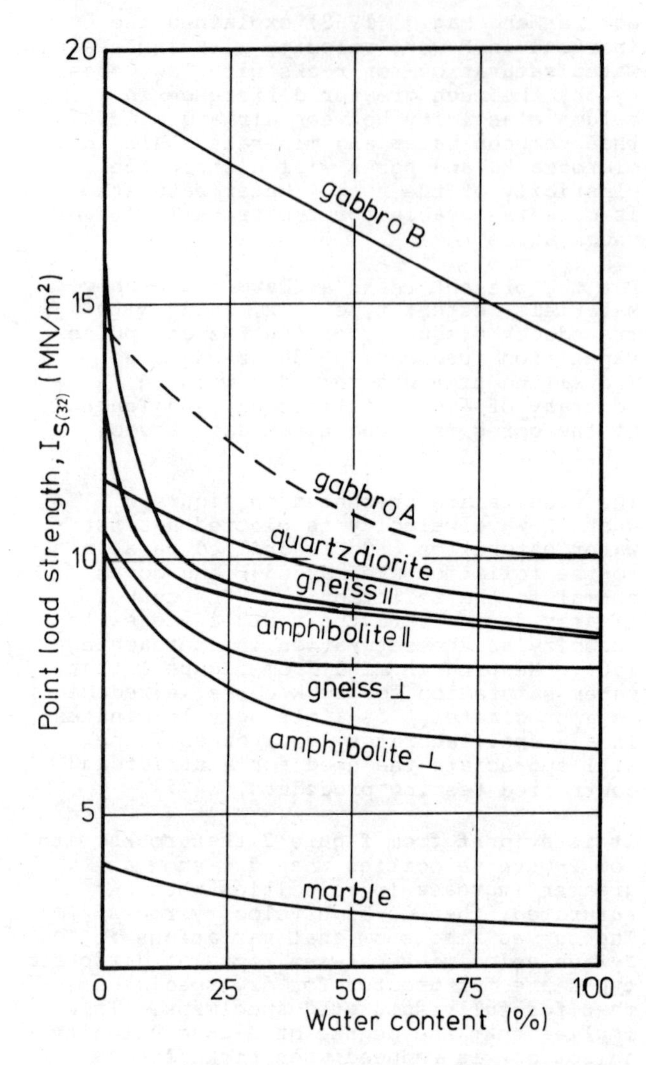

Figure 3 - Point load strength as a function of the water content in rock cores.

UNIAXIAL AND TRIAXIAL COMPRESSION STRENGTH.

Reduction in strength from dry to water saturated conditions for rocks in compression is reported by different authors. The uniaxial compression tests Colback and Wiid (1965) did on rocks with varying degree of saturation are already mentioned. The tests were performed on a quartzitic shale with a porosity of 0,28%. As might be expected, the strength/water saturation - curve is of the same form as the curves for anisotropic rocks presented in figure 3.

The same authors also carried out triaxial compression tests on the same rock and found that the shear strength curve of water saturated rock was merely a sealed down copy of the shear strength curve of the dry rock. This should imply that there is no change in internal friction when rocks are saturated with water. The shear strength reduction was explained mainly by the reduction in uniaxial compressive strength. This again was due to reduction in the free surface energy of the specimens as the rock was saturated by water. Similar explanations on strength reduction have been given by other authors.

Some authors claim that shear strength reduction is due to a reduction in the internal friction, as for instance Byrlee (1967) who performed tests on a granite.

For the present tests a "Hoek Triaxial Cell" was used. This is described in detail by Hoek and Franklin (1968). The axial load was applied by means of a 1500 MN hydraulic press. Both axial stress, σ_1, and confining stress, σ_3, were applied at a low and constant rate. Tests were carried out at five different stages of σ_3; i.e. 0, 10, 20, 30 and 50 MN/m^2. At every stage four specimens of each rock were tested and the average values were computed. The length/diameter ratio of the cores was 2,5, and the parallelity of the ends was better than 0,04 mm. Point load strength tests were performed as described in the previous chapter.

The results from the uniaxial compression tests, σ_c, and the point load tests, I_s, are presented in Table 1 together with the calculated strength reduction in percent. For the gneiss cores parallel as well as normal to the foliation were tested.

Rock	σ_c (MN/m^2)			I_s (MN/m^2)		
	Dry	Sat.	Red.	Dry	Sat.	Red.
Quartzdiorite	241	162	33%	11,4	8,9	22%
Gabbro	324	189	42%	14,2	10,0	30%
Gneiss, norm.	179	84	53%	5,0	2,7	46%
Gneiss, par.	184	115	38%	18,4	11,8	36%

Table 1 - Uniaxial compressive strength and point load strength for 32 mm cores tested in oven dry and fully water saturated conditions. Strength reductions in percent.

For the gneiss specimens cored parallel to the foliation the strength reduction is approximately equal for the two tests. For the other rocks the compressive strength suffers a greater reduction when saturated with water, than does the point load strength. For the two isotropic rocks the ratio of strength reduction between the two tests is as high as 1,45.

The results from the triaxial compression tests are presented in figure 4. Failure curves are fitted to the points. For the two isotropic rocks this curve fitting is done with good accuracy. The parallelity of the failure curves for dry and water saturated rocks respectively is very good.

Although the gabbro has a porosity of only 0,5% whilst the quartzdiorite has a porosity of 0,9%, the former shows a considerably greater loss of strength than does the latter.

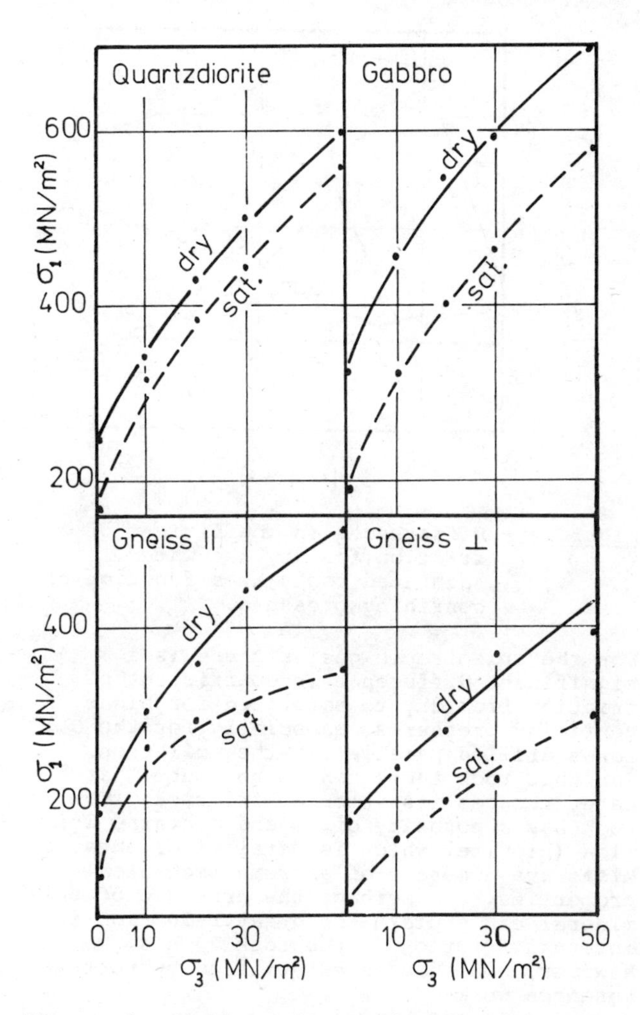

Figure 4 - Failure curves for dry and water saturated rocks.

Fitting failure curves to the results for the anisotropic gneiss was a less accurate task. For this rock the parallelity between the failure curves is lost.

To study the influence of water saturation on the internal friction of the rocks, Mohr circles were drawn for all results and Mohr envelopes fitted. For every circle the angle of friction, ϕ, was measured, and the coefficient of friction calculated as $\mu = tg\phi$.

The differences in μ for dry and saturated rocks at varying confining pressures are plotted for the different rocks in figure 5. The isotropic rocks, i.e. the quartzdiorite and the gabbro, plot very close to the zero difference line. For these rocks one must assume that the strength reductions are due to something other than change of internal friction; they may be due to the reduction in surface energy as claimed by some authors.

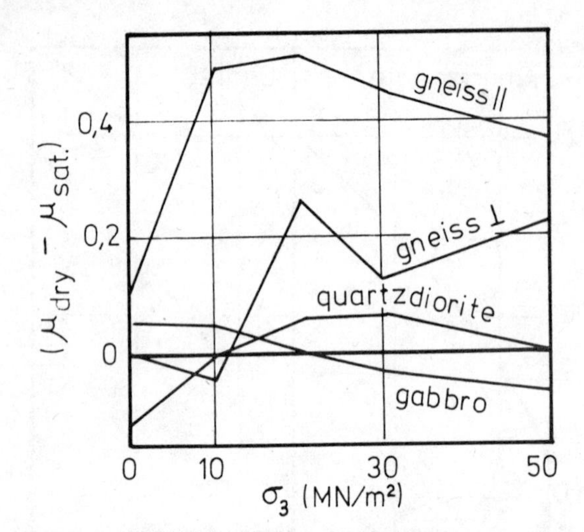

Figure 5 - Differences in coefficient of friction for dry and water saturated rocks as a function of confining pressure.

For the anisotropic gneiss there is a significant difference in coefficient of friction from dry to saturated for higher confining pressures, especially for the cores drilled parallel to the foliation. For this rock there can be no doubt that water reduces its internal friction. The rock has a porosity of 1% and contains 15% mica (biotite) which is parallel orientated. Micas are minerals of extreme mechanical properties, and perhaps the presence of this mineral can explain the great reduction in internal friction of the rock. This, however, can only be established by further research work.

ACKNOWLEDGEMENTS.

The author is thankful to Mr. P.R. Neeb and Mr. S.I. Leivestad who as students carried out all the laboratory work in a very concientious way. The specimen preparation was paid through a grant from Norges Tekniske Høgskoles Fond.

REFERENCES.

BROCH, E., 1971, Point load testing of rocks. Geologisk Institutt, Ingeniørgeologi, Rep. No. 4. 87 pp.

BROCH, E. and FRANKLIN, J.A., 1972, The point load strength test. International Journal of Rock Mechanics and Mining Science, Vol. 9, pp. 669 - 697.

BYRLEE, J.D., 1967, Theory of friction based on brittle fracture. Journal of Applied Physics, Vol. 38, pp. 2928 - 2934.

COLBACK, P.S.B. and WIID, B.L., 1965, The influence of moisture content on the compressive strength of rocks. Proceedings of the 3rd Canadian Symposium on Rock Mechanics, Toronto, pp. 65 - 83.

DORTMAN, N.B. and MAGID, M.S., 1968, Velocity of elastic waves in crystalline rocks and its dependence on moisture content. Doklady of the Academy of Sciences of the U.S.S.R., Earth Science Sections, Vol. 179, pp. 1 - 3.

FRANKLIN, J.A., BROCH, E. and WALTON, G., 1971, Logging the mechanical character of rock. Transactions/Section A of the Institution of Mining and Metallurgy, Vol. 80 pp. A 1 - 9. Discussion in Vol. 81, pp. A 43 - 51.

HOEK, E. and FRANKLIN, J.A., 1968, Simple triaxial cell for field or laboratory testing of rock. Transactions/Section A of the Institution of Mining and Metallurgy, Vol. 77, pp. A 22 - 26.

WYLLIE, M.R.J., GREGORY, A.R. and GARDNER, L.W., 1956, Elastic wave velocities in heterogeneous and porous media. Geophysics, Vol. 21, No. 1, pp. 41 - 69.

ESSAI DE POINÇONNAGE DES ROCHES - BASE D'UNE CLASSIFICATION INTERNATIONALE AU POINT DE VUE DE LEUR DESTRUCTIBILITÉ

ROCK-PIERCING TEST - BASE FOR AN INTERNATIONAL CLASSIFICATION WITH REGARD TO THEIR DESTRUCTIBILITY

VERSUCH EINES GESTEINSDURCHSCHLAGES - GRUNDZÜGE EINER INTERNATIONALEN KLASSIFIZIERUNG

J. BRYCH

Faculté Polytechnique de Mons

Mons, Belgium

RÉSUMÉ: Après de nombreuses analyses et recherches, il semble que les essais de poinçonnage sont les plus efficaces, les plus proches de la réalité et les plus précis en ce qui concerne la détermination des propriétés physico-mécaniques des roches pour étude de leur destructibilité par outils de forage et de sciage. Il est recommandé que l'essai de poinçonnage Schreiner avec les modifications apportées par d'autres chercheurs devienne la base d'une classification internationale des roches au point de vue de leur destructibilité.

SUMMARY: After much analysis and research, it appears that the piercing tests were the most effective, the closest to actual conditions, and the most accurate in defining the physical-mechanical properties of rocks in the study of their destructibility by drilling and cutting tools. It is recommended that the SCHREINER piercing test, with the modifications provided by other researchers, become the basis for an international classification of rocks from the point of view of their destructibility.

ZUSAMMENFASSUNG: Nach einer Anzahl erstellter Analysen und durchgeführter Versuche scheint es, dass die Gesteinsdurchschlagsversuche die effektivsten waren, die den normalen Bedingungen gleichkamen und die die physikalischen Eigenschaften der Gesteine während des Studiums auf ihre Zerstörbarkeit mittels Bohr- und Schneidgeräte genau definieren. Es wird empfohlen, dass die SCHREINER-Durchschlagsversuche, die mit von anderen Forschern gemachten Veränderungen versehen werden, als Grundlage zur internationalen Klassifizierung der Gesteinszerstörbarkeit angehen werden.

Les outils de forage et/ou de sciage utilisés en sondages profonds de prospection géologique, pétrolière, minière, en travaux publics ou en carrières pour scier les pierres dures, attaquent les roches de façons différentes. En principe, il s'agit du poinçonnage statique ou dynamique (avec ou sans influence au bord d'une rainure), de découpage suivant une trajectoire linéaire ou rotative, sans ou avec les effets de percussion, vibration, etc. ....

La base de tous ces différents processus de destruction est en principe commune pour tous les systèmes mécaniques actuellement connus. Le forage, le sciage, etc. ... peuvent, en principe, avoir lieu, si la surface active de l'outil en question (totale ou partielle) est en correspondance avec la résistance du matériau à détruire et l'effort total exercé sur l'outil. Se l'effort critique exigé par la roche (par rapport à la géométrie de l'outil), la destruction ne peut pas être efficace. L'outil peut dans ce cas pénétrer tout de même dans un matériau rocheux, mais lentement en général, et perdant l'efficacité technique et économique du processus. Plusieurs chercheurs ont décrit cette façon de destruction des roches comme pénétration sous régime de l'usure superficielle (SCHREINER (1), (2), (20), VOROPINOV-BROUL (3), VOROPINOV-KITTRICH (17), BRISON-BRYCH (11), (13), (16), ALPAN (23) ..)

Nombreuses recherches ont été entreprises dans ce domaine en vue de déterminer le type de résistance à vaincre, pour assurer la pénétration d'un outil de forage et/ou de sciage, sous un régime choisi, dans un matériau rocheux (SCHREINER-PETROVA (2), PAVLOVA-SCHREINER (6), GAUTHIER-BARON (9), VOROPINOV-KITTRICH (17), BROUL-HOFRICHTER (10), BRISON-BRYCH (11), (13), (16), HUCKA (14) ...).

Certains chercheurs ont basé leurs observations sur essais directs (tels que résistance à la compression, traction torsion, cisaillement, poinçonnage, etc. ...) d'autres sur les essais de rebondissement (SHORE et SCHMIDT (22)) et d'autres encore sur les essais indirects (essais ultrasoniques in situ et/ou au laboratoir).

Nos observations et études approfondies ont montré que les essais de poinçonnage (effectués au laboratoire ou in situ

(14)) sont les essais très efficaces, très proches de la réalité quant à l'attaque des roches par outils de forage et de sciage. Ils donnent un nombre suffisamment grand de renseignements bien déterminés et chiffrés en unités physiques, étant en rapport avec les résultats technologiques de forage et de sciage.

Un grand nombre de chercheurs, travaillant dans ce domaine a adopté le système de poinçonnage introduit par SCHREINER (1), (6), (2) ou l'ont amélioré (3), (10), (11), (17), (16), (14), (19) ... ou adapté aux conditions locales.

SCHREINER (1), (6) a introduit son essai au cours des années 1950, utilisant les poinçons à bout plat (1), (20), (17), (16) (fig. 1), pour éviter certains inconvénients que peuvent poser les matériaux fragiles en cas d'utilisation des poinçons côniques ou sphériques.

Examinant les roches d'après la méthode SCHREINER, on à la possibilité de chiffrer aisément différentes propriétés fondamentales de ces dernières (telles que Résistance au poinçonnage (1), Résistance réduite au poinçonnage (3), (16), coëfficient de plasticité (1), coëfficient de fragilité (17),(16), travail spécifique de contact (1), travail volumétrique de destruction (1), travail total de destruction (1), module d'élasticité statique (1), coëfficient de destructibilité d'une roche (3), (14), (16), (19), (21))et établir les classifications adéquates (1), (3), (6), (9), (13), (16), (17), (19), (20), (21) ....).

Un assez grand nombre de chercheurs, représentant plusieurs pays est en principe d'accord avec les essais de poinçonnage SCHREINER et leur application directe aux chantiers de forage, travaillant surtout avec les outils à molettes, où chaque dent, étant en contact avec la roche au fond du trou, ressemble à un essai de poinçonnage dynamique. Ainsi dans le cas des outils à molettes, l'utilistation des résultats de poinçonnage du laboratoire est quasi directement applicable au chantier. Une classification internationale des roches basée sur le poinçonnage SCHREINER et complétée par les interprétations d'autres chercheurs signifierait que chaque fabricant ou utilisateur des outils à molettes par exemple serait rapidement et suffisamment informé des propriétés fondamentales des roches à forer, d'où il pourrait juger si la géométrie des dents leur disposition sur les molettes, portance nécessaire des axes et des roulements .... et les régime de forage à appliquer sont en correspondance avec ces dernières. (Quant à l'usure, les essais d'abrasivité seraient à appliquer (1), (2), (3), (13), (16), (17), (19)..)fig. 1, 2 et 3, tabl. 1.

surtout avec les outils à molettes, où chaque dent, étant en contact avec la roche au fond du trou, ressemble à un essai de poinçonnage dynamique. Ainsi dans le cas des outils à molettes, l'utilisation des résultats de poinçonnage du laboratoire est quasi directement applicable au chantier. Une classification internationale des roches basée sur le poinçonnage SCHREINER et complétée par les interprétations d'autres chercheurs signifierait que chaque fabricant ou utilisateur des outils à molettes par exemple serait rapidement et suffisamment informé des propriétés fondamentales des roches à forer, d'où il pourrait juger si la géométrie des dents, leur disposition sur les molettes, portance nécessaire des axes et des roulements... et les régimes de forage à appliquer sont en correspondance avec ces dernières. (Quant à l'usure, les essais d'abrasivité seraient à appliquer (1), (2), (3), (13), (16), (17), (19)...) fig. 1, 2 et 3, tabl. 1.

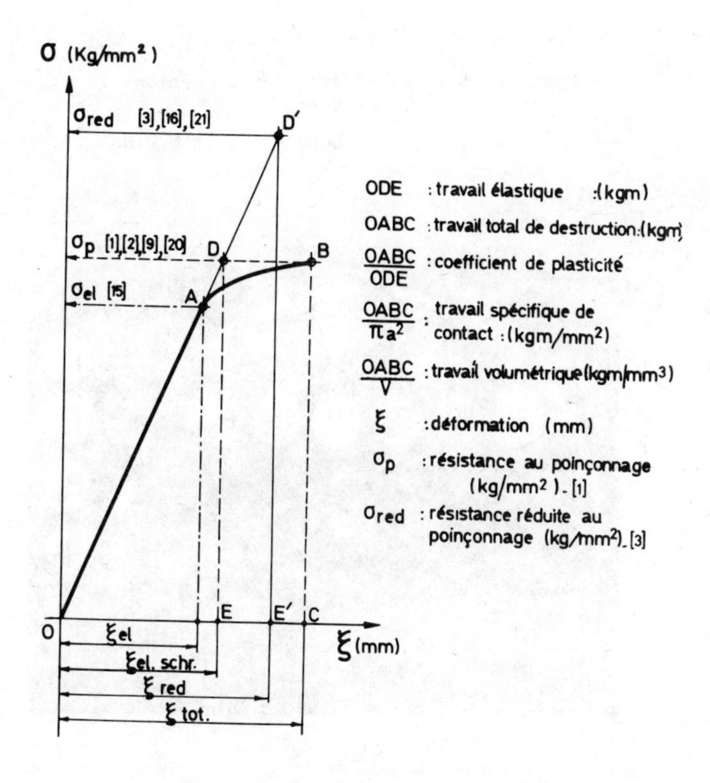

FIG. 1. ESSAI DE POINÇONNAGE.
[1],[3],[6],[9],[11],[14],[16],[17],[19],[20],[21]

FIG. 2.

Appareil universel F.P.Ms. utilisé pour les essais de O_P, Oc_P, O_{red}, E_{st}, G et les propriétés rhéologiques (creep).

(Photos archives F.P.Ms.)

FIG. 3.

Appareil triaxial F.P.Ms. pour les essais de poinçonnage en laboratoire.

(Photo archives F.P.Ms).

TABL. 1. Résultats d'essais de poinçonnage SCHREINER *)

Echantillon, nature.	N° F.P.Ms.	Résistance au poinçonnage. σ_p (kg/mm²)	Travail élastique. T_{el} (kgm)	Travail total de destruction. T_{TD} (kgm)	Coefficient de plasticité. C_{pl} —	Travail spécifique de contact. T_{spc} (kgm/mm²)	Travail volumétrique de destruction. T_{VD} (kgm/mm³)
Marbre COMBLANCHIEN	48/0	170,53	$3,29 \times 10^{-3}$	$5,27 \times 10^{-3}$	1,602	$1,60 \times 10^{-3}$	$5,97 \times 10^{-4}$
Calcaire SOIGNIES	2/17	121,52	$2,47 \times 10^{-3}$	$3,67 \times 10^{-3}$	1,486	$1,16 \times 10^{-3}$	$2,53 \times 10^{-4}$
Marbre SPRIMONT	47/0	129,55	$2,80 \times 10^{-3}$	$4,29 \times 10^{-3}$	1,532	$1,37 \times 10^{-3}$	$3,30 \times 10^{-4}$
Marbre ARDENNES	46/0	94,88	$8,06 \times 10^{-4}$	$2,07 \times 10^{-3}$	2,568	$6,59 \times 10^{-4}$	$5,90 \times 10^{-4}$

*) Poinçon cylindrique à bout plat Ø 2mm ; vitesse de mise en charge comprise entre 2,2 et 4,04 kg/mm sec.

Une autre situation se montre dans le domaine des outils autres que molettes dentées, par exemple dans le domaine des outils à lames, couronnes à prismes en carbure de tungstène, couronnes et trépans diamantés, pics classiques et autoaffûtants, montés sur les chaînes des haveuses-rouleuses, ... etc. En ce qui concerne ces catégories d'outils, les chercheurs de différents pays ne sont pas encore suffisamment unis quant à l'application directe des essais de poinçonnage. Certains chercheurs supposent que le processus de destruction des roches dans ce cas est très différent de celui du poinçonnage SCHREINER. D'autres expliquent dans leurs travaux que cette différence n'est qu'illusoire et que même dans le cas d'utilisation des outils de cette catégorie il serait possible de profiter des avantages d'une classification des roches, basée sur les essais de poinçonnage SCHREINER (1), (2), (3), (6), (11), (13), (14), (16), (17), (19), (20), (24)...

Les résultats de nos derniers travaux, effectués au laboratoire Mines-Sondages-Mécanique des Roches à la Faculté polytechnique de Mons et subsidiés par le Fonds National de la Recherche Scientifique de Belgique, ont prouvé que l'avancement d'un outil de forage ou de sciage s'effectue grâce à une série de poinçonnages dans le sens du déplacement de l'outil et/ou à des poinçonnages combinés avec les effets de bord (10), (14), (21) (Résistance au cisaillement par poinçonnage). Ces phénomènes sont observés quand le tranchant d'un outil a une forme d'un pic, d'un poinçon, d'un prisme en carbure de tungstène ou dans le cas des outils diamantés (11), (13), (14), (16), (21) et cela si on examine des roches dures ou en travaillant avec les matériaux équivalents au laboratoire (24) fig. 4, 5, 6, 7 et 8.

Les poinçons type "SCHREINER" du diamètre 2 mm, les poinçons diamantés, plaquettes de 8 x 8 x 0,8 et 8 x 8 x 1 mm en carbure de tungstène des outils autoaffûtants ont été utilisés pour ces essais de forage et de sciage au laboratoire en refroidissant le contact roche-outil à l'air comprimé, fig. 8. On observe que différentes roches, classées dans les catégories des roches plastiques, fragiles ou fragiloélastiques (d'après SCHREINER (1), (2), (3), (6), (9), (11), (14), (16), (17), (19), (20), (21), (24)) forment les rainures en correspondance avec les propriétés mécaniques de ces dernières.

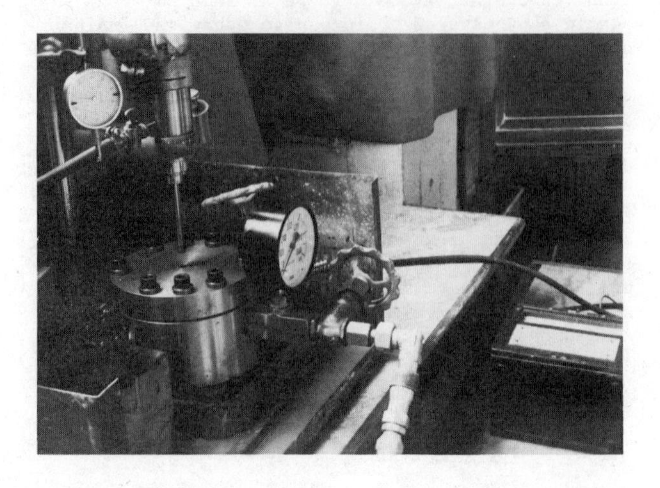

FIG. 4 .

Essai de forabilité dans des conditions triaxiales en laboratoire.

(Photo archives F.P.Ms).

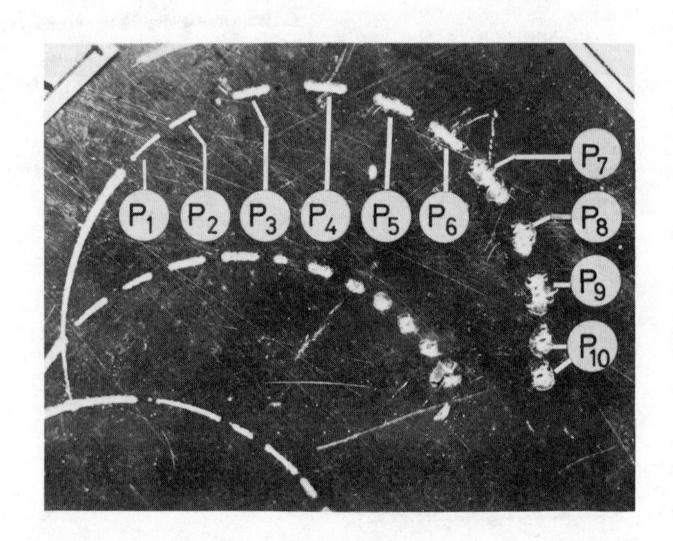

FIG. 5.

Destruction du calcaire crinoïdique de Soignies (éch 2/17) par un poinçon diamanté. Vitesse linéaire de déplacement du poinçon = constante. Poussée axiale variant de P_1 à P_{10}.

(Photo archives F.P.Ms).

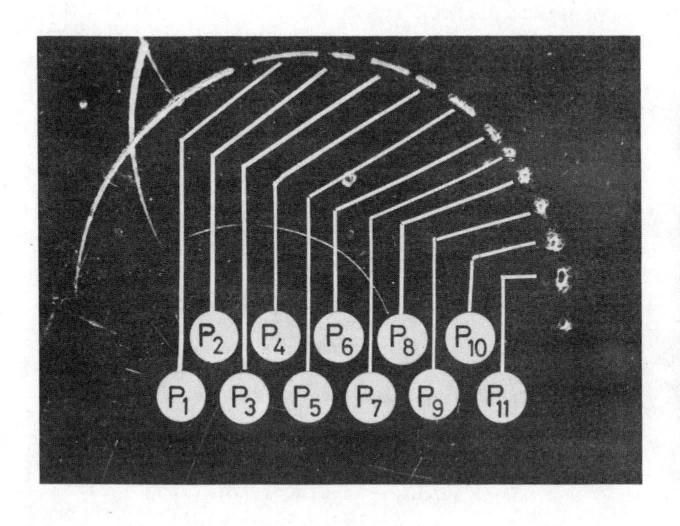

FIG. 6.

Destruction du marbre de Fontaine l'Evêque par un poinçon diamanté. Vitesse linéaire de rotation étant constante, poussée axiale sur le poinçon variant de P_1 à P_{11}.

(Photo archives F.P.Ms.).

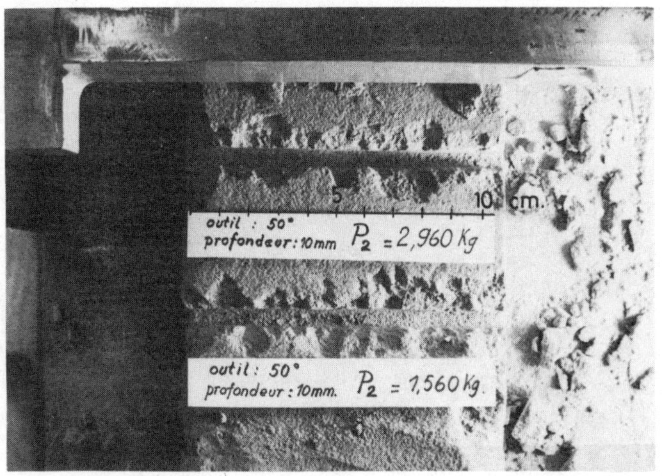

FIG. 8.

Destruction d'un matériau par l'outil de coupe. L'ondulation de la rainure est liée aux phénomènes de poinçonnage par saccades.

(Photo archives F.P.Ms.)

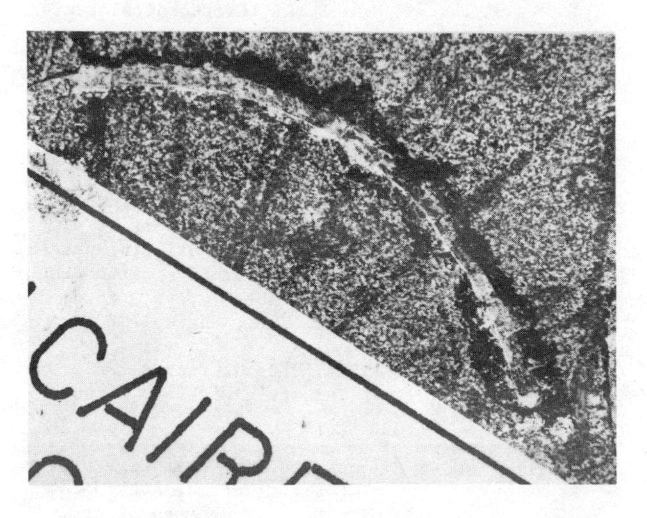

FIG. 7.

Destruction d'un calcaire de Soignies (éch 2/17) par un poinçon cylindrique à bout plat; vitesse linéaire = const.
Pax. = const. avec observation de poinçonnages par saccades liés aux ondulations de la rainure.

(Photo archives F.P.Ms.).

Plus il y a de fragilité du matériau à tester, plus il y a d'éclatements complémentaires autour de la rainure. Ces phénomènes sont les mêmes si l'outil tourne (le cas d'une foreuse ou d'une sondeuse) ou s'il se déplace linéairement sur une surface de roche en question. (le cas d'une chaine de haveuse-rouleuse).

Si nous comparons les résultats d'essai de poinçonnage Schreiner au point de vue du coëfficient de plasticité par exemple (Fig. 1, 3 et 9) nous constatons que la valeur de celui-ci change en fonction de profondeur, effectuant les tests de poinçonnage et les tests de forabilité dans les appareils triaxiaux, spécialement construits pour étudier ces phénomènes (influence de la contrainte latérale et de la pression d'une boue de forage sur le fond du trou fig. 9 (25)). Ces tests triaxiaux nous font comprendre entre autres pourquoi un outil de forage conçu pour les conditions de travail à la surface n'est plus valable pour le forage en grande profondeur, par exemple.

On peut déduire de nos observations que dans le cas du forage rotatif ou du sciage des roches, travaillant avec les outils autres que molettes, les phénomènes de poinçonnage ont lieu et cela sous différentes formes et que même dans le cas des outils autres qu'à molettes, le comportement physico-mécanique d'une roche peut être détecté par un essai de poinçonnage SCHREINER et complété par d'autres auteurs.

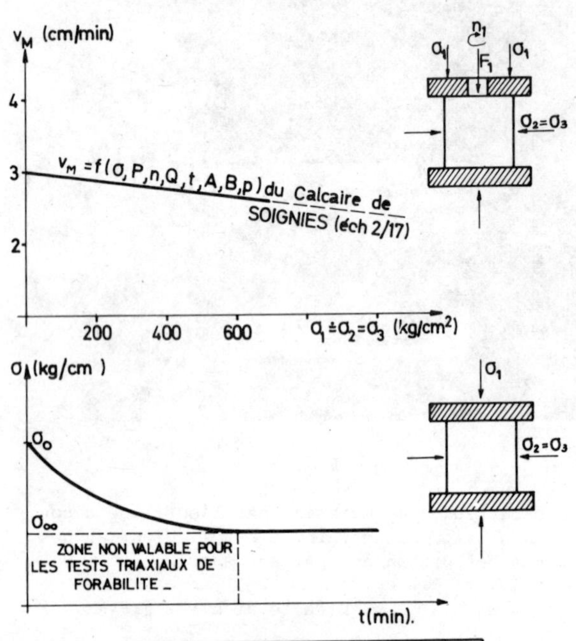

$\sigma_1 \pm \sigma_2 = \sigma_3$ (kg/cm^2)	vitesse de forage (cm/min)	σ_{RED} (kg/mm^2)
0	3	157,9
200	2,15	
400	2,85	
600	2,62	180,5

FIG. 9.

Paramètres technologiques _ ici forabilité en relation avec les paramètres mécaniques des roches et en fonction de la profondeur. $\sigma_1, \sigma_2, \sigma_3$ = contraintes; F_1 = poussée sur l'outil; n = nombre de tours de l'outil; Q = débit de la boue; p = pression hydrostatique de la boue sur le fond du trou; A = caractéristiques de l'outil; B = caractéristiques physico-mécaniques de la roche; t = temps de relaxation de la roche dans la cellule triaxiale.

Une classification des roches dans ce sens, à l'échelle internationale, à l'aide d'un essai standardisé permettrait aux nombreux chercheurs et surtout aux fabricants et utilisateurs d'outils de forage et de sciage d'utiliser un langage commun.

BIBLIOGRAPHIE

1 - SCHREINER : Klassifikacia gornych parod po mechaniceskim svojstvam (Moscou, 1958).

2 - SCHREINER - PETROVA : Zony plasticeskoj deformacii, Mechaniki razrusenija gornych parod (Gosinti, 1961).

3 - VOROPINOV - BROUL : Metodicke pokyny proklasifikaci soudrznych hornin privrtanź VSB Ostrava Duben, 1969).

4 - SNEDDON : Boussinesq's problem for a flet ended cylinder proceed of the Cambridge Phil. Soc. v. 42, 1946 p.l., pp.29-39.

5 - SOMMERTON : A laboratory study of rock breakage by rotary drilling (Trans. ASME, 216, 92, 1959).

6 - PAVLOVA - SCHREINER : Razrusenije gornych parod pri dynamiceskom nagruzenii (Nedra - Moscou, 1964).

7 - ADAMS COKER : An experimental investigation into the flow of rocks (The Amer. Jour. of Science, v. XXIX, n° 174, 1910).

8 - ROWLEY HOWER DEILY : Laboratory drilling performance of the full-scale rockbit (I. Petroleum Technology, v. 13, N. 1, 1961).

9 - GAUTHIER-BARON : Classement des roches préliminaires à une méthode de forabilité (IFP 1963/3).

10 - BROUL - HOFRICHTER : A composition of four different methods of determining the shear strength of Rocks (Geotechnical conference, Oslo, 1967).

11 - BRISON - BRYCH : Influence des propriétés physicomécaniques sur le processus de découpage des roches (Annales des Mines de Belgique, 1971/1).

12 - REICHMUTH : Corrélation of force-displacement data with physical properties of rock for percussive drilling systems (Proceding of fifth symposium School of Mines and Metallurgy, Oxford, London, New York, Paris, 1963).

13 - BRISON - BRYCH : Abrasivité des roches (Revue de l'Industrie Minérale, France 1/1970).

14 - BRYCH - HUCKA : A new test for disintegrability of Coal. (Int. J. Rock Mech. Min. Sci. et Geomech Abstr., vol. 10, 1973.

15 - DAS - HUCKA : Penetration strength of Coal (Canad. Min. Journal, 1973).

16 - BRYCH : Mécanique des roches I, vol. I (notes de cours Faculté polytechnique de Mons, 1972).

17 - VOROPINOV - KITTRICH : Mechanika Hornin I (SNTL Praha, 1966).

18 - WAGNER - SCHUMANN : The stamp boad bearing s strength of rocks and experimental and theoretical investigations (Rock Mechanics I. 3,185-207, vol.3/4 -1971).

19 - SCERBA : Laboratorní vyzkum vrtatelnosti hornin a optimalisace parametru vrtaní (Ugi Brno, 1968) I.A.E.G. - IGHP N.P. Zilina).

20 - SCHREINER : Fyziceskie osnovy mechaniky gornych parod (Gostoptechizdat, 1950).

21 - BRYCH : Destructibilité des roches (Annales des Mines, 1973, n° spécial).

22 - SHEPHERD : Physical properties and drillability of mine Rocks Colliery Eng. January , 1961).

23 - ALPAN : Factors apeecting the speed of penetration of bits in Electric Rotary Drilling (Coll. Gnard. 22.9.1951, p. 325.)

24 - BRYCH - BRISON - TEKADIOMONA : Utilisation de matériaux équivalents pour l'étude préliminaire en laboratoire du découpage du charbon (Annales scientifiques F.P.Ms. n° 1 1973).

25 - BRYCH : Drillability tests of rocks under natural conditions (Geological Survey n° 3 - 1968).

GEOSTRUCTURAL, GEOPHYSICAL AND GEOMECHANICAL SCHEMES OF ROCK MASSES

SCHEMAS GÉOSTRUCTURAL, GÉOPHYSIQUE ET GÉOMÉCANIQUE DU MASSIF ROCHEUX

DIE GEOSTRUKTURELLEN, GEOPHYSIKALISCHEN UND GEOMECHANISCHEN SCHEMEN EINES FELSMASSIVS

A.M. GUREEV Engineer

O.K. VORONKOV M.Sc.

The B.E. Vedeneev All Union Research Institute of Hydraulic Engineering

Leningrad, U.S.S.R.

SUMMARY

Discussed in this paper are the techniques followed in developing the geostructural, geophysical and geomechanical schemes of a rock mass in order to establish its mechanical behaviour. Considered are the static modulus of deformation, static Poisson's ratio, the compression strength, the coefficient of mollifiability, frost resistance factor and their correlation with the physical rock properties determined by geophysical methods. The relationships obtained are recommended for establishing structural properties of rock masses from geophysical data prior to static investigations.

RESUME

Dans le rapport on décrit des méthodes visant à développer les schémas géostructural, géophysique et géomécanique du massif rocheux pour déterminer ses propriétés mécaniques. On considère le module de déformation statique, le coefficient de Poisson statique, la résistance à la compression, le coefficient de ramollissement et le coefficient de résistance au gel en corrélation avec les propriétés physiques définies par les méthodes géophysiques. On recommande d'utiliser les relations obtenues pour évaluer les propriétés techniques de la roche sur la base des données géophysiques avant la réalisation des essais statiques.

ZUSAMMENFASSUNG

Die Aufbauverfahren von geostrukturellen, geophysikalischen und geomechanischen Schemen eines Felsmassivs werden beschrieben, um seine mechanischen Eigenschaften zu bestimmen. Es wurde auch folgendes festgestellt, und zwar: statischer Verformungsmodul, statische Poissonzahl, Druckfestigkeit; Erweichungs- und Frostbeständigkeitskoeffizienten und ihre Korrelation mit den physikalischen Eigenschaften, die mit Hilfe der geophysikalischen Methoden bestimmt werden. Die ermittelten Abhängigkeiten werden empfohlen, zur Bestimmung der Baueigenschaften von Massivsgesteinen nach den geophysikalischen Angaben vor der Durchführung von statischen Untersuchungen zu verwenden.

Rock masses in hydraulic structure foundations unlike soft soils are characterized by much more complex geology, an appreciable non-homogeneity and notorious anisotropy in strength, deformation and percolation properties. These specific features of rock masses are strongly dependent on the effect of jointing whose character and development is determined by the history of formation, evolution and decay of rock masses and on a wide variety of rock genesis. The primary purpose of field and laboratory examinations of rock masses is to establish the characteristic features noted above, as well as to analyse and generalize the survey data for constructing a rock-engineering model (scheme). The model is to simulate with an accuracy sufficient for design purposes the general layout of three-dimensional rock mass elements with quasihomogeneous structural properties. It is to cover a system of vertical and horizontal layers modelled to scales of 1:1000 - 1:500. Such a model includes a number of partial models (schemes), viz. a geostructural, geophysical, hydrogeological and geomechanical correlated models.

Based on the geostructural model the geomechanical scheme is developed, both being linked by the geophysical scheme with respect to the extension of point data on the mechanical characteristics of a rock mass as a whole.

The feasibility of transforming the geophysical scheme into a geomechanical one is supported by the correlation between physico-mechanical properties of rock and its indices (such as the velocity of elastic wave propagation, the modulus of elasticity, Poisson's ratio, relative electric resistance, total and open porosities etc.) found by geophysical methods.

1. A geostructural scheme of a rock mass.

The geostructural scheme of a rock mass shows by appropriate contours on foundation cross-sections the position in space, conditions of bedding and stratigraphical correlations of structural petrological three-dimensional elements (structural petrological zones - SPZ and structural petrological blocks - SPB), which are quasihomogeneous in composition and structure. The quasihomogeneity of an element is determined by the following features: a) mineral composition; b) structure (texture and bed composition dependent upon the block-forming joints); c) state (interstitial and crack porosity, crack and pore fillers); d) properties of the rocks and of rock filler.

The procedure of constructing the geostructural scheme is described below:

1. Proceeding from a composite lithological stratigraphic cross-section and laboratory test results, some syngenetic relatively weak zones are identified in rock mass and checked with the fault bedding-plane displacements established in the course of the geological geophysical examination.
2. From data of the geological and geophysical investigations postgenetic fault rock zones of weakness are established as well as extended release cracks. The spatial distribution of the syngenetic and postgenetic zones of weakness are compared. The general scheme of the space lattice for zones of weakness is developed.
3. Based on geological geophysical characteristic features and the available experimental data defined are the boundaries of a postgenetic zone of release and weathering according to the following zonules: A (a zonule of elution), B (a zonule of pronounced release and weathering), C (a zonule with slight traces of release and weathering), D (well preserved rock), with the geomorphology and hydrogeology of the valley considered. Intersection of the A, B, C, D zonule boundaries with those of structural petrological zones of weakness and well preserved rock blocks indicates the contours of engineering geological zones (EGZ) and engineering geological blocks (EGB), respectively. Both (as distinguished from SPL and SPB) are quasihomogeneous not only in composition and structure, but also in their state and properties.
4. Jointing data compiled from EGZ and EGB are systematized and statistically treated according to the following indices: a) the areal crack porosity coefficient $K_{c.p.}$ (%.),numerically equal to the area of joints per 1 m^2; b) mean volume of a joint block in the rock mass; c) mean crack and vein density for each block-forming joint system, this criterion being of importance in determination of the shape, size and orientation of joint blocks in the rock mass.
5. Then the physico-mechanical properties of the rock investigated experimentally are systematized and analysed statistically.
6. The findings of field studies on the percolation, deformation, elasticity (velocity of elastic wave propagation) and electrical properties enable all the above indices to be related with the depth individually for the channel, right-bank and left-bank sections of the rock mass.
7. Field and laboratory data on the rock properties obtained are plotted in the geostructural scheme. By superposition of the geostructural and geophysical schemes of one cross-section the structure of the rock mass is interpreted and the boundaries of EGL and EGB are verified.

The geostructural cross-section of the Toktogul dam foundation as an element of the geostructural scheme is exemplified in Fig. 1. The cross-section was schematized at the Middle-Asian Branch of the Gidroproekt Institute. The order and in-filling material of each large crack is denoted in the geostructural scheme; in Fig. 1 these designations are omitted.

In case of the Toktogul dam foundation the mean width of cracks of the 3d, 4th, 5th and 6th order can be stated to be 64, 18, 11 and 10 mm, respectively. The filler is represented (beside air) by friction breccia, shattered limestone, leader stone.

2. A geophysical scheme of a rock mass.

The geophysical model of rock masses is to show the regularities of variation in space of physical (elastic, electrical, magnetic etc.) rock properties, determined by geophysical exploration methods. The geophysical scheme is plotted on the basis of the data obtained at individual observation points and those along certain profiles on the day surface, in shafts and tunnels, in the course of coring, from investigations of rock between shafts and drill holes as well as from testing of rock samples in the laboratory. A more rational application of various geophysical methods is promoted by a comprehensive geophysical scheme of a rock foundation which is based on the seismic-geological scheme and supplemented by the data of other investigations (mostly of coring). The seismic-geological scheme presents the distribution of the elastic properties (C_p and C_s - velocities) of the rock masses as a field of isotachs (lines of equal velocity).

The following three types of a non-homogeneous seismic-geological scheme are possible:

The Ist type is a scheme for layered (zoned) rock mass; being considered as a preliminary scheme it can be obtained from the data of geophysical studies. Such a scheme demonstrates mostly rock mass weakening due to release and weathering.

The II nd type is a scheme which is concerned with a zoned large block rock mass and shows structural petrological blocks separated by rather large structural faults and zones of weakness of various genesis.

The IIId type is a scheme for a zoned small-block rock mass indicating the orientation of rock joint blocks of various types and sizes.

These three types of schemes are characterized by a different degree of accuracy in reflecting the actual structure of rock masses and the distribution of their elastic properties. When designing large engineering structures it has become necessary to construct the type II schemes and in a number of cases even the type III schemes (e.g. in experimental designing).

From the standpoint of physics the seismic-geologic scheme is substantiated by relating wave propagation velocity with jointing, porosity, crack and pore fillers and mineralogical composition. Within a joint block of a quasihomogeneous petrography jointing is the main factor governing the velocity of elastic waves. The procedure of generalization of geological and geophysical data to be used for plotting the seismic-geological II type scheme is as follows:

Stage 1 includes an analysis of data from rock samples permitting to establish: a) mineral composition and its variants; b) total, open and close porosity, their distribution and interconnection; c) distribution of C_p and C_s in samples; d) $C_{m(p)}$ and $C_{m(s)}$-values in the mineral (solid) portion of the rock mass, their variations due to mineral composition; e) influence of the texture of samples on the C -value and its anisotropy with the state of rock (air dry, water saturated or frozen) taken into account; f) the variation pattern of C with the pressure in monolithic and jointed samples of different lithological types studied in dry, saturated and frozen states. Results are presented as variation curves, correlations etc.

Stage 2 envisages zoning of a schematized rock mass cross-sections aimed at outlining: a) zones of rock with different petrographic composition and $C_{m(p)}$, $C_{m(s)}$ - values; b) zones with different

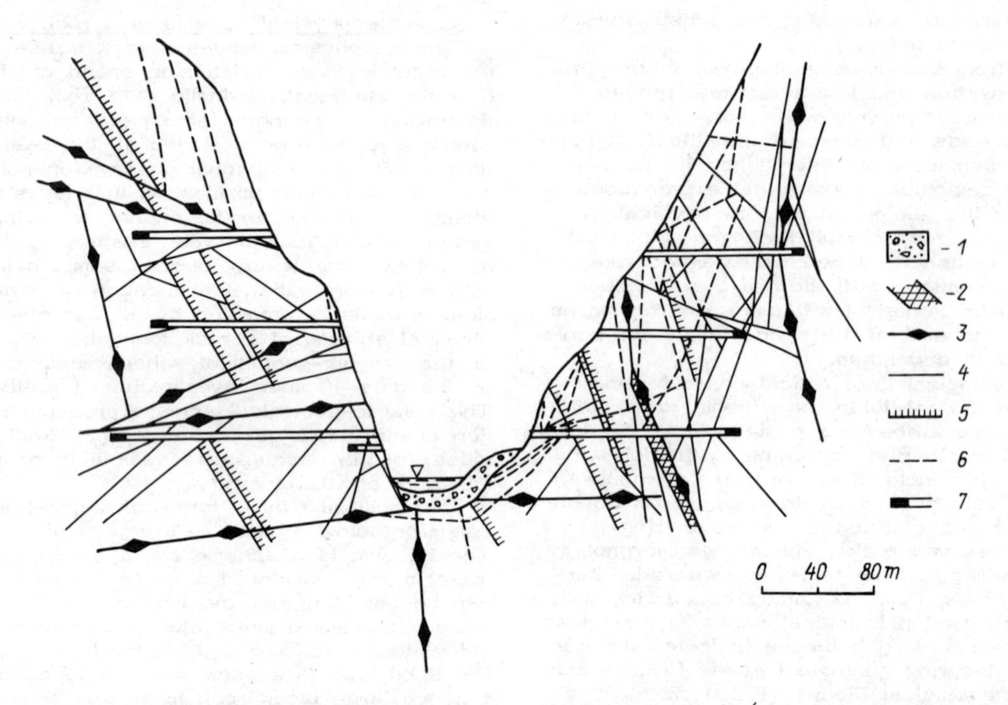

Fig. 1. Geostructural cross-section of the Toktogul Dam foundation (According to V.V.Kayakin et al.) 1 - alluvium and talys deposits, 2 - layer of dark limestone with lenses and interlayers, 3 - joints of the 3d order, 4 - tectonic joints of the 4-6th order, 5 - bedding joints of the 4-6th order, 6 - release cracks in walls and bottom of the valley, 7 - adits.

crack and pore fillers; c) a zone of rock surface weathering and release (according to the A, B, C zonules).

Stages 3 consists in constructing fields of isotachs for the selected cross-sections of rock masses with zoned block structure: a) plotting the main elements of the geostructural scheme in the selected cross-sections; b) marking the C_p and C_s-values (obtained by profiling, sonic logging, coring) and velocity-correlated values (relative electric resistance, specific water absorption, the modulus of deformation, the depth along the vertical etc.) these correlations being essential for the region under study; c) determination of the effect of faults of various orders and weak zones of some other genesis on the C_p or C_s-values; in this case due consideration should be given to the anisotropy in the velocity, induced by jointing anisotropy; the isotachs are drawn according to the velocity values measured along directions almost normal to joint planes; d) interpolation and extrapolation of wave velocity values on the geostructural scheme with a distinct identification of structural elements either affecting the velocity or not. When plotting the isotachs attention is to be paid to the position of boundaries of rock blocks characterized by different petrographic composition and fillers as well as by varying depth from the day surface of rock mass zones.

The seismic-geological sections as elements of the geophysical schemes are illustrated in Figures 2 and 3.

Geophysical schemes permit a proper estimation of the state of appropriate rock zones from numerous measurements of geophysical parameters. Thus the geophysical scheme is to be considered as a connecting link between the geostructural and geomechanical schemes.

3. Application of correlations between rock properties to plotting of a geomechanic scheme of rock masses

The geomechanic scheme of rock masses discloses the inhomogeneity and anisotropy in deformation and strength properties of jointed rock taken to a depth somewhat exceeding that of the active zone which is affected by the structure under design. For large engineering structures (e.g. high-head concrete dams) it is important: a) to evaluate the inhomogeneity of the deformation properties of foundation rock; b) to find the planes of potential shear, i.e. extended joint planes and layers of weakness. Therefore the geomechanic scheme of rock masses can be presented as partial schemes developed in terms of the following characteristics: a) the modulus of deformation, E_o; b) Poisson's ratio, ν; c) shear resistance parameters, c and ϕ; d) compressive strength, σ_c; e) coefficient of mollifiability, K_m; e) frost resistance factor, K_f, etc.

M o d u l u s o f t o t a l d e f o r m a t i o n, E_o (MN/m^2) of rock is determined at individual points of a mass with the help of 1 m dia. round plates (or square plates of 1x1 m).

The experimental E_o-values are extended to the whole mass using a) the geostructural and geophysical schemes, b) correlations of E_o to the indices of the rock properties and the state established by geophysical methods. The indices include C_p and C_s-values; the dynamic elastic modulus, E_d; the total porosity, n; the open porosity, n_o; the crack porosity, $K_{c.p.}$ etc. The correlation between E_o and C_p, C_s, E_d-indices, determined in the course of a seismic survey were reported elsewhere (Gureev, 1968; Savich et al., 1969; Ukhov and Panenkov, 1968). E_o as a function of porosity and jointing established by geological and geophysical methods, is given

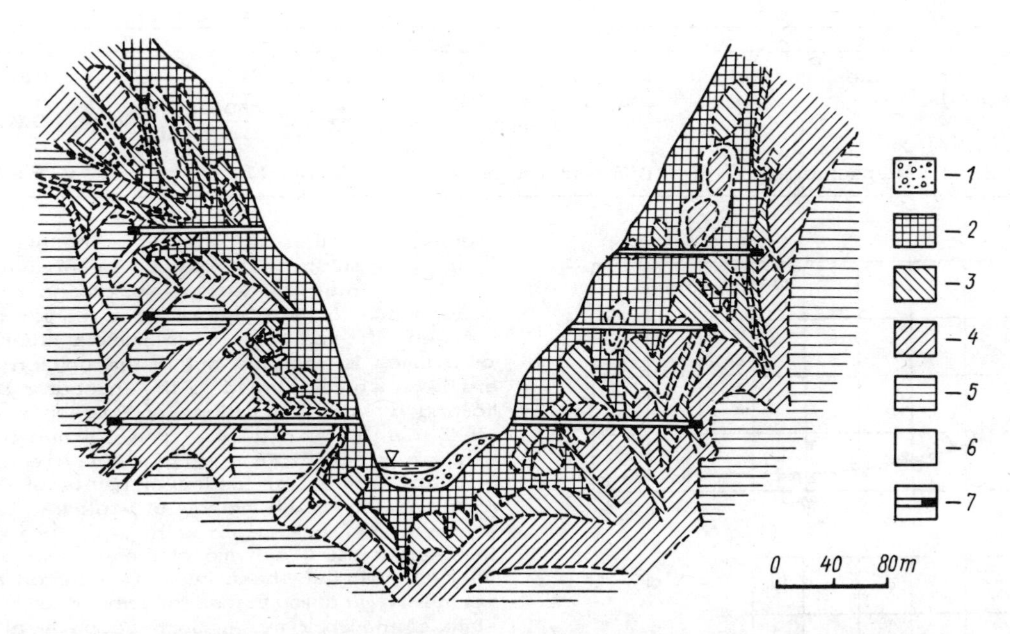

Fig. 2. Seismic-geological cross-section of rock foundation of the Toktogul Dam. 1 - alluvium and talus deposition, 2 - region of 1 km/s < C_s < 1.5 km/s, 3 - region of 1.5 km/s < C_s < 2.0 km/s, 4 - region of 2.0 km/s < C_s < 2.5 km/s, 5 - region of C_s > 2.5 km/s, 6 - isolines of transverse seismic wave velocities, 7 - adits.

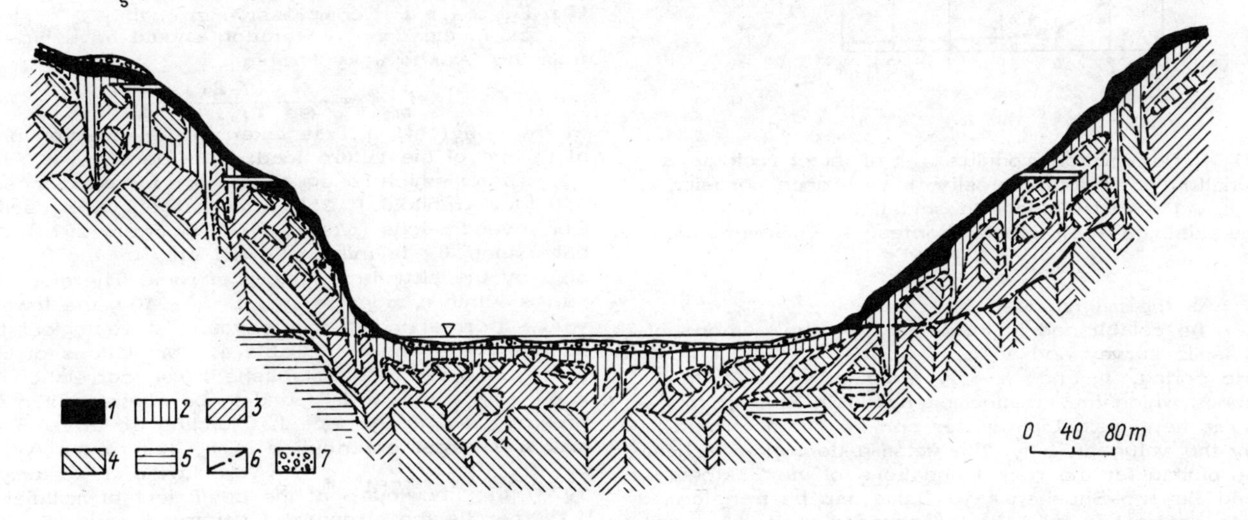

Fig. 3. Seismic-geological cross-section of rock foundation of the Sayano-Shushenskaya Dam. 1 - region of C_p < 2.5 km/s, 2 - region of 2.5 < C_p < 4 km/s, 3 - region of 4 km/s < C_p < 5 km/s, 4 - region of 5 km/s < C_p < 6 km/s, 5 - region of C_p > 6 km/s, 6 - isolines of longitudinal seismic wave velocities, 7 - alluvium and talus deposition.

in Table 1 and Fig. 4.

Table 1

Relation of $E_o (MN/m^2)$ to $K_{c.p.}$ (%), n(%) and n_o(%) of rocks

Rock	Site	E_o	Correlation factor	Author
1	2	3	4	5
Metamorphic chlorite schists (in-situ)	The Andijan Dam	$E_o = 7870\ K_{c.p.}^{-0.475}$	-0.82	A.S.Panenkov, S.B.Ukhov
Traps (in-situ)	The Ust-Ilim Dam	$E_o = 8550\ K_{c.p.}^{-0.725}$	-	B.D.Zelensky
Gneisses, crystalline schists (in-situ)		$E_o = 8550\ K_{c.p.}^{-0.725}$	-0.76	N.Kh.Vitkina
Quartz-porphiries (in-situ)	The Kapchagai Dam	$E_o = 11500\ K_{c.p.}^{-0.83}$	-0.88	E.I.Tkachuk

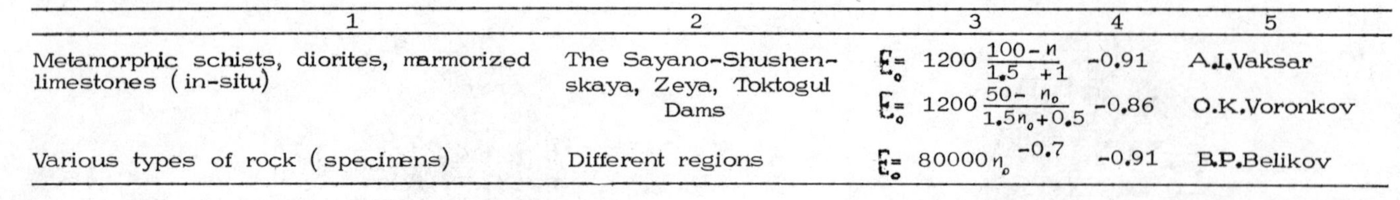

1	2	3	4	5
Metamorphic schists, diorites, marmorized limestones (in-situ)	The Sayano-Shushenskaya, Zeya, Toktogul Dams	$E_o = 1200 \frac{100-n}{1.5n+1}$	-0.91	A.I.Vaksar
		$E_o = 1200 \frac{50-n_o}{1.5n_o+0.5}$	-0.86	O.K.Voronkov
Various types of rock (specimens)	Different regions	$E_o = 80000\, n_o^{-0.7}$	-0.91	B.P.Belikov

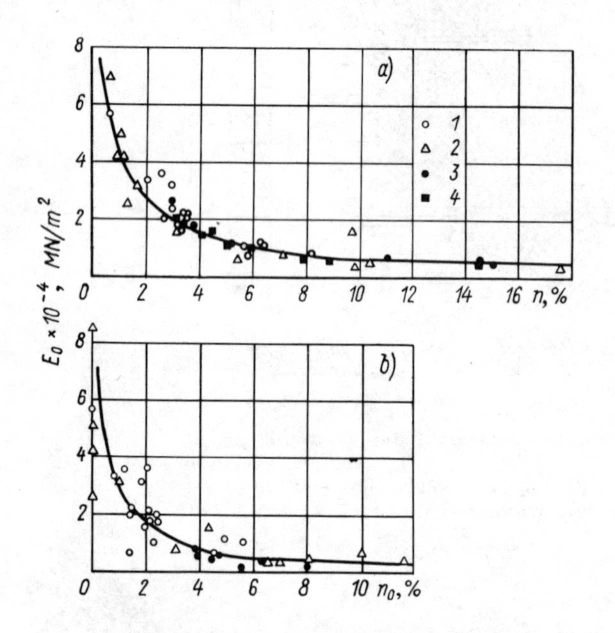

Fig.4. Deformation modulus E_o of intact rock as a function of a) total porosity, n ; b) open porosity, n_o . 1 - crystalline orthoschist, 2 - crystalline paraschists, 3 - amphibole diorites, 4 - marmorized limestone.

As the magnitudes of n and n_o, E_d, C_p can be established in intact rock by the methods of seismic survey and acoustic coring, n_o - by electric coring, n and n_o - by radioactive coring, the zones which are quasihomogeneous in respect to some geophysical parameter can be characterized by the value of E_o. The seismic-geological schemes plotted for the rock foundations of the Toktogul and Sayano-Shushenskaya Dams can be transformed into geomechanical schemes proceeding from E_o and the data given in Tables 2 and 3.

Table 2

Transverse wave velocity, C_s ; total porosity, n and deformation modulus, E_o, in the Toktogul Dam foundation composed of marmorized limestone

C_s in km/s	n in %	E_o x10^{-2} in MN/m^2
1.0-1.5	10.5-5.9	30-50
1.5-2.0	5.9-3.3	50-100
2.0-2.5	3.3-1.6	100-300
$>$2.5	$<$ 1.6	$>$ 300

P o i s s o n ' s   r a t i o for most rocks ranges from 0.1 to 0.4. The dynamic value of Poisson's ratio, ν_d , is commonly calculated from the measured relation of C_p to C_s . The static value, ν_{st} , is seldom determined. The analysis of the ν_d / ν_{st} ratio for various rocks and non-rock soils points to the absence of a regular difference between ν_d and ν_{st} . Sometimes a difference by 2 or 3 times is reported but in the opinion of the writers it can be attributed to the inaccuracy of both static and dynamic estimations of Poisson's ratios.

T h e c a n d φ - p a r a m e t e r s o f s h e a r i n g r e s i s t a n c e o f r o c k resulting from shear testing of pillars of well preserved rock and those with planes of weakness are extended to cover the rock mass as a whole, proceeding from the geostructural scheme of the mass and with the filler of potential shear joints recognized as well as weathering and roughness of joint walls and the stress state of the rock mass. Some geophysical methods (the seismic survey, resistivity prospecting) help to reveal potential shear cracks, the others (the electric, acoustic and radioactive coring) - to characterize the crack filler and the water content of rock. U n i a x i a l compressive strength, σ_{comp} (MN/m^2) of rock in the zone of aeration should be estimated from the Lyakhovitsky formula

$$\sigma_{comp\,1} = \frac{C_p^2 \rho (1-2\nu_d)}{196 \cdot C_1 (1-\nu_d)}$$

where C_p (m/s) is taken in the direction normal to that of the failure load; ρ - density (g/sm^3); C_1 - factor, which is equal to 900 (for sandstones), 950 (for granitoids), 1500 (for carbonbearing soils). Our investigations (Voronkov, Rostomyan, 1973) indicated that C_1 is influenced not only by the type but also by the structural history of rock. Therefore C_1 varies within a wider range of 550-2400, the lowest values corresponding to the youngest geological formations as is shown in Table 4. Correlations of $\sigma_{comp.1}$ to n and n_o are also established. The correlation between $\sigma_{comp.1}$ and n_o is found to be closer, which is probably due to the fact that jointing governing $\sigma_{comp.1}$ makes a larger contribution to n_o than to n . As $\sigma_{comp.2} = \sigma_{comp.1} K_m$ (Voronkov and Rostomyan, 1973) the knowledge of the coefficient of mollifiability K_m permits the strength of saturated rock $\sigma_{comp.2}$ to be obtained.

T h e c o e f f i c i e n t o f m o l l i f i a b i l i t y K_m of rock characterizes variation in the compressive strength of saturated rock $\sigma_{comp.2}$ as compared to that of dry rock $\sigma_{comp.1}$:

$K_m = \sigma_{comp.2} / \sigma_{comp.1}$. The relationship between K_m and the total porosity n (%) of rock is established by experiment. For types of rock insensitive or almost insensitive to saturation with water (i.e. practically all the igneous and metamorphic rocks with the exception of fine fragmented tuffs; siliceous quartzitic sandstones also refer to this group) $1/K_m = 1+0.009\,n$ at $0\% \leqslant n \leqslant 14\%$.

For the great majority of sedimentary rocks (carbonaceous rock and sandstones) as well as for fine fragmented tuffs $1/K_m = 1+0.075\,n$ at $0\% \leqslant n \leqslant 30\%$.

T h e f r o s t r e s i s t a n c e f a c t o r K_f stands for the total effect of water saturation and negative temperatures on the rock strength. It is equal to the ratio of the ultimate compressive

Table 3

Longitudinal wave velocity, C_p ; total porosity, n , and deformation modulus, E_o , in the Sayano-Shushenskaya Dam foundation composed of metamorphic schist

C_p in km/s	Above the ground water table		Below the ground water table	
	n in %	$E_o \times 10^{-2}$ in MN/m^2	n in %	$E_o \times 10^{-2}$ in MN/m^2
< 2.5	> 10	< 30	-	-
2.5 - 3.0	10 - 6.3	30 - 100	> 10	< 30
3.0 - 4.0	6.3 - 4.2	100 - 140	10 - 7.3	30-90
4.0 - 5.0	4.2 - 2.4	140 - 230	7.3 - 4.0	90-150
5.0 - 6.0	2.4 - 1.1	230 - 400	4.0 - 2.0	150-270
> 6.0	< 1.1	> 400	< 2.0	> 270

Table 4

C_1 - values for various rocks

Rock	Age	C_1
Intrusive rock (granites)	Jurassic-Cretaceous	650
Intrusive rock (granites)	Devonian	850
Intrusive rock (granites)	Silurian	1200
Effusive rock (andesites, basalts, tuffs, slags etc.)	Quarternary	600
Effusive rock (andesites, basalts, tuffs, slags etc.)	Permian-Triassic	1850
Metamorphic rock (except clay and coaly shales)	various	1800
Clay and coaly shales	various	1400
Sedimentary rock (sandstones and siltstones)	Early Cretaceous	550
Sedimentary rock (sandstones and siltstones)	Carboniferous	1800
Sedimentary rock (limestones)	Various (from Neogene to Devonian)	2400

strength of saturated rock samples (after 25 alternative cycles of freezing down to -20°C and thawing) to the initial compressive strength of dry samples, i.e. $K_f = \sigma_{comp.3} / \sigma_{comp.1}$. The results obtained from low porosity rock ($n \leqslant 4\%$) at $\sigma_{comp.1} \geqslant 80$ MN/m^2 show that, as a rule, $K_f = 1 - 0.18n$, where n is given in %. Experiments on relatively weak rocks of high porosity ($\sigma_{comp.1} \leqslant 80$ MN/m^2) yield for the frost resistance factor $K_f = 1 - 6 \times 10^{-3} \sigma_{comp.1}$, where $\sigma_{comp.1}$ is in MN/m^2, the formula being valid within the range of 10 $MN/m^2 \leqslant \sigma_{comp.1} \leqslant 80$ MN/m^2.

REFERENCES

1. Belikov, B.P., Alexandrov, K.S., Ryzhova, T.V.,- Elastic properties of rock-forming minerals and rocks, "Nauka", Moskva, 1970, 276 p.

2. Voronkov, O.K., Rostomyan, T.V., - On determination of ultimate uniaxial compressive strength, mollifiability and frost resistance factors of rock by geophysical methods, Izvestia VNIIG, vol.101, 1973, pp.222-234.

3. Gureev, A.M., - Principles of engineering geological zoning of rock masses at the sites of high dams, Sbornik "Voprosy inzhenernoi geologii i gruntovedeniya", Vyp.2, 1968, pp.213-228.

4. Gureev, A.M., Voronkov, O.K., Motorin, G.A., - Procedures for constructing seismic-geological models of rock masses from seismic survey data, Trudy koordinatsionnykh soveshchanii po gidrotekhnike, Vyp.77, 1972, pp.18-22.

5. Savich, A.I., Koptev, V.I., Yashchenko L.G., - Seismoacoustic methods of exploring rock masses, "Nedra", 1969, 240 p.

6. Ukhov, S.B., Panenkov, A.S., - On correlation between static and dynamic deformation indices of rock, obtained from large-scale testing on undisturbed rock mass, Gidrotekhnicheskoye stroitelstvo, no.11, 1968, pp.38-37.

VORSCHLAG ZUR GRUNDLEGENDEN BESCHREIBUNG UND KLASSIFIZIERUNG DES GEBIRGES FÜR ALLGEMEIN-TECHNISCHE ZWECKE

PROPOSAL FOR THE BASIC DESCRIPTION AND CLASSIFICATION OF THE ROCK MASS FOR GENERAL TECHNICAL PURPOSES

PROPOSITION POUR LA DESCRIPTION ET CLASSIFICATION FONDAMENTALE DE ROCHE POUR DES BUTS TECHNIQUES EN GÉNÉRAL

Helmut HABENICHT

Hochschulassistent

Montanistische Hochschule Leoben

Leoben, Austria

Zusammenfassung

Es wird auf den zunehmenden Bedarf einer materialorientierten Klassifikation des Gebirges hingewiesen, die als Grundlage für den Aufbau allfälliger und verschieden gearteter zweckorientierter Klassifikationen dienen soll. Nach einer Besprechung allgemeiner Gesichtspunkte zur Klassifizierung, wie der Definition, der Elemente einer Klassifizierung und der Anforderungen an eine Klassifizierung, wird ein Vorschlag einer materialorientierten Klassifizierung gebracht. Dieser enthält umfassende Eigenschaften des Gebirges und der in ihm aufscheinenden Gesteine. Dabei werden die Eigenschaften und Klassen weitgehend auf die meßtechnische Erfassung der charakteristischen Größen abgestimmt, weil es immer mehr erforderlich wird, Zahlenangaben über das Gebirge zur Verfügung zu haben.

Summary

The increasing demand for such a materialrelated classification of the rock mass is stressed, which can serve as a basis for the superposition of eventually required purpose-related classifications of specialized nature. A discussion of general aspects like the definition, the elements of a classification, and the requirements of the same is followed by a proposal of a material-related classification. This one includes far reaching properties of the rock mass and of the contained rocks. Thereby the properties and classes are mainly built on the determination of the characteristic quantities by measurement, because quantitative data about the rock mass become more and more required.

Résumé

La demande croissante pour une classification de roche en relation matériel est montrée quelle peut servir comme fondement pour la superposition eventuelle d'une classification en relation à l'application de mode diverse. Après d'une discussion des points de vue generals, une proposition d'une classification en relation matériel est presentée. Elle comprends des propriétés de roche embrassantes et des roches contenues. Les propriétés et les classes sont extensivement considerées pour la determination par mesure comme il-y-a la demande croissante pour des renseignements quantitativs.

Einleitung

Stetig nimmt das Ausmaß zu, in dem sich die Menschheit mit der festen Erdkruste als Gegenstand mechanischer Eingriffe zu befassen hat. Sowohl in industrieller als auch in wissenschaftlicher Sicht sind hauptsächlich die Fachbereiche der Bergbautechnik und der Bautechnik dieser Entwicklung unterworfen. Für beide sind die Probleme der Stabilität von Auffahrungen und der Gewinnbarkeit des gewachsenen Gebirges gleichermaßen von Bedeutung. Und für beide treten eine Reihe von Fragenkreisen auf, die kurz wie folgt unterschieden werden können (HABENICHT und BRENNSTEINER, 1971):

Standfestigkeit von Wänden und Böschungen in Tagebauen und an Baustellen;
Standfestigkeit von Grubenräumen einschließlich Abbauen und von untertägigen Hohlräumen für Verkehrs-, Speicher- und Schutzzwecke, sowie Wasserkraftanlagen;
Entwurf von Ausbausystemen zum Offenhalten der untertägigen Hohlräume;
Kontrolle und Steuerung von Bruch- oder Absenkungsvorgängen im Gefolge des Abbaus;
Abschätzung und Einschränkung der Gebirgsschlaggefahr;
Entwurf von Auflagern wie Dammgründungen, Brückenwiderlagern und Verankerungen;
Abschätzen der Leistung bei der Gebirgszerlegung wie beim Bohren, Schneiden, Sprengen;
Auslegung von Bohr- und Schießschemen;
Beurteilung von Zerkleinerungsvorgängen wie Brechen und Mahlen.

Die wirkungsvollste Maßnahme, den Bautechniker und den Bergmann oder den Gebirgsmechaniker in seinen Bestrebungen bei der Erfassung des Gebirgsverhaltens zu unterstützen, wäre die, fürjeden Fragenkreis die Gebirgsarten in Klassen nach ihren Reaktionen einzuteilen. Jeder solchen Klasse könnte dann die erforderliche technische Maßnahme gegenübergestellt werden. Mittels eines Katalogs solcher Maßnahmen würde die Entscheidung der Techniker erleichtert und beschleunigt werden. Es bestünde dabei nur das Problem, die Klasse der Gebirgsarten rechtzeitig zu erkennen.

Der derzeitige Stand der Kenntnisse ist noch weit von dieser Idealvorstellung entfernt. Als wesentlichste Hindernisse stehen einerseits die Vielartigkeit des Gebirges und die Vielzahl der wichtigen Eigenschaften, andererseits die Vielartigkeit der technischen Eingriffe im Wege. Wohl sind in manchen Fragenkreisen schon bedeutende Fortschritte erzielt worden, wie etwa beim Tunnelausbau durch die Arbeiten von LAUFFER (1958).

Dieser Erfolg ist das Ergebnis einer besonderen Denkweise, in der allein die dem Fragenkreis zugeordneten Eigenschaften betrachtet und klassifiziert werden. Danach können spezifische, problembezogene Kriterien für die Aufstellung einer Klassifizierung dienen, die sich für besondere technische Zielsetzungen eignet. Solche Klassifizierungen sollen im folgenden als zweckorientierte Klassifizierungen bezeichnet werden. Verfolgt man diesen Gedankengang konsequent, so kann man die Idealvorstellung erfüllen.

Hiebei ist jedoch zu berücksichtigen, daß nicht in allen Fällen eine Klassifizierung für nur einen technischen Zweck verlangt ist, sondern daß sich häufig mehrere Fragenkreise überschneiden. Diese Tatsache hat besonders dort große Bedeutung, wo langfristige Projekte in ein und derselben Gebirgszone umgehen, wie z.B. bei der Bergbautätigkeit. Dort kommt zur Vielartigkeit der Zielsetzungen noch die zeitliche Fortentwicklung der Technik, sodaß eine größere Anzahl von Eigenheiten interessant erscheint. Zu diesen Eigenheiten zählen dann nicht nur die zweckorientierten, sondern auch solche, die allgemein bedeutende Charakteristiken des Materials wiedergeben und die im folgenden als materialorientierte Eigenheiten (entsprechend: materialorientierte Klassifizierung) bezeichnet werden sollen.

Es soll Aufgabe dieses Beitrages sein, eine solche materialorientierte Klassifikation vorzuschlagen. Diese Gelegenheit wird auch zum Anlaß genommen, einige allgemeingültige Gesichtspunkte für die Klassifizierung aufzuzeigen.

Definition

Nach der Encyclopedia Britannica (1962) versteht man unter dem Begriff Klassifikation eine Anordnung von Dingen in Klassen entsprechend den Eigenschaften, die sie gemeinsam haben.

Streng genommen können demnach jene Dinge oder Begriffe nicht klassifiziert werden, die keine gemeinsamen Eigenschaften aufweisen. Solche Dinge können nur gruppiert werden. Dabei ist es allerdings möglich, solche Gruppen zu bilden, in denen gewisse Eigenschaften als charakteristisch hervorstechen oder zumindest bei allen Elementen einer Gruppe auftreten, sodaß eine Gruppe z.B. nach einer der Eigenschaften bezeichnet werden kann. Innerhalb einer solchen Gruppe ist es dann möglich, entsprechend dem Ausbildungsgrad einer Eigenschaft eine Klassifizierung vorzunehmen, d.h. eine Klassifikation zu erstellen.

Elemente der Klassifizierung und Probleme

Im Zuge der Klassifizierung muß ein in verschiedenen Erscheinungsformen auftretender Begriff oder ein Ding entweder direkt in Klassen oder zuerst in Gruppen und innerhalb derselben in Klassen untergliedert werden. Hiebei lassen sich grundsätzlich vier Elemente unterscheiden:

a) Der Begriff:
Unter Begriff wird der eigentliche Gegenstand verstanden, der zu klassifizieren ist. Dieser kann konkreter oder abstrakter Natur sein und umfaßt eine Vielfalt von Erscheinungsformen, die sich im gesamten oder gruppenweise durch bestimmte Eigenschaften auszeichnen. Er soll systematisch in Gruppen oder Klassen untergliedert werden, wobei für die Systematik gewisse Gesichtspunkte maßgebend sind, die durch das jeweils vorschwebende Ziel bestimmt werden.

b) Das Ziel
Ganz allgemein gesehen ist es das Ziel einer Klassifizierung, die in den Begriffsbereich gehörenden Erscheinungsformen übersichtlich einzuordnen. Im besonderen gilt jedoch, daß dieses Einordnen immer im Hinblick auf einen konkreten Zweck vorgenommen wird, der einen von außen her vorgegebenen Wertmaßstab für das Einordnen liefert. Dieser Zweck muß also vor Beginn der Klassifizierung gegeben sein. Der Zweck bestimmt vorwiegend die Auslegung der Gruppen. Der Wertmaßstab bestimmt die Systematik der Klassenbildung.

c) Die Eigenschaften
Grundsätzlich werden für das Gruppieren solche Eigenschaften bevorzugt, die in Hinsicht auf den Zweck die größte Aussagekraft besitzen. Die Wahl der Eigenschaften stellt sich immer als ein Problem eines Kompromisses dar. Denn das Bestreben des Einordnens verlangt nach Vollständigkeit, was eine Vielzahl von Gruppen und somit auch von gewählten Eigenschaften zur Folge hat. Das Bestreben der Übersichtlichkeit verlangt wenig Gruppen oder Eigenschaften, und eine einfache Zusammenstellung derselben. Somit besteht

nicht nur das Problem einer zweckgerechten Auswahl der Eigenschaften, sondern auch einer günstigen Auslese ihrer Anzahl.

Auf dem Gebiet der angewandten Wissenschaften kann man durchwegs zwei Gruppen von Eigenschaften unterscheiden: solche, die spezifisch zweckorientiert sind und solche, die im Sinne einer allgemeinen Information als materialorientiert (begriffsorientiert) angesehen werden können. Die erstgenannten beschreiben im besonderen die Eignung des Begriffes für einen technischen Zweck und die zweitgenannten umfassen die sachbezogenen Eigenschaften allgemein wissenschaftlicher Natur. Daraus resultieren die zweckorientierten bzw. die materialorientierten Klassifikationen.

d) Die Klassen
Als Klassen werden die mehr oder weniger quantifizierbaren Stufen des Ausbildungsgrades einer Eigenschaft bezeichnet. Ein Begriff kann also unmittelbar in Klassen eingeteilt werden, wenn die Klassifizierungseigenschaft allen seinen Erscheinungsformen gemein ist. Trifft dies nicht zu, müssen Gruppen gebildet werden, die ihrerseits in Klassen geteilt werden können.
Auch für die Wahl der Klassen trifft eine Problematik der Kompromißerfordernis zu. Je mehr Klassen gebildet werden, desto treffender oder genauer wird die Aussage. Weniger Klassen vereinfachen die Übersicht. Es wird besonders dort erforderlich sein, mehr Klassen zu wählen, wo die Veränderlichkeit der Klassifizierungseigenschaft groß ist.

Anforderungen an eine Klassifizierung

Die vielartigen Gesichtspunkte, die für die erfolgreiche Verbindung der Elemente einer Klassifizierung ausschlaggebend sind, können in Form von 6 Anforderungen wiedergegeben werden. Diese sind:

a) Optimierung der Ausdrücke:
Die Wahl der charakteristischen Eigenschaften und der Klassen soll so geschehen, daß mit einer möglichst geringen Zahl an Ausdrücken eine dem Zweck entsprechende optimale Aussagefähigkeit erzielt wird.

b) Einfachheit der Mittel:
Die Wahl der charakteristischen Eigenschaften und Klassegrenzen soll so erfolgen, daß ihre Erfassung mit möglichst einfachen Mitteln erfolgen kann.

c) Vielartigkeit der Mittel:
Die Wahl der charakteristischen Eigenschaften und Klassegrenzen soll so erfolgen, daß diese mit möglichst vielen Mitteln und Methoden festgestellt werden können.

d) Ausschließlichkeit der Ausdrücke:
Die gewählten Eigenschaften und Klassen sollen so geartet sein, daß sie einander in der Bedeutung ausschließen.

e) Normung der Ausdrücke:
Die Festlegung von Eigenschaften und Klassen soll möglichst nach bestehenden Normen erfolgen.

f) Aussagebeständigkeit:
Die Wahl der Eigenschaften und Klassen soll so erfolgen, daß die Beurteilung der Begriffe auch bei verschiedener technischer Zielsetzung gleich bleibt.

Vorgeschlagene Klassifikation

Die in nachstehender Tabelle 1 vorgeschlagene Klassifikation des Gebirges soll als materialorientierte verstanden werden. Sie enthält zwar nur Eigenschaften mechanischer

Tabelle 1: Vorschlag zur Klassifizierung des Gebirges nach materialorientierten Eigenschaften

I. Fundort:

Bezeichnung: Lage: Zeitpunkt:

Bereichsgröße B:

Homogenitätsbereich H: $H < B$, $H > B$

Besonderheiten des Aufbaus von B:

II. Stratigraphische Einordnung von B:

III. Beteiligte Gesteine: Anzahl:

Für jedes Gestein:

1. Name:
2. Bildungsweise:

magmatogen:	sedimentär:	metamorph:
Plutonit	a) autochthon	katazonal
Eruptivgestein	allochthon	mesozonal
Ganggestein	b) mechanisch	epizonal
	chemisch	anchimetamorph
	biogen	

3. Petrographische Gefüge: massig (amorph, krypto-, mikro-, makro- oder phanerokristallin)
   lagig (schwach, deutlich, stark ausgeprägt)
   schieferig (gut, mäßig, schlecht)
4. Festigkeit (einachsige Druckprobe):

Stufe I $\sigma_B > 2500$ kp/cm^2 ($2{,}5.10^8$ N/m^2)
Stufe II 2500 kp/cm^2 ($2{,}5.10^8$ N/m^2) $> \sigma_B >$ 1000 kp/cm^2 ($1{,}0.10^8$ N/m^2)
Stufe III 1000 kp/cm^2 ($1{,}0.10^8$ N/m^2) $> \sigma_B >$ 500 kp/cm^2 ($0{,}5.10^8$ N/m^2)
Stufe IV 500 kp/cm^2 ($0{,}5.10^8$ N/m^2) $> \sigma_B >$ 300 kp/cm^2 ($0{,}3.10^8$ N/m^2)
Stufe V 300 kp/cm^2 ($0{,}3.10^8$ N/m^2) $> \sigma_B$

5. Verformungsverhalten:

Elastisch: Verformungsverhältnis $= \varepsilon_{hyst}/\varepsilon_{Bruch} < 0{,}25$

a) Linearität:
   Linear: Linearitätsabweichung < 10 %
   Nicht linear: Linearitätsabweichung > 10 %

b) Elastizitätsbereich:
   hoch .... über 75 % der Bruchlast
   mittel .... 25 % - 75 % der Bruchlast
   niedrig .... unter 25 % der Bruchlast

Fortsetzung der Tabelle:

c) E-Modul:
sehr hoch ...... über 8.10^5 kp/cm^2 (8.10^{10} N/m^2)
hoch .... $1.10^5 - 8.10^5$ kp/cm^2 ($1.10^{10} - 8.10^{10}$ N/m^2)
niedrig .... $0{,}5 .10^5 - 1.10^5$ kp/cm^2 ($0{,}5.10^{10} - 1.10^{10}$ N/m^2)
sehr niedrig ... unter $0{,}5.10^5$ kp/cm^2 ($0{,}5.10^{10}$ N/m^2)

Nicht elastisch: Verformungsverhältnis $\varepsilon_{hyst}/\varepsilon_{Bruch} \geq 0{,}25$
elastoplatisch ...... $\varepsilon_{hyst}/\varepsilon_{Bruch}$ von $0{,}25 - 0{,}75$
plastisch .... $\varepsilon_{hyst}/\varepsilon_{Bruch} > 0{,}75$
viskos .... bei Belastung von 50 % der einachsigen Druckfestigkeit nimmt die Dehnung um $2.10^{-6}/h$ zu.

IV. Tektonische Eigenheit : ungefaltet — ungestört
gefaltet — verworfen

V. Kontinuität:
1. Ungeklüftet:
2. Geklüftet:
Unsichtbare Klüfte:
Sichtbare Klüfte:
A) unverheilt: dicht, offen, wasserführend
B) verheilt: Füllstoff, schwächer, gleich, fester als Nebengestein

Zahl der Kluftscharen:
tabular (1 Schar von Kluftflächen)
säulig (2 Scharen von Kluftflächen)
blockig (3 Scharen von Kluftflächen)
komplex (>3 Scharen von Kluftflächen)
unregelmäßig zerbrochen (keine durchlaufenden Kluftebenen)

Dichte der Kluftscharen:
weit ...... Kluftflächenabstand > 2 m
mäßig ..... Kluftflächenabstand 2 m – 20 cm
mittel .... Kluftflächenabstand 20 cm – 20 mm
eng .... Kluftflächenabstand < 20 mm

Natur, doch sind diese im Sinne der Gebirgsmechanik so allgemeiner Art, daß der Vorschlag nicht als zweckorientierter aufgefaßt werden kann. Im Gegenteil soll der Vorschlag betont die allgemein technischen Gebirgseigenschaften so weitgehend erfassen, daß er als alleinige Grundlage gebirgsmechanischer Information für die allgemeinen Gesichtspunkte dienen kann. Er ist demnach als breiteste Grundlage gedacht und soll generell als Vorstufe für eventuell darüberhinaus noch zu erstellende zweckorientierte Klassifikationen angesehen werden.

Damit soll der Vorschlag eine Lücke füllen, die sich immer deutlicher abzeichnet, zumal die zunehmenden Eingriffe in die Erdkruste und das steigende Niveau der technischen Hilfsmittel es immer mehr verlangen, daß breitgespannte Kenntnisse über Zustand und Eigenschaften des Gebirges zur Verfügung stehen. Zusätzliche zweckorientierte Klassifikationen können im Falle besonderer Problemstellung hier in beliebiger Zahl hinzugefügt werden.

Es besteht noch ein weiteres Problem bei der Wahl der Eigenschaften und Klassen. Obwohl nämlich in den Anforderungen verlangt wird, daß sie aus genormten Größen ausgewählt werden, ist dies nicht immer möglich. Denn vielfach bestehen hiefür keine Normen. Es besteht also die Frage, ob sich ein Klassifizierungsvorschlag streng im Bereich genormter Begriffe bewegen soll oder ob er darüber hinaus auch Eigenschaften und Klassen beinhalten soll, die zwar zweckmäßig, aber nicht genormt sind. Im letztgenannten Fall würde eine Klassifizierung der Normung vorausgreifen und gewissermaßen richtungsweisend für erforderliche Schritte der Normung dienen.

Eine solche vor allem auf den aktuellen Fragen aufbauende Klassifizierung wurde hier angestrebt. Diese gewissermaßen vorausschauende Orientierung der Klassifizierung wurde deshalb angenommen, weil die Entwicklung im Fluß ist, und darauf hingewiesen werden soll, welche Eigenschaften und Klassen normierungswürdig erscheinen.

Auch ist in dem Vorschlag zu erkennen, daß er eine Reihe von Kriterien enthält, die nicht mehr qualitativ, sondern nur durch Messung festgestellt werden können. Damit wird auch deutlich der Standpunkt vertreten, daß eine meßtechnische Erfassung der Gebirgscharakteristik immer mehr erforderlich wird, und nicht dabei verblieben werden kann, nur qualitative Ausdrücke und eine meßungsfreie Beurteilung zu verwenden.

Der dargebrachte Vorschlag ist eine Weiterentwicklung der Klassifikation, welche von HABENICHT und BRENNSTEINER (1971) veröffentlicht wurde. Seine Weiterentwicklung geschah mit der fruchtbaren Unterstützung der Mitglieder des Arbeitskreises für technische Gebirgsbeschreibung des Bergmännischen Verbandes Österreichs.

Es wurde dabei besonders darauf Wert gelegt, die bedeutenden Erscheinungsformen des Gebirges zu berücksichtigen und die innerhalb desselben aufscheinenden Gesteine als Untergruppen zu erfassen.

Unter den Eigenschaften der Gesteine wurde auch das Verformungsverhalten eigens klassifiziert. Dabei wird zwischen elastischem und nichtelastischem unterschieden. Zur Abgrenzung zwischen beiden wurde das Verformungsverhältnis $\varepsilon_{hyst}/\varepsilon_{Bruch}$ verwendet. ε_{hyst} bedeutet darin die Restdehnung nach Durchlaufen eines Be- und Entlastungsspieles und wird abgelesen an der Dehnungskoordinate des σ-ε Diagrammes. ε_{Bruch} bedeutet die Bruchdehnung der Probe. Da es praktisch nicht möglich ist, ein Hysterese-Spiel unter Erreichen der Bruchdehnung durchzuführen, wird vorgeschlagen, ε_{Bruch} aus dem Druckversuch zu bestimmen und ε_{hyst} aus einem Be- und Entlastungsspiel für das die Belastung nur auf 75 % der Bruchdehnung gesteigert wird.

Die für die Linearität herangezogene Linearitätsabweichung soll als Standardabweichung von der Regressionsgeraden eines Belastungsspiels an einem oder mehreren Prüfkörpern verstanden werden. Der E-Modul soll ebenfalls aus der Regressionsgeraden ermittelt werden.

Für die Bestimmung des Elastizitäsbereiches wird das Verhältnis jener Last zur Bruchlast herangezogen, für welches die Forderung $\varepsilon_{hyst}/\varepsilon_{Bruch} < 0{,}25$ erfüllt ist.

Obwohl das Festigkeits- und Verforumgsverhalten auch durch in-situ Prüfungen des Bereiches sozusagen als Gebirgseigenschaft ermittelt werden kann, wurde von einer Einbeziehung solcher Werte hier abgesehen, da die Art der Prüfung in solchen Dimensionen noch stark variiert.

Vielmehr wurde das Gebirgsverhalten durch die Ausbildung der Tektonik und des Kluftgefüges berücksichtigt.

Schluß

Der dargebrachte Vorschlag zur technischen Klassifizierung des Gebirges zeichnet sich dadurch aus, daß er nur materialorientierte Eigenschaften enthält und daß er hiemit als eine Grundlage allgemeiner Information angesehen werden kann, die durch beliebig viele zweckorientierte Klassifikationen ergänzt werden kann.

Sie enthält bewußt solche Eigenschaften, die nicht dem üblichen Stand entsprechend, geschätzt werden oder qualitativ beurteilt werden können, sondern die ein meßtechnisches Vorgehen erfordern. Deshalb enthält sie auch keine bereits genormten Größen oder Klassen, sondern weist eher selbst den Weg für eine erforderliche Normung. Sie stellt es aber frei, eines der verschiedentlich bereits genormten Verfahren zur größenmäßigen Erfassung der Eigenschaften zu verwenden.

****

Literaturstellen

ENCYCLOPEDIA BRITANNICA, INC. (1962), Encyclopedia Britannica, Vol. 5.

HABENICHT, H. und BRENNSTEINER, E. 1971, Über den Stand der Entwicklung auf dem Gebiet der Gebirgsklassifizierung, Berg- und Hüttenmännische Monatshefte, 116, Heft 4, S. 138 - 149.

LAUFFER, H., 1958, Gebirgsklassifizierung für den Stollenbau, Geologie und Bauwesen 24, Nr. 1, S. 46 - 51.

METHODS OF MODELLING IN ENGINEERING GEOLOGY AND GEO-ENGINEERING

DE LA MÉTHODOLOGIE DE L'ÉLABORATION DES MODÈLES DE GÉOLOGIE DE L'INGÉNIEUR ET DES MODÈLES GÉOTECHNIQUES

ÜBER DIE METHODE DER ERARBEITUNG INGENIEURGEOLOGISCHER UND GEOTECHNISCHER MODELLE

Branislav KUJUNDŽIĆ
Professor
Jaroslav Černi Institute for Development of Water Resources
Belgrad, Yugoslavia

Abstract. Engineering-geological and geo-engineering models represent the foundation for design of structures in or on rock. They constitute the final presentation of measurements of various parameters, e.g. deformability, shear strength, permeability, natural undisturbed stress state, etc.

Résumé. Les modèles de géologie de l'ingénieur et les modèles géotechniques constituent les données de base qui sont directement utilisées dans l'élaboration des projets des ouvrages de génie civil dans les masses rocheuses. Ils sont exécutés comme présentation final des résultats des travaux de reconnaissance d'après chacun des parametres tels que: déformabilité, resistance au cisaillement, perméabilité, état des contraintes naturel et autres.

Kurzfassung. Ingenieurgeologische und geotechnische Modelle stellen grundlegende Unterlagen dar, die unmittelbar zur Erarbeitung von Projekten für Bauanlagen in Felsmassen genützt werden. Sie werden als abschliessende Darstellung von Ergebnissen der Forschungsarbeiten nach einzelnen Parametern, wie: Verformbarkeit, Scherfestigkeit, Wasser - durchlässigkeit, Naturspannungszustand usw. bearbeitet.

1.1 Introduction

Research whose purpose is to provide base data for design and construction of structures on or in rock must in essence be a complex. Usually it involves the investigation of a number of parameters, and only a comprehensive work-up of the results can yield the information necessary for predicting with the desired accuracy the engineering-geological conditions under which the construction will have to be executed, and the behavior of the rock mass in interaction with the structure in use.

The practical final objective of pre-design research is to define in the rock of the construction location quasi-homogeneous zones within which the rock mass can be considered to have uniform properties, especially mechanical properties, and to experimentally investigate and numerically express all parameters relevant to design and construction.

The acheivement of this objective is greatly facilitated in practice by presenting research results in the form of engineering-geological sections (EGS), engineering-geological models (EGM) and geo-engineering models (GEM).

EGS are made up from measurements and study of particular characteristics of the rock mass, e.g. of: jointing, lithology, deformability, velocity of longitudinal elastic waves, permeability, resistivity, etc. An EGS is in fact a way of displaying the data yielded by these measurements and study.

An integral engineering-geological section (IEGS) is obtained by superimposing the EGS for each individual parameter, along with the necessary work-up and interpretation in order to tie all the research results into a logical whole.

EGM's are set up for parameters of key importance in design, such as jointing, deformability, permeability, undisturbed stress state, etc. As such they are to a greater or lesser extent simplified representations of the actual medium, broken down into quasi-homogeneous zones.

On EGS and IEGS all engineering-geological measurement or test points are plotted.

GEM's are representations of the rock mass divided up into zones within which different construction or geo-engineering improvement works must be designed and executed, e.g.: excavation, consolidation grouting, grout screens, anchoring, drainage, etc.

EGS, EGM's, the IEGM and the GEM are usually presented graphically on a suitable scale in vertical section along the axis of the planned structure and in plan projection (as a map). In complicated cases a number of vertical and horizontal sections may be necessary. The graphical material is accompanied by the necessary written information, which apart from the key to the diagrams will also present basic conclusions and observations regarding the properties of the rock mass, any relationships established, and suggestions for design and construction.

The proposed methods can in principle be applied to any civil engineering structure whether on the surface or underground. They will be illustrated on examples of exploratory works for the foundations of large concrete dams. Due to space limitations it is not possible to present all EGS, EGM's and GEM's.

1.2 Engineering-geological Sections (EGS)

The EGS of a dam site are usually vertical sections at right angles to the river; longitudinal vertical and horizontal sections are also made when required.

For large concrete dams EGS are most often made of the following properties: lithology, jointing (discontinuity of the rock mass), weathering, velocity of longitudinal elastic waves (v_l), resistivity (ρ), deformability (D, E, E_{dyn}), shearing strength (c, φ), permeability (Lu). They may also be made for, e.g., natural stress state, hardness, etc.

Lithology EGS. The results of prospecting are plotted on the EGS as contours of zones in the rock mass of different lithology and genesis. The genetic and lithological breakdown may also indicate the age of the formations, facies and other stratigraphic features. The EGS may also give information about the degree of disturbance of the formations, faulting, overthrusts, and the number of geotectonic units.

EGS of jointing. The investigation of the jointing of the rock mass should aim to provide information about the jointing in terms of the following parameters: location (position), strike and dip, length, gap width, wall configuration, type of fill.

Large joints are primarily plotted on the EGS, since they determine the chief preferred directions of shear, i.e. potential failure trajectories. For smaller fissures zones within which all systems have similar properties, i.e. quasi-homogeneous zones in the parameter of fissuring are determined and displayed on the EGS.

The gap width of cracks is important from the mechanical aspect since it influences the mobility of monolithic blocks in the rock mass and hence the deformability of the latter. It is often also one of the factors determining permeability. The wall configuration can essentially influence the resistance to shear in the direction of the crack. The type and characteristics of the fill are another factor determining the mobility of blocks and hence also deformability, the behavior of the rock in shear and the permeability. The effect of water on the rock mass and its suitability for grouting also depend on the fill characteristics.

Jointing is quantitatively expressed in terms of the coefficients of linear and planar discontinuity, and the so-called fissure porosity. Quasi-homogeneous zones in the parameter of jointing are defined by consideringspecific fissure systems, the characteristics of the joints, and the coefficients just referred to.

Figure 1 shows a fissuring EGS for the Mratinje arch dam (H = 220 m) on the Piva, in a vertical section at right angles to the river valley.

For stability calculations for arch dams, i.e. for identification of potential failure surfaces, it is also usual to make detailed engineering-geological maps of fissuring in a selection of horizontal sections at different elevations.

EGS of physical and chemical disintegration. EGS for this parameter show the weathering zone, i.e. that part of the rock mass which has undergone severe physical,

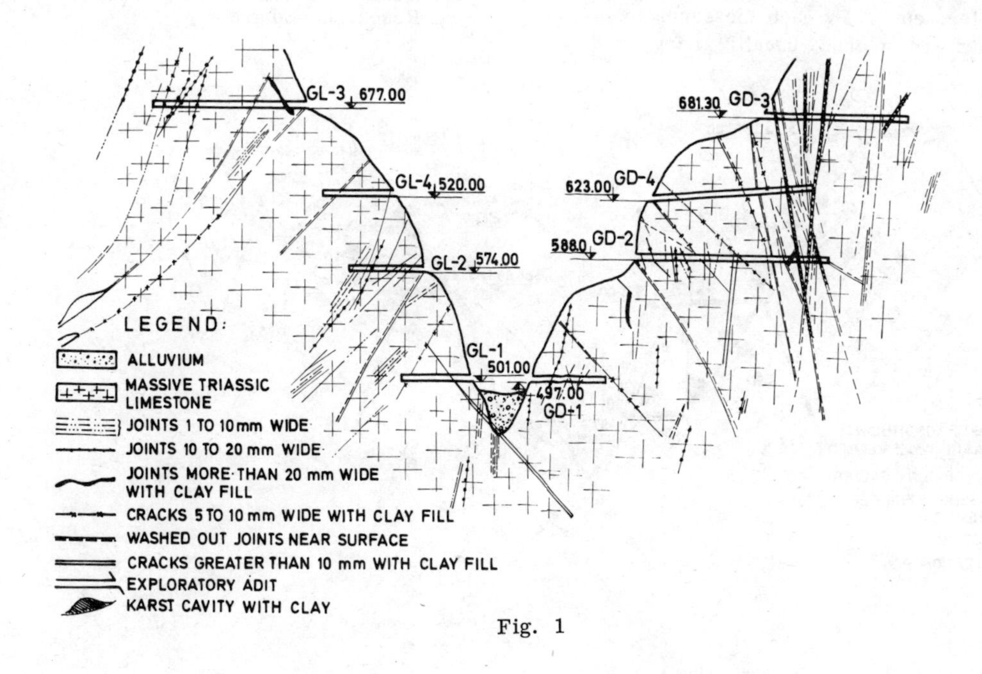

Fig. 1

mechanical changes of its properties in comparison with the sound rock. It should show the types of physical and chemical change and demarcate the subzones: surface weathering, deep weathering, block weathering.

EGS of the longitudinal elastic wave velocity. Field measurements are made by the seismic transmission ("en transparent") method. The seismic detectors are located, for example, in one exploratory adit, and pulses generated in another. Hence the travel time measured is that of direct arrivals whose trajectories pass trough the rock between excitation point and detection point.

All the exploratory adits, shafts and boreholes between which measurements have been made are drawn in on the EGS. The trajectories along which travel times have been measured are drawn and on them the velocities calculated from these measurements are entered.

Figure two shows a velocity EGS for the Mratinje dam site.*

Resistivity EGS. Electrical prospecting methods are used on dam sites to locate and delimit different types of rock, and especially to determine the depth to bedrock. Resistivity prospecting is also useful in karstic terrain since it can locate karstic collectors and the base of karstification, i.e. the depth limit of karstification. For the same purpose resistivity prospecting is often combined with refraction seismics.

The resistivity EGS is drawn to show quasi-homogeneous zones in this parameter.

Deformability EGS. On this EGS data from field deformability measurements are plotted. It is generally a vertical section through the foundation line of the dam. The drawing is made to show all test locations, adits, shafts, boreholes etc., and all the points at which measurements were made, with appropriate symbols for the method of measurement (hydraulic spanner, hydraulic flat jack, borehole dilatometer, etc.). By each measuring point the results obtained are entered, usually giving: modulus of deformation D, modulus of elasticity E, dynamic modulus of elasticity E_{dyn}, longitudinal elastic wave velocity v_l.

For the sake of a clearer visual impression the deformation characteristics at each measuring point are also shown graphically as vertical columns or columns oriented in the direction of the force applied in the test.

Figure 3 presents a deformability EGS for the Mratinje dam site.

Shear strength EGS. The data shown by this EGS are the results of field and laboratory tests of shearing in the sound rock and at joints. The test locations are drawn in with appropriate symbols showing the methods used. The results are entered by each measuring point, usually as the shear strength parameters c and ρ.

Permeability EGS. This EGS is drawn to show the data obtained by field measurements of permeability, usually, by Lugeon tests in boreholes. The permeability is expressed in Lugeon units: 1 Lu = 1 lit/min/m/10 at. The results are shown on the EGS by a graph of the test pressure drawn on one side (usually the right) of the borehole and on the other side the permeability expressed in Lugeon units.

1.3 The Integral Engineering-Geological Section (IEGS)

The IEGS synthesizes all the EGS for individual parameters. It is made by superimposing all the single-parameter EGS on one drawing. Its function is to facilitate a comprehensive, integral interpretation of all the measurement data for the given site and their synthesis into a logical unity.

At each point of the IEGS the data must all be consistent. For example, if at a certain point v_l is

---

* Longitudinal wave velocity measurements on the Mratinje dam site were made by the Institute for Geological Research, Belgrade.

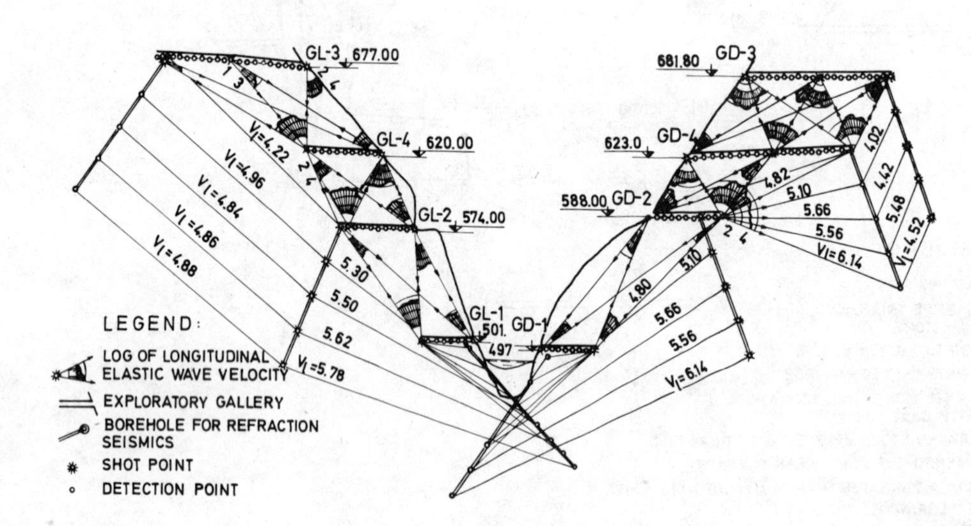

Fig. 2

small, then generally speaking the jointing at that point must be high, as must the permeability. If this consi - stency is lacking at certain points, the reason for it must be sought and the apparent contradiction explaiend.

The IEGS, with the combined results of all exploratory work, constitutes the basis for design. It is usually given as a vertical projection.. It is accompanied by a written report which contains a key to the graphi - cal presentation, and given the basic data on various characteristics quantitatively expressing different proper - ties of the rock mass, formulates conclusions, and ma- kes recommendations for design.

The IEGS makes it possible to set up EGM´s and GEM´s.

1.4 Engineering- geological Models (EGM)

EGM´s are made for those parameters which are important for design. They are to a gre- ater or lesser extent simplified representation of the actual medium, i.e. the foundation rock. Where possi- ble the model shows the boundaries of quasi- homogene - ous zones in the parameters required in design, with nu - merical values for the relevant characteristics in each such zone.

For designing large concrete dams EGM´s are most often made for the following parameters: de - formability, shear strength permeability, natural stress state.

Deformability EGM. The data for setting up this model are obtained by combined application of static and dyna - mic tests, viz. by establishing the correlation between deformation moduli and the velocity of propagation of elastic waves. With these results the rock mass of the dam site can be divided into quasi- homogeneous zones in deformability.

Although the resulting model involves a certain amount of simplification, it can supply a sufficiently accurate foundation for a stress-strain analysis of the dam or for the construction of a physical model if mo- del experiments are planned.

Figure 4a shows a deformability EGM for the Mratinje dam site. It may be seen that the rock mass has been divided up into a number of quasi- homogene - ous zones, delimited both by surface contours and depth- wise. Figure 4b shows the correlation $D = f(v_1)$, ob - tained by measuring moduli of deformation by the flat hydraulic jack method and the average v_1 by polar mi - croseismic tests at the same points.

Shear strength EGM. In setting up this kind of model two possible cases may be distinguished. The first arises with soft or degraded rock which lends itself to division in zones quasi- homogeneous in shear strength and where numerical values can be given which are va - lid for an entire quasi- homogeneous zone, whether this be in all directions or in certain preferred directions in case of a rock mass with shear strength anisotropy.

The second case arises with more rigid rock masses whose block have high deformation moduli, but which exhibit pronounced jointing. In this research must first make an identification of the different types of jo - inting present in terms of the parameters used in describing joints, and on this basis a relative classifi - cation must be made. Shear strength values associated with given types of joints can be arrived at by genera - lizing the shear behavior recorded in tests in different locations, and these are entered alongside the joints type designation in the EGM.

Thus in this case the shear strength EGM is in fact an EGS of joint with shear strength values for each joint and all the types of joint identified entered on it.

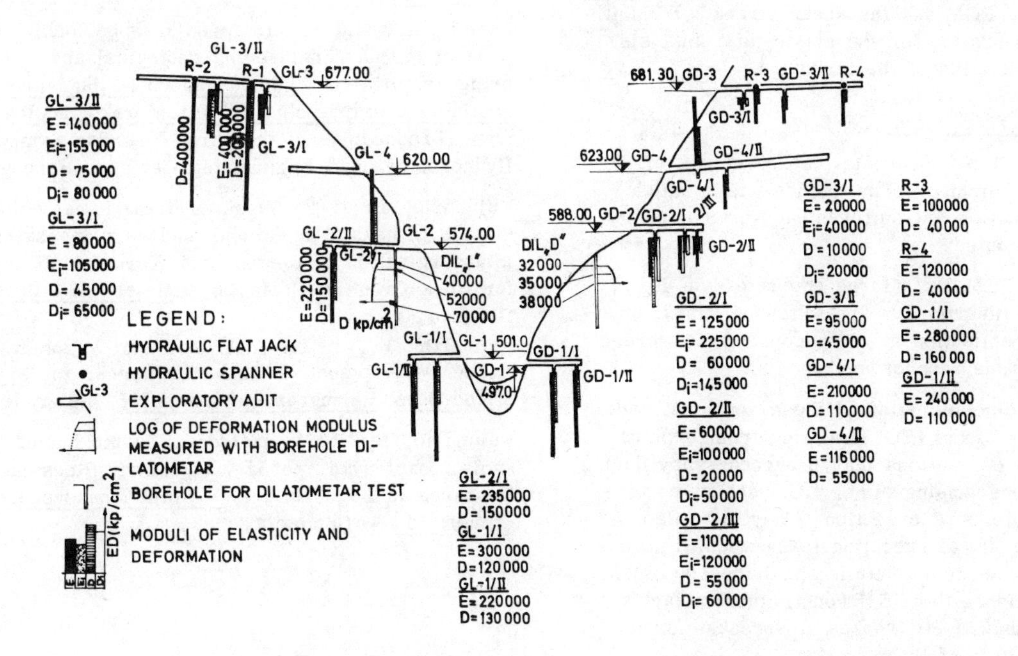

Fig. 3

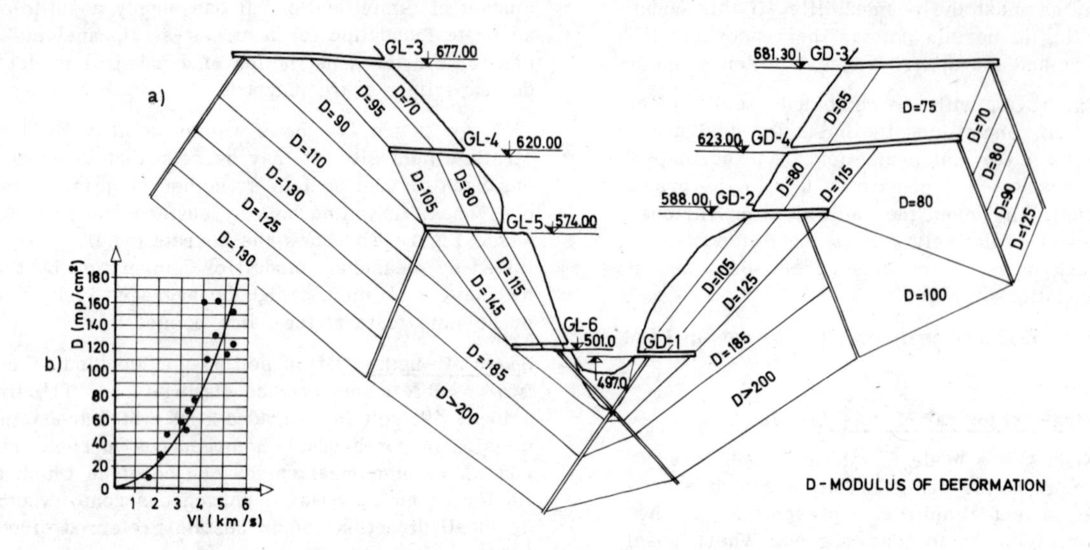

Fig. 4

Permeability EGM. This is set up using the results of permeability tests and their graphical presentation on an EGS.

Usually, points of equal permeability as determined Lugeon tests are joined up to obtain lines of equal permeability. These lines are checked for consistency with other data on the IEGS, especially with fissuring, in order to be able to logically incorporate them into the overall picture. One can then proceed to identify quasi-homogeneous zones within which the permeability is approximately constant.

EGM of the natural stress state. This model is set up using data from in situ measurements. Together with the deformability EGM and the shear strength EGM it makes up the foundation for the elastostatic analysis and stability estimation of the structure.

1.5 Geo-engineering Model (GEM)

The GEM represents the rock mass of the construction site divided up into zones within which specified construction or improvement works must be designed and executed.

The GEM for a large concrete dam is usually made to discriminate the following zones: excavation zone, consolidation grouting zone, grout screen zone, drainage zone, anchorage zone.

The discrimination of these zones is made from an analysis of the IEGS resulting from exploratory works, and corrections may provenecessary during design for reasons arising either from design requirements or problems of execution. They may also be corrected during actual execution (excavation, improvement works) when more details about the rock mass come to light. Hence the GEM constitutues in fact a carefully and exhaustively worked up forecast for the design and execution of these works.

Acknowledgements

This paper was written as part of the study "Strength and Deformability of Foundation Rock and Stability of Large Concrete Dams" jointly undertaken by the Jaroslav Černi Institute for Water Resource Development, Belgrade (with financial support from the Community for Scientific Work of the Socialist Republic of Serbia, Belgrade) and VNIIG im. B.E.Vedeneeva of Leningrad. In this part the author was directly assisted by Prof. M. Janjić as a geology expert, and by M. Tomaš in the preparation of illustrations. Data on fissuring at the Mratinje dam site were kindly made available by J. Obradović.

References

Janjić, M. et al, 1971, Inženjerskogeološki i geotehnički preseci terena (Engineering-geological and Geo-engineering Sections) in Zbornik radova 1. jugoslovenskog simpozijuma o hidrogeologiji i inženjerskoj geologiji, Hercegnovi, (Proceedings of the First Yugoslav Symposium on Hydrogeology and Engineering Geology, Hercegnovi

Kujundžić, B, 1967, Tipski sadržaj i metodologija izrade glavnih projekata injekcionih radova u stenskim masama (Standardization of Content and Work-up of Main Designs for Rock Grouting Projects) - Materijali i konstrukcije, Beograd

Kujundžić, B., 1970, Contribution of Yugoslav Experts to the Development of Rock Mechanics, in: Proceedings of the Second Congress of the ISRM, Belgrade

Kujundžić, B., 1971, Issledovaniia mekhanicheskih svoistv skal´nykh porod v Iugoslavii (Rock Mechanics Research in Yugoslavia) - Vestnik Moskovskogo Universiteta - Geologiia.

EVALUATION OF STRENGTH INDEXES OF ROCK MATERIALS BY MEANS OF THE IRREGULAR LUMP TEST

ÉVALUTATION D'INDICES DE RÉSISTANCE DE MATÉRIAUX ROCHEUX MOYENNANT L'ESSAI D'ÉCRASEMENT EFFECTUÉ SUR DES SPECIMENS INFORMES

BEWERTUNG DER WIDERSTANDSZAHLEN VON GESTEINSMATERIALIEN MITTELS ZERDRÜCKUNGSVERSUCHE AN FORMLOSEN PROBEN

S. MARTINETTI Italian State Electricity Board - Enel, Geotechnical Service, Collaborator with the CNR Research Center for Technical Geology

R. RIBACCHI Professor of Rock Mechanics, Institute of Mining, Faculty of Engineering University of Rome

Rome, Italy

SUMMARY - From the crushing load C_r of irregular lumps stressed along their shortest dimension $\underline{h}$ it is possible to define three strength indexes

$$I_A = C_r/S_m \qquad I_B = C_r/h^2 \qquad I_C = C_r/V^{2/3}$$

where S_m is the average contact surface between the lump and the platens and V the volume of the lump. Our investigation has established the validity and significance of the indexes I_B and I_C ; some conceptual doubts remain for index I_A, which, besides, is more time consuming to evaluate. The coefficient of variation of a strength index for a given rock is usually about 30 - 40% and practically does not seem to be influenced by the homogeneity of the rock; this means that 40 - 50 irregular lumps should be crushed to obtain a good estimate of the mean value of the indexes. All indexes are well correlated with one another and with the simple compressive and "Brazilian" tensile strength of the materials. From the bilogarithmic scatter diagrams reported and discussed in the paper it is possible to estimate the various indexes fairly accurately, on the basis of any one of them determined experimentally. In particular from the irregular lump indexes I_B and I_C a good estimate of the Brasilian tensile strength of rock can be obtained by means of the relations $I_B = I_C = 1.1\,\sigma_t$

RÉSUMÉ - En se rapportant à la valeur de la charge d'écrasement C_r d'échantillons informes sollicités selon la dimension mineure $\underline{h}$, il est possible de définir trois indices de résistance:

$$I_A = C_r/S_m \qquad I_B = C_r/h^2 \qquad I_C = C_r/V^{2/3}$$

où: S_m est la surface moyenne de contact entre l'échantillon et la plaque de chargement, et V est le volume de l'échantillon. Notre étude, a permis d'établir la validité et la qualité significative des indices I_B et I_C; quelques incertitudes demeurent à l'égard de l'indice I_A. Le coefficient de variation de chacun des indices de résistance pour un type donné de roche est compris, généralement, entre 30 e 40%, et il ne parait pas être pratiquement par le degré d'homogénéité de la roche elle même; ceci signifie qu'il este nécessaire d'assujettir aux assais 40÷50 spécimens informes si l'on veut obtenir un'évaluation satistaisante de la valeur moyenne des indices. Tous les indices presentent une bonne corrélation entr'eux, soit avec la résistance à la compression uniaxe, soit enfin avec la résistance à la traction "brésilienne" du matériel. En particulier, en partant des indices de résistance caractéristiques des spécimens informes I_B et I_C il est possible d'obtenir une bonne évaluation de la résistance à traction "brésilienne", ayant recours à la relation $I_B = I_C = 1,1\,\sigma_t$

ZUSAMMENFASSUNG - Anhand des Zerdruckunsbelastungswertes C_r an formlosen Proben, die gemass des Kleinmasses $\underline{h}$ beansprucht werden, kann man drei Widerstandszahlen festlegen

$$I_A = C_r/S_m \qquad I_B = C_r/h^2 \qquad I_C = C_r/V^{2/3}$$

wo S_m die durchschnittliche Berührungsfläche zwischen der Probe und der Belastungsplatte und V das Probevolumen ist. Unser Studium hat uns ermöglicht, die Gültigkeit und die Bedeutung der Zahlen I_B und I_C festzulegen. Einige Zweifel bleiben für die Zahl I_A. Der Änderungswert von jeder Widerstandszahl für eine bestimmte Gesteinsart liegt allgemein bei 30÷40%. Er scheint praktisch nicht von dem Grad der Homogenität des Gesteins beeinlussbar zu sein. Das bedeutet, dass 40÷50 formlose Proben einer Untersuchung zu unterstellen sind, um eine gute Bewertung des Durchschnittwertes der Zahlen zu erhalten. Alle Zahlen scheinen untereinander gut korreliert zu sein, sei es mit der Einaxial-Druckfestigkeit, sei es mit dem "brasilianischen" Zugwiderstand des Materials. Insbesondere ist es möglich, von den Widerstandszahlen, die für die formlosen Proben I_B und I_C charakteristisch sind, eine gute Bewertung des brasilianischen Zugwiderstandes zwischen dem Verhältnis $I_B = I_C = 1,1\,\sigma_t$ zu erhalten.

1. STRENGTH INDEXES FROM IRREGULAR LUMP TESTS

In the irregular lump test the crushing load C_r of an irregular specimen inserted between the platens of a press is determined. The most common strength indexes, denoted by I_A, I_B, I_C, are respectively defined by the following relations:

$$I_A = C_r/S_m \quad I_B = C_r/h^2 \quad I_C = C_r/V^{2/3} \qquad [1]$$

S_m is the average contact area between the specimen and the loading platens at failure; h is the heigth of the specimen in the direction of the applied load (that is, the distance between the press platens); V is the volume of the specimen. The I_A index was introduced by Hobbs (1967), on the assumption that failure of the lump is bought about essentially by the high concentration of compressive stresses generated around the areas in contact with the platens. The I_B index was introduced by Hiramatsu and Oka (1966) on the hypothesis that failure is caused by tensile stresses that are generated at the center of the specimen and are similar in magnitude to those induced by diametral compression of a sphere having a diameter equal to the height of the irregular specimen in the direction of the applied load. The third index, I_C was introduced by Protodiakonov (1960), on the basis of dimensional and empirical considerations; however, it is the most utilized and has also been considered for standardization. The various authors have not espressed a great variance of opinions on the practical of the test, except for the direction in which the load should be applied to the specimen. Some authors (Erock and Franklin, 1972) following Protodiakonov (1960) prefer to apply the load in the direction of the maximum elongation of the specimen for the determination of the I_C index. The supporters of the I_A and I_B indexes have always applied the load along the shortest dimension of the irregular specimen; this was found convenient by many researchers, including ourselves (Diernat and Duffault, 1966; Martinetti and Ribacchi, 1968) also for the determination of the I_C index.

2. AIMS AND METHODS OF THE RESEARCH

The research was conducted mainly to derive reliable elements of judgment for the assessment of the practical advantage of using one or the other of the indexes, especially as concerns the rapidity of their determination and their significance and to verify the existence of close correlations between the strength indexes obtained with the irregular lump test and those obtained with conventional laboratory tests. In this research, twenty-three rock materials were submitted to irregular-lump and conventional tests. The materials differed greatly in their petrographic characteristics, homogeneity and mechanical behavior, especially as concerns their strength and brittleness. The rock materials tested were: lithic tuffs and ignimbrite from the Quaternary eruptive centers in Latium (Nos. 1 to 6); lavas from the Quaternary eruptive centers in Latium (Nos 7 to 9); ores from the evaporitic Miocene formation, Pasquasia mine, Sicily (Nos. 10 to 12) (10: coarse-grained kainite; 11: fine-grained kainite; 12: halite); triassic gypsum with anhydrite inclusion, from Tuscany (No. 13); travertine from Latium (No. 14); limestones from the Cretaceous formations of Central Appennines (Nos. 15 & 16); Carrara marble from Tuscany (No. 17); sandstones from Central Italy (Nos. 18 to 19); coarse-grained granite from Central Sardinia (No. 20); porphiry (Permian rhiolitic ignimbrite) from Eastern Alps (No. 22); phyllitic micaschist from Central Alps (No. 23). Each type of rock was subjected to:

- uniaxial compression tests on cylindrical specimens having a length-to-diameter ratio of 2 (usually 15 tests);
- "Brazilian" tensile tests on cilindrical specimens having the same diameter as above and a length-to-diameter ratio of 0.5 (usually 15 tests);
- irregular lump tests, for the determination of I_B and I_C, on about 50 specimens having volumes nearly the same as those used for the uniaxial compression tests. In addition:
- I_A was determined on seven different types of rock (Nos. 1, 4, 6, 9, 16, 17, 19, 21);
- I_B and I_C were determined on irregular lumps having volumes comprised in a much wider range (from a few cm^3 to 5000 cm^3) for a more careful study of the scale effect (on rocks Nos. 1, 4, 6, 9, 15, 16, 17, 19 and 21).

For the determination of I_A the areas of contact at failure were measured by placing sheets of carbon paper and graph paper between the specimen and each platen and couting the blackened squares (Hobbs, 1967). Such a procedure is rather time consuming and conflicts with the principle of developing simple and quick methods for the determination of rock strength. For the determination of I_C it is necessary to measure the volume of the specimen; in practice, however, it is sufficient to weigh the specimen and derive the volume through an average value of the unit weight of the material. Quite often results of unit weight measurements of the rock material tested are available; at any rate, if need be, the unit weight can be estimated for most rocks without any test and with a 5% precision. So, in pratice the determination of I_C can be done as easily and quickly as the determination of I_B which entails only the measurement of the distance between the press platens during the test. The irregular lumps were crushed with loads applied parallel to the smallest dimension.

3. REVIEW OF THE RESULTS AND THEIR INTERPRETATION

Since the definition of the indexes provided by equations [1] can be considered valid, the crushing load C_r must be well correlated to S_m, h and V over the range in which these quantities are involved in the performance of the tests. In view of Equations [1] and since it is reasonable to expect an increase in the scattering of the results as the crushing load increases, the actual esistence of a relation between the variables C_r, S_m, h and V can be investigated better with a statistical model of linear regression among the logarithms of the variables. The validity of the indexes is ensured when the determination coefficient is very near unity and the coefficients of the regression lines differ little from unity for the correlation C_r-S_m, from 2 for the C_r - h correlation and from 0.67 for the C_r- V correlation. If a "scale effect" is significant, these coefficient should be slightly lower than their theoretical values. For nine rocks we have adopted a wide range of geometrical parameters of the lumps and we have obtained very satisfactory results. The determination coefficients r^2 are usually greater than 0.9; for the same material they are very close to one another even if it appears that the crushing load C_r is systematically related better to volume V. For all the materials, the regression coefficients approach and are slightly lower than the theoretical values. Therefore, the definition of the strength indexes from Eqns[1] seems reliable. Less simple it is to establish which of the indexes, I_A, I_B and I_C, is most significant, that is, which of the three parameters S_m, h and V is actually most important to determine the crushing point of an irregular lump. The difficulties arise from the fact that these three geometrical parameters are generally well correlated with one another; in particular, the relation between V and h for all the tested materials has determination coefficients r^2 higher than 0.95. But it is just for this reason that a more extensive investigation of the subject would have only theoretical and conceptual interest: from the practical standpoint, one or the other index could be used, and the choice be made only on the basis of the case of measurement of the parameter involved. An investigation on the relative importance of parameters V and h was performed, however, by means of a multiple-regression analysis and the following conclusions could be drawn:

a) The volume of the irregular specimen has a more fundamental influence on its strength and therefore the index I_C should be considered more representative of the strength properties of the rock. A similar conclusion was arrived at by Duffaut and Maury (1970)
b) The strength of an irregular specimen could be better predicted from its volume and a "shape factor" h/V according to a power law of the type

$$C_r = I_{BC} \, V^{2/3} \, (h^3/V)^{\beta_2} \qquad [2]$$

in which I_{BC} is a proportionality factor that could be used as a more refined strength index and β_2 is approximately equal to 0.15.

The theoretical analysis becomes even more complex when we try to analyze the significance of parameter S_m and thus the conceptual validity of index I_A. A multiple correlation analysis indicates that at parity of volume and height, there is a significant relation between S_m and the crushing load C_r. However S_m cannot be considered an "independent" variable in the same sense as V and h, which are measured before the test. In fact, it is reasonable to expect that for a given material, specimens of equal volume and height will present an "intrinsic" strength variability when subjected to crushing and will thus give different results, scattered around an average value. Under these conditions it is likely that the average contact surface S_m will be greater at higher loads owing to the spreading of the volume of the plasticized rock near the platens and the load variations would be at least in part the "cause" for S_m variations.

It is well known that in many types of rock, the volume of the specimen affects its strength considerably (Bieniawski, 1970). Indicating with I a generical strength (tensile, flexural, compressive) the influence of the volume V is well represented by an equation of the following type:

$$I_1 / I_2 = (V_1 / V_2)^{\alpha} \qquad [3]$$

The value of α is on the order of -0.1 in most cases. Also in the irregular lump test an appreciable scale effect was noted for some materials (Table 1) but only for the indexes I_B and I_C; for the index I_A irregular or abnormal results were obtained.

TABLE 1

Values and standard deviations of the b coefficients of the equations IxV^b which express the scale effect on the strength indexes. The • indicates when the scale effect is significant for the I_B and I_C indexes

		I_A - V		I_B - V		I_C - V	
		b	s(b)	b	s(b)	b	s(b)
1 Tuff	•	-0.01	0.03	-0.07	0.02	-0.01	0.03
4 "		0.04	0.03	0.05	0.03	-0.01	0.03
6 "		0.06	0.03	0.00	0.03	0.04	0.03
9 Lava	•	0.01	0.04	-0.01	0.04	-0.07	0.03
15 Limestone	•	–	–	-0.13	0.02	-0.15	0.02
16 "	•	0.17	0.03	-0.08	0.03	-0.10	0.03
17 Marble		0.14	0.04	0.01	0.04	0.00	0.03
19 Sandstone	•	0.09*	0.04	-0.07	0.03	-0.05	0.03
21 Porphiry	•	0.10	0.04	-0.08	0.03	-0.07	0.03

The existence of a scale effect dictated the advisability of refering the strength indexes - when determined on specimens having a wide range of volumes - to one common volume, that is, the volume on which the uniaxial compressive strength on the same material was determined (usually about 100 cm^3). The strength indexes, scaled on the basis of the values of Table 1, are summarized in Table 2, together with the strength obtained in the conventional laboratory test and their variation coefficients.

Independently from the type of test, the standard deviation of the distribution of the strength of a rock material is usually proportional to the mean value of the strength itself. In these conditions the statistical parameter most suited to express the scattering of the results -- and possibly the homogeneity of the material -- is the coefficient of variation v which is the ratio of the standard deviation to the mean value. As can be seen in Fig. 1, the coefficient of variation for index I_C is comprised, for all materials, within the range 30%-40%; for index I_B the range is just as narrow, but the coefficients of variation are usually slingthly higher, as observed also by DUFFAUT and

TABLE 2

Strength indexes (MN/m^2) from conventional and irregular lump tests.

Rock	σ_f		σ_t		I_A		I_B		I_C	
	$\bar{\sigma}_f$	%	$\bar{\sigma}_t$	%	$\bar{I}_A$	%	$\bar{I}_B$	%	$\bar{I}_C$	%
1	6.86	11	1.11	13	15.20	29	1.44	27	1.48	33
2	14.50	24	1.27	16	-	-	1.24	39	1.40	33
3	12.20	18	1.19	32	-	-	1.64	33	1.82	31
4	27.90	18	3.82	11	44.40	47	3.04	42	2.94	36
5	35.30	14	2.45	33	-	-	1.96	38	2.35	29
6	29.40	14	3.13	14	87.80	34	3.43	45	3.43	37
7	41.20	28	4.21	18	-	-	3.23	39	3.82	34
8	39.70	26	5.09	15	-	-	5.58	35	5.98	31
9	145.00	36	11.30	19	226.00	39	13.40	42	12.40	38
10	7.06	16	6.37	39	-	-	0.49	59	0.49	55
11	44.60	16	3.72	17	-	-	2.94	43	3.04	28
12	35.30	8	2.45	11	-	-	3.23	47	3.04	44
13	23.00	48	1.96	31	-	-	3.04	50	3.33	43
14	34.80	25	5.88	26	-	-	7.25	29	7.94	23
15	57.30	30	3.92	33	-	-	4.80	45	5.19	42
16	137.00	25	8.53	28	167.00	40	11.80	38	10.50	32
17	84.30	15	6.17	13	132.00	32	7.35	28	6.66	27
18	115.00	4	7.84	11	-	-	8.92	44	9.02	42
19	153.00	8	12.40	14	145.00	45	11.80	37	11.60	37
20	145.00	12	8.43	21	-	-	11.20	30	11.30	31
21	185.00	9	10.68	17	218.00	47	11.90	39	12.40	36
22	119.00	30	9.21	27	-	-	10.50	46	9.31	38
23	80.40	26	13.70	28	-	-	13.30	54	9.12	52

Maury (1970). Although these coefficients are high in absolute value, they confirm the significativity of the indexes obtained from rough tests, such as the irregular lump test may appear to be. In fact, 40-60 test on irregular specimens should be enough to provide an estimate of the mean value of the "strength" of the material with a standard mean deviation on the order of 5% of the mean value -- which is sufficient for most pratical purposes. For any one material, the comparison of the coefficients of variation of index I_B and of the resistence to simple compression σ_f (fig. 1) and Brazilian tension σ_t indicates that although the latter are lower on the average, they are comprised within a wider range (8-30%). Usually the coefficient of variation for tests on regular specimens increases directly with the degree of dishomogeneity of the material evaluated by visual examination. A reasonable explanation of these observations can be derived from an examination of the factors that may affect the scattering of the results of a strength test. The overall variability (expressed by the variance of the distribution) can be considered as the sum of a portion due only to the characteristics and modalities of the test and of another portion depending on the "intrisic" variability of the material on laboratory test scale; in other words, we may write;

$$v_r^2 = v_m^2 + v_{tr}^2 \qquad [4]$$

$$v_i^2 = v_m^2 + v_{ti}^2 \qquad [5]$$

where v_r and v_i are the coefficients of variation obtained respectively with regular and irregular specimens of given rock, having an "intrisic" variability induced respectively by the regular and ir-

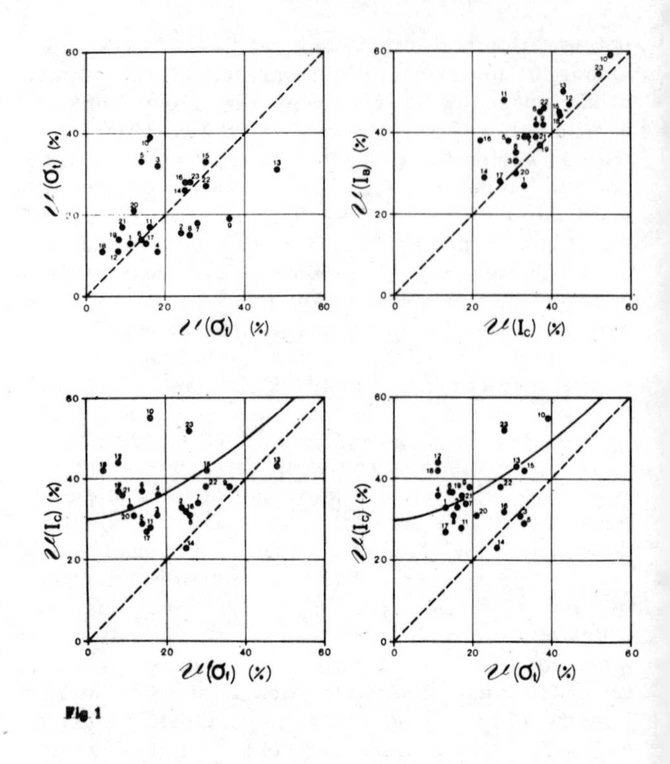

Fig. 1

regular lump tests. From Eqns [4] and [5] the following equation may be obtained

$$v_i = \sqrt{v_{ti}^2 - v_{tr}^2 + v_r^2} \qquad [6]$$

v_{ti} and v_{tr} cannot be assessed directly; a reasonable estimate for v_{ti} could be a few tens per cent and for v_{tr} a few units per cent. For merely indicative purposes, fig. 1 shows the relation

$$v_i = \sqrt{0{,}0925 + v_r^2} \qquad [7]$$

obtained by assigning v_{ti} a value of 0.3 and v_{tr} a value of 0.05. The resulting curve is in good agreement with the experimental values. In conclusion, the degree of homogeneity of the rock can be reliably assessed only through conventional tests because in the irregular lump test it is almost completely concealed by the variation induced by the test itself.

Use was made of statistical methods, and specifically of regression and structural analysis, to study also the relations among the "strength" values that can be evaluated from classical laboratory tests and from irregular lump tests. In this analysis the data rock from No. 23 were omitted because the significanc of the irregular lump test for strongly anisotropic rock requires more detailed investigations.
The problem consists in ascertaining the possibility of estimating any one index with sufficient approximation on the basis of another index determined experimentally. It must be taken into account that the absolute deviation of the estimated value from the theoretical one is not as important as the percentual deviation; therefore the relations between any two indexes can be better evaluated, for instance, by

means of the logarithms of the variables. Scatter diagrams for the various strengths are reported in Figs. 2 - 3. The significance and closeness of the relationships are best expressed through the coefficients r(or their square, the determination coefficients r^2) which are given in Table 3. They are all very high, which would confirm the opinion that the indexes are actually the expression of related physical characteristics.

TABLE 3

Determination coefficients r^2 and parameters of the structural relationships $y = Ax^b$ and $= A^* x$

Relation	Numb. obser.	r^2	A	b	A^*
$\sigma_f \propto \sigma_t$	22	0.916	8.770	1.192	11.500
$I_B \propto I_C$	22	0.992	0.920	0.961	0.980
$I_A \propto \sigma_f$	9	0.931	3.770	0.787	1.530
$I_A \propto \sigma_t$	9	0.883	14.120	1.122	10.660
$I_B \propto \sigma_f$	22	0.877	0.143	0.894	0.095
$I_B \propto \sigma_t$	22	0.944	0.990	1.067	1.090
$I_C \propto \sigma_f$	22	0.870	0.169	0.856	0.097
$I_C \propto \sigma_t$	22	0.941	1.070	1.024	1.115

Of special interest is the existence of a very close correlation between I_B and I_C, and the fact that significativity of the correlations among the strength indexes obtained from irregular lump tests and from classical laboratory tests is nearly the same as that characterizing the correlation between the uniaxial compressive and tensile strengths. Besides, the results clearly indicate that I_B and I_C are on the whole, correlated best to the tensile strength; these indexes therefore can be used in practice as a measurement of a form of "strength" of the material which is closely related to the conventional tensile strength. The information available on index I_A appears to be less reliable, since it was derived from a smaller number of materials. Anyway, it seems that this index is better related to the uniaxial compressive strength. (Fig. 4).

The parameters of the relationships could be estimate through regression analysis; however, taking into account the fact that none of the variables could be considered "independent" and that all are subject to error, it is felt that ML estimation of the structural relationship (Kendall e Stuart 1963) is best suited to the problem. The parameters obtained for the relationships $y = Ax^b$ between the strength indexes are also given in Table 3. From an examination of the table, it is apparent that some of the exponents of the power law are quite near unity; therefore, a linear equation could be adopted in these cases. Such linear equations, which have the advantage of simplicity, hold good for the mutual relationships of the strength indexes I_B, I_C, and σ_t, but are quite less satisfactory in the other cases. The parameter A^* of the linear equation $y = A^* x$ is given in Table 3 for all the relations between the strength indexes; as in the previous case, it was calculed by ML estimation of the structural relationship between the logarithms of the parameters. It is possible to write with very good approximation

$$I_B = I_C = 1,1 \ \sigma_t$$

Only as a first approximation it is besides possible to write

$$\sigma_f = 11.5 \ \sigma_t$$

$$I_A = 1.53 \ \sigma_f$$

$$I_B = I_C = 0.096 \ \sigma_f$$

$$I_A = 10.65 \ \sigma_t$$

In the latter case the true relationships are however clearly non linear, and the ratio between the compressive strength and any one of the parameters σ_t, I_B, or I_C increases with the strength of the material.

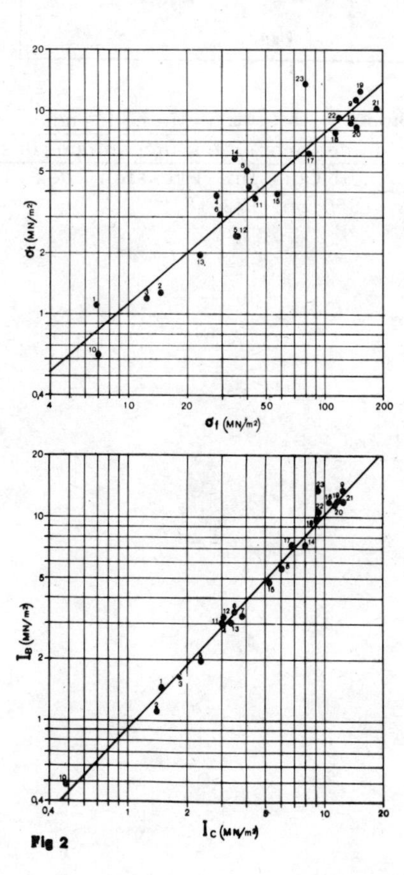

Fig 2

ACKNOWLEDGMENTS

This work was partially supported by CNR (contracts Nos. 70.01953.05 and 72.00351.05).

Thanks are due to A. Straulino and M. Delfini for their help in laboratory investigation.

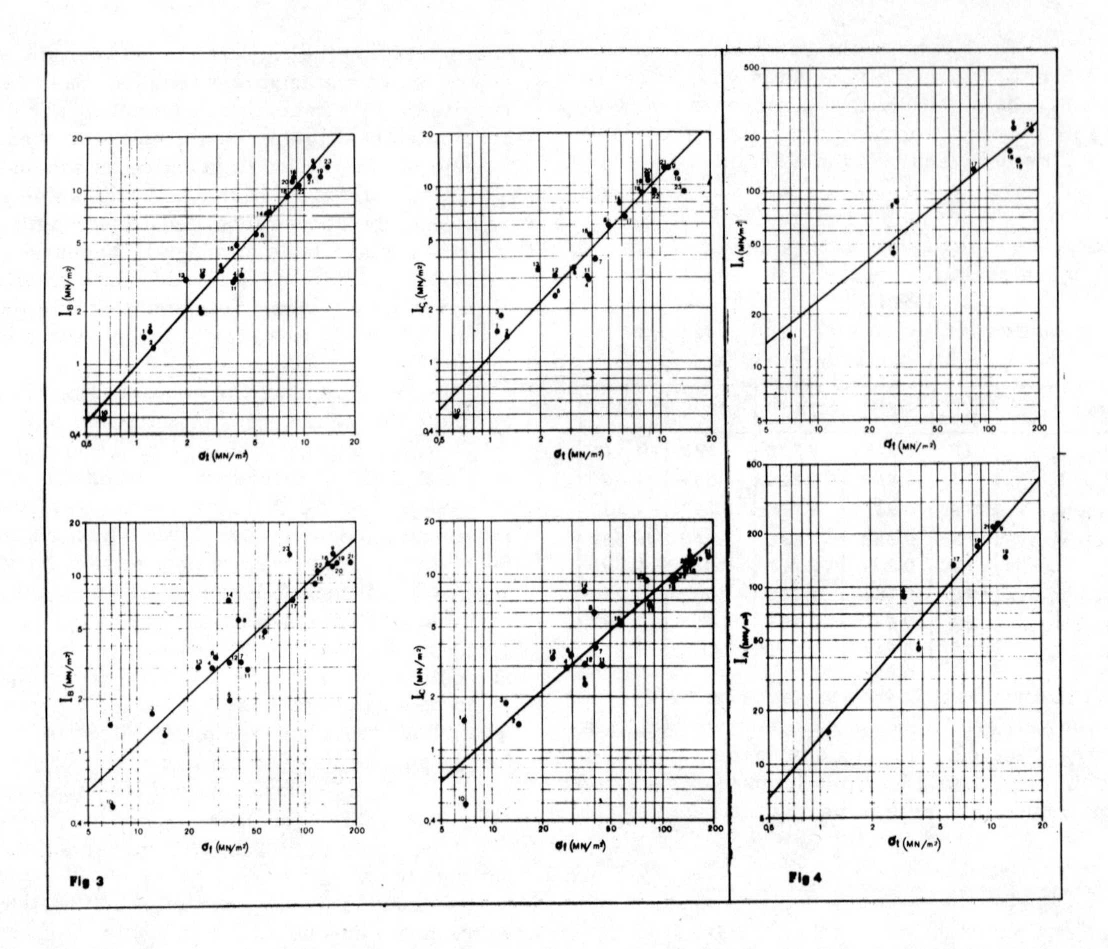

Fig 3

Fig 4

REFERENCES

Bieniawski, S. T. - The effect of specimen size on compressive strength of coal. Int. J. Rock. Mech. Min. Sci. 5, 1968, pp. 325-335.

Brogi , E. ;. Franklin , J. A. -The point load strength test. Int. J. Rock. Mech. Min. Sci. 9,1972, pp.669-697.

Diernat, F. ;Duffaut, P. -Essais sur échantillons de forme irréguliéere. Proc. I Congr. Int. Rock. Mech. Lisbona 1966, Vol. I, pp. 405-409.

Duffaut , P. ;Maury, V. - Etude photoélastiques pour l'essai Protodjakonov, Proc. II Congr. Int. Soc. Rock. Mech. 1970, Vol. III paper 5-15.

Hiramatsu, Y.; Oka, Y. - Determination of the tensile strength of rock by compression test of an irregular tests piece. Int. J. Rock. Mech. Min. Sci. 3 1966, pp 89-99.

Hobbs, D. W. - Rock tensile strength and its relationship to a number of alternative measures of rock strength. Int. J. Rock. Mech. Min. Sci. 4, 1967, pp. 115 - 127.

Kendall, M. G. ;Stuart, A. - The advanced theory of statistics, London, 1967

Martinetti, S. ; Ribacchi, R. -Validità e significato delle prove meccaniche su campioni informi di roccia. IX Convegno di Geotecnica, Genova, 1968, pp.1-6

Protodiakonov, M. M. -Méthodes nouvelles de détermination des propriétés mécaniques des terrains miniers. III Conf. Int. Pression des Terrains, Paris, 1960, pp. 172-181.

WEATHERING AND ITS RELATION TO MECHANICAL PROPERTIES OF GRANITE

RELATION ENTRE LES CARACTÉRISTIQUES DES INTERSTICES ET LES PROPRIÉTÉS MÉCANIQUES SUR LES GRANITE DÉSAGRÉGÉS

ÜBER DEN ZUSAMMENHANG ZWISCHEN DER FUGENHAFTEN DES VERWITTERTEN GRANITS

T.F. ONODERA
R. YOSHINAKA
M. ODA

Dept. of Foundation Engineering
Saitama University, Japan

SUMMARY

Relation between characteristics of interstices and mechanical properties of weathered granite has been studied on rock pieces and rock mass of various stages of weathering. The following results have been obtained:-

Degree of chemical weathering is designated as shown in Fig. 1 and degree of mechanical weathering is designated as shown in Fig. 3. Porosity of granite is due to two modes of microcracks development in the rock the one is the increase of crack number and the other is the expansion of crack opening.

Porosity causes important effect on the mechanical properties of weathered granite; on Shore hardness (Fig. 4), on Young's modulus (Fig. 5), on triaxial shearing strength (Fig. 9) and on residul strain ratio (Fig. 6).

Shearing characteristics of granite can be expressed by $q' = \alpha\sigma_c + \beta p'$, where α and β are constants, $q'(kg/cm^2) = (\sigma_1 - \sigma_3)/2$ and $p'(kg/cm^2) = (\sigma_1 + \sigma_3)/2$ and σ_c is unconfined compressive strength. Strength and deformation characteristics of granite rock mass in-situ depend seriously on the properties of drilled core pieces and on the properties of cracks.

Bore hole deformation modulus by Pressiometer have relation to Shore hardness of the core specimen as shown in Fig. 11.

Shearing characteristics of granite rock mass in-situ are designated by Fig. 12 and 13 expressed as RQD and Shore hardness as parameter respectively. Essential informations on the mechanical rock mass quality of the test adit where in-situ tests have been carried out are simply defined by RQD of the pilot boring, Shore hardness, porosity and so on of the core specimens (Fig. 14).

ZUSAMMENFASSUNG

Der Zusammenhang zwischen der Charakteristik der Fuge und den mechanischen Eigenschaften vom verwitterten Granit wurde anhand der die verschiedenen Verwitterungsstufen angezeigten Gesteinund Felsenstücke untersucht. Daraus ergaben sich folgende Ergebnisse:

Der chemische Verwitterungsgrad ist in Fig. 1 dargestellt und der mechanische Verwitterungsgrad ist in Fig. 3 angezeigt. Die Porosität des Granits ist von der Mikrokrachentwicklung der Krachenöffnung.

Die Porosität an sich hat bedeutende Einflüsse auf solch mechanischen Eigenschaften vom verwitterten Granit, wie auf Shore-Härte (Fig. 4), Elastizitätmodul (Fig. 5), dreiachsige Abscherungsfestigkeit (Fig. 9) und Restspannungsratio (Fig. 6).

Die obenerwähnten Einflüsse ändern sich mit einer Ubergangsporosität ($3 \sim 4\%$), wobei die Mikrokrache von unterbrechlicher zur kontinuierlichen Stufe sich überschreitet. Die Scherungseigenschaften des Granits kann mittels der Gleichung von $q' = \alpha\sigma_c + \beta p'$, $q'(kg/cm^2) = (\sigma_1 - \sigma_3)/2$ und $p'(kg/cm^2) = (\sigma_1 + \sigma_3)/2$ ausgedrückt werden, wobei α von 0.05 bis 0.12, β von 0.88 bis 0.95 und σ_c Druckfestigkeit sind.

Die Beziehung zwischen Deformationsverhältniszahl des Bohrlochs und Shore-Härte des Bohrkerns ist in Fig. 11 gezeigt.

Die Schereigenschaft des Granitfelsens in-situ kann mittels Parameter von RQD (Fig. 12) und Shore-Härte (Fig. 13) dargestellt werden. Die Festigkeits- und Deformationseharakteristik des Granitfelsens in-situ ist von Eigenschaft des Bohrlochs und deren der Kluft stark abhängig. Verschiedene Informationen der Felsqualität der die Felsenprüfung stattgefundenen Stolle können mit RQD des Führungsbohrens, Shore-Härte des Bohrlochs, Porosität u.s.w. ohne Schwierigkeit sich ausdrücken lassen (Fig. 14).

RESUME

Relation entre les caractéristiques des interstices et les propriétés des roches et des rochers des granits désagrégés a été étudiée, et on a obtenu des résultats suivants. Pour étudier la relation entre la désagrégation chimique (Fig. 1) et celle mécanique (Fig. 3), on a trouvé les méthodes de désignation qui sont aptes pour chacune de celle-ci.

La porosité est causée des microfissures, et concernant la fac on de ses développements, il y a celle par l'augmentation de leurs nombres et celle par l'expansion de la distance des interstices. La porosite donne une influence importante sur les proprietes mecaniques; la durete Shore (Fig. 4), le module d'elasticite (Fig. 5), la resistance au cisaillement triaxial (Fig. 9), le taux de la formation residuelle (Fig. 6).

Cette influence différente à partie du taux interstitiel (3 ~ 4%) ou les microfissures se changent de celles intermittentes aux continues. La propriété de la résistance au cisaillement des granits est exprimé par $q' = \alpha\sigma_c + \beta q'$, et ici$\alpha = 0.05 \sim 0.13$,$\beta = 0.88 \sim 0.95$, $q'(kg/cm^2) = (\sigma_1 - \sigma_3)/2$, $p'(kg/cm^2) = (\sigma_1 - \sigma_3)/2$, σ_c est la résistance a la compression. Il y a une relation entre le coefficient de deformation par le pressiomètre du trou de perforation et la dureté Shore de la carotte comme montrée à la figure 11. Les caractéristiques de cisaillement du rocher in-situ peuvent etre désigner en utilisant RQD (Fig. 12) et la dureté Shore (Fig. 13) comme perametres.

La resistance du rocher in-situ et les caractéristiques de déformation dépendent gradement aux caractéristiques des carottes de perforation et la nature de la fissure. Les informations peuvent etre designer simplement par l'etat du rocher de la galerie à flanc, le RQD de la perforation pilote, la durete Shore et la porosité de cette carotte où les essais du rocher ont été exécutés (Fig. 14).

1. INTRODUCTION

This paper presents basic physical and chemical points accompanied with weathering of granite and their influence upon the mechanical properties of granite as a rock and rock mass.

Rock samples for this study were taken from the fresh to the highly decomposed masa in the neighbourhood of Innoshima, Onomichi City and Shimotsui, Kojima City on the Setouchi Sea, Japan.

2. MICROCRACKS OF WEATHERED GRANITES

Changes of the rock by weathering are roughly classified into chemical and physical ones, both having a remarkable effect on the mechanical strength of the rock.

The former is the alteration of the rock or the clay-forming phenomenon by the decomposition or solution of rock-forming minerals, while the latter causes the disintegration of the rock by the mechanical action from unloading, thermal expansion, freezing, growth of minerals, etc.

Since the leaching of SiO_2, Na_2O, CaO and Mgo with the advancing weathering of granite is more considerable as compared with that of Al_2O_3 and K_2O, the ratios Na_2O/K_2O, $Al_2O_3/(SiO_2+Al_2O_3)$ and $(Na_2O+K_2O+CaO+MgO)/Al_2O_3$ may be used as the indices of chemical weathering.

Thus, chemical analysis and microscopic observation were done for a series of ten weathered rock samples in order to know the degree of chemical weathering.

From these observations it was known that in spite of the increased porosity on the physical side no considerable leaching of SiO_2, Na_2O, K_2O, CaO and MgO was observed on the chemical side.

Besides, from the X-ray analysis and the observation by polarization microscope it was revealed that the clay formation by the dissolution had scarcely been in progress.

This means that the chemical weathering is immature compared to the erosion of granite caused by perolating water.

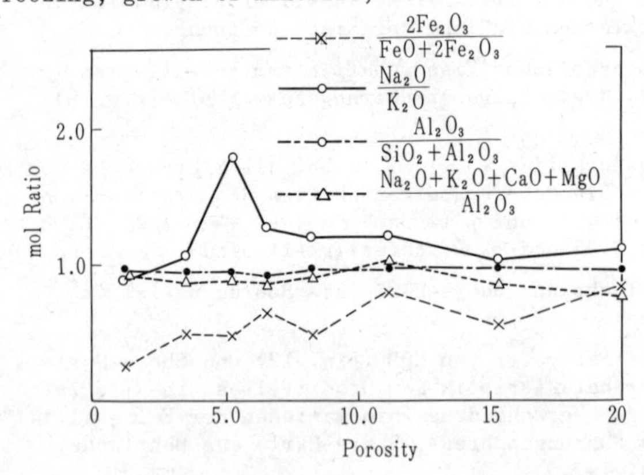

Fig. 1 Variation of molar ratio with porosity
Fig. 1 Variation vom Molverhaltnis mit Porositat
Fig. 1 Variation du taux de mole avec celle de la porosité

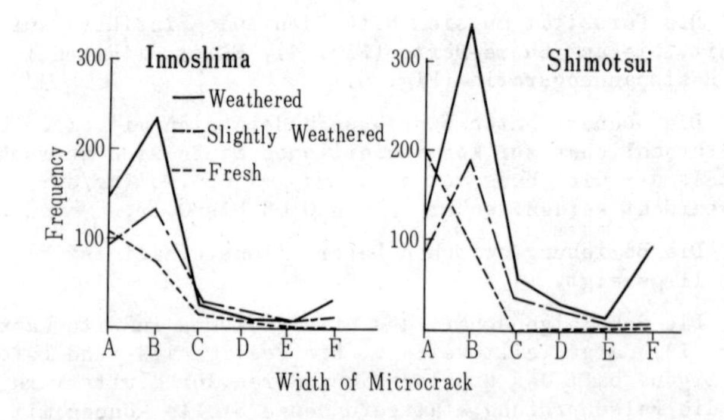

Fig. 2 Frequency of microcracks
Fig. 2 Frequenz vom Mikrokrach
Fig. 2 Fréquence des microfissures

Accordingly, the distinct increase of porosity (0 → 15) accompanying to the weathering of granite in this district seems to reflect the increase of the number or breadth of cracks mostly from mechanical causes.

Even in the process of such weak alteration, however, the change of ferrous to ferrics iron oxide in biotite is seen, and showing this change by $2Fe_2O/(FeO+2Fe_2O_3)$ (molar ratio), we find a relation as shown in Fig. 1 between it and porosity, which may be used as an index of chemical weathering.

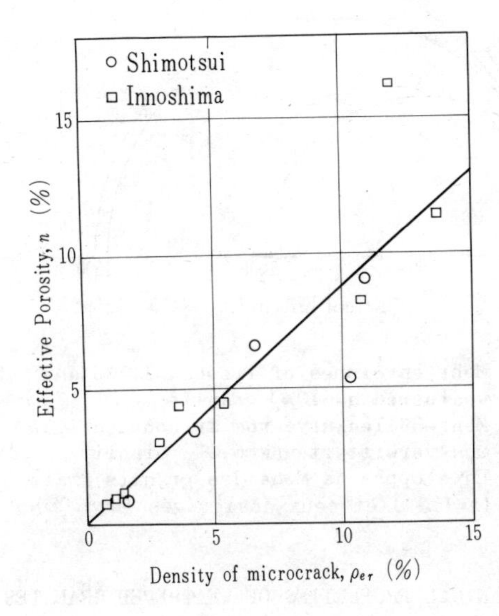

Fig. 3 Relation between porosity and density of microcracks

Fig. 3 Zusammenhang zwischen Porosität und Mikrokrachendichte

Fig. 3 Relation entre la porosité et la densité de microfissures

The number and breadth of cracks in thin sections of rocks were measured under the microscope by the following manner.

Along the measuring lines of various directions (total length 24 cm) cracks were observed, which were classified according to their breadths as A(0-0.0016mm), B(0.0016-0.016mm), C(0.016-0.032mm), D(0.032-0.048mm), E(0.048-0.064mm) and F(more than 0.064mm) and the crack frequencies belonging to each of such ranks were obtained (Fig. 2).

According to this result, with the progressing weathering the number of cracks and, at the same time, the proportion of open cracks increase. Then the density of microcracks was defined as follows, and this was used as an index of physical weathering of rocks.

Density of microcracks ρ_{cr} =100 × (total of breadth length of crack)/(length of measuring line).

as an index of physical weathering is in such relation with porosity n as shown in Fig. 3, and since the increase of n almost wholly depends upon that of ρ_{cr}, the proportion of voids chemically produced by the dissolution is supposed to be very small.

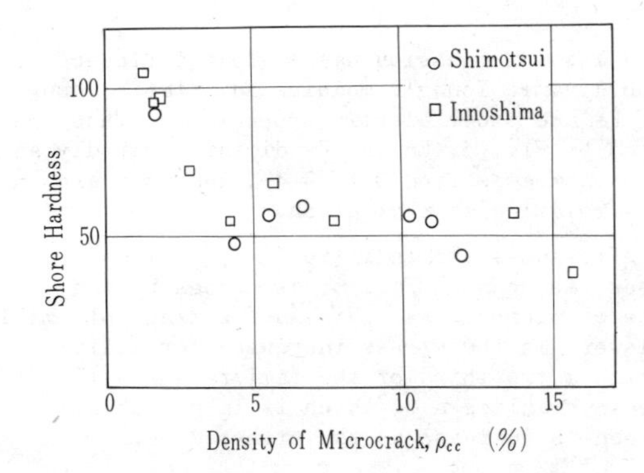

Fig. 4 Influence of density of microcracks on Shore hardness

Fig. 4 Einflu der Mikrokrachendichte auf die Shore-Härte

Fig. 4 Influence de la densité de microfissures sur la dureté Shore

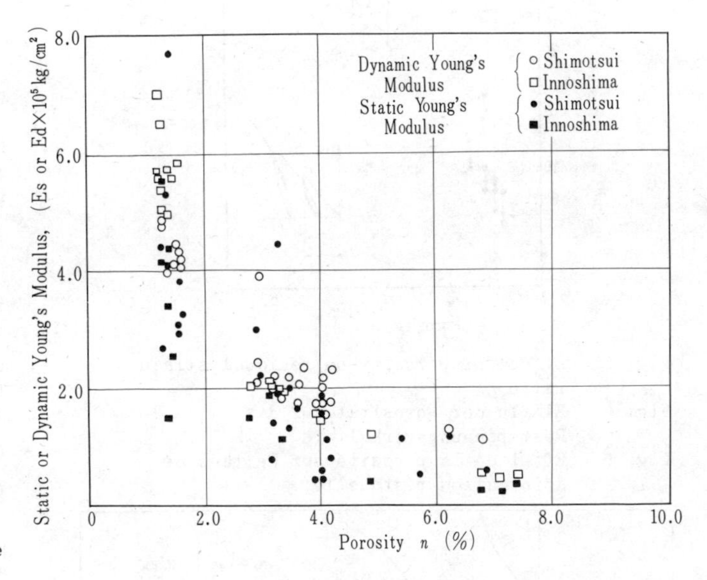

Fig. 5 Relationship between Young's modulus and porosity

Fig. 5 Zusammenhang zwischen Dehnungs-Koeffizient und Porosität

Fig. 5 Relation entre le module d'élasticité de la porosité

The lowering of Shore hardness Sh of the rock is generally caused by that of the hardness of constituent minerals and their cohesion, and since quartz and orthoclase of this granite have scarcely undergone weathering, the Shore hardness struck these minerals is supposed to express the degree of loosening of rock structure.

As shown in Fig. 4 the increase of ρ_{cr} (=n) lowers Sh, and this tendency is conspicuous in the range of ρ_{cr} =0 3-4%.

From this fact it seems that the loosening of bond between the constituent mineral grains is especially promoted in this range of ρ_{cr} resulting in the loss of the greater part of cohesion.

The loss of cohesion has a great influence upon the dynamic Young's modulus Ed, static Young's modulus Es and other elastic properties. Thus, as indicated by Fig. 5, Ed and Es diminish rapidly as $n(=\rho c r)$ increases from 0 to 3-4%, and they are in the same relation as that of Sh.

The residual strain ratio $(1-\frac{\varepsilon e}{\varepsilon T})$x100 increases, as seen in Fig. 6, as n does by the increase of microcracks. Within the range of small n, it lowers as the stress increases for a limit of load up to a two-third of the failure strength, whereas in granites n of which is larger than 3-4% it is seen to increase as the stress does.

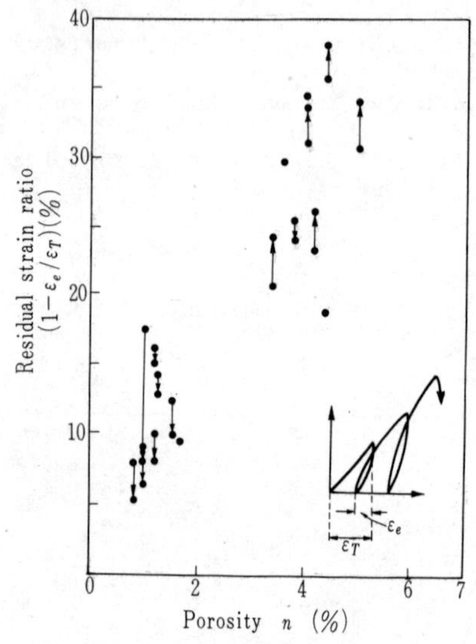

Fig. 6 Effect of porosity on residual strain ratio
Fig. 6 Einflu der Porosität auf das Restspannungsverhältnis
Fig. 6 Effet de la porosité sur le taux de déformation résiduelle

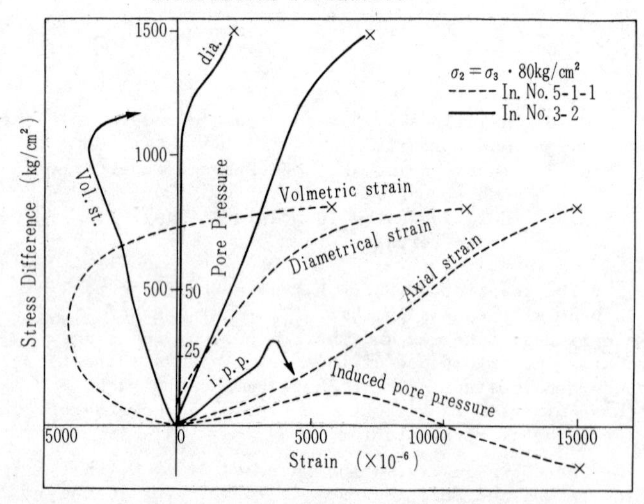

Fig. 7 Stress-strain and strain-pore pressure curves(No.5.1.1; n=6.0%, No.3,2; n=1.3%)
Fig. 7 Dehungs-Spannungs und Spannungs-Porosität-Druckkurve(No.5.1.1; n=6.0% No.3.2; n=1.3%)
Fig. 7 Courbes de pression de l'eau de la deformation-effort et celles de la deformation-porosite

Such essential change in the nature of the interstice with the boundary of n=3-4% is also expressed in the stress-strain relation, etc. of granites.

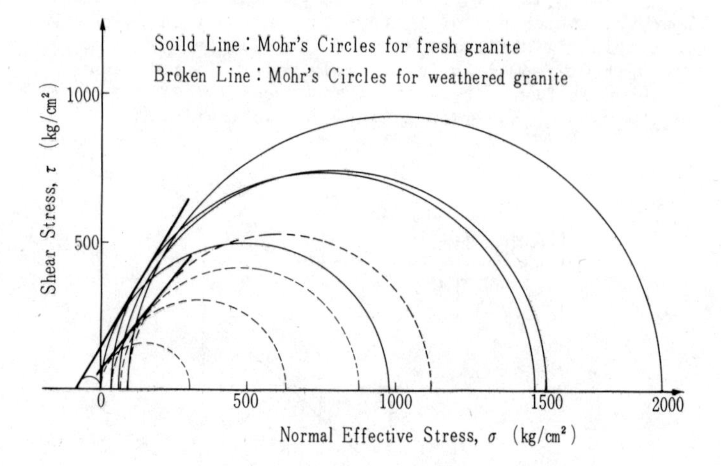

Fig. 8 Mohr envelopes of fresh(n=1.3%) and weathered(n=6.0%) granite
Fig. 8 Mohr-Hüllenkurve vom frischen(n=1.3%) und verwitterten(n=6.0%) Granit
Fig. 8 Enveloppes de Mohe des granits frais (n=1.3%) et ceux désagrégés (n=6.0%)

3. MECHANICAL PROPERTIES OF WEATHERED GRANITES

For weathered granites triaxial compression tests were done in the following manner.
The test pieces are columnar in shape, 5 cm in diameter and 10 cm in height, with tightly attached 2 cm resistance-wire strain gauge in the axial and cross-axial directions, and these test pieces were immersed in water for a week.

In this period air was expelled by the vacuum-pump at least for twelve hours to promote water saturation.

At the experiment with these test pieces a back-pressure at 10-20 kg/cm^2 was given to complete the water saturation, and thereupon the maximum confining pressure of 100 kg/cm^2 was exerted upon them with a loading rate of 5-10 kg/cm^2/min.

As the results of the test the stress-strain relations of unweathered granites are expressed by full lines in Fig. 7 while that of weathered granites by dotted lines in the same figure.

For several test pieces made from a granite blocks of each varied stages of weathering a series of undrained triaxial compression tests was done, and for each block the envelopes of Mohr's circles at the $\tau-\sigma$ effective stress diagram.

In this case the envelopes for the Mohr's circles of failure at a range of smaller than 200 kg/cm^2 were assumed approximately as straight lines. Fig. 8 shows two examples out of these results.

It is noted that the envelopes drawn as such are roughly parallel with each other both for unweathered and weathered rocks.

Obtaining the strength values τ_0' and ϕ' for granites in various stages of weathering by such envelopes and examining the relation between such strength values and porosities, we have the relation as shown in Fig. 9.

Dividing the average mean stress p' and the the maximum shearing stress q' divided by uniaxial compressive strength σ_c , making them non-dimensional, the writes are expressed their relation in Fig. 10.

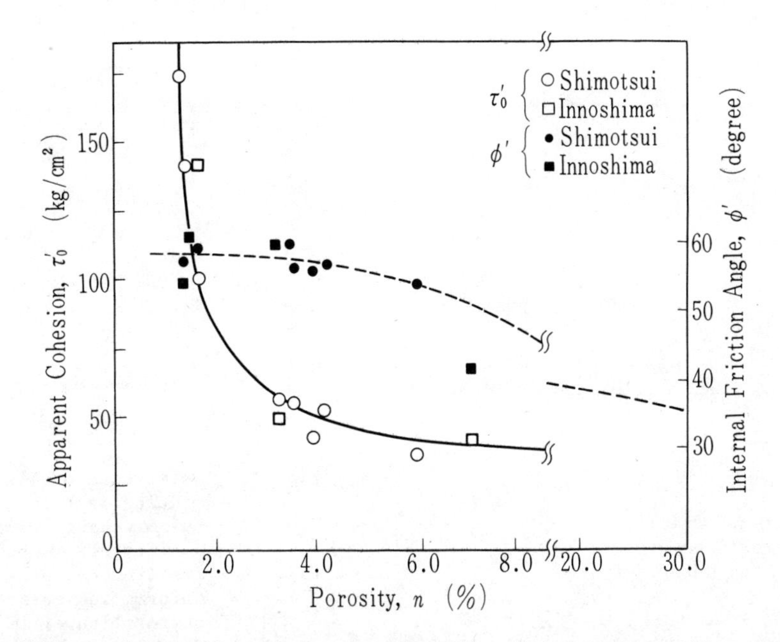

Fig. 9 Effect of porosity on cohesive strength and internal friction angle of granite
Fig. 9 Einflu der Porosität auf die Klebfähigkeit und den Innenreibungswinkel vom Granit
Fig. 9 Effect de la porosité sur la force cohésive et l'angle de frottement interne des granits

The value of ϕ' for the variation of n changes as weathering proceeds from 60° - 50° in relatively fresh rocks to 40° - 30° in highly weathered rock, masa, and for a range of n=0-7% in the lower degree of weathering the extent of decrease of ϕ' with increasing n is small.

While, for τ_0', with increasing n from 1.1% to 4.0% decreases rapidly from 150 kg/cm^2 to 50 kg/cm^2.

This relation is also conformable with the before-mentioned relation of n to Shore hardness, modulus of elasticity and density of microcracks, and this is supposedly due to the loss of the most bond of rock-forming minerals by the physical injury of the rock by the time of the increase of n to the order 3-4%.

Further increase of n from this value means the further advance of weathering, with which the strength value of granite lowers more gradually, approaching to that of masa, and τ_0'becomes at last zero.

It is noted, however, that even the granite whose porosity is more than 3-4% still has 0-50 kg/cm^2 of τ_0'.

This may be due, apart from the effect of some residual cohesion of constituent grains, to certain structural cohesion due to the interlocking effect of grains, and when porosity becomes more than 15-20% disintegration would have advanced to such a degree that the structural cohesion is no longer exhibited.

From this it is known that rocks in varied stages of weathering with their different porosities are all plotted almost on a straight line, and that the relation of p' and q' is simply expressed, with σ_c as a parameter, as $q' = \alpha\sigma_c + \beta p'$, where α and β are in the range of 0.05-0.12 and 0.76-0.90, respectively.

This equation might be accepted as giving a general strength relation of weathered granites for a range of n=1-7%.

4. STRENGTH AND DEFORMATION CHARACTERISTICS OF ROCK MASS AND THE NATURE OF ROCK

In the preceding chapter it was stated that the mechanical strength of rocks is influenced by the development of microcracks, and the amount of them is evaluated by the porosity of rocks.

This is suggestive of the nature of a rock mass as an apparently continuous body which is mostly characterized by the existence of cracks such as joints, etc. The detailed study for this problem is to be expected for the future, and here only some comparative examination with previous in situ measurements on rock mass will be made.

In Fig. 14 are illustrated the fundamental mechanical properties of rock mass and rocks in an adit where in site tests of shearing and deformation tests were performed.

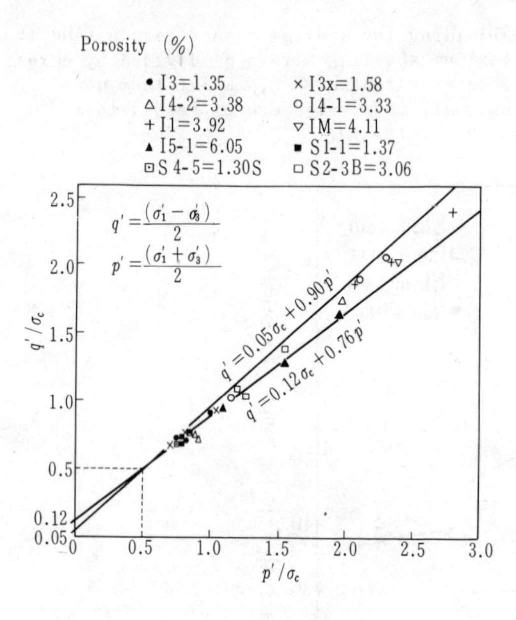

Fig. 10 Strength of granite
Fig. 10 Festigkeit vom Granit
Fig. 10 Résistance des granits

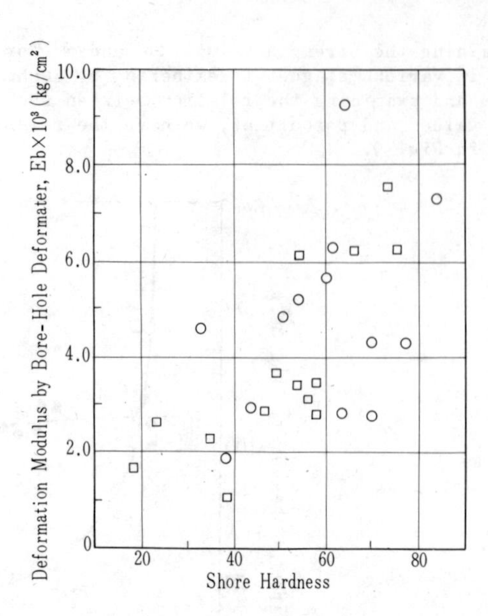

Fig. 11 Relationship between deformation modulus in bore-hole and Shore hardness
Fig. 11 Zusammenhang zwischen Verformungskoeffizient im Bohrloch und Shore-Härte
Fig. 11 Relation entre le coefficient de déformation mesurée dans le trou de perforation et la dureté Shore

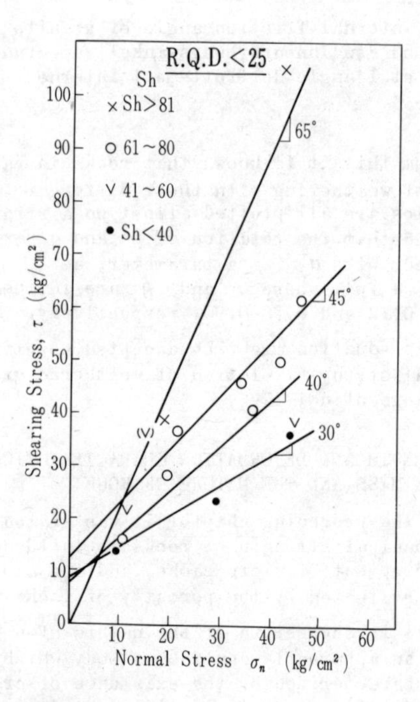

Fig. 12 Shearing strength of rock mass and Shore hardness (RQD=const.)
Fig. 12 Abscherungsfestigkeit vom Felsen und Shore-Härte (RQD=konst.)
Fig. 12 La dureté Shore et la résistance de cisaillement du rocher (RQD=const.)

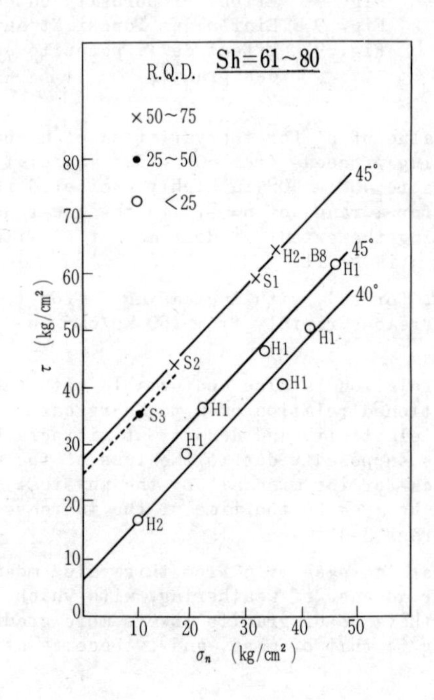

Fig. 13 Shearing strength of rock mass and RQD,(Sh=const.)
Fig. 13 Abscherungsfestigkeit vom Felsen und RQD (Sh = konst.)
Fig. 13 Résistance de cisaillement du rocher et RQD (Cis.=const.)

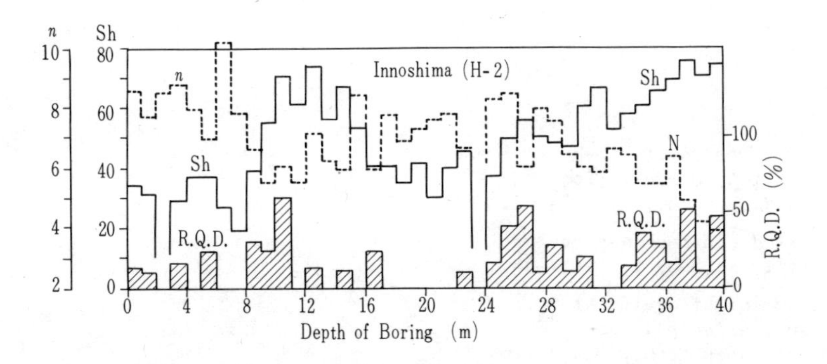

Fig. 14 Representation of test adit by boring core tests
Fig. 14 Darstellung vom Versuchsstollen durch Bohrkernversuche
Fig. 14 Désignation de la galerie à flanc d'essai par l'essai de carotte de la perforation

For these measurements cores of pilot borings were used, and the properties of rocks were expressed by Shore hardness and porosity and those of rock mass by the RQD designation (Deere, 1967).

As both are obtained by simple methods of test, they have the great advantage of being able to give detailed measuring values over the whole rock mass.

As seen in Fig. 3 the Shore hardness may be realized as an expression of elastic property which strongly reflects the nature of microcracks in the rock.

Fig. 11 shows the relation between modulus of deformation of rock mass measured in the bore holes and Shore hardness of corresponding core rocks.

Though the former is a value affected by microcracks in the rock mass, certain relation is seen between it and Shore hardness, and this represents the degree of relation between the properties of the rock body and those of the rock. Again, if the amount of cracks is used as a parameter, a more strong relation may be expected.

Fig. 12 and 13 show the relations of Shore hardness representing the properties of rock, RQD representing the properties of rock mass to the shearing strength of rock mass.

From these figures it is known that the Shore hardness has a strong relation with τ_o', and, accordingly, these values may be used as important indices for evaluating the strength of the rock mass.

CONSLUSIONS

Relation between characteristics of interstices and mechanical properties of weathered granite has been studied on rock pieces and rock mass of various stages of weathering from fresh rock up to weathered rock of which porosity is about 15%. The following results have been obtained:-

1. Appropriate methods to define the degree of chemical weathering(Fig. 1) and of mechanical weathering(Fig. 3) have been found in examining the relation between chemical weathering and mechanical weathering of granite.

2. Porosity of granite used in this study is attributed to microcracks developed in the rock and two modes are discriminated in the development of microcracks, the one is the increase of crack number and the other is the expansion of crack opening.

3. Porosity caused important effect on the mechanical properties of weathered granite; on Shore hardness as shown in Fig. 4, on Young's modulus as shown in Fig. 5, on triaxial shearing strength τ_o' and ϕ' as shown in Fig. 9 and on residual strain ratio as shown in Fig. 6.

4. Shearing characteristics of granite can be expressed by the following equation Fig. 10):-

$$q' = \alpha\sigma_c + \beta p'$$

where $\alpha = 0.05\text{–}0.12$, $\beta = 0.76\text{–}0.90$, $q'(kg/cm^2) = (\sigma_1 - \sigma_3)/2$ and $p'(kg/cm^2) = (\sigma_1 + \sigma_3)/2$ and is unconfined compressive strength.

5. Strength and deformation characteristics of granite rock mass in-situ depend seriously on the properties of drilled core pieces and on the properties of cracks.

Essential informations on the mechanical rock mass quality of the test adit in which in-situ tests have been carried out are simply defined by RQD of the pilot boring, Shore hardness, porosity and so on of the core specimens(Fig. 14).

6. Shearing characteristics of granite rock mass in-situ are designated by Figs. 12 and 13.

7. Bore hole deformation modulus by Pressiometer have relation to Shore hardness of the core specimen as shown in Fig. 11.

ACKNOWLEDGEMENT

This study was supported by the Honshu-Shikoku Bridge Authority. The authors are grateful to members of the Foundation Survey and Design Sections in the Authority for the considerable assistance and encouragement. The authors are indebted to Rock Engineering Laboratory members of the Saitama University.

* * * * * *

REFERENCES

Deere, D. U., et al, 1967, Design of sub-surface and near-surface construction in rock, Proc. of the Eighth Sympo. on Rock Mech., p. 237-302.

Goldich, S.S., 1938, A study in rock weathering Jour. of Geology, vol. VI, No. 1, P. 17-58.

Heck, W.J., 1968, Development of equipment for studying pore pressure effects in Rock, Proc. of the Tenth Sympo. on Rock Mech., P. 243-266.

Onodera, T.F., R. Yoshinaka and M. Oda, 1973, Relation between characteristics of interstices and mechanical properties on weathered granite, Proc. of the Fourth National Symposium on Rock Mechanics, Japan, P. 121-126.

Ruxton, B. P., 1968, Measures of the degree of chemical weathering of rocks, Jour. of Geology, P. 518-527.

Yoshinaka, R., 1973, Mechanical properties of granitic rock foundation, Jour. of the Bridge and Foundation Engineering, vol. 7, No. 10, P. 88-3 (in Japanese)

A CONSPECTUS OF AGGREGATE STRENGTH AND THE RELEVANCE OF THIS FACTOR AS THE BASIS FOR A PHYSICAL CLASSIFICATION OF CRUSHED ROCK AGGREGATE

UNE VUE D'ENSEMBLE DE LA FORCE DE L'AGRÉGATE ET DE L'APPLICABILITÉ DE CE FACTEUR COMME BASE D'UNE CLASSIFICATION PHYSIQUE DE L'AGRÉGAT DE ROCHE BROYÉE

ÜBERSICHT ÜBER DIE AGGREGATSTÄRKE UND DIE BEDEUTUNG DIESES FAKTORS ALS GRUNDLAGE FÜR DIE PHYSIKALISCHE KLASSIFIZIERUNG VON REIBUNGSSTEINAGGREGATEN

I.M. SPENCE
Research Assistant, Department of Civil Engineering, University of Dundee, Scotland
D.M. RAMSAY
Head of Geology Department, University of Dundee
R.K. DHIR
Lecturer in Department of Civil Engineering, University of Dundee, Scotland

SUMMARY Crushed rock aggregate strength is measured by the Aggregate Impact and Crushing Values. The numerical values obtained are governed by intrinsic geological factors namely, petrology, petrography and the structure of the rock together with clast fabric. Non-standard residue values were introduced to augment knowledge on the toughness and effects of cataclasis of the aggregate. The standard and residue values are sensitive indicators of the various factors and related in a simple fashion, i.e. IV or ACV = C + nI_F; IVR or ACVR = C - nI_F. In view of the consistent pattern of strength values this attribute forms a suitable basis for a practical classification of roadstone. Three primary Grades are recognised which embrace a large proportion of the tougher rocks employed in Scotland.

RESUME On mesure la roche broyée par l'épreuve pour choc et pour broyage de l'agrégat. Les résultats numériques qui en reviennent sont régis par des facteurs géologiques intrinsiques—c'est-à-dire, la pétrologie, la pétrographie, la formation des roches et leur qualité clastique. Des épreuves de résidu de type exceptionnel ont été introduites pour ajouter à nos connaissances de la résistance et des effets cataclasiques de l'agrégat. Les épreuves normales de résidu indiquent de façon sensible les facteurs divers et s'apparentent simplement—par exemple IV ou ACV = C + nI_F; IVR ou ACVR = C - nI_F. D'après ce modèle consistent des épreuves de force, cette qualité fournit une base propre à la classification de pierre pour les routes. On reconnaît trois qualités principales qui renferment la plupart des roches les plus résistantes dont on se sert en Ecosse.

ZUSAMMENFASSUNG Die Stärke eines Reibungsgesteins-Aggregats wird bestimmt durch den Aggregatdruck und durch Reibungswerte. Die daraus erhältlichen Zahlenwerte werden von spezifisch geologischen Faktoren bestimmt: Petrologie, Petrographie und Gesteinsstruktur zusammen mit der Struktur klastischer Sedimente. Es wurden nichtstandardisierte Werte eingeführt, um mehr Kenntnisse über die Härte und die Wirkung der Aggregatkataklase zu erhalten. Die Standard und die Restwerte sind genaue Indikatoren der verschiedenen Faktoren und folgen der einfachen Gleichung: IV or ACV = C + nI_F; IVR or ACV = C - nI_F. Angesichts des feststehenden Musters der Stärkewerte bildet diese Eigenschaft die brauchbare Grundlage für die Klassifizierung von Strassenschotter. Man erhält drei Primärgrade, die einen Grossteil des in Schottland verwendeten (Schotter-) Gesteins ausmachen.

INTRODUCTION

In Great Britain the assessment of crushed-rock aggregate quality is achieved through a suite of predictive tests designed to evaluate different facets of physical behaviour such as strength, susceptibility to polishing, attrition and abrasion (BS 812: 1967). There is however, no single, consistent or unique pattern of rock response to these different physical tests. The present account is concerned with aggregate strength for which two tests have been designed to provide Aggregate Impact (IV) and Aggregate Crushing (ACV) Values. These values provide some insight into the potential stand-up life and dependability of the aggregate, factors relevant to any primary investigation of a potential aggregate or comparative assessment of different materials.

The aim of this study was an evaluation of the significance of the values obtained in both tests, with particular reference to the geological factors responsible for the wide variation in values which can occur within and between different rock groups. When geological and methodological variables are duly assessed the rational pattern of the results make it possible to erect a practical classification of crushed-rock aggregate based on physical parameters, in contrast to the chemical-mineralogical basis of existing classifications.

To this end more than 3000 tests have been performed on aggregate from 40 sources, covering the spectrum of rocks employed as roadstone in Scotland and including granite, granodiorite, dolerite, teschenite, porphyry, porphyrite, basalt, andesite, phonolite, dacite, felsite, psammite, quartzite, marble, greywacke, flagstone and limestone.

AGGREGATE STRENGTH

Tests

For the quantitative estimation of aggregate strength two tests are quoted in British Standards namely, Aggregate Impact (IV) and Crushing (ACV) Values (BS 812: 1967).

By employing different loading systems these tests investigate different aspects of aggregate toughness. In both tests the samples used are in the particle size range 12.76mm—9.52mm, a typical grade in the wearing courses of asphalt roads. In the Impact Test the sample is subjected to the repeated impact of 15 blows from a 13.6—14.1kg. hammer, falling through 381 ± 6.5mm. In the Crushing Test continuous loading is applied through a piston set in a compression testing machine and the load is increased to reach a total of 398.56kN in 10 mins. In the resulting cataclasis the fine material which is produced and passes BS 2.40mm sieve is calculated as a weight percentage of the original sample and is expressed as the Aggregate Impact (IV) and Aggregate Crushing (ACV) Values respectively (BS 812: 1967). In both of these tests lower numerical values represent superior strength.

Aggregate strength, gauged as it is by the degree of granulation, differs significantly from the strength which is measured in intact rock samples. IV and ACV are really indices of pulverisation, reflecting toughness or tenacity under loading beyond the point of failure, as opposed to the stress level corresponding to fracture of the conventional strength in intact rock. As such the values obtained for aggregate strength are dimensionless numbers. Moreover both IV and ACV are bulk and generalised values for a particulate sample, unlike the results of intact rock testing which are obtained from individual specimens. As a result of these differences it is difficult to correlate particular values of the aggregate tests with those obtained from intact specimens (Dhir, et al, 1971). In general terms however, the pattern of aggregate strength values agrees with what might be anticipated from the intact rocks, for example volcanic igneous rocks yield lower IV and ACV than plutonic igneous types. Exceptions do occur however, and greywacke which might be anticipated to be weaker than fine-grained igneous rocks yield comparable values, while limestones yield lower and therefore superior values to those granites.

From aggregate strength tests it is difficult to predict the performance of the material in asphalt mixtures. This is not surprising however, when one considers that even in the loose condition of the strength tests the present programme has revealed a number of geological and methological variables which influence results and impair reproducibility.

Prior to the present investigation the pattern of results was somewhat inconclusive and even within restricted petrological types appeared to display a high degree of inconsistency. It remains a difficulty in roadstone investigation therefore to be able to test samples in conditions representative of the 'in service' situation and reconcile field conditions with laboratory results.

The merit of the existing physical tests on loose aggregate becomes more obvious where one is concerned with macadamised or simpler dirt-surfacing in which the aggregate particles are not encased and buffered with bituminous material. These tests seem particularly apposite when considering vehicular loads concentrated by use of studded tyres etc.

Impact and crushing residue values

The choice of the sieve size 2.40mm as the definitive measure of IV and ACV is quite arbitrary and it became obvious during the early stages of the present investigation that some attention should be paid to the coarser products of cataclasis. Any good aggregate should exhibit minimum break-up to particles of any size and the standard IV and ACV tests take no account of the coarser products produced. From this viewpoint a more realistic measure of aggregate soundness is the proportion of material remaining within the original size range (12.7—9.52mm) after the test. This additional non-standard value in both tests was differentiated and expressed as Impact Value Residue, IVR (Ramsay, 1965) and Aggregate Crushing Value Residue, ACVR (Dhir, et al, 1971).

The significance of IVR can be illustrated from one inferior andesite product which has an IV of 16, some 25% higher than normal values for such rock types. The IVR however was only 14.0 as against values of 35 for the normal product.

Correlation between standard and non-standard values

When both standard values are related to their appropriate residue values, curves of steep gradient result (Fig. 1) indicating the sensitivity of the residue values to factors which increase IV or ACV.

A high degree of correlation obtains between IV—ACV and IVR—ACV as shown in Fig. 2, a synoptic diagram for all the diverse rock types tested. This close correlation implies that IV can be confidently employed as the test for aggregate strength. The test has the advantage over ACV of simplicity and cheapness in operation and does not require the more elaborate facilities of a testing laboratory. The equipment is portable and the small sample required make it a particularly useful value in the question of quality control.

Influence of geological factors

The published spread of values for the standard aggregate strength tests, both within and between rock groups, is so large that considerable overlap exists, blurring the differences between very different rock types (Shergold, 1950). This imprecision has led to an ambivalent attitude to strength tests by many operators and users alike.

By working within a restricted framework of specific rock types rather than the broader and mineralogically similar groups of conventional petrological classifications a consistent and rational pattern of behaviour emerges. One can differentiate several geological and methodological factors affecting results and assess their influence on aggregate behaviour (Ramsay, et al, 1973). In the rock suites investigated to date the significant geological factors to emerge are texture, grain-size and anisotropy. In addition to these intrinsic characters of the rock material itself and independent of their influence, the shape distribution of the constituent particles in particular the flakiness index, exerts a consistent and important effect on aggregate response to the strength tests.

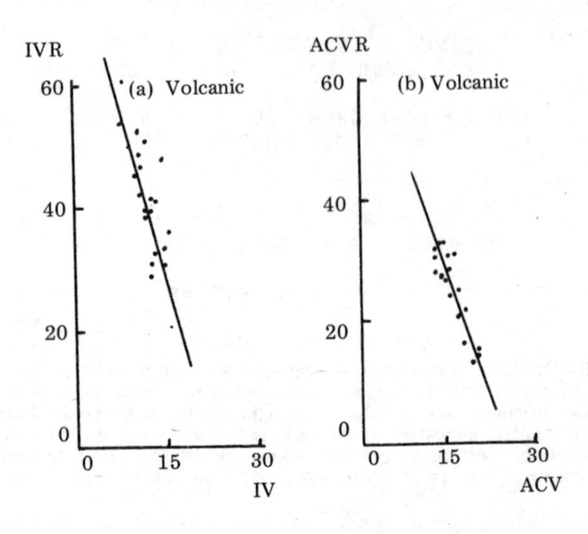

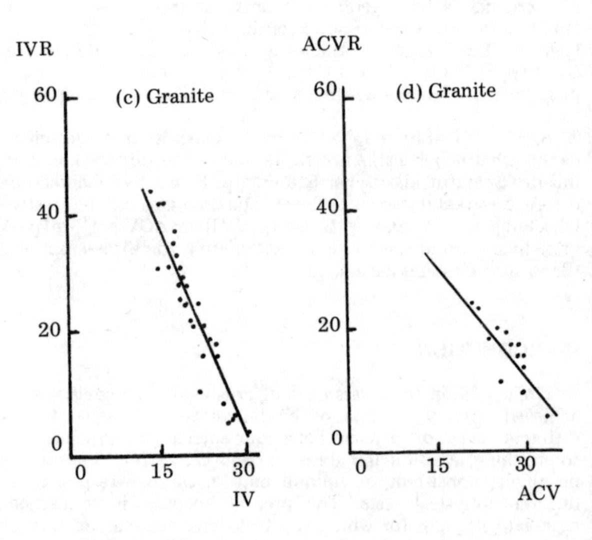

Fig. 1 Relationship between IV—IVR and ACV—ACVR for granitic and volcanic rocks.

Connexité entre IV—IVR et ACV—ACVR pour des roches d'épanchement et granatiques.

Abb. 1 Verhältnis von IV—IVR und ACV—ACVR für Granit und Vulkangestein.

CLAST FABRIC

From BS specifications one can distinguish four principle categories of particle shape in a crushed-rock aggregate namely, cuboidal (irregular and angular equidimensional particles), elongate, flaky and flaky-elongated. Flaky particles have lowest mass and are defined as those with smallest dimension a maximum of 0.6 times the mean sieve size. Elongate particles are those whose maximum dimension is more than 1.8 times the mean sieve size (BS 812: 1967). Employing standard BS shape gauges one can obtain the weight percentage of each type and compute the significant indices of flakiness (I_F) and elongation (I_E). The values obtained for these indices depend on rock character, crushing-equipment employed and production technique.

Both IV and ACV are sensitive to variation in flakiness and increase linearly with increasing I_F (Ramsay, 1965; Dhir, et al, 1971). The

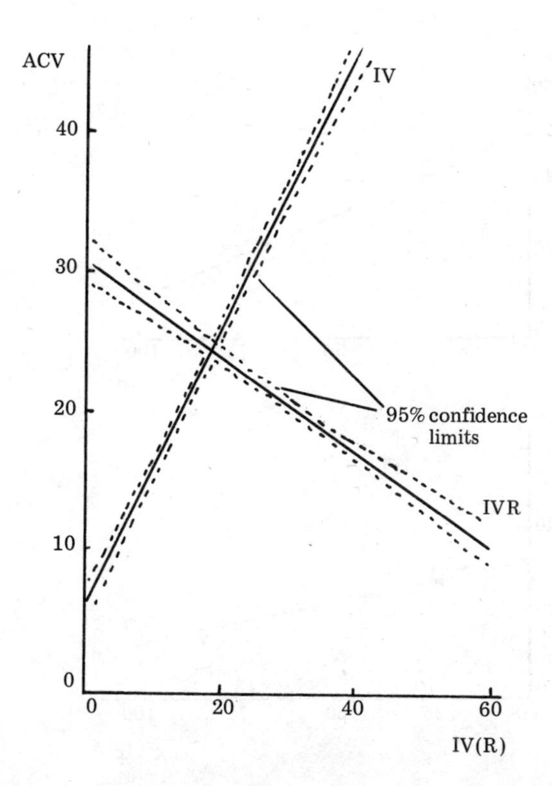

Fig. 2 Relationship between ACV and IV or IVR for 19 rock types.

Connexité entre ACV et IV ou IVR pour 19 types de roches.

Abb. 2 Verhältnis von ACV und IV oder IVR für 19 Gesteinsarten.

relationship is of the simple form, IV or ACV = $C + nI_F$, where C is a petrological constant and n is the coefficient of flakiness.

In normal quarry products I_F falls between 15 and 40 and only exceeds this in inferior products. Artificial variation of I_F from 0-100 for each rock type confirmed the linear relationship with IV and ACV (Fig. 3). I_E on the other hand exerts no significant effect on either aggregate strength value. The influence of flakiness is consistent throughout the range of rocks tested, although the gradient of the curves may vary with rock type, but in general it falls in the range 0.04-0.08.

Residue values for both tests are also related in a simple linear fashion to I_F as IVR or ACVR = $C - nI_F$. From the steeper gradient of these curves (n = 0.16 - 0.38) it is obvious that the residue values are even more sensitive indicators of the influence of aggregate shape than the standard IV and ACV (Fig. 3).

The effect of the strength tests on the flaky particles present in the aggregate can be appreciated from Fig. 4, in which it can be seen that these constituents undergo preferential elimination. The break-up of such particles is principally to fragments coarser than BS 2.40mm, so that despite production of some fine sand which raises the IV and ACV values in proportion to the I_F, the increase in value in absolute terms is not spectacular, even for high I_F. In andesite with I_F = 30 for example, the IV is 13, while for another poorer andesite product with I_F = 53, IV is 16. The increase in IV is 25 percent and the higher value of 16 would suggest a material comparing favourably in strength with the soundest granites. The error of this conclusion can be seen by comparing IVR values in both materials, where the flaky andesite (I_F - 53) retains only 13.9 percent of the sample in the original size range as against 30 for the granites. The poor quality of this material is masked in the standard IV and ACV values as the bulk of the cataclastic products are in the disregarded 9.52—2.40mm size range. In samples with I_F up to 60 the reduction in flakiness during the test is between 50 and 100 percent (Fig. 4).

INFLUENCE OF ROCK FABRIC AND PETROLOGY

The different families of rocks have IV—I_F and ACV—I_F curves cutting the ordinate (I_F = 0) at distinctive intercepts. At I_F = 0 the aggregate is free from the influence of adverse clast shape and the ordinate intercept (C) reflects the inherent characteristics of the rock material itself. The lower the value of C the tougher and more resistant is the rock material.

Although the IV—I_F and ACV—I_F curves are simple, consistent and rational the petrological constant C for the rock material is a complex value. In an earlier study which concentrated on igneous and metamorphic rocks of comparable but restricted characters Ramsay (1965) proposed that C was a reflection of the petrography, especially grain-size and anistropy. As the project developed it became apparent that C is a compound value summing the influence of several geological elements, each of which may vary in its contribution to the numerical value of C, within and between rock types and groups, for example, $C = \sum_{i=1}^{3} c_i$ where c_1 is petrology, c_2 is petrography and c_3 is structure, see Table I.

Fine-grained igneous rocks and massive, well-cemented, fine-grained greywackes which display homogeneous fabrics free from adverse textural and structural elements approach the optimum conditions for obtaining the maximum possible value for the strength of silicate aggregate material. In such rocks the value of C in the impact test is 6-8. As the fabric becomes modified by coarsening grain-size, foliation, alteration, the numerical value of C is increased. For volcanic rocks therefore $C = c_1$ while for plutonic rocks $C = c_1 + c_2$ and in schistose rocks $C = c_1 + c_3$ and perhaps c_2 (Table 1). This can be appreciated by comparing IV—I_F curves for volcanic and plutonic rocks, schistose and non-schistose psammites or marbles (Fig. 5).

Any disturbance of the primary fabric by weathering or deuteric alteration also dramatically increases the value of C to a level which overshadows or swamps the influence of clast shape so that IV = C (Ramsay, 1965).

An important feature to emerge from the study of igneous rocks is that chemical-mineralogical variation has no effect on strength values. In the volcanic suite rocks ranging in composition from basalt to felsite display IV and ACV within one narrow family curve. This reflects the comparable physical properties of the common rock forming silicates.

Although mineralogical variation within related groups of rocks has no influence on IV or ACV there are gross mineralogical-chemical differences between groups which are significant. The common rocks utilised in roadstone aggregates fall into two broad mineralogical categories, calcareous and silicate. The former includes limestones, dolomites and marbles, while the latter includes psammites, igneous and meta-igneous, and arenaceous sedimentary rocks. The difference in physical properties between the carbonate and silicate mineral families is reflected in the fundamentally weaker nature of the carbonate rocks, provided other features of the fabrics are constant.

CLASSIFICATION

In view of the consistent and rational behaviour of aggregates in the Impact and Crushing tests aggregate strength emerges as a viable basis for a simpler and more utilitarian classification of roadstones than standard geological classifications.

The American classification of aggregates described in ASTM C294-50 (ASTM, 1965) does not have a consistent basis and specific rock types are grouped into broader divisions with petrographic similarities in some and petrological similarities in other instances. These larger sub-divisions transect natural geological boundaries. For metamorphic and sedimentary types the groupings reflect consistent mineralogy, while for igneous rocks they reflect textural-environmental similarities. The British classification of roadstones given in BS 812, 1967 assembles specific rock types into a number of Trade Groups of comparable mineralogical or grain-size character.

Petrologically based classifications provide little help in predicting

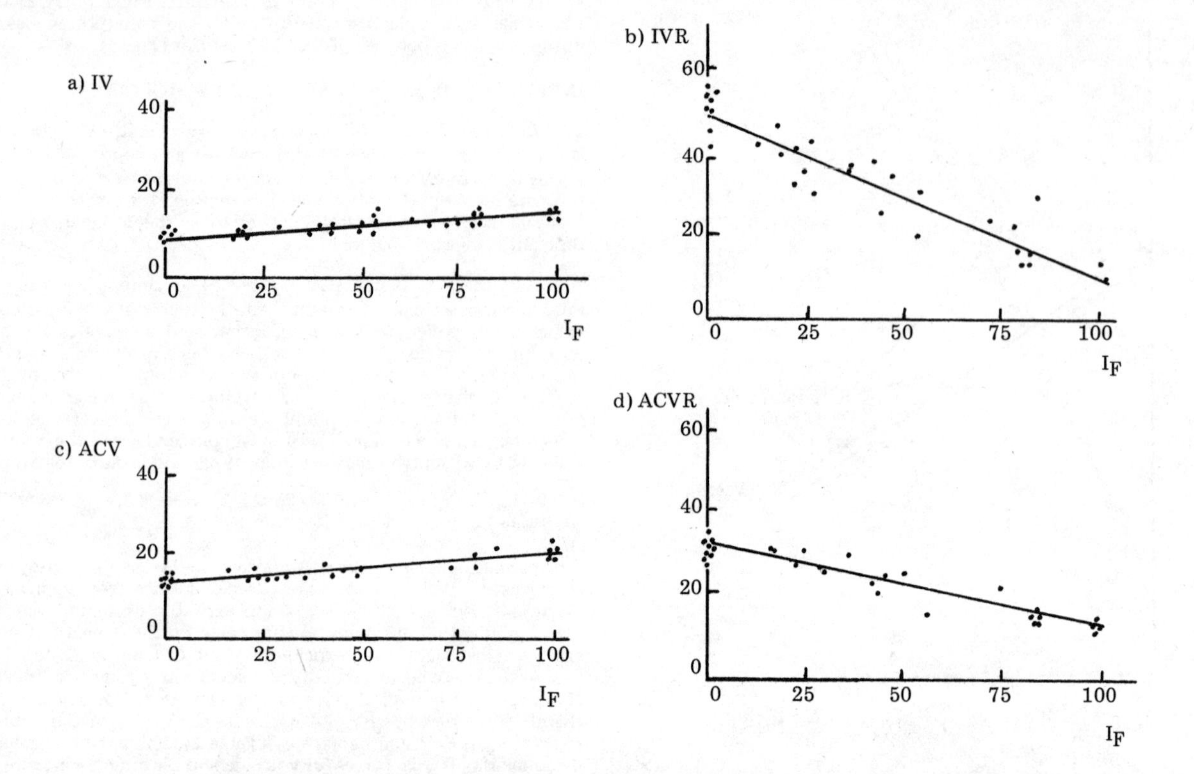

Fig. 3 Influence of flakiness Index on IV (a), IVR (b), ACV (c) and ACVR (d) for fine and medium-grained igneous rocks.

Influence de l'Indice de'écaille sur IV (a), IVR (b), ACV (c) et ACVR (d) dans les roches pyrogènes à grain fin et moyen.

Abb. 3 Einfluss des Schieferungsindex auf IV (a), IVR (b), ACV (c) unde ACVR (d) für feines und mittelkörniges Erruptivgestein.

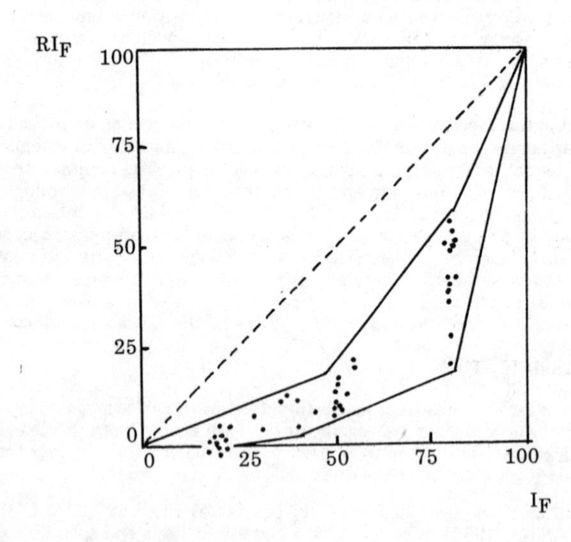

Fig. 4 Relationship of pre-test, Flakiness Index (I_F) and post-test Flakiness Index (RI_F).

Connexité de l'Indice de'écaille avant l'essai (I_F) avec l'Indice après l'essai (RI_F).

Abb. 4 Verhältnis von Schieferungsindex vor (I_F) und nach dem Test (RI_F).

physical performance in other than general terms. This is borne out in published synoptic summaries of IV and ACV for all Trade Groups (Road Research Laboratory, 1959) where the range of possible values in each group is so large and overlapping that their possible significance as predictive indicators is blurred. In view of the demonstrated influence of the several geological factors any one rock type can exhibit a spectrum of physical behaviour.

The basic units of the proposed classification are, as in the other classifications, specific Rock Types, e.g. basalt, greywacke, marble, within which mineralogy is statistically consistent. For these basic units IV and ACV are governed by inherent rock and clast fabric parameters in a simple rational fashion, e.g. IV or ACV = $C + nI_F$; IVR or ACVR = $C - nI_F$.

Rock Types can be collated into Rock Groups (Table I) of consistent petrogenetic import and within which petrological characteristics are reasonably consistent or vary within narrow limits (Table I). It should be pointed out that the classification at present embraces only fresh rock types and ignores more complex factors like weathering, deuteric alteration etc. There is no doubt that such factors could be incorporated into the scheme although this has not yet been attempted. Within the Rock Groups rock types may vary considerably in mineralogy and chemistry, for example the volcanic igneous group ranges from basalt to felsite. Strength values of such groups are reasonably consistent or vary in a rational fashion, and for each there are distinctive curves or families of curves relating IV or ACV to I_F. The rock types and groups listed in Table I embrace a significant proportion of the common aggregate types and the majority of the types utilised in Britain. The names applied to the Rock Groups describes the essential characters of the constituent types, for

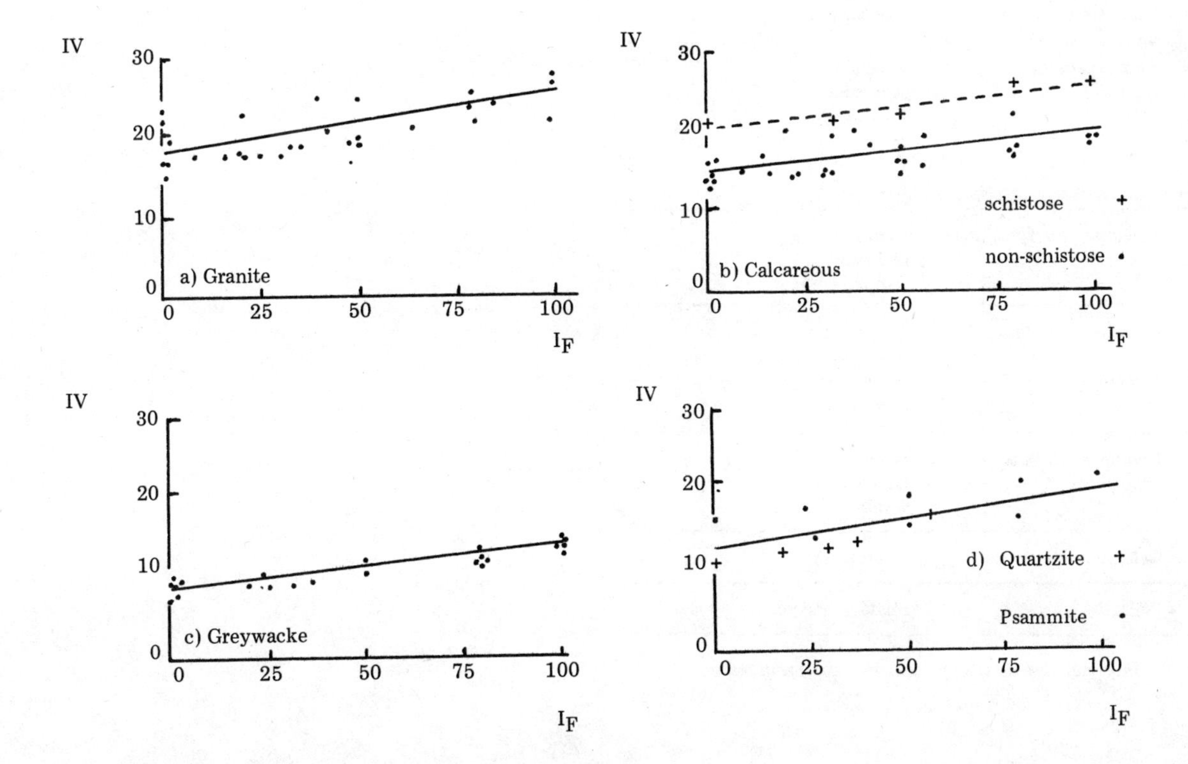

Fig. 5 Influence of Flakiness Index on Impact Value for (a) granites, (b) calcareous rock, (c) greywacke, (d) quartzite and psammite.

Influence de l'Indice d'écaille sur l'épreuve pour choc par rapport aux (a) granits, (b) roches calcaires, (c) greywacke, (d) quartzites et psammites.

Abb. 5 Einfluss des Schieferungsindex auf den Schlagwert von (a) Granitgestein, (b) Kalkgestein, (c) Grauwacke, (d) Quarz und Psammit.

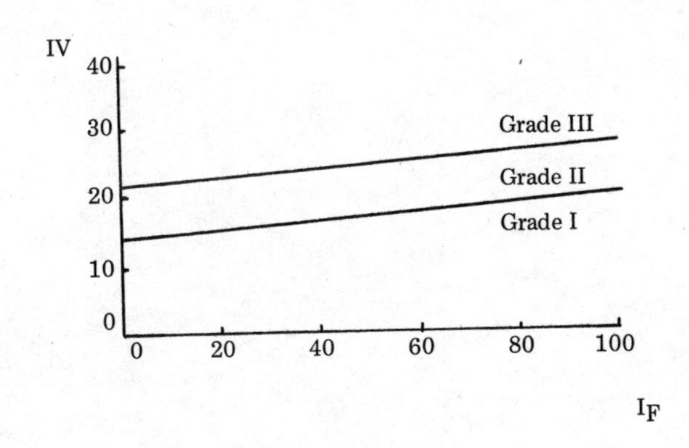

Fig. 6 Influence of Flakiness index on rock grade boundaries.

Influence de l'Indice de'écaille sur les teneurs des limites des roches.

Abb. 6 Einfluss des Schieferungsindex auf Gesteinsgradbegrenzungen.

example Fine and coarse crystalline, silicate metacrystalline, calcareous cemented etc., (Table I).

All rock types and groups can be assembled simply into at least three major Grades which, focussing on the physical characteristics, are independent of common petrological boundaries, see Table I. The numerical limits placed on each are somewhat arbitrary but allow rational differentiation of the rock types and groups of comparable quality. For the construction of such a classification the influence of *aggregate flakiness is removed, i.e.* $I_F = 0$. Grade I is the soundest grade characterised by C in IV falling below 14. In Grade II the value of C falls between 14 and 22, while in Grade III it exceeds 22. This classification will allow further grades to be introduced as the investigation extends to the several categories of weaker rocks. When aggregate flakiness is considered in the scheme it can be appreciated that the Grade boundaries will be influenced (Fig. 6). Before any aggregate can be placed in its appropriate Grade the flakiness index must be determined and the rock fabric scrutinised carefully.

This proposed classification does not imply rejection of standard classifications but rather it provides an ancillary or complimentary classification of more practical value.

CONCLUSIONS

Intrinsic geological factors such as petrology, petrography and structure together with clast fabric underlie the numerical values obtained in the predictive tests for the strength of crushed rock aggregate. The strength of the material in both Aggregate Impact and Crushing tests as reflected in the pulverisation and surviving fraction, is related to the geological and fabric factors in a simple linear fashion, e.g. IV or ACV = C + nI_F and IVR or ACVR = C - nI_F.

Grade	Rock Group	Rock Type	Significant constants
I	Fine crystalline (volcanic)	Basalt	c_1
		Andesite	c_1
		Porphyrite	c_1
		Porphyry	c_1
		Dolerite	c_1
		Felsite	c_1
I	Silicate metacrystalline	Psammite	c_{1-3}
		Quartzite	c_1
		Amphibolite	c_{1-3}
I	Silicate cemented	Greywacke	c_{1-2}
I-III		Sandstone	c_{1-3}
II	Calcareous metacrystalline	Marble	c_{1-3}
II-III	Coarse crystalline (Plutonic)	Granite	c_{1-2}
		Diorite	c_{1-2}
		Gabbro	c_{1-2}
II-III	Calcareous cemented	Limestone	c_{1-2}
III	Pelite	Shale-mudstone	c_{1-3}

Table I. Physical classification of crushed rock aggregate

The values obtained for strength display a consistent and rational pattern for the common rocks exploited as crushed rock aggregate. This pattern has been demonstrated to transgress conventional petrological boundaries and provides the basis for a simple and practical physical classification of such aggregates. Three grades have been recognised from the broad spectrum of rocks investigated, although it has been recognised that this may be extended for weaker rocks and synthetic materials.

REFERENCES

ASTM 1965, Standard descriptive nomenclature of constituents of natural mineral aggregate, *ASTM Standards Part 10 C294-56.*

B.S.812: 1967, Methods for sampling and testing of mineral aggregates, sand and fillers. *British Standard Institution.*

DHIR, R.K., RAMSAY, D.M. and BALFOUR, N. 1971, A study of the aggregate impact and crushing values tests. *Journal of the Institute of Highway Engineers*, vol. 18: 17-27.

RAMSAY, D.M. 1965, Factors influencing aggregate impact value in rock aggregate. *Quarry Managers' Journal* April, Vol. 49: 129-34.

RAMSAY, D.M., DHIR, R.K. and SPENCE, I. 1973, Non-geological factors influencing the reproducibility of results in the aggregate impact test. *Quarry Managers' Journal*, May, Vol. 57, No. 5, 179-181.

ROAD RESEARCH LABORATORY, 1959, Roadstone test data presented in tabular form.

SHERGOLD, F.A., 1950. The classification and mechanical testing of road making aggregates. *Quarry Managers' Journal*, July, Vol. 34: 27-35.

THE USE OF THE STANDARD PENETRATION TEST IN CLASSIFYING ROCKS

L'EMPLOI DE L'ESSAI DE PÉNÉTRATION STANDARD POUR LA CLASSIFICATION DES ROCHES

DER GEBRAUCH DES STANDARD-PENETRATIONTESTS IN FELSKLASSIFIZIERUNG

A. C. STAMATOPOULOS
P. C. KOTZIAS
Soils Consultants
Athens, Greece

SUMMARY The standard penetration test which is one of the routine tests for classifying soils in-situ, can be used also for classifying rocks. This method is particularly adaptable to weak rocks where other methods do not apply readily. Test results can be used effectively in identifying quantitatively variations of rock properties in borings. This paper includes 1209 results obtained on 7 lithological types, and statistical correlations with laboratory test results.

SOMMAIRE L'essai de pénétration standard qui est une méthode de routine pour la classification des sols en place, peut être aussi employé pour la classification des roches. Cette méthode est adaptable particulièrement au cas des roches de résistance faible où les méthodes courrantes ne peuvent pas être appliquées facilement. Les résultats des essais peuvent être employés effectivement pour constater des variations des propriétés des roches dans les sondages. Cet exposé contient 1209 résultats tirés de 7 types lithologiques, et des correlations statistiques avec des résultats de laboratoire.

ZUSAMMENFASSUNG Der "Standard Penetration Test", der als Rutine-Versuch für die Klassifizierung der Bodenablagerungen genutzt wird, kann auch für die Einteilung der Felsen verwendet werden. Dieser Versuch ist besonders an weichen Felsen anwendbar, wo andere übliche Methoden nicht bereits angänging sind. Anhand dieser Methoden kann man Felseigenschaften durch Bohrungen quantitativ anerkennen. Der vorliegende Beitrag enthält 1209 Versuchsergebnisse, die aus 7 verschiedenen lithologischen Gruppen entstehen. Statistische Zusammenhänge mit Labor-Versuchsergebnissen sind dargestellt.

INTRODUCTION AND DEFINITION OF PENETRABILITY

The standard penetration test (ASTM D1586), which is instrumental in the classification of soils in-situ, has been found useful also for the classification of rocks. This application of the standard penetration test is exemplified employing 1209 results from 17 investigated sites. These sites are at 9 different geographic locations and involve 7 lithological types.

In soils, the standard penetration test involves the measurement of the number of blows required to advance the penetration device three consecutive increments of penetration, 15 cm each. The accepted test procedure calls for a maximum of 100 blows for the second and third increments. The number of blows required for the first increment is considerably lower than 100, since it is expended primarily for seating.

In rocks, 100 blows will normally cause a penetration of less than 15 cm. Increasing the number of blows to, say, 200, would augment somewhat the length of penetration, but would result in disproportionally higher wear of the equipment.

The standard penetration test, as used herein, consists of recording the length of penetration caused by the application of 60 blows. The penetration device and driving energy of blows are the same as described in ASTM D1586. The results of the standard penetration test as recorded for rocks is expressed in

$$\frac{\text{length of penetration}}{60 \text{ blows}} \quad \text{or} \quad (\text{number}) \times \frac{\text{cm}}{\text{blows}}$$

It is the inverse of the expression used for soils, which is

$$\frac{\text{number of blows}}{30 \text{ cm of penetration}} \quad \text{or} \quad (\text{number}) \times \frac{\text{blows}}{\text{cm}}$$

Since in the case of soils the reported result is called "penetration resistance", it is appropriate to refer to the inverse result as "penetrability".

TEST PROCEDURE

In order to eliminate errors introduced by the accumulation of debris at the bottom of the borehole, it is advisable to disregard the penetration caused by the first 10 blows. Therefore, the test procedure should consist of first applying 10 blows and then measuring the penetration caused by the following 60 blows.

SUBSURFACE SECTIONS

If standard penetration tests are performed in boreholes at regular depth increments such as every 1 m of boring, it is possible to detect changes in the properties of rock during field investigatigations. If adjacent borings show matching results, it is possible to infer the existence of layering or continuous pockets of large extent. If a pocket or layer of weak rock is delineated it can lead to additional investigations and/or special precautions during construction.

The example of Figure 1 is taken from an investigation in central Athens, in an area underlain by shale. The investigation was made for a high-rise building with basements extending to a depth of 14 m. The excavation had to be carried to a depth of 16 m below road level. Measurements of penetrability indicated considerable differences between borings 1 and 2. These differences could not be expressed quantitatively simply by observing macroscopically the cores extracted from the boreholes. During construction, the sides of the excavation near boring 1 were unstable and had to be supported to prevent a major slide. The slide was not prevented altogether, and the adjacent road pavement developed cracks about 2 cm wide, parallel to the edge. The side of the excavation near boring 2 stood nearly vertically without showing instability.

RANGE OF RESULTS

The histograms of Figure 2 indicate the range of penetrability of 7 lithological types as obtained from 1209 test results. It is observed that in most cases the results are in the range of 3 to 8 cm/60 blows. Penetrabilities less than 3 cm/60 blows usually indicated rock with very good to excellent characteristics, whereas penetrabilities more than 8 cm/60 blows indicated weak rock and a potentially troublesome area (e.g. instability of the sides of a deep excavation).

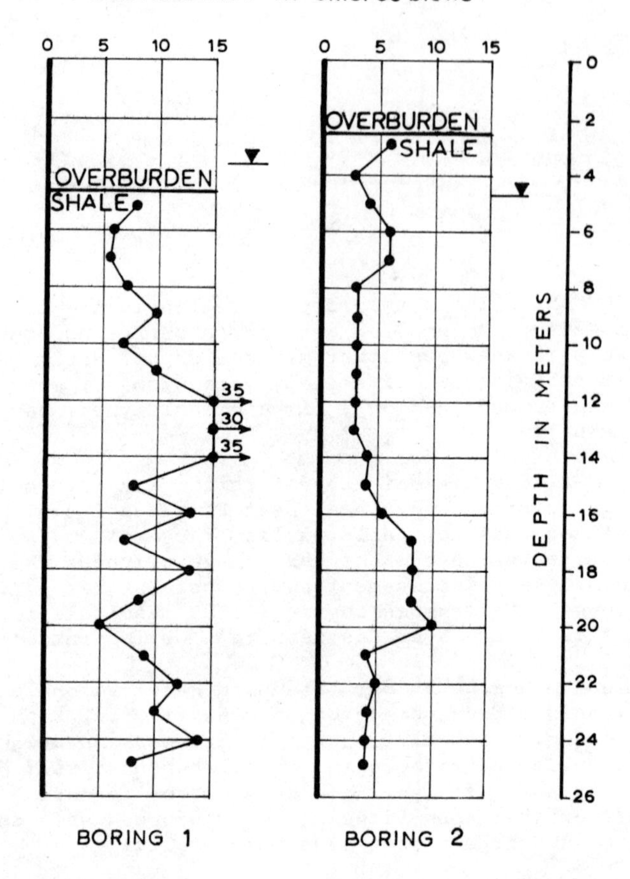

Fig. 1 Penetrability vs Depth. Two Borings in Shale at a Site in Central Athens.

CLASSIFICATION ACCORDING TO PENETRABILITY

The standard penetration test is particularly adaptable to weak rock, with properties lying between those of typical intact rock and compact soil. Comparing with other current methods of classification, it is noted that rock quality designation (RQD) (Deere, 1969) is based on counting "hard and sound" pieces of core, therefore, it presupposes the existence of rock with rather good characteristics which may not exist in a formation of weak rock. Classification by RQD also requires double tube core barrel of at least NX size which may not be available.

Laboratory tests, in particular uniaxial compression tests, which are used in classifying rock of medium and high strength, are of limited applicability in the case of weak rock. Referring to the classification chart for intact rock shown in Figure 3

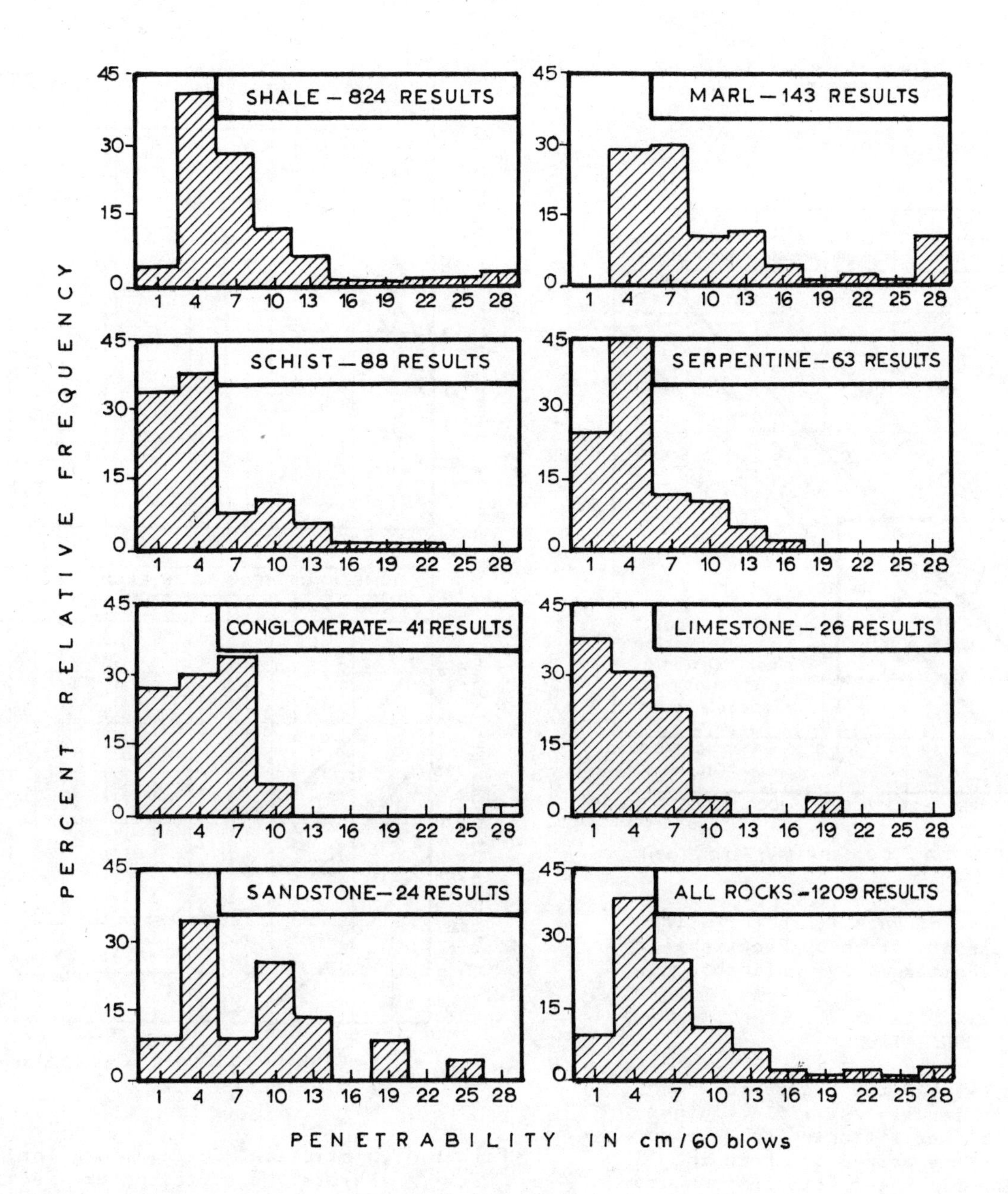

Fig. 2 Frequency Diagrams of Penetrability for Tested Rocks

(Deere, 1969), the classification by penetrability can be applied to rocks with strengths rated as "low" (D) and "very low" (E), and can be extended to rocks with strengths lower than "very low".

The histograms of Figure 2 suggest the classification of table 1 set on a geometric progression of penetrability values.

Table 1. Classification by Penetrability

Penetrability (cm/60 blows)	Rating
0 and 1	very low
2 to 4	low
5 to 8	medium
9 to 15	high
16 to 30	very high

Beyond 30 cm/60 blows the rock could, for engineering purposes, be classified as soil.

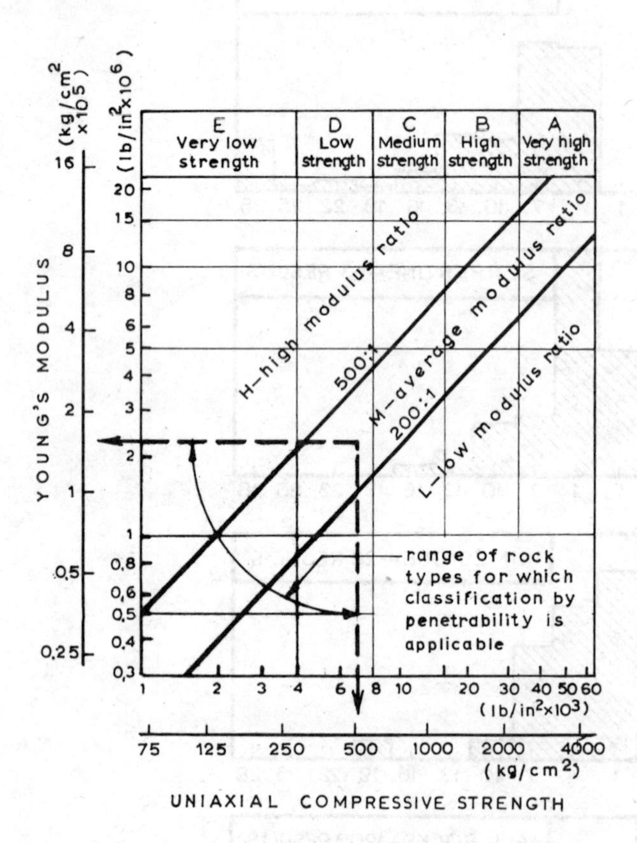

Figure 3 Range of Rock Types for which Classification by Penetrability is Particularly Applicable

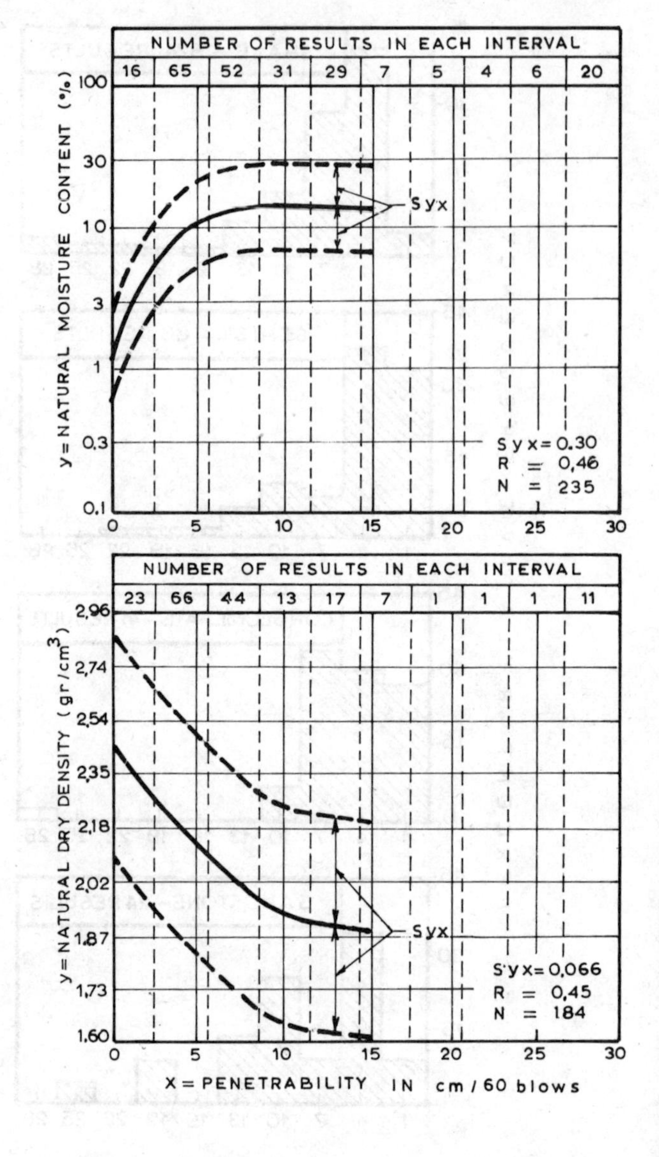

Figure 4 Statistical Correlations for Natural Moisture and Dry Density

STATISTICAL CORRELATIONS

In order to examine the degree to which penetrability results may reflect other properties, it was attempted to develop statistical correlations as shown in Figures 4 and 5. These correlations are based on results of laboratory tests performed on core samples obtained from borings, within 50 cm from the depths of penetrability measurements.

In the cases of water content, dry density and uniaxial compressive strength the number of results are more than 100. This number of results is sufficiently high to justify the calculation of the equation of the best fitting curve (method of least squares).

In the cases of Young's modulus and constrained modulus, the number of results are only 20 and 24, respectively. Because of the limited number of results, only the individual points and a freehand fitting curve are shown (Figure 5). These correlations should be regarded as highly tentative.

In pursuing the equations of the best fitting curves it was assumed that they can be written in the form y = f (x) and/or log y = f (x) where x is the penetrability in cm/60 blows, considered as the independent variable, y is the property being correlated with penetrability, considered as the dependent variable, and f (x) is a polynomial of the first to the fifth degree. The standard error of estimate Syx and the coefficient of correlation R for each of the cases attempted is given in table 2. It is observed that the form log y = f (x) produced in two of the three cases a higher coefficient of correlation than the form y = f (x). The coefficient of correlation is 0.46 - 0.64 which can be regarded as

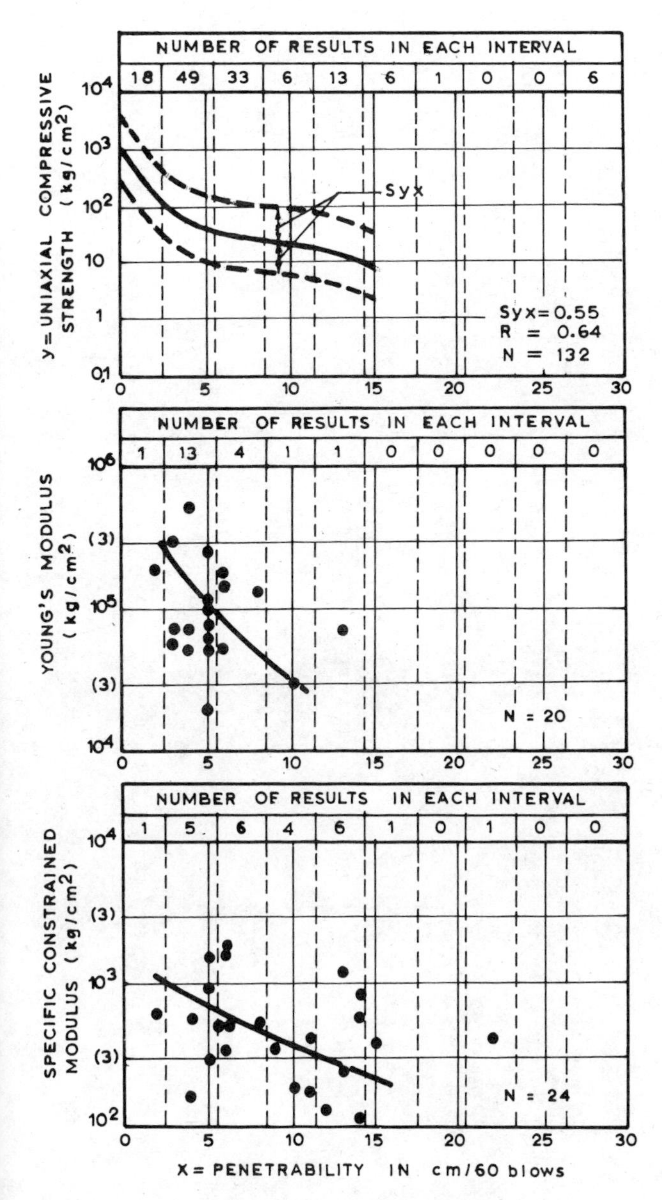

Fig. 5 Statistical Correlations for Mechanical Properties

satisfactory. The curves of Figures 4 and 5 correspond to the following expressions:

Water content : $\log y = 0.0565+0.379x - 0.0486x^2+0.00291x^3-0.0000832x^4 + 0.000000914x^5$

Dry density : $\log y = 0.390-0.0112x - 0.000519x^2+0.0000751x^3-0.00000166x^4$

Compressive strength : $\log y = 3.034-0.534x + 0.0664x^2-0.00363x^3+0.0000639x^4$

These equations apply in the range of penetrability values between 0 and 15 cm/60 blows.

TABLE 2. Values of the Standard Error of Estimate Syx and Coefficient of Correlation R for Polynomial Expressions of Best Fitting Curves

Type of Function	Degree of Polynomial	Parameter	Water Content (%)	Dry Density (gr/cm^3)	Uniaxial Compressive Strength (kg/cm^2)
ARITHMETIC : $y = f(x)$	1st	Syx	6.4	0.33	120
		R	0.26	0.36	0.36
	2nd	Syx	6.3	0.32	110
		R	0.31	0.42	0.45
	3rd	Syx	6.2	0.32	110
		R	0.37	0.44	0.51
	4th	Syx	6.2	0.32	110
		R	0.37	0.45	0.52
	5th	Syx	6.2	0.32	110
		R	0.37	0.45	0.53
LOGARITHMIC : $\log y = f(x)$	1st	Syx	0.32	0.068	0.58
		R	0.26	0.36	0.59
	2nd	Syx	0.31	0.066	0.57
		R	0.36	0.42	0.61
	3rd	Syx	0.30	0.066	0.57
		R	0.44	0.44	0.61
	4th	Syx	0.30	0.066	0.55
		R	0.45	0.45	0.64
	5th	Syx	0.30	0.066	0.55
		R	0.46	0.45	0.64
Number of Results = N			235	184	132

ACKNOWLEDGMENT

The computer programs for the statistical correlations were prepared by COUMOULOS D.G.

REFERENCES

ASTM Designation D1586-64T, Penetration Test and Split-Barrel Sampling of Soils.

Deere, D.U., 1969, Geological Considerations, Rock Mechanics in Engineering Practice, edited by Stagg and Zienkiewicz, John Wiley.

THEME 1

THÈME 1

THEMA 1

B

Static or Quasi-Static Deformation and Strength Tests

B

Déformation statique ou quasi-statique et essais de résistance

B

Feststehende oder quasi-feststehende Deformierungen und Stärkeversuche

DIRECT TENSILE TESTING OF ANISOTROPIC ROCKS

ESSAIS DE TRACTION DIRECTE SUR DES ÉCHANTILLONS DE ROCHE ANISOTROPE

DIREKTE ZUGVERSUCHE ÜBER ANISOTROPISCHE FELSPROBEN

G. BARLA L. GOFFI

Politecnico di Torino

Torino, Italy

SUMMARY

The different problems which were met in setting up a unit to be used for direct tensile testing of cylindrical rock specimens are described. Numerical results, obtained by the finite element method, which let one choose the most adequate cap for cementing the rock specimen, are presented. A series of tests on anisotropic rocks, with a transversely isotropic behavior, carried out in order to determine the strength and deformation characteristics, as a function of the inclination of the laminations with respect to the direction of loading, are discussed.

RESUME

L'on discute les différents problèmes de la mise au point d'un équipement pour l'exécution de l'essai de traction directe sur des échantillons cylindriques de roche . En particulier l'on examine les résultats (obtenus à l'aide de la méthode des éléments finis) qui ont permis de choisir la tête d'ancrage pour fixer l'extrémité de l'échantillon de roche . Enfin l'on donne les resultats d'une série d'essais sur deux rochers orthotropes, ayant le but de déterminer les caractéristiques de résistence et déformabilité en fonction de la différente direction d'application de la charge.

ZUSAMMENFASSUNG

Die Probleme der Ansetzung eines Gerätes für die Zugversuche zylindrischer Felsenproben und die Ergebnisse der Berechnungen (durch "Finite Element Method"), um die beste Verankerung der Proben zu wählen, werden dargestellt und diskutiert.

Nachdem illustriert man die Ergebnisse einiger Versuche über orthotropen Felsen, für die Darstellung der Festigkeits - und Verformbarkeitseigenschaften nach den verschiedenen Richtungen der Belastung.

INTRODUCTION

The purpose of the work reported in the present paper has been the setting up of a testing unit to be used in order to determine the strength and deformation characteristics of a rock subjected to tensile stress. Subsequently, a series of preliminary tests on transversely isotropic rock specimens has been carried out with the aim to predict the change in the value of the elastic modulus with the direction of load application, with respect to the plane of isotropy.

The direct tensile test (i.e. the uniaxial tensile test) presents many difficulties, which must be overcome if it is to be performed correctly. Careful consideration is to be given to the problem of applying the tensile load without transmitting bending stresses to the specimen. Furthermore, the ways of attaching the rock to the testing unit are to be analysed in order to avoid any anomalous concentration of stress in the specimen.

On the contrary, the indirect methods for tensile testing are conveniently used. However, they are generally applied to homogeneous and isotropic rocks, as the formulae which are adopted for calculating the tensile strength are based upon the assumptions of the classical theory of elasticity. Therefore if anisotropic rocks are to be studied, with consideration being given to the deformation behavior, the use of the direct tensile method seems to be the most appropriate.

DIRECT TENSILE TESTING

The problems which are met in performing correctly the uniaxial tensile test, are to be found mainly in achieving a perfectly axial application of the tensile load. Furthermore, the transmission of the tensile stress to the rock must avoid stress concentrations in the specimen, which can often make, due to brittle behavior of the material, the test unacceptable.

The first problem is often tackled in many Rock Mechanics laboratories by using a ball joint (Hawkes and Mellor, 1970). This system shows however a disadvantage, because even at small loads friction is difficult to be avoided.

The second problem could be solved by adopting carefully shaped specimens in order to ensure that a uniform stress state be applied (Brace, 1964). However, the preparation of these specimens is extremely difficult for many rocks. The practice of cementing with epoxy resin the specimen to caps to be attached to the testing unit is consequently preferable (Hawkes and Mellor, 1970).

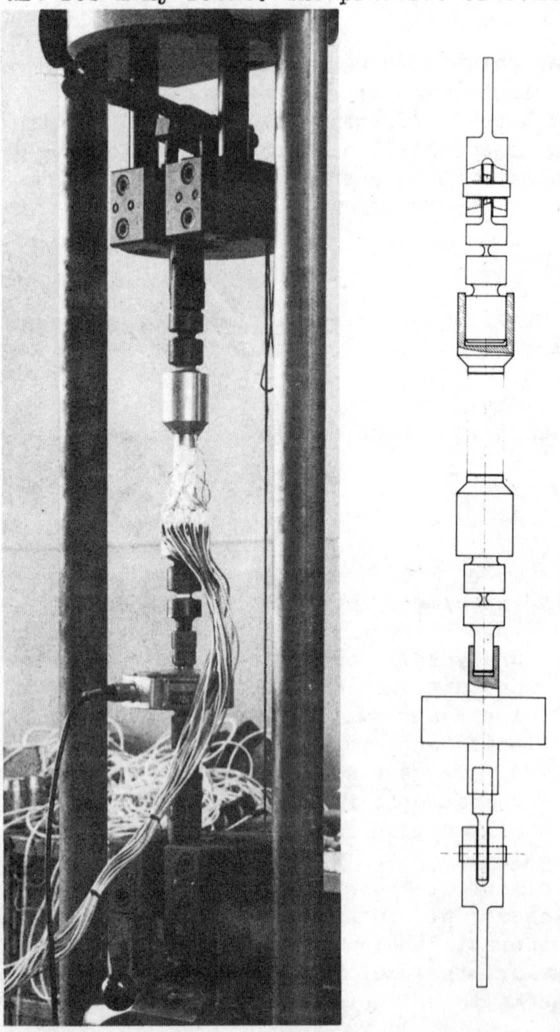

Figure 1 - A view of the testing unit

AXIAL LOAD APPLICATION

An elastic joint (Figure 1), similar to the one used by Dubois (1970), has been adopted in the present work. The main advantage of this system, with respect to the ball joint, is found in its great efficiency, which is increased with the increase in the value of the load being applied.

An aluminium specimen, with the same dimensions as the rock specimen to be used in subsequent tests (Figure 1), was subjected to uniaxial tensile load, applied through the elastic joint. The measurement of strains by means of electric strain gauges cemented on the surface of the specimen allowed a careful check of the system to be made. It may be observed that the difference in the values of the strain, measured along diametrally opposite sides of the specimen, is of the same order of the precision of instrument used.

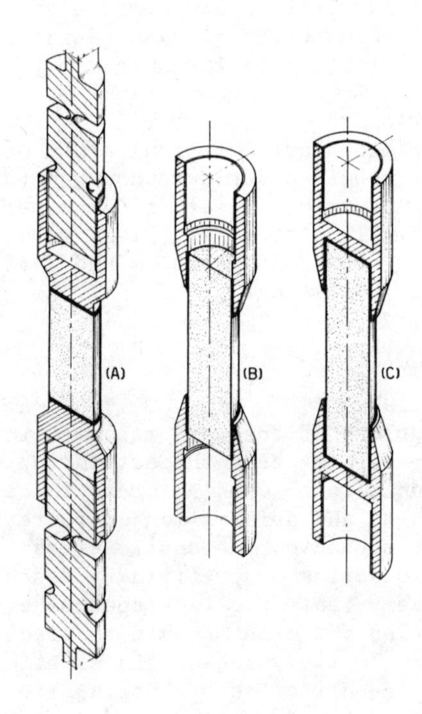

Figure 2 - Caps for applying the tensile stress to the specimen

METHOD FOR HOLDING THE SPECIMEN

The ends of the cylindrical rock specimen are cemented with epoxy resin to caps of a different type (Figure 2).

A problem which is to be solved is the determination of influence of the cap shape on the distribution of stresses in the specimen. In order to clear up this point, a finite element study was carried out which let the most appropriate cap be chosen, so that stress concentration could be avoided.

NUMERICAL RESULTS

The three caps considered in this study are shown in Figure 2 where: in a) the rock specimen is simply cemented through the end faces (Model 1), in b) the connection is obtained with cementation on the sides (Model 2), in c) both end faces and sides are used in order to hold the specimen (Model 3).

The finite element model for each case is axially symmetric; both quadrilateral and triangular constant stress elements were employed in order to carefully reproduce the shape of the various caps.

Due to the symmetry conditions for geometry and loading, only one fourth of the specimen was considered in each case and the boundary conditions were represented as shown in the Figures 3 to 5. A uniform load was applied on the upper surface of each cap and continuity of stresses and displacements was assumed between this and the rock specimen.

The following elastic constants were assumed: for the rock, E (Young's modulus) = 60,000 MN/m^2; ν (Poisson's ratio) = 0.25; for the cap, supposed to be of aluminium, E = 60,000 MN/m^2, ν = 0.35.

The numerical results for displacements and stresses are shown for each case in Figures 3 to 5. It is noticed that stresses are here reckoned as positive when tensile, negative when compressive. In each case normalized values are reported as each stress is referred to the applied uniform stress $\bar{\sigma}_z$ on the boundary.

The following observations can be made: a) the axial stress (σ_z) for model 1 (Figure 3) is practically uniformly distributed when compared with the same stress obtained

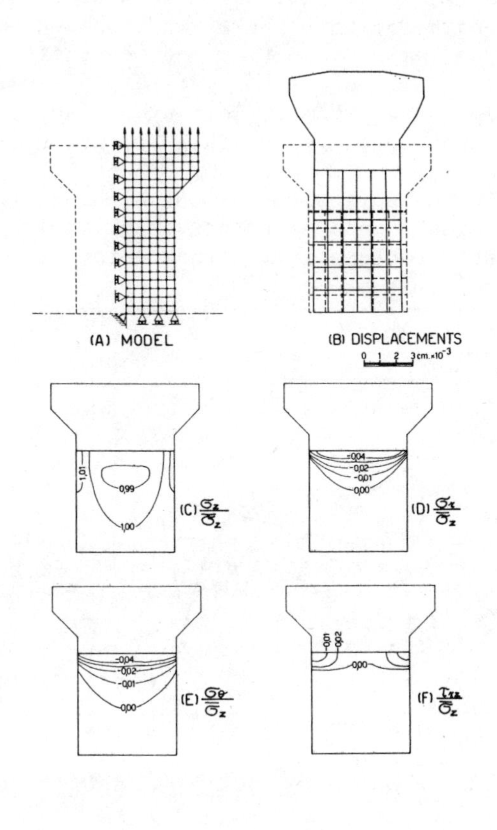

Figure 3 - Displacements and stresses in model 1

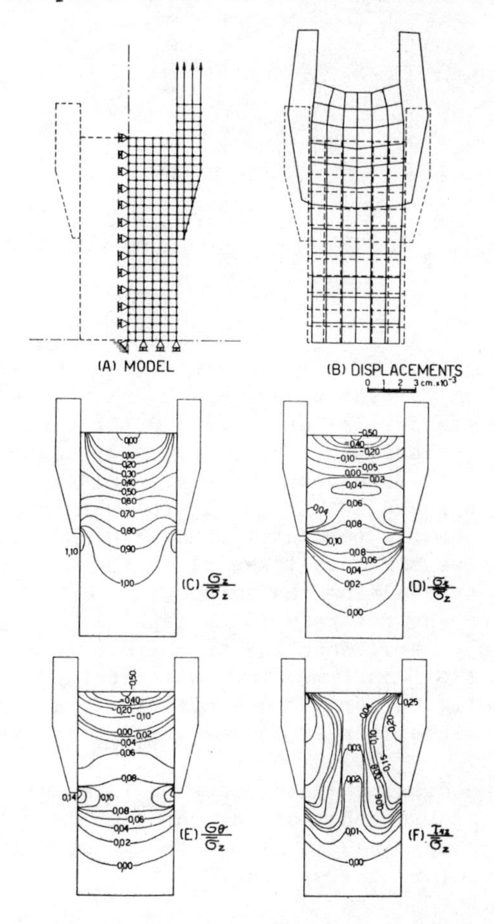

Figure 4 - Displacements and stresses in model 2

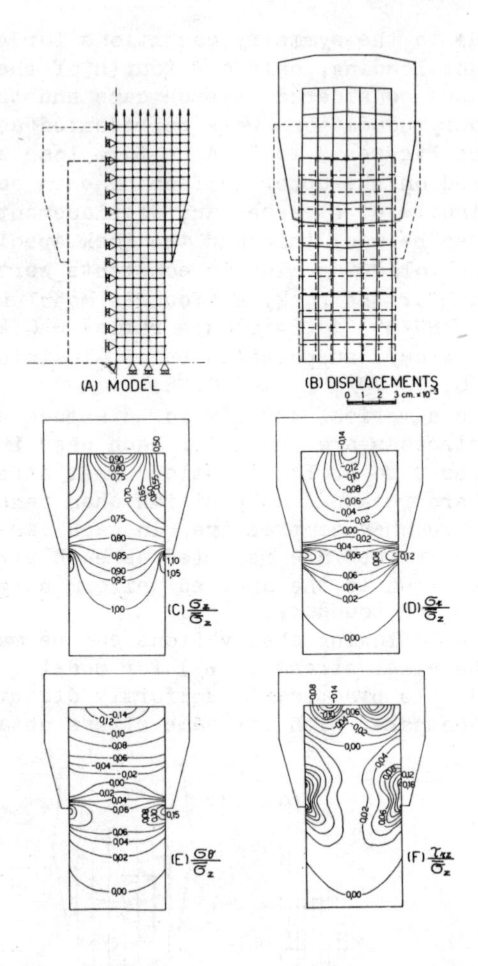

Figure 5 - Displacements and stresses in model 3

for model 2 (Figure 4) and 3 (Figure 5). The maximum percent change which one observes near the cap is less than 1.0 per cent.

b) Compressive radial (σ_r) and tangential (σ_ϑ) stresses occur more extensively for models 2 and 3 than for 1; furthermore, a considerable percental change in the value of these stresses takes place in both models when approaching the caps.

c) The shear stress in the specimen is approximately zero, when the cap of model 1 is used; this fact confirms, for this model, the prevalently uniform stress distribution and the negligible stress concentration near the caps.

d) The displacements observed in model 1 show a favorable behavior for this cap under load, if a comparison is made with the results obtained for models 2 and 3.

EXPERIMENTAL RESULTS

Laboratory tests were performed on various specimens of a Carrara marble, which exhibits ideal characteristics for isotropy and homogeneity. These tests allowed a check to be made of the numerical results reported above and the preference of cementing the cylindrical specimen through end faces (Barla and Goffi, 1973). Subsequently, a series of tests on two transversely isotropic rocks - a gneiss from Entracque (Val Gesso, Italy) and a serpentineous schist from Val Malenco, Italy, - was carried out.

Cylindrical specimens (diameter = 29.7 mm, height = 2.5 diameter) were drilled from squared blocks. These specimens were obtained so that different inclinations (angle α in Figure 6) of the plane of laminations could be considered (serpentineous schist: four specimens, for each α , at 15 degrees increment; gneiss: three specimens, for each α , at 15 degrees increment, except for $\alpha = 15$ and 75 degrees). The cylinders were thus cemented to model 1 caps, by using an epoxy resin with 23 MN/m^2 tensile strength.

The results for the tensile strength (T_o) of both rocks are reported in Figure 6 as a function of the angle α (the values shown are average values). In this Figure $(T_o)_\alpha$ is referred to $(T_o)_{90}$, which is the tensile strength for both rocks, when loaded parallel to the laminations (for the serpentineous schist: $(T_o)_{90} = 10$ MN/m^2; for the gneiss: $(T_o)_{90} = 7.3$ MN/m^2). Some specimens, in the way they appear after failure, are shown in Figure 7.

The measurements for the strains ε_1 (longitudinal) and ε_3 (transversal) present different problems if the rock deformability is to be derived:

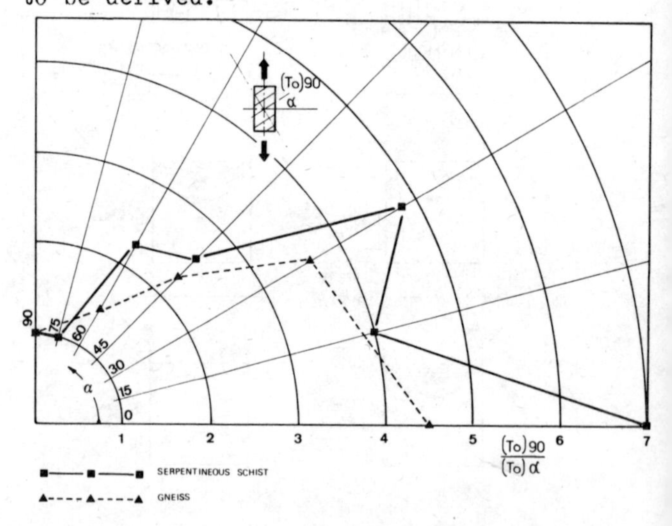

Figure 6 - Ratio of the tensile strengths $\frac{(T_o)_{90}}{(T_o)_\alpha}$ versus α .

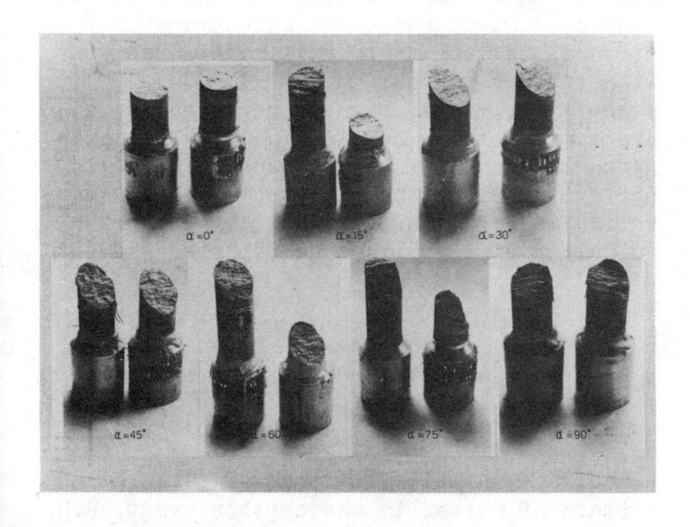

Figure 7 - A view of the specimens of serpentineous schist after testing

1) the transversal strain ε_3, measured for the gneiss specimens, exhibits the same sign of the corresponding longitudinal strain ε_1;
2) when the above phenomenon does not occur for the serpentineous schist, the values measured for the transversal strain ε_3, are very small, i.e. of the same order of magnitude of the instrument precision;
3) the limited number of tests carried out, consideration being given also to the dispersion of the experimental results, which is known to characterize the tensile strength of rock.

It is of interest to evaluate, for each specimen, the tangent modulus $\bar{E}_2$, in the loading direction, when the applied stress is equal to half the tensile strength. The results are reported for both rocks in Figures 8 and 9, where the ratio $E_1/\bar{E}_2$ is given (E_1 is the tangent elastic modulus measured in the direction of laminations).

If one assumes the rocks tested in the present work to behave as transversely isotropic, linearly elastic, and homogeneous media (Lekhnitskii, 1963), with 5 elastic constants (E_1, E_2 = elastic modulus; ν_1, ν_2 = Poisson's ratio; G_2 = independent shear modulus), the modulus $\bar{E}_2$ is

$$\bar{E}_2 = \frac{E_1}{\sin^4\alpha + \frac{E_1}{E_2}\cos^4\alpha\ \left(\frac{E_1}{G_2} - \nu_2\frac{E_1}{E_2}\right)\sin^2\alpha\cos^2\alpha}$$

The curves reported in Figures 8 and 9 are obtained by using the above relationship and by introducing different assumptions for

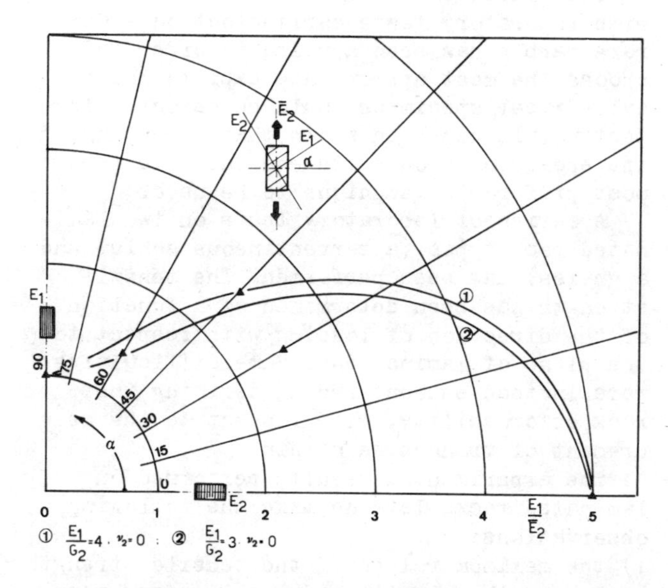

Figure 8 - Ratio of the elastic moduli $\frac{E_1}{\bar{E}_2}$ for gneiss versus α

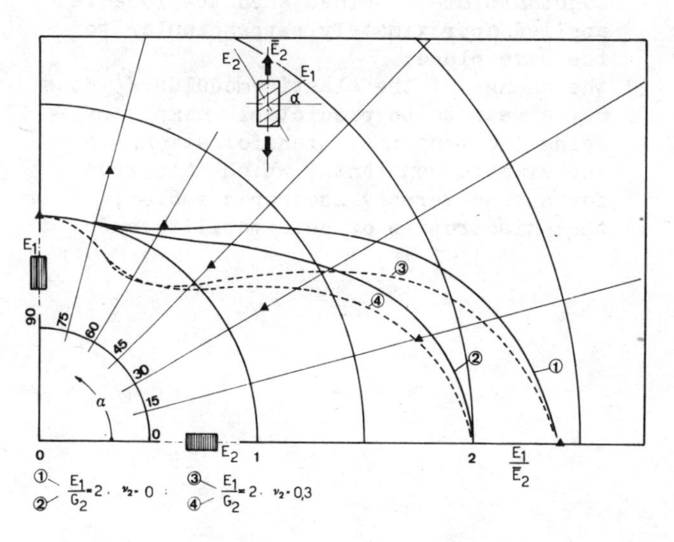

Figure 9 - Ratio of the elastic moduli $\frac{E_1}{\bar{E}_2}$ for serpentineous schist versus α

the values to be given to $\frac{E_1}{G_2}$ and ν_2.

CONCLUSIONS

The method used in the present work for the direct tensile testing of cylindrical rock specimens appears to be quite satisfactory. In particular, the problems of applying a perfectly uniaxial load and of attaching the specimen to the testing unit, without inducing unacceptable stress concentrations, have been considered.

The finite element method in conjunction with laboratory tests carried out on a Carrara marble has been applied in order to choose the most appropriate cap, to which cylindrical specimens could be cemented for testing. It has been shown that cementing the specimen through its end faces is the most preferable technique to be used.

A series of laboratory tests on two laminated rock types (a serpentineous schist and a gneiss) has been performed. The tensile strength has been determined as a function of the direction of loading with respect to the plane of laminations. Some difficulties were instead encountered in defining the rock deformability, with respect to the measurement of transverse strain.

The experimental results performed on laminated rocks let one make the following observations:

1) the maximum values of the tensile strength T_o and the elastic modulus $\bar{E}_2$ occur when the tensile load is applied parallel to the plane of laminations;
2) the minimum values for the above material constants are obtained when the load is applied approximately perpendicular to the same plane;
3) the change of the elastic modulus $\bar{E}_2$ does not appear to be predictable simply by using the tensorial transformations for the elastic constants, which hold true for a transversely isotropic medium;
4) the anisotropies of deformability and strength are shown to coincide for the gneiss; however this does not hold for the serpentineous schist, where the anisotropy of strength is seen to prevail considerably with respect to that of deformability;
5) the experimental results reported above are limited in number if a consideration is given to the difficulties generally met in performing direct tensile tests; this observation asks for further work to be carried out along similar lines as reported above.

REFERENCES

Barla, G. and Goffi, L. Prove di trazione diretta su roccia, Secondo Congresso Nazionale AIAS, Genova, 1973.

Brace, W.F. Brittle fracture of rocks in State of stress in the earth's crust, W.R. Judd (Ed.), New York, Elsevier, 1964, pp. 111-174.

Dubois, M. Experimental study of strain gauge high precision dynamometers at the O.N.E.R.A. Modane test centre, 1970.

Hawkes, I. and Mellor, M. Uniaxial testing in rock mechanics laboratories, Eng. Geol., 4, 1970, pp. 179-285.

Lekhnitskij, S.G. Theory of elasticity of an anisotropic elastic body, Holden-Day Inc., San Francisco, 1963.

Wilson, E.L. Structural analysis of axisymmetric solids, J.A.I.A.A., vol. 3, 1965, pp. 2269-2274.

MICROMÉCANISME DE DÉFORMATION PLASTIQUE D'UN SOLIDE MINÉRAL CRISTALLISÉ

PLASTIC DEFORMATION MICROPROCESS OF A MINERAL CRYSTALLIZED SOLID

MIKROPROZESS DER PLASTISCHEN VERFORMUNG EINES KRISTALLISIERTEN MINERALKÖRPERS

J. BERGUES
P. HABIB — Laboratoire de Mécanique des Solides, Ecole Polytechnique, Paris

M. CHAYE d'ALBISSIN — Laboratoire de Géologie Dynamique, Universite de Paris VI

J. DESPUJOLS
H. MOINEAU — Laboratoire d'Électronique et Rayons X, Reims

C. TOURENQ — Laboratoire Central des Ponts et Chaussées

France

RESUME. - Une étude utilisant différentes techniques d'analyses a été effectuée en vue de relier le comportement rhéologique d'un calcaire cristallin isotrope soumis à différents types de contraintes mécaniques aux divers micromécanismes de déformation des agrégats de cristaux de calcite.

Les résultats font apparaître l'importance du trajet de chargement sur le comportement de la roche au delà de la limite élastique. La déformation résulte de différents mécanismes qui se succèdent ou interviennent simultanément : maclage, mouvements intergranulaires, microfissuration, glissements intracristallins, torsion des cristaux et macrofissuration.

SUMMARY. - A study has been made with the different techniques of analysis in order to establish a relationship between the rheological behaviour of an isotropic crystalline limestone subjected to various types of mechanical stresses and different strain microprocesses of calcite crystal aggregates.

The results bring out the importance of the loading conditions for the rock behaviour beyond the elastic limit. The strain is the result of different successive or simultaneous processes : twinning, intergranular movements, microcracking, intercrystalline gliding, crystal torsion and macrocracking.

ZUSAMMENFASSUNG. - Eine verschiedene Analysentechnik benutzende Untersuchung wurde durchgeführt, um das rheologische Verhalten eines isotropen kristallinen Kalksteins unter verschiedenartigen mechanischen Spannungen mit verschiedenen Verformungs -Mikroprozessen von Kalzitkristall-Aggregaten zu verbinden.

Die Ergebnisse bringen zum Vorschein die Bedeutung der Belastungsbedingungen für das Verhalten des Gesteins über der Elastizitätsgrenze. Die Verformung ist auf verschiedene aufeinanderfolgende oder gleichzeitig verlaufende Prozesse zurückzuführen : Zwillingskristallausbildung, intergranulare Bewegungen, Mikrorissebildung, intrakristalline Gleitung, Torsion der Kristalle und Makrorissebildung.

Une étude a été effectuée en vue de relier le comportement rhéologique d'un calcaire cristallin isotrope soumis à différents types de contraintes mécaniques aux divers micromécanismes de déformation des agrégats de cristaux de calcite. Un marbre de Carrare a été sélectionné pour cette étude en fonction de sa pureté relative (99% de calcite), de son homogénéité, de la régularité de taille et de forme de ses cristaux, de son isotropie et de son absence de fissuration naturelle.

Une analyse détaillée de la microstructure des échantillons non déformés et déformés a été effectuée en faisant intervenir plusieurs techniques permettant une approche du phénomène de l'échelle du cristal à celle du réseau cristallin.

I - Conditions expérimentales

A) Essais mécaniques

Les essais ont été réalisés dans des cellules triaxiales avec des éprouvettes cylindriques équipées de jauges longitudinales et transversales.

Trois modes d'expérimentation ont été testés :

a) mise en charge de l'éprouvette sous une pression de confinement qui reste constante au cours de l'essai.

b) essai à chargement radial $\sigma_1/P = C^{te}$,

c) essai à déformation transversale nulle $\varepsilon_2 = \varepsilon_3 = 0$.

B) Examens au microscope optique

- Des surfaces polies parallèles aux génératrices des éprouvettes ont été photographiées avant et après déformation en des points repérés,
- Des sections axiales des éprouvettes ont été polies après déformation expérimentale puis imprégnées d'une résine epoxy chargée en colorant minéral qui se localise préférentiellement dans les fissures.

C) Examens au microscope électronique à balayage (MEB)

Nous avons observé quelques surfaces polies mais principalement des surfaces de rupture qui sont plus riches en information.

D) Examens aux Rayons X

Des examens ont été effectués avec un diffractomètre vertical Philips, équipé d'un compteur proportionnel et d'un dispositif d'avance pas à pas, d'intervalle 0,01°, en utilisant principalement la réflexion 10.4 des rayonnements K_α et K_β du cuivre.
Le broyage semblant influer sur W, largeur à mi-hauteur des pics de diffraction, les mesures ont été

effectuées sur des plaquettes découpées dans les éprouvettes suivant la direction perpendiculaire à σ_1.

Compte tenu de l'inhomogénéité des éprouvettes et des erreurs expérimentales, l'erreur sur les mesures de W a été chiffrée à 3/1000 de degré en 2 θ.

E) Irradiation et thermoluminescence (TL)

Des fragments provenant de la partie centrale de toutes les éprouvettes étudiées ont été réduits en grains de 250-315 μ. La courbe de TL naturelle a été enregistrée puis les mêmes échantillons ont été soumis à une irradiation γ de 3.10^5 rads et les courbes de TL artificielle enregistrées.

II - Données de l'expérimentation

A) Essais à confinement constant

1°) contraintes sphériques

Des éprouvettes ont été soumises à des pressions hydrostatiques. Jusqu'à 2000 MPa de confinement, aucune variation de structure n'a été observée aussi bien au microscope par réflexion qu'aux Rayons X.

2°) contraintes cylindriques

L'essai s'effectue en deux temps :
- mise en charge hydrostatique jusqu'à la pression de confinement désirée : $\sigma_1 = \sigma_2 = \sigma_3 = P$,
- mise en charge axiale en maintenant constante la pression latérale $\sigma_1 > P$ = constante.

Le matériau a été testé au voisinage de la limite élastique, dans le domaine plastique et à la rupture.

a) comportement au voisinage de la limite élastique

La limite élastique est définie comme étant l'état de contrainte pour lequel il n'y a plus linéarité des courbes "effort-déformation" ; ce seuil élastique est donc le point où les premiers désordres apparaissent, ces désordres pouvant être essentiellement une microfissuration ou une déformation plastique de l'agrégat cristallin.

Des courbes ont été tracées pour l'essai en compression simple, en portant séparément les valeurs de la limite élastique données par les jauges longitudinales σ_{1L} et les jauges transversales σ_{1T} en fonction du déviateur. Ces courbes montrent l'existence de deux limites élastiques bien distinctes, correspondant aux deux directions de mesure. Cette dualité (Morlier, 1971) qui est habituellement caractéristique des matériaux fragiles est encore observable pour les échantillons déformés sous une pression de confinement constante de 10 MPa. Au delà de cette valeur, les deux limites sont confondues.

D'une façon générale, on interprète l'existence de ces deux limites par l'apparition de microfissures se propageant dans la direction de la contrainte maximale.

Une observation au microscope par réflexion des surfaces polies d'échantillons non déformés, puis des mêmes échantillons déformés au-dessous de la limite élastique montre qu'entre 50 et 90% de la limite élastique apparaissent quelques macles très fines affectant une faible proportion des grains (moins de 10%). Ces macles ne modifient pas les comportements élastiques du matériau et ne sont pas décelables sur les courbes "efforts-déformations" avec le matériel d'enregistrement dont nous disposions. Au voisinage de la limite élastique, les macles se multiplient, certains joints de grains s'ouvrent alors que d'autres demeurent presque invisibles.

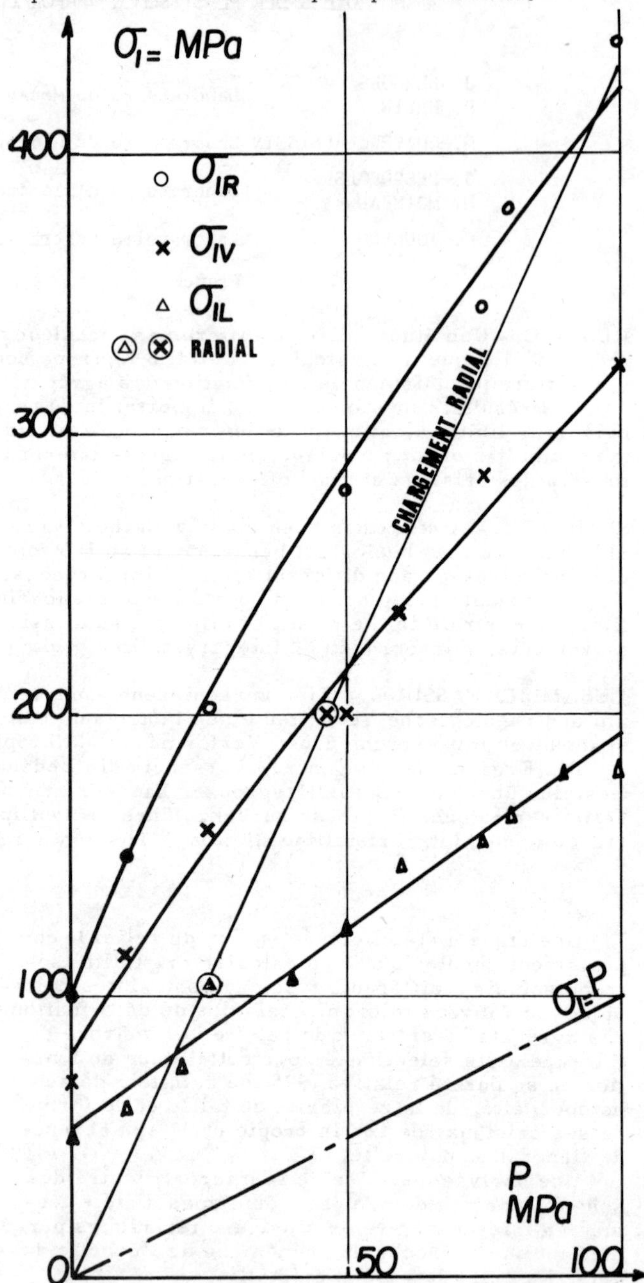

Fig. 1 : Représentation des résultats expérimentaux dans le plan $\sigma_1 = f[P]$ (P=pression de confinement).

b) comportement au voisinage de la rupture

Les résultats des essais sont mentionnés sur la figure 1 où nous avons porté :

σ_{1R} = contrainte maximum à la rupture

σ_{1V} = contrainte majeure pour laquelle la dérivée des courbes $\sigma_1 = f[\Delta V/V]$ tend vers l'infini avec $\Delta V/V = \epsilon_1 + 2\epsilon_2$ défini à partir des courbes "efforts-déformations".

La comparaison des courbes montre que l'écart

entre ces deux valeurs croît avec la pression latérale, ce qui met en évidence le caractère fragile du matériau aux basses pressions de confinement. Au cours de ces essais, le volume des éprouvettes diminue puis augmente.

σ_{1V} peut être interprété comme étant l'état de contrainte pour lequel il se produit un début de foisonnement, c'est-à-dire qu'au delà de cette valeur, le coefficient de Poisson correspondant à la tangente à la courbe $f[\Delta V/V]$ devient supérieur à 0,5.

c) domaine de la déformation plastique

Des séries d'échantillons ont été étudiées en faisant varier successivement le taux de déformation, la pression de confinement et la vitesse de déformation.

1 - influence du taux de déformation

α) Des observations ont été effectuées sur les éprouvettes ayant été déformées jusqu'à la rupture.

L'examen à l'œil nu et au microscope optique des sections axiales de ces éprouvettes polies après déformation puis imprégnées de colorant montre qu'il se produit au contact des plateaux de la presse des cônes résultant d'un phénomène de frettage (fig. 2). Ces cônes sont dépourvus de fissures alors que le reste de l'éprouvette présente un abondant réseau de fissures verticales intergranulaires et intracristallines. La densité des fissures augmente proportionnellement à la pression de confinement et inversement proportionnellement à la distance à la zone de rupture.

Le foisonnement observé correspond, d'une part à l'ouverture de fissures produites au delà de la limite élastique, d'autre part à la création de nouvelles fissures au cours du chargement (fig. 3).

Il n'a pas été possible d'observer avec ces échantillons les glissements intracristallins qui sont susceptibles de se produire dans les échantillons soumis à une déformation plastique et laissent peu de traces visibles au microscope. Cependant, on sait que ces glissements sont accompagnés par la formation de défauts de structure du réseau cristallin (Handin et al., 1957). Au cours d'une irradiation X ou γ, ces défauts favorisent la création de centres colorés. Il résulte de ceci qu'un tel échantillon, soumis à un rayonnement X ou γ, prend une teinte bleue prononcée et qu'il apparait, sur les courbes de TL de l'échantillon un pic inconnu dans les roches non affectées par de tels glissements. Nous avons observé de tels changements de couleur et des modifications de forme des courbes de TL dans les échantillons de cette série soumis à des pressions de confinement de 50, 75 et 100 MPa.

Une étude aux Rayons X de la même série d'échantillons a montré l'existence d'une relation linéaire entre W (largeur à mi-hauteur des pics de diffraction) et la déformation totale (ε totale).

β) Des observations ont été effectuées sur une deuxième série d'éprouvettes soumises à différentes pressions de confinement, avec un déviateur égal à environ 80% de celui déterminant la rupture. Il s'agissait donc d'éprouvettes ayant été chargées légèrement au-dessus de la limite de foisonnement. Les valeurs de σ_{1V} correspondant à cette série d'essais ont été portées sur la figure 1. On peut noter une bonne corrélation de ces valeurs avec les résultats de la précédente série d'essais.

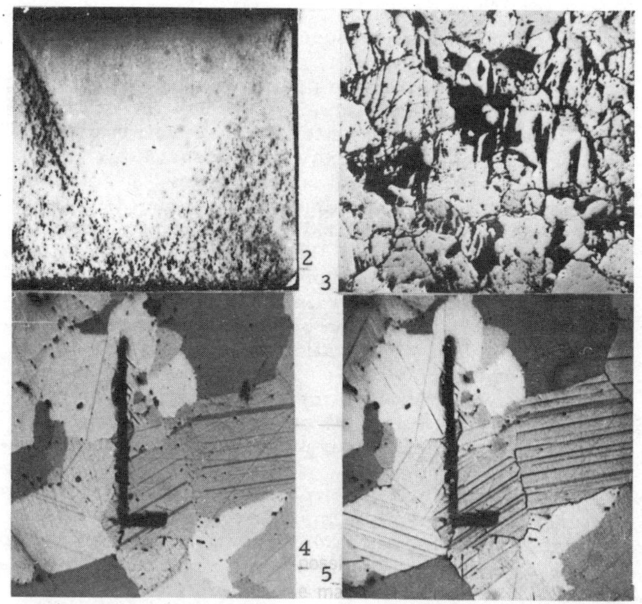

Fig. 2 : Eprouvette déformée jusqu'à rupture (P= 10 MPa) sciée suivant un plan diamétral montrant le cône non fissuré résultant du frettage.

Fig. 3 : Eprouvette déformée jusqu'à rupture (P= 80 MPa); surface polie après déformation montrant le foisonnement (LN x 35).

Fig. 4 : Eprouvette polie : structure avant déformation (LP x 50).

Fig. 5 : Même zone de l'éprouvette polie de la fig. 4 déformée (P = 25 MPa) (LP x 50).

Fig. 6 : Surface de rupture avant déformation ; cristal maclé (MEB x 300).

Fig. 7 : Surface de rupture d'une éprouvette déformée (P = 100 MPa) ; structure en feuillets liée au maclage (MEB x 1500).

Fig. 8 : Eprouvette polie puis déformée (P=100 MPa), surface modifiée par des mouvements intergranulaires (MEB x 1000).

Fig. 9 : Eprouvette déformée jusqu'à rupture (P = 80 MPa) ; surface polie montrant des cristaux maclés et tordus (LP x 430).

L'examen des surfaces axiales polies après déformation, puis imprégnées de colorant montre que, dans ces éprouvettes, la pénétration du colorant est faible, la distinction entre la zone frettée et la zone non frettée est moins nette et l'observation des fissures n'est possible qu'au microscope.

Sur les surfaces polies, on observe au microscope avant déformation quelques macles (fig. 4). Après déformation apparaissent de nombreuses macles (fig. 5). Certaines d'entre elles qui étaient interrompues au milieu d'un grain se trouvent prolongées jusqu'au joint de grain.

Au MEB, alors qu'on observe sur les surfaces de rupture avant déformation une mosaïque de cristaux présentant quelques rares macles (fig. 6), on constate après déformation une multiplication des macles donnant à la surface des cristaux un modelé en forme de gradins pouvant aller jusqu'à un véritable feuilletage (fig. 7).

Ce maclage est accompagné par des mouvements intergranulaires qui se manifestent clairement. La surface des éprouvettes devient rugueuse. Au microscope optique certains cristaux ne réfléchissent plus la lumière. On note des ruptures intracristallines suivant des plans de clivage facile. Certains cristaux sont tordus (fig. 8). Au MEB on perçoit nettement la différence de niveau existant d'un cristal à l'autre (fig. 9).

Les examens par TL et irradiation montrent que des glissements intracristallins se sont produits dans les échantillons soumis à des confinements de 80 et 100 MPa.

Les mesures effectuées aux Rayons X mettent en évidence une relation linéaire entre W et la déformation totale (ϵ totale) (fig. 10).

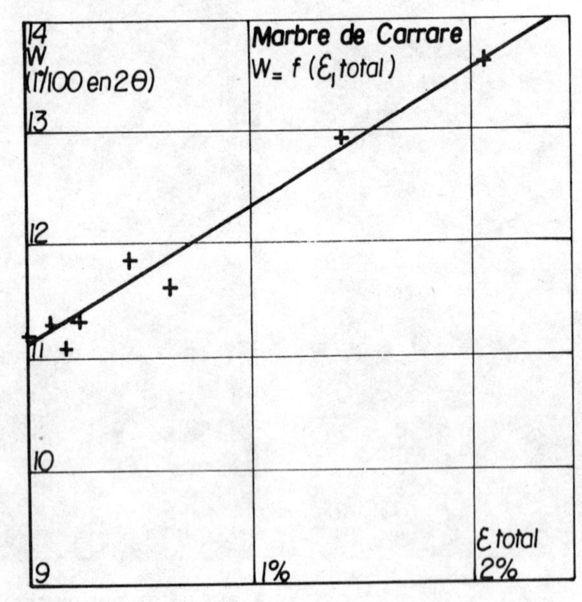

Fig. 10 : Variation de W en fonction de la déformation totale ϵ.

2 - influence du confinement

Pour un taux de déformation constant, on observe une nette influence de la pression de confinement sur le maclage :

	confinement en MPa			
	25	50	75	100
grains intacts %	44	48	53	79
grains très maclés %	56	52	47	21

L'augmentation de la contrainte latérale semble donc limiter nettement les possibilités de maclage des cristaux.

3 - influence de la vitesse de déformation pour une pression de confinement de 100 MPa

Des essais donnant une déformation de 1% en 1 minute et 1% en 100 minutes montrent qu'une déformation plus rapide entraine un maclage plus intense et des mouvements intergranulaires plus importants. De nombreux cristaux ne réfléchissent plus la lumière , ce qui correspond à une légère rotation.

B) Essais à chargement radial

La mise en charge de l'éprouvette a été réalisée en maintenant le rapport σ_1/P constant.

Le rapport des contraintes utilisé $\sigma_1/P = 4,3$ ne nous a pas permis d'atteindre la rupture de l'échantillon avec le matériel dont nous disposions. De cet essai, nous avons tiré les caractéristiques mécaniques suivantes.

Dans la partie linéaire des courbes $\epsilon = f(\sigma)$:

$E = 81\,000$ MPa, $\nu = 0,33$

La limite élastique est obtenue pour :

$\sigma_1 = 110$ MPa, $P = 26$ MPa

Ces dernières caractéristiques se recoupent bien avec les résultats déjà mentionnés ; on peut donc dire que le trajet de chargement n'a aucune influence sur les caractéristiques élastiques du matériau.

Des courbes ont été tracées de façon à comparer la variation de ϵ_1 en fonction de σ_1 dans le cas des essais à chargement radial et dans celui des essais à confinement constant, en déduisant de ces derniers les valeurs des déformations pour des états de contrainte donnés du chargement radial (fig. 11).

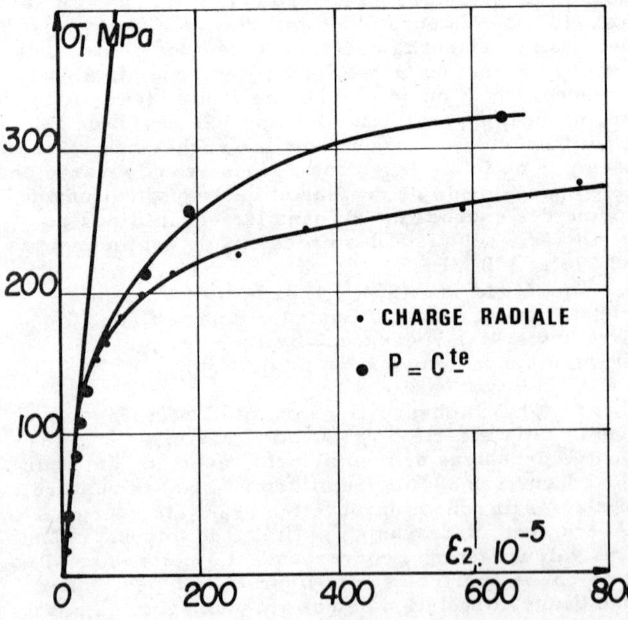

Fig. 11 : Courbes "efforts-déformations" $\sigma_1 = f(\epsilon_2)$

Nous pouvons remarquer, à partir de ces courbes que, dans le domaine non linéaire, le comportement rhéologique est différent suivant le trajet de chargement, surtout à partir du foisonnement qui, ici, est atteint pour l'état de contrainte suivant :

$$\sigma_{1V} = 2000 \text{ MPa}, \quad P_V = 220 \text{ MPa}$$

A la dispersion près, ces valeurs concordent bien avec celles trouvées au cours des essais menés jusqu'à la rupture des éprouvettes.

Au delà de cet état de contrainte, le foisonnement est beaucoup plus important. Ceci est bien mis en évidence en portant sur le même graphique les courbes $\sigma_1 = f[\Delta V/V]$ dans le cas d'un chargement radial et dans celui d'essais sous pression de confinement constante (fig. 12).

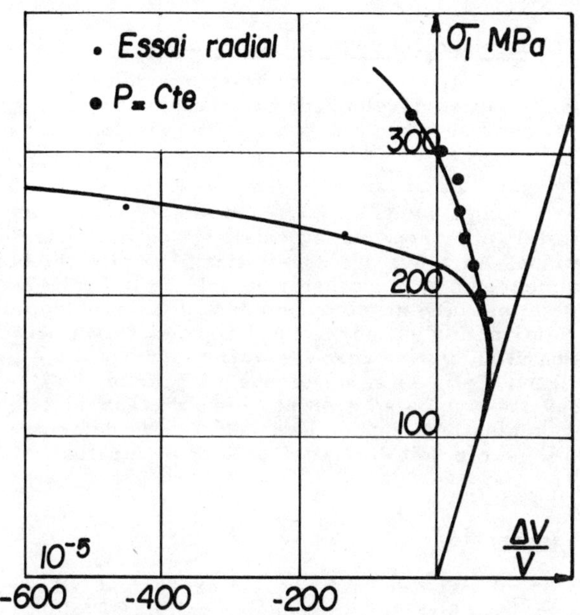

Fig. 12 : Courbe de variation de volume $\sigma_1 = f[\Delta V/V]$

C) Essai à déformation transversale nulle

Un essai a été réalisé jusqu'à une pression de confinement de 100 MPa en maintenant la déformation transversale nulle $\varepsilon_2 = \varepsilon_3 = 0$.

Les équations de l'élasticité nous permettent d'écrire : $P = \nu(\sigma_1 + P)$.

La courbe représentative de $P = f(\sigma_1 + P)$ (fig. 13) présente une rupture de pente pour :

$$\sigma_1 = 124 \text{ MPa}, \quad P = 50 \text{ MPa}$$

valeurs qui correspondent bien à la limite élastique de la figure 1.

Par ailleurs, la courbe représentative de $\sigma_1 = f(\varepsilon_1)$ (fig. 14) indique un franchissement de la limite élastique pour le même état de contrainte.

Il est intéressant de noter, de plus, qu'à partir d'un certain état de contrainte, les déformations longitudinales restent constantes.

Le module élastique déduit de la partie linéaire de la figure 14 est de 84 500 MPa, ce qui est conforme aux résultats précédemment obtenus.

De la figure 13 peuvent être déduits deux coefficients de Poisson :

$\nu_1 = 0,32$ (valeur trouvée au cours des 1° essais conduits jusqu'à la rupture).

$\nu_2 = 0,50$

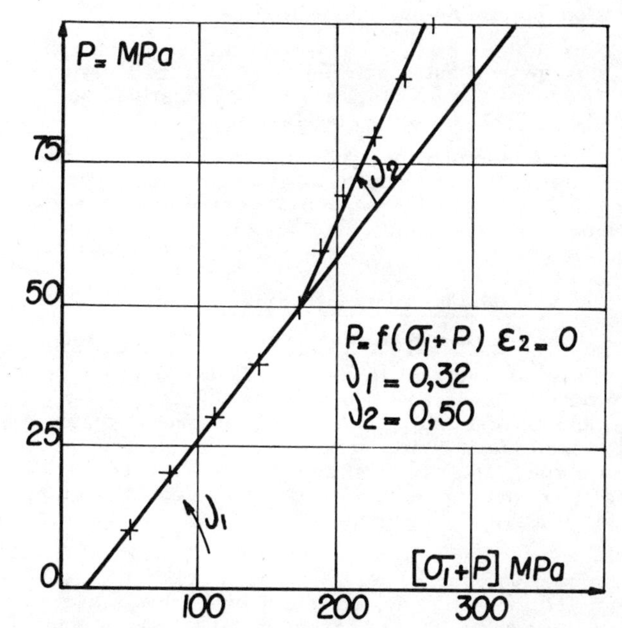

Fig. 13 : Chargement avec $\varepsilon_2 = 0$, $P = f[\sigma_1 + P]$

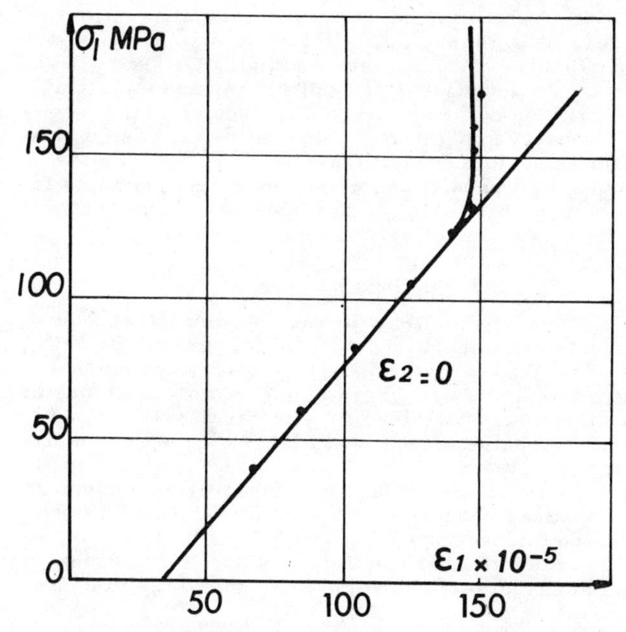

Fig. 14 : Chargement avec $\varepsilon_2 = 0$, $\sigma_1 = f(\varepsilon_1)$

Ces valeurs ne peuvent s'expliquer que par un franchissement du domaine élastique et une fissuration. En effet, l'augmentation de σ_1 entraîne une ouverture des fissures qui se referment sous l'effet de la pression de confinement.

Aux Rayons X, aucun élargissement des raies de diffraction n'a été observé, ce qui confirme l'existence d'un lien entre largeur de raies et déformation.

III - Discussion et interprétation des résultats

De l'ensemble des recherches effectuées ressortent un certain nombre de faits.

- Dans le domaine des essaismécaniques : le trajet de chargement est sans effet sur la limite élastique mais affecte les mécanismes de déformations se situant au delà de la limite élastique.

- Pour la déformation à l'échelle du cristal et à celle de l'agrégat polycristallin on constate l'intervention de plusieurs mécanismes qui sont différemment influencés par les conditions dans lesquelles sont effectués les essais.

A) Les déformations intracristallines

1°) maclage et glissement intracristallin

- le maclage suivant le plan {10. 2} débute avant la limite élastique et se poursuit jusqu'à ce que l'ensemble des cristaux soit maclé. Il se produit d'autant plus facilement que la pression de confinement est peu élevée. Pour un confinement donné, il est favorisé par une augmentation du taux de déformation et de la vitesse de chargement.

- lorsque l'échantillon a atteint un certain taux de déformation pour lequel la plupart des cristaux sont complètement maclés, ceux-ci peuvent continuer à se déformer par glissement par translation suivant le plan {10. 1} (Turner et al., 1954). La mise en mouvement de ces glissements qui suppose une multiplication et une mise en mouvement des dislocations affectant le réseau cristallin ne semble pas pouvoir se produire en compression simple. On l'observe à partir d'un confinement de 50 MPa dans la série d'échantillons déformés jusqu'à la rupture alors qu'on ne l'observe qu'à partir d'un confinement de 80 MPa dans la série d'échantillons déformés à 80% de la rupture. Il parait donc exister une relation entre le taux de déformation, la pression de confinement et l'apparition des glissements intracristallins.

2°) déformations du réseau

A ces déformations intracristallines sont associées des déformations du réseau, décelables aux Rayons X ; les distorsions angulaires, responsables de l'astérisme des diagrammes de monocristaux, ne sont pas enregistrables dans le cas des polycristaux pour lesquels la forme et la largeur des pics de diffraction dépendent :
- de la taille des domaines diffusant le rayonnement de manière cohérente, qui peut être reliée à la densité de dislocations,
- de la déformation élastique résiduelle du réseau cristallin qui est une variation locale de la distance réticulaire,
- de la présence de fautes d'empilement.

Paterson (1959) et Gross (1965) ont reconnu la quasi impossibilité de séparer de façon formelle les trois effets indiqués plus haut ; ils ont cependant déduit de leurs expériences, menées avec des échantillons de marbre et de calcaire de Solenhofen très déformés, que l'effet de déformation élastique était prédominant.

Dans le cas présent, nous avons pu vérifier que la largeur des raies était une fonction linéaire de la déformation totale ; la pente de la droite de la figure 10, extrapolée, conduirait à des largeurs voisines de celles observées par Paterson et Gross ; l'élargissement des pics parait en première approximation indépendant du mode de déformation de l'échantillon.

3°) ruptures intracristallines

Dans les échantillons très déformés apparaissent au sein des cristaux des ruptures qui empruntent souvent les plans de clivage facile de la calcite. Lorsqu'on atteint la limite de foisonnement, on assiste à une multiplication de ces ruptures et à une destruction de plus en plus avancée du réseau cristallin.

B) Les mouvements intergranulaires

Parallèlement au maclage se produisent des mouvements intergranulaires qui, à pression de confinement constante, sont favorisés par une augmentation du taux de déformation et de la vitesse de chargement.

C) Les décollements intergranulaires

Ceux-ci apparaissent au voisinage de la limite élastique et se développent au delà de cette limite. Ils peuvent servir d'amorce à la fissuration.

D) La fissuration

En compression simple, une microfissuration parallèle à σ_1 apparait au voisinage de la limite élastique. Au cours des essais triaxiaux elle semble commencer à se manifester au delà de la limite élastique et est bien développée à 80% de la rupture, taux de déformation qui correspond approximativement à l'apparition d'une macrofissuration perceptible à l'œil nu. Celle-ci se développe à l'échelle de l'éprouvette jusqu'à sa rupture. Pour un taux de déformation plastique donné, l'essentiel de la déformation mesurée doit être attribué à la fissuration.

Bibliographie

GROSS, K.A., 1965, X ray line broadening and stored energy in deformed and annealed calcite, Philos. Mag., G.B., vol. 12, pp. 801-813.

HANDIN, J., HIGGS, D.V., LEWIS, D.R. and WEYL, P.K., 1957, Effects of gamma radiation on the experimental deformation of calcite and certain rocks, Bull. Geol. Soc. Amer., vol. 88, pp. 1203-1224.

MORLIER, P., 1971, Sur le comportement des roches fragiles avant la rupture, Symposium Soc. Intern. Mécanique des Roches, Nancy.

PATERSON, M.J., 1959, X ray line broadening in plastically deformed calcite. Philos. Mag., G.B., vol. 4, pp. 451-466.

TURNER, F.J., GRIGGS, D.T. and HEARD, H., 1954, Experimental deformation of calcite crystals, Bull. Geol. Soc. Amer., vol. 61, p. 1512.

THE INFLUENCE OF FABRIC ON THE DEFORMABILITY OF ANISOTROPIC ROCKS

L'INFLUENCE DE LA STRUCTURE SUR LA DÉFORMABILITÉ DES ROCHES ANISOTROPES

DER EINFLUSS DES GEFÜGES AUF DAS VERFORMUNGSVERHALTEN DER ANISOTROPISCHEN FELSEN

P. BERRY Research Associate, Institute om Mining, University of Rome , Italy
G. CREA Italian Bureau of Mines, National Hydrocarbons Division, Rome
D. MARTINO Italian Bureau of Mines, National Hydrocarbons Division, Rome
R. RIBACCHI Professor of Rock Mechanics, Institute of Mining, Univ. of Rome

SUMMARY The characteristics of the anisotropy of rocks - both metamorphic and sedimentary - under condition of uniaxial and triaxial compression are discussed here. The anisotropy of the rock materials is due, essentially, to the characteristics and distribution of the existing cracks in the rock, and only subordinately to the orientation of the minerals of which it is composed. The effect of open and closed cracks in rock deformation and the influence of progressive closing of the cracks are examined, evidencing the "non-linear" stress-strain behaviour of the strongly anisotropic rocks. In fact, the anisotropy ratio is found to be strongly dependent on the applied stress and the variation of elastic constants with the orientation of the sample is quite different from that foreseen by the theory of elasticity. Finally, the necessity of analysing deformation measurements with statistical methods in determining "elastic constants" is stressed and derivant problems are discussed.

RESUME On a étudié les caractéristiques d' anisotropie de plusieurs roches. Cette anisotropie est lié essentiellement aux caractéristiques des microfissures presentes dans la roche et seulement subordonnément à l' orientation des minerais composants. On discute le rôle des microfissures "ouvertes" et "serrées" sur les caractéristiques de déformabilité et l' influence de la serrure progressive des microfissures mêmes, qui détermine un comportement nettement "non-linéare" des roches plus fortement anisotropes. Un tel comportement "non-linéare" se manifeste soit avec une sensible variation du rapport d' anisotropie avec la contrainte appliée, soit avec une loi de variation des constants élastiques avec l' orientation des échantillons différent de celle qui prévoit la théorie de l' élasticité.

ZUSAMMENFASSUNG In diesem Text sind die anisotropischen Kennzeichen einiger Felsen behandelt worden. Diese Anisotropie ist tiefst mit den Merkmalen der in den Felsen vorhandenen Mikrospaltungen verbunden und nur in niedrigerem Masse mit dem Gefuege der die Felsen bildenden Mineralien. Man illustriert auch die Rolle der offenen und der geschlossenen Mikrospalten, sowie den Einfluss des progressiven Verschusses der Mikrospalten. Daraus ergibt sich ein "unlineares" Verhalten der staerker anisotropischen Felsen. In der Tat erscheint das Anisotrop-Verhaeltnis tief von der gegebenen Spannung beeinflusst; ausserdem ist die Abhaengigkeit der Elastizitaetsmodulen von der Orientierung des Probestabs anders als die aufgrund der Elastizitätstheorie vorhergesehenen.

INTRODUCTION

In problems of rock mechanics an isotropic behaviour is often assumed, whereas experience has proved that many rocks have anisotropic characteristics and moreover such anisotropy is often connected with a strongly non-linear behaviour. In the present study, the structural factors at the root of such behaviour are examined and some typical deformability patterns of methamorphic and sedimentary rock are presented.

THEORETICAL CONSIDERATIONS

The anisotropy of a rock is caused by a non-statistically isotropic orientation (in a broad sense, symmetry) of one or more of the following structural elements:

(i) the crystal lattices of the component minerals;
(ii) non-equidimensional voids, particularly open or closed microfissures;
(iii) non-equidimensional grains or crystal (taking only their form into account).

In comparison with the former two, it is to be noted that this latter type of structural elements, in the case of rocks, has a negligible influence on anisotropy. In the majority of cases a more or less close connection is observed between the orientation of the three types of structural elements. Accordingly, the third type, immediately apparent, can provide a guide-line for the study of the anisotropy of the rock, although, essentially, such anisotropy depends on the first two types. A typical example is the case of the schistose rocks.

As for crystal lattice orientation, a study of petrostructural literature shows a prevalence of monoclinic or triclinic symmetries. Even in these cases it is often reasonable to assume axial symmetry transversal isotropy) or orthorombic symmetry (orthotropy), purposely overlooking the contribution of less important structural elements. In this way the number of the "elastic constants" of the rock can be considerably reduced and anyway the approximations thus introduced can prove of little relevance in comparison to those caused by non-linear behaviour of the rock.

In the hypothesis that only crystal lattice orientation is relevant, the elastic properties of a rock can be calculated using various averaging techniques.

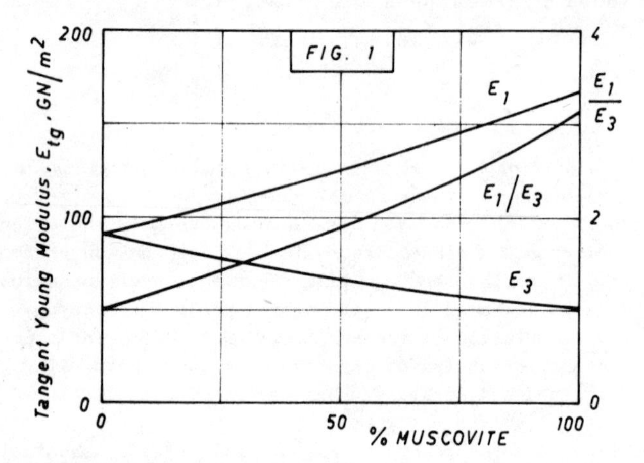

For instance, Figure 1 shows the elastic characteristics as calculated theoretically in a micaschist with a perfect orientation of the crystal lattices in the phillosilicate levels (muscovite) but with a statistically isotropic orientation in the quartz levels.

Results would vary little in the presence of feldspar. Such averaging techniques have proved quite satisfactory in conditions of high isotropic stress (Brace, 1965). However within the range of stress of primary interest to mining and civil engineering (e.o. 0 - 50 MN/m^2) the values portrayed in Figure 1 overestimate the values of the moduli and the ratio of anisotropy E_1/E_3. This is due to the considerable influence of the voids and cracks in the rocks.

Crack effect on deformability of isotropic rocks had been analytically evaluated by Walsh (1965a, 1965b) and by Brady (1969). Making use of the same techniques as the aforementioned authors, it is possible to evaluate the anisotropy of deformability caused by a system of cracks having the same orientation.

In an uniaxial test on a sample in which the crack group lies at an angle θ to the base of the cylindrical sample (Figure 2), we can affirm :

$$\frac{d\varepsilon_a}{d\sigma} = \frac{1}{E} = \frac{1}{E^*} + \frac{1}{E^*}\left(4\pi n b^3 \cos^2\theta\right)$$

$$\frac{d\varepsilon'_t}{d\sigma} = \frac{\nu'}{E} = \frac{\nu^*}{E^*}, \quad \frac{d\varepsilon''_t}{d\sigma} = \frac{\nu''}{E} = \frac{\nu^*}{E^*} \tag{1}$$

the elastic characteristics of the solid matrix being indicated by *, while b refers to the half length of the cracks and n to their density.

While the cracks remain open, the material has a linearly elastic behaviour, hence, the stress-strain curve is reversible and the superposition principle can be applied in the case of triaxial stresses. The relation between Young's moduli and the inclination of the crack system is shown in Figure 3.

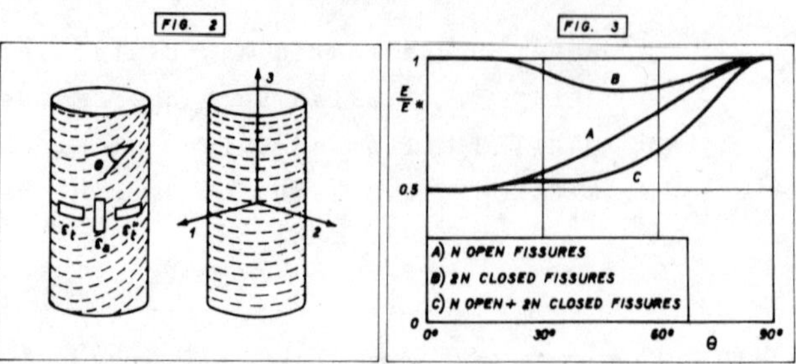

The cracked material has a transversely isotropic behaviour with the following elastic characteristics:

$$\frac{1}{E_1} = \frac{1}{E^*}, \quad \frac{1}{E_3} = \frac{1}{E^*} + \frac{1}{E^*}\left(4\pi n b^3 \cos^2\theta\right)$$

$$\frac{\nu_{12}}{E_1} = \frac{\nu_{31}}{E_3} = \frac{\nu^*}{E^*} \tag{2}$$

$$\frac{1}{G_{13}} = \frac{1}{E_1} + \frac{1}{E_3} + \frac{2\nu_{31}}{E_3}$$

It is, therefore, a particular type of transversal isotropy, characterised by only 3 independent elastic constants (instead of 5 in the general case).

When a system of closed cracks is present, if σ_3/σ_1 denotes the ratio between the confining and the major principal stresses and φ is the friction angle on the crack surfaces, the result is:

$$\frac{1}{E} = \frac{1}{E^*} + \frac{1}{E^*}\left\{4\pi n b^3 \frac{\sin 2\theta}{2}\left[\left(1 - \frac{\sigma_3}{\sigma_1}\right)\frac{\sin 2\theta}{2} - tg\,\varphi\left(\cos^2\theta + \frac{\sigma_3}{\sigma_1}\right)\right]\right\}$$

$$\frac{\nu'}{E} = \frac{\nu^*}{E^*}, \quad \frac{\nu''}{E} = \frac{\nu^*}{E^*} + \left(\frac{1}{E^*} - \frac{1}{E}\right) \tag{3}$$

which are valid if:

$$\frac{\left(1 - \sigma_3/\sigma_1\right)\sin 2\theta}{2\left(\sigma_3/\sigma_1 + \cos^2\theta\right)} > tg\,\varphi \tag{4}$$

otherwise, the elastic constants of the body are the same of the solid matrix.

Figure 3 (curve B) denotes the relation between Young's moduli and the inclination of cracks system in uniaxial compression. It is apparent that closed cracks are considerably less effective than open ones in the reduction of the elastic modulus of the rock and that their effect is only evident when the samples are angled with relation to crack planes.

The relation between Young's moduli and the crack system orientation does not correspond to that of a linear anisotropic material, no matter how the elastic constants are selected; this is due to the non linearity introduced by frictional sliding at the crack surfaces.

Only by way of preliminary approximation we can assume:

$$\frac{1}{E_1} = \frac{1}{E_3} = \frac{1}{E^*}$$

$$\frac{\nu_{12}}{E_1} = \frac{\nu_{31}}{E_3} = \frac{\nu^*}{E^*} \qquad (5)$$

$$\frac{1}{G_{13}} \simeq \frac{1}{G^*_{13}} + \frac{1}{E^*}\left[4\pi n b^3\left(1-\frac{\sigma_3}{\sigma_1}\right) - \left(1+\frac{2\sigma_3}{\sigma_1}\right)\operatorname{tg}\varphi\right]$$

The expression of the shear modulus indicates that it strongly depends on the value at the confining stress σ_3. In particular, it would be far lower in conditions of pure shear alone and would increase as the confining stress until reaching the value corresponding to the solid matrix.

Because both open and closed cracks are present in the rock, its total deformation is made up of the sum of the uncracked solid deformation plus the open and closed cracks deformations (Figure 3, curve C). Also in this case, therefore, the behaviour of the material will not correspond exactly with that of a classical anisotropic body.

Another important factor causing non linearity in rock materials is the gradual complete closure of initially open cracks. In uniaxial compression, such closure occurs under stress corresponding to:

$$\sigma_1^{(cl)} \simeq 2\alpha E/\cos^2\theta \qquad (6)$$

where α stands for the initial ratio between the width and length of the cracks. Beyond this critical value, rock deformability may be calculated by equations (3) valid for a body with closed cracks. In hydrostatic loading, closing takes place at the following stress:

$$\sigma_{hydr}^{(cl)} \simeq 2\alpha E \qquad (7)$$

Should differential stress be applied subsequently the deformability can be calculated by equations similar to (3), substituting the term σ_3/σ_1 with $\sigma_3 - \sigma_{hydr}^{(cl)}/\sigma_1 - \sigma_{hydr}^{(cl)}$.

It is to be noted that the following approximations are assumed to arrive at the equations (1) to (7). In the first place it is assumed that the uncracked solid has an isotropic behaviour - which may appear uncorrect given that we are dealing with anisotropic rocks. In many cases, however, as will be shown later, such an hypothesis is quite sound, inasmuch as the anisotropy is essentially due to the cracks and not to the matrix properties. A further hypothesis is that the cracks have equal form, dimension and orientation; this is certainly not verified in reality, but the actual deformation may be evaluated as the sum of the deformations deriving from each type of crack. And finally we assume that the crack density is so low as not to cause significant interferences between the state of stress and deformation caused by each separate crack. This is undoubtedly true in the cases studied by Walsh and Brace but in many anisotropic rocks the crack density is very high; as a result the equations (1) - (3) are only an approximation and likely underestimate the true deformability of the rock.

EXPERIMENTAL RESULTS

The tests were carried on five rock types:

A) Fine-grained gneiss ("beola") of the Western Alps composed by about 12% micas, 44% quartz and 44% feldspar;

B) Medium-grained gneiss ("serizzo") of the Western Alps composed by 10% micas, 75% feldspar and 15% quartz;

C) Phillitic micaschist from the Central Alps composed of about 50% micas, 40% quartz and 10% feldspar;

D) Miocenic sandstone from Calabria with calcitic cement;

E) Ignimbrite ("Viterbo Peperino") from the Northern Lazio composed of vitreous material having a markedly fluidal structure in which fragments of minerals and scorias are included.

With the exception of rock C), the samples for testing were drilled from a single block. In the case of phillitic micaschist the samples were taken from boreholes with varying orientations - a fact that accounts for the greater dispersion of the results obtained in this rock.

The fine-grained gneiss ("beola") was decidedly orthotropic, but only the results relative to the principal plane containing the two axes of deformability, maximum and minimum, will be discussed here. The other rocks had a transversally isotropic behaviour.

The relation between the principal moduli and the uniaxial or triaxial compressive stress is presented in Figure 4.

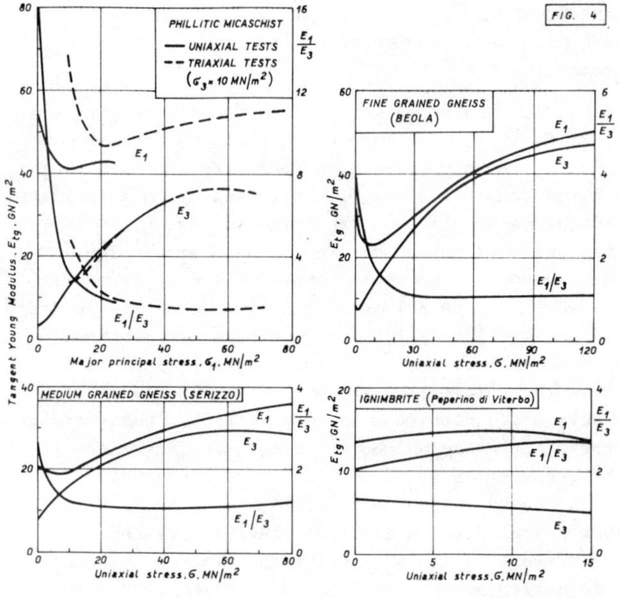

For the two gneiss (A and B) the ratio of anisotropy, initially high, lowers with the increase of load and equals about 1 when the stress reaches values of about 20 MN/m^2. It may be inferred that the anisotropy of these rocks is due solely to the cracks and that the solid matrix can be considered isotropic. Also in the phillitic micaschist C) the ratio of anisotropy drops rapidly with the increase of load but reaches final values of about 1.6. This different behaviour is likely due to the higher percentage of phillosilicates in the latter rock.

For all the three rocks, even under high compressive stresses, the elastic moduli are lower than those theoretically calculated for the solid matrix by the averaging methods and they continue to rise regularly as the compressive stress. Such behaviour can be explained on the hypothesis that there are two sets of cracks in the rock. The first set has an orientation corresponding to that of the schistosity plane; its cracks are very flattened and, accordingly, can be closed at low compressive stresses. The second set has statistically isotropic orientation and is characterized by cracks with a rather less flattened form that close progressively under higher stresses.

Our diagrams also evidence a lowering of the moduli at initial loading before the successive rise caused by the closing of the cracks. The fall is very marked in samples where schistosity is at an angle of 90° to the sample base, but hardly noticeable or even absent in those where this angle is 0°. It could possibly be caused by the presence of some closed cracks that only begin to slide when a certain level of compression value is reached. From a study of (3) it can be deduced that in a uniaxial compression test this can occur in the event of "residual" compressive stress being present between some cracks surfaces even when the sample is unloaded; this may be due to the non-homogeneity of the rock. Possibly, besides, at the beginning of the test some cracks are only potential (for instance crystal boundaries that fail prematurely). In samples where $\theta = 0°$, this effect is disguised by the more important phenomenon of the closing of open cracks.

Loading and unloading cycles under increasing uniaxial compression allow an evaluation of the importance of various factors on rock deformability. Total deformation is the sum of the following contributions:
(i) the deformation of the solid matrix
(ii) the deformation due to closed cracks which is composed of a reversible component and an irreversible one which can be attribued to slidings of the surfaces of cracks either potential or closed by internal stresses before any macroscopic compression is applied
(iii) the deformation caused by the closing of open cracks which also comprises an reversible part, and an irreversible one which may be due, for instance, to the crushing of solid bridges between cracks.

In Figure 5 the contributions of these factors to incremental deformability of the fine-grained gneiss are presented. It is apparent that the irreversible deformation makes a restricted contribution to rock deformability at low loads and that the anisotropy is essentially due to the presence of a set of initially open parallel cracks.

Ignimbrite (rock E) present a quite different behaviour pattern in respect to the first three rock types. The minor principal modulus decreases and the ratio of anisotropy increases with the applied stress. Such behaviour can be attributed to the fact that the material was never subject in situ to litostatic loads greater than about 0.5 MN/m^2 and, moreover, that it is very porous (about 20%).

A considerable amount of the deformation, then, can derive from irreversible flattening of open cracks and from the collapse of solid bridges existing between different cracks.

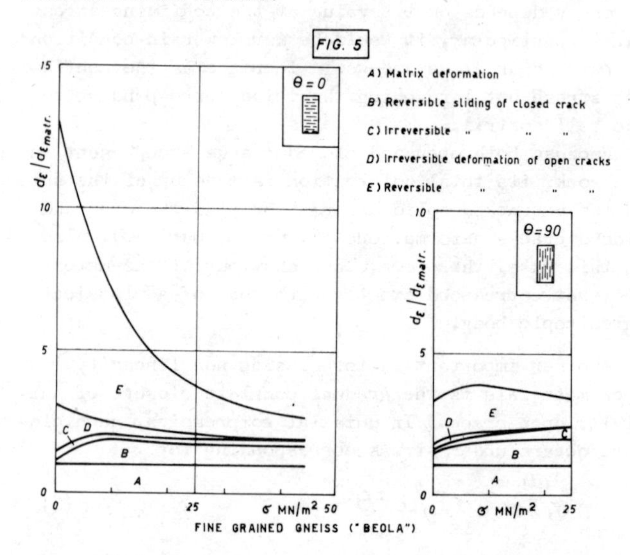

The deformability of the rocks in triaxial conditions was also investigated. For the phillitic micaschist the modulus curves in triaxial compression as a function of the major principal stress are a prolungation of the curves relative to uniaxial condition (Figure 4). A difference occur only when application of differential stresses is begun, insofar as the moduli are considerably higher in triaxial compression, especially when the sample axis is parallel to the schistosity. A quite similar behaviour is presented by the fine-grained gneiss (A).

From the first of the equations (3) this phenomenon can be attributed to the sticking of closed cracks due to hydrostatic compression, a sticking that is maintained until the differential stress reaches a given value.

When studying the dependency of the elastic constants on the orientation of the sample it is advisable to analyse the results of the experimental tests on the basis of the theoretical equations valid for an ideal anisotropic elastic body (Lekhnitscskii, 1963) because more workable parameters could be so obtained.

Naturally, both systematic differences, due to the non linearity effects above discussed, and a "casual" dispersion of the experimental data derived from non-homogeneity of the rock and the imperfections of test method are to be expected.

Axial deformability in a linear elastic body is expressed by:

$$\frac{\varepsilon_1}{\sigma} = \frac{1}{E} = \frac{1}{2}\left(\frac{1}{E_3} + \frac{1}{E_1}\right) + \frac{1}{2}\left(\frac{1}{E_3} - \frac{1}{E_1}\right)\cos^2\theta + \left(\frac{1}{G_{13}} - \frac{1}{\overline{G}_{13}}\right)\left(\frac{\sin 2\theta}{2}\right)^2 \quad (8)$$

where $\overline{G}_{13}$ denotes the shear modulus of a particular ideal anisotropic body, whose properties have been already discussed by Saint-Venant, and which is characterised by a shear modulus indipendent of the angle θ and equal to:

$$\frac{1}{\overline{G}_{13}} = \frac{1}{E_1} + \frac{1}{E_3} + \frac{2\nu_{31}}{E_3} \quad (9)$$

The validity of the Saint-Venant hypothesis (isoG) is often assumed in practical applications (for example, Niwa and others, 1968), since it simplifies many problems concerning anisotropic bodies. The isoG hypothesis is satisfied when the ratio $R_G = \overline{G}_{13}/G_{13}$ is equal to 1.

In quartz-phillosilicate rocks the anisotropy of the solid matrix due to an iso-orientation of mica flakes is characterized by values of $R_G > 1$. Examination of equation (2) shows that the anisotropy due to a set of open cracks has $R_G = 1$, whilst the anisotropy deriving from a set of closed cracks is characterized by values of R_G higher than 1.

The elastic parameters of the rock can be obtained from experimental measurements by means of eq. (8) applying a regression analysis which allows besides an evaluation of the significancy of the results. If the second coefficient of regression (that is the estimated value of $1/G_{13} - 1/\overline{G}_{13}$) is significantly different from zero, the isoG hypothesis cannot be assumed for the tested rock; if the first coefficient (that is the estimated value of $1/E_3 - 1/E_1$) is not significant, the behaviour of the rock is isotropic.

When the lateral deformations are measured as well, the following equations apply (Lekhnitskii, 1963):

$$\frac{\varepsilon'_t}{\sigma} = -\frac{\nu'}{E} = -\frac{\nu_{31}}{E_3} - \left(\frac{1}{G_{13}} - \frac{1}{\overline{G}_{13}}\right)\left(\sin\frac{2\theta}{2}\right)^2$$

$$\frac{\varepsilon''_t}{\sigma} = -\frac{\nu''}{E} = -\frac{\nu_{31}}{E_3} - \left(\frac{\nu_{12}}{E_1} - \frac{\nu_{31}}{E_3}\right)\sin^2\theta \quad (10)$$

The observed values of lateral deformations can also be treated by a regression analysis that provides an evaluation of the other elastic parameters of the rock and their confidence limits. In particular, the first equation of (10) offers another estimate of the correspondence of the rock to the isoG hypothesis, which should coincide with that obtained from the analysis of the axial deformations (8), within the confidence limits for the two regressions.

The necessity of analysing the results of deformability measurements by statistical methods, to establish the elastic constants of anisotropic rock, has been recognised earlier by other researchers (Loureiro Pinto, 1970; Tremmel and Widmann, 1970; Perez Rodriguez, 1970). The results of regression analysis for the tested rocks are, on the whole, satisfactory; Figure 6 shows the experimental values along with the theoretical curves (solid lines) obtained from the regression analysis. It must observed, however, that in rocks with a high ratio of anisotropy a standard regression analysis may provide sometimes abnormal results; some of the calculated moduli, for example, may prove negative. The results in Figure 7 referring to the phillitic micaschist were obtained precisely by this method.

In all the tested rocks (Figure 6 and 7) a progressive increase of R_G values in correspondence with the increase of stress was observed. This would comply with the fact that the influence of open cracks di-

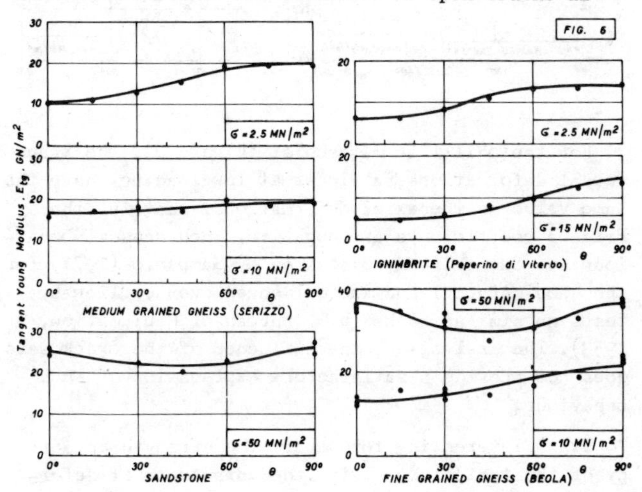

minishes as the applied stress increases, whilst that of closed cracks increases; at low values of the uniaxial stress, however, the R_G values sometimes prove less than 1, a result which does not appear justifiable in the light of the preceding considerations.

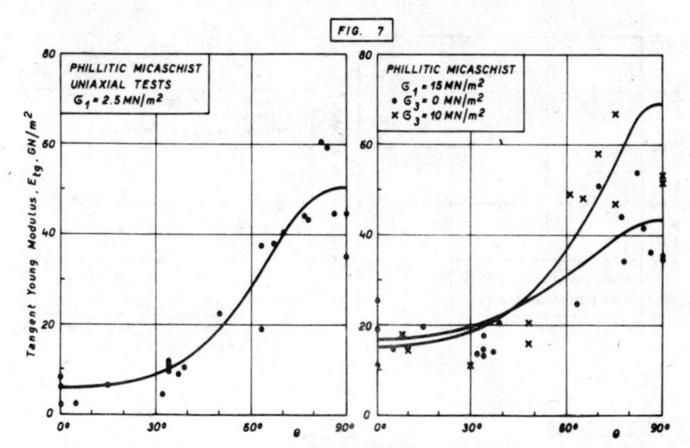

Figure 8 refers an example of regression analysis applied to the transversal deformations of the fine--grained gneiss (rock A).

At lowest loads, the two transversal deformabilities (ν'/E and ν''/E) are independent of sample orientation and are, moreover, equal to one another; inspection of equation (2) shows that such behaviour corresponds to that of a rock of which the anisotropy is determined essentially by a set of open cracks. At higher loads, however, the value of one of the two transversal deformabilities varies in correspondence with the angle θ , evidencing the increased effect of the closed cracks on the behaviour of the material.

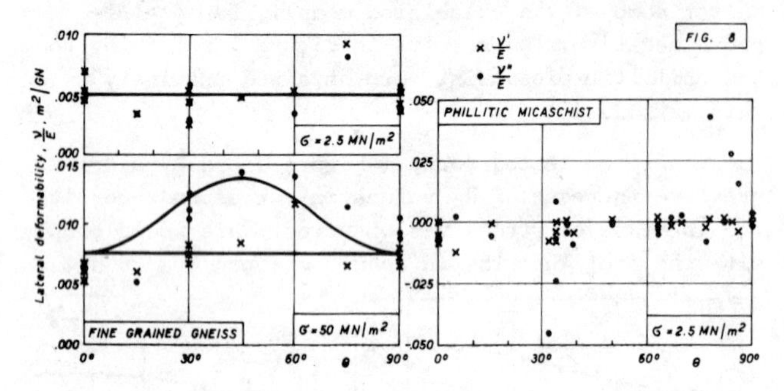

For the phillitic micaschist (Figure 8), the transversal deformations, at least at low loading, have the same value as the axial deformations, that is, the Poisson coefficients are negative. Such unusual behaviour has been already discussed by Sampaolo (1971) for the same material and was evidenced even earlier by tests on similar rocks (U.S. Bureau of Reclamation, 1953). The analysis of the influence of the crack sets does not provide a satisfactory explanation of such behaviour.

It is interesting to compare the strength anisotropy of the tested rocks with the anisotropy of deformability (Figure 9). It is apparent that the anisotropy of strength for the two gneiss and phillitic micaschist is somewhat less strong that the anisotropy of deformability. It is to be noted that in the sandstone and the ignimbrite strength anisotropy was not observed.

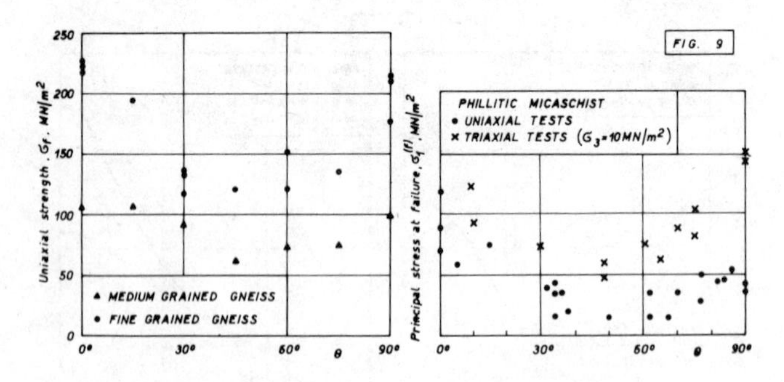

CONCLUSIONS

The anisotropy of the tested metamorphic rocks is mainly due to the existence of a set of iso-oriented open microcracks. The properties of the matrix have some influence only when a large amount of phillosilicates is present in the rock.

At low uniaxial loads the dependency of axial and lateral deformability on the orientation of the sample is in good agreement with that derived theoretically for a body containing a set of open microcracks. The progressive closing of microcracks is the cause of the strongly non-linear behaviour of the tested rocks; in uniaxial or triaxial conditions the anisotropy of the metamorphic rocks decreases as the major principal stress increases.

ACKNOWLEDGEMENTS

Thanks are due to the Dr. M. Sciotti for petrografic studies on the tested rocks.

This work was supported by E N E L (Contract CRIS 9-71) and by C N R (Contract No. 71.01244.05).

****

REFERENCES

Brace W.F., Relation of elastic properties of rocks to fabric, Journ. of Geoph. Res., Vol. 70, No. 22, 1965, pp. 5657-5667.

Brady B.T., The non linear mechanical behaviour of brittle rock. Part I - Stress- strain behaviour during regions I and II, Int. Journ. Rock Mech. Min. Sci., Vol. 6, 1969, pp. 211-225.

Lekhnitskii S.G., Theory of elasticity of an anisotropic body, Holden-Day Series in Mathematical Physics, S. Francisco, 1963.

Loureiro Pinto J., Deformability of schistous rocks, II Congr. Int. Soc. Rock Mech., I, Beograd,1970, pp. 591-496.

Niwa Y., Hobayashi S., Hirashima K., Determination of rock orthotropy by water chamber test, Int. Symp. Rock Mech., Madrid, 1968, pp. 59-64.

Perez Rodriguez F., Anisotropy of rocks, most probable surfaces of the ultimate stresses and of the moduli of elasticity, II Congr. Int. Soc. Rock Mech., Beograd, 1970, pp. 133-142.

Sampaolo A., Ricerche di laboratorio su rocce fortemente anisotrope, ENEL, D.S.R., C.R.I.S., Report No. 2181, 1971.

Tremmel E., Widmann R., Das Verformungsverhalten von gneis, II Congr. Int. Soc. Rock Mech., I, Beograd 1970, pp. 567-575.

U.S. Bureau of Reclamation, Physical properties of some typical foundation rocks, Concr. Lab.Rep. No. SP-39, Eng. Lab. Branch., 1953 (by Jaeger and Cook, Fundamentals of Rock Mechanics, London 1969).

Walsh J.B., The effect of cracks on the uniaxial elastic compression of rocks, Journ. of Geoph. Res., Vol. 70, No. 2, 1965a, pp. 399-411.

Walsh J.B., The effect of cracks in rocks on Poisson's ratio, Journ. of Geoph. Res., Vol. 70, No. 20, 1965b, pp. 5249-5257.

FRACTURE OF ROCK UNDER UNIFORM BIAXIAL COMPRESSION

CASSURE DU ROCHE UNIFORMÉMENT COMPRIMÉ SUR DEUX AXES

DER BRUCH VON GESTEIN UNTER GLEICHFÖRMIGEM DRUCK AUS ZWEI ACHSENRICHTUNGEN

E. T. BROWN
Associate Professor of Civil Engineering
James Cook University of North Queensland
Townsville, Australia

SUMMARY: The question of the behaviour of rock under biaxial compression is of both fundamental and practical significance. Experimental investigations of this problem have been limited by the difficulty in applying uniform load distributions free of the influence of end restraint. This difficulty can be overcome by using brush platens developed by Hilsdorf for testing concrete. Biaxial compression tests carried out on Wombeyan marble using brush platens yielded increases in strength of up to 15% of the uniaxial value. This result, when considered together with those obtained for concrete and plaster by other workers, suggests that for practical purposes, it may be imprudent to design for enhanced strength of brittle materials in biaxial compression.

RÉSUMÉ: La question du comportement du roc sous compression suivant deux axes est à la fois d'importance fondamentale et pratique. Les études expérimentales de ce problème ont été limitées par les difficultés à appliquer une pression uniformément répartie qui soit libre de toute influence de la butée d'extrémité. On peut surmonter cette difficulté en utilisant le système de "plateau en brosse" dont Hilsdorf se sert pour tester le béton. Les essais de compression suivant deux axes, effectués sur du marbre de Wombeyan en utilisant ce plateau en brosse ont produit des accroissements de force sur an axe allant jusqu'à 15%. Si on considère ce résultat avec ceux que d'autres chercheurs ont obtenus pour le béton et le plâtre, il apparaît que, en pratique, il peut être imprudent d'établir un plan en comptant sur une meilleure résistance de matériaux cassants en compression sur deux axes.

ZUSAMMENFASSUNG: Die Frage des Verhaltens von Gestein, das aus zwei Achsenrichtungen zugleich unter Druck gerät, ist sowohl von theoretischer als auch von praktischer Bedeutung. Untersuchungen dieses Problems auf dem Versuchswege waren bisher nur in begrenztem Masse möglich, weil es schwer ist, gleichförmige, von Einwirkung der Endsperre unbeeinflusste Belastungsverteilungen zu erzielen. Dieser Schwierigkeit kann durch Anwendung der von Hilsdorf zum Zwecke der Betonüberprüfung hergestellten Bürstenplatten vorgebeugt werden. Unter Verwendung von Bürstenplatten an wombeyanischem Marmor ausgeführte, zweiachsige Kompressionsversuche ergaben Stärkesteigerungen bis zu 15% der Werte, die für einachsige gelten. In Anbetracht der Ergebnisse, welche andere Forscher für Beton und Gips erhalten haben, ist dieses Resultat wohl als Hinweis darauf anzusehen, dass es in der Praxis unangezeigt sein mag, Entwürfe für erhöhte Festigkeit spröder Stoffe unter Druck aus Zwei Achsenrichtungen zu machen.

INTRODUCTION

Laboratory studies of the fracture of rock generally involve the uniaxial compression test or the so-called triaxial compression test. If σ_1, σ_2 and σ_3 are the principal stresses with compression positive, then for both tests $\sigma_2 = \sigma_3$, with $\sigma_1 > \sigma_2 = \sigma_3 = 0$ for uniaxial compression and $\sigma_1 > \sigma_2 = \sigma_3 \neq 0$ for triaxial compression. In most field situations, however, the applied stress field will be a general polyaxial one with $\sigma_1 \neq \sigma_2 \neq \sigma_3 \neq 0$. In a number of special cases, an approximately plane stress condition will apply ($\sigma_1 \neq \sigma_2 \neq \sigma_3 = 0$). This can occur where a free, unloaded surface forms part of a structure as in the face of a slope or the wall of an underground excavation. The case of biaxial compression ($\sigma_3 = 0$) is therefore of some significance in its own right. Perhaps the greater value of carrying out biaxial compression tests is that they will contribute data not obtainable from conventional tests which will be useful in the development of a general fracture criterion for rock.

The fact that the behaviour of intact rock and rock masses under uniform biaxial and polyaxial stresses have not been more thoroughly investigated is probably due to the very considerable experimental difficulties involved. The major difficulty is that of applying and maintaining uniform distributions of compressive load over the faces of prismatic specimens and eliminating the influence of frictional restraint. This paper describes a technique that has been successfully used to overcome this problem in biaxial compression tests on brittle materials, and presents and analyses results obtained for one rock, Wombeyan marble.

PREVIOUS STUDIES

Previous attempts to study the behaviour of rock under biaxial or polyaxial compression have been of two types - those in which an effort has been made to apply known principal stresses directly to the faces of rectangular prisms, and those in which non-homogeneous states of stress have been induced in hollow cylinders by internal pressure or torsion. The latter approach has been widely used but suffers from two major disadvantages that appear to be insurmountable. Since the intermediate principal stress is not applied directly, its value at each stage of the test must be inferred from the known values of the directly applied stresses. This requires the assumption of either elastic or plastic behaviour, neither of which can be expected to yield accurate results. Furthermore, the stress field is non-homogeneous, and fracture occurs in a zone of pronounced stress gradient making the determination of the failure stresses difficult. Although rock fracture does occur under stress gradients in practice, it is obvious that the introduction of this factor complicates the fracture problem considerably. Because of this and the uncertainties associated with tests of the second type, attention has been directed towards the former approach to the problem.

The difficulties associated with testing plates or cubes of material in biaxial compression have long been recognized. Föppl (1900) showed that a prismatic specimen subjected to uniaxial or biaxial compressive loads may be confined along its loaded surfaces due to friction between the specimen and the loading platens. Föppl recognized that this may result in an increase in the apparent strength of the test piece, and attempted to eliminate confinement by applying a lubricant at specimen - platen contacts. He found, however, that this could have a deleterious effect: soft packings or lubricating agents between specimen and loading platen cause lateral tensile stresses and a non-uniform stress distribution to be established in the specimen resulting in a reduction in its apparent strength.

Since this early recognition of the problem, little progress has been made towards its solution. In the several subsequent investigations of the behaviour of rock under biaxial compression, a number of techniques have been used in an effort to eliminate the effects of end restraint, but their effectiveness remains open to question. Details of several recent investigations are given in Table 1; the experimental results are summarized in Figure 1.

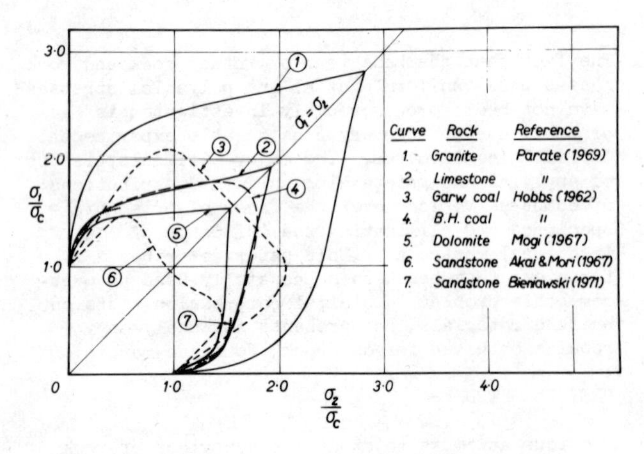

Figure 1 Results of previous biaxial compression tests on rock.

Although each of these investigations shows that some increase in the major principal stress required to cause failure (σ_1) results when the intermediate principal stress (σ_2) is applied, the observed relationships between σ_1 and σ_2 vary widely. This diversity in the results and the doubts that remain concerning end conditions, make it extremely difficult to draw meaningful general conclusions from these data.

An important contribution was recently made by Atkinson (1972) who developed an effective test cell for loading materials in uniform, multiaxial compression. The use of hydraulic loading through flexible membranes limits the capacity of the device which has been used for the determination of constitutive relations rather than fracture tests. Consequently, Atkinson's work is not referred to in Table 1.

BRUSH PLATENS

An ingenious approach to the end-effects problem was developed by Hilsdorf (1965) who used what he termed "brush bearing platens" in polyaxial tests on concrete. (A similar system had been used some 30 years earlier by Kjellman (1936) for multiaxial compression testing of soils.) These platens consist of a large number of closely spaced slender steel pins encased in a steel block at one end and bearing against the specimen at the other. Deformation of the specimen in any direction is accompanied by bending of the pins such that restraint at the specimen-platen contact is eliminated. Pins must be carefully designed so that they have sufficient flexibility to accommodate specimen deformations and sufficient strength to support combined axial loads and shear forces applied at their free ends without buckling.

In recent years, brush platens have been used with outstanding success in uniaxial and biaxial compression and/or tension tests on concrete and similar materials. A convincing demonstration of their efficacy is reported by Kupfer, Hilsdorf and Rusch (1969). Concrete prisms with various height to side length ratios were loaded in uniaxial compression with and without brush platens. When brush platens were used, the strength of the specimens was independent of their shape, and equal to the strength of prismatic specimens with a height to side length ratio of 4.

Similar results were recently obtained by Gonano and Brown (1973) in uniaxial compression tests on cylindrical specimens of Wombeyan marble and a gypsum plaster. This investigation provided important additional evidence of the usefulness of brush platens in that the shapes of the complete stress-strain curves determined using a servo-controlled testing system, were found to be sensibly independent of length to diameter ratio when brush platens were used, and quite variable with length to diameter ratio when solid steel platens of the same diameter as the specimens were used (Figure 2).

Ergun (1970) used a loading system incorporating the brush platen principle in biaxial compression tests on models of jointed rock. From photoelastic and strain gauge measurements he found that the compressive stresses applied to the edges of solid

Investigator(s)	Rock Type	Specimen Size	Uniaxial Compressive Strength, σ_c $MN\ m^{-2}$	Specimen - Platen Contact Conditions
Hobbs (1962)	Garw and Barnsley Hards coal	38 mm cubes	Garw ⊥ to bedding-11.9 B.H. parallel to bedding-19.3	Platens made of epoxy. No lubrication on inserts.
Akai and Mori (1967,1970)	Sandstone	55 mm cubes	117	0.23 mm thick soft rubber sheets covered with silicone grease inserted between platen and specimen.
Mogi (1967)	Dunham dolomite	10x16x37 mm	213	σ_1-rock attached to steel platen with epoxy. σ_2-contact lubricated from σ_2 up to $\sigma_c/2$ then unlubricated with correction applied to results.
Parate (1969)	Granite Limestone (dry and wet)	22 mm cubes	Granite 162 Limestone(dry)243 (wet)152	Cardboard sheet inserted between steel platen and specimen.
Bieniawski (1971)	Fine-grained sandstone	25 mm cubes	87.7	No special treatment.
Obermeier (1971)	Indiana limestone A.Isotropic B.Anisotropic	32x78x183 mm	A. 69.7 B. 31.2	Aluminium foil and very then film of silicone bearing grease and MoS_2 mixture between platen and specimen.

Table 1 Previous investigations of the behaviour of rock in biaxial compression.

glass and duralumin plates were uniform to within ±7% and that shear stresses on the edges were negligible.

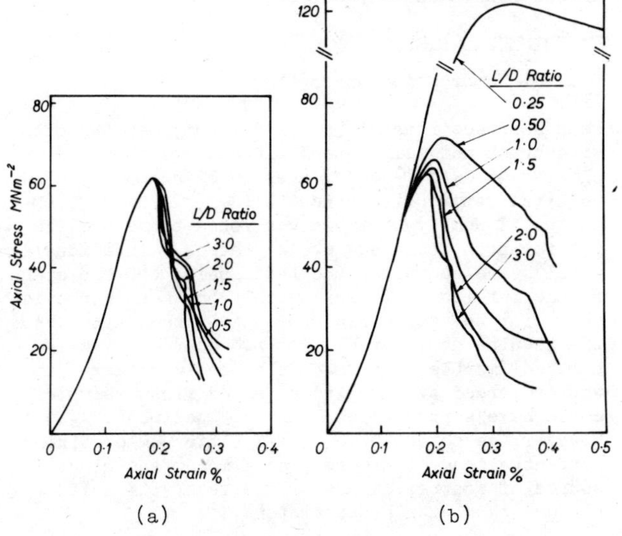

Figure 2 Complete uniaxial compression stress-strain curves for Wombeyan marble
(a) Brush platens
(b) Solid platens.

The results of typical biaxial compression tests (and, in some cases, biaxial tension and tension-compression tests) carried out on concrete and related materials using brush platens are shown in Figure 3. It is important to note that in no series of biaxial compression tests did the increase in strength over the uniaxial compressive strength exceed 25%. Increases of considerably higher magnitude than this have been obtained in tests on concrete in which solid steel platens were used (Kupfer et al, 1969).

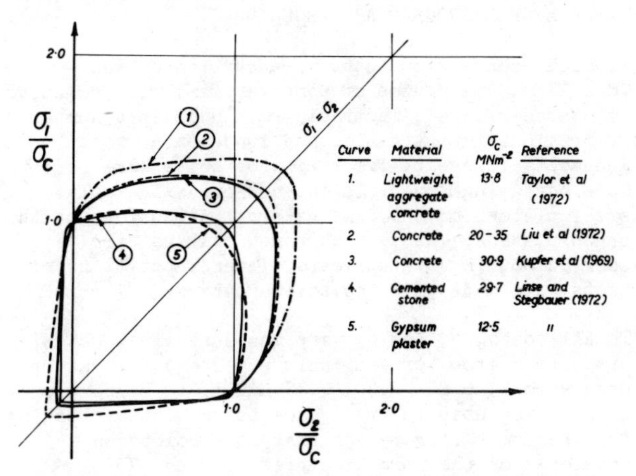

Figure 3 Biaxial compression test results for concrete and related materials tested with brush platens.

On the basis of this background, a set of brush platens was designed for the purpose of applying compressive stresses of up to 100 MN m^{-2} to the faces of 76x76x25 mm plates of rock. Four platens were built to the design shown schematically in Figure 4. Since the platens were designed for use in biaxial and uniaxial compression tests only, it was not necessary to allow for contraction of the specimen in the short lateral direction by the provision of gaps between the 3.2 mm square pins. Gaps of 0.2 mm were provided between all pins in the long dimension of the platen by inserting pieces of brass shimstock between the steel pins to the height of the steel holder. When each platen had been assembled the ends of the pins were ground flat and parallel to the base of the holder.

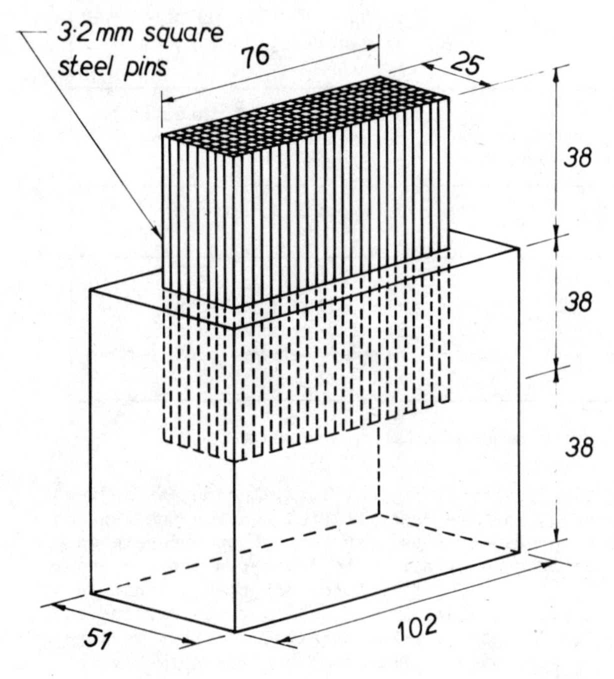

Figure 4 Schematic view of brush platen (Dimensions in mm)

EXPERIMENTAL PROGRAM AND TECHNIQUES

Biaxial compression tests were carried out on 76mmx76mmx25mm plates of Wombeyan marble, a relatively coarse-grained, isotropic rock used in a number of previous investigations of fundamental rock mechanics interest. Two series of tests were performed - one using brush platens and one using solid steel platens of the same external dimensions as the brush platens. Tests with brush platens were carried out in quintuplicate; fewer repetitions of tests were made with the solid platens.

In all tests, σ_1 and σ_2 were increased in constant proportion from zero to failure. The σ_2/σ_1 ratios used were 0, 0.25, 0.50, 0.75 and 1.0. Proportional loading was used in preference to sequential loading for the compelling reason that some points on envelopes of the form of curves 1, 2 and 3 in Figure 3 could never be reached by first applying σ_2 to its final value and then applying σ_1. Failure would occur in uniaxial compression when σ_2 exceeded σ_c.

Force was applied in the σ_1 direction by a 450 kN capacity servo-controlled jack operating in displacement control at a programmed strain rate of 5×10^{-5} sec^{-1}. Force was applied in the σ_2 direction by two 450 kN capacity jacks connected to a common hydraulic accumulator type pressure generating device. The pressure supplied to these two jacks was manually adjusted to required values throughout each test. Greater efficiency and accuracy in this operation could be achieved by the incorporation of a second servo-controlled jack into the system (e.g. Taylor et al, 1972). Deformation in the σ_1 direction were measured and recorded by two LVDT's. Other components of deformation were not measured.

It is well established that the standard of specimen preparation can have major influence on the behaviour of rock in laboratory compression tests. In the present experiments, particular care was taken in preparing specimens and aligning the loading platens. Pairs of opposite faces of specimens were ground flat and parallel to within ±0.01 mm. Closer tolerances were aimed for but could not be achieved with the equipment available. The nominally 76 mm dimensions of the specimens were made up to 1 mm oversize in order that there would be no interference of vertical and lateral platens at the corners as specimens were compressed.

The loading surface of each brush platen was ground flat and parallel to the base of its holder to within ±0.005 mm. When the platens were in place in the testing frame, the loading faces of each pair of platens were parallel to within ±0.01 mm. The alignment of the platens was repeatedly checked and adjusted during the course of the experimental program. The fact that the alignment was less than perfect is seen as the major reason for the scatter in the experimental results.

EXPERIMENTAL RESULTS

Biaxial Compression Strengths

Peak stresses reached in biaxial compression tests with brush and solid steel platens are shown plotted on σ_1/σ_c - σ_2/σ_c axes in Figure 5. The mean uniaxial compressive strength (σ_c) of 76x76x25 mm plates of Wombeyan marble was found to be 65.5 MN m^{-2} for both brush and solid platens. Individual results are shown for the tests using brush platens; in the interests of clarity only the mean curve is shown for the solid platen tests. The scatter in the results could arise from two sources. The block of marble from which the specimens were cut was traversed by limonite strained fissures which could have served to weaken some specimens. However, as noted above, difficulties in obtaining perfect alignment are seen as a more feasible source of scatter. Scatter was less with solid platens than with brush platens.

The mean curve for the brush platen tests shows a maximum strength of 15% above the uniaxial compressive strength. At $\sigma_1 = \sigma_2$, the strength is 1.03 σ_c. For solid platens the corresponding strength increases are 38% and 19% of σ_c respectively.

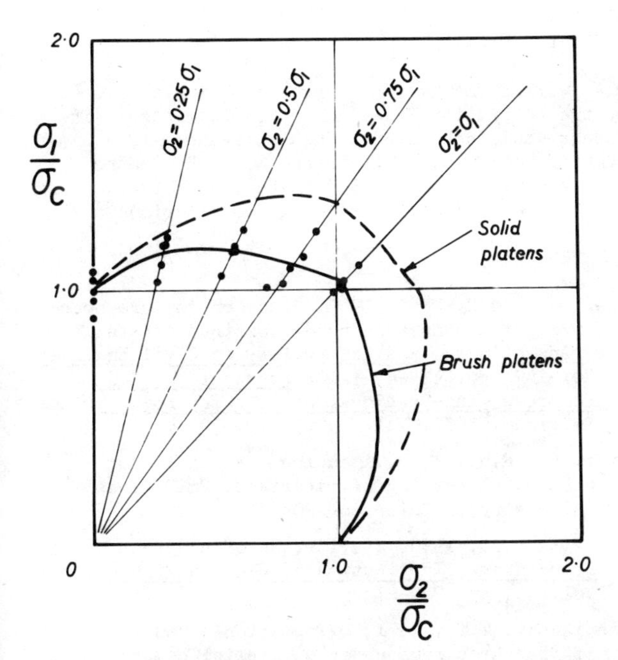

Figure 5 Biaxial compression test results for Wombeyan Marble.

Failure Modes

Although all tests were carried out using a servo-controlled jack, the test arrangement, loading frame stiffness and availability or feed-back signals were such that it was not possible to control fracture and obtain complete stress-strain curves. In a few tests, uncontrolled failure occurred with extraneous fracture planes being produced. In the majority of cases the test was stopped and the specimen unloaded at or shortly after the peak axial force had been reached but before explosive failure had occurred.

Generally in the tests carried out with brush platens, vertical fracture planes formed parallel to the $\sigma_1 - \sigma_2$ plane and perpendicular to the $\sigma_3 = 0$ direction. In controlled tests, these fractures were quite small at the peak load and often not apparent until the specimen had been sectioned and polished. When failure was uncontrolled, the specimen split into slabs parallel to the $\sigma_1 - \sigma_2$ plane. The fractures extended to the loading faces of the specimens. End cones were not formed.

In the tests carried out with solid steel platens end cones formed, and fractures coalesced into an hour-glass shape in the $\sigma_1 - \sigma_3$ plane. Similar results to these have been obtained in investigations of the behaviour of concrete under biaxial compression (e.g. Taylor et al, 1972).

FAILURE CRITERIA

A variety of failure criteria are available for consideration in the present context. They include the classical Mohr-Coulomb, maximum stress, Tresca, von Mises-Hencky and Griffith criteria of fracture or yield, and more recently developed theories of brittle fracture such as those of Trollope (1968), Wiebols and Cook (1968), Brady (1970), Baker (1970) and Lundborg (1972).

A generally valid failure criterion must satisfy two major conditions. It must be based on a realistic mechanism or model of fracture or yield, and must be capable of predicting failure stresses for all practicable combinations of stress. The classical theories all fail at least one of these tests. Acceptance of the observation that failure in biaxial compression is by a splitting rather than a shear mode, automatically rules out those criteria based on shear stress considerations. Many of the classical criteria (e.g. Mohr-Coulomb, Tresca) also suffer from the disadvantage that they either assume or predict that the intermediate principal stress has no influence on failure. The present experimental results would suggest that this disadvantage may be of greater theoretical than practical consequence.

The strain energy theories of failure do not suffer from the same disadvantage. The von Mises-Hencky or maximum strain energy of distortion criterion has found wide-spread use in describing the failure of metals under combined stresses. Hobbs (1962) applied it to the results of his biaxial compression tests on coal. It successfully predicts an increase in fracture stress at low values of the intermediate principal stress (σ_2), and a decrease in fracture stress at higher values of σ_2.

Wiebols and Cook (1968) have developed a criterion for brittle fracture under polyaxial stress based on the concept of the strain energy per unit volume stored around cracks as a result of sliding on cracks under an "effective" shear stress. Lundborg (1972) extended Weibull's tensile failure theory to the case of shear failure, and produced a criterion of which the Wiebols-Cook criterion is a special case. Lundborg's criterion contains two material constants, one of which is an index, and so it can be fitted to most sets of experimental data, including those reported here. The major difficulty with these theories is that they are based on shear failure when it is not at all clear that this is, in fact, the operative mechanism.

Brady (1970) developed an interesting theory also based on shear failure and the Griffith crack concept. His theory predicts that uniaxial ($\sigma_2 = 0$) and "biaxial" ($\sigma_1 = \sigma_2$) compressive strengths are equal, and that the maximum effect produced by σ_2 is an increase in strength of 0.20 σ_c. In the tests on Wombeyan marble the so-defined biaxial compressive strength was 1.03 σ_c, and the maximum increase in strength observed was 0.15 σ_c.

In terms of consistency with observed failure modes, those failure theories based on effective or induced tensile stress (Taylor et al, 1972; Trollope, 1968) or maximum extensional strain (Baker, 1970) are to be preferred. As noted previously, both concrete and rock specimens tend to divide into sheets or slabs parallel to the unstressed direction when biaxial loads are applied via brush platens.

Trollope's effective tensile stress theory of brittle fracture is based on a particulate or "clastic" model of material structure. It postulates that applied compressive stresses will induce effective tensile stresses in the orthogonal directions. Failure will occur by cleavage when the inter-particle or effective tensile stress reaches a critical value. In its present form this theoy does not account for the small observed increase in strength with increase in σ_2, but with suitable modification of parameters to take account of non-linear and anisotropic behaviour of rocks it could certainly do so.

Baker (1970) has shown that the maximum extensional strain theory of failure can be interpreted so as to produce envelopes such as those shown in Figures 3 and 5, rather than a decrease in σ_1 with increasing σ_2 as in the conventional statement of the theory. This interpretation depends on recognition of the fact that the parameters relating the components of stress and strain in materials such as concrete and rock tested to failure, are not the classical elastic constants, but parameters reflecting changes in material behaviour with stress level and the development of cracking. Baker applied this approach to a set of biaxial compression test results obtained for concrete, and was able to predict an increase in biaxial strength ($\sigma_1 = \sigma_2$) of 10% over the uniaxial strength.

In cases in which the material is more closely linear up to peak strength than was this material, and the variation in the stress-strain parameters with stress level is less, a decrease in σ_1 with increasing σ_2 can result. Such behaviour has been observed for gypsum plaster and "cemented stone" (reconstituted rock) by Linse and Stegbauer (1972) (see curves 4 and 5, Figure 3).

CONCLUSIONS

Since the new data presented were obtained from only one rock type, it is extremely difficult to formulate conclusions regarding the general behaviour of rocks in biaxial compression. Clearly, tests on a variety of other rock types must be carried out before conclusions of a general nature can be drawn. Nevertheless, the present results, when considered in conjunction with results obtained by other workers on other brittle materials such as concrete and plaster, would suggest that the following general conclusions probably apply.

1. Brush platens provide an effective means of overcoming the effects of frictional end-restraint.
2. The increases in compressive strength accompanying increases in the intermediate principal stress when the minor principal stress is zero, are likly to be small. Decreases in strength are possible in extremely brittle materials.
3. Consequently, when dealing with the case of biaxial compression in practice, it is inadviseable to design for a strength above the uniaxial strength.
4. In biaxial compression, failure will generally occur by extension in the $\sigma_3 = 0$ direction.
5. Failure criteria based on effective tensile stress or maximum extensional strain concepts can account for the experimental observations, and appear likely to provide the basis for a general criterion of rock fracture.

ACKNOWLEDGEMENTS

This work forms part of a project being sponsored by the Australian Research Grants Committee. The author would acknowledge the assistance given him by Professor D.H. Trollope and Mr. L.P. Gonano in discussion, and Mr. R.D. Matheson in fabricating the test equipment and running the experiments.

REFERENCES

Akai, K. and H. Mori, 1967, Study on failure mechanism of a sandstone under combined stress, Transactions, Japanese Society of Civil Engineers, No. 147, pp. 11-24. (Also Proceedings, 2nd Congress, International Society for Rock Mechanics, Belgrade, 1970, Vol. 2, pp. 285-290).

Atkinson, R.H., 1972, A cubical test cell for multiaxial testing of materials, Ph.D. Thesis, University of Colorado, 206 pp.

Baker, A.L.L., 1970, A criterion of concrete failure, Proceedings, Institution of Civil Engineers, Vol. 45, pp. 269-278.

Bieniawski, Z.T., 1971, Deformational behaviour of fractured rock under multiaxial compression, Structure, Solid Mechanics and Engineering Design, M.Te'eni (ed), London, Wiley-Interscience, Part 1, pp. 589-598.

Brady, B.T., 1970, Effect of the intermediate principal stress on the fracture of brittle rock, Rock Mechanics - Theory and Practice, W.H. Somerton (ed), New York, AIME, pp. 267-279.

Ergun, I., 1970, Stress distribution in jointed media, Proceedings, 2nd Congress, International Society for Rock Mechanics, Belgrade, Vol. 1, pp. 497-507.

Föppl, A, 1900, Die Abhangigkeit der Bruchgefahr von der Art des Spannungszustandes, Mitteilungen aus dem Mechanisch - Technischen Laboratorium, Technische Hochschule, Munchen, Vol. 27, 43 pp.

Gonano, L.P. and E.T. Brown, 1973, Brush platens for compression testing of rock, Australian Geomechanics Journal, Vol. G3.

Hilsdorf, H.K., 1965, Die Bestimmung der zweiachsigen Festigkeit von Beton, Proceedings, Deutsher Ausschuss fur Stahlbeton, Vol. 173.

Hobbs, D.W., 1962, The strength of coal under biaxial compression, Colliery Engineering, Vol. 39, pp. 285-290.

Kjellman, W., 1936, Report on an apparatus for consummate investigation of the mechanical properties of soils, Proceedings, 1st International Conference on Soil Mechanics and Foundation Engineering, Vol. 1, pp. 16-20.

Kupfer, H., H.K. Hilsdorf and H. Rusch, 1969, Behaviour of concrete under biaxial stress, Journal of the American Concrete Institute, Vol. 66, pp. 656-666.

Linse, D. and Stegbauer, A., 1972, Festigkeit und Bruchverhalten von Benton und Homogenen Baustoffen bei Zweiachsiger Beanspruchung, Veröffentlichungen des Institutes fur Bodenmechanik und Felsmechanik der Universitat Fridericiana, Karlsrube, Vol. 55, pp. 139-157.

Liu, T.C.Y., A.H. Nilson, and F.O. Slate, 1972, Stress-strain response and fracture of concrete in uniaxial and biaxial compression, Journal of the American Concrete Institute, Vol. 69, pp. 291-295.

Lundborg, N., 1972, A statistical theory of the polyaxial compressive strength of materials, International Journal of Rock Mechanics and Mining Sciences, Vol. 9, pp. 617-624.

Mogi, K., 1967, Effect of the intermediate principal stress on rock failure, Journal of Geophysical Research, Vol. 72, pp. 5117-5131.

Obermeier, S.F., 1971, Influence of imposed stress histories and plane stress-plane strain on the mechanical properties of two limestones, Ph.D. Dissertation, Purdue University, 300 pp.

Parate, N.S., 1969, Critère de rupture des roches fragile, Annales de l'Institut Technique du Batiment et des Travaux, No. 253, pp. 148-160.

Taylor, M.A., A.K. Jain, and M.R. Ramey, 1972, Path-dependent biaxial compressive testing of an all-lightweight aggregate concrete. Journal of the American Concrete Institute, Vol. 69, pp. 758-764.

Trollope, D.H., 1968, The mechanics of discontinua or clastic mechanics in rock problems, Rock Mechanics in Engineering Practice, K.G. Stagg and O.C. Zienkiewicz (eds.), London, John Wiley, pp. 275-320.

Weibols, G.A. and N.G.W. Cook, 1968, An energy criterion for the strength of rock in polyaxial compression, International Journal of Rock Mechanics and Mining Sciences, Vol. 5, pp. 529-549.

NUMERICAL AND PHYSICAL EXPERIMENTS WITH DISCONTINUA

EXPÉRIENCES NUMÉRIQUES ET PHYSIQUES DE DISCONTINUITÉ

NUMERISCHE UND PHYSIKALISCHE EXPERIMENTE IM DISKONTINUUM

Brian A. CHAPPELL

Maunsell and Partners, Melbourne, Australia

SUMMARY

Definition of stresses in a discontinuum requires a selection of representative units which will allow the transformation of the normal and shear forces acting between the units into stresses. The shape of the units Fig. 1 (a) determines whether moments are transmissible or not transmissible across the joint system.

It is found that with blocky units moments are transmitted across the joint system and a characteristic length or moment arm is required to convert the moments into forces which in turn are subsequently averaged to give stresses. Consequently, if the discontinuum is a blocky or interlocking material, and is analysed using structural continuum methods, moment transmission with the resultant stress gradients must be considered. In turn, if an analogue continuum representing a discontinuum is transformed into a structural lattice for the purpose of analysis, the characteristic length must be determined. This characteristic length is a function of the material properties and lattice geometry (Banks and Sokolowski, 1968).

It is shown here that it is not possible by just selecting geometrical configurations of various units, to represent the interacting forces in terms of stresses and strains. Comparison between the results of computer and photoelastic model studies are made.

ZUSAMMENFASSUNG

Die Bestimmung der Spannungen in einem Diskontinuum erfordert eine Auswahl von repräsentativen Elementen, die die Transformation der Normal-und Scherkräfte, die zwischen den Elementen wirken, in Spannungen ermöglicht. Die Form der Elemente Fig. 1 (a) ist entscheidend dafür, ob Momente über das Fugensystem übertragbar sind order nicht.

Es wurde gefunden, dass im Falle von blockförmigen Elementen Momente über das Fugensystem übertragen werden und eine charakteristische Länge oder ein Hebelarm erforderlich ist, um diese Momente in Kräfte umzuwandeln, deren Durchschnitt dann die Spannungen ergibt. Wenn das Diskontinuum also aus einem blockartigen oder ineinandergreifenden Material besteht und mit Methoden für ein strukturelles Kontinuum analysiert wird, muss die Uebertragung von Momenten mit den daraus resultierenden Spannungsgradienten in Betracht gezogen werden. Andererseits muss, wenn ein analoges Kontinuum, das ein Diskontinuum repräsentiert, für die Zwecke der Analyse in ein strukturelles Netzwerk transformiert wird, die charakteristische Länge bestimmt werden. Diese charakteristische Länge ist eine Funktion der Eigenschaften des Materials und der Netzwerk-Geometrie (Banks und Sokolowski, 1968).

RESUME

La définition des efforts dans une discontinuité nécessite une selection d'éléments représentatifs qui permettra la transformation des forces normales et de cisaillement agissant entre les éléments en efforts. La forme des éléments Fig. 1 (a) determine si les moments sont transmissibles ou non transmissibles à travers le système des joints.

L'on trouve qu'avec des éléments en blocs les moments sont transmis à travers le système des joints et une longueur caractéristique ou bras de levier du moment est requise pour convertir les moments en forces qui sont ultérieurement traduites en une moyenne pour donner les efforts. En conséquence, si la discontinuité consiste d'éléments en blocs ou emboités, et est analysée selon des méthodes de continuité structurale, il faut prendre en considération la transmission du moment avec les gradients des résistances qui en resultent. De même, si une fonction discontinue analogue représentant une discontinuité est transformée en une structure en treillis aux fins d'analyse, il faut déterminer la longueur caractéristique. Cette longueur caractéristique est fonction des propriétés de la matière et de la géométrie du treillis (Banks er Sokolowski, 1968).

INTRODUCTION

To date the main procedure when dealing with a discontinuum, is to take a representative unit, sometimes called a systone (Trollope, 1968) and from this define the stresses. Consequently the average stress summed over the representative unit represents the force acting over the actual areas of contact. This approach does not consider the variation of stress over the face or boundary of the unit, that is stress gradients are neglected. This representation is adequate when stress gradients are not prevalent within or between representative units, and, therefore, depicts the behaviour of a discontinuum when only thrust and shear forces are acting. When moments between units are introduced stress gradients have to be considered, (Chappell 1973), and the representative units chosen to date are inadequate for defining the stress system.

When moments are considered in a two-dimensional continuum another constant termed the characteristic length L is introduced (Mindlin and Tiersten, 1962). If a continuum is discretized to give an equivalent structural lattice (Banks and Sokolowski, 1968) this characteristic length is a function of both the lattice geometry and material properties. The implication is that where moments and hence stress gradients are prevalent in a discontinuum, the choice of a representative unit has to consider the above characteristic length before the continuum concepts of stress and strain can be used.

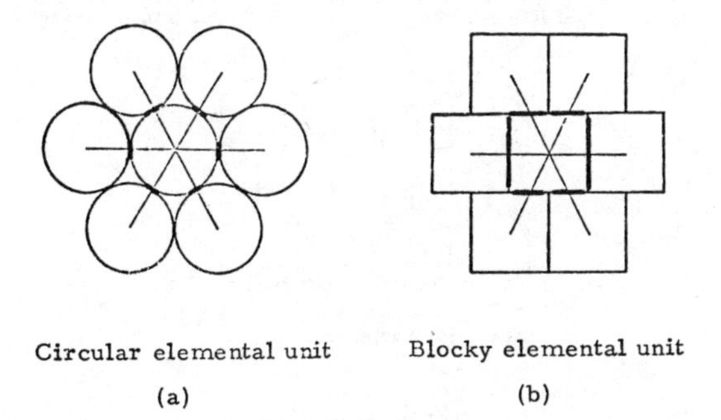

Circular elemental unit (a) Blocky elemental unit (b)

Fig. 1 Element representation of systone used to transform interacting forces to stresses.

If the area of contact between the representative units, Fig. 1(a), is relatively small compared to the individual units making up the representative units and the magnitude of the transmitted moments has a relatively small effect on the average stress distribution across the joint, the representative unit can represent the force system in terms of stress. For a blocky material, however, the elements are large compared to the size of the blocks, Fig. 1(b), and the effects of moments transmitted across the block faces cause significant stress gradients. In order to represent the forces acting on the faces of the block in terms of equivalent stresses the characteristic length, L, would have to be introduced.

INFLUENCE OF COUPLE STRESSES

If χ_{ij} is the intensity per unit area of the stress couple, where i denotes area and j the vector direction, it can be shown that for equilibrium

$$\sigma_{ij} - \sigma_{ji} = \sum_{L=1}^{3} \frac{\partial \chi_{ij}}{\partial L} \quad \ldots. (1)$$

where i, j, and k are all different and L is a characteristic length. Consequently, when considering the two-dimensional case, and when a couple stress exists, equilibrium is found to give the relation $\sigma_{xy} \neq \sigma_{yx}$. When this happens it follows that the path dependent movements in a blocky mass readily occur. That is the movements in a blocky mass as propounded by Bray (1965), where $\sigma_{xy} = \sigma_{yx}$ appears to be a requirement, are not as restrictive as they may first appear especially if moments, hence stress gradients, are transmitted across the joints. In fact where moments across joints are prevalent this mode of path dependent deformation readily occurs as is observed from experimental observation Chappell (1973).

DESCRIPTION OF THE MECHANISTIC FINITE ELEMENT METHOD

Burman (1971) using a method similar to the one used by Goodman, et al (1968), replaced the elastic blocks with rigid ones and used a joint element which includes both the block and joint response of stress versus strain and moment versus rotation. What this basically does is replace the discontinuum, which here is a system of blocks, with a structural frame, Figs. 2(a) and (b). The interaction between the blocks and joints is then represented by joint elements placed between the centroids of the blocks.

CHARACTERISTICS OF NON-LINEAR BLOCK INTERACTION

In the computer programme there are three deformation modes which contribute most significantly to the non-linear or in fact non-elastic response of the structure to load. These are:-

(a) the response normal to the joint is limited by the tensile strength,

(b) the shear strength of the joint is limited by Coulomb's shear strength criterion,

(c) a non-linear stress strain response for the joint may be included.

Analysis of non-linear behaviour can be approached by a constant or variable elastic matrix process as developed by Zienkiewicz and Valliappan (1968). The computer programme used here employs a constant elasticity approach in which the initial stress or strain is the variable. It is found that the initial stress approach operates successfully for conditions where a small increment of stress is accompanied by a relatively large change in strain, for example when residual or incremental shear stress mobilises large strains.

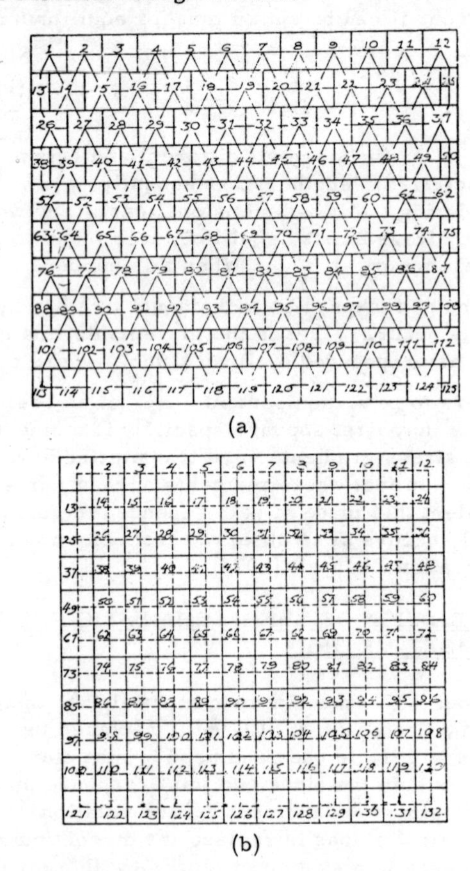

Fig. 2. Block arrangement representing structural configuration in both computer and physical experiments.

A non-linear relationship is obtained which connects each degree of freedom at the blocks centroid with the normal and shear stress at the centroid of each joint element surrounding the rigid block. The resultant data from this programme give the average stresses in the joint elements which are in fact the forces acting on the boundaries of the rigid blocks at the centroid of the chosen joint elements.

NUMERICAL AND PHYSICAL EXPERIMENTS

In the first instance a series of physical models were constructed (Chappell 1973) which consisted of square blocks of different sizes and differing aspect ratios of length to depth. Araldite D was the photoelastic material used for constructing these models. The boundary forces on these blocks were evaluated from the stresses within the individual blocks. Sequences of loading and block extraction were similar for both the physical and numerical experiments. Consequently for each of the numerical experiments described below physical experiments were performed in a similar manner.

Between 125 and 132 blocks were used in the experiments with different sequences of loading, joint properties and block stackings. Primarily, the object was to investigate the load distribution for excavations in and foundation loads imposed on a blocky material.

From the results of the numerical experiments the loads on specific blocks could be assessed, and the stresses induced within the blocks could then be evaluated using the now standard finite element approach.

Initially both the numerical and physical experiments were performed where certain blocks were removed before the loads were imposed, and then these experiments were repeated where all the blocks were left in place and the loads imposed and the same blocks as in the previous experiments subsequently removed.

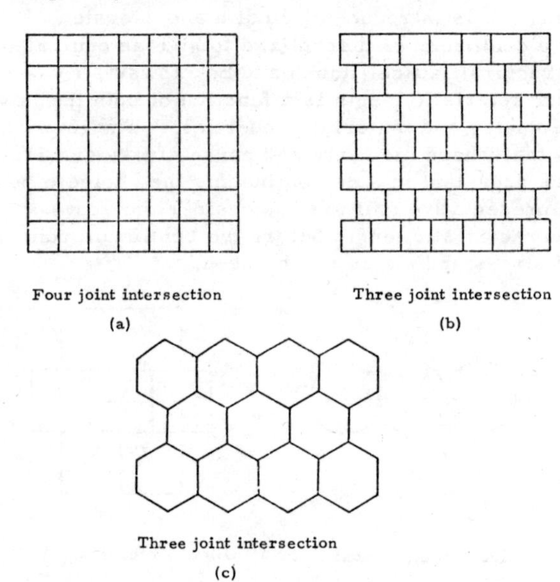

Fig. 3. Joint intersections at a point and the resulting effect on block arrangement.

HYDROSTATIC LOADING

Two stacking systems were used as shown in Figures 3(a) and (b). The first diagram, Figure 3(a) represents a three joint intersection problem (Lafeber, 1963) and Figure 3(b) represents a four joint one. Another three jointed system is the hexagonal one which does not however intersect at right angles, Figure 3(c). This latter system induces an order of complexity higher than that experienced for the square blocks, and in the opinion of the author is a specialised instance much less common than that encountered with the square blocks.

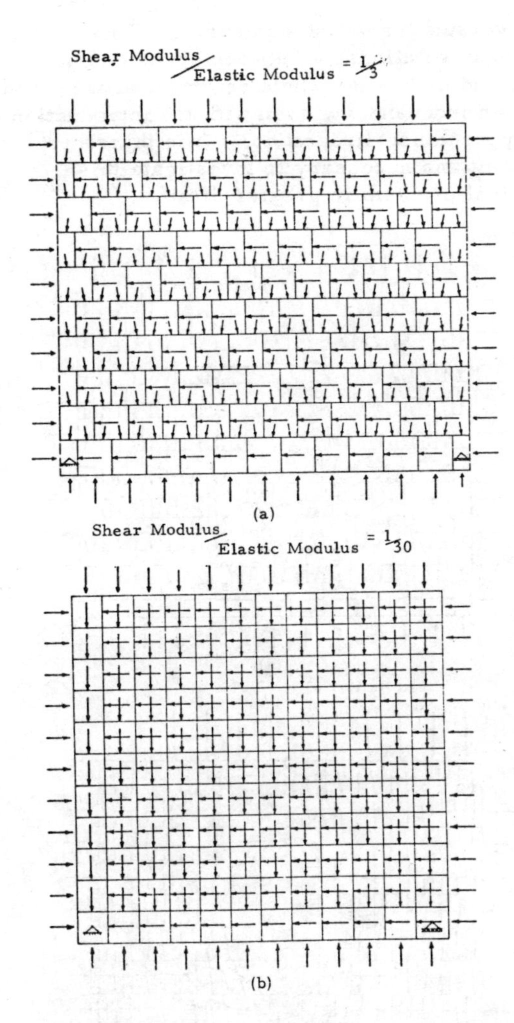

Fig. 4 Development of shear forces in the jointing system of a blocky mass.

When the blocks are stacked to give a model with staggered vertical joints and then a hydrostatic load imposed, shear forces in the jointing system are developed, Figures 4(a) and (b). These induced shear forces are dependent on the magnitude of the shear modulus of the joints and the relative movements between blocks in contiguous rows. Figure 4(a) shows the force field caused by the hydrostatic loading when the shear stiffnes is relatively high while Figure 4(b) depicts the force field when the shear stiffness is relatively low. Relatively high and low shear stiffnesses are defined as the ratio of the joint shear modulus to Young's modulus normal to the length of the joint. A value of 1/3 is considered high while 1/30 is low.

If the representative unit, such as in Figure 1(a), is used in this instance to define stress the consequent stress system satisfies equilibrium to within 1%.

BLOCK EXTRACTION

In a stacked block system it was found, that the development of shear force in the jointing system under hydrostatic load was dependent, in the main, on factors such as stacking geometry and shear stiffness of the jointing system. Because of the symmetry of the induced shear forces, however, there is no tendency for the blocks to rotate. If some blocks are now removed from the stacked system additional shear forces are induced. This imposes a rotative tendency on certain blocks especially those contiguous to the opening and destroys the symmetry of the forces acting on the blocks be they normal or shear forces.

It is found in the physical models that when certain blocks were extracted the mechanisms of slip and rotation were initiated. These mechanisms impose specific load distributions on the blocks which in turn control the stress distributions within the blocks. An important observation is that in most instances where rotation of the block occurred either a tensile stress or effective tensile strain was induced within the block (Chappell, 1973). It should go without saying that this characteristic has very important implications in the subsequent deformational behaviour and strength characteristics of the blocky mass.

BLOCKS EXTRACTED AND LOAD SUBSEQUENTLY IMPOSED

First 3, 5 and then 6 blocks were removed from the model and after each group of blocks had been extracted the boundary loads were applied. It was noted that when the joints were of low stiffness in shear, mechanistic beaming type forces were mobilised, and when the joints were of high stiffness, continuous beaming type forces were mobilised, Figure 5(a) and (b) respectively. When comparing the numerical and physical experimental results it was found that the load distribution for the numerical joints of low stiffness agreed remarkably well with the physical experiments where the blocks were loaded and the blocks subsequently extracted, Figure 5(a). Good correlation between the numerical joints of high stiffness and the physical experiment was obtained where the blocks were first extracted and the model subsequently loaded, Figure 5(b).

In the numerical experiments, it was noted that as soon as the moment transmitted across the joint became significant equilibrium of the representative unit, which was used to obtain the stresses, was no longer satisfied (20% to 30% error). However in areas of the same load field, generally some distance away from the opening where the moments transmitted across the joints were small, equilibrium of the representative units was satisfied to within 2%.

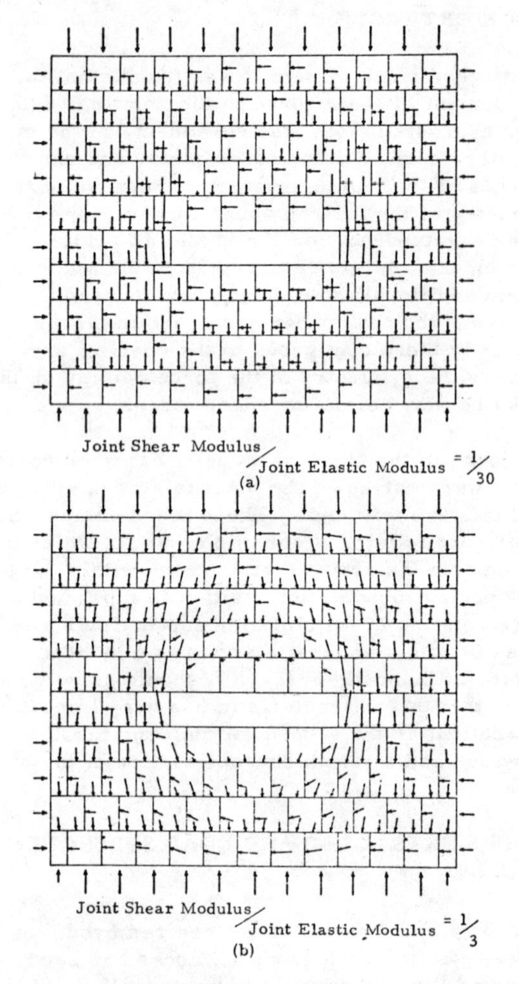

Fig. 5. Load distribution around an opening where the joint shear values differ.

BLOCKS EXTRACTED OR MINED OUT AFTER THE LOADS ARE APPLIED

In these numerical experiments the loads were first imposed and then specific blocks in groups of 3, 5 and 6 were mined out. The resultant magnitudes and patterns of force, Figure 6(a) and (b) were the same as those obtained when the blocks were first extracted and the loads subsequently applied. This would imply that the load distribution is independent of the load path, which is basically what Best (1971) and Burman (1971), among others, determined. The physical experiments showed that this determination is certainly not correct. It has been determined that the numerical result of load path independence is a result of the numerical iteration process, (Byrne, 1972).

Essentially the shear stress is a linear function of normal stress and the process of solving the finite element equations is by satisfying compatability. Therefore for each imbalance of strain at a node the strain correction brings the stress back onto another shear versus normal stress curve. This results in a linear relationship between shear and normal stress and makes the whole deformational response load path independent, even with the introduction of the supposed non-linearities. It is therefore important and necessary to investigate this numerical problem in greater detail.

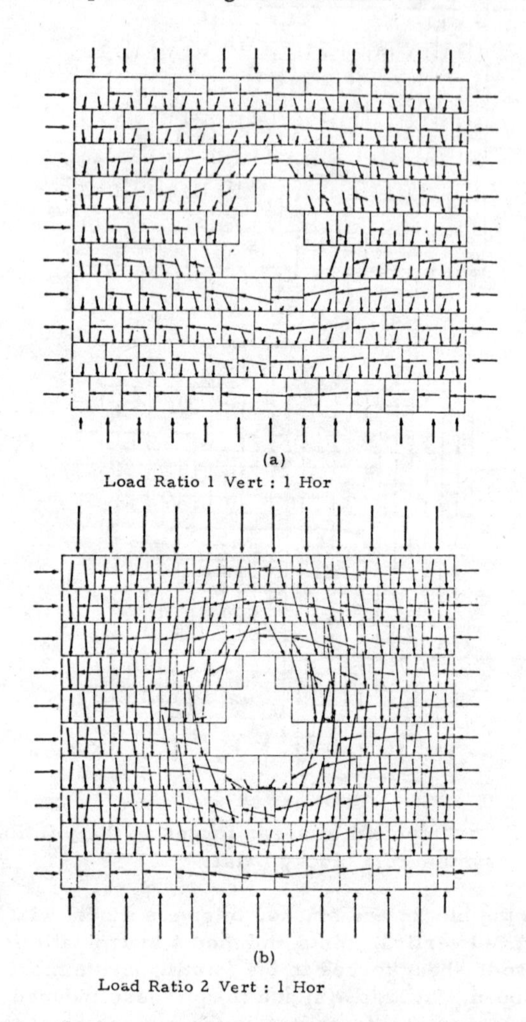

Fig. 6. Six blocks removed and the imposed load ratios vary Vert. load/Horiz. load - 1 then 2.

For the moment however, if the aforementioned limitation is recognised it is still possible to glean some very useful information from the numerical work and compare this with experimental work on some physical models.

INDIVIDUAL BLOCKS

In the numerical experiments performed it is found that the load distribution for the different geometries of block openings created is very much dependent on the mechanisms of slip and rotation which is basically a manifestation of geometry change. However, even with the one mechanism, namely rotation, incorporated in the numerical model it is found that comparable results with those of the physical photoelastic models are attainable and specific patterns of load distribution repeatedly appear on the boundaries of specific blocks. Once the overall boundary load distribution is determined the stress distribution within the individual blocks can be determined from another computer programme.

Figure 2(a) gives the block arrangement and the numbers used for their identification. Initially the three blocks 68, 69 and 70 were removed then 56 and 57 and finally 44.

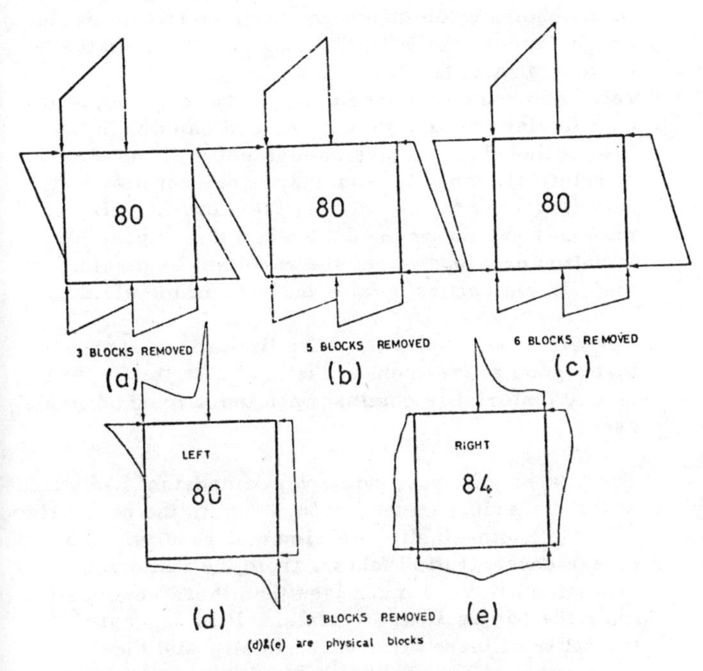

Fig. 7. Stress distribution on abutment block from both the numerical and physical models.

LOWER SUPPORTING ABUTMENT BLOCK NUMBER 80

As the blocks were extracted the loads on the supporting abutment block, number 80, remain much the same except for the horizontal thrust which increases, Figure 7(a) and (b) and (c).

CONTACT LOAD DISTRIBUTIONS ON A BLOCKY SUBGRADE

It is clear (Lee, 1963 and Chappell, 1967) that under certain conditions of foundation rigidity and Poisson's ratio the contact shear forces have little effect on the distribution of the normal contact forces. These contact shear forces however can change the normal load distribution considerably if slip and rotation of the material making up the supporting subgrade is possible.

In Figure 9 the contact stresses between a rigid and semi-flexible foundation on a blocky subgrade are shown. Here it is evident that the elastic interaction between the blocks and foundation is masked by slip and rotation of individual blocks, and as this slip is inhibited, the stress distribution tends to that of a continuum. The important point to note here is that the elastic interaction of the blocks and foundation give a definite stress distribution on the boundary of the blocks. This in effect can control subsequent mechanisms of deformation, especially rotation, and consequent failure modes.

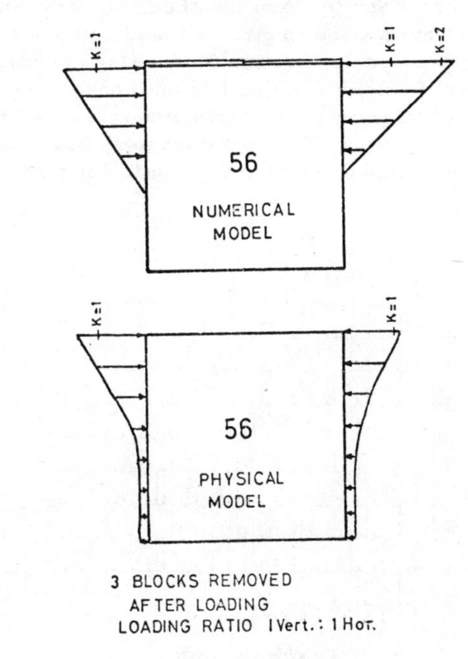

Fig. 8. Stress distribution on hanging wall block from both the numerical and physical models.

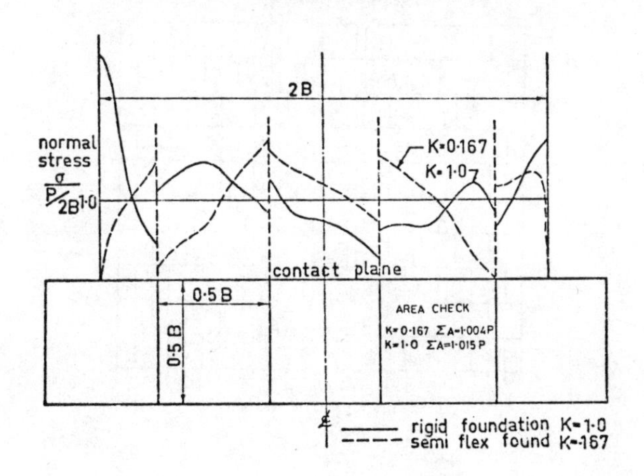

Fig. 9. Stress distribution at contact plane between foundations of varying stiffness and blocky subgrade.

Difficulty is encountered if the elasticity of each block is included in the general computer programme because of the large storage capacity required. Nevertheless if the load distribution in a blocky material is to be examined with a computer, especially if the failure of individual blocks is to be included, the elastic response of individual blocks should be considered.

LOAD DISTRIBUTION WITHIN A BLOCKY SUBGRADE

With the numerical experiments performed in this instance, two stacking geometries were examined, Figures 2(a) and (b), and the shear stiffness in these models were varied to give stiff and soft joints as defined previously, Section 5.1. Also examined was the effect load distribution has on blocks when either a flexible or rigid load distribution is applied to the blocky subgrade. The resultant load distributions from these experiments are given in Figures 10(a) and (b).

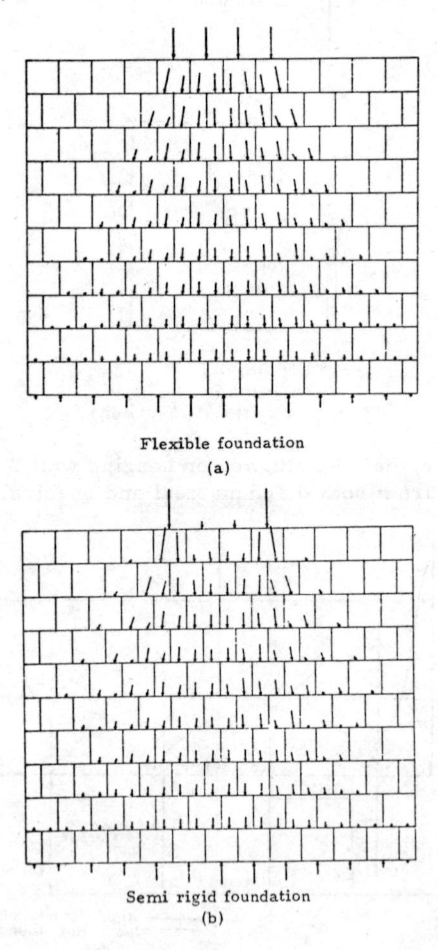

Fig. 10. Load distribution in block subgrade from flexible and semi rigid foundations.

DISCUSSION

Though the numerical method used in the experiments performed show general agreement with the form of results produced from the photoelastic method, the method still has limitations to its general applicability. Only one basic mechanism namely rotation, is included in the numerical model, where in the photoelastic models two are operative, namely slip and rotation. Another important factor not included in the numerical models is the elasticity of the individual blocks. This, however, only appears to be significant where the stress gradients are high in the region of large stress intensities. It is suggested that in these regions the deformations are relatively large so as to cause local geometry changes.

In the choice of elements and their distributions the programme is not sensitive enough to pick up the development of tension. That is, tension is relieved once it is experienced at the centroid of the chosen element and the load re-evaluated with the load relieved in the tension element. If the element is relatively long, tension may occur but not necessarily at the centroid of the element. Hence the loads are not re-evaluated and the impossible situation develops where the resultant load acting on the element occurs outside the area of the element.

Nevertheless, even with these limitations it appears that a good assessment of the load distribution in a blocky material is obtained with the numerical model used.

There are, however, some very important limitations to the numerical method brought out in the comparison with the photo-elastic experimental results. The stress concentration factors from the numerical examples are very much less than those obtained from the physical experiments. It is suggested that the cause of these differences is slip and the consequent geometry changes. In the numerical model slip is as yet not incorporated whereas in the physical models it is a reality and its effect is of some significance. The load distributions in individual blocks for the numerical and photoelastic models are much the same except the stress concentration on the blocks are less than those of the numerical models.

REFERENCES

BANKS, C. B., and Sokolowski, M., 1968, On Certain Two Dimensional Applications of the Couple Stress Theory, International Journal of Solids and Structures, Vol. 4, No. 1.

BEST, B. S., 1971, An Investigation into the Use of Finite Element Methods for Analysing Stress Distribution in Block Jointed Masses, Thesis (Ph. D.), James Cook University of North Queensland, Australia.

BRAY, J. W., 1966, Limiting Equilibrium of Fracture and Jointed Rocks, Proceedings, 1st Congress of the International Society for Rock Mechanics, Lisbon, Vol. 1, pp. 531-353.

BURMAN, B. C., 1971, Numerical Approach to the Mechanics of Discontinua, Thesis (Ph. D.), James Cook University of North Queensland, Australia.

BRYNE, J., 1972, Non Linear Numerical Model for Discontinua Rock Masses, Thesis (M. Eng. Sc.), James Cook University of North Queensland, Australia.

CHAPPELL, B. A., 1967, Stress Distribution in Discontinua, Thesis (M. Eng. Sc.), University of Melbourne, Australia.

CHAPPELL, B. A., 1973, Mechanics of Blocky Material, Thesis (Ph. D.), Australian National University.

GOODMAN, R. E., TAYLOR, R. L., and BREKKE, 1968, A Model for the Mechanics of Jointed Rock, Proceedings, A. S. C. E. Journal of Soil Mechanics and Foundations Division, Vol. 94 : SM3, pp. 637-59.

LAFEBER, D., 1963, On the Spatial Distribution of Fabric Elements in Rock and Soil Fabrics, 4th Australian and New Zealand Conference on Soil Mechanics and Foundation Engineering, Adelaide.

LEE, I. K., 1963, Elastic Settlement of Footage with a Rough Interface, 4th Australian and New Zealand Conference on Soil Mechanics and Foundation Engineering, Adelaide.

MINDLIN, R. D., and TIERSTEN, H. F. 1962, Effect of Couple Stresses in Linear Elasticity, Arch. Ration Mech. Analysis, Vol. 11, p. 415.

TROLLOPE, D. H., 1969, The Mechanics of Discontinua or Elastic Mechanics in Rock Problems, Rock Mechanics and Engineering Practice (ed. by Stagg and Zienkiewicz), Wiley and Sons.

ZIENKIEWICZ, O. C., and VALIAPPAN, S., and KING, I. P., 1968, Stress Analysis of Rock as a No Tension Material, Research Report, University of Wales, Swansea, Geotechnique, Vol. 28, p. 56.

L'INFLUENCE DES DIMENSION DE L'ÉCHANTILLON EXAMINÉ SUR LA RÉSISTANCE D'UN AXE RÉSISTANCE POLAIRE

DIMENSIONS INFLUENCE OF TESTED SAMPLE ON ITS SINGLE-AXIAL HARDNESS - POLAR HARDNESS

EINFLUSS DER ABMESSUNGEN DER GEPRÜFTEN PROBE AUF DEREN EINACHSIGE FESTIGKEIT - POLARFESTIGKEIT

Milan CVETKOVIĆ

Dipl.-Ing.

Faculté des Mines à Belgrade

Yugoslavia

Résumé

Vu des résultats jusqu'à présent de la recherche de l'influence des dimensions et des formes de l'échantillon examiné sur la valeur de la résistance d'un axe sur la pression, lesquels sont déterminés dans les laboratoires de monde entier, les relations de la recherche sont élargies dans ce travail. Il était suivi simultanément sur les matériels examinés et les roches tant l'influence des rapports h/a /rapport de l'hauteur et du côté du prisme/ que l'influence de la grandeur et de la forme de la surface de la coupe en travers de l'échantillon examiné. Embrassant au cours des essais tous ces rapports par un large spectre des valeurs différents, il est constaté par là, le rapport h/a où la dimension de l'échantillon n'influence pas sur la valeur de sa résistance d'un axe sur la pression. De cette manière, sans influence des dimensions, la résistance obtenue sur la pression, est définie comme RESISTANCE POLAIRE sur la pression d'un axe σ_{pp}-/$kpcm^{-2}$/.

Summary

Having in mind the up to now researching results of dimensions and tested sample effect on the value of uniaxial pressure hardness being established in the laboratories all over the world, the up to now applied relations in this kind of research work have been enlarged. Both the effect of the relation h/a /prism height and side relation/ and the effect of size and the shape of the tested sample cross section surface has been followed at the same time on the tested materials and stones. Including all these relations during experiments in wide spectrum of various values, such relation h/a has been defined - where the sample dimension has no effect to its uniaxial pressure hardness value. In this way the achieved pressure hardness has been defined as POLAR HARDNESS to the uniaxial pressure σ_{pp} - /$kpcm^{-2}$/ without dimensions effect.

Zusammenfassung

Mit Rücksicht auf die bisherigen Forschungsergebnisse des Einflusses der Abmessungen und Form der geprüften Proben, auf den Wert deren einachsige Druckfestigkeit, die in den Labors in der ganzen Welt festgestellt wurden, sind in dieser Tätigkeit die bisher angewandten Forschungsrelationen erweitert. An den geprüften Materialien und Feldern wurde gleichzeitig sowohl der Einfluss der Beziehungen h/a /Beziehung der Höhe und Seite des Prismas/ als auch der Einfluss der Grösse und Form der Fläche des Querschnittes der geprüften Probe verfolgt. Im Laufe der Experimente wurden alle diese Beziehungen mit einem weiten Spektrum verschiedener Werte umfasst und es wurde eine solche Beziehung h/a bestimmt, bei welcher die Abmessung der Probe keinen Einfluss hat auf den Wert deren einachsige Druckfestigkeit. Auf diese Weise wurde die Druckfestigkeit, erhalten ohne Einfluss der Abmessungen, als POLARHAERTE auf einachsigen Druck σ_{pp} / $kpcm^{-2}$/ definiert.

INTRODUCTION

Dans le dernier temps, une attention particulière est prêtée au problème de la classification des roches de la mécanique expérimentale. Un des critériums essentiels pour la classification des roches est basé sur la determination de la résistance d'un axe sur la pression. Ayant en vue ce critérium, il se pose sans équivoque la question de

./.

l'échantillon représentatif sur lequel sera la valeur de la résistatance d'un axe sur la pression. Néanmoins, le problème essentiel déterminera les dimensions de l'échantillon représentatif. Les recherches expérimentés de Kuznjecov, Protodjakonov, Kolfman, Ćirkov, ensuite les essais effectuées par Pforz, Veber, Rosetz etc. démontrent certainement l'influence des dimensions de l'échantillon sur la résistance d'un axe. Dans les laboratoires de mécanique des roches à la Faculté des Mines à Belgrade, à la Faculté des Mines à Tuzla ainsi qu'à l'Institut des Mines à Tuzla d'une part dans la laboratoire de l'Académie de Cracowie /Pologne/, l'auteur avait atteint à la recherche de l'influence des dimensions de l'échantillon examiné sur la valeur de la résistance d'un axe ainsi que sur les qualités de déformation du sel gemme et du béton. Le but essentiel de ces recherches était de définir par le moyen expérimental l'échantillon représentatif, c'est-à-dire l'échantillon dont la résistance d'un axe ne sera pas influencée par les formes et les dimensions.

E S S A I S

Au début de ces recherches, pour un des plus favorables roches est choisi le sel gemme des Mines Tušanj. Dans ce but, il était préparé 156o échantillons de diverses dimensions en forme prismatique de coupe carré en travers. Suivant la grandeur du côté du carré de la base, tous les échantillons sont divisés en lo séries, comme suit :

Série 3 -	avec coupe	en travers	F =	9	cm^2
Série 4 -	"	"	F =	16	cm^2
Série 5 -	"	"	F =	25	cm^2
Série 6 -	"	"	F =	36	cm^2
Série 8 -	"	"	F =	64	cm^2
Série 1o -	"	"	F =	1oo	cm^2
Série 15 -	"	"	F =	225	cm^2
Série 2o -	"	"	F =	4oo	cm^2
Série 3o -	"	"	F =	9oo	cm^2
Série 35 -	"	"	F =	1225	cm^2

Toutefois, toute la série comprenait les échantillons aux diverses valeurs du rapport de l'hauteur et du côté de la base - rapport h/a. Ce rapport avait les valeurs suivant dedans de chaque série: o,5 ; o,75 ; 1,oo ; 1,5o ; 2,5o ; 3,oo et 4,oo. Chaque rapport appliqué dans toutes les lo séries examinées, est le plus fréquamment recherché sur les 5o échantillons adéquats afin que les résultats soient définis avec certitude statistequement. Ce grand nombre des essias répétés était particulièrement indispensable à cause du grand dégré de l'anistropie mécanique des échantillons examinés du sel gemme. Cependant, par l'augmentation des dimensions de l'échantillon examiné leur nombre s'était diminué vu de la grande difficulté lors de la préparation des échantillons des dimensions assez grandes comme sont les échantillons de la série 2o, 3o et 35.

Fig. 1 - Aspect du groupe des échantillons du sel gemme des séries 15, 2o et 3o préparés pour les essais

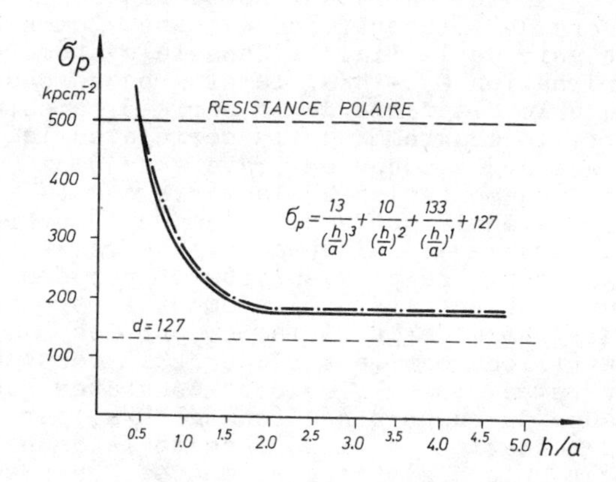

Fig. 2 - Interprétation graphique de la dépendance de la résistance d'un axe sur la pression du rapport h/a pour les échantillons de la série 4

Sur la base de l'interprétation graphique de tableau ainsi effectuée et de leur analyse, pour chaque série recherchée est tiré le terme mathematique définissant la dépendance de la résistance d'un axe /σ_p/ du rapport h/a. La dépendance constatée est définie par le polynome du troisième dégré, comme suit :

$$\sigma_p = \frac{A}{/\frac{h}{a}/^3} + \frac{B}{/\frac{h}{a}/^2} + \frac{C}{/\frac{h}{a}/} + D$$

dans lequel est :

σ_p - résistance d'un axe sur pression/$kpcm^2$/
h - hauteur de l'échantillon /cm/
a - côté de la base /cm/
A,B,C et D - coefficients dépandant de la grandeur de la coupe en travers de l'échantillon examiné

ANALYSE DES RESULTATS

Le diagramme de la dépendance σ_p du rapport h/a de chaque des lo séries recherchées démontre que la résistance d`un axe sur la pression est échangée considérablement avec la modification du rapport h/a à la même surface de la coupe en travers. Pourtant, on peut de même en conclure que dans la suite des valeurs h/a existe une valeur limite s`élevant h/a = 1,75. Pour toutes les valeurs h/a elevées de 1,75, la résistance sur la pression devient constante et le diagramme de la figure 2 s`approche à l`asymptote. En échangeant le rapport h/a au dessous de 1,75, la résistance d`un axe augmente brusquement pour atteindre au rapport h/a = o,5 la valeur de 5oo kpcm^2.
En vue d`une analyse plus facile des données obtenues, les résultats de toutes les recherches sont interprétés dans un système commun de coordination $\sigma_p$-h/a de la fig. 3. Grâce à l`analyse du diagramme de la fig. 3 représentant les résultats de 156o échantillons du sel gemme de differentes dimensions, on peut remarquer sauf la dépendance antérieurement prouvée σ_p au rapport h/a et la dépendance aussi de la résistance à la grandeur de la surface de la coupe en travers de l`échantillon examiné. Comme on peut voir de la fig. 3. dans le système de coordination $\sigma_p$ - h/a, la plus basse position a le diagramme de la série 3, c`est-à-dire le diagramme de la série avec la surface de la coupe en travers de 9 cm^2.
Avec l`augmentation de la série c`est-à-dire avec la surface de la coupe en **travers** le diagramme de la dépendance de résistance monte de plus en plus et par conséquent tout à fait sur le sommet se trouve le diagramme de la série 3o dont les échantillons ont la surface de la coupe en travers de 9oo cm^2. On peut constater que à cause du rapport non échangé h/a, par l`augmentation de la surface de la coupe en travers, la résistance augmente. Cependant, comme on peut conclure de la fig. 3, l`influence h/a σ_p par l`augmentation de la surface F devient moins accentuée et le diagramme des séries élevées se redresse.
Une donnée particulièrement remarquable sur le diagramme la fig. 3 est le point où les diagrammes de toutes les séries examinées se coupent. Ce point est nommé le POLE, c`est-à-dire la RESISTANCE POLAIRE. En ce cas, lors de la recherche du sel gemme, le pôle est défini dans le système de coordination σ_p-h/a par h/a = 0,5 par une ordonnée σ_p = 5oo kpcm^2. Etant donné que toutes les courbes des séries examinées se coupent dans un demi-point par rapport h/a = o,5, on peut conclure que les di-dimensions de l`échantillon n`ont pas de l`influence sur sa résistance d`un axe sur la pression si ses dimensions peuvent satisfaire la condition que h/a = o,5.
Puisque l`échantillon du rapport h/a = o,5 peut être défini par le rapport des surfaces en considération de la surface chargée, c`est-à-dire la surface sur laquelle agissent les coupes de mâchoire de la surface non chargée, c`est-à-dire sur la surface du revêtement, on peut conclure que lors de la détermination de la résistance d`un axe sur la pression des échantillons du sel gemme, l`effet des dimensions sur la valeur de la résistance pourra être évité uniquement dans le cas où l`échantillon satisfait la condition que h/a = o,5, ou que la surface chargée de l`échantillon - la surface de toutes les deux bases soit :gale à la surface du revêtement de l`échantillon examiné c`est-à-dire o/n = 1,o.

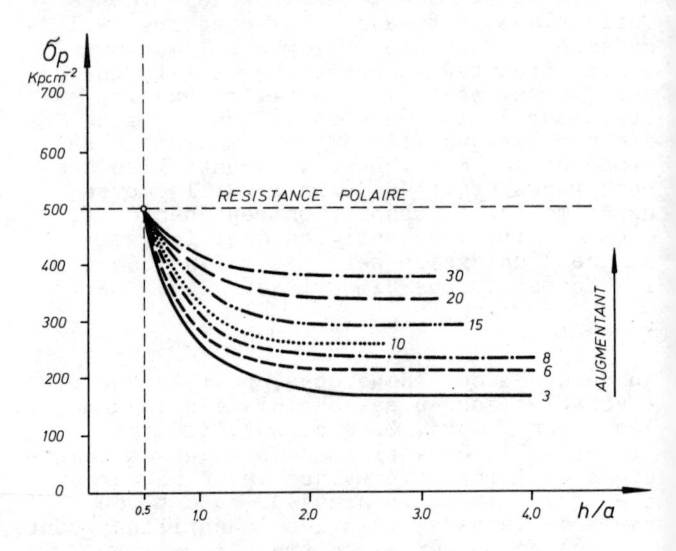

Fig. 3. Aperçu graphique de la dépendance de la résistance d`un axe sur la pression au rapport h/a et à la surface de la coupe en travers F pour le sel gemme

Dans ces conditions, la résistance définie sur la pression est nommée, comme on l`avait déjà dit, la RESISTANCE POLAIRE σ_{pp} /kpcm^2/.
Les 156o échantillons examinés du sel gemme des Mines Tušanj démontrent que la résistance polaire existe et qu`elle fait pour le sel gemme 5oo kpcm^2.
En ayant en vue la définition du pôle, les résistances polaires et les rapports des dimensions et des surfaces qui la conditionnent, on peut déterminer la résistance polaire sans égard de la grandeur absolue de l`échantillon examiné mais en satisfaisant les conditions pour h/a ou les conditions o/n.
Pour avoir la notion plus plastique de la dépendance σ_p au rapport h/a et à la grandeur de la surface de la coupe en travers, il est donnée leur interprétation graphique sur la fig. 4.
Vu que la résistance polaire est certainement définie pour le sel gemme, on pose sans équivoque la question si la résistance polaire est le phénomène constant qui est spécifique seulement pour les sels ou si la résistance polaire est la propriété de chque roche c`est-à-dire de

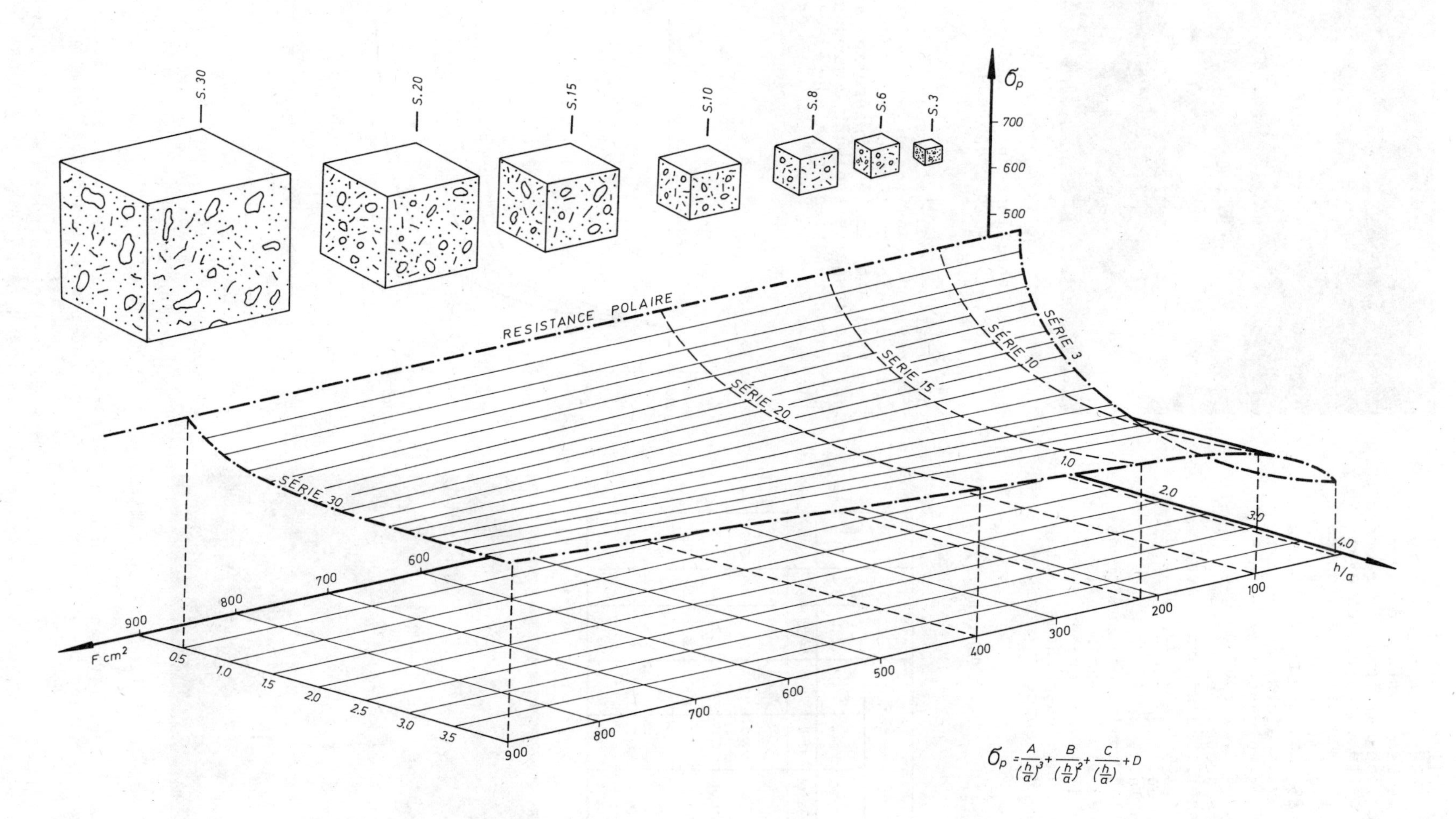

$$\sigma_p = \frac{A}{(\frac{h}{a})^3} + \frac{B}{(\frac{h}{a})^2} + \frac{C}{(\frac{h}{a})} + D$$

Fig. 4. Interprétation graphique d'espace de la dépendance σ_p à h/a et à la surface F determinée pour les échantillons du sel gemme

chaque matériel solide. Afin de répondre avec arguments à cette question, on avait abordé suivant le même système et avec le grand nombre des échantillons, le recherche du béton. Pour cette occasion, on avait préparé et examiné les séries suivantes : Série 3 - /F = 9 cm^2/, série 4 - /F=16cm^2/, série 5 - /F = 25 cm^2/, série 1o-/F=1oocm^2/. Le rapport h/a avait alors pour ces séries les valeurs suivantes h/a = o,5 ; 1,o ; 2,o ; 3,o et 4,o. Pour chaque rapport précité h/a dans toutes les séries était préparé 2o échantillons adéquats avec la composition granulométrique de sable définie, le facteur de ciment et d'eau bien determiné, avec la densité, la période de naturation, les conditions uniformes des contacts avec les éléments de la la presse au cours de la recherche, avec les vitesses strictement déterminées de la dispersion de la puissance au cours de la recherche etc.

Tableau 1.

DIMENSIONS a x b x c	h/a	$б_{(kpcm^{-2})}$			Koeficient des variations, ν %	Nombre des échantillons, n	Temps des essais, $t_{sec.}$
		$б_{min}$	$б_{max}$	б			
3×3×1 5	0,5	367,00	647,1	495,1	15,37	51	19-13
3×3×3	1	166,00	350,0	263,5	17,06	50	16-23
3×3×5	1,7	98,00	239,0	159,1	25,00	50	10-18
3×3×6	2	113,70	250,0	171,4	19,25	46	9-28
3×3×7,5	2,5	109,20	251,0	168,2	28,04	19	16-21
3×3×9	3	163,84	237,4	199,0	12,55	13	15-25
3×3×10	3,3	111,11	182,6	174,7	5,58	5	11-18
3×3×12	4,0	116,54	235,0	168,8	22,06	8	12-18

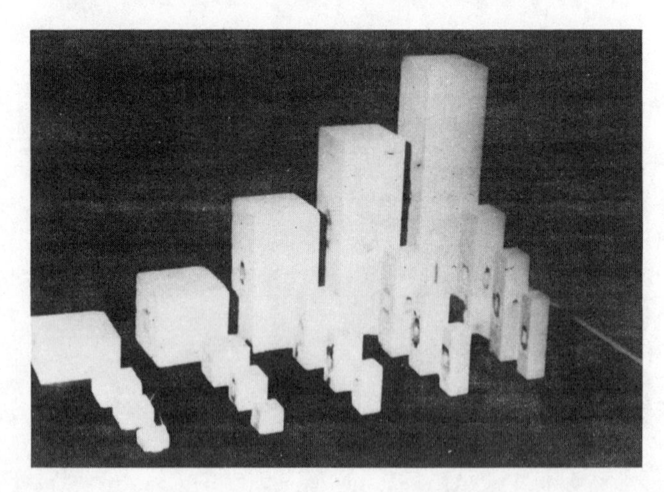

Fig. 5. Aspect des échantillons représentatifs du béton pour les séries particulières et les différents rapports h/a dans les séries recherchées

Fig. 6. Echantillons du béton des séries 3,4,5 et 1o préparées pour les essais

Tous les 4oo échantillons du béton ainsi préparés sont examinés à la même manière comme les échantillons de sel gemme. Les résultats sont inclus systèmatiquement et calculés dans les tableaux correspondantes. Leur interprétation graphique est donnée à la fig. 7.

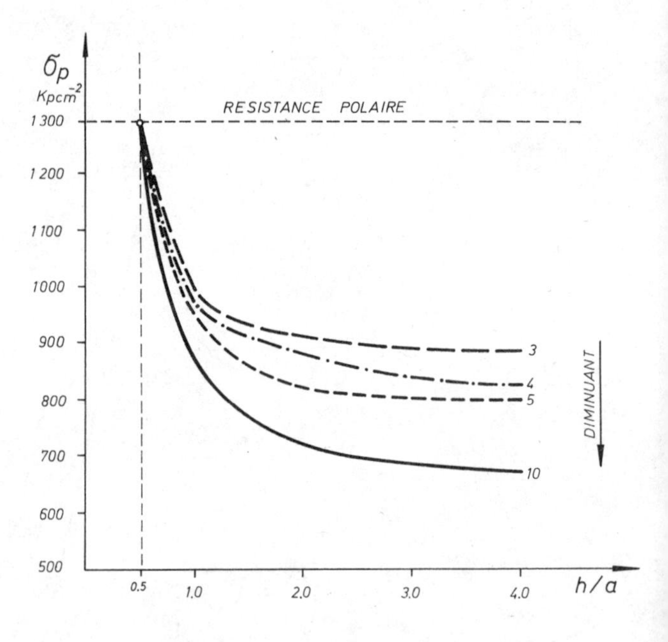

Fig. 7. Aspect graphique de la dépendance de la résistance d'un axe sur la pression du rapport h/a et de la graneur de coupe en travers de l'échantillon du béton

Grâce à l'analyse de la fig. 7. on peut constater quelques données importantes, comme suit :

- Toutes les courbes de la résistance d'un axe sur la pression au rapport h/a se

coupent à un point pareillement au sel gemme.
- L'effet de la grandeur de la surface de coupe en travers sur la valeur de la résistance à un axe sur la pression se manifeste à un ordre particulier, systematique de coupes des séries particulières.

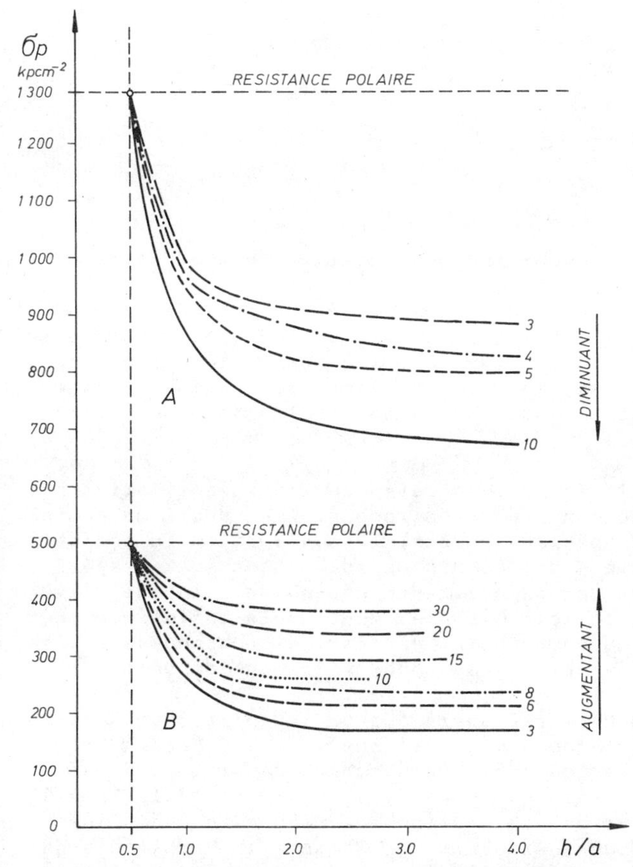

Fig. 8. Aperçu graphique de la dépendance de la résistance d'un axe sur la pression au rapport h/a et à la grandeur de la coupe en travers
A - béton ; B - sel gemme

Cependant, tant que pour le sel, par l'augmentation de la surface de la coupe en travers, les courbes dans le système de coordination $б_p$ - h/a montent de plus en plus, pour le béton il y a le cas contraire, c'est-à-dire par l'augmentation de la surface de la coupe de 9 à 1o cm^2, généralement dit, la résistance diminue et les courbes des séries particulières descendent. Etant donné que dans l'ensemble de ces essais sur le béton, les échantillons ne sont pas examinés avec les surfaces de coupe en travers inférieur de 9 cm et supérieur de 1oo cm^2, la dépendance ultérieure ne peut pas être annoncée. En général, ce qui est le plus important dans les essais rélatifs au béton, est la donnée que le béton ainsi que le sel gemme a sa RESISTANCE POLAIRE. Tant que pour le sel, elle s'éleve à 5oo $kpcm^{-2}$, pour le béton elle s'éleve à 13oo $kpcm^{-2}$.
Tandis que la résistance polaire pour le sel est définie avec 162 échantillons de différentes grandeurs absolus mais avec le rapport h/a = o,3 au coéfficient de la variation de 12%, la résistance polaire sur le béton est determinée avec 8o échantillons au coefficient de variation de 13,8%.
Si dans l'intérêt d'une analyse efficace des phénomènes de la résistance polaire, on présente les données rélatifs aux essais du sel gemme et du béton dans le système de coordination commun $б_p$ - h/a, on obtient la fig. 8. Afin d'eclaircir la résistance polaire comme une notion par les preuves nouveaux et les faits, on avait examiné en ce sens le plâtre et le grès. Le plâtre est examiné à l'aide des séries 3,4,5 et 1o avec le rapport h/a = o,5. La résistance polaire du grès est définie par les séries 3,4 et 5. La résistance polaire du plâtre est 16 $kpcm^{-2}$ tandis que la résistance polaire du grès est 43o $kpcm^{-2}$. Les valeurs de la résistance polaire du plâtre et du grès de quartz sont données dans le diagramme de la fig. 8 comme les points au rapport h/a = o,5.

C O N C L U S I O N

En examinant la résistance à un axe sur la pression des échantillons du sel gemme et du béton en forme prismatique de différentes dimensions et de leurs rapports, on avait constaté tels rapports où sans égards à la grandeur absolue de l'échantillon examiné, on a toujours la même valeur de la résistance de pression d'un axe pour le roche déterminé ou le matériel. Cette valeur dans le diagramme $б_p$ - h/a est determinée par le point où se coupent les diagramme des résistances des séries particulières. Le point de coupe est nommé le POLE et la valeur correspondante de la résistance est définie comme la RESISTANCE POLAIRE.
En recherchant le sel gemme, le plâtre et le grès de quartz où avait apparu le pôle, c'est-à-dire la résistance polaire, il est annoncé la possibilité que la RESISTANCE POLAIRE EST LA QUALITE DU MATERIEL.
Etant donné que la résistance polaire peut être définie soit sur les échantillons très grands et qu'elle reserve en elle-même l'effet des dimensions de l'échantillon examiné, on peut utiliser les échantillons très petits pour la recherche de la résistance à un axe sur la pression en vue d'étudier la classification mais à la condition que h/a = o,5, c'est-à-dire que la surface de toutes les deux bases où se fait la charge des échantillons soit égale au revêtement. Par conséquent, on peut conclure que le pilier d'entrechambre lors de l'exploitation du sel gemme ayant le rapport h/a = o,5 aura la même portance à cm^2 comme l'échantillon rélativement petit du sel gemme examiné dans le laboratoire avec le rapport h/a = o,5.

THE INFLUENCE OF UNEVENNESS OF LOADING SURFACES ON THE STRENGTH OF ROCK CUBES

L'INFLUENCE DE L'IRRÉGULARITÉ DES SURFACES DE CHARGEMENT SUR LA RÉSISTANCE DES CUBES DE ROCHE

DER EINFLUSS DER UNGLEICHMÄSSIGKEIT DER BELASTUNGSFLÄCHE AUF DIE FESTIGKEIT VON WÜRFELPROBEN DER GESTEINE

C. A. DEMIRIS

Dr. Eng. of Mines

Ministry of Public Works

Athens, Greece

SUMMARY The writer describes a method which he used for the quantitative determination of the unevenness of loading surfaces of cubic specimens of rocks. The degree of this unevenness is represented by an index da. Cubic specimens 10x10x10 cm of varying unevenness index da and of three different types of rock were tested under compression. It was concluded that the decrease of strength is in direct relation with the unevenness index and the compressive strength of the rock tested. The decrease in strength can exceed, in certain cases, 70% of the strength of the rock. A comparison of results obtained from rock specimens with results obtained from concrete specimens is also presented.

SOMMAIRE L'auteur décrit une méthode qu'il a utilisée pour la determination quantitative de l'irregularité des surfaces de chargement des spécimens cubes de roches. Le degré de cette irregularité est représenté par l'indice da. Des spécimens cubes, 10x10x10 cm, d'un indice d'irrégularité variant da et provenant de trois types différents de roches ont été essayé à la compression. Il a été conclu que l'abaissement de la résistance dépend de l'indice d'irrégularité et de la résistance en compression de la roche. L'abaissement de la résistance peut surpasser dans certains cas 70% de la résistance de la roche. Les résultats obtenus avec les spécimens de roche sont comparés avec des résultats obtenus avec des spécimens de béton.

ZUSAMMENFASSUNG Es beschreibt sich ein Verfahren des Verfassers für die quantitative Bestimmung des Ungleichförmigkeitsgrades der Ebenen der Würfelproben der Gesteine . Der Ungleichförmigkeitsgrad der Ebenen drückt sich mit dem Kennzeichen da aus. Darüberhinaus wurde studiert die Druckfestigkeit von Würfelproben drei vershiedenartiger Gesteine (Dimensionen 10x10x10 cm) mit Verschiedenem Ungleichförmigkeitsgrad (da) der Belastungsflächen. Aus diesem Studium haben sich ergeben Zusammenhänge der Verminderung der Druckfestigkeit der Würfeln im Verhältnis des Ungleichförmigkeitsgrades (da) und der Festigkeit der Gesteine . Somit würde durchgeführt eine Vergleichung zwischen Ergebnissen von Würfelproben aus Gesteinen und Würfelproben aus Beton.

INTRODUCTION

The compressive strength of natural rocks is determined by carrying out compression tests on cubic or cylindrical specimens. For this type of test it is necessary to form at least 2 surfaces which will serve as loading surfaces. Surfaces must be plane and smooth.

ASTM designation C170-50 states that the accuracy of strength results depends greatly on the uniformity of stress distribution on the loading surfaces and recommends an elaborate method for leveling and polishing these surfaces.

This paper attempts to study the effect of unevenness of loading surfaces on the compressive strength of cubic specimens, 10cm x 10cm x 10cm.

A number of tests were carried out on three of the most common rock types in Greece, i.e., marble, marly limestone, and marl. These rock types were selected because they cover a wide range of mechanical properties and because they lend themselves to the preparation of companion specimens of a high degree of similarity so that results are comparable.

For all rock types tested in compression, the load was applied in a direction perpendicular to the stratification of the rock.

DEFINITION AND METHOD OF DETERMINATION UNEVENNESS INDEX

In the course of this investigation it became necessary to introduce a parameter expressing arithmetically the degree of unevenness of the loading surfaces of specimens. This parameter was taken to be the mean distance of selected points on the loading surface, from the corresponding plane surface of the platens of the compression machine on which the specimens are placed during the test (Fig.2). This parameter is referred to as "unevenness index".

In the case of Fig.2, where the distance of the various points on the loading surface from the referenced plane are a_1, a_2, a_3, ... a_{16}, the unevenness index da in mm is equal to

$$da = \frac{a_1 + a_2 + \qquad + a_{16}}{16}$$

For the determination of the plane of reference (e) (Fig.2), and the unevenness index, the following method was applied:

The cube is placed on a machined cash-iron platen whose evenness has been checked. Readings are taken with a strain dial (sensitivity 0.0001 inch) mounted on a metalic stand that slides on the machined surface, as shown in Figure 1. The 16 readings obtained in this fashion are transferred onto graph paper, using a suitable scale, to show the relief of the surface. On this relief surface three points are selected in such a way that (a) the center of gravity of the relief surface falls within the triangle which is formed by the three points and (b) the plane formed by the three points does not intersect the relief surface.

Figure 1. Measurement of the unevenness of the loading surface of a 10cm cube of marl.

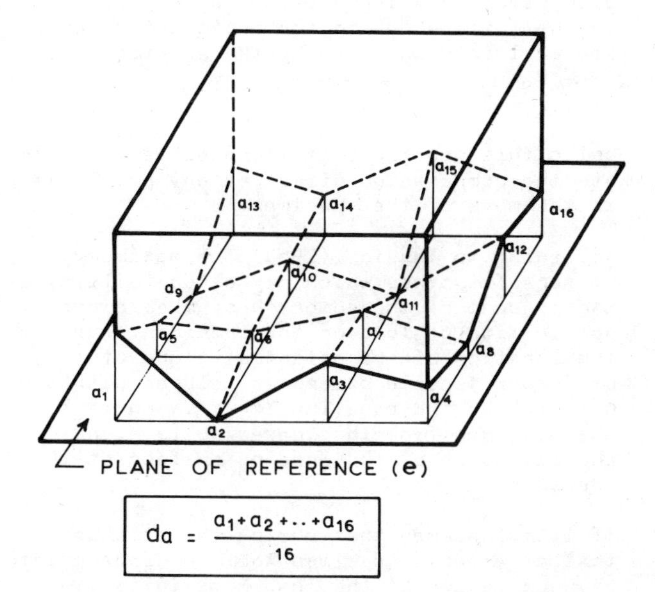

Figure 2. Specimen on level plate and determination of unevenness index da.

It is considered that this plane will coincide with the plane of the platen of the compression machine, i.e., this plane is taken as the reference plane for the determination of distances a_1, a_2, a_3,...... a_{16} and the unevenness index da (for more details see Demiris, 1973).

THEORETICAL ASPECTS ON THE BREAKING OF SPECIMENS WITH UNEVEN SURFACES.

The question of decrease of strength of cubic rock specimens due to the unevenness of the loading surfaces can be put forward as follows. Given a cubic specimen of rock with loading surfaces having an unevenness index da and elasticity modulus E, and then assuming that a load of magnitude P is transmitted by N loading points, it is necessary to find the distribution of stresses developed within the specimen and their unfavorable effects.

The cause of the experimentally observable decrease in strength of a cubic specimen with uneven loading surfaces can be attributed to (a) lateral tensile stresses which develop within the specimen and (b) the non-development of plane surfaces during loading by elastic and/or plastic deformations under a load considerably smaller than the load at failure.

Following Saint-Venant principle, a concentrated load applied on a section with width b will be linearly distributed along the whole section at a distance which for all practical purpose is equal to 2b.

According to Boussinesq theory, the compression stress p which develops at any point of the half space due to the action of a concentrated load P is given by the equation:

$$P = 3Pz/2\pi \sqrt{(r^2 + z^2)^5}$$

Using this equation, it is possible to estimate the compression stress at any point within the mass of the specimen.

According to Tassios (1958) the maximum lateral tensile stress which may cause failure, is independent of the number N of the points of application of load on the specimen, whereas the location of the potential plane of failure under tensile stress is related with the number N by the equation $Y = c/\sqrt{N}$ where Y is the distance from the loaded surface and c is the dimension of the loading surface of the specimen.

If it is assumed that during the breaking test of a cubic specimen the number of points of application of the load P is initially three (N=3), then the stresses developing at these three points are so high, that in spite of the induced triaxial stresses, there are plastic deformations tending to cause levelling of the surface, i.e., tending to increase the number of points N and to displace toward the loading surfaces the points of concentration of tensile stress. This displacement eliminates partially the undesirable tensile stresses, due to the development of frictional forces in the specimen close to the loading surfaces.

Therefore, in case of a low modulus of compressibility E this levelling action is obtained under relatively small loads and the remaining tensile stresses affect the failure of the specimen to a very small degree.

In the case of a rock specimen with a high modulus of elasticity, the relative magnitudes of loads are such that before they can induce the levelling action, they cause failure of the specimen.

It is consequently evident that it is more likely to have a large decrease of strength dB/B in a rock of high strength than in a rock of low strength. It is also evident that there is a higher likelyhood of failure of a cube of high strength along many vertical planes, due to the tensile stresses that will develop within the relatively free area of the specimen.

PREPARATION OF SPECIMENS - UNEVENNESS OF SURFACES.

A sufficient number of 10cm cubic specimens were prepared by a circular diamond cutting saw from the above mentioned three rock types. On the surfaces of the specimens measurements were made to determine the unevenness index da. The purpose of these determinations was firstly to draw conclusions on the unevenness created by cutting with the circular diamond saw on the surfaces during the preparation of the 10cm cubes, and secondly to classify the cubes in accordance with the degree of univenness of the loading surface.

From the evaluation of the above unevenness indices it was inferred that irrespective of the type of rock, the linear velocity, and the condition of wear of the cutting tool, the average unevenness index da was equal to approximately 0.116mm and the typical standard deviation σ was equal to 0.028mm.

In order to perform the investigation, the surfaces of specimens were leveled and polished, and in some cases, they were distorted so that the loading surfaces of each cube would have approximately the same unevenness index.

VARIATION OF CUBE STRENGTH AS A FUNCTION OF UNEVENNESS INDEX

The variation of the compressive strength of the prepared cubes with loading surfaces of varying unevenness index is shown in Figure 3. This diagram shows the percent decrease of the strength dB/B of the specimens as a function of the unevenness index of the loading surfaces. The curve (A) corresponds to marble cubes, the curve (B) to marly limestrone cubes and the curve (C) to marl cubes. The compressive strength B of each rock type, i.e., 1055 kg/cm^2 for the first type, 607 kg/cm^2 for the second and 159 kg/cm^2 for the third, was taken equal to the average strength of three cubes whose loading surfaces were carefully leveled and polished.

From the curves of Figure 3 it can be concluded that the decrease in strength dB/B of the cubes depends on the unevenness index da of the loading surfaces and on the strength of the rock. From this Figure it is noted that for any unevenness index the corresponding decrease in cube strength follows the order of the corresponding rock strengths. The case of marble cubes with da = 0.32 mm which showed a decrease dB/B larger than 70%, is characteristic. Similarly from the same Figure it is noted that up to about da=0.05 mm the decrease in strength in the weaker rock types is insignificant, whereas in the rock types of high strength this index causes a considerable decrease approaching in the case of marble 7.5%.

Figure 4 refers similarly to the decrease in strength of cubes, whose loading surfaces

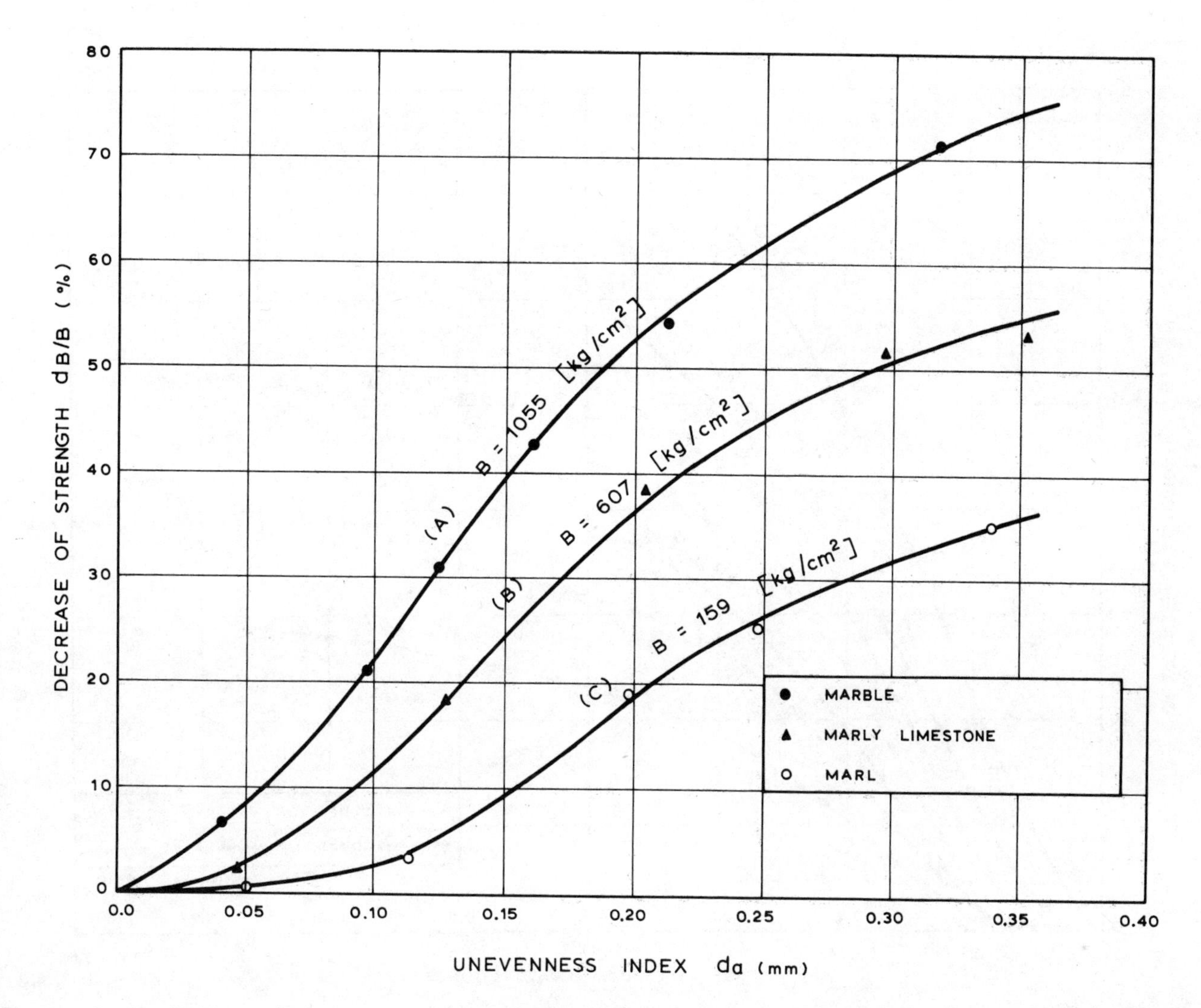

Figure 3 Variation of decrease of strength of 10cm cubes as a function of the unevenness index da and the strength of rock.

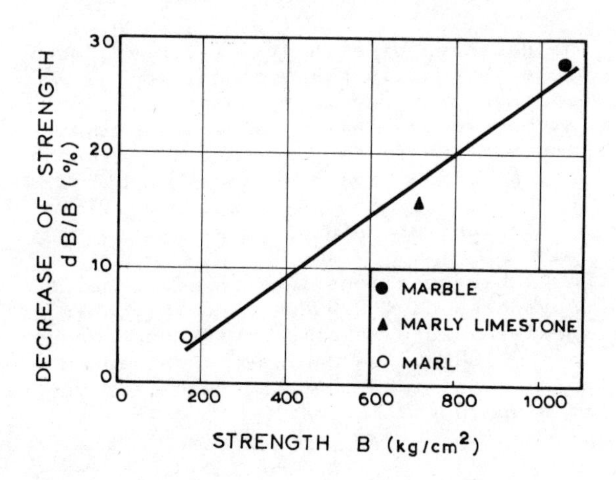

Figure 4 Decrease of strength of cubes with loading surfaces of da ≃ 0.116mm as a function of the strength of rock.

correspond to an unevenness index of about 0.116mm, relative to the compressive strength of the rock types. It is hereby reminded that this unevenness index is equal to the average index value that can be expected of the faces of 10cm cubes prepared by a circular cutting saw.

CORRELATION OF TEST RESULTS ON CUBES OF ROCK AND CUBES OF CONCRETE

As the structure of concrete resembles the structure of many types of natural rock, it was considered worthwhile to compare the results of tests on rock specimens with the results obtained with concrete specimens in the past by the writer (Demiris, 1973). Figure 5 which is similar to Figure 3, shows the change in decrease of strength of 10cm cubes made of natural rock, and the change in decrease of strength of 20cm cubes made of various classes of concrete. Due to the

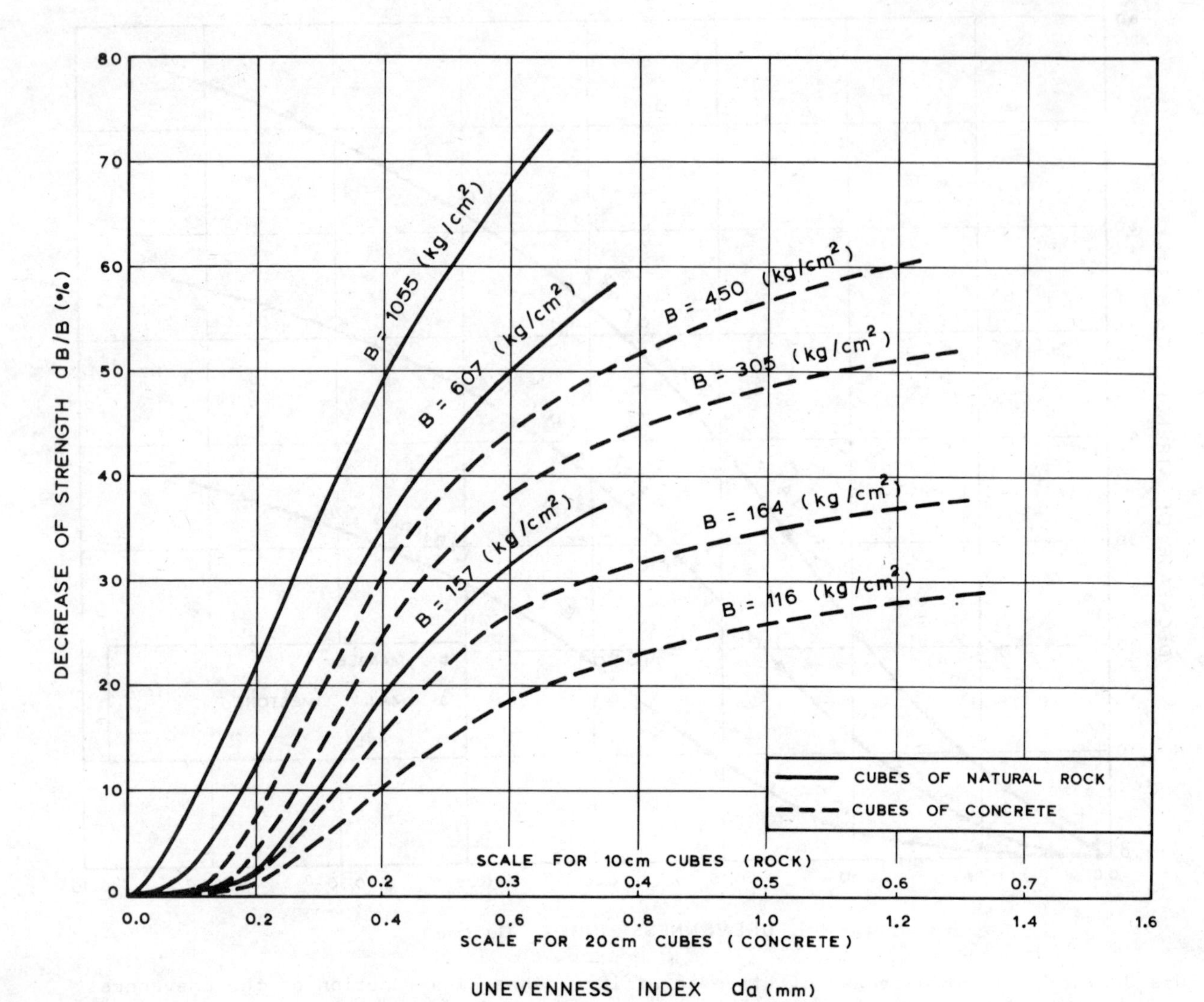

Figure 5 Comparison between tests on rock and tests on concrete (dB/B vs da).

difference between the size of specimens of concrete and natural rock, the unevenness index da (horizontal axis) of the cubic specimens of natural rock was halfed to make it correspond to the value of unevenness index of the cubic specimens of concrete.

From this Figure the following conclusions can be drawn:

1. The factor of one half by which the unevenness index of the smaller specimens was multiplied to obtain compatibility with the results obtained with the larger specimens (twice the size of the smaller ones) yielded a satisfactory comparison.
2. The results of tests on the four classes of concrete (compressive strength from 116 to 450 kg/cm^2) and the three types of rock, show that in both concrete and rock the decrease of compressive strength of cubes correlates with the unevenness index da in the same general manner.
3. The decrease of strength of cubes of concrete is equally proportional to the decrease of strength of cubes made of natural rock. This is shown also in Figure 6, where the decrease of strength refers to an unevenness index da=0.250mm in the case of concrete, and da=0.116mm in the case of natural rock.
4. For cubic specimens 10cm in size, having unevenness da $<$ 0.050mm, and for cubic specimens 20cm in size having unevenness da $<$ 0.100mm, the decrease in strength dB/B is not important, at least for values of B up to 450 kg/cm^2.

CASE OF TWO OPPOSITE LOADING SURFACES WITH DIFFERENT UNEVENNESS INDEX

The results discussed so far refer to tests performed on cubes having about the same unevenness index on both loaded surfaces. The

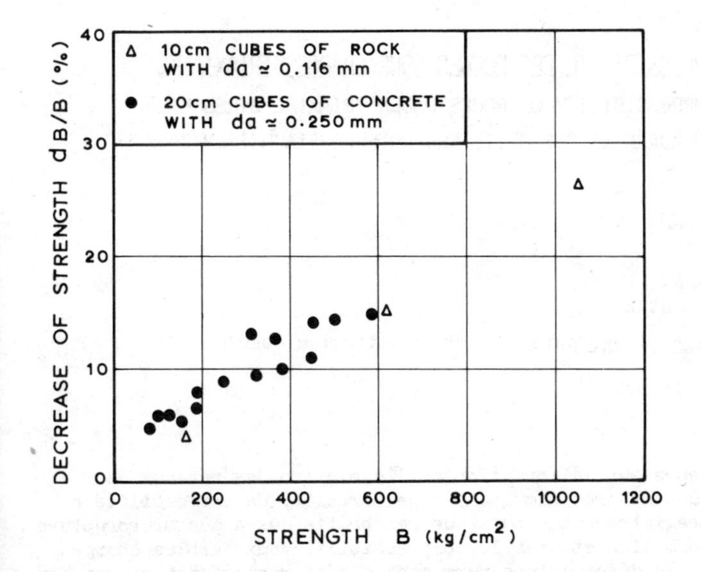

Figure 6 Comparison between tests on rock and tests on concrete (dB/B vs B).

similarity of results between tests performed on cubes of concrete and cubes of natural rock, as outlined in the previous section, suggests that it is possible to make certain predictions on the decrease of strength of cubes of natural rock, in the case where the two loaded sides have a different unevenness index, notwithstanding that this variant should be further investigated.

It has been observed from tests on cubic specimens of various classes of concrete where (a) the two loading surfaces had the same unevenness index (b) the unevenness index of one surface was equal to one half the unevenness index of the opposite surface and (c) one of the two loading surfaces was smooth (Demiris 1973), that the strength did not differ substantially. It is, therefore, inferred that also in the case of natural rock the decrease of strength of cubic samples must depend primarily on the surface having the greater unevenness index.

CONCLUSIONS

1. The decrease in strength of cubes of rock dB/B depends on the unevenness index da of the loading surface and on the strength B of the rock.

2. In rocks of high strength, there may be a decrease in strength of a cubic specimen of up to more than 70% of the strength of the rock, due to the unevenness of the loading surfaces.

3. The surfaces of cubes of rock, 10cm in size, cut by a circular diamond saw, have such an unevenness that a considerable decrease in strength may occur.

4. Cubes whose sides have an unevenness index da $\leq$ 0.05mm, showed a decrease in strength which is insignificant in the case of marl, marly sandstone, and other weak rocks, and which was considerable in the case of marble and other rocks of high strength.

5. The requirements for smoothness of the faces of cubic specimens destined for compression tests, should depend on the strength of the rock. For rocks of a very low strength the procedure of ASTM C170-50 may be simplified to include a simple levelling of the surfaces of the cubes to be tested.

6. There is a considerable similarity in the decrease of strength of cubes of natural rock and cubes of concrete.

REFERENCES

1. C. DEMIRIS: "Irregular Plane Faces of Concrete Moulds as a Cause of the Compressive Strength Reduction of Concrete Cube Specimens" First Greek Congress of Concrete, 1973.

2. TH. TASSIOS: "Sources of Scatter in Tests of Cement Mortar", Athens, 1958.

MICROFISSURATION, DÉFORMATION ET COMPRESSIBILITÉ DES ROCHES SOUS CHARGES TRIAXIALES

MICROFISSURATION, DEFORMATION AND COMPRESSIBILITY OF ROCKS UNDER TRIAXIAL STRESSES

MIKRORITZE, VERUNSTALTUNG UND ZUSAMMENDRÜCKBARKEIT DES GESTEINES UNTER DREIACHSIGEN DRÜCKEN

J. FARRAN
Professeur

R. PERAMI
Maitre-Assistant

Laboratoire de Minderalogie et Cristallographie de l'Université Toulouse

Toulouse, France

RESUME
L'effet des charges de confinement et celui des déviateurs sur la formation et l'évolution des réseaux de microfissures contenus dans les roches est étudié par des mesures simultanées de porosité, de perméabilité à l'air, de déformation axiale et transversale et par enregistrement acoustique des bruits dus à des microruptures. Le rôle essentiel de la porosité fissurale dans la déformation et dans la compressibilité aux faibles charges est mis en évidence et chiffré expérimentalement. Dans les déformations permanentes sans rupture des roches, on distingue la part revenant à la plasticité proprement dite et celle qui découle de l'extension ou de la fermeture du réseau de microfissures. Il est possible, ainsi, de faire apparaître différents types de comportement et de les rattacher aux caractères minéralogiques et structuraux des roches.

SUMMARY
The effect of confining pressures and deviatory stresses on formation and evolution of rocks microfissures is studied on different rocks, granites, limestones, dolomies, by means of simultaneous measures of porosity, air permeability, transversal and axial deformation and by acoustic recording of sounds produced by microbreakings. In deformation and compressibility under low pressures the essential role of fissural porosity is shown and experimentally figured. The considerable increase of deviatory stresses which are needed to get the microfissure system wider is analysed in terms of confinement. In permanent deformations without rock breakings, the part concerning the real plasticity is discerned from the one which concerns the extension and the closing of microfissures. So it is possible to make appear different kinds of reactions and to connect them with mineralogical and structural rock properties.

ZUSAMMENFASSUNG
Man prüft die Wirkung der Entsperrungsdrücken und die Wirkung der Drücken, die abweichen lassen auf der Bildung und auf der Entwicklung der Microritzennetzen, die in dem Gestein enthalten sind, durch gleichzeitige Maßnahmen und zwar die Porosität, die Luftdurchdringlichkeit, die senkrechte und quere Verunstaltung und das den Microbrüchen entsprechende Geräusch. Durch das Experiment bringt man ans Licht und beziffert man die Hauptrolle der spaltigen Porosität in der Verunstaltung und Zusammendrückarbkeit mit schwachen Drücken. In den bleibenden Verunstaltungen ohne Gesteinbrüchen, unterscheidet man die Verunstaltungen, dessen Ursache die Plastizität selbst ist, und die Verunstaltungen, dessen Ursache die Ausbreitung oder die Verschließung des Microritzennetzes ist. Dadurch ist es möglich, verschiedene Verhaltensarten hervortreten zu lassen und sie mit den mineralogischen und strukturaslischen Eigentümlichkeiten des Gesteines zu verbinden.

INTRODUCTION

Les roches renferment un grand nombre de discontinuités microscopiques qui peuvent être mises en évidence par injection de résine colorées très fluides (Farran, 1950), microcraquelures, entièrement situées à l'intérieur des cristaux et ne les traversant pas entièrement, microfissures ayant la dimension des cristaux, et microfractures recoupant un grand nombre de cristaux (Farran et Thénoz, 1965) - (Pérami, 1971). Ces discontinuités affaiblissent le matériau et le rendent plus déformable. De plus, la microfissuration dans une roche n'est pas une caractéristique stable ; elle peut varier avec l'altération et se modifier considérablement, aussi, au cours de sollicitations mécaniques, par déformations de microfissures anciennes ou par formation de microfissures nouvelles (Capdecomme et al., 1966). Les déformations linéiques ou volumiques des roches comprimées dépendent donc, à la fois, du comportement élastique et plastique de la matrice minérale et de l'existence des microfissures.

Nous étudierons, ici, les effets particuliers des microfissures anciennes et de la microfissuration nouvelle sur les déformations ainsi que sur la compressibilité des roches comprimées triaxialement. Nous nous limiterons aux effets des variations lentes de pression.

PRINCIPES DE DETERMINATION DE LA MICROFISSURATION ET DES DEFORMATIONS.

La microfissuration.

La formation d'une microfissure nouvelle s'accompagne d'accroissements de la porosité et de la perméabilité; elle est généralement brusque et se manifeste par un microchoc décelable acoustiquement. C'est par la mesure des variations de perméabilité et la détection simultanée des microbruits que nous caractérisons les évolutions de la microfissuration (Pérami, 1965) en dehors des mesures de déformation. Quand la charge croît progressivement, un seuil de microfissuration, caractérisé par un accroissement simultané de la perméabilité et des microbruits, est régulièrement mis en évidence. Ce seuil se situe entre deux phases successives :

- une phase de tassement, pendant laquelle les microdiscontinuités préexistantes tendent globalement à se fermer, ce qui entraîne une diminution de perméabilité;

- une phase de microfissuration, correspondant à l'ouverture de microfissures nouvelles qui accroissent la perméabilité en même temps que se multiplient les microbruits.

Les déformations.

Au cours de la compression d'une roche hétérogène, les contraintes et les déformations à l'intérieur du solide ne sont pas uniformes ; seules peuvent être commodément déterminées, sans ambiguité, les charges globales et les déformations globales de l'ensemble du volume hétérogène.

Si on considère une éprouvette cylindrique, la mesure de la déformation axiale moyenne ne présente pas, généralement, de difficultés particulières. Nous mesurons l'accourcissement total de l'échantillon R entre les pièces métalliques P_1 et P_2 qui transmettent la charge (figure 1) grâce à deux extensomètres E_1 et E_2 placés symétriquement par rapport à l'axe de compression. Un étalonnage préalable permet de tenir compte des déformations élastiques des pièces de compression P_1 et P_2.

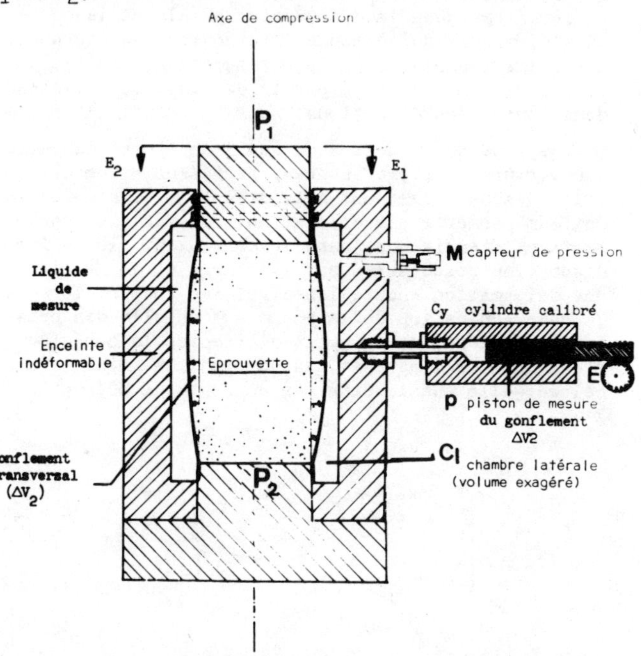

Figure 1 - MESURE DES VARIATIONS DE VOLUME DE L'EPROUVETTE (Schéma de principe).

La mesure des déformations transversales est plus délicate. Les mesures locales, effectuées sur une portion de la surface latérale des éprouvettes au moyen de jauges de contrainte, présentent des incertitudes analysées notamment par Morlier (1964). En particulier, le gonflement irrégulier de l'éprouvette en "tonneau" rend incertaine l'évaluation d'un gonflement moyen.

A la suite des expériences d'Adams et Williamson (1923) des mesures directes de déformations volumiques, basées sur le déplacement d'un liquide entourant l'éprouvette, ont été réalisées par Bridgman (1949) et c'est sur ce principe que nous avons effectué nos mesures. Dans le dispositif que nous avons mis au point (figure 1), l'éprouvette cylindrique enserrée par ses bases entre deux pistons de même diamètre P_1 et P_2 qui assurent la compression axiale, est enfermée dans une enceinte rigide remplie d'un liquide maintenu à une pression constante qui assure le confinement latéral. Cette pression est déterminée grâce à un capteur très sensible M. Le gonflement transversal ΔV_2 de l'éprouvette entraîne une diminution du volume annulaire dans la chambre latérale C_1 et un départ équivalent de liquide si la pression est maintenue constante ; ce liquide déplacé est recueilli dans un cylindre calibré C_y relié directement à l'enceinte. Le déplacement, dans ce cylindre, du piston de mesure (p) permet de déterminer, en pratique, des variations de volume de quelques mm^3 dans l'enceinte C_1. Un étalonnage, rendu nécessaire par les déformations de l'appareillage, est effectué en remplaçant l'éprouvette de roche par une éprouvette d'acier de modules élastiques connus.

Du gonflement transversal ΔV_2 de l'échantillon, on peut déduire une déformation transversale moyenne (d_2) considérée comme uniformément répartie sur toute la surface latérale du solide.

Sous charges triaxiales anisotropes, la déformation volumique ΔV est obtenue en retranchant, de la déformation transversale ΔV_2, la déformation volumique axiale ΔV_1 déduite de l'accourcissement axial moyen. Sous charges triaxiales isotropes, cas particulier du précédent, la détermination de ΔV permet de définir le coefficient de compressibilité de la roche et, par là, sa porosité (Capdecomme et al. 1966).

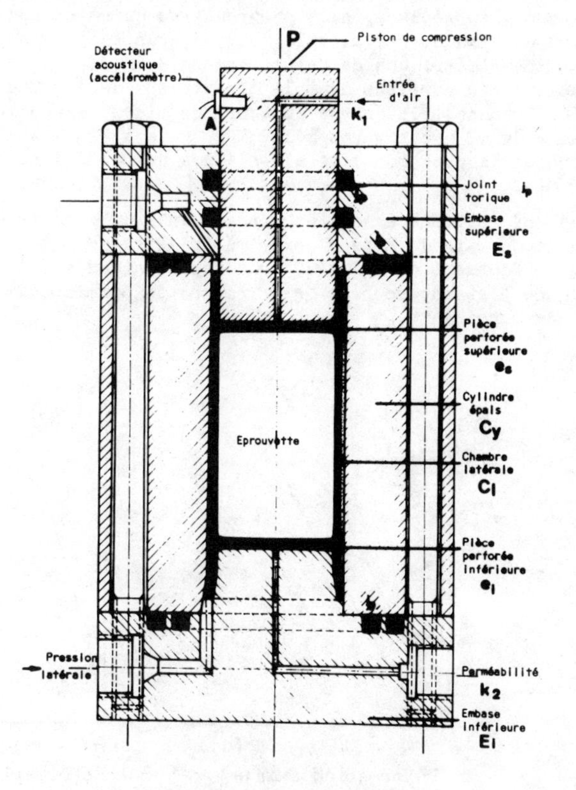

Figure 2 - CELLULE TRIAXIALE.

Finalement, nos mesures de déformation et de compressibilité qui s'appliquent à la totalité du volume de roche étudié, évitent toute ambiguité dans la définition des couples contraintes-déformations moyennes à l'intérieur des solides hétérogènes. Elles nous permettent d'atteindre des grandeurs mécaniques simples, commodément reliables entre elles, notamment un module d'élasticité moyen, un coefficient de Poisson moyen et un coefficient de compressibilité moyen.

EFFETS DE LA MICROFISSURATION SUR LES DEFORMATIONS SOUS CHARGES TRIAXIALES ANISOTROPES.

Le mode de déformation des microfissures a été étudié en complétant les mesures de perméabilité (k) et de déformation axiale (d_1) par des mesures de déformation transversale (d_2) dans une cellule de compression triaxiale spécialement réalisée (figure 2). Cet appareillage a déjà été décrit dans une publication antérieure (Pérami, 1971).

Sous confinement triaxiaux, les effets de la plasticité des minéraux prennent une importance croissante (Heard, 1960). Nous examinerons successivement la microfissuration et les déformations d'une roche très peu plastique (granite), puis celles d'une roche relativement plastique (calcaire).

Granite.

Comme on peut le prévoir théoriquement, sous charges triaxiales, les possibilités d'ouverture des microfissures par un déviateur de pression axial sont d'autant plus diminuées que la charge de confinement est plus forte. La charge correspondant au seuil de microfissuration est donc croissante, mais on retrouve, très nettement, comme dans les essais uniaxiaux, les deux phases successives de tassement et de microfissuration. Cependant, les variations de perméabilité sont, en général, plus progressives qu'en compression uniaxiale. Par exemple, sur un granite à cristaux centimétriques de Saint Germain de Modéon, exploité en carrière dans le département de la Côte d'Or (France), la charge au seuil de microfissuration passe de 60 MPa environ à 150 MPa, puis à 320 MPa lorsque la pression latérale s'élève de 0 à 25 puis 50 MPa.

Les déformations axiale et transversale du granite de Saint Germain de Modéon comprimé triaxialement sous un confinement de 25 MPa, sont représentées sur la figure 3 et rapprochées de la courbe de perméabilité k correspondante.

La déformation axiale (figure 3a) est quasi-linéaire de l'origine jusqu'à 300 MPa environ (branche OP) ; elle croît ensuite plus rapidement (branche PM_1). L'absence de courbure initiale indique le serrage quasi-complet des discontinuités préexistantes sous l'effet de la pression latérale. On comprend ainsi que, sous charges triaxiales, les roches obéissent plus rigoureusement aux lois de comportement mécanique des milieux continus (Habib, 1968). Le seuil de microfissuration, repérable sur la courbe de perméabilité (figure 3c) aux environs de 150 MPa, n'apparaît aucunement sur la courbe de déformation axiale. La forte courbure terminale de cette dernière ne résulte pas d'une déformation plastique du milieu continu, mais de l'ouverture de microfissures, car elle coïncide avec un fort accroissement de perméabilité entre P et M_1 (figure 3c) et avec une intensité sonore accrue (diagr. i, figure 3a).

La déformation transversale (figure 3b) présente les particularités suivantes :

- au début de la compression, mais seulement jusqu'au niveau İ du seuil de microfissuration S déterminé sur la courbe de perméabilité (figure 3c), la déformation transversale est approximativement linéaire ;
- au-dessus du seuil, l'accroissement de la fissuration entraîne un accroissement de la déformation transversale qui se manifeste à partir de İ, par une lente diminution de la pente de la courbe (figure 3b).
- au-dessus du point P et au même niveau de charge que P, la déformation latérale croît très fortement, en même temps que la déformation axiale et la perméabilité, tandis qu'augmente l'intensité des microbruits. Ces faits traduisent un accroissement généralisé de la porosité du solide à partir de fissures orientées dans toutes les directions.

On comprend qu'au-dessus du seuil de microfissuration l'ouverture de microfissures, préférentiellement orientées parallèlement à la direction de compression maximum permette une dilatation transversale supplémentaire, tandis que, dans le sens axial, le solide discontinu reste serré par la charge et donne lieu à une déformation encore linéaire. Par contre, lorsque la désorganisation de la roche à l'échelle des cristaux se généralise au point d'affecter la cohésion d'ensemble de l'agrégat, la déformation axiale s'accélère, elle aussi, dans une courbure de prérupture.

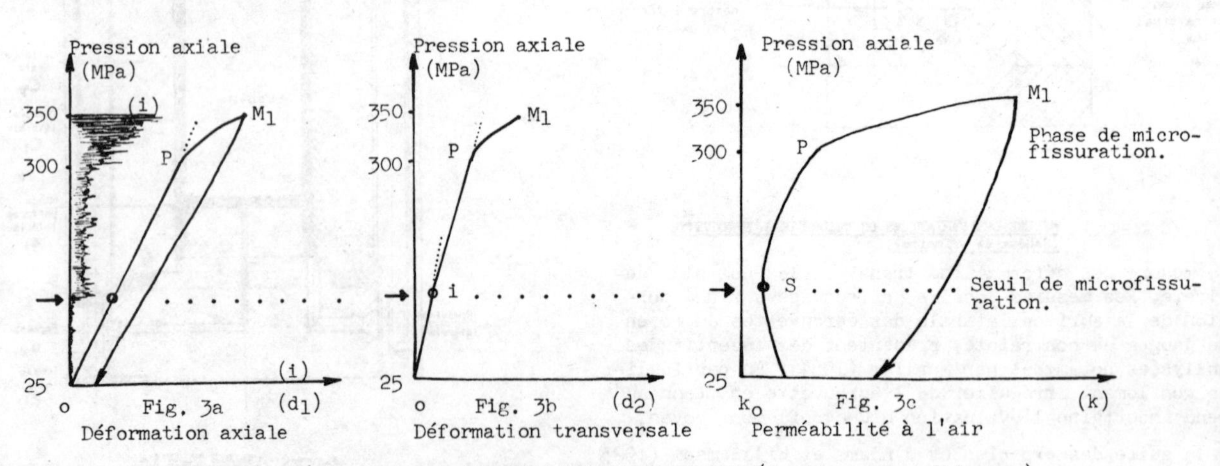

Figure 3 - COMPRESSION D'UN GRANITE DE SAINT GERMAIN DE MODEON (Confinement : 250 bars).

Ainsi, dans une roche cohérente comprimée triaxialement, le seuil de microfissuration n'apparaît pas sur la courbe de déformation axiale, mais se manifeste par un changement de pente sur la courbe de déformation transversale. Toutefois, la détermination du seuil de microfissuration à partir de cette seule courbe serait plus imprécise qu'à partir des courbes de perméabilité et des enregistrements acoustiques.

Des cycles successifs de compression-décompression entre 25 MPa et 350 MPa, sous un même confinement de 25 MPa, mettent en évidence l'importance des déformations résiduelles irréversibles successives, d_0d_1, d_1d_2, etc ... (figure 4a) sur les courbes de déformation axiale du granite de Saint Germain de Modéon. Ces déformations sont généralement interprétées comme d'origine plastique, les points P_1, P_2 etc ... étant considérés comme des seuils de plasticité. Cependant, dans cette phase de la compression, les déformations s'accompagnent d'accroissements permanents de perméabilité (figure 4b) et résultent donc, pour l'essentiel, de la formation des microfissures.

Nous appellerons déformations "pseudo-plastiques" ces déformations irréversibles liées à la microfragmentation. Elles peuvent se combiner ou non, à des déformations "plastiques vraies" dues à la plasticité de certains minéraux constituant la roche (feldspaths, par exemple).

L'effet cumulatif de "fatigue", produit, à chaque nouvelle alternance, par un nouvel accroissement de microfissuration, se manifeste sur les courbes de perméabilité par un abaissement progressif du seuil de microfissuration, S_1, S_2, S_3 etc ... (figure 4b); il n'apparaît pas sur les courbes de déformation qui conservent pratiquement la même pente, d'un cycle au suivant (figure 4a). Ainsi tant que la roche n'est pas complètement désorganisée sous la charge, la microfissuration nouvelle n'affecte pas notablement les déformations suivant l'axe de compression.

En définitive, des granites soumis à des alternances de compressions-décompressions triaxiales au-dessus du seuil de microfissuration, peuvent subir des déformations irréversibles importantes, à apparence plastique, mais qui s'accompagnent d'accroissements importants de perméabilité et résultent donc essentiellement d'une microfissuration.

Calcaire.

Rappelons que, sous charges uniaxiales, les calcaires cristallins, sont des roches relativement plastiques et peu microfissurables mécaniquement (Pérami, 1971). Par exemple, un calcaire de Saint Béat, à grains millimétriques (Haute-Garonne), soumis à une compression uniaxiale croissante, subit d'abord un tassement progressif jusqu'à un seuil de microfissuration élevé 80 MPa. Au-dessus de ce seuil, l'accroissement de perméabilité est le plus souvent brutal, par formation de grosses microfractures peu nombreuses. La rupture intervient, ensuite, assez rapidement, entre 100 et 120 MPa.

Sous charges triaxiales, les effets modérateurs de la plasticité de la calcite sur la microfissuration sont fortement accrus par le confinement. Avec le calcaire de Saint Béat, une pression latérale de 50 MPa suffit pour réduire considérablement les possibilités de microfissuration. C'est ainsi qu'une première compression jusqu'à 250 MPa ne produit qu'une variation relativement faible de la perméabilité (cycle 1, figure 5b). Par contre, la déformation résiduelle est très importante (cycle 1, figure 5a).

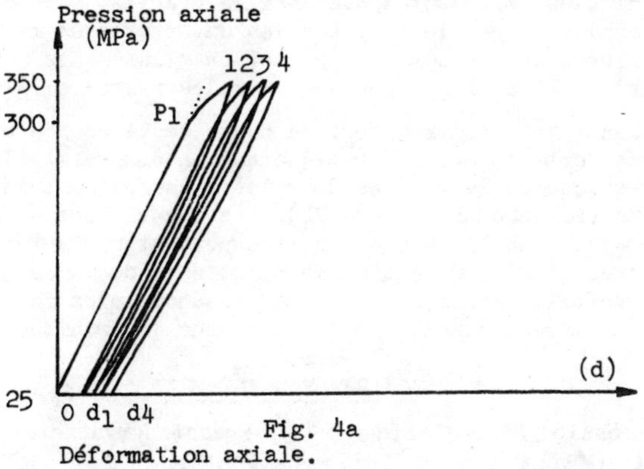

Pression axiale (MPa)
350
300
25
1234
P_1
(d)
0 d_1 d_4

Fig. 4a
Déformation axiale.

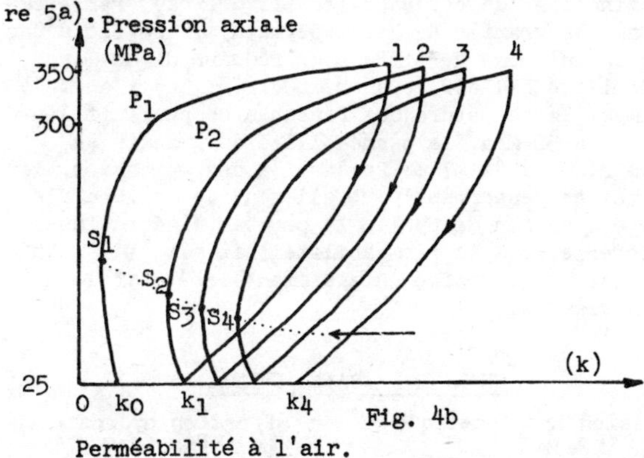

Fig. 4b
Perméabilité à l'air.

Figure 4 - GRANITE DE SAINT GERMAIN (Confinement 250 bars).

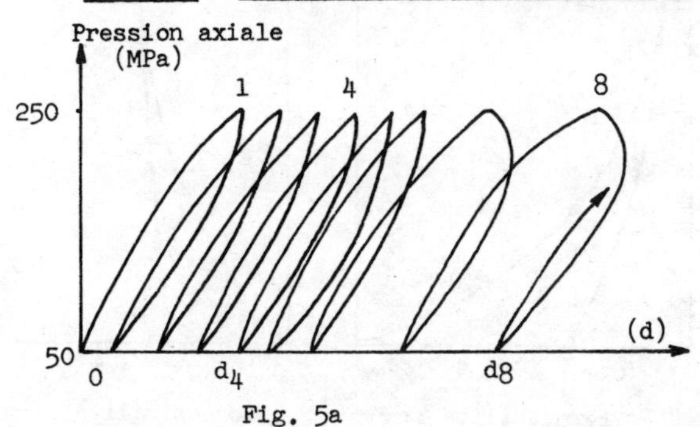

Fig. 5a
Déformation axiale.

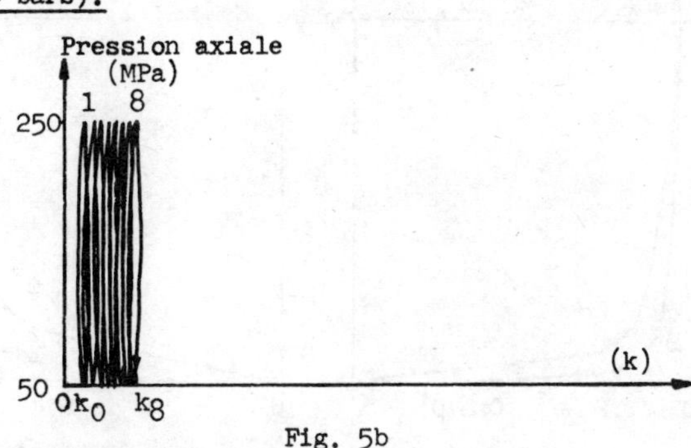

Fig. 5b
Perméabilité à l'air

Figure 5 - CALCAIRE DE SAINT BEAT (Confinement : 500 bars).

Des alternances de compression-décompression répétées entraînent de cycle en cycle, des augmentations de perméabilité très faibles (figure 5b), mais provoquent des déformations irréversibles considérables (figure 5a) donnant progressivement à l'éprouvette, initialement cylindrique, une forme en "barillet". Ce phénomène résulte des facilités de déformation plastique des cristaux de calcite (translations et macles mécaniques).

A la différence des granites les calcaires cristallins présentent donc des déformations irréversibles importantes qui ne s'accompagnent pratiquement pas d'accroissements de perméabilité parce qu'elles sont essentiellement dues à des déformations plastiques vraies.

Ainsi, les déformations irréversibles observées dans les différentes roches granites, calcaires, etc ... peuvent avoir des origines très distinctes, correspondant à des processus mécaniques de milieu continu ou de milieu discontinu et, parfois, à des processus mixtes où interviennent simultanément les déformations plastiques et la microfissuration.

EFFETS DE LA MICROFISSURATION SUR LES DEFORMATIONS SOUS CHARGES TRIAXIALES ISOTROPES.

Les charges hydrostatiques ont pour conséquences essentielles une diminution de la porosité et de la perméabilité. Toutefois, les résultats sont très différents suivant qu'il s'agit de roches peu plastiques (granites) ou très plastiques (calcaires).

Granite.

Si la charge hydrostatique est progressivement croissante, on constate que les discontinuités préexistantes se ferment très rapidement ainsi que la montre la diminution de perméabilité (figure 6a). Par exemple, sur le granite de Saint Germain, il suffit d'une pression uniforme de 5 MPa pour réduire de 80 % sa perméabilité à l'air (branche DC, fig. 6a) ; au-delà de 5 MPa, la fermeture des fissures se poursuit lentement ; à 50 MPa, la perméabilité du granite se trouve réduite de 97 %. Pendant la décompression, les fissures se desserrent partiellement de manière élastique et, en fin de cycle, la perméabilité résiduelle est inférieure à la perméabilité initiale (D') ; la compression a entraîné un tassement irréversible du réseau fissural.

La courbe des compressibilités du même granite (fig. 6b) concorde avec celle des perméabilités. Elle montre, de 0 à 5 MPa, une diminution du volume extrêmement rapide (C), puis de 5 à 50 MPa une diminution plus lente (CA). Par décompression, la roche recouvre incomplètement son volume initial comme le laissaient prévoir les courbes de perméabilité. La pente de la branche AB définit une compressibilité voisine de celle de la matrice non microfissurée. Comme le laissaient prévoir les courbes d'Adams et Williamson (1923), l'essentiel de la compressibilité globale du granite dans le domaine des pressions étudiées est dû aux microfissures et la compressibilité de la matrice minérale non fissurée est comparativement très faible.

Calcaire.

Nous prendrons encore comme exemple, le marbre de Saint Béat. Dans ,cette roche, quand la pression s'élève de 0 à 50 MPa, la perméabilité diminue très progressivement (figure 7a) sans présenter de tassement rapide dans la phase initiale de compression comme cela a lieu dans le granite. Au cours de la décompression, une faible partie seulement de la perméabilité initiale est recouvrée (30 à 40 % au lieu de 50 à 70 % pour le granite de Saint Germain).

Les déformations plastiques de la calcite ont ainsi diminué irréversiblement d'une manière considérable les vides préexistant dans la roche.

Sur la courbe de compressibilité (figure 7b) de 0 à 50 MPa, la diminution relative du volume est nettement plus faible que celle du granite précédemment examiné, ce qui peut tenir à une porosité initiale plus petite; de plus, cette diminution est moins brusque au début de la compression. La fermeture des microdiscontinuités nécessite dans le calcaire des charges relativement plus importantes que dans le granite. Cela peut s'expliquer par le fait que les ouvertures de microfissures ont pu s'y accompagner de glissements qui empêchent les fermetures par simples resserrements.

Pendant la décompression, la pente de la courbe est très forte et mesure pratiquement la compressibilité élastique de la matrice dont les fissures sont fermées (branche AB, figure 7b). C'est seulement en fin de cycle que les discontinuités peuvent s'ouvrir à nouveau (BC). Du fait de la plasticité de la calcite, la porosité ainsi rétablie est beaucoup plus faible relativement qu'elle ne l'était dans le granite.

GRANITE DE SAINT GERMAIN

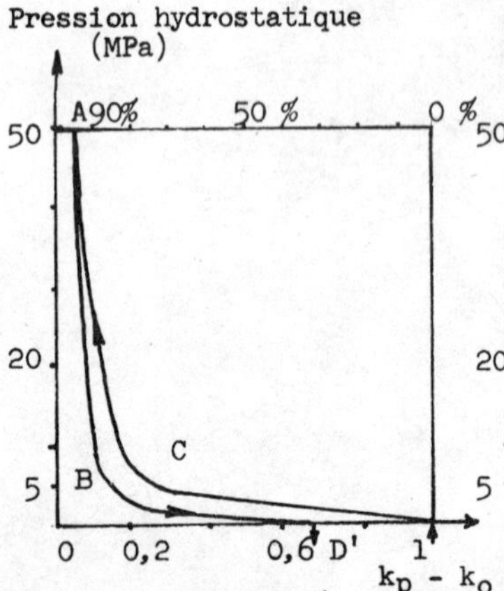

Pression hydrostatique (MPa)

Perméabilité : $\frac{k_p - k_o}{k_o}$

Figure 6a

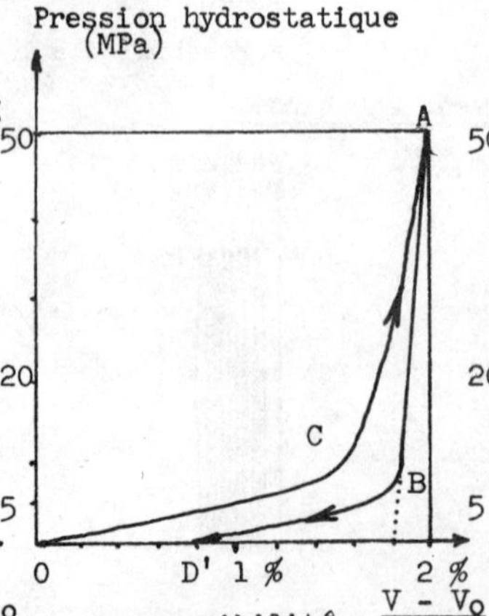

Compressibilité : $\frac{V - V_o}{V_o}$

Figure 6b

CALCAIRE DE SAINT BEAT

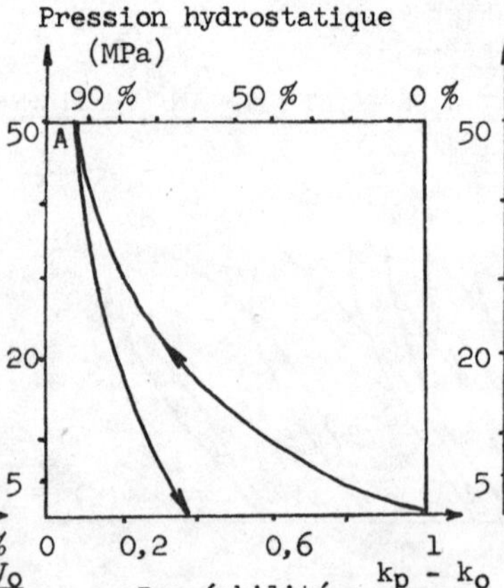

Pression hydrostatique (MPa)

Perméabilité : $\frac{k_p - k_o}{k_o}$

Figure 7a

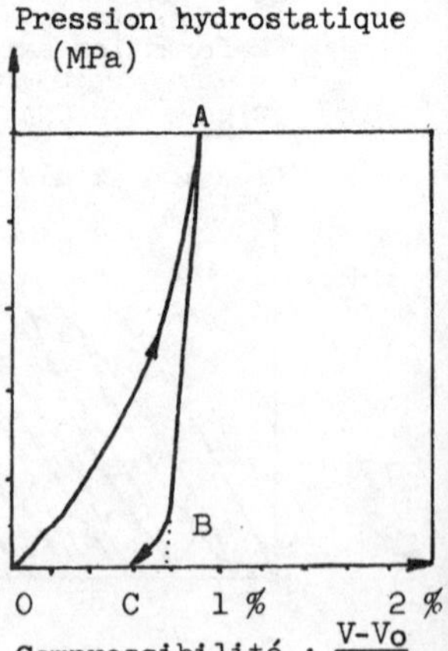

Compressibilité : $\frac{V-V_o}{V_o}$

Figure 7b

CONCLUSION.

L'analyse de l'évolution de la microfissuration sous charges triaxiales montre que dans les solides hétérogènes discontinus, les déformations globales peuvent dépendre considérablement de l'existence initiale ou de la formation progressive de microfissures, tandis que, dans les solides continus, elles se réduisent aux effets de l'élasticité et de la plasticité.

Ces observations ont été rendues possibles par la détection des microbruits -qui signalent les écrasements aussi bien que les ouvertures de microfissures nouvelles- et par les enregistrements de perméabilité à l'air -qui permettent de suivre le sens d'évolution du réseau de microdiscontinuités et de déterminer le "seuil de microfissuration".

L'examen simultané des courbes de compressibilité et de perméabilité nous a permis, ainsi, de distinguer dans une roche la compressibilité, généralement très faible, de la matrice continue, de celle, bien plus importante, aux faibles charges, qui découle des microfissures.

L'analyse directe des déformations linéiques, est, à elle seule, peu explicite sur la formation des microfissures. Cependant la comparaison des courbes de déformation longitudinale et de déformation transversale peut être significative dans les roches fragiles pourvu que les mesures effectuées se rapportent à la totalité de l'échantillon :

- les courbes de déformation longitudinale traduisent, par une courbure initiale plus ou moins prolongée, le tassement des microfissures suivant l'axe de compression sans que puisse être décelé le seuil de microfissuration ;
- les courbes de déformation transversale ne font pas apparaître le tassement initial mais elles signalent le seuil de microfissuration par un changement de pente qui se distingue de la courbe finale de prérupture.

Dans les roches plastiques, l'intervention de déformations non-linéaire irréversibles résultant de glissements plastiques et de maclages mécaniques, estompe l'ensemble des caractères précédents et rend incertaine toute détermination du seuil de microfissuration sur les courbes de déformation transversale. Cette remarque prend toute son importance dans le cas de confinements triaxiaux où les effets de la plasticité des minéraux sont accrus, tandis que les effets des microfissures préexistantes sont atténués par le frettage.

Plasticité et microfissuration interviennent dont très inégalement suivant les roches et suivant les sollicitations exercées. Bien qu'elles se traduisent par des déformations globales pouvant être confondues, celles-ci ne sont pas de même nature et leurs conséquences sur le comportement mécanique et physicochimique du matériau sont très différentes. Il nous paraît donc essentiel de distinguer, parmi les causes de déformations irréversibles observées, celles qui résultent de déformations plastiques vraies de celles qui résultent d'une microfissuration (déformations pseudo-plastiques). C'est ce que permettent les mesures de perméabilité associées aux enregistrements acoustiques.

-o-o-o-o-

REFERENCES.

Adams L.H. et Williamson E.D., 1923, The compressibility of minerals and rocks at high pressures. Journal Franklin Institute, t. 195, p. 475-529.

Bridgman, 1949, Volume change in the plastic stages of simple compression. Journ. Applied Physics, t. 20, p. 1241.

Capdecomme L., Farran J. et Pérami R., 1966, Mode de développement des microfissures dans les roches cristallines et notamment dans les granites soumis à des efforts uniaxiaux. Premier Congr. Int. Méca. Roches Lisbonne, t. 1, p. 621-624.

Farran J., 1950, Etude pétrographique du comportement des roches dans leurs applications en Génie Civil. Bull. Soc. Hist. nat. Toulouse, vol. 85, p. 331-337.

Farran J. et Thénoz B., 1965, L'altérabilité des roches, ses facteurs, sa prévision. Ann. Inst. Tech. Bât. Trav. Publ., n° 215, p. 1534-1548.

Habib P., 1968, Introduction à la fissuration des roches. Colloque Fissur. roches. Rev. In . Min. n° spécial, p. 5-8.

Heard H.C., 1960, Transition from brittle fracture to ductile flow in Solenhofen limestone as a function of temperature, confining pressure and interstitial fluid pressure. Bull. Soc. geol. Amer. vol. 79.

Morlier P., 1964, Etude expérimentale de la déformation des roches. Rev. Ind. Fr. Pétrole vol. XIX, n° 10, p. 1115-1147.

Pérami R., 1965, Sur les microfissures de roches soumises à des efforts uniaxiaux. C. R. Ac. Sc. Fr., t. 260, p. 1209-1212.

Pérami R., 1971, Contribution à l'étude expérimentale de la microfissuration des roches sous actions mécaniques et thermiques. Thèse Sciences Toulouse, 1 vol. 276 p.

-o-o-o-o-

THE RECTANGULAR-PRISMATIC TEST SPECIMEN WHOSE CENTER COINCIDES WITH THE ORIGIN OF COORDINATES AND WHOSE SURFACES ARE PARALLEL TO THE PLANES OF COORDINATES

SPECIMEN D'ESSAI RECTANGULAIRE-PRISMATIQUE DONT LE CENTRE COINCIDE AVEC L'ORIGIN DES COORDONNÉES ET DONT LES SURFACES SONT PARALLÉLES AUX PLANS DES COORDONNÉES

ÜBER DEN RECHTECKIG-PRISMATISCHEN PROBEKÖRPER, DESSEN MITTELPUNKT IM KOORDINATEN-URSPRUNG LIEGT UND DESSEN WÄNDE ZU DEN KOORDINATENEBENEN PARALLEL STEHEN

I. C. GANEV

Professor Bulgarian Academy of Sciences, Inst. of Techn. Mech., Sofia
Bulgaria

Summary: In the introduction is presumed that the test specimen is made of transversally isotropic (monotropic) material of the most general kind for which there exist full theoretical solutions [1]. The geometrically symmetric specimen should be symmetric also with regard to load, being loaded uniformly and centric as usual. Since the influence of body forces in test specimens is insignificant and can be neglected, there should be made use only of the general part (1) of the full theoretical solutions. For satisfying all conditions of symmetry the system (1) of equations is transformed into the equations (4), (5), and (6) in which the arbitrary functions f must be odd functions of ζ and η.

In the following development only the case is discussed in which the friction on all surfaces of contact is practically eliminated by adequate lubrication, while all surfaces stand under uniformly distributed load. It has come out that all boundary conditions are satisfied by choosing the six arbitrary functions as linear functions of ζ and η. It can easily be proved too that the attained solutions (9) do satisfy on the whole the fundamental elastic equations (10) belonging to general orthotropy. Therefore in all kinds of orthotropy (down to isotropy) the final solutions for the three displacements U, V, and W are given by the equations (15) in sequence of which there arise the equations (16) for the deformations and (17) for the stresses.

The attained results in the case of test specimens with adequately lubricated surfaces of contact show that: (1) In all points of the test specimen the normal stresses are principal stresses and the state of stress is uniform all over the test specimen; (2) the dimensions of the test specimen do not influence its mechanical state, so that the so called "scale effect" does not appear; and (3) the test specimen may not be necessarily a cube, and in the case of a "test cube" there is only necessary that the mutual perpendicularity of its edges should be kept strictly.

Résumé: Dans l'introduction on considere tout d'abord que l'échantillon est composé de matiere transversalement isotrope (monotrope) du type le plus général, pour laquelle existent des solution théoriques completes [1]. L'échantillon géométriquement symmétrique doit etre par conséquent symmétrique ainsi par rapport a la charge, lorsque'il est en général chargé uniformément et centriquement. Puisque dans les échantillons, l'influence des forces de masse est minime et peut etre négligée, il suffit d'utiliser la partie générale (1) des solutions théoriques completes. Pour satisfaire a toutes les conditions de symmétrie, le systeme d'équations (1) est réduit aux équations (4), (5), et (6) ou les fonctions arbitraires f doivent etre des fonctions inpaires de ζ et η.

Dans le développement suivant on considere uniquement le cas ou le frottement sur tous les cotés de l'échantillon disparait pratiquement par suite d'une lubrification adéquate; les memes cotés se trouvent alors sous une charge normale uniformément répartie. Il s'avere alors que toutes les conditions limites sont remplies, puisque les six fonctions arbitraires sont des fonction lineaires de ζ et η. On peut aussi établir facilement, que les solutions (9) ainsi obtenues satisfont pleinement les équations d'élasticité fondamentales (10), valables pour l'orthotropie générale. C'est ainsi que pour tous les genres d'orthotropie (isotropie inclue) les solutions finales des trois déplacements U, V, et W sont données par les équations (15), desquelles on obtient les équations (16) pour les déformations et (17) pour les tensions.

Des résultats obtenus dans le cas d'un échantillon aux cotés lubrifiés, on peu constater immédiatement que: (1) Partout les tensions normales sont principales et leur intensité est la meme pour tout point de l'échantillon; (2) les dimensions de l'échantillon n'ont aucune influence sur son état mécanique, l'effet appelé "effet de l'échelle" ne se manifeste donc pas; et (3) il n'est pas nécéssaire que l'échantillon soit obligatoirement un cube, ainsi dans "l'échantillon cube" avec des aretes pas exactement égale, il suffit seulement qu'elles soient exactement perpendiculaires l'une par rapport a l'autre.

Zusammenfassung: In der Einleitung wird zunächst angenommen, daß der Probekörper aus transversal isotropem (monotropem) Material allgemeinster Art hergestellt ist, für welches vollständige theoretische Lösungen bereits vorliegen [1]. Der geometrisch symmetrisch Probekörper soll auch in Bezug auf die Belastung symmetrisch sein, indem er gleichmäßig und mittig belastet wird, wie das üblich ist. Da bei Probekörpern der Einfluß der Massenkräfte verschwindend klein ist und vernachlässigt werden darf, kommt nur der allgemein Teil (1) der vollständigen theoretischen Lösungen zur Anwendung. Um allen Symmetrie-Bedingungen zu genügen, wird das Gleichungsstem (1) in die Gleichungen (4), (5), und (6) übergeführt, in welchen die willkürlichen Funktionen f ungerade Funktionen von ζ and η sein müssen.

In der weiteren Entwicklung wird nur der Fall behandelt, wo die Reibung an allen Kontaktflächen des Probekörpers durch geeignete Schmierung praktisch beseitigt ist, während die Seitenflächen unter gleichmäßig verteilter Normalbelastung stehen. Es hat sich heraus gestellt, daß alle hierzugehörigen Grenzbedingungen erfüllt werden, wenn die sechs willkürlichen Funktionen lineare Funktionen von ζ und η sind. Es kann auch leicht festgestellt werden, daß sich die daraus ergebenden Lösungen (9) auch die für allgemeine Orthotropie geltenden Elastizitäts-Grundgleichungen (10) restlos befriedigen. Daher werden für alle Arten von Orthotropie (bis herunter zu Isotropie) die endgültigen Lösungen für die drei Verschiebungen U, V., und W durch die Gleichungen (15) gegeben, woraus die Ausdrücke (16) für die Verformungen und (17) für die Spannungen folgen.

Aus den erhaltenen Ergebnissen ist für den Fall des Probekörpers mit passend geschmierten Kontaktflächen sofort zu ersehen: (1) Die Normalspannungen sind durchweg Hauptspannungen und der Spannungszustand ist in allen Punkten des Probekörpers der gleiche; (2) die Abmessungen des Probekörpers haben keinen Einfluß auf seinen mechanischen Zustand, so daß der sogenannte "Maßstabeffekt" nicht auftritt; und (3) der Probekörper braucht nicht notwendig ein Würfel zu sein, so daß es beim "Probewürfel" mit nicht ganz gleichen Kantenlängen nur notwendig ist, daß die Kanten genau senkrecht zueinander stehen.

As introduction a specimen may be considered, built of transversally isotropic material of the most general kind, whose elastic constants A_{mn} satisfy the following relations:

$$A_{22} = A_{11};\ A_{23} = A_{31} = A_{13} = A_{32};\ A_{12} = A_{21} = A_{11} - 2A_{44};\ A_{55} = A_{66}$$

corresponding to transversal isotropy (monotropy) perpendicular to the Z-axis of coordinates.

The five elastic constants A_{11}, A_{33}, $A_{31} = A_{13}$, A_{44} A_{66} may be considered as independent on each other.

The dimensions of the specimens being sufficiently small, the influence of the body forces can be neglected, so that the solution for the discussed specimens can be founded on the basis of the following general solutions for transversely isotropic elastic continua of the most general kind, the transverse isotropy being perpendicular to the Z-axis of coordinates [1]:

$$U_o = \frac{a}{a^2+b^2}\left[f_1(\zeta_1)+f_2(\eta_1)\right] + \frac{a}{a^2+b^2}\left[f_3(\zeta_2)+f_4(\eta_2)\right] + \frac{b}{a^2+b^2}\left[f_5(\zeta_3)+f_6(\eta_3)\right]$$

$$V_o = \frac{b}{a^2+b^2}\left[f_1(\zeta_1)+f_2(\eta_1)\right] + \frac{b}{a^2+b^2}\left[f_3(\zeta_2)+f_4(\eta_2)\right] - \frac{a}{a^2+b^2}\left[f_5(\zeta_3)+f_6(\eta_3)\right] \qquad (1)$$

$$W_o = i\,\frac{A_{11}-A_{66}\alpha^2}{(A_{31}+A_{66})\alpha}\,\frac{1}{\sqrt{a^2+b^2}}\left[f_1(\zeta_1)-f_2(\eta_1)\right] + i\,\frac{A_{11}-A_{66}\beta^2}{(A_{31}+A_{66})\beta}\,\frac{1}{\sqrt{a^2+b^2}}\left[f_3(\zeta_2)-f_4(\eta_2)\right],$$

where the designations

$$\zeta_1,\eta_1 = ax + by \pm i\alpha\sqrt{a^2+b^2}\,z$$
$$\zeta_2,\eta_2 = ax + by \pm i\beta\sqrt{a^2+b^2}\,z \qquad (2)$$
$$\zeta_3,\eta_3 = ax + by \pm i\sqrt{\frac{A_{44}}{A_{66}}}\sqrt{a^2+b^2}\,z$$

$$\alpha^2,\beta^2 = \frac{\left[\sqrt{A_{33}A_{11}-A_{31}^2} \pm \sqrt{A_{33}A_{11}-(A_{31}+2A_{66})^2}\right]^2 + 4A_{66}^2}{4A_{33}A_{66}}, \qquad (3)$$

have been used. The free parameters a and b have the dimension: length^{-1}.

The discussion of the transversal isotropy perpendicular to the Z-axis of coordinates does not confine the generality of investigation, since the system of coordinates can always be chosen in such a way that the Z-axis of coordinates should be perpendicular to the planes isotropic in themselves.

The test specimens stand usually under uniformly distributed and centric load, so that in sequence of the geometric and load symmetry all mechanical quantities (displacements and stresses) become also symmetrical with regard to the system of coordinates. To guarantee the symmetry of the solution it is necessary and sufficient to assume the arbitrary functions to be odd functions of ζ and η, and the general solutions (1) must be so reformed that (a) to the expressions depending on the arbitrary functions of ζ_1 and η_1 and ζ_2 and η_2, should be <u>added</u> expressions of the same kind, in which the free parameter b is substituted by -b; and (b) from the expressions depending on the arbitrary functions of ζ_3 and η_3, should be <u>subtracted</u> expressions of the same kind, in which the free parameter b is also substituted by -b.

The general solutions for the displacements U, V, and W thus adapted to the necessity of symmetry accept the form:

$$U_o = \frac{a}{a^2+b^2}\left\{\left[f_1(\zeta_1^+)+f_2(\eta_1^+)\right]+\left[f_1(\zeta_1^-)+f_2(\eta_1^-)\right]\right\} + \frac{a}{a^2+b^2}\left\{\left[f_3(\zeta_2^+)+f_4(\eta_2^+)\right]+\left[f_3(\zeta_2^-)+f_4(\eta_2^-)\right]\right\} + \frac{b}{a^2+b^2}\left\{\left[f_5(\zeta_3^+)+f_6(\eta_3^+)\right]+\left[f_5(\zeta_3^-)+f_6(\eta_3^-)\right]\right\}; \qquad (4)$$

$$V_o = \frac{b}{a^2+b^2}\left\{\left[f_1(\zeta_1^+)+f_2(\eta_1^+)\right]-\left[f_1(\zeta_1^-)+f_2(\eta_1^-)\right]\right\} + \frac{b}{a^2+b^2}\left\{\left[f_3(\zeta_2^+)+f_4(\eta_2^+)\right]-\left[f_3(\zeta_2^-)+f_4(\eta_2^-)\right]\right\} - \frac{a}{a^2+b^2}\left\{\left[f_5(\zeta_3^+)+f_6(\eta_3^+)\right]-\left[f_5(\zeta_3^-)+f_6(\eta_3^-)\right]\right\}; \qquad (5)$$

$$W_o = i\frac{A_{44}-A_{66}\alpha^2}{(A_{31}+A_{66})\alpha}\frac{1}{\sqrt{a^2+b^2}}\left\{\left[f_1(\zeta_1^+)-f_2(\eta_1^+)\right]+\left[f_1(\zeta_1^-)-f_2(\eta_1^-)\right]\right\} + i\frac{A_{11}-A_{66}\beta^2}{(A_{31}+A_{66})\beta}\frac{1}{\sqrt{a^2+b^2}}\left\{\left[f_3(\zeta_2^+)-f_4(\eta_2^+)\right]+\left[f_3(\zeta_2^-)-f_4(\eta_2^-)\right]\right\} \qquad (6)$$

where the designations

$$\zeta_1^+,\eta_1^+ = ax + by \pm i\alpha\sqrt{a^2+b^2}\,z;\quad \zeta_1^-,\ \eta_1^- = ax - by \pm i\alpha\sqrt{a^2+b^2}\,z$$
$$\zeta_2^+,\eta_2^+ = ax + by \pm i\beta\sqrt{a^2+b^2}\,z;\quad \zeta_2,\eta_2 = ax - by \pm i\beta\sqrt{a^2+b^2}\,z \qquad (7)$$
$$\zeta_3^+,\ \eta_3^+ = ax + by \pm i\sqrt{\frac{A_{44}}{A_{66}}}\sqrt{a^2+b^2}\,z;\quad \zeta_3^-,\eta_3^- = ax - by \pm i\sqrt{\frac{A_{44}}{A_{66}}}\sqrt{a^2+b^2}\,z$$

have been used, and α^2 and β^2 are to be derived from (3).

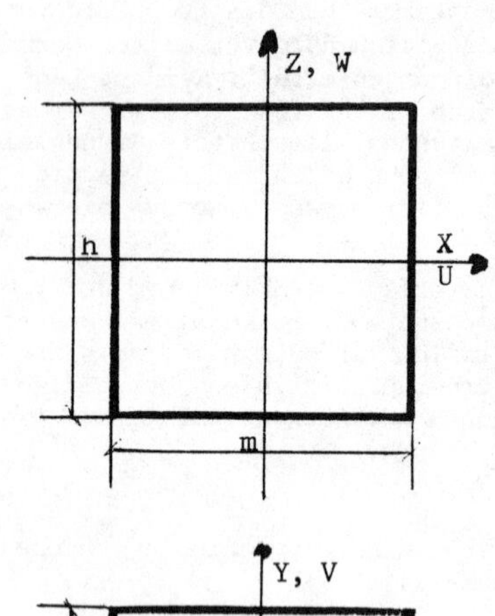

A rectangular-prismatic test specimen with the dimensions shown on the left, shall now be discussed under the assumption of eliminated friction at all its surfaces of contact, as this can be obtained by using an adequate grease (for instance MoS_2) with an accuracy sufficient for practical needs.

This specimen should stand under the following uniformly distributed normal loads: P_x at the surfaces perpendicular to the X-axis of coordinates; P_y at the surfaces perpendicular to the Y-axis of coordinates and P_z at the surfaces perpendicular to the Z-axis of the coordinates.

In this case the boundary conditions are reduced only to the boundary conditions depending on the stresses as follows: (a) the shearing stresses at all six surfaces of the specimen must be equal to zero: $\tau_{xy} = \tau_{yx} = 0$; $\tau_{yz} - \tau_{zy} = 0$; $\tau_{zx} = \tau_{xz} = 0$; (b) the normal stresses at all six surfaces of the specimen must have the values: $\sigma_x = p_x$; $\sigma_y = p_y$ and $\sigma_z = p_z$.

To satisfy all this boundary conditions or, what is the same to solve the problem, it is sufficient to take the arbitrary functions in the simplest possible form, that is to take the linear forms:

$$f_1(\zeta_1) = \frac{A}{4}\zeta_1 \quad f_2(\eta_1) = \frac{A}{4}\eta_1; \quad f_3(\zeta_2) = \frac{B}{4}\zeta_2 \quad f_4(\eta_2) = \frac{B}{4}\eta_2;$$
$$f_5(\zeta_3) = \frac{C}{4}\zeta_3 \quad f_6(\eta_3) = \frac{C}{4}\eta_3, \tag{8}$$

wherein A, B, and C are pure dimensionless numbers.

By means of the assumption (8) and in virtue of the equations (4), (5), (6), and (7) the solutions:

$$U_o = \left(A\frac{a^2}{a^2+b^2} + B\frac{a^2}{a^2+b^2} + C\frac{ab}{a^2+b^2}\right)x = M_x$$
$$V_o = \left(A\frac{b^2}{a^2+b^2} + B\frac{b^2}{a^2+b^2} - C\frac{ab}{a^2+b^2}\right)y = N_y \tag{9}$$
$$W_o = -\left(A\frac{A_{11}-A_{66}\alpha^2}{A_{31}+A_{66}} + B\frac{A_{11}-A_{66}\beta^2}{A_{31}+A_{66}}\right)z = P_z$$

for the three displacements are obtained, wherein U, N, and P are also pure dimensionless numbers.

The solutions (9) for the three displacements U, V, and W satisfy the boundary conditions with respect to the shearing stresses for all values of U, N, and P.

The satisfying of the boundary conditions with respect to the normal stresses is achieved by the adequate determination of the quantities M, N, and P.

Remark: The same equations (9) are obtained also then, when going out of the general solutions for transversally isotropic elastic continua of the two other kinds, and also for completely isotropic elastic continua. On the other side the forms (9) of the expressions for the three displacements satisfy the fundamental elastic equations for general orthotropic continua which have the following form valid for the present case:

$$A_{11}\frac{\partial^2 U}{\partial x^2} + A_{44}\frac{\partial^2 U}{\partial y^2} + A_{66}\frac{\partial^2 U}{\partial z^2} + (A_{12}+A_{44})\frac{\partial^2 V}{\partial x\partial y} + (A_{31}+A_{66})\frac{\partial^2 W}{\partial x\partial z} = 0$$

$$A_{44}\frac{\partial^2 V}{\partial x^2} + A_{22}\frac{\partial^2 V}{\partial y^2} + A_{55}\frac{\partial^2 V}{\partial z^2} + (A_{23}+A_{55})\frac{\partial^2 W}{\partial y\partial z} + (A_{12}+A_{44})\frac{\partial^2 U}{\partial y\partial z} = 0 \tag{10}$$

$$A_{66}\frac{\partial^2 W}{\partial x^2} + A_{55}\frac{\partial^2 W}{\partial y^2} + A_{33}\frac{\partial^2 W}{\partial z^2} + (A_{31}+A_{66})\frac{\partial^2 U}{\partial z\partial x} + (A_{23}+A_{55})\frac{\partial^2 V}{\partial z\partial y} = 0$$

In consequence thereof the boundary conditions with respect to the normal stresses are always satisfied through the determination of the values of U, N, and P not only in the case of general orthotropy, but also for transversal isotropy of the three possible kinds and finally for complete isotropy, if for the normal stresses the values are used which are given by HOOKE's law referring to general orthotropy. The values of U, N, and P referring to the other special cases will be obtained by taking into account the special relations between the elastic constants A_{mn} which belong to the concrete case.

When going out of the widened HOOKE's law, in virtue of which the normal stresses σ_x, σ_y, and σ_z are given by the equations

$$\sigma_x = A_{11}\frac{\partial U}{\partial x} + A_{12}\frac{\partial V}{\partial y} + A_{13}\frac{\partial W}{\partial z}$$
$$\sigma_y = A_{21}\frac{\partial U}{\partial x} + A_{22}\frac{\partial V}{\partial y} + A_{23}\frac{\partial W}{\partial z} \tag{11}$$
$$\sigma_z = A_{31}\frac{\partial U}{\partial x} + A_{32}\frac{\partial V}{\partial y} + A_{33}\frac{\partial W}{\partial z}$$

as the functions of the deformations $\epsilon_x = \frac{\partial U}{\partial x}$, $\epsilon_y = \frac{\partial V}{\partial y}$ and $\epsilon_z = \frac{\partial W}{\partial z}$ for the determination of the values of U, N, and P the following system of three linear algebraic equations

$$A_{11}M + A_{12}N + A_{13}P = p_x$$
$$A_{21}M + A_{22}N + A_{23}P = p_y \tag{12}$$
$$A_{31}M + A_{32}N + A_{33}P - p_z$$

comes forth, whose solutions are:

$$M = \frac{D_{11}}{D}p_x - \frac{D_{21}}{D}p_y + \frac{D_{31}}{D}p_z$$
$$N = -\frac{D_{12}}{D}p_x + \frac{D_{22}}{D}p_y - \frac{D_{32}}{D}p_z \tag{13}$$
$$P = \frac{D_{13}}{D}p_x - \frac{D_{23}}{D}p_y + \frac{D_{33}}{D}p_z$$

The common denominator D is given by

$$D = \begin{vmatrix} A_{11} & A_{12} & A_{13} \\ A_{21} & A_{22} & A_{23} \\ A_{31} & A_{32} & A_{33} \end{vmatrix}, \tag{14}$$

and D_{mn} denotes the subdeterminants of A_{mn}.

In this way the solution for the rectangular prism as

test specimen, whose center coincides with the origin of coordinates and whose surfaces are parallel to the planes of coordinates, loaded by uniformly distributed loads, has the following form, valid for eliminated friction:

(a) Displacements

$$U = \frac{D_{11}}{D} px - \frac{D_{21}}{D} py + \frac{D_{31}}{D} pz \quad x$$

$$V = -\frac{D_{12}}{D} px + \frac{D_{22}}{D} py - \frac{D_{32}}{D} pz \quad y \qquad (15)$$

$$W = \frac{D_{13}}{D} px - \frac{D_{23}}{D} py + \frac{D_{33}}{D} pz \quad z$$

(b) Deformations

$$\epsilon_x = \frac{D_{11}}{D} px - \frac{D_{21}}{D} py + \frac{D_{31}}{D} pz$$

$$\epsilon_y = -\frac{D_{12}}{D} px + \frac{D_{22}}{D} py - \frac{D_{32}}{D} pz \qquad (16)$$

$$\epsilon_z = \frac{D_{12}}{D} px - \frac{D_{23}}{D} py + \frac{D_{33}}{D} pz$$

(c) Stresses

$$\sigma_x = p_x; \qquad \sigma_y = p_y; \qquad \sigma_z = p_z \qquad (17)$$

$$\tau_{xy} = \tau_{yx} = 0; \quad \tau_{yz} = \tau_{zy} = 0; \quad \tau_{zx} = \tau_{xz} = 0$$

This form of solution shows (1) that the dimensions of the adequate greased rectangular-prismatic test specimen do not influence its mechanical state, that is the so-called "scale-effect" does not appear; (2) that the normal stresses are principal normal stresses and that the stress distribution is the same in all points of the adequate greased rectangular-prismatic test specimen.

The fundamental solution (15) and the ensuing equation groups (16) and (17) which comprise all possible cases of general orthotropy, transversal isotropy and complete isotropy, can be used for discussing and estimating of the behavior of the subject rectangular-prismatic test specimen in the different cases.

A. Linear Strain

This form of strain can be established in rock specimens by means of special built steel devices, for instance the so-called "pressure device" which has been used in the experiments in Leipzig: [3] and [4] (figs. 1 and 2).

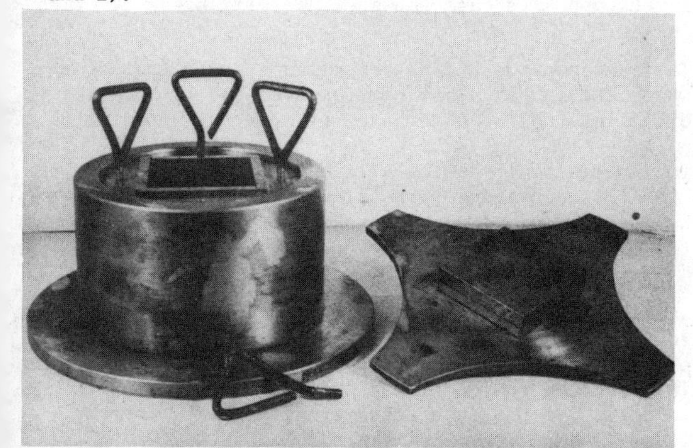

FIGURE 1. - Steel Device for Establishing of Linear Strain (open).

FIGURE 2. - Steel Device for Establishing of Linear Strain (closed).

Here $\epsilon_x = 0$ and $\epsilon_y = 0$; but $\epsilon_z \neq 0$.

The deformations ϵ_x and ϵ_y equalling zero lead to the resulting form (6) system of two algebraic equations for determining p_x and p_y as functions of p_z:

$$D_{11}p_x - D_{21}p_y = -D_{31}p_z$$
$$-D_{12}p_x + D_{22}p_y = D_{32}p_z \qquad (18)$$

from which in sequence of

$$\begin{vmatrix} D_{11} & -D_{21} \\ -D_{12} & D_{22} \end{vmatrix} = A_{33}D; \quad \begin{vmatrix} -D_{31} & -D_{21} \\ D_{32} & D_{22} \end{vmatrix} = A_{13}D; \quad \begin{vmatrix} D_{11} & -D_{31} \\ -D_{12} & D_{32} \end{vmatrix} = A_{23}D \qquad (19)$$

the expressions come forth:

$$p_x = \frac{A_{13}}{A_{33}} p_z \text{ and } p_y = \frac{A_{23}}{A_{33}} p_z. \qquad (19)$$

Substituting the values (18) of p_x and p_y in the third equation (16) there arises the equation

$$\epsilon_z = \frac{p_z}{A_{33}} \qquad (20)$$

giving the relation between ϵ_z and p_z.

The uniformly distributed loads p_x and p_y are exerted by the side walls of the "pressure device" as resistance, if these walls are sufficiently unyielding with sufficient for the practical needs exactness.

When the linear strain is parallel to the Y-axis or to the X-axis of coordinates, there is obtained correspondingly:

$$p_a = \frac{A_{32}}{A_{22}} p_y \text{ and } p_x = \frac{A_{12}}{A_{22}} p_y \qquad (19')$$

$$\epsilon_y = \frac{p_y}{A_{22}}; \qquad (20')$$

and

$$p_y = \frac{A_{21}}{A_{11}} p_x \text{ and } p_z = \frac{A_{31}}{A_{11}} p_x \qquad (19'')$$

$$\epsilon_x = \frac{p_x}{A_{11}} \qquad (20'')$$

B. Linear Stress Situation

This form of stress situation parallel, for instance, to the Z-axis of coordinates appears when

$p_x = 0$ and $p_y = 0$, but $p_z \neq 0$

which corresponds to uniformly distributed load parallel to the Z-axis.

From the equations (16) the expressions for the (positive or negative) elongations are directly derived

$$\epsilon_x = \frac{D_{31}}{D} p_z = - \frac{A_{22}A_{13} - A_{12}A_{23}}{D} p_z$$

$$\epsilon_y = - \frac{D_{32}}{D} p_z = - \frac{A_{11}A_{23} - A_{21}A_{13}}{D} p_z \qquad (21)$$

$$\epsilon_z = \frac{D_{33}}{D} p_z = \frac{A_{11}A_{22} - A_{21}A_{12}}{D} p_z.$$

Under compressive load the deformations ϵ_x and ϵ_y are always positive, and the deformation ϵ_z is, on the contrary, negative.

It is evident that

$|\epsilon_z| > |\epsilon_x|$ and $|\epsilon_z| > |\epsilon_y|$.

In the cases of linear stress situation parallel to the Y-axis or X-axis of coordinates there is obtained correspondingly

$$\epsilon_x = - \frac{D_{21}}{D} p_y = - \frac{A_{12}A_{33} - A_{32}A_{13}}{D} p_y$$

$$\epsilon_y = \frac{D_{22}}{D} p_y = \frac{A_{11}A_{33} - A_{13}A_{31}}{D} p_y \qquad (21')$$

$$\epsilon_z = - \frac{D_{23}}{D} p_y = - \frac{A_{11}A_{32} - A_{31}A_{12}}{D} p_y$$

and

$$\epsilon_x = \frac{D_{11}}{D} p_x = \frac{A_{22}A_{33} - A_{32}A_{23}}{D} p_x$$

$$\epsilon_y = - \frac{D_{12}}{D} p_x = - \frac{A_{21}A_{33} - A_{31}A_{23}}{D} p_x \qquad (21'')$$

$$\epsilon_z = \frac{D_{13}}{D} p_x = - \frac{A_{31}A_{22} - A_{21}A_{32}}{D} p_x$$

It is self-evident that in the case of these two kinds of linear stress situation under compressive load ($p_y<0$), $p_x<0$) the deformations perpendicular to the direction of the load are also positive, and the deformations parallel to it are negative. It is self-evident too, that the absolute values of the longitudinal deformations considerably surpass the absolute values of the transverse deformation.

If there can be assumed that the linear HOOKE's law may still be applied when the deformations have reached the neighborhood of the strength limit, there can be accepted that the expressions for ϵ_x, ϵ_y, and ϵ_z do keep their validity with a correctness sufficient for the practical needs. It is evident too that the breaking load $\max|P|$ will be that one which corresponds to the absolutely less ultimate deformation. In the case of rocks this occurs with one of the transversal deformations which are, according to their absolute value, considerably less than the longitudinal deformations. On this reason the rectangular-prismatic test specimen whose axes are parallel to the principal axes of orthotropy and whose surfaces are free of friction, fail usually by subdividing into plates or columns parallel to the monoaxial load. After this the single plates and columns fail by buckling.

It is worth emphasizing that the failing (subdividing) in the directions transversal to the compressive load comes forth without appearance of tensile stresses, when the surfaces of the rectangular-prismatic test specimen, whose axes are parallel to the principal axes of orthotropy, are free of friction.

C. Spatial Stress Situation

A spatial stress situation exists in a test specimen which is enclosed in a pressure camera with internal pressure p and which is loaded, for instance, in the direction of the Z-axis of coordinates with a uniformly distributed load p_z.

The deformations ensuing directly from the equation (16) are

$$\epsilon_x = \frac{D_{11} - D_{21}}{D} p + \frac{D_{31}}{D} p_z$$

$$\epsilon_y = \frac{D_{22} - D_{12}}{D} p - \frac{D_{32}}{D} p_z \qquad (22)$$

$$\epsilon_z = \frac{D_{13} - D_{23}}{D} p + \frac{D_{33}}{D} p_z.$$

Introducing the designations

$$\epsilon_{xp} = - \frac{D_{11} - D_{21}}{D} p = - \frac{A_{22}A_{33} - A_{12}A_{33} + A_{32}(A_{13} - A_{23})}{D} p$$

$$\epsilon_{yp} = - \frac{D_{22} - D_{12}}{D} p = - \frac{A_{11}A_{33} - A_{21}A_{33} + A_{31}(A_{23} - A_{13})}{D} p \qquad (23)$$

$$\epsilon_{zp} = - \frac{D_{13} - D_{23}}{D} p = \frac{A_{11}A_{32} + A_{22}A_{31} - (A_{31}A_{12} + A_{32}A_{21})}{D} p.$$

the equations (22) can be brought in the form

$$\epsilon_x + \epsilon_{xp} = \frac{D_{31}}{D} p_z$$

$$\epsilon_y + \epsilon_{yp} = \frac{D_{32}}{D} p_z \qquad (24)$$

$$\epsilon_z + \epsilon_{zp} = \frac{D_{33}}{D} p_z.$$

It can easily be seen on the basis of (21) and (23) that the complementary quantities ϵ_{xp}, ϵ_{yp}, and ϵ_{zp} have the same signs as ϵ_x, ϵ_y, and ϵ_z, so that the breaking load increases by adding them. It is evident that the relation between p_z and p is linear.

Whether in this case the test specimen will fail by subdividing into plates and columns parallel to p_z, depends on the condition, whether the left sides of the first two equations (24) reach the limit values ($\max \epsilon_x + \epsilon_{xp}$) and ($\max \epsilon_y + \epsilon_{yp}$) before the left side of the third equation (24) has reached its limit value ($\max|\epsilon_z| + |\epsilon_{zp}|$).

In the opposite case the specimen will break by crushing.

The same considerations are valid also in the cases where the longitudinal compressive load is parallel to either of the two other axes (Y or X) of coordinates.

The theoretical results attained to this point for the linear strain and for the linear stress situation can be used for simultaneous experimental determination of the group of elastic constants A_{mn} (m,n = 1,2,3) of orthotropic elastic continua by application of monoaxial compressive loads on the rectangular-prismatic test specimen in the direction of each of the three principal axes of orthotropy - in every direction once in the condition of linear strain and once more in the condition of linear stress situation.

This possibility has been already utilized in the above mentioned experiments in Leipzig, whose theoretical argumentation and method of execution is given in the works of the same author [2] and [3]. In these works the groups of formulae (20), (20'), and (20'') and (21), (21'), and (21'') have been applied, although having been derived in a different way. The results of these experiments attained until now have been published in the works of the same author [3] and [4].

By the methods of the Leipzig experiments the values of the elastic constants A_{mn} (m,n - 1,2,3)

A_{11}, A_{22}, A_{33}, $A_{12} = A_{21}$, $A_{23} = A_{32}$ and $A_{31} = A_{13}$

can only be obtained, which connect the normal stresses with the corresponding deformations according to HOOKE's law (11).

The elastic constants A_{44}, A_{55}, and A_{66} (the moduli of elasticity in shear) are to be determined by the formulae

$$A_{44} = \frac{\sqrt{A_{11}A_{22}} - A_{12}}{2}; \quad A_{55} = \frac{\sqrt{A_{22}A_{33}} - A_{23}}{2}; \quad A_{66} = \frac{\sqrt{A_{33}A_{11}} - A_{31}}{2} \tag{25}$$

which represent the relationship between the moduli of elasticity in shear and the usual moduli of elasticity (in tension and compression).

In conclusions it is worth to be pointed out that the theoretical results here obtained show that the rectangular-prismatic test specimen with eliminated friction at all surfaces may not be necessarily a cube. It is only sufficient that the mutual perpendicularity of the edges and the ensuing plane-parallelity of the opposite surfaces of the approximately cubiform specimen be strictly kept, while the imperfect parity of the edges has to be taken into account when processing the experimental information.

REFERENCES

1. GANEV Iwan Chr. - Full solution of the differential equations of transversally isotropic (monotropic) continua of the most general kind (in Bulgarian). ANNUARY of the Technical Institutes - Applied Mechanics, Sofia, 1967, vol. III, No. 2, p. 35-51.

2. _____. Übergang von räumlichen zu ebenen und linearen Verhältnissen bei den Elastizitäts-Grundgleichungen des orthogonal-anisotropen (orthotropen) elastischen Körpers und von der Benutzung der beiden linearen Zustände zur Ermittlung der technischen Konstanten. BERICHT über das 5. Ländertreffen des I.B.G. in Leipzig 1963, S. 169-177.

3. _____. On simultaneous experimental determination of the elastic constants of orthotropic rocks by monoaxial pressure (in Bulgarian). ANNUARY of the Mining and Geological Institute, Sofia, 1964/65, vol. XI, No. 1, p. 49-62.

4. _____. Über eiu experimentelles Verfahren zur Ermittlung von Elastizitäts-Konstanten stetiger orthotroper elastischer Medien unter Annahme der Linearität (Gültigkeit des HOOKEschen Gesetzes). BERICHT über das 10. Ländertreffen des I.B.G. in Leipzig 1968, S. 767-779.

IN-SITU STRENGTH PREDICTION OF MINE PILLARS BASED ON LABORATORY TESTS

LA PRÉDICTION DE LA RÉSISTANCE UNIAXIALE D'UN PILIER DE MINERAI BASSE SUR DES ESSAIS DE LABORATOIRE

VORHERSAGE DER FESTIGKEIT EINES UNTER TAGE PFEILERS AUFGRUND VON LABORUNTERSUCHUNGEN

G. HERGET Research Scientist

K. UNRUG Post Doctorate Fellow

Elliot Lake Laboratory, Mines Branch, Mining Research Centre,
Department of Energy, Mines and Resources, Elliot Lake, Ontario, Canada

SUMMARY Three hundred and fifty sound and broken samples of siderite with diameters between 2.2 cm (0.875 in.) and 24.1 cm (9.5 in.) were tested under triaxial conditions to estimate the strength of a mine pillar. The Mohr envelopes obtained show the size effect over the whole range of confining pressures employed. The uniaxial compressive strength was interpolated. The prediction of the pillar strength by a log volume/log strength relationship is unrealistically low. As the mean uniaxial compressive strengths of broken and sound samples converge with increasing size, this convergence is used to estimate the strength of the pillar. This yields a value of 79.3 ± 31 MPa (11500 ± 4500 psi).

RESUME 350 échantillons, massifs et cassés, de siderite, ayant un diamètre de 2.2 cm (0.875 p.) à 24.1 cm (9.5 p.), furent essayés sous conditions triaxiales afin d'estimer la solidité d'un pilier de minerai. Les enveloppes Mohr obtenus démontrent l'effet de faille (grandeur) à travers le champ entier de pressions confinantes utilisées. La résistance uniaxiale à la rupture fut interpolée. La prédiction quant à la résistance d'un pilier conformèment au rapport log volume/log résistance, est trop basse et irrealiste. A mesure que les résistances uniaxiales moyennes des échantillons cassés et massifs convergent avec un accroissement de la grandeur, cette convergence est utilizée pour évaluer la résistance du pilier. On obtient une valeur de 79.3 ± 31 MPa (11500 ± 4500 psi).

ZUSAMMENFASSUNG 350 solide und zerbrochene Siderit Proben mit Durchmessern zwischen 2,2 cm und 24,1 cm wurden im dreiachsialen axisymmetrischen Spannungsbereich getestet und die Mohr'schen Hüllkurven zeigen für den gesamten Bereich der benutzten Seitenspannungen einen Einfluß der Probengröße. Die einachsiale Druckfestigheit wurde interpoliert. Die Vorhersage der Pfeilerfestigkeit mit Hilfe einer Beziehung log Volumen/log einachsiale Druckfestigkeit führt für diese Proben zu unrealistisch niedrigen Werten. Da jedoch eine Konvergenz der einachsialen Druckfestigkeit für zerbrochene und solide Proben mit zunehmender Größe zu beobachten ist, wird diese Konvergenz benutzt, um die Druckfestigkeit der Pfeiler zu bestimmen. Dieses liefert einen Schätz-Wert von 79.3 ± 31 MPa für die Pfeilerfestigkeit.

INTRODUCTION

An attempt was made to estimate the strength of mine pillars in a siderite ore body by testing progressively larger sizes of drill core under triaxial conditions. The samples were obtained from an iron mine on the NE shore of Lake Superior (Figure 1). The siderite zone strikes ENE-WSW and dips between 65 and 75° south. The hanging wall consists of basic volcanics and the footwall of acid tuffs. Many hanging wall and footwall contacts have been sheared and the ore has been displaced along NNW- to NW-trending faults. Some of these faults have been filled with diabase dikes. Mining is done by blasthole open stoping with stopes about 70 m (230 ft) high and about 18 to 23 m (60 to 75 ft) wide. Pillars are between 21 and 25 m along strike (70 and 80 ft). The ore thickness varies between 12 and 75 m (40 and 250 ft).

SAMPLING, SPECIMEN PREPARATION AND TESTING PROCEDURES

The samples were obtained at about 305 m (1000 ft) below surface in the M2373 footwall drive, halfway between hanging wall and footwall; see Figure 2.

The sampling was done in a regular pattern to prevent bias towards the strong samples. Three sizes of drill cores were obtained in three diameters -- 5.4 cm (2.125 in.), 7.3 cm (2.875 in.), and 24.1 cm (9.5 in.). As shown in Figure 2, all samples were removed from the ground at regular intervals after rejecting the first 15 cm (6 in.) at the collar to eliminate the influence of blasting. The samples obtained were subdivided into groups of sound and broken specimens. Some of the samples were so badly broken that they could not be prepared for testing. Their strengths were to be estimated at the end of the testing series on the basis of their fracture orientations and their probable coefficient of friction and cohesion intercepts. The total number of samples obtained was as

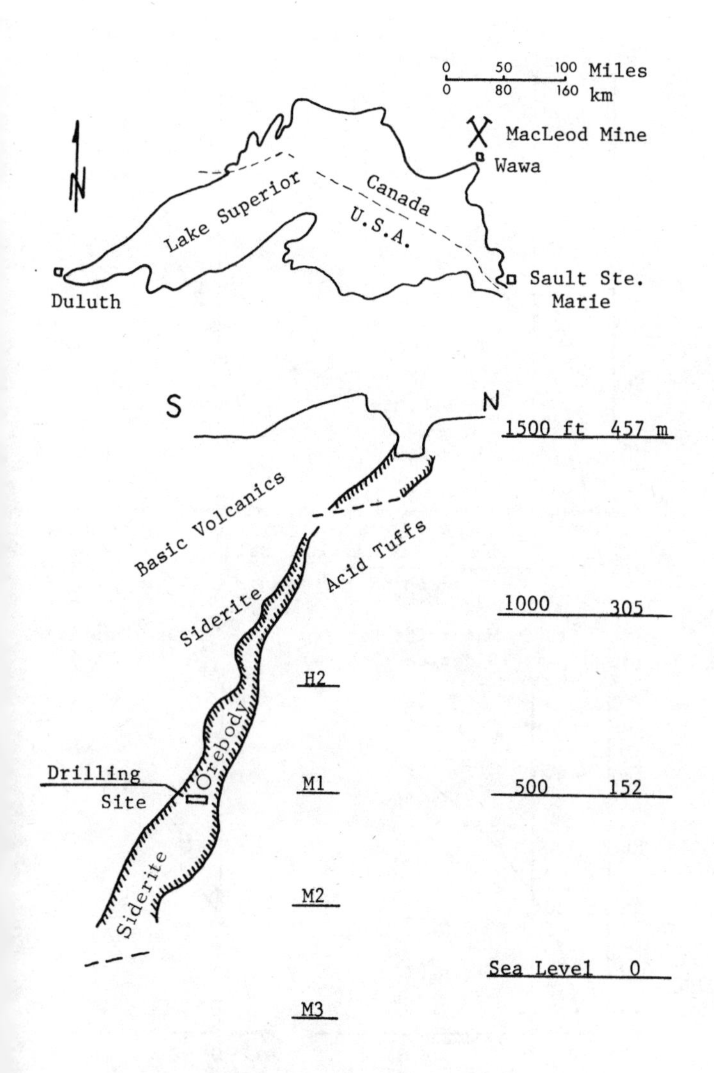

Figure 1: Location of MacLeod Mine, Wawa, and N-S Section through Siderite Ore Zone.

follows:

5.4-cm (2.125-in.) diameter	74	(32),
7.3-cm (2.875-in.) diameter	60	(39),
24.1-cm (9.5-in.) diameter	46	(18).

The number of samples which could not be tested is given in brackets. In addition to the above samples, 2.2-cm-diameter core was drilled from short pieces of large core not suitable for testing. This coring was done in the general drilling direction.

For each sample interval, one sample for compression testing was prepared. If, within one sampling interval, a sound or broken specimen could be selected by shifting the sample boundaries, the broken specimen was preferred. The ends were ground flat and to within 0.003 cm (0.001 in.) of parallel for the smaller cores, and to within 0.013 cm (0.005 in.) of parallel for the larger cores. The length:diameter ratio was 2:1, except for three large-diameter samples for which the length:diameter ratio was 1.6:1.

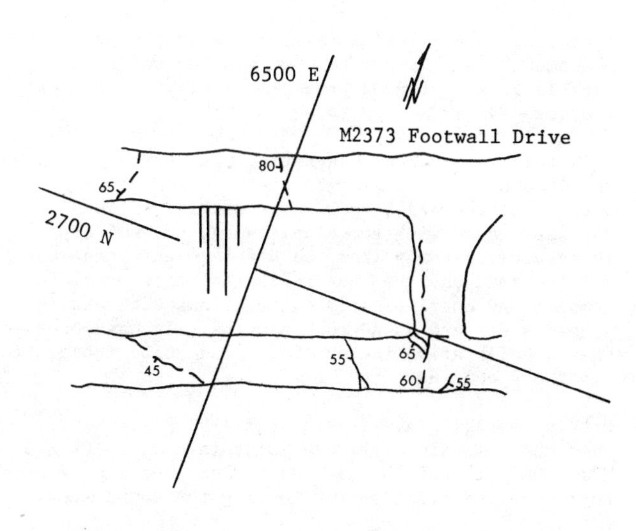

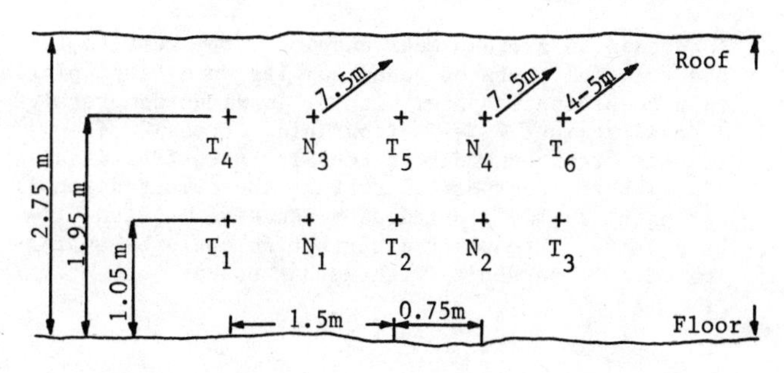

T_1 = 24-cm samples taken at 71-cm intervals,
N_2, N_3 = 7.3-cm samples taken at 24-cm intervals,
N_4, N_1 = 5.4-cm samples taken at 20-cm intervals.

The first 15 cm of each core was rejected.
All drill holes were drilled in the direction S20°E/05° up.

Figure 2: Sampling Site and Drilling Pattern.

Specimens for indirect tensile testing (Brazilian disc test) were prepared from parts of the drill core not used for compression testing. The thickness of the discs was generally 2.5 cm (1 in.); only for the 24 cm core was this increased to 6.4 cm (2.5 in.).

The testing was done with the aim of obtaining Mohr's envelope for the specimen because this would allow the evaluation of strength of broken samples in relation to the shear strength determined for critically oriented chlorite-coated fractures. Triaxial tests were done for the 2.2 cm core up to a confining strength of 55.1 MPa* (8000 psi). For the remainder of the cores the confining pressure varied between 1, 10, 26, and 31 MPa (150, 1500, 2500, and 4500 psi). Tests were done with a 2000-ton testing machine and under triaxial conditions the compression system was stiff enough to break a specimen and to enable post-failure strength tests under various confining

* MPa = 10^6 N/m^2 = 145 lb/in.^{2}

pressures. A triaxial chamber was specially built to accommodate the large-diameter samples and to be capable of a confining pressure of 41 MPa (6000 psi) (Herget, 1972).

This triaxial chamber was fitted with three displacement transducers to measure the relative movement between piston and vessel. The smaller triaxial vessel was fitted with two displacement transducers. The average reading from the displacement transducers was recorded and the true axial displacement of the samples was obtained from calibrations with strain gauged steel and sound rock samples. It was observed that a calibration factor of 1.8 had to be applied for all the specimens.

Within the triaxial vessels, parallel platens were used and a loading rate was maintained at about 3.5 MPa (500 psi) per second. No teflon sheets were used to reduce end friction for testing the sound samples.

RESULTS FROM TRIAXIAL TESTING

To obtain an average Mohr envelope, the results from the triaxial tests on sound samples were first plotted in a co-ordinate system with σ_1 (maximum compressive stress) against $\sigma_3 = \sigma_2$ (confining stress). The results from the indirect tensile tests (Brazilian discs) were incorporated so that the computed tensile strength (T) was plotted as a negative σ_3 with σ_1 being zero. The point distribution could be approximated by a parabola (Figures 3A to 3F):

$$\sigma_1^2 = 2p\,(\sigma_3 + T),$$

where: σ_1 = maximum principal compressive stress,
σ_3 = minimum principal compressive stress,
T = tensile strength, and
2p = parameter of parabola.

To obtain the best-fit parabola, all σ_1 values were squared and a linear regression was run with σ_1^2 the dependent and σ_3 the independent variable.

From the relationship,

$$\sigma_1^2 = \sigma_1' = m\sigma_3 + n,$$

the best-fit parabola was calculated, where 2p = m and T = n/m. This smoothed-out σ_1/σ_3 relationship was then used to plot Mohr's envelope. The family of Mohr's envelopes for the different sizes of the sound samples is given in Figure 4. This shows quite clearly that a size effect exists for the mean strength values from the smaller to the larger samples.

To this plot, the results from testing the shear resistances of geological fracture planes in siderite were added (Herget, et al, 1973). This had given an average shear stress/normal stress ratio for chlorite-coated fracture surfaces of 0.75 (tan 37°) and delineates the lower mean boundary of the pillar strength. Shear stress/normal stress ratios lower than 0.75 do exist on some smooth chlorite-coated surfaces of shear planes that possess very little interlock; however, due to their curvature and lack of continuity in the orebody, they are unlikely to affect the over-all strength of the pillar. They can cause undesirable rock falls; however, this is only of local significance. This line represents the lowest boundary of the pillar strength.

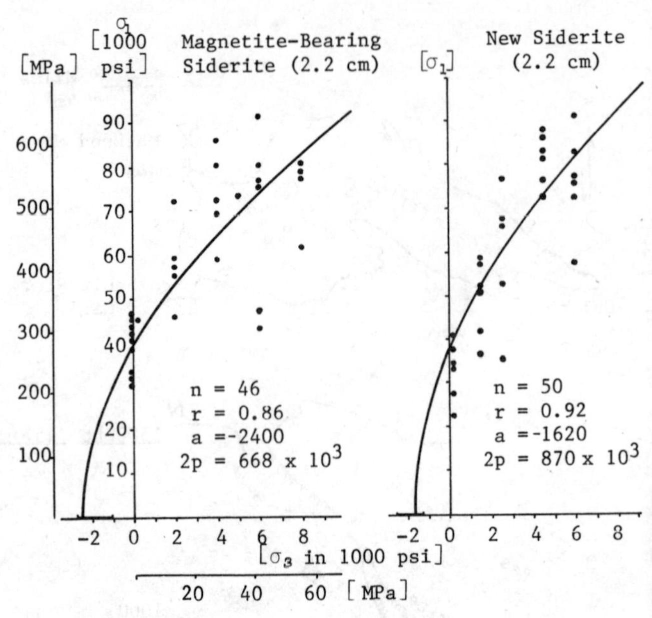

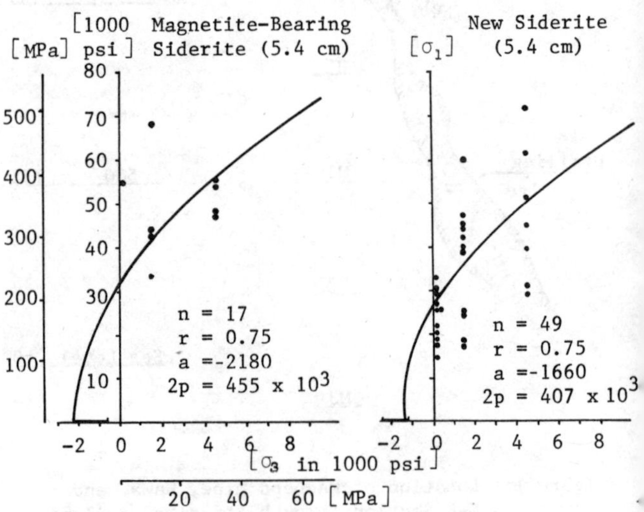

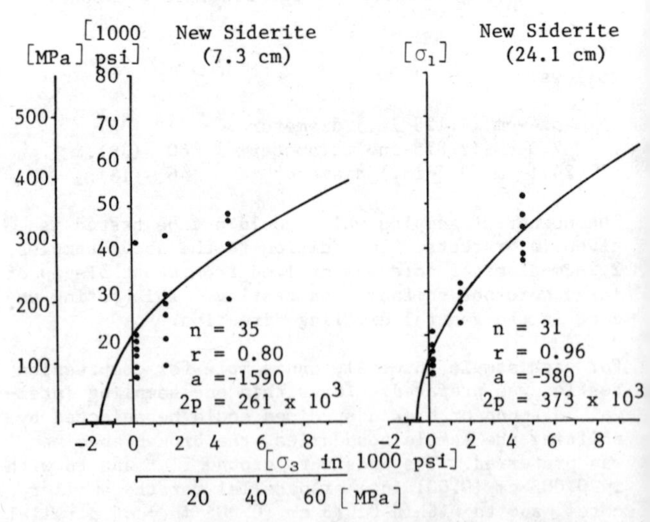

Figure 3: σ_1/σ_3 Parabola for Triaxial Compression Tests for Sound Specimens. (n = number of observations, r= correlation coefficient, a= position of apex , $y^2 = 2p(x+a)$).

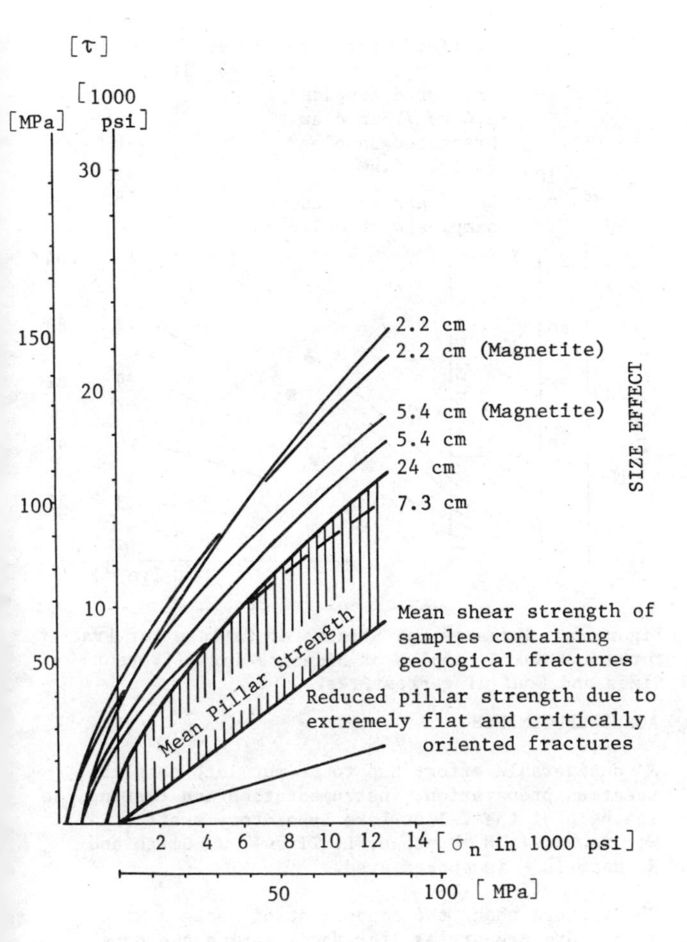

Figure 4: Mohr Envelopes of Siderite for Different Size Specimens and Shear Resistance of Geological Fractures.

To obtain the uniaxial compressive strength for the sound samples, the individual failure points shown on Figures 3A to 3F were moved parallel to the best-fit curve until the σ_1 axis was intersected ($\sigma_3 = 0$). For all the tested samples the uniaxial compressive strength was determined and the mean and standard deviation are given in Table 1. Table 1 indicates a size effect in regard to uniaxial compressive strength, tensile strength, and standard deviation of strength for the sound samples. Following the analysis of several investigators (Lundborg, 1967; Kostak and Bielenstein, 1971), a regression analysis of log strength against log volume gave the following results:

$$\log \text{strength (psi)} = (4.58 \pm 0.04) - (0.136 \pm 0.027) \log \text{volume (in.}^3\text{)},$$

$$\log \text{Std. Dev. (psi)} = (4.125 \pm 0.072) - (0.118 \pm 0.040) \log \text{volume (in.}^3\text{)}.$$

An extrapolation into the size of pillars in the siderite orebody, 67.3 x 10^3 m^3 (2.4 x 10^6 cu ft), yields a uniaxial compressive strength of about 12.9 MPa (1870 psi) and a standard deviation of 6.7 MPa (970 psi). This value appears to be unrealistically low. Investigations of Protodiakonov (1964), Bieniawski et al (1969), and Pratt et al (1972) have

TABLE 1

Uniaxial Compressive Strength in MPa[1] of Broken and Sound Samples of Various Sizes

Diameter (cm)		Mean	Std.Dev.
Sound Samples			
2.2[2]	(29)[3]	273	81
2.2	(30)	242	70
5.4[2]	(9)	232	93
5.4	(30)	171	78
7.3	(17)	136	66
24.1	(17)	100	30
Broken Samples (Uniaxial Compression)			
5.4	(44)	33	19
7.3	(43)	30	5
24.1	(29)	56	61
Sound Samples (Tensile Strength)			
2.2[2]	(14)	135	3
2.2	(20)	115	2
5.4[2]	(8)	95	2
5.4	(19)	110	2
7.3	(18)	112	2
24.1	(14)	4	1

[1] 1000 psi = 6.89476 MPa
[2] Magnetite bearing
[3] Number of observations

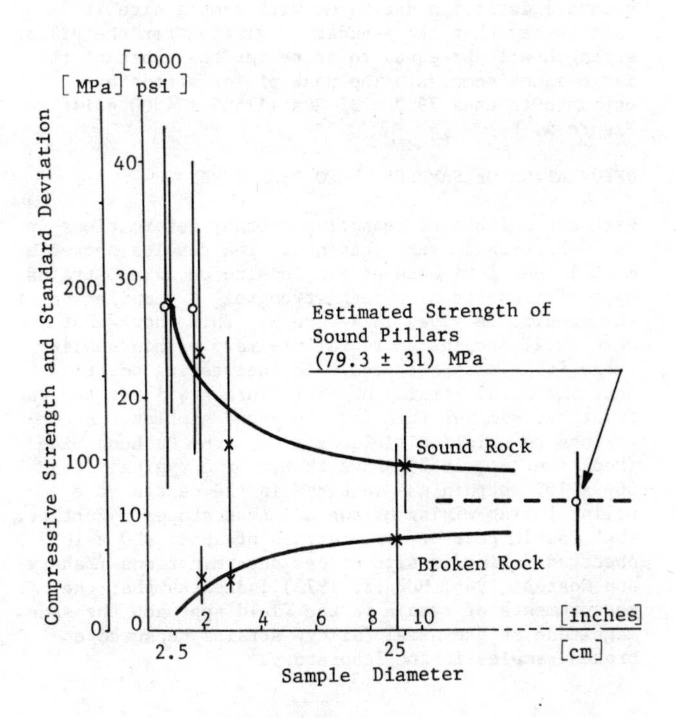

Figure 5: Estimate of Pillar Strength from Compression Tests.

shown that for sound specimens a limit strength value is approached with increase in size which makes an extrapolation of an experimental log strength/log volume relationship over orders of magnitude questionable.

In the case of the siderite, the limit strength value was not known and the results from testing the broken samples were used to obtain a substitute.

The triaxial strength values of the broken samples were plotted in a σ_1/σ_3 diagram, and the uniaxial compressive strength was determined by moving the σ_1 values along the best-fit line until $\sigma_3 = 0$ was reached. Some of the observed variations could be explained by different inclinations of geological fractures. With this information, the strength of the non-testable samples was estimated. The results are given in Table 1.

A plot of the mean strength of the broken siderite samples against size shows an increase with size (Figure 5). This increase of the mean strength can be explained by observing the failure modes of fractured small and big samples. The probability of failure occurring along a fracture without mobilizing the full rock material strength due to interlock is considerably higher for small samples than for larger samples where the larger surface area of the fractures provides more interlock and mobilizes a larger amount of the rock material strength.

In this study it appears, therefore, justifiable to estimate the strength of a sound pillar at Wawa as being halfway between the mean strength of the large broken samples and the large sound samples. As the standard deviation decreases with sample size it is safe to say that the standard deviation for the pillar strength will be equal to or better than that of the large sound samples. The peak pillar strength estimate is thus 79.3 ± 31 MPa (11500 ± 4500 psi); see Figure 5.

DEFORMATION OF SAMPLES UP TO PEAK STRENGTH

With the calibrated measuring system, deformations up to peak strength were obtained. The results showed a much lesser influence of sample size on axial strains up to failure than on peak strength. A compilation of the results is given in Figure 6. This shows that mean axial strains up to failure vary within smaller ranges than peak stresses. An interesting point is that the axial strains up to failure are lower for the fractured samples than for the sound samples. A comparison to existing field data from the MacLeod Mine (Hedley et al, 1968) shows that, for a typical case, 500×10^{-6} strain was measured in the centre of a pillar during mining of the adjacent stopes. Further, the elastic recovery from strain of about 300×10^{-6} observed during in-situ stress determinations (Zahary and Coates, 1966; Herget, 1973) indicates that the measurements of strain in the field approach the same magnitude as the axial failure strains measured on broken samples in the laboratory.

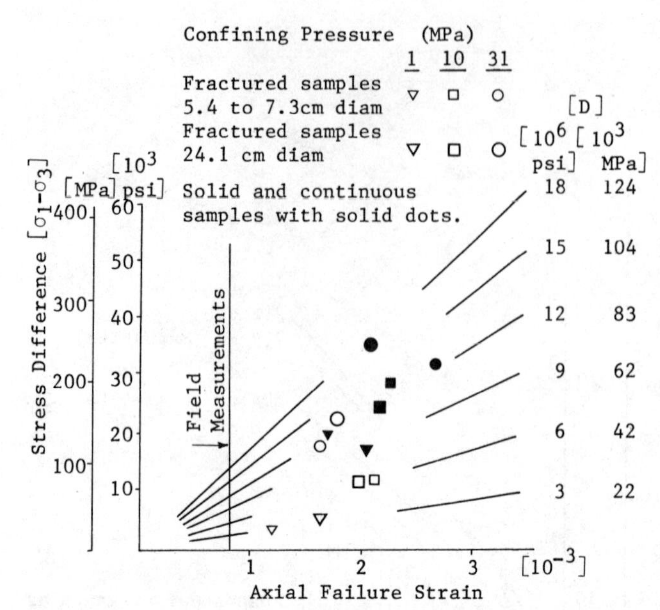

Figure 6: Stresses and Strains at Failure for Fractured and Solid Samples of Siderite for Different Sizes and Confining Pressures.

ACKNOWLEDGEMENTS

A considerable effort had to be put into sampling, specimen preparation, instrumentation and testing, so the help of the Elliot Lake Laboratory staff - Wm. Zawadski, H. Montone, L. Tirrul, J. Smith and N. Capozio - is appreciated.

The authors thank the management of MacLeod Mine, Algoma Ore Properties, for facilitating the core sampling.

REFERENCES

Bieniawski, Z.T., Denkhaus, H.G. and Vogler, U.W., 1969, Failure of fractured rock, International Journal of Rock Mechanics and Mining Sciences, Vol. 6, pp. 323-341.

Hedley, D.G.F., Zahary, G., Soderlund, H.W. and Coates, D.F., 1968, Underground measurements in a steeply dipping orebody, Proceedings, 5th Canadian Rock Mechanics Symposium, Toronto.

Herget, G., 1972, A cylindrical pressure vessel for testing 10-inch diameter specimen under a confining pressure of up to 6000 psi, Mining Research Centre, Ottawa, IR 72/24. Unpublished.

Herget, G., 1973, Variation of rock stresses with depth at a Canadian iron mine, International Journal of Rock Mechanics and Mining Sciences, Vol. 10, pp. 32-51, Pergamon Press.

Herget, G., Unrug, K., and Capozio, N., 1973, Shear strength and failure strains of geological and artificial fractures in siderite under triaxial conditions, Mining Research Centre, Ottawa, IR 73/61. Unpublished.

Kostak, B. and Bielenstein, H.U., 1971, Strength distribution in hard rock, International Journal of Rock Mechanics and Mining Sciences, Vol. 8, pp. 501-521.

Lundborg, N., 1967, The strength-size relation of granite, International Journal of Rock Mechanics and Mining Sciences, Vol. 4, pp. 269-272.

Pratt, H.R., Black, A.D., Brown, W.S. and Brace, W.F., 1972, The effect of specimen size on the mechanical properties of unjointed diorite, International Journal of Rock Mechanics and Mining Sciences, Vol. 9, pp. 513-523.

Protodiakonov, M.M., 1964, Methods for evaluation of cracks and strength of rock systems in depth, 4th International Conference on Strata Control and Rock Mechanics, Henry Crumb School of Mines, Columbia University, New York, Addendum.

Zahary, G. and Coates, D.F., Rock mechanics investigations 1964/1965 at the MacLeod Mine, Algoma Ore Properties, Wawa, Ont., Mining Research Centre, Ottawa, FMP 66/117. Unpublished.

CONTRAINTES DANS LES MODÈLES DES MASSIFS ROCHEUX FISSURES SANS POUSSÉE HORIZONTALE

STRESSES IN MODELS SIMULATING THRUSTLESS JOINTED ROCK MASSES

SPANNUNGEN IN MODELLEN VON KLUFTARTIGEN FELSMASSIVEN OHNE HORIZONTALSCHUB

I.I. KANDAOUROV
Professeur

L.A. OUVAROV
cand. es sc.

N.M. KARPOV
ing.

Institut de Recherches Hydrotechniques B.E. Védénéev

Leningrad, U.R.S.S.

RESUME

Dans le rapport il s'agit des résultats des études de la répartition des contraintes dans les modèles en blocs des fondations rocheuses stratifiées et fissurées. Les essais expérimentaux ont montré que la répartition des contraintes dans les blocs portait un caractère non uniforme. Aussi, lors de l'analyse de l'état de contrainte du milieu tout entier convient-il de mesurer les contraintes en plusieurs points des blocs en déterminant leurs valeurs moyennes. Ensuite il faut examiner la répartition dans le massif de ces valeurs moyennes des contraintes qui ont été obtenues pour un nombre assez grand de blocs.

Les essais ont permis de constater que la répartition des contraintes verticales σ_z dues à l'action des charges verticales sur les faces de modèle obéit à la loi normale. Le degré de concentration des contraintes σ_z dans la direction de la charge dépend des propriétés structurales du milieu, c'est-à-dire des dimensions, de la forme et de l'arrangement des blocs dans le massif, ainsi que des propriétés physico-mécaniques tant des blocs eux-mêmes que de leurs surfaces de contact. L'angle de la zone sollicitée est défini par la structure du massif.

Les particularités de répartition des contraintes dans les modèles en blocs, mises en lumière par les essais montrent que pour l'évaluation de l'état de contrainte et de déformation des fondations rocheuses fissurées il est rationnel d'employer la mécanique des milieux discontinus.

SUMMARY

Presented are the results of investigations on the distribution of stresses in block-jointed models reproducing jointed stratified rock of structure foundations. As evidenced by experimental studies, the pattern of stress distribution varies from block to block. Therefore, when analysing the stress state of the whole rock mass it is necessary to measure stresses at a series of points of individual blocks and to determine their average values. Further analysis should be based on the distribution of these average stresses obtained for a fairly large number of blocks.

The distribution of vertical stresses σ_z induced by a vertical load applied to the model has been shown to obey the normal law. The degree of concentration of stresses σ_z in the direction of load is governed by the structural features of the medium, namely, the size, shape and arrangement of blocks in the rock mass, as well as by the physico-mechanical characteristics of both the blocks themselves and their contact surfaces. The inclination of the stressed zone is determined by the rock structure.

The stress distribution patterns obtained on block models suggest that the stress-strain state of jointed rock of structure foundation can be described fairly well in terms of mechanics of descrete media.

ZUSAMMENFASSUNG

Im Bericht werden die Untersuchungsergebnisse der Spannungsverteilung in blockgegliederten Modellen der geschichteten klüftigen Felsfundamente dargelegt. Die experimentellen Untersuchungen haben gezeigt, dass die Spannungsverteilung in Blöcken einen ungleichmässigen Charakter hat. Im Zusammenhang damit ist es bei der Analyse eines Spannungszustandes des ganzen Mediums notwendig, die Spannungen in vielen Punkten der Blöcke zu messen und ihre Mittelwerte zu bestimmen. Ferner muss man die Verteilung dieser für eine genug grosse Anzahl von Blöcken ermittelten Mittelwerte im Massiv untersuchen.

Die Untersuchungen erlaubten auch festzustellen, dass die Verteilung der vertikalen Spannungen σ_z unter der Wirkung der vertikalen Belastung auf die Modellseiten einem normalen Gesetz unterworfen wird. Der Konzentrationsgrad der Spannungen σ_z in der Richtung der Belastung hängt von den Struktureigenschaften der Blöcke, d.h. von den Grössen, der Form und Lagerung der Blöcke, sowie von ihren physikalischmechanischen Charakteristiken und Kontaktflächen ab. Ein Winkel der beanspruchten Zone wird durch die Struktur des Massivs bestimmt.

Die während der Versuche bestimmten Besonderheiten der Spannungsverteilung in den blockgegliederten Modellen haben gezeigt, dass der Verformungs-Spannungszustand mit Hilfe der Mechanik von diskreten Medien genug gut beschrieben werden kann.

Lors de l'établissement du projet des ouvrages il est très important d'évaluer correctement l'état de contrainte et de déformation de leurs fondations rocheuses. Ce problème est particulièrement actuel pour les ouvrages transmettant de grandes charges aux massifs rocheux. A présent, il existe quelques méthodes théoriques pour l'évaluation de l'état de contrainte et de déformation des fondations rocheuses. Ces méthodes se distinguent par le choix d'un modèle théorique de la fondation rocheuse de l'ouvrage. Parmi elles on peut citer deux méthodes principales: la première méthode permet de considérer la fondation rocheuse comme un massif continu et la seconde méthode comme un massif discontinu constitué de nombreux éléments.

Dans la première méthode d'étude de l'état de contrainte et de déformation des fondations rocheuses qui sont considérées comme un milieu continu le plus souvent on utilise les solutions de la théorie de l'élasticité d'un corps isotrope ou anisotrope. Dans l'autre méthode c'est un modèle du milieu granulaire créé par les savants de notre pays qui sert d'un modèle théorique de la fondation rocheuse de l'ouvrage. Dans ce modèle le massif rocheux est considéré comme un ensemble d'éléments disposés d'une façon éventuelle l'un par rapport à l'autre.

La plupart des fondations rocheuses se distinguent par les conditions complexes de gisement des roches, leur fissurité, ainsi que par les propriétés mécaniques non uniformes, La fissurité définit essentiellement l'état de contrainte et de déformation, les propriétés de résistance et de filtration des massifs rocheux.

Les fondations rocheuses horizontalement stratifiées découpées par des fissures horizontales et verticales présentent une des formes types de la structure des massifs rocheux. La répartition des contraintes dans le massif est influencée par le degré d'ouverture des fissures verticales et le caractère d'interaction des blocs. En présence des fissures verticales ouvertes, les massifs rocheux peuvent être considérés comme des milieux granulaires sans poussée horizontale. A une telle structure, les fissures verticales empêchent le transfert des efforts entre les blocs de la même assise et diminuent considérablement les déformations transversales du massif entier.

Etant donné la structure des massifs rocheux fissurés horizontalement stratifiés, il convient d'attendre dans les zones où agissent les charges extérieures une grande concentration des contraintes verticales et de plus grands tassements par rapport à un milieu continu isotrope. C'est pour cette raison que pour la solution de nombreux problèmes de la construction il est important d'étudier les milieux granulaires sans poussée horizontale, comme des modèles des massifs rocheux fissurés, ayant une capacité de distribution des contraintes plus faible par rapport aux milieux d'autres structures.

Nous avons effectué les études de l'état de contrainte des milieux en blocs sur les modèles à deux dimensions par une méthode de polarisation optique, ainsi que par une méthode qui prévoit la mesure directe des pressions de contact entre blocs. Les essais par la méthode optique avaient pour but de 1. Déterminer l'état de contrainte des modèles à deux dimensions des milieux granulaires sans poussée horizontale pour différents rapports des côtés des blocs de modèle. 2. Comparer les contraintes expérimentales à celles obtenues selon la mécanique des milieux granulaires sans poussée horizontale et par la théorie de l'élasticité. 3. Determiner dans les modèles essayés l'angle de la zone sollicitée.

Les essais ont ete réalisés sur trois modèles des milieux granulaires sans poussée horizontale, les rapports entre la largeur et la hauteur des blocs étant 2,22:1; 1,67:1; 1:1. La hauteur de tous les blocs de modèle essayés était de $1{,}8 \cdot 10^{-2}$m et la largeur était de $1{,}2 \cdot 10^{-2}$m. L'appareil des blocs de tous les modèles était admis uniforme. La hauteur des assises (au nombre de 7) et le caractère des surfaces de contact étaient les mêmes pour tous les modèles. Les blocs de modèles fabriqués d'un matériau photoélastique à base de la résine époxyde ЭД-6 ont été posés par assises horizontales avec jeux entre les faces verticales, ce qui permet de considérer les modèles testés comme modèles sans poussée horizontale.

L'installation expérimentale a été executée en forme d'un cadre fermé. Les charges de calcul verticales étaient créées à l'aide d'un vis et les valeurs des charges étant mesurées par un dynamomètre à ressort. La charge verticale était transmise par une charnière au poinçon métallique qui s'appuyait contre le bloc supérieur des modèles au moyen d'un join en caoutchouc. Grâce à ce joint en caoutchouc la charge exercée sur le bloc peut être considérée comme uniformément répartie.

La singularité spécifique des études expérimentales réside dans la détermination de l'état de contrainte des blocs constituant un massif rocheux. La définition des contraintes s'effectuait pour les 3ième et 5ième assises de blocs des modèles essayés. Pour chaque bloc essayé, après les mesures réalisées tous les $(2 \div 3) \cdot 10^{-3}$m suivant la longueur des blocs, on a fait une intégration numérique des équations d'équilibre. Pour vérifier les résultats des mesures on a rempli la condition d'égalité à zéro des valeurs des contraintes horizontales σ_x sur les faces de bloc verticales non sollicitées. La deuxième vérification consistait à remplir la condition d'équilibre des projections des forces sur l'axe vertical.

Les expériences ont permis de constater que la charge verticale n'est supportée que par les blocs situés au triangle avec sommet près du bloc sous le poinçon. Cela est montré sur une image d'isochromes obtenue lors des essais du premier modèle (fig.1).

Fig.1. Lignes isochromatiques observées dans le premier modèle soumis à la triple charge de calcul

On peut voir sur la figure que les isochromes à l'intérieur de chaque bloc sollicité sont non uniformes. La construction des courbes de toutes les composantes des contraintes pour les blocs des 3ième et 5ième assises des modèles essayés a montré que toutes les courbes ont un caractère irregulier accentué selon la longueur des blocs. Il en résulte que pour déterminer l'état de contrainte des milieux en blocs discontinus il est nécessaire d'effectuer les mesures des contraintes en plusieurs points des blocs. Les mesures des contraintes en un ou en deux points des blocs conduiront évidemment aux erreurs dans la détermination de l'état de contrainte de tout le milieu.

Lors de la réalisation des expériences sur les milieux en blocs, malgré le polissage des surfaces de contact des blocs, pratiquement il semble impossible d'obtenir une égalité des efforts sur des blocs disposés symétriquement par rapport à l'axe de la charge. Pour rendre symétriques les courbes σ_z et τ_{xz}, les aires des courbes correspondantes pour les blocs symétriques par rapport à l'axe de la charge exercée ont été moyennisées et distribuées uniformément selon la longueur des blocs, les points expérimentaux étant portés sur les parties medianes des blocs.

En comparant les courbes expérimentales de répartition des contraintes normales et tangentielles à celles théoriques, on a pris en considération le fait que pour la théorie de l'élasticité le schéma de calcul, en raison de la continuité du milieu, serait présenté par une charge uniformément répartie d'une intensité de $12{,}5\cdot10^5$ N/m² qui s'exerce sur un tronçon de demi-surface d'une longueur respectivement 4,0, 3,0 et $1{,}8\cdot10^{-2}$m. Dans un modèle discontinu la charge de même intensité était répartie sur un seul bloc d'une longueur de 4,0, 3,0 et $1{,}8\cdot10^{-2}$m et c'est pourquoi elle se réduisait à une résultante d'une intensité, respectivement, de 50, 37 et $22{,}5\cdot10^5$ N/m². Une telle comparaison des courbes expérimentales σ_z et τ_{xz} à celles théoriques pour différents schémas de calcul de la théorie de l'élasticité et de la mécanique des milieux granulaires (Kandaourov, 1966) est expliquée par les différents caractères spécifiques des modèles de milieu eux-mêmes.

Les figures 2 et 3 fournissent les courbes de répartition des contraintes verticales et tangentielles pour trois modèles essayés comparées à celles théoriques obtenues selon la mécanique des milieux granulaires sans poussée horizontale et la théorie de l'élasticité. A la figure 2 on peut voir que dans les modèles essayés la concentration des contraintes dans la direction de la charge est plus grande que dans un milieu continu. Dans ce cas la position des courbes expérimentales est conditionnée par les propriétés structurales du milieu: lorsque le rapport entre la largeur et la hauteur des blocs diminue, les courbes expérimentales des contraintes verticales et tangentielles et les courbes théoriques obtenues selon la mécanique des milieux granulaires se rapprochent sensiblement. Un tel rapprochement a lieu aussi suivant la profondeur avec l'augmentation de la coordonnee z.

L'aplanissement des courbes expérimentales des contraintes verticales σ_z s'effectuait par la méthode des moments de Pearson. Les valeurs des paramètres des équations de contraintes verticales, aux charges moyennisées sur les blocs symétriques par rapport à l'axe vertical du modèle, ont été déterminées par les expressions:

$$a = 0; \quad \sigma^2 = \sum_1^n p_i x_i^2 \qquad /1/$$

où a - attente mathématique; σ^2 - dispersion de distribution; p_i - probabilité égalée à la partie totale de la charge agissant sur le i ième bloc; x_i - coordonnée du centre du i ième bloc suivant l'axe d'abscisses.

Connaissant la dispersion de distribution et la valeur de la charge extérieure on a établi, pour les modèles essayés, les équations déterminant les contraintes verticales σ_z. Pour les premier et troisième modèles ces équations s'écrivent comme suit:

Modèle I.

3ième assise de blocs:

$$\sigma_z = \frac{12{,}5\cdot4\cdot10^5}{\sqrt{2\pi}\cdot2{,}8}\exp\left(-\frac{x^2}{2\cdot2{,}8^2}\right) \qquad /2/$$

5ième assise de blocs:

$$\sigma_z = \frac{12{,}5\cdot4\cdot10^5}{\sqrt{2\pi}\cdot3{,}58}\exp\left(-\frac{x^2}{2\cdot3{,}58^2}\right) \qquad /3/$$

Modèle III.

3ième assise de blocs:

$$\sigma_z = \frac{12{,}5\cdot1{,}8\cdot10^5}{\sqrt{2\pi}\cdot1.17}\exp\left(-\frac{x^2}{2\cdot1{,}17^2}\right) \qquad /4/$$

5ième assise de blocs:

$$\sigma_z = \frac{12{,}5\cdot1{,}8\cdot10^5}{\sqrt{2\pi}\cdot1{,}53}\exp\left(-\frac{x^2}{2\cdot1{,}53^2}\right) \qquad /5/$$

Les expériences ont permis de constater que sous l'action de la charge verticale dans les blocs de modèle apparaissent les contraintes horizontales σ_x dont les valeurs diminuent jusqu'à zéro près des faces verticales non sollicitées des blocs. Les essais ont montré que si les charges de calcul s'exercent sur les blocs supérieurs ce n'est qu'une zone limitée par les contours des blocs supportant la charge extérieure qui travaille, mais non pas toute la demi-surface. L'angle de la zone sollicitée pour les premier, deuxième et troisième modèles était respectivement β_1 = 0,84 rad; β_2 = 0,7 rad; β_3 = 0,46 rad, ce qui peut s'écrire par la relation (Ouvarov, 1970):

$$\beta = \arctan\frac{b}{2h} \qquad /6/$$

où b et h sont les valeurs moyennes de la largeur et de la hauteur des blocs de modèle.

Cela montre que la diminution du rapport entre la largeur et la hauteur des blocs médianes conduit à la diminution de l'angle de la zone sollicitée, à la concentration élevée des contraintes dans la direction de la charge et aux grands tassements.

Les essais sur les modèles de matériau photoélastique ont permis de mettre en évidence un certain nombre de particularités de la répartition des contraintes dans les milieux formés de blocs. Il s'est avéré que la répartition des contraintes dans un milieu réel s'accorde qualitativement avec les résultats des solutions théoriques (Kandaourov, 1966). Cependent, pour les calculs pratiques des fondations des ouvrages concrets il est indispensable de déterminer les paramètres de calcul intervenant dans les relations. Dans ce but, nous avons entrepris les essais expérimentaux visant à étudier la nature des paramètres qui caractérisent la répartition des contraintes dans le milieu en blocs et à mettre en évidence l'influence sur ces paramètres de différents facteurs propres aux massifs rocheux. Comme le montrent les essais précédents, au nombre de facteurs principaux se rapportent la structure du massif et les propriétés physico-mécaniques des blocs et de leurs contacts, par exemple les propriétés de frottement des surfaces de blocs, leur déformabilité, etc. (Karpov, 1973).

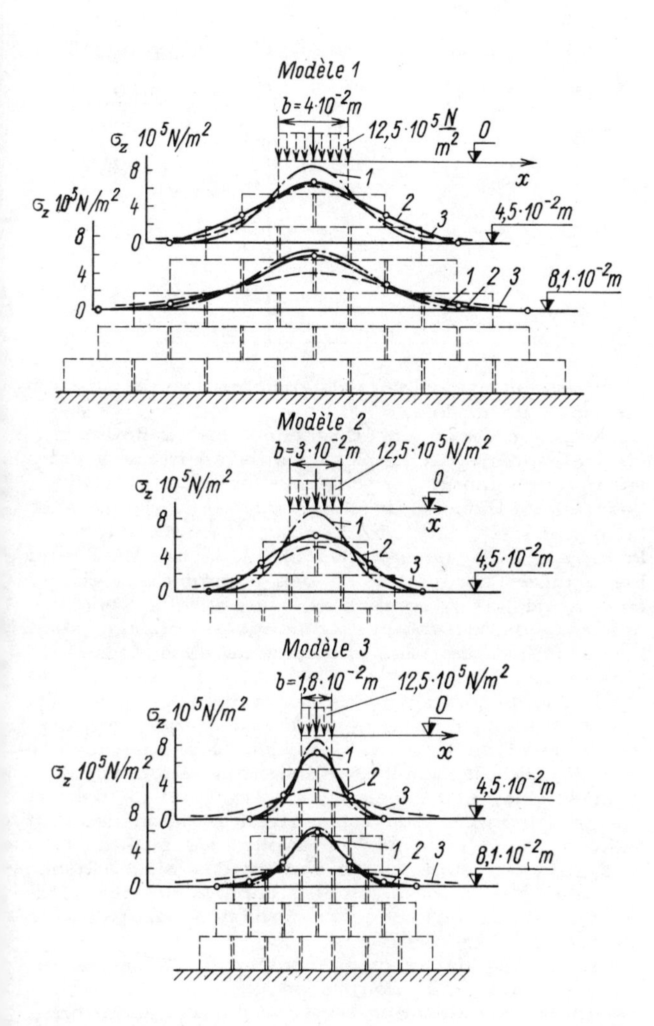

Fig.2. Courbes de contraintes verticales σ_z pour trois modèles testés
1 - selon la mécanique des milieux granulaires sans poussée horizontale
2 - courbe expérimentale
3 - selon la théorie de l'élasticité.

Pour l'étude de l'influence de ces facteurs, ont été effectués les essais des modèles formés de blocs ayant différents dimensions, formes et arrangements dans le massif. Au total, on a realisé 8 modèles de différente structure dont les caractéristiques sont groupées dans le tableau ci-dessous.

Les essais des modèles structuraux de la fondation rocheuse étaient réalisés pour deux valeurs des paramètres de la résistance au cisaillement selon les joints entre blocs: 1/ μ = 0,25 et c = 0; 2/ μ = 0,85 et c = 0. En outre, les modèles étaient testés à condition que les blocs soient collés selon les surfaces horizontales. Pour les essais on a utilisé un stand d'épreuve vertical de 1,0x1,0 m. En tant que matériau de blocs on a utilisé le plâtre dont les propriétés mécaniques représentaient celles des roches réelles.

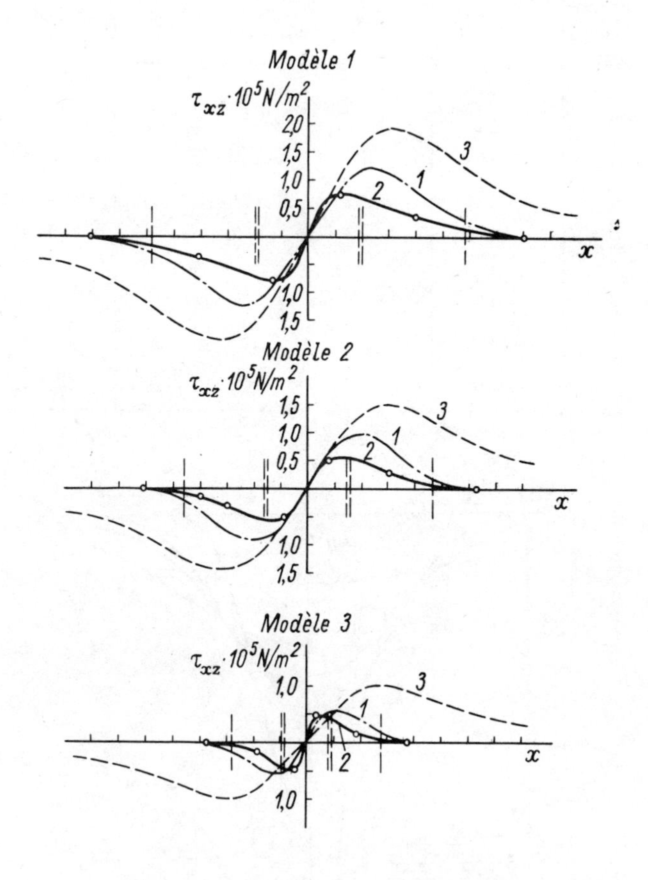

Fig.3. Courbes de contraintes tangentielles pour 3ième assise de blocs des modèles testés.
1 - selon la mécanique des milieux granulaires sans poussée horizontale
2 - courbe expérimentale
3 - selon la théorie de l'élasticité.

Les mesures des contraintes de contact entre blocs (à l'action de la charge verticale sur les surfaces du modèle) s'effectuaient par les jauges de pression créées spécialement pour ce but, leur principe de fonctionnement étant basé sur la variation de la résistance électrique de contact due à l'effort de compression.

Sur la figure 4 sont données les courbes expérimentales de répartition des contraintes verticales à une profondeur de 0,52 m de la surface du massif, entre 13ième et 14ième assises. Les courbes montrent que la répartition des contraintes dans un massif formé de blocs est conditionnée par sa structure et dépend des dimensions, de la forme et de l'arrangement des blocs. Outre cela, les résultats des essais démontrent que la concentration des contraintes σ_z dans la direction de la charge dépend, quantitativement, du coefficient de frottement dans les joints entre blocs et de la cohésion (courbes I, II et III).

Une fois les essais effectués, on peut faire les conclusions suivantes:

Tableau

n° modèle	Hauteur des blocs $h \cdot 10^{-2}$, m	Dimension moyenne suivant horizontale (largeur) $b \cdot 10^{-2}$, m	Angle de la zone sollicitée $\beta°$, rad	$\tan\beta$ pour le massif	Coefficient de non-uniformité de l'appareil κ	Indice de structure $\alpha = \frac{4h\kappa^2}{b^2} \cdot 10^{-2}$, 1/m
1	4	8	0,787	1,00	1	0,25
2	4	6	0,645	0,75	1	0,445
3	4	4	0,465	0,5	1	1,00
4	4	4	0,465	0,5	1	1,00
5	4	5,34	0,465	0,5	1,335	1,00
6	4	6	0,465	0,5	1,5	1,00
7	4	4	0,245	0,25	2	4,00
8	4	4	0,198	0,2	–	–
			0,552	0,615		

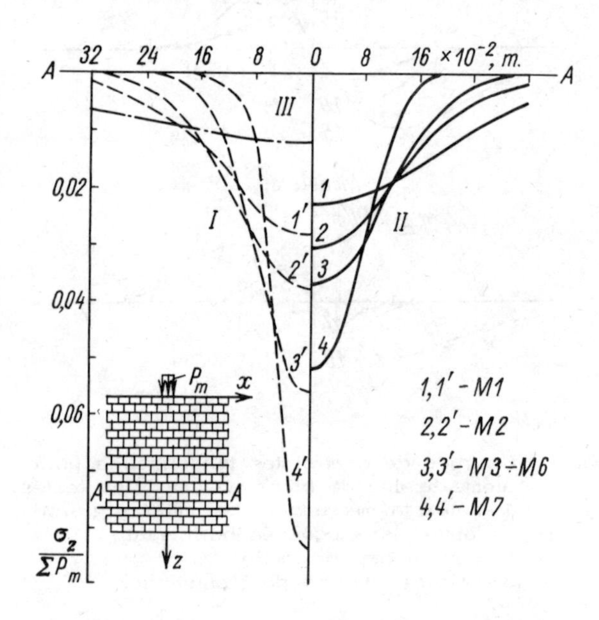

Fig.4. Répartition des contraintes normales verticales σ_z dans le milieu en blocs suivant la ligne AA en fonction du coefficient de frottement des surfaces de bloc μ et de l'indice de structure α
I – μ = 0,25; II – μ = 0,85; III – blocs collés.

1. Pour les études expérimentales de l'état de contrainte dans les modèles des massifs rocheux fissurés sans poussée horizontale, il est rationnel d'utiliser la méthode de polarisation optique. En étudiant par cette méthode les contraintes dans les blocs, sans changer la structure du milieu, on peut obtenir les données sûres concernant la répartition des contraintes verticales et tangentielles pour les assises choisies.

2. Dans les modèles d'un massif rocheux fissuré sans poussée horizontale la concentration des contraintes verticales dans la direction de la charge est plus grande que dans un milieu continu isotrope. La répartition des contraintes est limitée par la zone dont les dimensions sont déterminées par la structure du milieu de modèle.

3. Les courbes expérimentales des contraintes verticales dans les modèles testés se trouvent entre les courbes théoriques obtenues selon la mécanique des milieux discontinus sans poussée horizontale et la théorie de l'élasticité. Lorsque le rapport reliant la largeur et la hauteur des blocs de modèle diminue, les courbes expérimentales des contraintes verticales et tangentielles s'approchent, suivant la profondeur des modèles, des courbes théoriques obtenues selon la mécanique des milieux discontinus sans poussée horizontale.

4. La concentration des contraintes σ_z dans la direction de la charge dépend de la forme, des dimensions et de l'arrangement des blocs. Le coefficient κ caractérisant l'arrangement des blocs dans le massif, leurs dimensions et formes est un des paramètres importants du milieu. La répartition des contraintes σ_z dépend des paramètres de frottement μ et c sur les surfaces de contact des blocs: la concentration des contraintes σ_z dans la direction de la charge augmente avec la diminution des paramètres μ et c.

5. Les essais effectués ont permis de mettre en évidence un certain nombre de particularités de la répartition des contraintes σ_z dans un milieu formé de blocs. Ils ont montré que pour évaluer l'état de contrainte-déformation des fondations rocheuses fissurées, il est rationnel d'utiliser la mécanique des milieux discontinus. C'est un modèle de milieu en blocs sans poussée horizontale qui peut servir d'un modèle théorique des fondations stratifiées altérées et décomposées ayant les fissures à remplissage tendre (matériau broyé, argile, etc.).

REFERENCES

1. Kandaourov I.I., – Mécanique des milieux granulaires et son emploi dans la construction, Stroiizdat, 1966, p.318.

2. Karpov N.M., – Influence des caractéristiques structurales des massifs rocheux sur leur état de contrainte et de déformation, Izvestia VNIIG, v.102, 1973, p.74-81.

3. Ouvarov L.A., – Sur le problème du choix de la zone sollicitée dans les fondations rocheuses fissurées sans poussée horizontale, Sb.dokladov po gidrotekhnike, vyp.11, Energia, v.102, 1970, p.74-81.

THE BEHAVIOR OF ROCK-LIKE MATERIALS IN SOME CONTROLLED STRAIN STATES

COMPORTEMENT DES MATÉRIAUX SEMBLABLES AU ROCHER DANS CERTAINES DÉFORMATIONS CONTROLÉES

VERHALTEN VON DEN STEINARTIGEN STOFFEN IN DEN BESCHRÄNKTEN VERZERRUNGSBEDINGUNGEN

Toshikazu KAWAMOTO Professor, Earth Pressure Research Laboratory, Nagoya University, Nagoya, Japan

Toshiaki SAITO Lecturer, Dept. of Marine Civil Engineering, Tokai University, Shimizu, Japan

SUMMARY The servocontrolled triaxial compression testing machine with the loading capacities of 100 ton in two horizontal axes and 200 ton in vertical axis was used to study the mechanism of failure and the behavior in post-failure of rock-like materials such as cement mortar, sandstone and tuff. The uniaxial compression test was, first, performed for the 10 cm cubic specimens of cement mortar in order to determine the relationships between the stiffness of testing machine and the strain rate. The relationships between the strain rate and the ultimate strength, the strain at strength failure and the postfailure behavior of cement mortar were observed from the results of uniaxial test. It was found that the strength increased as applied strain rate was increased but the strain at strength failure was hardly affected by strain rate. Next, the biaxial compression test in plane strain condition and the stress relaxation test with various initial confining strain were performed, and the mechanism of failure in this condition and the stress relaxation behavior of the rock-like materials were investigated. Furthermore, the triaxial compression tests were carried out under the various controlled strain paths from some initial strain conditions and the behavior of failed materials was discussed.

RÉSUMÉ Une machine d'essai servo-contrôlée de la compression triaxiale, d'une capacité de charge de 100 tonnes dans les deux axes horizontaux et de 200 tonnes dans le vertical, fut ulitisée pour examiner le mécanisme de la rupture et le comportement aprèsla rupture des matériaux semblables au rocher comme mortier de ciment, grès et tuf. L'essai de la compression uniaxiale fut d'abord réalisé avec de pièces cubiques de 10 cm de côté en mortier de ciment afin de déterminer la relation entre la rigidité de la machine d'essai et le taux de la déformation. La relation entre le taux de la déformation et la résistance ultime et celle entre la déformation à la résistance de rupture et le comportement après la rupture du mortier de ciment furent examinées avec le résultat de l'essai uniaxial. Il fut démontré que la résistance accroit avec l'auguementation du taux de la defórmation, tandisque la déformation à la résistance de rupture est tres peu affectée par le taux de la déformation. Dans la suite, l'essai de la compression biaxiale sous la déformation plane et l'essai de la relaxation des tensions avec diverses déformations intiales confinées furent executés, et le mécanisme de la rupture dans la defórmation plane et le comportement de la relaxation des tensions des matériaux semblable au rocher furent analysés. En fin l'essai de la compression triaxiale fut effectue en contrôlant des passages divers de la déformation à partir de son état intial certain, et le comportement des matériaux semblables au rocher défaillis fut discuté.

ZUSAMMENFASSUNG Zur Untersuchung des Bruchmechanismus und des Verhalten nach der Zerstörung von den steinartigen Stoffen wie Zementmörtel, Sandstein und Tuff wurde eine dreiachiale, servogesteuerte Druckprüfmaschine mit zwei 100 ton waagerechten- und einen 200 ton senkrechten Achsen benutzt. Zuerst wurde einachsiger Druckversuch der kubischen Proben mit einer Seitenlänge von 10 cm des Zementmörtels durchgeführt, um das Verhältnis zwischen die Steifigkeit der Prüfmaschine und die Verzerrungsgeschwindigkeit zu bestimmen. Die Verhältnisse zwischen die Verzerrungsgeschwindigkeit und höchste Festigkeit, dazu gehörige Verzerrung und Verhalten nach der Zerstörung von Zementmörtel wurde durch den einachsialen Versuch untersucht. Dadurch wurde die Tatsache festgestellt, dass die Festigkeit mit der Zunahme der Verzerrungsgeschwindigkeit zunimmt, aber kein Einfluss auf den Verzerrungswert am Bruch daraus geübt wird. Dann wurden die zweiachsiale Druckversuche unter der ebenen Verzerrungsbedingungen und die Spannungsrelaxationsversuche mit den verschiedenen anfänglichen Umschnürungsbedingungen durchgeführt und der Bruchmechanismus unter den ebenen Verzerrungsbedingungen und das Verhalten der Spannungsrelaxation von steinartigen Stoffen untersucht. Noch dazu wurden die dreiachsiale Druckversuche unter den aus den einigen anfänglichen Verzerrungsbedingungen heraus verschiedenen eingeschränkten Verzerrungsvorgängen und das Verhalten nach der Zerstörung von steinartigen Stoffe erörtert.

INTRODUCTION

There has long been an interest in the measurement of mechanical properties of rock for use in the stress analysis and the stability analysis of rock mechanics problems. For rock specimens the modulus of deformation or stress-strain relationship, Poisson ratio and the variation of failure strength with confining stress can be found from uniaxial and triaxial compression tests, which commonly are done under controlled loading and confining stress state. These tests have shown that the violent disintegration occurs in rock prior to fracture in compression because of uncontrolled release of energy from the testing machine into the rock, so the details of the failure process and the behavior in postfailure of rocks can not be obtained. Consequently, the stiff testing machines have been developed to control rock failure and used to study rock propertis that are unaffected by the characteristics of testing machine.

(Wawersik,1970, Bieniawski, 1970, Wawersik, 1971, Peng and Podnieks, 1972).

Several studies have shown that the dedormation behavior and the mechanism of failure of rock-like materials has different characteristics in relation to the confining stress state. Many presented investigations of failure mechanism or failure criterion , hitherto, are almost discussed on the state of applied stress and are hardly based on the strain state. Therefore, they did not fit to all the case of the various stress conditions. There are some examples for the failure criterion considering the strain state. Many of them, however, treat only the axisymmetric state of stress, in which the influence of the intermediate principal stress can not be observed.

In this study attempt to control failure is extended to triaxial compression by using the pure triaxial compression testing machine in which strains in three perpendicular axes can be respectively controlled by means of servocontrol system. Some characteristic features of complete stress-strain curves and the stress relaxation behavior of rock-like materials such as cement mortar, sandstone and tuff were investigated in some controlled strain conditions. From the observed results, the material characteristics in the confining strain states, the behavior in post-failure, the failure criterion in the strain state and the stress relaxation behavior will be discussed.

EXPERIMENTAL PROCEDURES

Specimens

The 100 mm cubic specimens of cement mortar and the 50 mm cubic specimens of Izumi sandstone and tuff were used in uniaxial and triaxial compression tests. The specimens of cement mortar were made of ordinary Portland cement and Toyoura standard grained sand. Their mix proportion in weight is as follows:

Water : Cement : Sand = 0.65 : 1 : 2

The cement mortar specimens were cured for twenty six days in water under the temperature at 20 ± 1 °C, and then for one day in the atmosphere. The age of specimens at experiment was twenty eight days.

Experimental equipment

The servocontrol system was equipped into the pure triaxial compression testing machine with the loading capacities of jacks of 100 ton for horizontal two pairs and 200 ton for vertical one pair in order to control the strain rate (Kawamoto, et al, 1970). This apparatus has also the automatic loading system controlling stress and the deformation reader system attached to the loading platens. The operational principle of the servocontrolled closed-loop system is shown in Figure 1.

The displacement rate of platens is able to be controlled in the range of $10^{-4} \sim 10^{-2}$ mm/sec. The relationships between strain rate $\dot{\varepsilon}$ and effective unloading stiffness of system K_r is given by Rummel and Fairhurst (Rummel and Fairhurst, 1970) as follows:

$$K_r = K_s + \frac{A\,k}{V_0}\cdot\frac{\dot{Q}}{L\,\dot{\varepsilon}}\,, \qquad (1)$$

where K_s is the unloading stiffness of loading system, A is the cross-sectional area of the pressurized cylinder, V_0 is the fluid volume in the pressurization system, k is the apparent bulk modulus of the fluid system, $\dot{Q}$ is the pumping rate and L is the length of

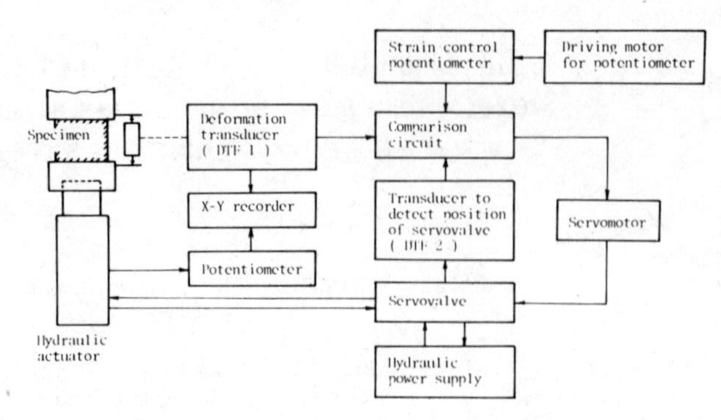

Fig. 1 Servocontrolled closed-loop system

specimen. Since A, k, V_0 and $\dot{Q}$ take the constant values determined for the loading system, respectively , it is necessry to decrease further the strain rate or to increase the length of specimen in order to increase more the stiffness of system. In this study, the appropriate displacement rate of platens which gives the complete stress-strain curve for uniaxial compression is used for all the other experiments.

Testing procedure

The teflon sheets wetted with silicon grease were inserted between the loading platens and the specimen in order to reduce the friction between them. The loading system with command and feedback signals was servocontrolled through the deformation transducers equipped between the platens. In this study the command signal was constant deformation rate and the load-deformation curves were recorded by X-Y recorders.

All the specimens were, first, preloaded to 5 ~ 10 per cent of the uniaxial compressive strength before actual tests in order to make better contact between the platens and the surfaces of specimen. Then, the preload was decreased to 1 per cent of the uniaxial strength and this state was assumed to be zero-strain state.

The loading patterns are as follows:

(1) Uniaxial loading with constant strain rate $\dot{\varepsilon}_1$ and zero or constant confining stresses σ_2 and σ_3.
(2) Uniaxial loading with constant strian rate $\dot{\varepsilon}_1$ and constant confining strains ε_2 and ε_3.
(3) Biaxial loading with different strain rates $\dot{\varepsilon}_2$ and $\dot{\varepsilon}_3$ and constant strain ε_1.
(4) Hydrostatic loading with same strains and same strain rates in three principal directions ($\varepsilon_1 = \varepsilon_2 = \varepsilon_3$, $\dot{\varepsilon}_1 = \dot{\varepsilon}_2 = \dot{\varepsilon}_3$).
(5) Uniaxial relaxation test (ε_1 = constant, $\sigma_2 = \sigma_3 = 0$) and relaxation test in hydrostatic strain state ($\varepsilon_1 = \varepsilon_2 = \varepsilon_3$ = constant).

EXPERIMENTAL RESULTS

Uniaxial loading tests

To test the effect of strain rate on the stress-strain curves of cement mortar, sandstone and tuff, uniaxial compression tests were carried out at various strain rates. The stress-strain curves for cement mortar are shown in Figure 2 and seem to be affected by the different applied strain rates from $6.0 \times 10^{-5} \sim 7.0 \times 10^{-6}$/sec. For the strain rates from 6.0×10^{-5}

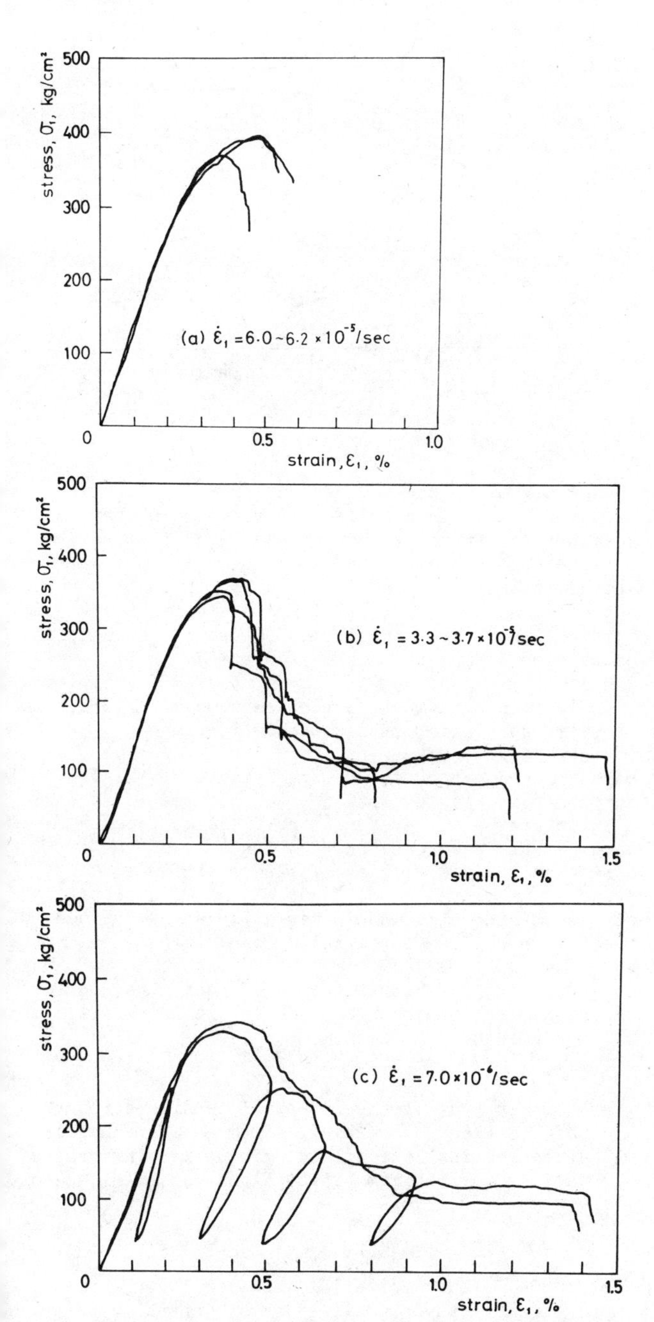

Fig. 2 Stress-strain relationships for cement mortar in uniaxial compression with various strain rates

to 3.7×10^{-5}/sec, the complete curves in postfailure region can not be obtained because of insufficiency of the stiffness of loading system as shown in Figures 2 (a) and (b). The complete stress-strain curves can , however, be obtained at the strain rates below about 7.0×10^{-6}/sec. It seems that the strain at the maximum compressive stress (strength failure) takes a mean value of about 0.40 % in spite of the different applied strain rates. Young's modulus and uniaxial compressive strength of cement mortar used in this study are 1.5×10^5 kg/cm² and 350 kg/cm², respectively.

Since sandstone and tuff are stiffer than cement mortar and the dimension of their specimens are smaller than cement mortar specimens, it is necessary to decrease further the strain rate for the specimens of sandstone and tuff. The stress-strain curves are shown in Figures 3 and 4 for sandstone and tuff, respectively. In these cases, the strain rate $\dot{\varepsilon}_1$ was decreased to 8.0×10^{-7}/sec, but this rate could not give the enough stiffness of loading system yet as shown in the figures. These figures show a considerable scatter in the measured values of uniaxial compressive strength and suggest that the values of strain may indicate the strength failure because the strains take almost the same value in spite of the values of strength and strain rate. The strains at strength failure are about 0.78 % and 0.76 % for sandstone and tuff, respectively.

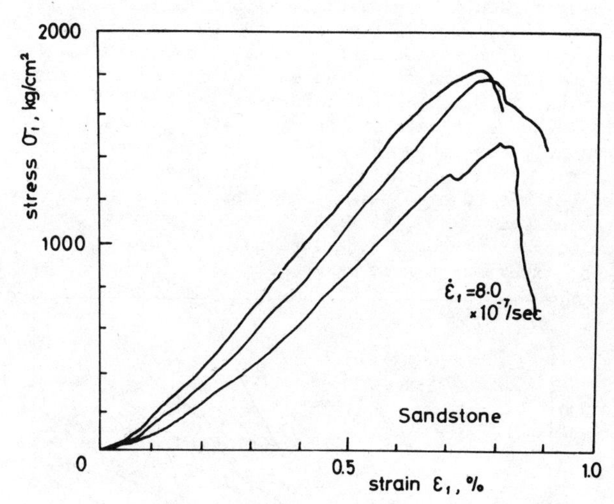

Fig. 3 Stress-strain relationships for sandstone in uniaxial compression

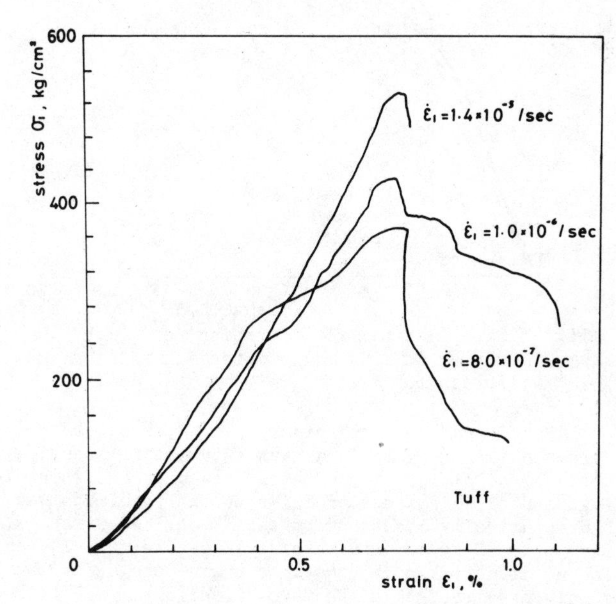

Fig. 4 Stress-strain relationships for tuff in uniaxial compression with various strain rates

Triaxial tests with different confining strain states

The triaxial compression test was carried out by loading at constant strain rate in one direction and holding the strains constant in other two directions. This test is formally equivalent to the ordinary triaxial compression test at the confining pressure. In the experimental procedure, the strains in three directions were hydrostatically increased to the prescribed magnitude of strain and then the strain in one direction was successively increased in the fixed strain states in other two directions.

For cement mortar, the stress-strain relationships in the loading direction with the different confining strains are shown in Figure 5, where the confining strain is expressed in values relative to the strain ($\varepsilon_p = 0.40$ %) at the strength failure for uniaxial compression test. As is evident from the figure, the slope of the stress-strain curve increases with the increase of confining strain, and the slope of the curve at each confining strain increases gradually for the strains in the loading direction above a certain magnitude in the postfailure region and becomes to be equal to the slope at the hydrostatic loading. It seems that the deformation behavior at the confining strains of $0 \sim 2.0\ \varepsilon_p$ in these experiments were essentially the same.

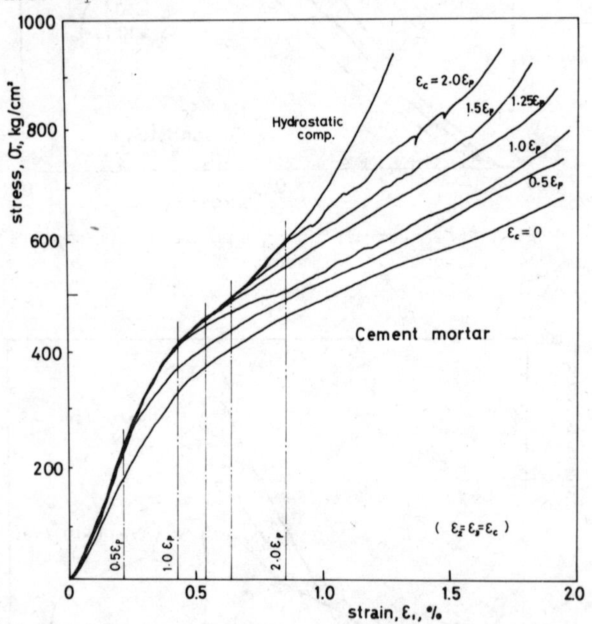

Fig. 5 Stress-strain relationships for cement mortar in triaxial compression with various confining strain

For comparison with Figure 5, the stress-strain curves obtained by the ordinary triaxial compression test at the different confining pressures are shown in Figure 6. In these experiments the specimens were hydrostatically loaded up to the prescribed stresses from 0 to 50 kg/cm^2 and then were successively loaded in one direction at a constant strain rate under these confining stresses in othe two directions. It is found from Figure 6 that the slope of the stress-strain curve in postfailure decreases with the increase of confining stress and becomes to be almost horizontal at the confining stress of 50 kg/cm^2.

In the strain control test the specimen can be

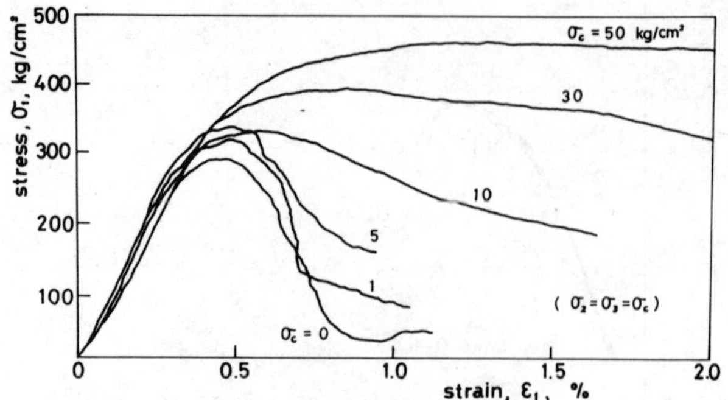

Fig. 6 Stress-strain relationships for cement mortar in triaxial compression with various confining stresses

loaded up to failure through any arbitrary strain paths. A failure surface in the strain state may be expressed by the values of strain at failure obtained by such experiment. Such failure surface enables one to study about a new conception of failure and the behaviors in postfailure are effectively used for nonlinear stress analysis because of the complete expression of material characteristics.

In this study, the experiments were performed for the various strain paths on Rendulic plane. The whole failure surface in strain state for cement mortar could not be shown here because of the limitation of capacity of loading machine used in the triaxial tests. Therefore, the yield surface in strain state was found by plotting the values of strain at the yield point of stress-strain curves as shown by a solid line in Figure 7. The elastic stress-strain relationship may at least be defined in the inside region of the solid line.

Assuming the Mohr's theory of rock strength for cement mortar, the Mohr's quadratic failure criterion is expressed by

$$\tau^2 = (\sqrt{n+1} - 1)^2 S_t (S_t - \sigma) \qquad (2)$$

where S_t and n denote the uniaxial tensile strength and the brittleness, respectively. The equation (2) changes into the following equation in terms of the maximum and minimum principal stresses, σ_1 and σ_3.

$$(\sigma_1 - \sigma_3)^2 + 2(\sqrt{n+1} - 1)^2 S_t (\sigma_1 + \sigma_3) = (\sqrt{n+1} - 1)^2 (2 - n + 2\sqrt{n+1}) S_t^2 \qquad (3)$$

The Mohr's failure criterion expressed by the principal strains can be obtained by substituting the following stress-strain relationship to the equation (3) assuming isotropic linear elastic material for cement mortar :

$$\sigma_{ij} = \lambda e_{\alpha\alpha} \delta_{ij} + 2G e_{ij} \qquad (4)$$

Now, calculating the failur condition in strain state by using the equations (3) and (4) and assuming that Young's modulus, Poisson's ratio, brittleness and uniaxial compressive strength of cement mortar are $E = 1.50 \times 10^5 kg/cm^2$, $\nu = 0.25$, $n = S_c/S_t = 8$ and $S_c = 350\ kg/cm^2$, respectively, the failure surface is found as the dotted line in Figure 7.

The effect of some confining strain ($\varepsilon_2 = \varepsilon_3$) on the stress-strain curves of sandstone and tuff is demonstrated by the set of curve in Figure 8. The study of sandstone and tuff was quite limited. In few experiments conducted, the similar behavior to cement mortar observed in the confining strain states.

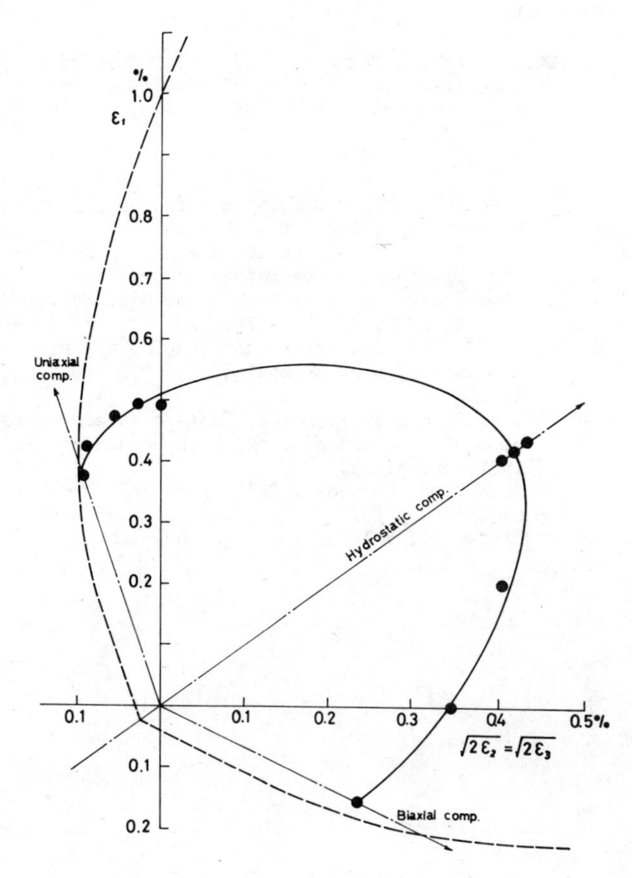

Fig. 7 Yield surface of cement mortar in strain state

Relaxation

Relaxation is the time-dependent behavior of stress within a stressed elastic body and can be observed by measuring the stress drop at the constant strain. To study the phenomenon of relaxation in the uniaxial and triaxial strain states, the specimen of cement mortar was held at constant deformation for 2 hours at the various magnitudes of strain in uni- and triaxial compression tests.

The relationships between the stress drop and the time (log t) are shown in Figure 9 for the uniaxial relaxation behavior of cement mortar. In these experiments, the deformation of platen was held constant to give the prescribed strains from 0.25 ε_p to 1.5 ε_p in the loading direction where ε_p was the strain at the strength failure. The specimens were loaded to the strain levels of 1.0 ε_p, 1.25 ε_p and 1.5 ε_p to verify the relationship between inelastic behavior and relaxation. These experiments show that $\sigma_1 \sim \log t$ relationship is linear for each fixed strain and its slope is affected by the fixed strain. The stress relaxation behavior is observed even in the elastic region from $\varepsilon/\varepsilon_p = 0.25$ to $\varepsilon/\varepsilon_p = 0.5$ and the stress drop rate in the relaxation increases with the increase of the fixed strain from $\varepsilon/\varepsilon_p = 0.8$ to $\varepsilon/\varepsilon_p = 1.25$. But the slope of $\sigma_1 \sim \log t$ line becomes to be flat and the stress relaxation behavior becomes considerably weaken at the fixed strain above $\varepsilon/\varepsilon_p = 1.5$. These phenomena suggest that the relaxation behavior seems to be closely related to the development of local failure or the initiation and propagation of cracks in addition to the viscoelastic property.

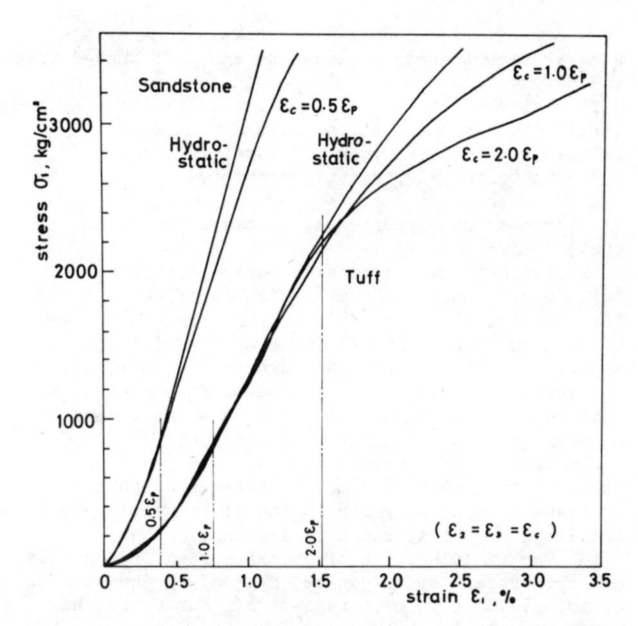

Fig. 8 Stress-strain relationships for sandstone and tuff in triaxial compression with various confining strain

The relationships between the drop of mean stress and the time (log t) is shown in Figure 10 for the stress relaxation behavior of cement mortar in the hydrostatic fixed strain states from $\varepsilon/\varepsilon_p = 0.25$ to $\varepsilon/\varepsilon_p = 2.0$. It is also found from the figure that its relation is linear for each fixed strain and the slope of $\sigma_m \sim \log t$ line becomes to be steep with the increase of the fixed strain in the extent of strain applied in these experiments.

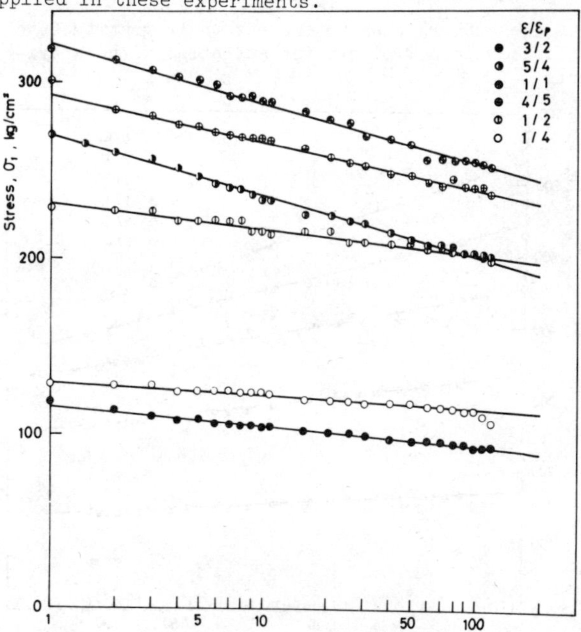

Fig. 9 $\sigma_1 \sim \log t$ relationships in relaxation behavior in uniaxial fixed strain state

CONCLUSION

Experiments conducted of rock-like materials such as cement mortar, sandstone and tuff showed that the deformation behavior in postfailure region has different characteristics in relation to the confining strain state and the stress relaxation is closely related to the development of local failure in addition to the viscoelastic property.

From these experiments, it can be concluded that:

(1) The maximum compressive stress (strength failure) in uniaxial compression is affected by the strain rate, but the strain at the strength failure takes a constant value in spite of the different applied strain rate and the magnitude of maximum compressive stress. The strains at the strength failure are 0.40 %, 0.78 % and 0.76 % for cement mortar, sandstone and tuff, respectively.

(2) The slope of stress-strain curve in the confining strain state becomes to be steep with the increase of confining strain and to be nearly equal to the slope at the hydrostatic loading.

(3) The yield surface of cement mortar on Rendulic plane in strain state can be obtained by the strains at the yield point of stress-strain curves in the confining strain state.

(4) In the stress relaxation behavior of cement mortar under the uniaxial fixed strain, $\sigma_1 \sim \log t$ relationship is linear for each fixed strain and the stress drop rate becomes to be the steepest at the fixed strain of 1.25 ε_p. The stress drop is recognized even in the elastic region and the relaxation behavior becomes considerably weaken at the fixed strains above 1.5 ε_p.

(5) In the stress relaxation behavior of cement mortar under the triaxial (hydrostatic) fixed strains, $\sigma_m \sim \log t$ relationship is also linear and the stress drop rate increases with the increase of fixed strain.

ACKNOWLEDGEMENTS

The authors wish to express their gratitude to K. Ishikawa and T. Ishii for assisting with experiments.

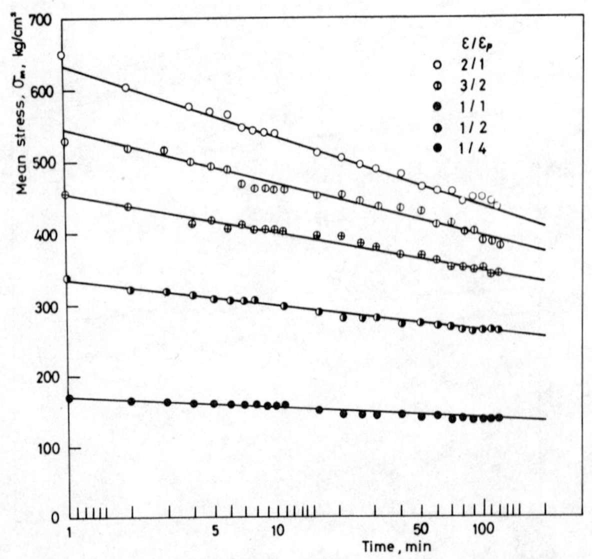

Fig. 10 σ_m log t relationships for relaxation behavior in hydrostatic fixed strain state

REFERENCES

Kawamoto, T. et al, *Characteristics of Deformation of Rock-like Materials under Triaxial Compression* Proc. 2nd Congress of ISRM, 2 - 2, Beograd, 1970, pp. 1-7.

Rummel, F. and C. Fairhurst, *Determination of the post-failure behavior of brittle rock using a servo-controlled testing machine,* Rock Mechanics, 2, 1970, pp. 189-204.

Wawersik, W. R. and C. Fairhurst, *A study of brittle rock fracture in laboratory compression experiments,* Int. J. Rock Mech. Min. Sci., Vol. 7, 1970, pp. 561-575.

Bieniawski, Z. T., *Time-dependent behavior of fractured rock,* Rock Mechanics, 2, 1970, pp. 123-137.

Wawersik, W. R. and W. F. Brace, *Post-failure behavior of a granite and diabase,* Rock Mechanics, 3, 1971, pp. 61-85.

Peng, S. and E. R. Podnieks, *Relaxation and the behavior of failed rock,* Int. J. Rock Mech. Min. Sci., Vol. 9, 1972, pp. 699-712.

THE ENERGY BALANCE THEORY AND ROCK FRACTURE ENERGY MEASUREMENTS FOR UNIAXIAL TENSION

LA THÉORIE DU BILAN ÉNERGÉTIQUE ET LES MESURES DE L'ÉNERGIE DE RUPTURE DES ROCHES EN CONTRAINTES UNIAXIALE

DIE THEORIE DER ENERGIEBILANZ UND MESSUNGEN DER BRUCHENERGIE FÜR GESTEINE UNTER EINACHSIGER SPANNUNG

Warren W. KRECH
Mining Engineer
Twin Cities Mining Research Center
Twin Cities, Minnesota, U. S. A.

SUMMARY

A new application of the basic Griffith theory of rupture of brittle solids, based on direct measurement of fracture energy requirements, is presented. The energy balance hypothesis is demonstrated by direct experiment, and nonrecoverable energy used in fracturing rock is directly measured. Ten rock types were tested in uniaxial tension under closed-loop control. Observation of test results and measurements of fracture energy are presented.

SOMMAIRE

On présente une nouvelle application de la théorie fondamentale de Griffith concernant la rupture des solides fragiles. La méthode est basée sur la mesure directe de l'énergie nécessaire pour causer la rupture. On démontre l'hypothèse de la balance énergétique par des essais directs. L'énergie non-récupérable dépensée durant la fracturation de la roche a été mesurée. Des essais ont été faits sur dix types de roches, en traction uniaxe dans un système d'essai a servo-contrôle à boucle fermée. On a mesuré l'énergie de fracturation et observé les résultats des essais.

ZUSAMMENFASSUNG

Eine neue Anwendung der grundlegenden Griffith Theorie der Sproedebruch der festen Koerper, basiert auf der unmittelbaren Messung der Bruchenergieforderungen wird vorgestellt. Die Hypothese des Energiegleichgewichtes wurde nachgewiesen durch unmittelbare Erprobung und eine direkte Messung der nichtwiedergewinnbaren Energie, verbraucht in Gesteinszerbrechung, wurde durchgefuehrt. Zehn Gesteinsarten sind in einachsigen servogesteuerten Zugversuchen mit geschlossener Regelkreis-Regulierung versucht worden. Die Versuchsergebnisse wurden beobachtet und die Bruchenergie wurde gemessen.

INTRODUCTION

The application of results of what is commonly called the Griffith theory of brittle failure to engineering materials, that of material failure being dependent upon reaching a critical stress, has required continual adjustment to a degree almost equal to the number of applications. Modifications like the classical extension of the Griffith theory to three-dimensional crack analysis (Sack, 1946) use the same basic approach used by Griffith, and have encountered problems similar to the original method.

Griffith developed his critical stress theory on the basis of observations made on uncontrolled failure in glass rods and fibers (Griffith, 1921). Although the development of the theory is based on this limited experimental observation, and although no consistent proof of the theory or modifications of the theory have ever been offered, the scientific and engineering community has turned to the critical stress concept for brittle fracture analysis and design.

Recent development of closed-loop servocontrolled test systems has allowed experimenters to obtain new information on material behavior (Hudson, Crouch, and Fairhurst, 1972; Krech and Chamberlain, 1974), that information being for controlled fracture in rock. Controlled failure is accomplished by supplying to the specimen under closed-loop control just sufficient energy to cause failure of the specimen such to reduce its load carrying capacity to zero.

The purpose of this paper is to demonstrate a modification of Griffith's energy balance hypothesis by direct experiment, and to show the means to directly determine the nonrecoverable energy (fracture energy) consumed in fracturing of a specimen. The direct measure of fracture energy yields a material property for application to problems involving fracture in brittle solids. Fracture energy values then replace critical stress values as the failure criterion for brittle materials. Servocontrolled uniaxial tension tests conducted on 10 rock types ranging from Berea Sandstone to Dresser basalt are evaluated and offered as the direct evidence of the validity of the theory.

A THEORETICAL CRITERION OF FRACTURE

All the basic theorems and the hypothesis made by Griffith (Griffith, 1921) are accepted herein. Two new hypotheses are added, one is an extension of the Griffith hypothesis. Of greatest interest, and that in need of restatement, is the Griffith hypothesis of energy balance: A crack will extend as long as the potential energy available to the crack is greater than the surface energy required to extend the crack (generate a surface). Because the extension of a single crack in an otherwise perfect material is not the manner of failure in real materials, and because the divergence from the perfect material differs for each real material considered, the author finds it necessary to consider the macrobehavior of a material rather than the microbehavior. The author's first hypothesis is that a crack will extend as long as the potential energy available to the crack is greater than the surface energy required to extend the crack, that cracks within a volume of a specimen will extend within that volume where sufficient energy is available to extend those cracks, that macrocrack extension is associated with extensive microfracture extension, and that the total energy consumed in extending a macrofracture is the summation of surface energy requirements at the many microfracture sites and all other dissipative energies associated directly with the formation of the macrofracture. This total energy requirement will be called fracture energy to distinguish it from surface energy alone. The author's second hypothesis is that equivalent fracture topography characteristics are generated under equivalent strain energy regimes for a given material.

APPLICATION OF THE ENERGY BALANCE THEORY TO A UNIAXIAL TENSION SPECIMEN

The theory of elasticity for a homogeneous isotropic material does not apply in defining a failure criterion for real materials, although strain energy within a specimen or structure determined by elasticity methods does hold to a high degree. However, there is not the need to consider strain energy if changes in the specimen due to fracture propagation are evaluated for conditions of zero load on the specimen when evaluating the fracture energy requirement of the uniaxial tension specimen. The work done on the specimen is simply an integration of the force-deformation history undergone by the specimen. (Such history must be known both for the loading and unloading of the specimen.)

If the energy balance requirement holds, then

$$\frac{\partial}{\partial C}(W - U) = 0, \qquad (1)$$

where W = strain energy,
U = fracture energy,
and C = crack length,
according to Griffith (Griffith, 1921) for any one crack extension, and according to the extended hypothesis of this paper for a real material.

EXPERIMENTAL VERIFICATION OF THE THEORY

To test the new hypotheses, 10 rock types were loaded in uniaxial tension under closed-loop control. These rock types were Baltic Amygdaloid, Barre Granite, Berea Sandstone, Calumet and Hecla Conglomerate, Dresser basalt, Holston Limestone, St. Cloud Gray Granodiorite (Charcoal granite), Salem Limestone, Sioux Quartzite, and Westerly Granite.

Samples 25 mm in diameter by 51 mm long were prepared according to ASTM specification for uniaxial tensile tests (ASTM, 1972). The specimens were cemented to threaded end pieces that were then attached to two spherical-rod-end bearings for application of the tensile load (Krech and Chamberlain, 1974). Various numbers of specimens were tested with controlled failure attained. No statistical analysis of the results is presented because the purpose of the tests is to demonstrate the validity of the energy balance hypothesis and not to provide statistically evaluated data.

To demonstrate the energy balance hypothesis, potential energy in the form of strain energy must be added to the specimen in a controlled manner so that only the amount of energy necessary to supply the fracture energy requirements is available at any time during the macrofracture extension process and a stable macrofracture extension is demonstrated.

This control of input of external work is possible with closed-loop control techniques (Krech and Chamberlain, 1974). Two commercial deflectometers were mounted diametrically opposite on the specimen to monitor axial extension of the specimen. The output from the deflectometers form the feedback signal to the servocontroller. The closed-loop servocontrolled test system is programed to control the axial extension of the specimen. Since energy can be added to the specimen by an axial force only if there is also an axial extension, control of the axial extension controls the energy input to the specimen. The amount of energy stored within the control loop at a given force level is dependent upon the amount of axial extension over the length of the control gage spacing for that load. The amount of axial extension within the control loop is dependent upon the distance between the attachment points of the deflectometer, thus the energy stored within the control loop for a given test situation and a given applied force is dependent upon the extensometer gage spacing. It is only the energy within the control loop that is available to the macrofracture, the energy outside the loop cannot cross into the loop.

The series of 10 rock types was tested with a 25 mm deflectometer gage spacing. With that gage spacing, five rock types yielded complete load-deformation curves; i.e., stable fracture conditions were attained. The other five rock types showed uncontrolled fracture growth upon reaching the peak load point. Reduction of the gage spacing showed controllability of fracture propagation, with all 10 rock types, indicating stable fracture growth with a 2.4-mm deflectometer gage spacing.

Axial strain rate (extension) was controlled at 1.6 x 10^{-6}/sec. Variation of this rate over two orders of magnitude did not effect stable fracture growth. On numerous occasions the axial extension rate was temporarily held at zero. No change in axial force occurred during the hold periods, and no specimens showed any apparent physical change during those periods. The point during the load-deformation history at which this check was conducted ranged from points on the pre-peak portion of the curve to near the zero level of the post-peak portion. No difference was observed with position on the load-deformation curve.

Several specimens were unloaded and reloaded during the post-peak portion of the curve. Upon reloading, the maximum load reached would be very near that load where unloading was commenced. Numerous specimens were unloaded and removed from the machine when the post-peak load was just slightly greater than zero. Those specimens had a visually apparent crack formed around the circumference of the specimen.

A circumferential notch was machined into those specimens tested with extensometer gage spacings of less than 25 mm to assure macrofracture initiation within the control loop, and not to create special "stress concentration" conditions. Specimens of Charcoal granite, which had showed controlled failure with the 25 mm gage spacing, were tested with a 4.1 mm gage spacing after being notched. No change in fracture energy requirements were found due to the notch.

Figures 1-10 show typical complete load-deformation curves for the 10 rock types tested. It should be understood that the shape detail of the load-deformation curve is a result of the rock behavior and the gage spacing. The integration of the force-deformation curve gives a constant number for a given cross-section size, which is the total work done on the test section. Thus, the total nonrecoverable energy is proportional to the cross-sectional area of the specimen in the plane of the fracture. The division of the nonrecoverable energy by the cross-sectional area of specimen is the fracture energy value for the material represented by the specimen.

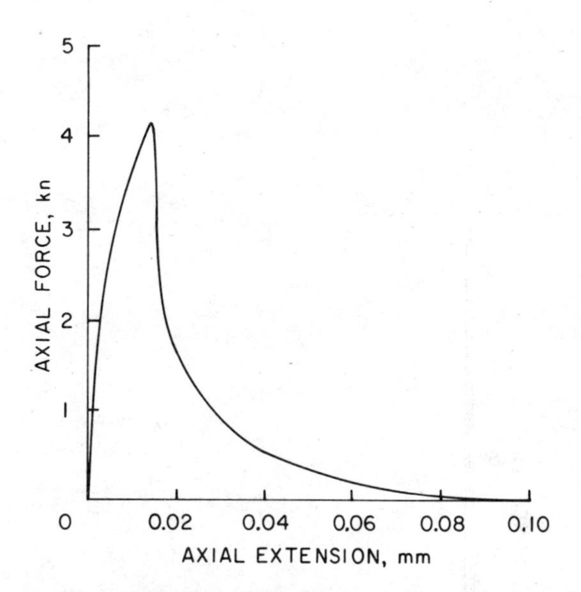

FIGURE 2.-Complete Uniaxial Tensile Load-Deformation Curve for Barre Granite.

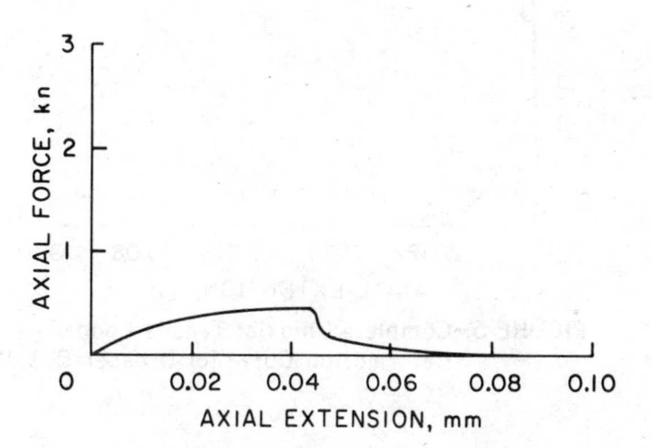

FIGURE 3.-Complete Uniaxial Tensile Load-Deformation Curve for Berea Sandstone

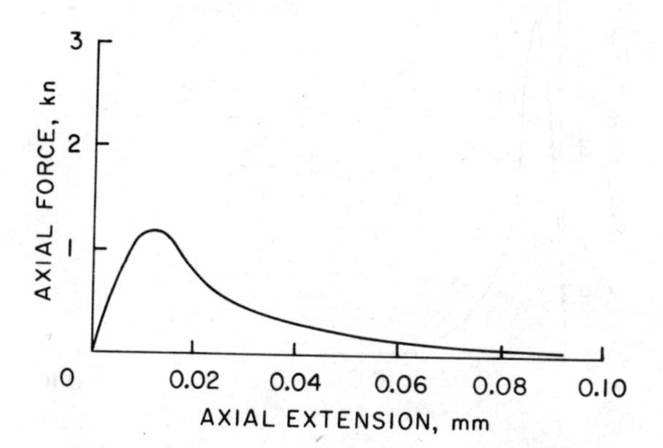

FIGURE 1.-Complete Uniaxial Tensile Load-Deformation for Baltic Amygdaloid.

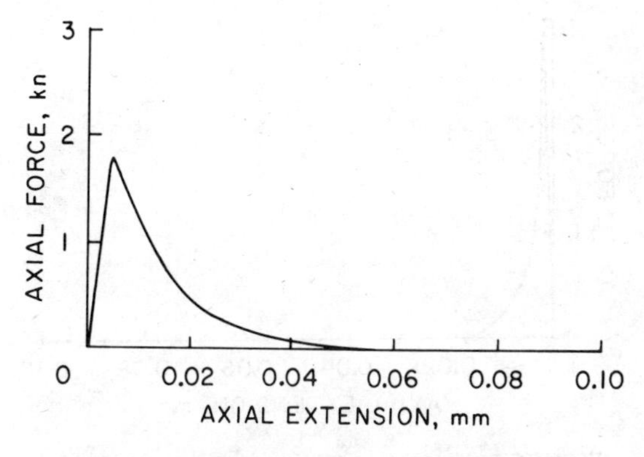

FIGURE 4.-Complete Uniaxial Tensile Load-Deformation Curve for Calumet and Hecla Conglomerate.

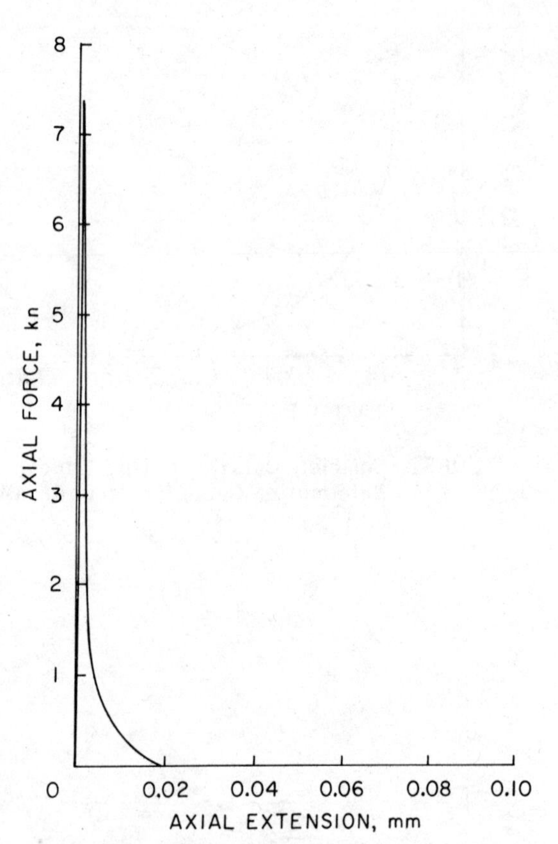

FIGURE 5.-Complete Uniaxial Tensile Load-Deformation Curve for Dresser Basalt.

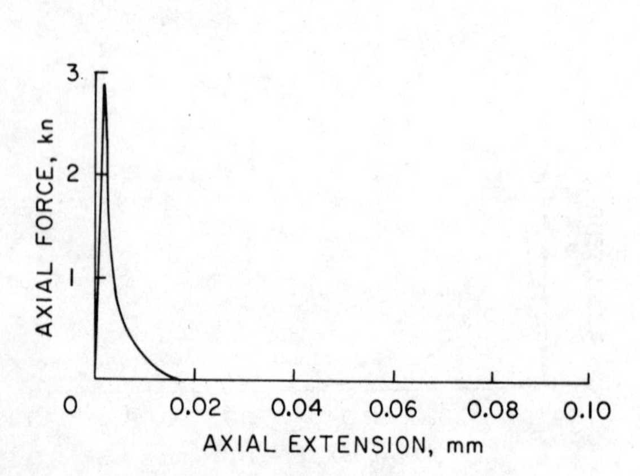

FIGURE 6.-Complete Uniaxial Tensile Load-Deformation Curve for Holston Limestone.

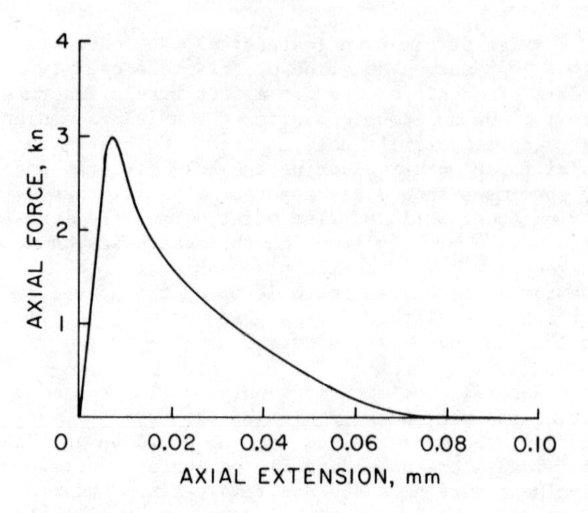

FIGURE 7.-Complete Uniaxial Tensile Load-Deformation Curve for St. Cloud Gray Granodiorite.

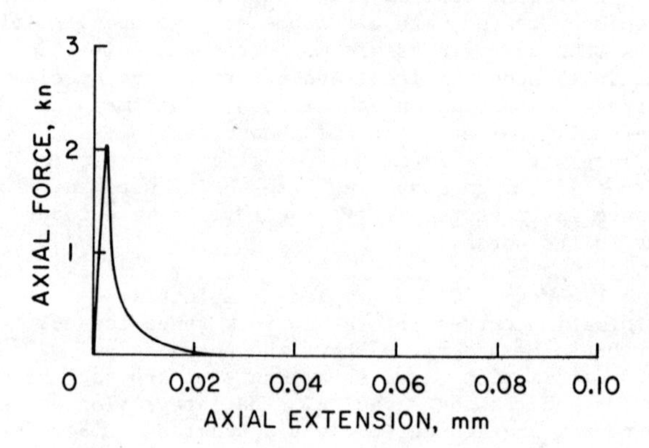

FIGURE 8.-Complete Uniaxial Tensile Load-Deformation Curve for Salem Limestone.

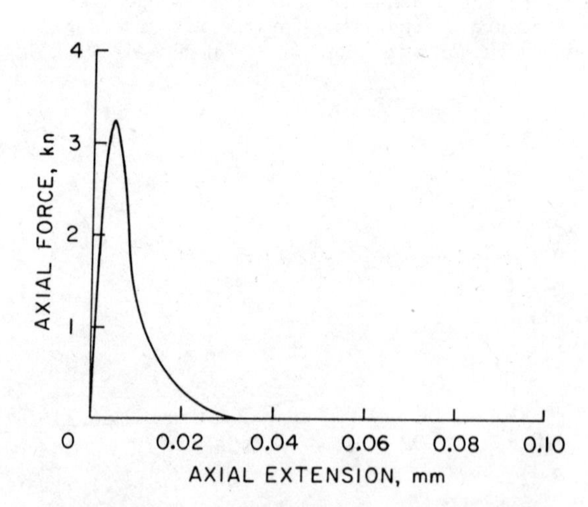

FIGURE 9.-Complete Uniaxial Tensile Load-Deformation Curve for Sioux Quartzite.

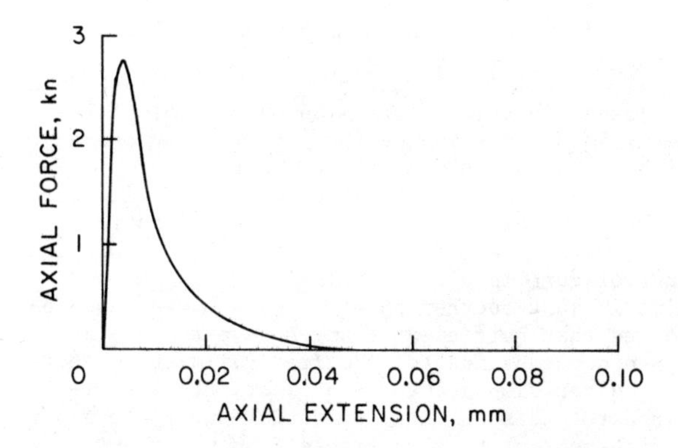

FIGURE 10.-Complete Uniaxial Tensile Load-Deformation Curve for Westerly Granite.

Figure 11 shows the effect of control gage spacing on the controllability of tensile failure for Salem Limestone. Available potential energy is reduced by reducing the total potential energy within the control loop until stability is achieved. Further reduction in control gage spacing results in a change in load-deformation curve shape, but not in indicated fracture energy within reasonable limits. Figure 12 shows the results for Dresser basalt of simultaneous measurement with a 25-mm gage spacing while controlling and measuring with a 2.4-mm gage spacing. Again, the shapes of the load-deformation curves are different, but the indicated energy is the same. Tests of this type on several of the rock types indicated a small variation in fracture energy with spacing, with the outer loop energy level being either slightly higher or slightly lower than the inner loop.

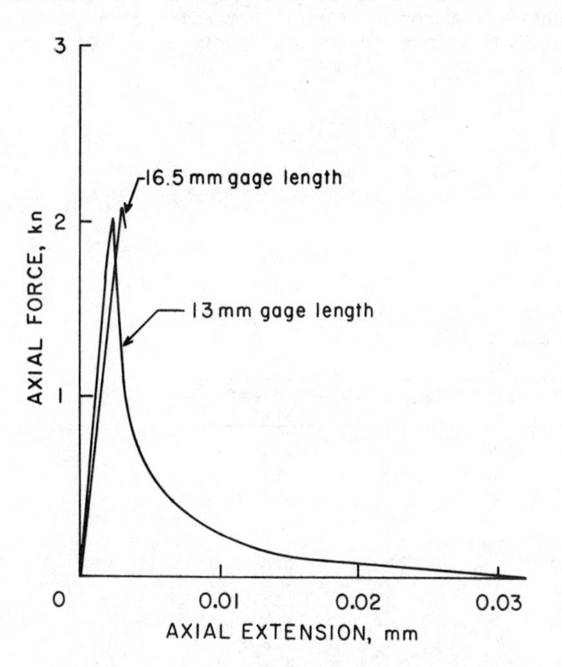

FIGURE 11.-Effect of Gage Length on Controllability of Tensile Failure in Salem Limestone.

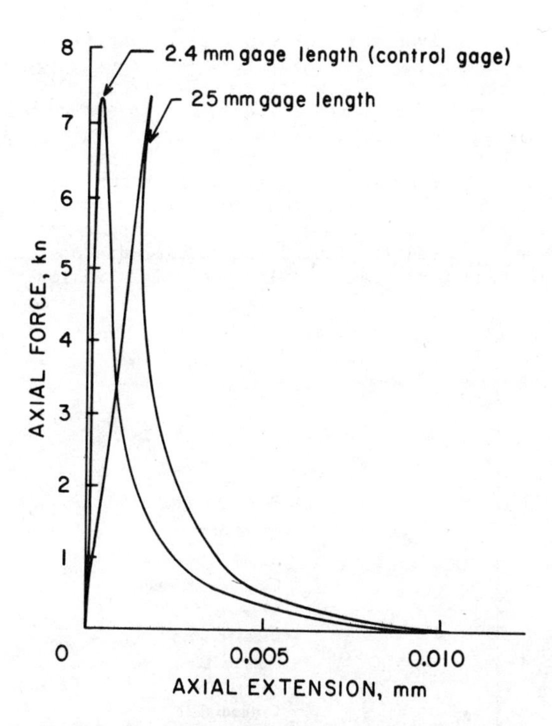

FIGURE 12.-Simultaneous Measurement of Uniaxial Tensile Load-Deformation Curve with Two Gage Lengths on Dresser Basalt.

Figure 13 shows the comparison of notched and unnotched Charcoal granite specimens. No significant difference in fracture energy is noted between the notched and unnotched samples.

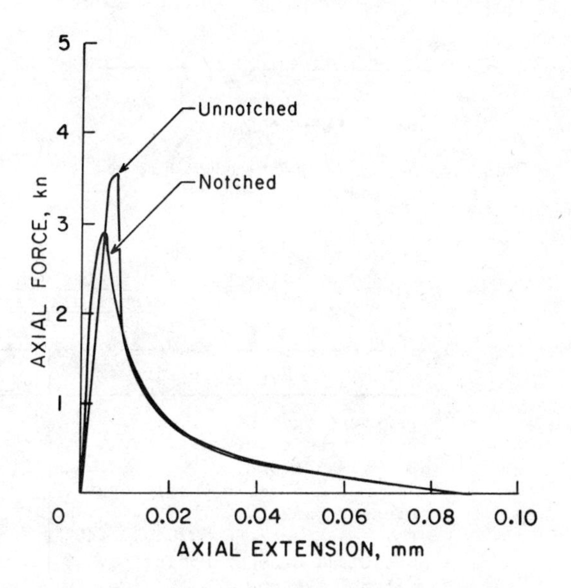

FIGURE 13.-Effect of Square Circumferential Notch on Uniaxial Tensile Load-Deformation Curve for Charcoal Granite.

Table 1 gives the rock type, test conditions, fracture energy, and uniaxial tensile strength for the 10 rock types. Uniaxial tensile strength is given for reference purposes, no worth is assigned to it as a rock property by the author and by others (Hardy, Hudson, and Fairhurst, 1973). Figure 14 shows a plot of peak tensile strength (uniaxial tensile strength) versus fracture energy value for the 10 rock types. No relationship is apparent, as would be expected in view of the earlier discussion on the meaning of peak load in a uniaxial tension test.

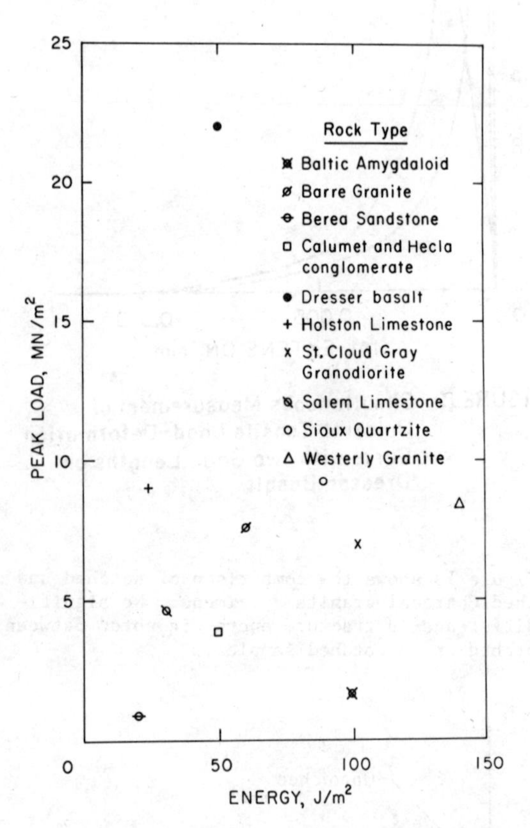

FIGURE 14.-Uniaxial Tensile Strength vs. Fracture Energy for Ten Rock Types.

DEDUCTIONS FROM EXPERIMENTAL RESULTS

The control of fracture growth in a rock specimen loaded in uniaxial tension by control of the energy input is evidence for proof of the energy balance hypothesis. According to the energy balance hypothesis, localized failures can take place within the rock specimen when the load applied to the specimen has reached any possible value within the range of zero load to peak load. The peak load point is just another point on that curve, and indicates that sufficient changes have taken place in the specimen due to localized failures so that for a given displacement increment, the load required to add sufficient potential energy to assure an increment of further stable fracture growth does not need to increase over that in the last increment, but rather needs to decrease relative to its value in the last increment. This peak load point is both material dependent and test dependent.

The material characteristics that influence the peak load are the surface energy (bond strength) requirements, and the distribution of bond strength and flaw sizes within the rock volume. The test characteristic that influences peak specimen load is the distribution of strain energy within the test specimen and thus the availability of that energy to the fracture sites due to the test configuration.

Nothing in the brittle failure theory as presented requires the consideration of the peak load as determined by a laboratory test. An analysis of the peak-load-carrying capacity of a structure can be made in terms of fracture energy requirements and energy distribution if proper account of energy requirements is made on an element by element basis within the structure as load is applied to the structure. It is important to emphasize that this peak load does not necessarily relate to a tensile strength in terms of a maximum tensile stress as determined from a laboratory specimen loaded in uniaxial tension.

TABLE 1. - Uniaxial tensile fracture energy and uniaxial tensile strength for 10 rock types

Rock type	Test condition	Fracture energy, J/m²	Tensile strength, MN/m²
Baltic Amygdaloid.............	U[1]	100	1.6
Barre Granite.................	U	60	7.7
Berea Sandstone...............	U	20	1.1
Calumet and Hecla Conglomerate.	U	50	3.9
Dresser basalt................	N[2]	50	21.9
Holston Limestone.............	N	23	9.0
St. Cloud Gray Granodiorite....	U	102	7.0
Salem Limestone...............	N	30	4.6
Sioux Quartzite...............	N	89	9.2
Westerly Granite..............	N	139	8.4

[1]/Unnotched.
[2]/Notched.

The observation that the fracture energy measurement within a 25-mm gage length is essentially the same as within a 2.4-mm gage length on the same rock indicates that nonrecoverable energy losses are associated with the macrofracture over a relatively narrow band width measured perpendicular to the macrofracture plane. This observation lends support to the fracture topography hypothesis, but is not offered as evidence of proof.

The comparison of the results of notched with unnotched Charcoal granite specimens shows that the effect of the notch is not significant relative to energy requirements for tensile failure. The peak load is changed to a small degree disproportionate to the cross-sectional area reduction. Concentration of strain energy in the vicinity of the notch is such that localized failures initiate in that vicinity at a lower peak load on the specimens; however, the fracture energy requirement is not changed. As soon as the fracturing is removed from the vicinity of the notch by progression of the development of the macrofracture, the energy balance requirements continue to control in a manner that does not reflect the presence of the notch. Thus, notch effects on peak load are dependent upon the relationship of the notch and its effect on strain-energy distribution to that of the natural heterogeneity of the rock and its effect on strain-energy distribution.

The observation that load does not decrease when deformation is held constant at any point on the stable fracture curve indicates that relaxation is a function of energy input; if energy balance is present at any time, then relaxation will not occur. Since relaxation does not occur at constant deformation when energy balance exists, it can also be said that creep will not occur if energy balance is present. Over the quasi-static loading range, stable fracture growth is not dependent upon the rate of load application. No tests were conducted where loading rates approached maximum crack propagation velocity. Although the energy balance hypothesis is not stated in terms of loading rate, proof of its validity at high loading rates remains to be established by direct experimentation.

The theory as presented is not dependent upon material. The limitation on experimental proof for all brittle materials with uniaxial tension tests may lie in the capability of the experimenter to limit total energy within the control loop to such a small value that the energy balance requirements for stable fracture growth can be attained. Indeed, the whole concept of brittle versus ductile behavior needs redefinition in terms of the energy balance concept, but the range of behavior is too broad to define within the scope of this paper.

CONCLUSIONS

The energy balance hypothesis is demonstrated by direct experiment. Stable fracture growth is attained in a uniaxially loaded specimen by control of energy supplied to the test section. This stability is maintained throughout the growth of the macrofracture, up to the point of zero-load-carrying capacity of the specimen.

The fracture topography hypothesis is strengthened by the observation of a limited region around the macrofracture section where energy is dissipated, thus fracture energy requirements being independent of specimen shape or volume for a given location of a macrofracture.

The concept that a crack will grow in an unstable manner once a critical stress level is reached in a uniaxial loaded specimen is disproved. Likewise, the generally held hypothesis that the slope of the load-deformation curve for a specimen loaded in uniaxial tension must be greater than zero for stability within the specimen is disproved.

The material property describing tensile failure in brittle materials is fracture energy.

REFERENCES

American Society for Testing Materials. Standard Method of Test for Direct Tensile Strength of Rock Core Specimens. D 2936-71 in 1972 Annual Book of ASTM Standards: Part 11, Bituminous Materials for Highway Construction, Waterproofing, and Roofing; Soils; Peats, Mosses, and Humus; Skid Resistance. Philadelphia, Pa., 1972, pp. 909-911.

Griffith, A. A. The Phenomena of Rupture and Flow in Solids. Phil. Trans. Roy. Soc. (London), v. A 221, 1921, pp. 163-198.

_____. The Theory of Rupture. 1st Internat. Congress of Appl. Mech. Proc., Delft, Netherlands, 1924, pp. 55-63.

Hudson, J. A., S. L. Crouch, and C. Fairhurst. Soft, Stiff, and Servocontrolled Testing Machines. Eng. Geol., v. 6, No. 3, October 1972, pp. 155-189.

Krech, W. W. and P. G. Chamberlain. New Techniques for Rock Fracture Energy Measurements. Soc. Petrol. Eng. J., v. 14, No. 2, June 1974 (in press).

Sack, R. A. Extension of Griffith's Theory of Rupture to Three Dimensions. Phys. Soc. (London), v. 58, 1946, pp. 729-736.

DISCONTINUITY ANISOTROPY OF ROCK MASSES

ANISOTROPIE DE LA DISCONTINUATION DES MASSES ROCHEUX

ANISOTROPIE DER DISKONTINUITÄT VON GESTEINSMASSEN

Petar LOKIN

School of Mining and Geology

University Belgrade

Yugoslavia

SUMMARY

Two methods are proposed in the paper,one analytical and one graphical, for calculating discontinuity anisotropy. Discontinuity anisotropy can be expressed in terms of the degree of inequality of the frequency of intersection of discontinuities with straight lines drawn in different directions from a given point. The analytical method consists in finding (analytically) the distances between successive discontinuities of a given family along the axes of a coordinate system. Hence it is possible to calculate the frequency of discontinuities of that family, and by summing the frequencies of all the families the frequency of the whole system of discontinuities in a given direction is obtained. The graphical method makes use of an equivalent area projection. In this projection each family is mapped as lines of equal frequency of discontinuities (Figs. 3,4,5). The frequency of discontinuities of the whole system is obtained by summing the values given by the lines of equal frequency of each family (Figs. 6,7,8).

RÉSUMÉ

Dans ce travail on propose deux methodes: première analytique et seconde graphique, par les quelles on peut faire un calcul de l'anisotropie de la discontinuation des masses rocheuses. On la concoit comme une propriété susceptible de posseder une fréquence diverse de la discontinuité ayant de differentes directions du meme point. La solution analytique comprend une détermination de la distance moyenne de deux discontinuités voisines de la famille à la direction des axes de coordonnées. A la base de tout cela on peut calculer la frequence de la discontinuité de cette famille, mais de l'adittion de celle.ci, il resulte la frequence d' un système de la discontinuité mise à la direction déterminée.Pour faire une solution graphique, on peut servir d'une projection équivalente de la sphere. Chaque famille de la discontinuité est representée à cette projection par les isolignes de la fréquence discontinuée (Fig. 3,4,5). Après avoir adittionné leurs valeurs, on peut obtenir la fréquence du systeme de la discontinuité à toutes les directions en espace (Fig. 6,7,8).

ZUSAMMENFASSUNG

Für die Berechnnung der Anisotropie der Diskontinuität von Gesteinmassen werden zwei Arbeitsmethoden vorgesehen: eine analytische und eine graphische. Die Anisotropie der Diskontinuität der Gesteinsmasse wird als ihre Eigenschaft begriffen, verschiedenartige Frequenz der Diskontinuität in verschiedenen, aus demselben Punkt gezogenen Richtungen aufzuweisen. Die analytische Lösung besteht darin, dass die durschnittliche Entfernung zwischen zwei benachbarten Diskontinuitäten einer Familie in der Richtung der Koordinatenachsen mathematisch bestimmt wird. Aus diesem Grund wird die Frequenz der Diskontinuität dieser Familie ausgerechnet, und durch Addieren der Diskontinuitäten sämtlicher Familien, wird die Frequenz des Diskontinuitätssystems in bestimmter Richtung bekommen. Für die graphische Lösung dient die flachentreu Projektion des Kugels. Jede Familie der Diskontinuität wird auf dieser Projktion mit den Isolinien der Diskontinuitätsfrequenz dargestellt (Fig. 3,4,5) Durch Addieren der Werte von Isolinien der Diskontinuitätsfrequenz sämtlicher Familien bekommt man die Frequenz des Diskontinuitätssystems in allen Richtungen im Raum (Fig. 6,7,8).

INTRODUCTION

The physical and mechanical properties of rock masses depend in large measure on the number and distribution of discontinuities in the rock. A need therefore arises to express rock discontinuity properties in terms of quantitative parameters, so that they can be taken into account in geostatic calculations. Efforts in this direction have on the whole reduced to:

- study of discontinuities on test pieces,
- study of discontinuities "in situ"

by geophysical prospecting methods,
- direct examination of discontinuities, but as an isolated phenomenon.

The first method suffers from the failing that the small size of a test piece makes scaling up unjustified. The basic shortcoming of the second is that the quantitative data afforded by geophysical prospecting cannot be uniquely interpreted. It is usually impossible to determine to what extent this data is determined by a given state of discontinuity and to what extent by other factors. Direct examination of individual discontinuities gives no clue to their function as a system in deformation or failure of the rock mass.

In order to be able to make more reliable predictions of the behavior of rock masses interacting with artificial structures, discontinuities must be studied as a feature of the rock as part of the given formation, and the characteristics of the system of discontinuities as a whole expressed in terms of quantitative parameters.

The present paper describes an attempt to develop a procedure for calculating the degree of discontinuity anisotropy of rock masses, this anisotropy being one of the principle causes of anisotropy of the physical and mechanical properties.

2. SOME ESSENTIAL DEFINITIONS

Discontinuity in a rock mass - any space inside the rock which is not occupied by firmly bonded mineral matter, but is filled with gas, fluid, or incoherent or only weakly bonded mineral matter. Such spaces are as rule physical and mechanical discontinuities where the physical and mechanical properties of the rock mass change abruptly.

Family of discontinuities - an ensemble of discontinuities with the same or at least similar characteristics (mode of origin, shape, orientation, dimensions, type of fill wall surface configuration).

System of discontinuities - all discontinuities in a given body of rock.

Discontinuity of a rock mass - the (global) property of containing discontinuities. It can be expressed in terms of the degree and mode of discontinuity.

Anisotropy of discontinuity - the property whereby the frequency of discontinuities is different in different directions from a point in the rock mass, the frequency of discontinuities being defined as the number of discontinuities per unit length in a given direction.

Degree of discontinuity anisotropy of a rock mass, chosen as a measure of anisotropy, defined as

$$1 : \frac{G_y}{G_x} : \frac{G_z}{G_x} : \dots \frac{G_n}{G_x}$$

wherw G_i is the frequency of discontinuities in direction $\underline{i}$.

The procedures proposed in this paper for calculating the anisotropy are only applicable to discontinuities which can be approximated by a plane.

3. DETERMINATION OF THE DISCONTINUITY ANISOTROPY OF A ROCK MASS

3.1. Analytical solution

In order to arrive at an analytical expression for the anisotropy of a given system of discontinuities, let us first consider a family of discontinuities. We shall assume that the members of this family are parallel discontinuities at equal spacing in the direction of their common normal. In practical applications the average dip elements and spacing of the family obtained by statistical processing of measurements would be used.

In Fig.1 the plane ABC represents a typical member of the family, i.e. a discontinuity with the dip elements of the family, in a three-dimensional rectangular coordinate system. The distance of this plane from the origin (i.e. distance along the normal OM) is equal to the distance between members of the family.

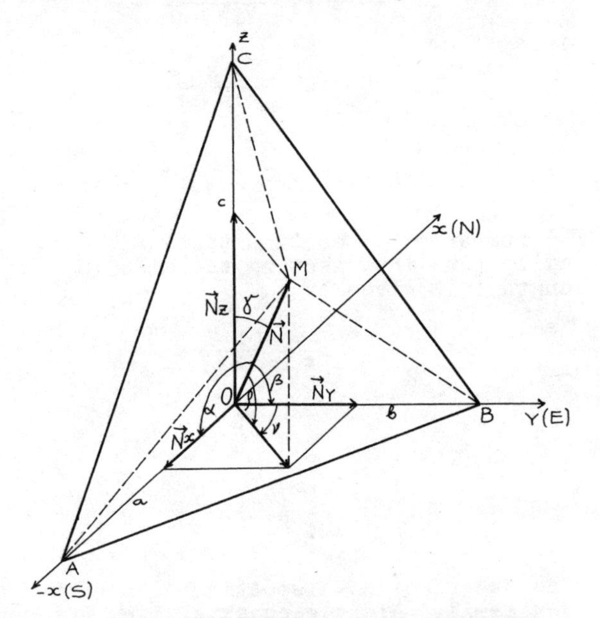

Fig.1. Schematic representation of a discontinuity showing the dip elements of the family to which it belongs in the geographical coordinate system.

Notation:

$\vec{N}$ - vector of the normal to the discontinuity plane, of magnitude proportional to the distance between discontinuities of the family (d),

$\vec{N}_x, \vec{N}_y, \vec{N}_z$ - vector components of $\vec{N}$ parallel to the axes

α, β, γ - angles which $\vec{N}$ makes with the axes

a,b,c - intercepts of the plane of the discontinuity on the axes

ν - angle between the x axis and the projection of $\vec{N}$ on the xy plane

ϱ - angle between $\vec{N}$ and the xy plane

If the coordinate system is so chosen that x and y coincide with the geographical coordinate axes N-S and E-W, and z with the vertical, then some of the above symbols also have the following significance:

ν - dip azimuth of the plane of discontinuity

γ - angle of dip of the plane of discontinuity

ϱ - angle of dip of the normal to the plane of discontinuity ($\varrho + \gamma = 90°$)

Knowing d, γ, ν (obtained as averages of field measurements) the intercepts a, b, c, i.e. distances between discontinuities of the family along the axes, can be obtained by straightforward application of trigonometry:

$$a = \frac{d}{\sin\gamma \cos\nu}$$

$$b = \frac{d}{\sin\gamma \sin\nu}$$

$$c = \frac{d}{\cos\gamma}$$

The number of discontinuities of the given family ($_1n$) intersecting the axes in a length L is given by

$$_1n_x = \frac{L}{a}$$

$$_1n_y = \frac{L}{b}$$

$$_1n_z = \frac{L}{c}$$

The frequency of discontinuities of the given family, along each axis, i.e. the number of discontinuities of that family intersecting the axis over a length of one meter, is given by:

$$_1G_x = \frac{_1n_x}{L} \quad \text{(discontinuities/m')}$$

$$_1G_y = \frac{_1n_y}{L} \quad \text{"}$$

$$_1G_z = \frac{_1n_z}{L} \quad \text{"}$$

The frequency of discontinuities of all other families making up the system ($_2G$, $_3G, \ldots {}_nG$) is determined in the same way. The sum of the frequencies of all the families gives the frequency of the system of discontinuities (G) for the specified axis:

$$G_x = \sum_{i=1}^{i=n} {}_iG_x = {}_1G_x + {}_2G_x + {}_3G_x + \ldots {}_nG_x$$

$$G_y = \sum_{i=1}^{i=n} {}_iG_y = {}_1G_y + {}_2G_y + {}_3G_y + \ldots {}_nG_y$$

$$G_z = \sum_{i=1}^{i=n} {}_iG_z = {}_1G_z + {}_2G_z + {}_3G_z + \ldots {}_nG_z$$

The discontinuity anisotropy for the axes of the geographical coordinate system will be:

$$1 : \frac{G_y}{G_x} : \frac{G_z}{G_x}$$

We have started by determining anisotropy with respect to the three axes of the geographical coordinate system because field measurements yield data about the orientation of discontinuities with respect to this coordinate system.

To obtain a more complete picture of the discontinuity anisotropy, and for the solution of practical problems, the frequency of discontinuities may be calculated for other directions as well. Practical tasks in engineering geology and geotechnique often call for determination of the frequency of discontinuities in directions or planes fixed by the layout of the field test or the configuration of the artificial structure involved or some part of it. The frequency of discontinuities in any other direction can be found either by setting up a new coordinate system or determining the angle between the new direction and $\vec{N}$.

3.2. Graphical solution

A graphical solution will also be sought by considering one family of discontinuities, making the same assumptions about it as in 3.1. The interval between the intersections of two neighboring discontinuities with an an arbitrary straight line (d') depends only on the angle this line makes with the normal to the discontinuities:

$$d' = \frac{d}{\cos \psi}$$

where

d is the distance between successive discontinuities in the direction of the normal;

ψ is the angle between $\bar{N}$ and the direction for which the frequency of discontinuities is to be calculated.

Hence for a given value of d the angles which directions with specified discontinuity frequencies make with $\bar{N}$ can be calculated. In an equal-area projection the poles of all straight lines making the same angle ψ with $\bar{N}$ lie on a minor circle whose center is the pole of the normal and whose radius corresponds uniquely to ψ (Fig.2):

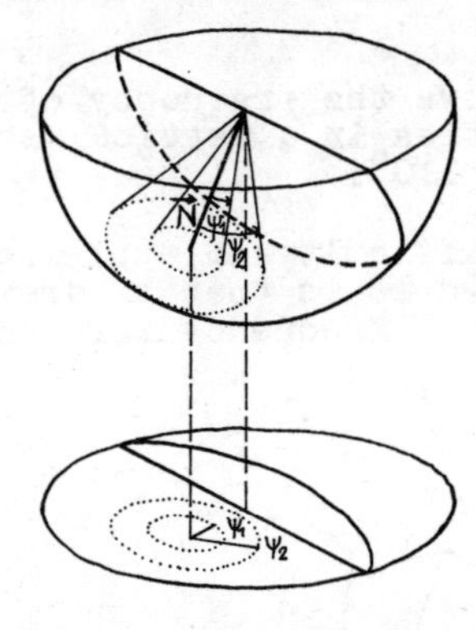

Fig.2. Mapping lines of equal frequency of discontinuities of one family in an equal area projection.

Different values of ψ give a set of concentric circles. For $\psi = 90^{\circ}$ the poles of the straight lines lie on a circle representing the intersection of the discontinuity with the sphere. Thus the locus of the poles of the straight lines making an angle ψ with $\bar{N}$ is a circle corresponding to directions of ewual frequency of discontinuities of the giveb family, i.e. the concentric circles about the normal are lines of equal frequency of discontinuities of that family.

Figure 3 shows lines of equal frequency of discontinuities of a family (I) with dip elements 70/45 and a distance between discontinuities d = 30 cm (Fig.3-a).

Hence the equal area projection provides a sufficiently accurate graphical presentation of the anisotropy associated with one family of discontinuities. The same procedure can be applied for all the other families making up a system under consideration.

Figures 3-b and 3-c show lines of equal discontinuity frequency for a family (II) with dip elements 180/68 and d = 80 cm, and a family (III) with dip elements 255/18 and d = 120 cm.

The total frequency of discontinuities of the system consisting of these theree families can also be found graphically by summing the values given by the lines of equal frequency for all theree families. This is easiest done by mapping the lines of equal frequency of all the families on the same diagram (Fig. 4-a). After summing the values given by the lines (Fig. 4-b), points of equal total frequency of discontinuities are found by interpolation and lines of equal total frequency drawn by joining them up (Fig.4-c).

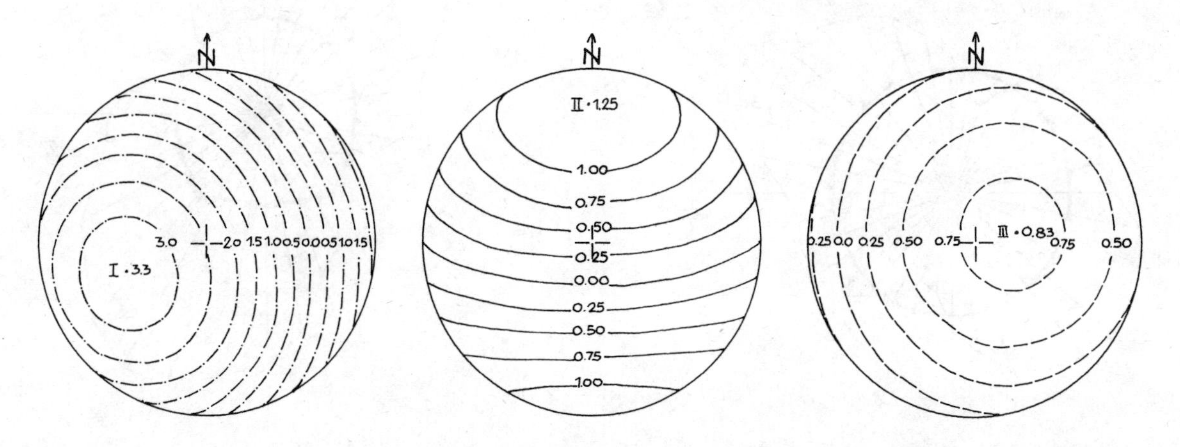

Fig.3. Lines of equal frequency of discontinuities (in equal-area projection) for a family with dip elements 70/45 (a), 180/68 (b) and 255/18 (c), and spacing betwen discontinuities d=30 cm(a), d=80 cm(b) and d=120 cm(c).

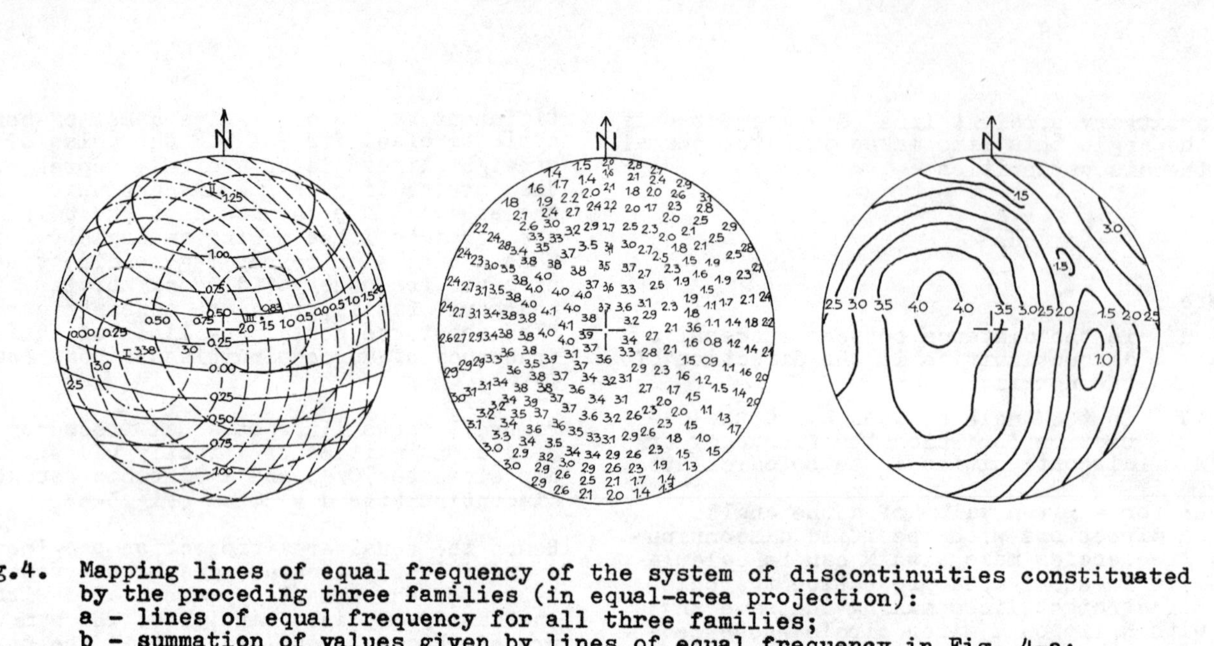

Fig.4. Mapping lines of equal frequency of the system of discontinuities constituated by the proceding three families (in equal-area projection):
a - lines of equal frequency for all three families;
b - summation of values given by lines of equal frequency in Fig. 4-a;
c - lines of equal frequency of the system of discontinuities.

The resulting graphical representation can be used to determine the frequency of discontinuities along any desired direction. Hence a plot such as that shown in Fig.4-c provides a complete representation of the three-dimensional discontinuity anisotropy of the rock mass.

To illustrate some possible applications of data about the frequency of discontinuities, let us consider Fig.5 which shows the frequency of discontinuities in a horizontal plane. The figure was drawn using the data from Fig.4-c.

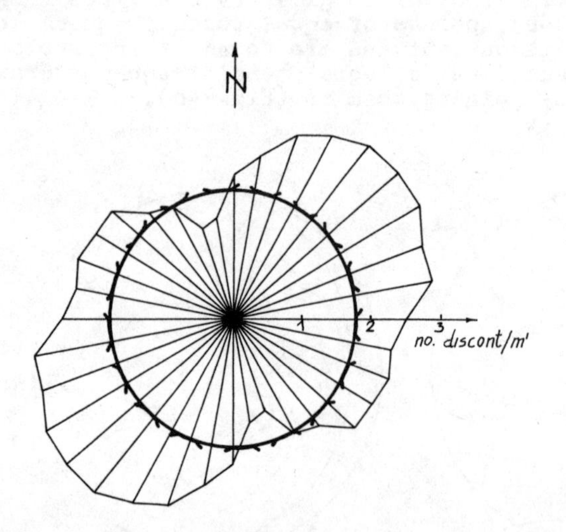

Fig.5. Frequencies of discontinuities plotted in a horizontal section through a shaft (data as in Fig.4-c).

Figure 6 shows the frequency of the same discontinuities in a vertical section of orientation 110°.

The chief difficulty in applying this graphical procedure is that of drawing all the lines of equal frequency for each family of

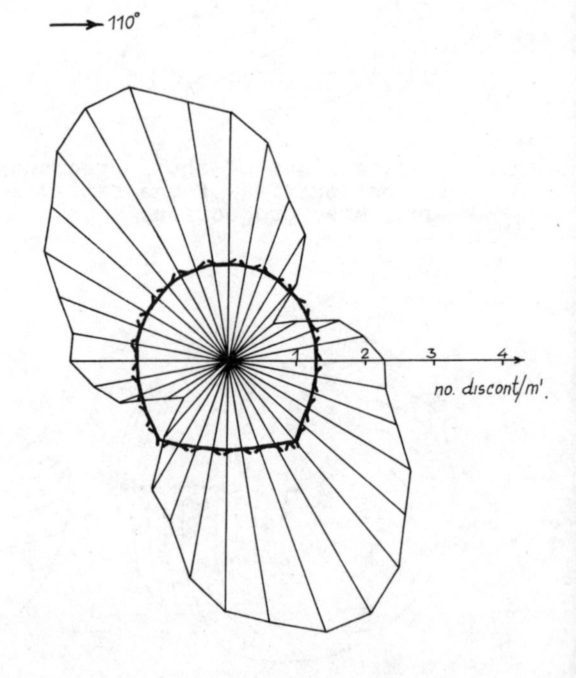

Fig.6. Frequencies of discontinuities plotted in a vertical section at right angles to the axis of a tunnel (data as in Fig.4-c).

discontinuities, especially if there is rather a large number of families. In order to facilitate its application a set of grids has been constructed with the poles of the normals to families of discontinuities with different specified angles of dip. With the aid of these grids the lines of equal frequency can be quickly drawn for a family with any dip elements and any distance between discontinuities.

4. CONCLUSION

The methods proposed here for calculating the discontinuity anisotropy of rock masses make use of data on the orientation and spacing of the discontinuities. Other properties of the discontinuities, such as their dimensions, shape, type of fill, etc., are not taken into account. These properties may however have a significant influence on the role of discontinuities in rock deformation or failure. Therefore, when analyzing the influence of discontinuities on the physical and mechanical properties of a rock mass, and in particular on the anisotropy of these parameters, one must give due attention to all those properties of individual discontinuities and families of discontinuities which are relevant to the problem in hand. If they are characterized by numerical parameters it is possible to take them into account as well when calculating the discontinuity anisotropy of the rock.

The calculation of discontinuity anisotropy as proposed in this paper can only be done for a volume of rock in which the orientation and density of discontinuities are statistically homogeneous, i.e. within which the frequency of discontinuities interesecting any straight line is constant along that line. Therefore, when studying the discontinuity of a given body of rock it is necessary to carry out preliminary zoning according to the degree and style of jointing, then proceeding to examine the discontinuity anisotropy of each homogeneous zone.

In principle it is also possible to analyze the discontinuity anisotropy of a volume of rock which is heterogeneous as regards the orientation and spacing of discontinuities if ine takes into account the variability of the frequency of discontinuities as well as the frequency itself: the frequency variability can also be different in different directions from a given point.

The procedures described here assume families of mutually parallel discontinuities. They of course do not exist in nature. Therefore the result obtained for the discontinuity anisotropy by using the average of the measured dip elements for a given family will embody a certain error whose magnitude will depend on how much the discontinuities of the family in fact deviate from parallelism. This can be estimated from the scattering of the measured dip elements for members of the given family.

The fact that the length of the discontinuities does not figure anywhere in the calculation umplies that it is assumed to be of the same order as the dimensions of the homogeneous zone for which the anisotropy is being calculated. For some classes of discontinuity such as interbed jointing, schistosity, etc., this may be the case, but for others it will usually not be so. Allowance can be made for this by introducing a correction for the average distance between discontinuities.

Despite the enumerated limitations, it is believed that the methods described here for calculating discontinuity anisotropy can find useful application both in theoretical considerations and in practical tasks of engineering geology and geo-engineering. A knowledge of rock discontinuity anisotropy can be of particular value when investigating the deformability and strength properties, in geostatic calculations, and in analyzing the feasibility of rock improvement measures.

A STATISTICAL THEORY OF THE POLYAXIAL STRENGTH OF MATERIALS

UNE THÉORIE STATISTIQUE DE LA RÉSISTANCE POLYAXIALE

EINE STATISTISCHE THEORIE DER MEHRACHSIGEN FESTIGKEIT

N. LUNDBORG

Swedish Deton Research Foundation

Stockholm, Sweden

SUMMARY

A complete model of the strength in the principal stress space has been derived from a probabilistic model of the strength distribution. Some well known strength criteria are found to be special cases of the present criterion. The independent parameters of the theory are theinternal friction coefficient and the variance of the strength distribution. Both of these are derivable from simple experiments. The theory shows good agreement with experimental results. One feature of the theory is that it gives a smooth yield surface without the sharp corners inherent for example in the Mohr-Coulomb and Tresca criteria.

RESUME

Un modèle complet de la résistance dans la surface de contrainte principale a été derivé d´un modèle de la probabilité de la distribution de résistance. On a trouvé que quelques critériums de résistance bien connus sont des cas particuliers du critérium présent. Les paramètres indèpendants de la théorie sont le coefficent de la frottement interne et la variance de la distribution de résistance. Tous les deux ont été derivés des expériments simples. La théorie est en accord avec les résultats expérimentaux. Une caractère de cette théorie est qu´elle permet une surface lisse d´élasticité sans les coins aigus qui sont compris dans les critériums de Mohr-Coulomb et de Tresca.

ZUSAMMENFASSUNG

Ein vollständiges Modell der Festigkeit im Hauptspannungsraum ist aus einem Wahrscheinlichkeitsmodell der Festigkeitsverteilung hergeleitet worden. Es hat sich gezeigt, dass einige bekannte Festigkeitskriterien Spezialfälle des Kriteriums der vorgelegten Theorie sind. Die unabhängigen Parameter der Theorie sind der innere Reibungskoeffizient und die Varianz der Festigkeitsverteilung. Diese beiden sind aus einfachen Experimenten ableitbar. Die Theorie steht in guter Übereinstimmung mit experimentellen Resultaten. Aus dieser Theorie resultiert u.a. eine glatte Festigkeitsfläche ohne die scharfen Ecken, die zu den Mohr-Coulomb und Tresca-Kriterien gehören.

INTRODUCTION

The basic concept of the present theory has been described previously by assuming a statistical distribution of the strength of a material and the appearance of an internal friction depending of the normal stress (Lundborg 1972).

When a material has the same strength in all directions and there is no internal friction, fracture occurs when the shearing stress in any direction reaches a critical value, the shearing strength of the material. This is the well known Tresca criterion.

When there is no internal friction, but the local strength is statistically distributed, the resulting strength of the material is given by the integral of the probability for fracture over the entire volume of the material. This reasoning forms the basis for the Weibull statistical theory characterizing the strength of materials.

When a material exhibits both internal friction and a statistically distributed strength, the resulting strength of the material must be found by integrating the probability for fracture over all local shearing planes where the effective shearing stress is positive. This is the basic concept used in the present theory where the probability for fracture has been integrated over the solid angle in the stress space where the effective shearing stress is positive.

Because of its ease in representation the Weibull distribution has been used in this treatment, but naturally it is possible to use other probabilistic models, such as the normal distribution.

STRESSES IN THE POLYAXIAL STRESS FIELD

In the polyaxial stress state we can calculate the stresses in a plane, whose normal (OP Fig. 1) has the direction cosines l, m and n to the σ_x, σ_y and σ_z axes, respectively. These are:

$$\sigma_n = l^2\sigma_x + m^2\sigma_y + n^2\sigma_z \quad \ldots\ldots\ldots\ldots (1)$$

and

$$\tau_n^2 = l^2\sigma_x^2 + m^2\sigma_y^2 + n^2\sigma_z^2 - \sigma_n^2 \quad \ldots\ldots (2)$$

where

$$l^2 + m^2 + n^2 = 1. \quad \ldots\ldots\ldots\ldots (3)$$

From Fig. 1 we get the relations

$$\left.\begin{aligned} l &= \cos\alpha\cos\lambda \\ m &= \cos\alpha\sin\lambda \\ n &= \sin\alpha \end{aligned}\right\} \quad \ldots\ldots\ldots\ldots\ldots\ldots\ldots\ldots (4)$$

Let us now define the effective shearing stress as

$$\tau_e = |\tau_n| - \mu\sigma_n \quad \ldots\ldots\ldots\ldots\ldots\ldots\ldots\ldots (5)$$

where $\mu\sigma_n$ is the internal friction stress.

By using equations (1)-(5) we can calculate the solid angle (Ω) where $\tau_e > 0$, which are the surface areas shown in Fig. 2 divided by the unit radius.

The results for Ω shown in Fig. 2 correspond to σ_x = 8 kb, σ_z = 1 kb, μ = 1, and σ_y as a parameter. In the shaded angle where $\tau_e < 0$ no rupture can

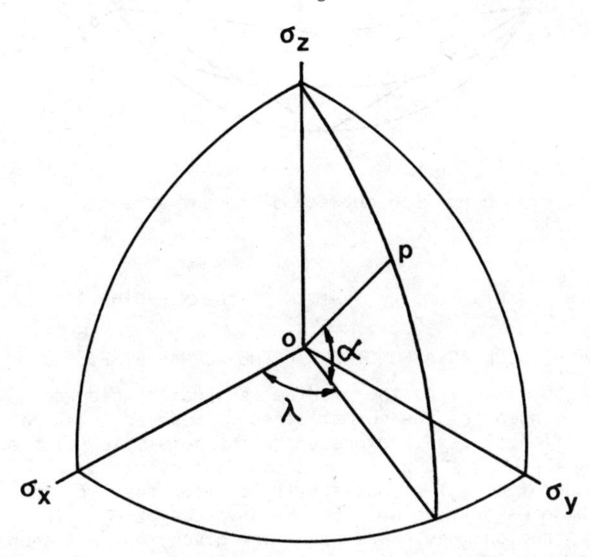

Fig. 1. Unit sphere with principal stress axes.

take place for any value of σ_y between σ_x and σ_z. It is also evident that the solid angle where fracture can occur at first decreases with increasing σ_y, reaches a minimum, and then again increases when $\sigma_z < \sigma_y < \sigma_x$. This fact indicates that the strength has a maximum when the intermediate principal stress lies approximately half-way between the other two.

CALCULATION OF THE STRENGTH

By using the Weibull distribution, the probability of rupture may be expressed in the form:

$$S = 1 - \exp(-kX) \quad \ldots\ldots\ldots\ldots (6)$$

where

$$X = \int \tau_e^M \, d\Omega \; (\tau_e > 0) \quad \ldots\ldots (7)$$

and k and M are Weibull parameters.

Substituting in equations (1) to (5), experimental strength values from a uniaxial compression test, corresponding to 50 per cent rupture, where kX = ln 2, or any other simple strength test, we get the X-value from (7). We can then calculate the strength at any combination of the principal stresses by setting X equal to this value. This is easily done by using a computer. Values of μ and M are determined in the manner described in a subsequent section.

The strength is presented in Fig. 3 on the σ_x, σ_y plane with σ_z = 0 and μ = 1 for the cases of M = 2, 3, 5 and ∞. Note that the results are normalized with respect to C the uniaxial compression strength.

We note that the influence of the intermediate principal stress decreases with increasing M, and when M tends to infinity the results are in agreement with the classical Mohr-Coulomb theory. For M = 2 and μ = 0, the result will coincide with the von Mises theory, and the strength curves become ellipses.

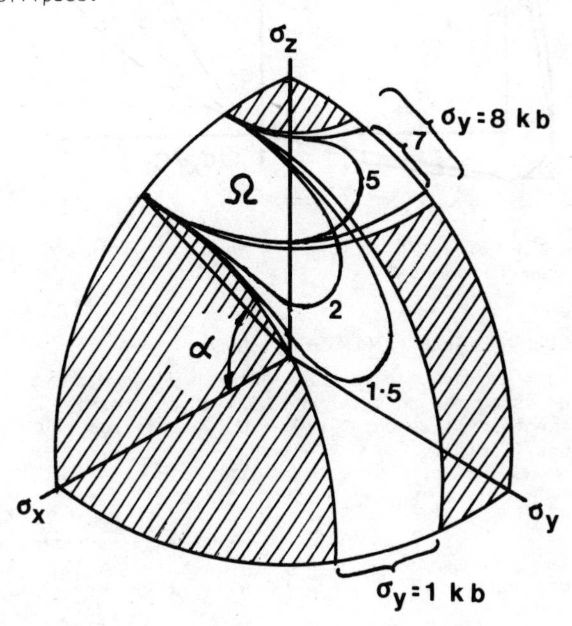

Fig. 2. Solid angles for $\tau_e > 0$ with σ_x = 8 kb, σ_z = 1 kb, μ = 1 and σ_y as a parameter.

A comparison between different strength criteria is shown in Fig. 4 for the deviatoric plane in the principal stress space where the statistical theory is calculated for the mean stress σ_o equal to zero, a uniaxial strength of 2 kb, μ = 1, and M = 2.

For special combinations of μ and M the statistical theory coincides with earlier strength criteria as shown in Table 1.

Table 1. Values of μ and M for which the statistical theory coincides with other criteria

Strength criteria	μ	M
von Mises	0	2
Tresca	0	∞
Mohr-Coulomb	arbitrary	∞

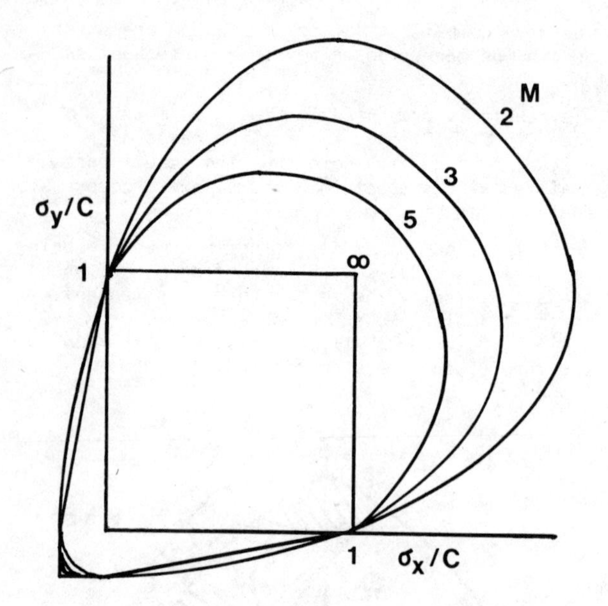

Fig. 3. Strength variation with σ_x at different M when $\mu = 1$ and $\sigma_z = 0$.

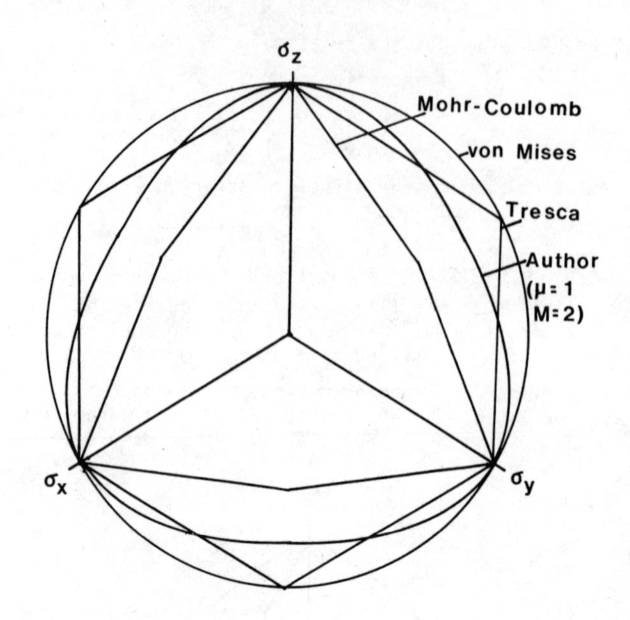

Fig. 4. Comparison between different strength theories.

RELATION BETWEEN STRENGTH, μ AND M

Determination of a relation between μ and M can be made using the uniaxial and biaxial compressive strength. If we put $\sigma_z = \lambda = 0$, we get from equations (1)-(5).

$$\sigma_n = l^2 \sigma_x \quad (8)$$

$$\tau_n = l \cdot n \sigma_x \quad (9)$$

and

$$\tau_e = l(n - \mu l)\sigma_x \quad (10)$$

From Fig. 1 or 2 it may be seen that this state of stress is held constant when rotating OP around either the $\sigma_x(\sigma_y = \sigma_z)$ or $\sigma_z(\sigma_y = \sigma_x)$ axis.

Using equation (4) in (10) this gives for $\lambda = 0$

$$\tau_e = \sigma_x \cos\alpha\,(\sin\alpha - \mu\cos\alpha) \quad (11)$$

When X is held constant as stated above, equations (7) and (11) give

$$\left(\frac{\sigma_{20}}{\sigma_{10}}\right)^M = \frac{\int_{\alpha_0}^{\pi/2} [\cos\alpha(\sin\alpha - \mu\cos\alpha)]^M \sin\alpha\, d\alpha}{\int_{\alpha_0}^{\pi/2} [\cos\alpha(\sin\alpha - \mu\cos\alpha)]^M \cos\alpha\, d\alpha} \quad (12)$$

where σ_{10} and σ_{20} are the uniaxial and biaxial compressive strengths, respectively. For $\alpha = \alpha_o$ τ_e is zero and (11) gives

$$\mu = \operatorname{tg}\alpha_o \quad (13)$$

It can be shown (see Appendix) that equation (12) gives

$$\left(\frac{\sigma_{20}}{\sigma_{10}}\right)^M = \sqrt{1 + \mu^2} + \mu. \quad (14)$$

This is a useful relationship between the Weibull parameter, friction coefficient and strength ratio.

Note in this section that α is the α-value for $\lambda = 0$.

THE μ-VALUE AS A FUNCTION OF THE NORMAL STRESS

In the literature the μ-value is usual considered independent of the normal stress. However, when the friction stress is expressed with the simple relation $\tau_f = \mu(\sigma_n)\sigma_n$, μ is not a constant over a wide range of normal stresses. It is noted that τ_f increases slowly with σ_n for high values of σ_n. In this region many expressions are given that all show a decreasing μ-value with increasing σ_n. Lundborg (1968) has used the relation

$$\mu = \mu_o/(1 + \mu_o \sigma_n/\tau_x) \quad (15)$$

which is based on experimental results. μ_o is a constant and τ_x the friction stress when σ_n tends to infinity. By using a computer, the expression (15) may easily be used instead of a constant μ-value.

COMBINED TENSILE AND COMPRESSIVE STRESSES

It is possible to extend the analysis to combined tensile and compressive stresses, in a number of different ways.

In this paper, it is assumed that the friction will still decrease when $\sigma_n < 0$ so that the calculation will hold throughout the region. Other alternatives may be to let the friction be zero for $\sigma_n < 0$, or according to Griffith (1924) let the calculation hold only when $\sigma_1 + 3\sigma_3 > 0$ and then let σ_3 be constant (σ_1 and σ_3 are the major and minor principal stress respectively).

COMPARISON BETWEEN EXPERIMENTAL AND CALCULATED STRENGTH

Experimental results from Hoskins (1969) on trachyte and from Akai and Mori (1967) on sandstone have given

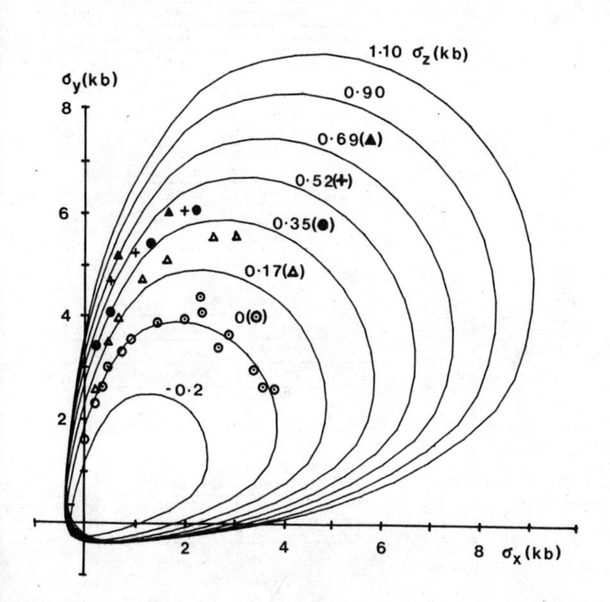

Fig. 5. Comparison between calculated strength and Hoskins' experimental values on trachyte. The symbols indicate different σ_z used by Hoskins corresponding to the calculated lines in the figure.

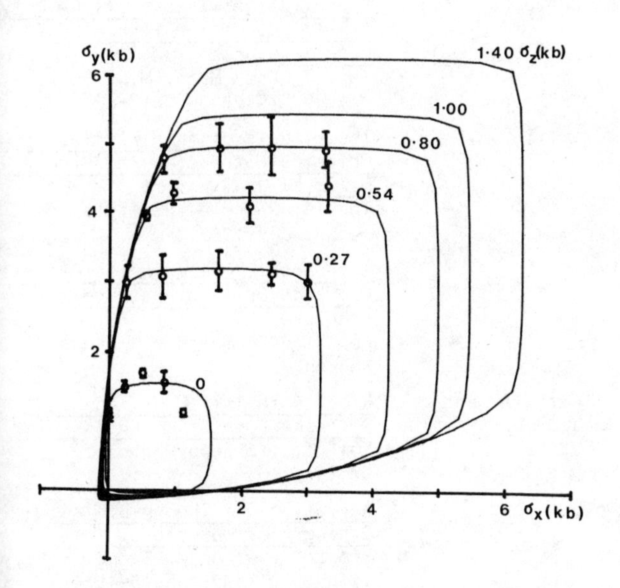

Fig. 6. Comparison between calculated strength and experimental values from Akai and Mori on sandstone.

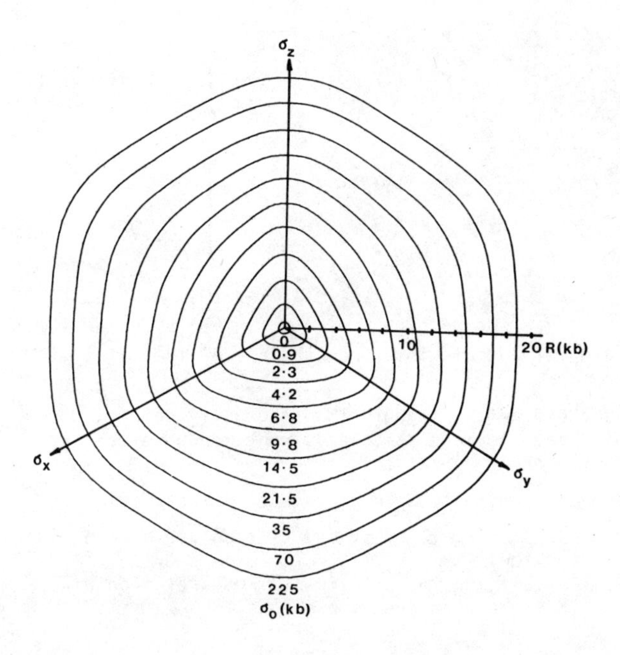

Fig. 7. Calculated strength criteria of trachyte for the deviatoric plane in the principal stress space at different mean stresses σ_o. The R-scale shows the radius of the yield surface, and the σ-axes the direction of the principal stresses.

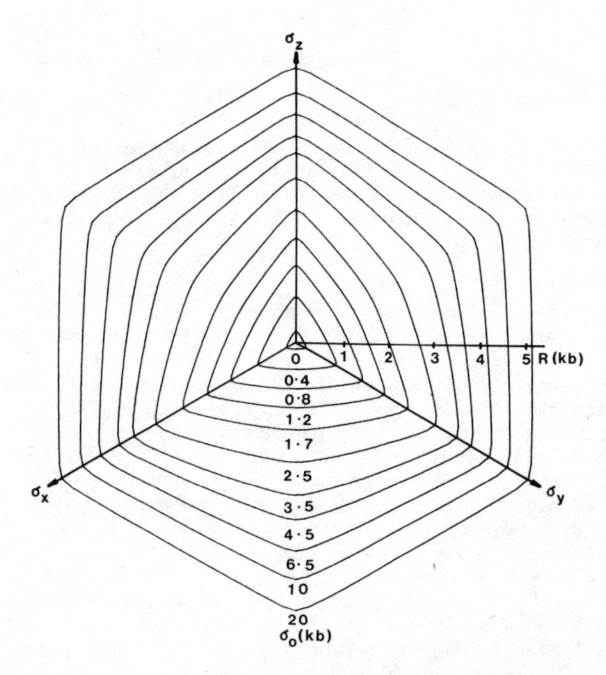

Fig. 8. Calculated strength criteria of limestone for the deviatoric plane in the principal stress space at different mean stresses σ_o. The R-scale shows the radius of the yield surface, and the σ-axes the direction of the principal stresses.

$$\left.\begin{aligned} \mu &= 0.9/(1 + \frac{0.9\sigma_n}{12}) \\ M &= 1.2 \\ X &= 0.2702 \end{aligned}\right\} \quad \ldots\ldots\ldots\ldots (16)$$

for trachyte and

$$\left.\begin{aligned} \mu &= 1.4/(1 + \frac{1.4\sigma_n}{3.8}) \\ M &= 7.0 \\ X &= 0.3904 \cdot 10^{-5} \end{aligned}\right\} \quad \ldots\ldots\ldots\ldots (17)$$

for sandstone.

By using the strength relation $\sigma_1 = f(\sigma_3)$ for $\sigma_2 = \sigma_3$ the μ-value is found. Then by using the uniaxial and biaxial strength in (14) the value of M is found.

As the biaxial strength is not exactly determined we will have to make some adjustment for a better fit to the experimental points.

The calculations may now be made in two ways:

1. Calculating $\sigma_y = f(\sigma_x)$ at fracture when σ_z is constant.
2. Calculating the principal stress relation at fracture when the mean stress

$$\sigma_o = \frac{\sigma_x + \sigma_y + \sigma_z}{3} \text{ is constant.}$$

These two methods are equivalent with cutting the space model of the strength perpendicular to the σ_z and space diagonal, respectively.

Fig. 5 and 6 give example of calculated strength curves for constant σ_z compared with experimental results. From the Figures we note that the calculated results are in good agreement with experimental values.

Fig. 7 and 8 show the calculated strength for constant mean stresses σ_o. The curves have shapes which show reasonable agreement with experimental result and are in agreement with what many scientist have expected (Mazanti 1967), (Sjibata and Karube 1965) and (Paul 1968).

CONCLUSIONS

The present theory has been able to, from a physical point of view, explain the variation in strength with different combinations of the principal stresses. By determining for example the uniaxial compressive strength, the internal friction coefficient $\mu(\sigma_n)$, and the variance in strength distribution M, a complete model of the strength of a material may be calculated. The calculated strength shows a result that many scientists have expected and experimental works have shown. For reasonable values of M the curves have no discontinuities or sharp corners. For great mean stresses where $\mu\sigma_n$ tends to a constant value τ_x the curves become Tresca hexagonals with rounded corners. For smaller σ_o the curves will have triangular forms.

ACKNOWLEDGEMENT

This work has been carried out at the Swedish Detonic Research Foundation, with financial support from the Swedish Board for Technical Development, Nitro Nobel AB and Atlas Copco AB. The author would like to express his thanks to Dr. P.A. Persson and Mr. F. Ouchterlony for useful discussion, and to Mr. R. Holmberg for writing the computer programs.

REFERENCES

Akai, K. and Mori, H. — Study of the Failure Mechanism of a Sandstone under Combined Compressive Stresses. Proc. Soc. Civ. Engrs No 147, 1967, pp. 11-24. (In Japanese). Proc. Sec. Congr. Int. Soc. Rock Mech. Belgrade 1970, (In German)

Griffith, A.A. — The Theory of Rupture. Proceedings of the First International Congress on Applied Mechanics, Delft, 1924, pp. 55--63.

Handin, J., Heard, H.C. and Magouirk, J.N. — Effects of the Intermediate Principal Stress on the Failure of Limestone, Dolomite and Glass at different Temperatures and Strain Rates. J. geophys. Res., Vol. 72, 1967, pp. 611-640.

Hojem, J.P.M. and Cook, N.G.W. — The Design and Construction of a Triaxial and Polyaxial Cell for Testing Rock Materials. S. Afr. Mech. Engr. Vol. 18, 1968 pp. 57-61.

Hoskins, E.R. — The Failure of Thick-Walled Hollow Cylinders of Isotropic Rock. Int. J. Rock Mech. Min. Sci., Vol. 6, 1969, pp. 99-125.

Lundborg, N. — Strength of Rock-Like Materials. Int. J. Rock Mech. Min. Sci., Vol. 5, 1968, pp. 427-454.

Lundborg, N. — A Statistical Theory of the Polyaxial Compressive Strength of Materials. Int. J. Rock Mech. Min. Sci., Vol. 9, 1972, pp. 617-624.

Mazanti, B.B. — The Effects of the Intermediate Principal Stress on the Strength of Rock. Thesis, Georgia Institute of Technology 1967.

Paul, B. — Macroscopic Criteria for Plastic Flow and Brittle Fracture. Fracture, Vol. 11, 1968, pp. 313-496. Academic Press N.Y., London.

Sjibata, T. and Karube, D. — Proc. 6 th Int. Conf. on Soil Mech and Foundation Engineering Vol. 1, 1965, pp. 359-363, Un. of Toronto.

Weibull, W. — A statistical Theory of the Strength of Materials. Proc. R. Sw. Acad. Engng. Sci., Vol. 151, 1939, pp. 5-45.

Wiebols, G.A. and Cook, N.G.W. — An Energy Criterion for the Strength of Rock in Polyaxial Compression. Int. J. Rock Mech. Min. Sci., Vol. 5, 1968, pp. 529-549.

APPENDIX

Deduction of the Relation Between Strength, μ and M

By the substitution of eqn (13) and

$$\alpha = \frac{\pi}{4} + \frac{\alpha_o}{2} + x \qquad (A.1)$$

in equation (12) we get

$$\left(\frac{\sigma_{20}}{\sigma_{10}}\right)^M = \frac{\int\left[\cos\left(\frac{\pi}{4}+\frac{\alpha_o}{2}+x\right)\cos\left(\frac{\pi}{4}+\frac{\alpha_o}{2}-x\right)\right]^M \sin\left(\frac{\pi}{4}+\frac{\alpha_o}{2}+x\right)dx}{\int\left[\cos\left(\frac{\pi}{4}+\frac{\alpha_o}{2}+x\right)\cos\left(\frac{\pi}{4}+\frac{\alpha_o}{2}-x\right)\right]^M \cos\left(\frac{\pi}{4}+\frac{\alpha_o}{2}+x\right)dx} \qquad (A.2)$$

where the integration is carried out for $x = -\left(\frac{\pi}{4}-\frac{\alpha_o}{2}\right)$ to $\left(\frac{\pi}{4}-\frac{\alpha_o}{2}\right)$

$$\left(\frac{\sigma_{20}}{\sigma_{10}}\right)^M = \frac{\int[\ ]^M\left[\cos\left(\frac{\alpha_o}{2}+x\right)+\sin\left(\frac{\alpha_o}{2}+x\right)\right]dx}{\int[\ ]^M\left[\cos\left(\frac{\alpha_o}{2}+x\right)-\sin\left(\frac{\alpha_o}{2}+x\right)\right]dx} \qquad (A.3)$$

$$= \frac{\int[\ ]^M\left(\cos\frac{\alpha_o}{2}\cos x - \sin\frac{\alpha_o}{2}\sin x + \sin\frac{\alpha_o}{2}\cos x + \cos\frac{\alpha_o}{2}\sin x\right)dx}{\int[\ ]^M\left(\cos\frac{\alpha_o}{2}\cos x - \sin\frac{\alpha_o}{2}\sin x - \sin\frac{\alpha_o}{2}\cos x - \cos\frac{\alpha_o}{2}\sin x\right)dx} \qquad (A.4)$$

The expression in the square brackets is an even function of x. Thus all integrals containing sin x are equal to zero and we get

$$\left(\frac{\sigma_{20}}{\sigma_{10}}\right)^M = \frac{\cos\frac{\alpha_o}{2}+\sin\frac{\alpha_o}{2}}{\cos\frac{\alpha_o}{2}-\sin\frac{\alpha_o}{2}} = \frac{1+\sin\alpha_o}{\cos\alpha_o} \qquad (A.5)$$

Finally we get from (13) $\mu = \mathrm{tg}\,\alpha_o$ and (A.5) becomes

$$\left(\frac{\sigma_{20}}{\sigma_{10}}\right)^M = \sqrt{1+\mu^2} + \mu \qquad (A.6)$$

Deduction of the above relation may also be done by using Guldin's rule.

EFFECTIVE STRENGTH OF ROCK SALT

LA RÉSISTANCE MÉCANIQUE EFFECTIF DU SEL GEMME

EFFEKTIVE FESTIGKEIT DES STEINSALZES

Enver MANDŽIĆ
Dipl.Min.Eng.

Faculty of Mining Tuzla
Yugoslavia

Summary

Uniaxial compressive strength of rock salt samples from Tušanj Rock Salt Mine has been considered through variation of dimensionsrelations. The test specimens were in cubic and prismatic forms. The height-to-breadth ratio, (h:h), chosen for specimens tested in this program were, h:h = o.5;1;2;3 and 4. The breadth of quadratic base was b = 3;4;5;6;8;1o;15;2o and 3o cm. The uniaxial compressive strength of rock salt crystal with b = o.4 - 2.5 cm, and h:b = o.5;1;2 and 3, has also been shown. Ratio between the breadth of the largest and the smallest sample was lo:l.

Plots the stress vs specimen size show that we have had three areas of change of the strength with changing dimensions of specimens.

The first area, where we have considerable decrease in strength with increasing specimen size until minimum is reached. Second area, with considerable increase in strength with increasing specimen size. Third area, with slowly increasing specimen size untill the strength asymptoticaly approaches a value of σ_{ult} = 5oo kpcm^{-2}. For the first time, in the references known to the author, a curve with minimum was obtained by investigating uniaxial compressive strength vs samples dimensions.

The strength of specimen in the point of minimum is caled "strength at critical grain size relation".

Alimit strength value, σ_{ult} = 5oo kpcm^{-2}, called "effestive strength" was determined by extrapolating the results of testing. We shall consider the samples with dimensions of b$\geqslant$7o cm, uniaxial compressive strength testing for rock salt Tušanj, as a limiting value, when a value close to the effective strength has been achieved.

Zusammenfassung

Die einachsigen Druckfestigkeit eines Steinsalzprobestückes der Grube "Tušanj" wurde bei veschiedenen Grössenverhältnissen bestimmt. Die Würfel und prissmenförmigen Proben hatten ein Verhältnis h:b = o,5; 1;2;3 und 4, und eine Breite b = 3;4;5;6;8;1o;15;2o und 3o cm. Bestimmt wurde auch die einachsige Festigkeit des Salzkristalls mit b = o,4 - 2,5 cm, bei h:b = o,5;1;2;3. Die Breite des grössten Probestückes war lo mal grösser als die des kleinsten.

Auf dem Diagramme sind drei Gebüte der Festigkeitsveränderungen in Bezug auf die Grösse der Probestücke gegeben. Im ersten Gebiete sinkt die Festigkeit mit der Zunahme der Grösse schnell ab und erreicht einen kleinsten Wert. Im zweiten Gebiete wächst mit der Zunahme der Grösse sehr schnell auch die Festigkeit. Im dritten Gebiete steigt die Kurve sehr langsam.

Die Festigkeit der Probe an der Stelle des kleinsten Wertes wurde von den Verfassern mit "Die Festigkeit beim kritischen Verhältnis der Kerngrösse" benannt. Rechnerisch wurde auch der Festigkeitsgrenzwert mit σ_{ult} = 5oo kpcm^{-2}, genannt "effektive Festigkeit" bestimmt. Die Grössen der Steinsalzproben b$\geqslant$7o cm bei einachsiger Druckbelastung können, wenn sie einen der effektiven Festigkeit nahen Wert erreichen, als analitische angenommen werden.

Résumé

La résistence à la compression uniaxe des échantillons du sel gemme de la Mine "Tušanj" à Tuzla est considérée par la variation des relations des dimensions. On a examiné de échantillons dans les formes du cube et du prisme, avec la relation de l'hauteur et de largeur b; h:b = o,5;1;2;3;4, et avec la largeur de la base carrée b = 3,4,5,6,8,1o,15,2o,3o cm. La résistence uniaxe des cristaux du sel est indiqué aussi, avec b=o,4 - 2,5 cm et avec la relation h:b = o,5;1;2;3;4.

Sur les diagrammes sont embranchées trois zones des changements de résistence avec lechangement des relations dimensionnelles des échantillons. La zone premiére, où la résistence décroit rapidement avec l'agrandissement de la résistence d'éćhantillon et atteint le minimum; la zone seconde, où la résistence augmente rapidement avec l'agrandissement de l'échantillon; et la zone troisième, où la courbe prend un cours doux d'accroissement. Pour la première fois on a obtenu dans la litterature, conue aux auteurs, de l'examination de dépendance de la résistence uniaxe à la compression de la grandeur d'échantillon, des courbes qui ont le minimum. La résistence d'échantillon au point du minimum est conditionellement démommée "la résistence de la relation critique de la finesse du grain". Par l'extrapolation des résultats d'examination une valeur limite de résistence est déterminée, σ_{ult} = 5oo $kpcm^{-2}$, dénommée la résistence effective. La dimension de l'échantillon b $\geqslant$7o cm, dans l'examination de la résistence uniaxe pour le sel gemme "Tušanj" peut être considérée comme finale, quand on atteint une valeur qui est très proche à la résistence effective.

1. INTRODUCTION

Since the first tests for the determination of uniaxial compression strength up to our days the investigation of the factors that influence the variation of strength degree has passed a very long development way. On this development way the correlatives have been determined (by investigating different samples of rock material), so that at present one starts with the experience, instead of having as clear image of normas and standards as possible. The problem has become more complecated by establishement of the influences of volume greatness of the sample, of width-to-height ratio, of contact surface, of contact conditions, the degree to which the sample has been treated, the degree of mechanical anisotropy, rate of load increase, duration of testing, creep effect, ambient temperature and moisture content, the amount of moisture present in the pore spaces, envairments, etc. For this reason the investigations today are reduced to (by experience applicable) shape formation that corresponds to natural, concrete conditions.
With all this, there have still remained vaguely established related influences incorporated in so-called factor of safety, or better said, "ignorance factor". Many authors, after having investigated the types of rock material have determined the area of validity and application of general factor and astablished a whole range of theories. By doing so, the characteristics of rock material have still been reduced only to a norrow area of what had been investigated and apriori determined, in spite of the desire to unify. The quoting and copying from the original and the generalization of the conditions result in any desired estimations having unforeseeable consequences for the mining and the investigations in general. The investigation determines the tendency of incorrect dependences, establishes validity and apllication areas, and reduces emprical assumptions and dimensional unhomogeneity.

2. SHORT HISTORICAL BECKGROUND

From historical point of view an important consideration in the determination of the mechanical properties of rock is the effect of specimen size on strength. It will be apparent from this consideration and through the report "Suggested Methods for Determining the Uniaxial Compressive Strength of Rock Materials" from "ISRM Commission on Standardization of Laboratory and Field Tests" that the simple compression test is far from being simple. At present there are conflicting observations on the role of specimen size for many reason.
On the one side, a decrease in strength with increasing specimen size has been reported by Melikidze 1959, andezit and bazalt andezit, Baron 1959, 1972, Kurbatova 1959, Ilinitskaja 1962, 1969, marble, Koifman 1962, coal, Polak 1967, brown coal, Bieniawski 1968 coal, Pratt and other 1971, diorit, and many other authors.
On the other side, no effect on the strength properties with an increasing in the specimen size was observed by Bauschinger 1876, (Koifman 1962), on different rock types, Obert 1946, on numerous rock types, Polak 1967, tertiary claystone, Hodgson and Cook 197o, shale and quartzite, and many other.
There is the third possibility an increase in strength with specimen has been reported by Koifman 1962, on numerous rock types, Stamati and Teodoresku 1935, rock salt, Kuznjecov 1947, rock salt, Penkov 195o, rock salt, Gimm 1966, rock salt, Mandžić and Cvetković 1972, rock salt, Proskurjakov 1973, carnalyt and rock salt.
By the above cited statements we are far from having exhausted the whole list of authors who have been working on this problem and still are.

3. SAMPLE AS A PART OF ROCK MASSIF

Rock salt deposit "Tušanj" in Tuzla has a form of asymmetrical, deformed syncline, and from the morphological point of view it belongs to the type of stratified lenticular-stratified deposit. Salt series in its construction have the form of slightly bent monoclinal folds, with smaller or greater concentrations of salt in synclinal, trough shaped part of the structure. Inner tectonics of salt strata in the deposit is manifested in the form of numerous and various micro and macro-structures. The most important forms of structural shaping are as follows: complex plicate folds, bed folds, micro-overl-aps, micro-diapirs, all kinds of fissures, intermediate

fissure dislocations, micro-faults, brecciated zones, salt spiring into fissures, mylonitization, budinage, schistosity, cleavege, etc.
The greatest part of all forms in their micro and macro proportions are present also in the salt samples that have been laboratory tested.
Just these inner macro and micro tectonic deposits have conditioned the great number of samples to have been taken for laboratory testing. In this way are determined statistically the most probable strength values for the samples representing crystal aggregates. In this, a special attention is paid also to the results the appearance probability of which is very small. With the samples having the dimensions of b = 3,4,4 cm, 5o samples have been tested for each point on the curve. By increasing the samples dimensions their number to be tested is reduced. The larger the specimen the smaller dependence of strength on the dimensions of the specimen.

4. OBJECT AND CONDITIONS OF TESTING

The object of testing is to determine the dependence of uniaxial compression strengt on the test body size - the sample. Some 175 samples of rock salt in the form of a half of the cube, 231 samples in the form of the cube, 2o2 samples in the form of the prism with h:b = 2, and 89 samples in the form of the prism with h:b = 3 have been tested. The height of the(h:b=1) samples was h = 3;4;5;6;8;1o;15;2o;3o cm, with the width of quadratic base b = 3;4;5;6;8;1o;15;2o;3o cm. The samples were cut into required seizes in the laboratory by dry procedure out of greater ore lumps. The terminal surfaces of the samples to be in contact in the press were specially treated. The influence of the different degree of mechanical anisotropy was reduced to the average size by using a great number of samples for one form element. Thus, for example, for the dimension of hxhxl = 4x4x4 cm we are tested 5o samples. For big samples, for example, hxbxl = = 3ox3ox3o cm, 3 samples have been tested, with very small ratio of variations in the data on the strength.
During the testing direct contact of steel plates of the press and the rock salt samples at the parallel contact surface has been always realized. There was no use the copping materials of the end surface treatments other then machining. The maximum load on the specimen was recorded in kilopound within 1%. Load on specimen were apllied continuosly at a constant stress rate so that the failure will occur within 5 to 15 minutes of loading, alternatively the stress rate was within the limits of 5 - 1o $kpcm^{-2} \cdot sec^{-1}$.
The uniaxial compressive strength of the specimen was calculated by dividing the ma imum load carried by the specimen during the test, by the original cross--sectional area computed by averaging two breadths at right angles to aech other at about the upper-height, the mid-height and the lower height of the specimen.
Formula for computed uniaxial compressive strength was $\sigma_{ult} = F/A\ kpcm^{-2}$.

5. RESULTS OF TESTING

Based on the above stated tests the curves of the dependence of the strength on the sample size have been determined, as shown in Fig.1.By separating the phenomenon into three characteristic areas, the object of investigation is branched into several essential questions.

I. With small sample size increase the strength is rapidly decreased. At the beginning from the theoretical strength, σ_{ult} = 2o,ooo $kpcm^{-2}$, (Zwicky 1921, Poloni 1922, Joffe 1924), up to the crystal of greater dimensions, h x 2.5 x 2.5 cm. For the dimensions greater then 3 cm the samples are crystal aggregats of rock salt ore.
II. From the clearly expressed established minimum the strength of the sample is further increased by further increase of the sample. The strength growth is great with small growth of sample size. The curve has such run up to the size of loxloxh cm.
III. The third area is characterized by slightly increasing run from $h \approx$ lo cm, therefore, the strenght is slowly increasing for great sample size growth.

The object of our further investigation is what assential changes are going on within the sample that result in phenomenon of singularity, phenomenon of minimum, and the presented curves forms.
According to the literature, that has been known to the author, it is the first time that the curves of such a form have been registered. Especially significant is the phenomenon of minimum and it asks for an essential explanation. The phenomenon is conditionally explained by so called, "critical relation of grain finess",that is, by the relation of dimensions of unit crystals of aggregates to the total sample volume.

Our aim in this work is to determine also the final test sample size, then its further increase would not result in in increase or decrease of its uniaxial strength. For this reason we to the investigation only a part of the curve, from minimum towards the greater sample dimensions. The diagram indicates clearly that the strength has the constant value of σ_{ult} = 5oo $kpcm^{-2}$ for the samples with the relation of h:b = o.5, regardless the sample size. All other curves tend towards this walue as asymptote. When the curve reaches 99.o% of the value σ_{ult} = 5oo $kpcm^{-2}$, we consider that the curve was practically transformed into asymptote. For the increasing part of the curve, from the point of minimum, the basic equation of general form has been established;

$$\sigma_{ult} = q - p_i e^{-r_i (b_i - 5)}$$

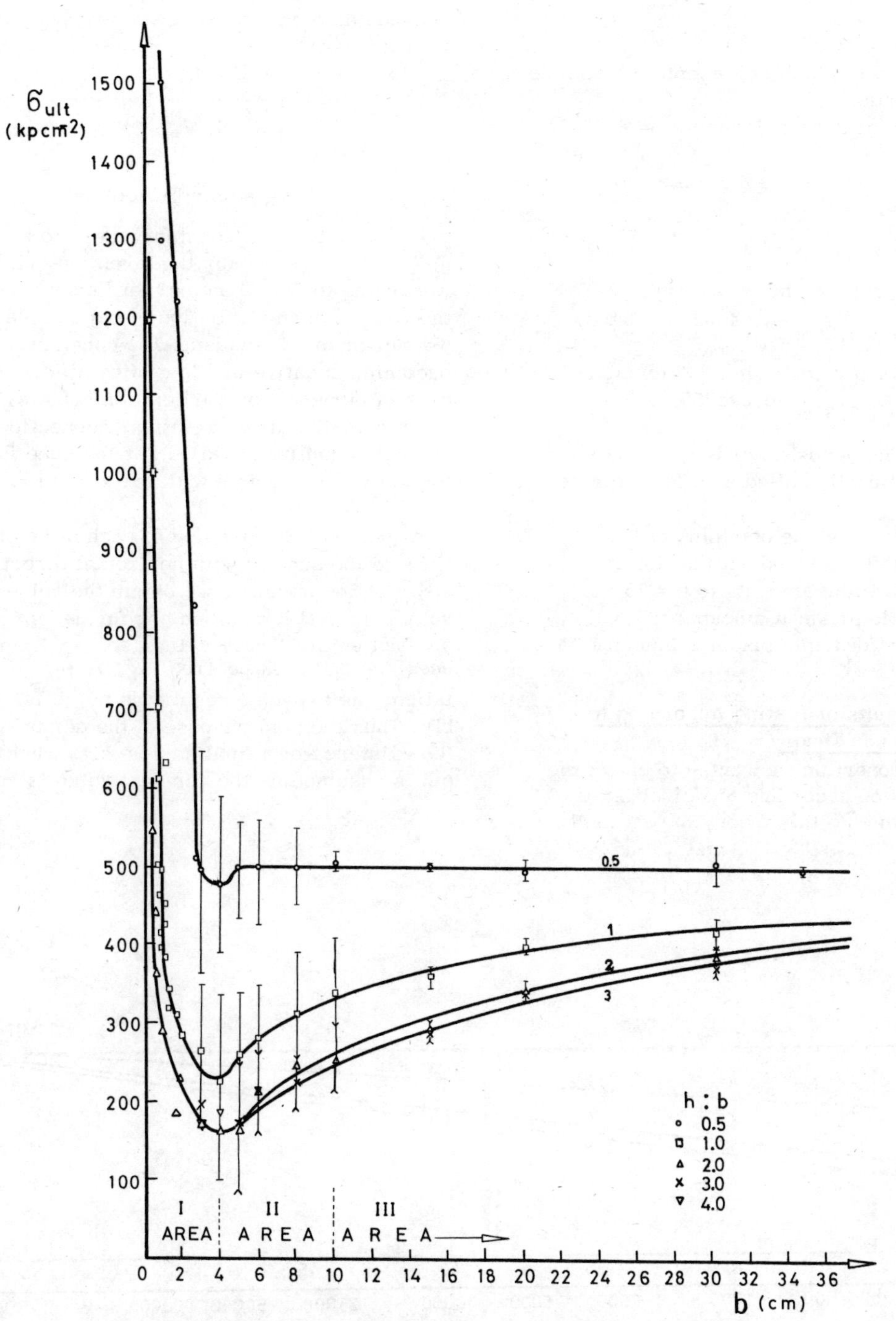

Fig. 1 The Effect of Specimen Size on Strength of Rock Salt

Bild 1 Der Einfluss der Probegrösse auf die Festigkeit

Fil. 1 L'influence de la dimension de l'échantillon sur la résistance mécanique du sel gemme

where is,

q,p and r - constants

b_i - variable which represents the sample breadth

e - base or natural logoritam = 2,71828

An equation has been found for each of represented curves, therefore the curve has the following shape for the form of cube;

$$\sigma_{ult} = 5oo - 217{,}9o6e^{-o{,}o43478\,(b-5)}.$$

For the dimensional relation h:b = 2 formć

$$\sigma_{ult} = 5oo - 3o4{,}268e^{-o{,}o4o355\,(b-5)}$$

and for the dimensional relation h:b = 3 form,

$$\sigma_{ult} = 5oo - 313{,}326e^{-o{,}o4o355\,(b-5)}.$$

Limes of each equation tends towards the value of 5oo, which is conditionally called as effective strength.

By solving the equation for the obtaining of limit values of sample width we found out that for the given cube form this width amounts to b = 95 cm, for the form of double prism it amounts to b = lo7 cm, and for the form of triple prism it amounts to b = llo cm.

5.1. Checking of Results of Testing According to WEIBULL'S Volume Theory

Using the log-log proportion we wanted to check the results of investigation according to Weibull statistical theory. According to this theory the strength depends also on the volume of test body through the relation as follows:

$$m \log \frac{(\sigma_{ult})_1}{(\sigma_{ult})_2} = \log \frac{V_2}{V_1}$$

where are:

V_1, V_2 - sample volume

m - constant that is to be determined for the given material.

According to Fig. 2 an extraordinary accordance of the results of investigation of big samples with Weibull theory is evident. The constant, m, is becoming negative and is getting different values for each of curves. For the relation h:b = o.5, m = o, therefore, the direct relation (connection) of strength equality is valid. For the cube form m=-13.8, for the form of prism with h:b = 2, m = -8.3, and with h:b = 3, m = - 7.9.

Considering the extension of each of belonging directions to the section with horizontal direction, to σ_{ult} = 5oo kpcm^{-2}, we obtain the value of final volume of test body when any further strength growth does not exist. These values are b$\geqslant$ 7o cm. As we used the curve shape from Fig. 1. for such interpretation, the expected results do not differ considerably. Thus the real purpose of the demonstration of the existence of a final sample size when the strength is assumed as the constant value is realized.

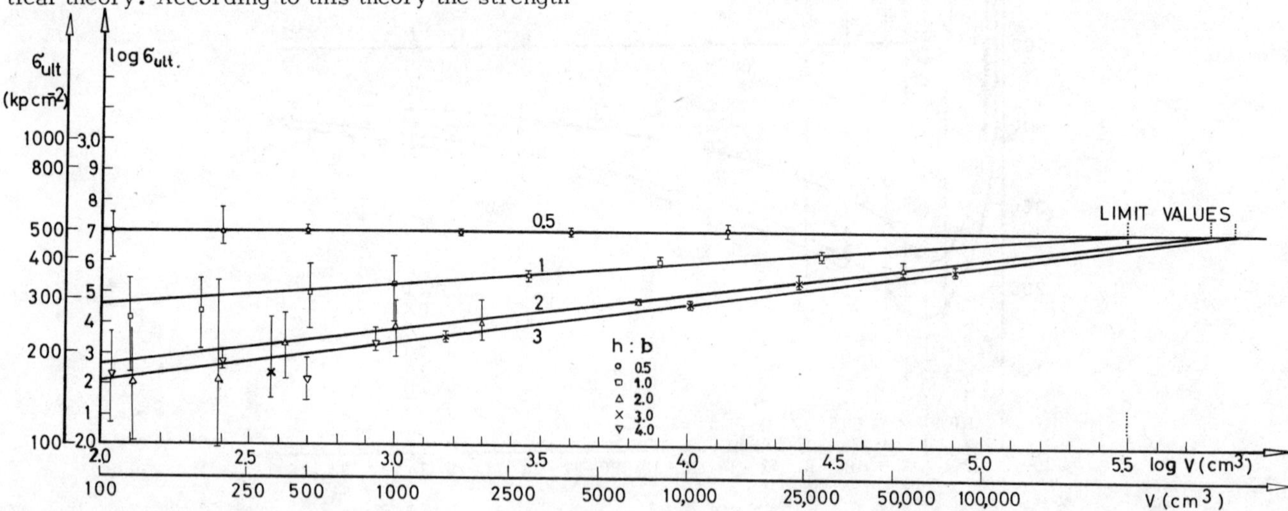

Fig. 2 Strength-Specimen Volume Relationship for Rock Salt; Experimentally and According to Weibull's Formula

Bild 2 Die Abhâgigkeit der Probegrösse von der Druckfestigkeit des Steinsalzes; Eksperimentele Daten und verbindung auf Weibull-s theorie

Fig. 2 La résistance mécanique du sel gemme comme fonction de la dimension de l'échantillon données expérimentales et relation avec la théorie de Weibull

6. PRACTICAL APPLICATION AND THE SIGNIFICANCE OF RESULTS OBTAINED

By establishing that the increase of sample dimensions, from one determined size of this sample, does not result in the increase of strength of the given rock material, a constant for calculation of the pillars in the mine is determined. Such strength is conditionally called "effective strength of rock material". In order to check the above statements experiments on big samples are going to be performed "in situ".

By experiments on big samples the phenomenon is going to be clearly determined, and by means of theoretical assumptions and proofs the performed considerations are going to acquire their confirmation. This opens broad possibilities for safe and economic design of mine rooms, and determines the clear orientation with resprect to investigations and testings of strength of rock salt and of other rock material as well.

7. CONCLUSION

By this work the basic points of the dependence of uniaxial compression strength and of sample proportion for the rock salt "Tušanj" determined. According to the results of investigation the values of strength of the pillars in the pit can be initiated. It has been found out that for the rock salt samples with the basewidth of $b \geq 7o$ cm, the effective compression strength would amount to σ_{ult} = 5oo kpcm^{-2}, for the dimensional relation of h:b = 1;2;3; and 4. The small ratio of variation in the strength during the testing of great size samples shows that we do not need a great number of tests in situ.

Reference

Bieniawski Z.T., 1968, The effect of Specimen Size on Compresive strength of Coal, Int. J. Rock Mech. Min. Sci. Vol. 5, pp 325-355.

Bieniawski Z.T., 1968, Eeine Studie des Brushmechanismus von Kohle in situ, Bericht über des 9. Landertreffen des Internationalen Büros für Gebirgsmechanik, Leipzig.

Baron L.I. and Kurbatova V.M., 1959, K voprosu o vlijanii masštabnogo faktora pri ispitanii gornih porod na razdovlivanie. V sb. "Naučnie issledovanija po razrabotke ugolnih i rudnih mestoroždenii". Ugletehizdat.

Baron L.I., 1972, Koeficienti kreposti gornih porod, Nauka, Moskva.

Bauschienger. 1876, 1882, 1892, Mitt. aus. d. mech. Laboratorium d. Techn. Hochschule, München.

Gimm W., 1966, Kali-und Steinsalz Bergbau. Bd. 1. Aufschluss und Abbau von Kali-und Steinsalzlagerstätten, Leipzig.

Hodgson K. and Cook N.G.W., 197o, The Effects of Size and Stress Gradient on the Strength of Rock, Proceedings of the Second Congress of the Internatonal Society of Rock Mechanics, Belgrade, Vol. 2, Paper 3 - 5.

Ilinitskaja E.I., 1962, Vlijanie masštabnogo faktora na pročnosnie svoistva gornih porod. V sb. "Fizikomehaničeskie svoistva, davlenie i razrušenie gornih porod". Izd. AN SSSR.

Ilinitskaja E.I. and other, 1969, Svojstva gornih porod i metodi ih opredelenija, Moskva.

Joffé A. and other, 1924, Deformation und Festigkeit der Kristalle, Zeitschrift für Physik, Bd. XXII, pp. 286-3o2.

Koifman M.I., 1962, O vlijanii razmerov na pročnost obrazcov gornih porod, V. sb. "Issledovanie fiziko-mehaničeskih svoistv gornih porod". Izd. Akademii Nauk SSSR.

Kuznjetzov G.N., 1947, Mehaničeskie svoistva gornih porod, Moskva.

Melikidze I.G., 1959, O vlijanii formi i razmerov obrazcov na ih mehaničeskie svoistva, Gornoi žurnal, No. 9.

Mandžić E. and Cvetković M., 1972, O uticaju razmjere na čvrstoću uzoraka kamene soli Tušanj, Saopštenje 3. simpozija iz mehanike stijena, Tuzla, Ref. 1 - 3.

Obert L. and others, 1946, Standardized Tests for Determining the Physical Properties of Mine Rock, U.S. Bureau of Mines Report of Investigation 3891.

Penkov A.M. and Vopilkin A.A., 195o, Rasčet opornih celikov pri dobiče kamenoi soli, Kiev, Izd. AN SSSR.

Polak V., 1967, Zkošenosti s pravádeňím laboratornich zkoušek pernosti hornin v tlaku a ve strihu, Výsledky Bánkého Výzkumu, Vol 5, pp. 96-1o6.

Pratt H.H. and others, 1972, The Effect of Specimen Size on the Mechanical Properties of Unjointed Diorite, Int. J. Rock Mech. Min. Sci, Vol. 9, pp 513-529.

Proskorjakov N.M. and other, 1973, Fiziko-mehaničeskie svoistva soljanih porod, Leningrad.

Poloni M., 1921, Über die Natur des Zerreissvorganges. Zeitschrift für Physik, Bd. XX, pp. 323-327.

Stamativ M. and Teodoresku H., 1935, Recherches sur la resistance aux efforts mechaniques du sel gemme roumain, Congress Internationale des Mines de la metallurgie et de la geologie appliquee, V. session, Paris.

Zwicky F., 1923, Die Reissfestigkeit von Steinsalz, Physik. Zeitschrift, Vol XXIV, pp. 131-137.

COMPRESSION STRENGTH OF GUALBA MARBLE RELATED TO ITS PETROGRAPHICAL CHARACTER

LA RÉSISTANCE A LA COMPRESSION DU MARBRE DE GUALBA EN RÉLATION AVEC SON CARACTÈRE PÉTROGRAPHIQUE

DIE DRUCKSTÁRKE DES GUALBA MARMORS IN BEZUG AUF SEINEN PETROGRAPHISCHEN CHARAKTER

M. MONTOTO Head, Dpt. of Petrology, University of Oviedo, Spain

J. ORDAZ Assistant Professor of Petrology, University of Oviedo, Spain

Summary

The mechanical behaviour of Gualba (Barcelona, Spain) marble - granoblastic, 95,6% calcite - under uniaxial compression is described.
Its low strength,376 bars, the nature of the failure, and deviation of the results (about 15% std. dev.) are explained in the light of its most significant petrographical and textural aspects.
Among them stand out: a) relatively coarse and heterometric grain size (2.5 - 0.1 mm., average 1.2 mm.); b) weak interlocking allowing slips between calcite grain boundaries; c) previous geological cataclastic deformation; d) slight textural anisotropy and e) abundance of fissures and cracks all over the rock.

Resumé

On décrit le comportement mécanique du marbre (granoblastique, 95,6% calcite) de Gualba (Barcelona - Espagne), sous compression uniaxial.
Sa faible résistance, 376 Bars, la nature de la fracture, et la déviation des resultats (aprox. 15% dév. standard) sont expliquées a la lumière de ses aspects pétrographiques et texturales les plus signifiants.
Les plus relevants, ce sont: a) dimension de grain relativement gros et hétérométrique (2,5 - 0,1 mm., moyenne 1,2 mm.); b) faible entrelacement qui permet des glissements entre les limites des grains de calcite; c) déformation cataclastique géologique préalable; d) legère anisotropie tecturale, et; e) abondance de fissures et microfissures partout la roche.

Zusammenfassung

Es wird das mechanische Verhalten des granoblastischen Marmors, 95,6% Kalzit, aus Gualba (Barcelona, Spanien) unter einachssigem Druck beschrieben.
Seine geringe Druckfestigkeit von 376 bar, die Bruchart und die Abweichung der Resultate (ungefähr 15% Standard Abw.) werden im Hinblick auf die wichtigsten petrographischen und gefügemässigen Gesichtspunkte hin ausgewertet.
Darunter treten besonders hervor: a) relativ grobe und heterometrische Kőrngrossen (2.5-0.1mm dürchschnittlich 1.2 mm.); b) schwache intergranulare Verbindungen, die ein Abrutschen zwischen den einzelnen Kalzitkorn-Abgrenzungen ermöglichen; c) vorangehende geologische kataklystische Verformungen; d) Leichte Anisotropie des Gefüges; e) reinchliches Vorhandensein von Rissen und Spalten im ganzen Gestein.

Mineralogy and texture

Gualba marble mineralogical composition is: calcite 95,6%, accessories 2,4% and secundaries 2%. Forsterite, diopside, brucite, epidote, etc. are the most frequent rock-forming accessory minerals in these rocks; all of them are characteristical silicates in carbonate metamorphic rocks.
Some correlations can be established between primary and secundary minerals: chlorite from diopside, antigorite from forsterite, etc.; ferric hidroxide minerals can be observed filling fissures and cracks.
The rock texture is granoblastic, 1.2 mm. being the average diameter of the calcite grains, sizes ranging from 0.1 to 2.5 mm. Nevertheless unusual large grains, 5 - 7 mm. can be found.
Microgranulation phenomena has affected the boundaries of calcite grains during the tectonic history of this marble. On account of this, the most frequent grain size in the rock is under its average size.
The size of the accessory minerals are usually less than 1 mm. and most of them are present as inclusions inside the calcite grains. The calcite grain shape tends towards xenoblastic habit; elongated and ellipsoidal forms are also very common. The shape factor (maximum/minimum grain diameter) is roughly 1.5, which indicates a slight morphometrical anisotropy or, in other words, a given dimensional orientation.
In general the grains show not sutured sharp

boundaries and tend to present rounded sides more or less rugose. They do not however show polygonal outlines, limited by flat faces, so common in recrystallization textures. That causes rather weak poorly interlocked intergranular links.
The above mentioned intergranular microgranulation also contributes to giving an appearance of local weakness in the marble rock-forming mineral cohesion.
Some 10% of the calcite grains present twinning phenomena, as individual or polysynthetic twins. Most of them as $(01\bar{1}2) = e$.
In the intact rock-mass some textural aspects of general cataclasis can be seen, evidencing previous tectonic processes. Among these textural aspects stand out: calcite wavy extinction as well as optical anomalies like biaxicity in some grains, intracrystalline mechanical deformation, bended cleavage planes, microcracks, microgranulation inside and in the border of the grains, etc.
Referring to the natural microfissuration of the Gualba marble, open and closed microfissures of different kinds and lengths can be observed. The closed ones are the most abundant, 64% of all of them, being intragranular and sometimes considered as microfractures. Much less abundant are those longer, trans-intergranular microfissures or mixtes, 21%; the others are open microcracks.
The average lengths of the longest microfissures range from 3 to 7 mm. The average density of microfissures by cm. is about 9, being variable along the same thin section, depending on the area considered.
The percentage of pores and voids is under 2%, determined by optical methods on surfaces of 1 cm. of thin section.

Compression tests
Ten cylindrical specimens of 52 mm. in diameter and slenderness = 2 (height/diameter relation) were used. They were drilled from homogeneous, unjoined and unweathered blocks selected in the Gualba quarries, and later their circular surfaces ground, being 0,05 mm. the maximum error in their parallelism. The load application velocity ranged between 6 and 7 bar/s. for the different series of specimens but in each one it was maintained constant during all the test.
The obtained results are summarized in Table I.

TABLE I

Specimens no.	Rc (bar)	Range (bar)
5	368	431-300
5	385	525-337

It can be said, according to the Deere and Miller mechanical classification of rocks (1966), that the Gualba marble presents a low strength under compression (class "C"), lower than the strength usually obtained in the most common marbles.
The standard deviation of the results is approximately 15%. According to the different tests which have been carried out en the Gualba marble, one can state that it is a sistematic characteristic of the rock.
In order to be able to establish some correlations between the above mentioned results, with other mechanical properties of the rock, the direct and indirect -"brazilian" test- tensile strength data of this marble, Ordaz (1973 a y b) are presented in Tables II and III.

TABLE II

Specimens no.	Rtd (bar)	Range (bar)
10	32	26-39

TABLE III

Specimens no.	Rtb (bar)	Range (bar)
7	49	41-59

Fractography
On account of the soft loading machine, Tonindustrie 200 Tm, used for this study, the fracture of the specimens was developed in a violent and uncontrolled way.
The nature of the fracture of the cylindrical specimens is predominantly by cataclasm, characterized by a high internal fracturation of the rock, Gramberg (1965).
The observed crumbling is produced by means of a multiple growth and development of micro fissures scattered all inside the mass specimen. They tend to orientate along the direc tion of the applied stress. When the specimen collapse is reached, two cones opposed along their vertexes are formed. In the external zones of the sample long splinters form due to the development of more or less longitudinal fissures macrocopically noticeable.
In some specimens, axial cleavage fracture or vertical splitting appear which are characterized by axial master fissures. They form vertical slabs parallel to the applied load.
Pure shearing fractures were not observed.
But mixed types formed so cataclasm and/or axial cleavage develop oblique shearing surfaces to the compressive axis. In these zones of maximum stresses, a very strong microgranulation took place changing the marble into a pulverulent material.
Marked signals of intense cataclasis can be observed in the microscopic texture of the marble specimens tested under compression up to the final failure. This is especially noticeable in the interior regions of the specimens supporting the highest stresses, principally in the central portion, (Fig. 1).
The newly formed cataclastic microstructures are higher than those of tectonic origin, especially when frictions along the grain boundaries and intergranular movements leading to

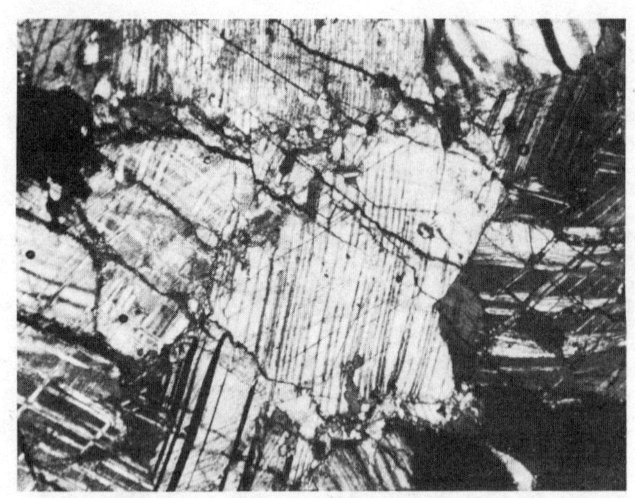

Fig. 1 (C.N.x13)

a grain size decrease - microgranulation - are considered.
The calcite cleavage planes generally appear bended, distorted, evidencing translations and intracrystalline slips. The crystalline lattice of many calcites was deformed during the tests as their wavy optical extinction shows.
Referring to the calcite twinning before and after loading, the differences are evident. Not only the percentage of twinned grains is increased but the intensity of the twinning as well. For example, mechanical conjugate twins not observed prior to the tests, were evident after the tests.
The bibliography concerned with marbles deformedunder triaxial conditions presents many examples of the above mentioned peculiar kind of mechanical twinning in calcite. They are usually present in highly tectonized rock masses, as we were able to observe in some samples taken from the Gualba marble area. In our tests, certain levels of compressive stresses, close to the rupture of the rock, were enough to bring on this kind of mechanical dislocation in some crystalline lattices favourably oriented.
Table IV shows the percentages of twinned and non-twinned calcite grains referred to different twinning levels. The percentages were calculated over 300 calcite grains in thin sections of the marble before and after the tests. During the counting operations, deformation bands and very thin twins were not taken into account.
A close relation exists between the marble texture and the growth and development of the microfissures under compression loads. As polarizing microscopy observations proved the microfissure nucleation takes place predominantly in textural defects or weaker zones, such as cleavage planes, grain boundaries, daries, inclusions and pre-existing microfissures. The density of those formed microfissures depends - for a given applied deformation - on those discontinuities already existing in the rock, Montoto and Esbert (1971).
The natural microfissuration that Gualba

TABLE IV

Twinning in calcite grains	Non tested specimen	%	Tested specimen	%
Non twinned	274	91.3	254	84.6
1-3 twins	15	5.0	25	8.3
4-6 twins	7	2.3	10	3.3
More than 6 twins	4	1.3	9	3.0
Conjugate twins	-	-	2	0.6
Total grains	300	99.9	300	99.8

marble presents is very significative and its intergranular unions are not very strong as we presented before. Thus in this rock the experimentally developed microfissures usually appear at relatively low level stresses. The intragranular fissures are the most frequent in this rock, followed by the longest-open or closed - trans- and/or intergranular types.
Those microfissures longer than 2.5 mm. tend to concentrate parallely to the maximum compression axis. Deviations lower than 15° to that axis are commonly observed. Nevertheless, the smaller microfissures - generally the intragranular ones - do not present such a clear spatial orientation.
The percentages of the microfissures ranging in length from 0.1 to 4.0 mm. are presented in Table V. They were measured and counted by means of thin sections taken from tested and untested marble specimens.

TABLE V

Microfissures	Non tested specimen		Tested specimen	
Length (mm)	no.	%	no.	%
0.1-1.0	159	90.8	263	82.1
1.0-2.5	14	8.0	44	13.7
2.5-4.0	2	1.1	13	4.0
0.1-4.0	175	99.9	320	99.8

According to the Koide and Hoshino index (1967) the microfissure density in those highly stressed zones usually ranges from 6 to 8. In the failed Gualba marble specimen, the relation between transgranular and intergranular microfissures, T/I, is roughly 3. This can be interpreted as an easier propagation of microfissures through the calcite grains; on their way they usually take the weakest directions existing inside the crystal, such as cleavage planes, dislocations, intragranular microfractures, etc.
However this is not the case when the propagation of the advancing microfissure presents a non-favourable orientation to the affected crystalline lattice. On account of this, the mentioned microfissure tends to follow the grain boundaries. (Fig. 2).
Willard and Mc Williams (1969) showed that in marbles the T/I ratio was inversely pro-

portional to the failure strength. Thus the greater mechanical strength of marbles is, the less the ratio between the total lengths of microfissures present in the rock.

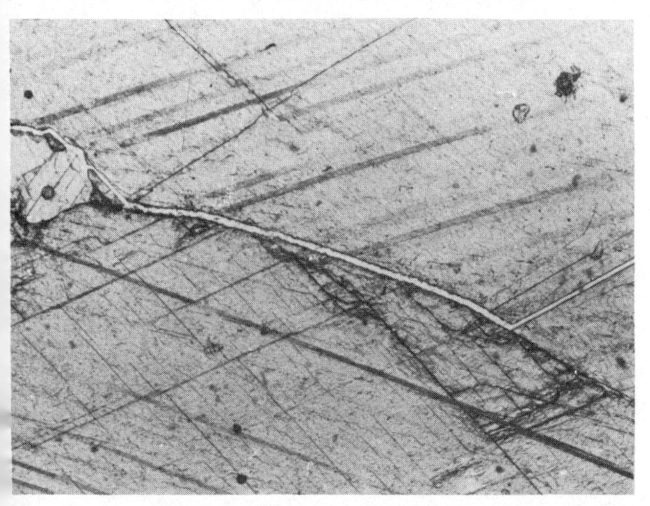

Fig. 2 (P.N.x33)

Conclusions

A highly intense post-failure cataclasis clearly observed in the rock is principally due to microgranulation of the original grains and crystalline deformations. 15% of calcite grains are affected by twinning, especially of polysynthetic nature. Post-tests polarizing microscopy studies show conjugate mechanical twins not present before the load application.

The microfissuration developed inside the marble samples during the compression tests are really important. Most microfissures, in general 70% or more, belong to the intragranular type. The others, larger in length, tend to grow parallel to the maximum compression direction inside the marble specimen. On their way, transgranular lengths predominate over the intergranular ones (ratio T/I ≈3). It can be concluded that fissures have a major facility for propagating through the calcite grains, by following the weakest planes, namely cleavage. (Fig. 3).

Cataclasmic and/or vertical splitting is the most common type of final fracture in Gualba marble cylindrical specimens tested under uniaxial compression.

The low mechanical strength of Gualba marble uniaxial compression can be explained by means of some petrographic factors:

(a) easy mechanical deformation of calcite grains.

(b) heterometric and coarse grain size.

(c) slight dimensional anisotropy.

(d) weak intergranular unions, having poorly interlocked grain boundaries, and absence of sutures, allowing movements between grains.

(e) the marble was slightly deformed during its tectonic history and some cataclasis was developed in it, as well as abundant fissures and microfissures.

In our opinion, the dispersion of results is partially (not counting other possible extrinsic factors) to (b)and(c), and to the aleatory and variable character of fissures and microfissures referred to in (d).

Fig. 3.- Development of microfissures inward from grain boundary.P.N.(x 33).

Acknowledgements

We would like to express our sincere gratitude to Aymar, S.A. in the Gualba marble quarries and to Mr. E. Vázquez in the "Servicio Regional de Materiales, Ministerio de Obras Públicas", Barcelona (Spain).

****

References

DEERE, D. and MILLER, R.D.,1966, Engineering classification and index properties for intact rock, Techn. Rept. nº AFWL-TR-65-116. Air Force Weapons Lab. Kirtland Air Force Base, New Mexico, U.S.A.

GRAMBERG, J., 1965, The axial cleavage frac-

ture I: axial cleavage fracturing, a significant process in mining and geology, Eng. Geol. Vol 1 (1), p 31-72.
KOIDE, H. and K. HOSHINO, 1967, Development of microfractures in experimentally deformed rocks, Zisin. Vol. 20, p 85-97.
MONTOTO, M. and R.M. ESBERT, 1971, Deformación y rotura de rocas: criterios petrográficos para su estudio, I Congr. Hispano-Luso-Americano de Geología Económica. Madrid-Lisboa, E-5-11, p 129-148.
MONTOTO, M. and J. ORDAZ, 1971, Características petroestructurales de significado mecánico en el mármol de Gualba, Publ. Inst. Inv. Geol. de la Diput. Prov. Barcelona, Vol. XXVI, p 57-75
MONTOTO, M. and J. ORDAZ, 1972, Características mecánicas del mármol de Gualba (Barcelona) bajo compresión uniaxial, Acta Geológica Hispánica, Año VII, nº 4, p 113-116.
MONTOTO, M. and J. ORDAZ, 1973, Interpretación petroestructural del comportamiento del mármol de Gualba (Barcelona) bajo compresión uniaxial, Bol. Geol. y Min. T-LXXXIV, (3), p 157-196.
ORDAZ, J., 1973a, Resistencia a la tracción directa del mármol de Gualba (Barcelona), Estudios Geológicos, n° 3, p 239-246.
ORDAZ, J., 1973b, Estudio petrográfico del comportamiento mecánico de los mármoles bajo esfuerzos uniaxiales, (Thesis), Departamento de Petrología, Fac. de Ciencias, Univ. de Oviedo, 226 p.
WILLARD, R.J. and J.R. Mc WILLIAMS, 1969, Microstructural techniques in the study of physical properties of rocks, Int. J. Rock Mech. Min. Sci., Vol. 6, p 1-12.

****

EFFECTS OF COUPLE-STRESSES ON STRESS DISTRIBUTION IN SPECIMENS OF LABORATORY TESTS

LES EFFETS DES COUPLE-TENSIONS SUR LA DISTRIBUTIONS DES CONTRAINTES DANS LES SPECIMENS EN LABORATOIRE

WIRKUNGEN DER MOMENT-SPANNUNGEN AUF SPANNUNGSVERTEILUNGEN IM MUSTER EINES LABORATORIUMTESTES

Yoshiji NIWA
Professor, Dept. of Civil Engineering Kyoto University, Kyoto, Japan

Shoichi KOBAYASHI
Asst. Professor, Dept. of Civil Eng. Kyoto University, Kyoto, Japan

SYNOPSIS Although the theory of elasticity is successfully applied in the stress analysis of ordinary problems, it may fail in predicting real behaviors of materials when the average dimension of the intrinsic discontinuities of the materials becomes comparable to the dimension of the portion concerned with problems as may be in the case of polycrystalline materials. In such a situation, the couple-stress theory, which reflects the effects of the intrinsic discontinuities, may find applications.
The present paper is concerned with the effects of couple-stresses on stress distributions in the typical specimens commonly used in a laboratory.
The analytical results show that the effects of couple-stresses are remarkable, especially in the indirect tests. In the disc test, the magnitude of stresses on the diametral plane in the loading direction, specifically in tension, decreases rapidly as the intrinsic internal length of materials increases. The stresses on the diametral plane perpendicular to the loading direction develop more uniformly with an increase of the internal length. In the ring test, stresses are also drastically reduced and become more uniform as the internal length increases. In the uniaxial compression test, however, the effects of couple-stresses are rather limited near the boundaries of the specimen and the more uniform stresses develop as the internal length increases. It may be suggested that test results in a laboratory must be suitably interpreted by taking account of the effects of the internal length of materials.

RESUME La théorie de l'élastisité est appliquée avec succès à l'analyse des contraintes des problèmes ordinaires, mais elle ne peut pas prédire les comportements des matériaux où la dimension moyenne des discontinuités intrinseques des matériaux devient comparable à la dimension de la portion des problemes, par exemple, dans le cas d'analyse les matériaux polycristallines. En pareil cas, la théorie avec couple-tensions est applicable, parce qu'elle estime les effets des discontinuités intrinséques.
Ce rapport présente les effets des couple-tensions sur les distributions des contraintes dans les spécimens en laboratoire.
Les résultats analytiques indiquent que les effets des couple-tensions sont remarquables, particulièrement dans les essais indirects. Dansl'essai du disque, la grandeur des contraintes sur le plan diamétral dans la direction du chargement, particulièrement des tensions, diminue rapidement avec la augmentation de la longueur intérieure intrinséque des matériaux. Les contraintes sur le plan diamétral et parpendiculaire dans la direction du chargement deviennent plus uniformément à la fois. Dans l'essai du ring, la grandeur des contraintes diminue aussi remarquablement et la distribution des contraintes devient plus uniformément avec une telle augmentation. Dans l'essai à la compression uniaxiale, les effets des couple-tensions sont limités un peu près des bordures du spécimen et les contraintes deviennent plus uniformément à mesure que la longueur intérieure intrinséque augmente. Il est suggéré qu'on doit interpréter proprement les résultats de l'essai considérant les effets par la longueur intérieure intrinséque.

ZUSAMMENFASSUNG Obwohl die Elastizitätstheorie mit Erfolg in der Spannungsanalyse von gewöhnlichen Problemen angewandt wird, ist sie vielleicht nicht dazu tauglich, das wirkliche Verhalten von Materialien vorherzusagen, wenn die durchschnittliche Dimension der eigentlichen Diskontinuität des Materials mit der Dimension eines Teiles vergleichbarist, zum Beispiel im Fall von polykristallinen Materialien. In diesem Fall lässt sich die Elastizitätstheorie mit Momentenspannungen, die sich auf die Wirkung der eigentlichen Diskontinuität bezieht, anwenden. Dieser Aufsatz beschreibt die Wirkungen der Momentenspannungen auf Spannungsverteilungen in den typischen Mustern, die gewöhnlich in Laboratorium verwendet werden.
Die analytischen Ergebnisse beweisen, dass die Wirkungen der Momentenspannungen besonders beim indirekten Test merkwürdig sind. Im Scheibe-Test nimmt die Grösse der Spannungen auf der diametralen Ebene in der Belastungsrichtung, besonders bei Zugspannung, schnell ab, während die eigentliche innere Lange des Materials zunimmt. Die Spannungen auf der diametralen Ebene, die senkrecht zur Belastungsrichtung steht, entwickeln sich noch gleiförmiger mit der Zunahme der inneren Länge. Im Ring-Test, vermindern sich die Spannungen drastisch und werden noch gleichförmige, wenn die innere Länge zunimmt. Im einachsigen Drucktest werden die Wirkungen der Momentenspannungen jedoch begrezt in der Nähe der Grenze der Musters und noch gleichförmigere Spannungen entwickeln sich mit der Zunahme der inneren Länge. Die Testergebnisse veranschaulichen, dass auf die Wirkungen der inneren Länge der Materialien Rücksicht zunehmen ist.

INTRODUCTION

Knowledge of stress distributions in specimens of laboratory tests is a basic prerequisite in order to estimate the strength of materials.
Much work has been done for the analysis of stresses in specimens based on the classical theory of elasticity. As is well known, the classical theory of elasticity assumes the homogeneity of the constituent materials to the infinitesimal element of volume, that is, mass density is continuous and remains constant if any volume element is continuously shrunk to zero.
This continuum approximation is violated for many real materials, for example, for polycrystalline mixtures such as rocks, and composite materials.
The classical theory of elasticity is successfully applied to the analysis of stresses whenever the overall dimension of the problem is larger than the average dimension of the intrinsic discontinuities in materials such as the average grain size and inter-grain distance. However, the average internal length of the material becomes comparable to the overall dimension of the problems concerned, the classical theory of elasticity is expected to fail in accurate estimation of stress distributions. In such a case, the more precise theory which reflects the effects of the constituent materials must be sought for.

The couple-stress theory (Mindlin, 1963; Mindlin and Tiersten, 1962) or the micropolar theory (Eringen, 1968) may find applications in a wide variety of situations from crystal lattices to rocks or composite materials. As discussed by Eringen (Eringen,1968) and Cowin (Cowin, 1970), the couple-stress theory is an extreme of the micropolar theory and the classical theory of elasticity is another extreme. In other terms, real responses of materials fall between those predicted by the couple-stress theory and those predicted by the classical theory of elasticity.

Based on both theories, the present paper discusses the effects of the average internal length of materials on stress distributions in the specimens commonly used in a laboratory, such as a rectangular specimen under uniaxial compression and a disc or a ring specimen subjected to diametral compression.

DESCRIPTION OF THE PROBLEMS

Three types of problems are considered. The first is as shown in Fig.1; a rectangular block specimen with unit thickness and $2a$ and $2b$ in width and in height, respectively, compressed uniaxially between rigid rough platens. The second shown in Fig.2 is a disc specimen with unit thickness and radius a subjected to diametral compression. The third shown in Fig.3 is a ring specimen with unit thickness and a and b in outer and inner radii, respectively, subjected to diametral compression.
As the reference coordinates, we use the rectangular Cartesian coordinates for the rectangular specimen and the polar coordinates for the disc and ring specimens, respectively.
These specimens are assumed to obey the couple-stress theory and the classical theory of elasticity, and also to be in a state of plane strain.

According to Mindlin and Tiersten (Mindlin and Tiersten, 1962), the governing equations of the couple-stress theory in a state of plane strain are expressed

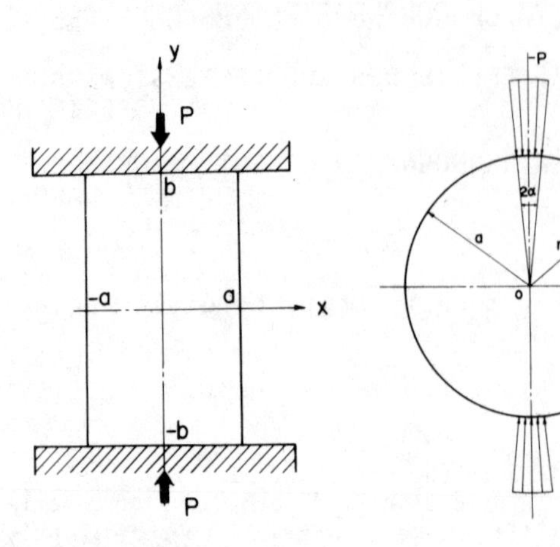

Fig.1 The rectangular specimen snd the coordinates.

Fig.2 The disc specimen and the coordinates.

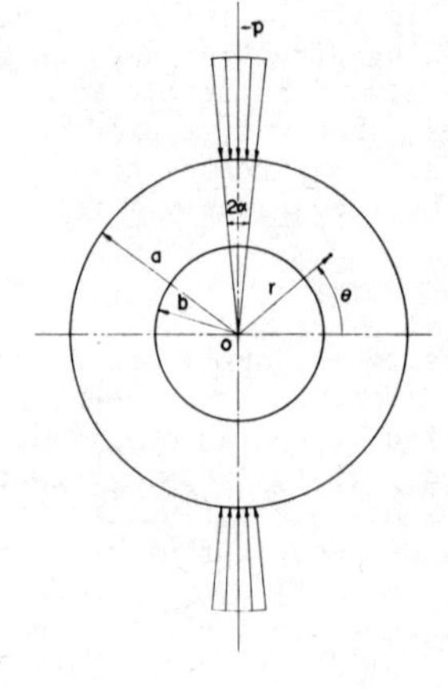

Fig.3 The ring specimen and the coordinates.

in the general coordinates x^α (α =1,2) by the two stress functions ϕ and ψ as follows;

$$\nabla^4\phi=0 \tag{1}$$

$$(1-\ell^2\nabla^2)\nabla^2\phi=0 \tag{2}$$

$$(1-\ell^2\nabla^2)\psi|_\alpha=-2(1-\nu)\ell^2\varepsilon_{3\alpha\beta}g^{\beta\gamma}\nabla^2\phi|_\gamma \tag{3}$$

where $\nabla^2=\frac{1}{\sqrt{g}}\frac{\partial}{\partial x^\alpha}(\sqrt{g}\,g^{\alpha\beta}\frac{\partial}{\partial x^\beta})$, $\nabla^4=\nabla^2\nabla^2$, $g=det|g_{\alpha\beta}|$, $g_{\alpha\beta}$, $\varepsilon_{3\alpha\beta}$, ν and ℓ are the fundamental metric tensor, thepermutation tensor, the Poisson's ratio and the intrinsic internal length of materials implying the bending rigidity of a micro-element, respectively, and $\psi|_\alpha$ implies the covariant derivative of ψ with respect to x^α.

Stresses are expressed

$$\tau^{\alpha\beta}=\varepsilon^{3\alpha\gamma}\varepsilon^{3\beta\delta}\phi|_{\gamma\delta}+\varepsilon^{3\gamma\alpha}\psi|^\beta_\gamma \tag{4}$$

$$\mu_{3\alpha}=\psi|_\alpha \tag{5}$$

where $\tau^{\alpha\beta}$ and $\mu_{3\alpha}$ are the Cauchy stress and the couple-stress, respectively.

Kinematical relations are expressed

$$e_{\alpha\beta} = \frac{1}{2}(u_\alpha|_\beta + u_\beta|_\alpha) \tag{6}$$

$$\omega_3 = \frac{1}{2}(u_2|_1 - u_1|_2) \tag{7}$$

$$\kappa_{3\alpha} = \omega_3|_\alpha \tag{8}$$

where $e_{\alpha\beta}$, ω_3, $\kappa_{3\alpha}$ and u_α are strain, rotation, curvature and displacement, respactively.

Constitutive relations are

$$e_{\alpha\beta} = \frac{1}{2G}[\tau_{(\alpha\beta)} - \nu g_{\alpha\beta} \tau^{\gamma}_{\gamma}] \tag{9}$$

$$\kappa_{3\alpha} = \frac{1}{4G\ell^2} \mu_{\alpha 3} \tag{10}$$

where $\tau_{(\alpha\beta)}$ and $\mu_{\alpha 3}$ are symmetric part of the Cauchy stress and the couple-stress, respectively, and G means shear modulus.

When ℓ=0 in Eqs. (1) to (3), all the relations mentioned above are reduced to those of the classical theory of elasticity.

ANALYTICAL RESULTS AND DISCUSSIONS

The governing equations of respective problems are solved with appropriate boundary conditions. Analytical solutions were obtained by Fourier series for the rectangular specimen and Fourier-Bessel series for the disc and the ring specimens. Since they are described elsewhere (Niwa, et al, 1971a; 1971b; Kobayashi and Fukui, 1971), some of the results for stress distributions are illustrated in the present paper in Figs.1 to 8.

On the effects of couple-stresses on stress distributions the followings may be concluded.

(a) For the rectangular specimen (see Fig.4):
1. The larger the internal length of materials ℓ becomes, the more uniform stresses are expected.
2. The effects of couple-stresses are limited near the boundaries of the specimen and rapidly fade out as it goes away from the boundaries.
3. As might be expected from the theory, stresses based on the couple-stress theory approaches to those based on the classical theory of elasticity as the internal length decreases to zero.
4. Stresses based on the couple-stress theory behave differently from those based on the classical theory of elasticity at the corner of the specimen.

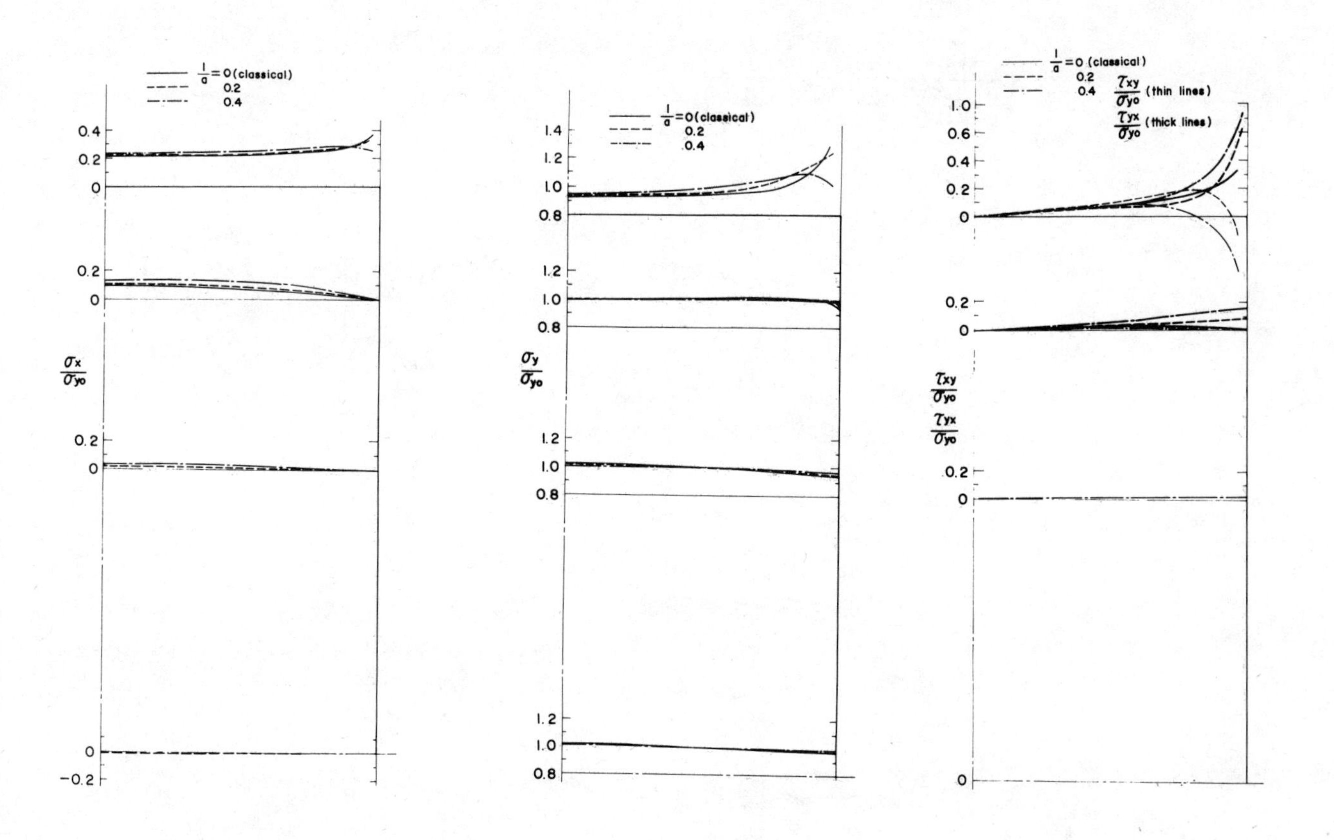

Fig.4 Effects of couple-stresses on normalized stresses, σ_x/σ_{yo}, σ_y/σ_{yo}, τ_{xy}/σ_{yo} and τ_{yx}/σ_{yo}. (σ_{yo} means the average stress, Poisson's ratio is 0.2, height-to-width ratio is 2.0)

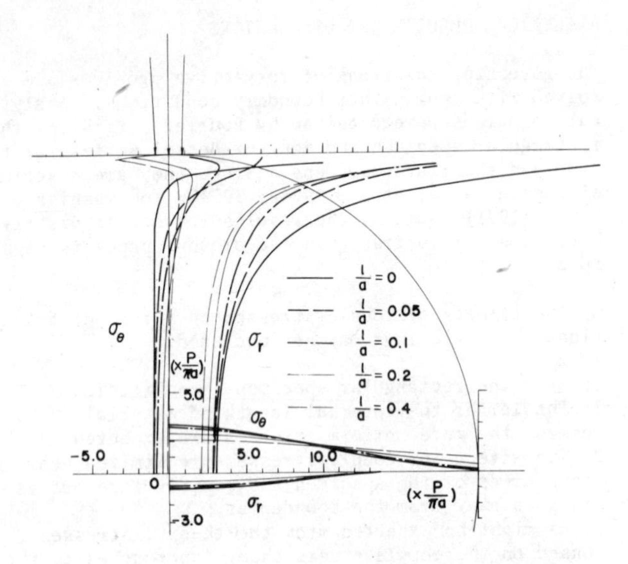

Fig.5 Effects of couple-stresses on stresses in diametral planes. (Poisson's ratio is 0.2, angle of loaded arc is 2.5°)

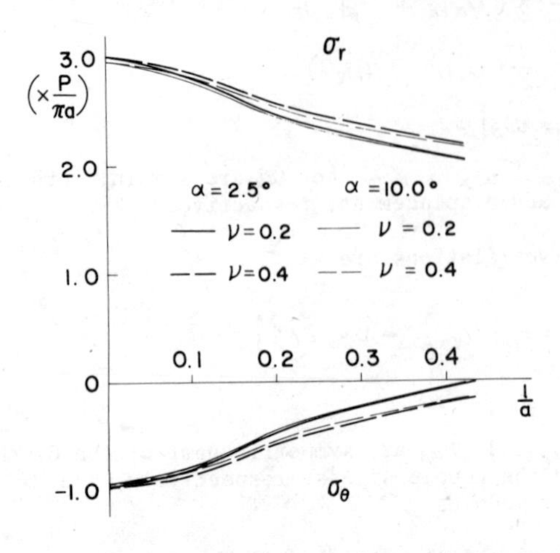

Fig.6 Variations of tensile and compressive stresses with the ratio l/a at the center of the disc specimen.

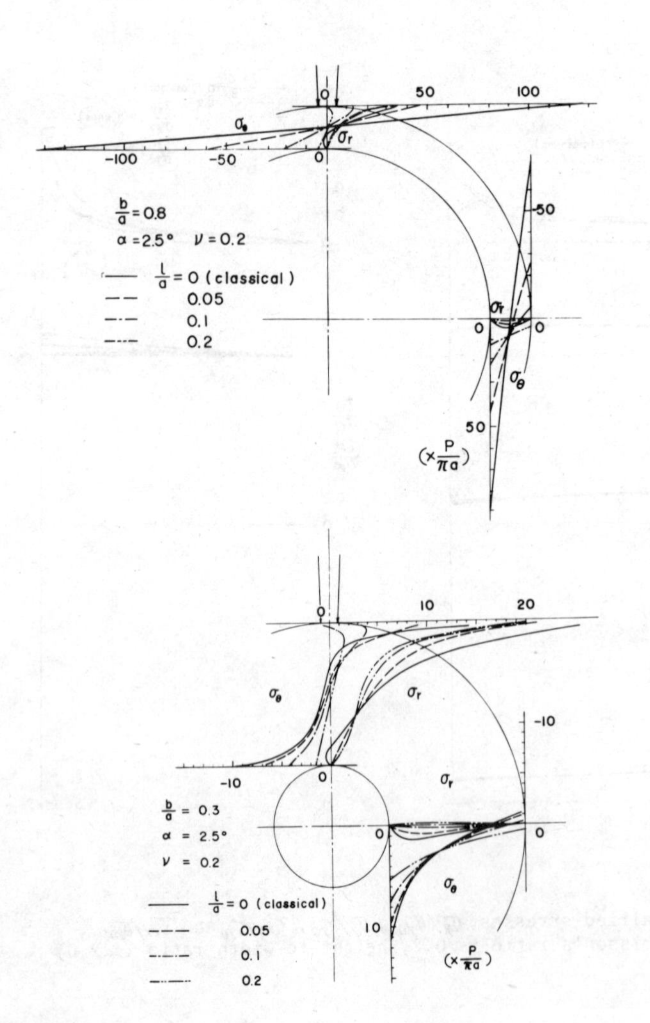

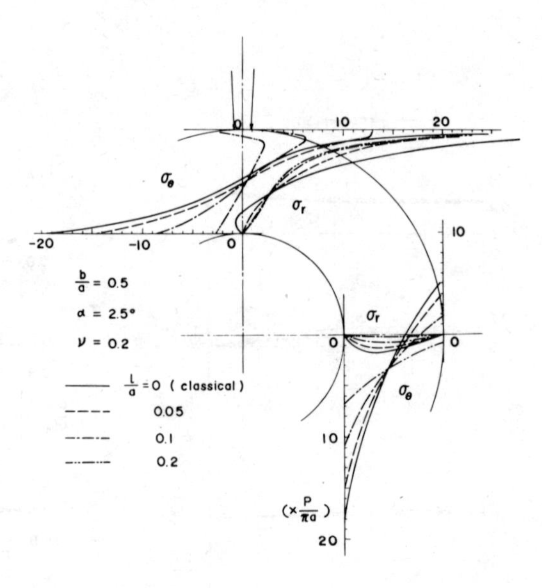

Fig.7 Effects of couple-stresses on stresses in diametral planes.

5. The magnitude of the shear stress acting on the plane perpendicular to the loading direction is larger in general than that acting on the plane parallel to the loading direction. The shear stress based on the classical theory of elasticity falls between the two types of shear stresses.

(b) For the disc specimen (see Figs.5 and 6):
1. When the internal length ℓ is very small, stress distributions are similar to the well-known one obtained by the classical theory of elasticity. As the internal length increases, the magnitude of stresses on the diametral plane in the loading direction reduces, especially remarkably in tension.
2. As the internal length increases, the turning point of stress σ_θ from tension to compression is shifted toward the center, and σ_θ near the loading boundaries changes from compressive to tensile.
3. The stresses on the diametral plane perpendicular to the loading direction become more uniform with an increase of the ratio
4. The magnitude of both tensile and compressive stresses at the center of the specimen decreases rapidly as the ratio ℓ/a increases.

(c) For the ring specimen (see Figs.7 and 8):
1. As the internal length ℓ increases, stresses are strikingly reduced and become more uniform.
2. As the ratio of the inner radius to the outer increases, stresses may be approximated by those expected from the bending theory of curved bars. On the other hand, as the ratio decreases, stresses are expected to become more and more uniform over the whole region of the specimen except near the inner boundary, as expected from the results of the disc test.
3. Stresses at the inner edge on the diametral section in the loading direction are reduced with an increase of the internal length as is shown in Fig.8.

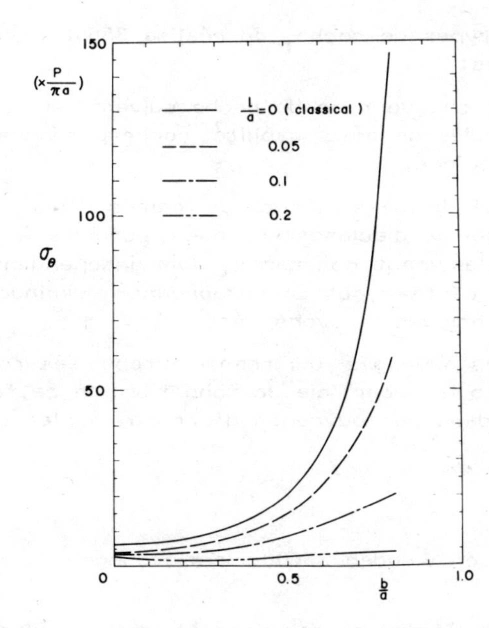

Fig.8 Variations of stresses with the ratio at the inner edge on the diametral plane in the loading direction.

From the results obtained herein, it may safely be said that the stress concentrations in small specimens are less than those in large specimens if both specimens are made of the same materials. This may be one reason for that small specimens show higher strength than large specimens, besides the statistical distributions of flaws in specimens.

It may be interpreted from these results that the wide scatter of brittleness index, that is, the ratio of compressive strength to tensile strength, for similar materials is caused by the intrinsic internal length of materials, since tensile strength is strikingly affected by the internal length while compressive strength is not.

Taking the effects of the intrinsic internal length of materials into account, it may also be explained such paradoxical variation of tensile strength between the disc test and the ring test that tensile strength increases with a decrease of hole size while the strength of the disc test remains constant (Hudson, 1969).

CONCLUDING REMARKS

Judging from the results obtained herein, it is suggested that the test results should be adequately interpreted based on the appropriate model as close to real materials as possible. The closer the model is to real materials, the more realistic behaviors may be estimated.

ACKNOWLEDGMENTS — The authors wish to express their gratitude to Mr. Moritake and Mr. Fukui for the computational work.

* * * * * * *

REFERENCES

Cowin, S.C., An Incorrect Inequality in Micropolar Elasticity Theory, ZAMP, Vol. 21, pp.494-497, 1970.

Eringen, A.C., Theory of Micropolar Elasticity, Chapt. 7 in "FRACTURE, VOL. 2", H. Liebowitz (ed.), pp.621-729, Academic Press, 1968.

Hudson, J.A., Tensile Strength and the Ring Test, Int. J. Rock Mech. Min. Sci., Vol. 5, pp.91-97, 1969.

Kobayashi, S. and T. Fukui, Effects of Couple-Stresses on Stress Distributions in a Ring Test Specimen, Memo. Faculty Eng., Kyoto Univ., Vol. 33, pp.233-242, 1971.

Mindlin, R.D., Influence of couple-stresses on stress concentrations, Exp. Mech., Vol. 3, pp.1-7, 1963.

Mindlin, R.D. and H.F. Tiersten, Effects of Couple-Stresses in Linear Elasticity, Archiv Rat. Mech. Anal., Vol. 4, pp.415-448, 1962.

Niwa, Y.,S. Kobayashi and T. Fukui, Effects of Couple-Stresses on Stress Distributions in a Disc Specimen Subjected to Diametral Compression, Memo. Faculty Eng., Kyoto Univ., Vol. 33, pp.118-127, 1971.

Niwa, Y., S. Kobayashi and S. Moritake, Influence of Couple-Stresses on Stress Distributions in Rectangular Specimen Compressed Between Rough Platens, Memo. Faculty Eng., Kyoto Univ., Vol. 33, pp.35-50, 1971.

INFLUENCE OF THE SCALE EFFECT OVER ROCK MASS SAFETY AGAINST DEFORMABILITY

L'INFLUENCE DE L'EFFET D'ÉCHELLE SUR LA SÉCURITÉ À LA DÉFORMABILITÉ DES MASSIFS ROCHEUX

DER EINFLUSS DER SKALENWIRKUNG AUF DIE VERFORMUNGSSICHERHEIT DER GEBIRGE

F. PERES-RODRIGUES

Research Officer, Division Head, LNEC

Lisboa, Portugal

SYNOPSIS

In simple compression tests on three types of rock 35600 determinations were carried out which have made it possible to develop the following conclusions:

- The values of unit strains measured on each type of rock follow a normal distribution and thus the mean value of the corresponding moduli of deformability is the harmonic mean of the unit strain values.

- The mean values of the moduli of deformability of rock masses are independent of the test area and of the gauge length, these rock masses being supposed to be homogeneous and divided by a system of joints supposed to be normal to the direction along which the force is applied, and the intensity of jointing being constant. Corresponding standard deviations decrease as the gauge length augments, asymptotically tending to zero.

- Safety against deformation increases with the foundation area, for structures that convey identical stresses to the same rock mass. Thus it will be possible to make savings in those works within the present safety criteria.

RÉSUMÉ

Au cours d'essais de compression simple sur trois types de roche, on réalisa 35600 déterminations qui ont permis de tirer les conclusions suivantes:

- Les valeurs des dilatations linéaires mesurées sur chaque type de roche suivent une distribution normale; de ce fait, la valeur moyenne des modules de déformabilité correspondants est la moyenne harmonique des valeurs des dilatations linéaires.

- Les valeurs moyennes des modules de déformabilité de massifs rocheux formés d'une certaine roche, supposée homogène, et divisée par une famille de diaclases supposée normale à la direction d'application de la force, et d'intensité de diaclasement constante, sont indépendants de la superficie d'essai et de la base de mesure, et les écarts-types correspondants diminuent tandis que la base de mesure augmente, tendant assymptotiquement vers zéro.

- La sécurité par égard à la déformabilité, pour des ouvrages qui transmettent des contraintes égales à un même massif rocheux, augmente avec la superficie de fondation; de ce fait on peut envisager l'hypothèse de réaliser des économies dans ces ouvrages d'accord avec les critères de sécurité actuels.

ZUSAMMENFASSUNG

Mittels einfacher Druckversuche an drei Gesteinstypen wurden 35600 Bestimmungen durchgeführt, die es erlauben folgende Schlüsse zu ziehen:

- Die gemessenen Verformungswerte folgen bei allen Gesteinstypen einer Normalverteilung, sodass also der Mittelwert der entsprechenden Verformungsmoduli das harmonische Mittel jener Werte ist.

- Die Mittelwerte der Verformungsmoduli von Gebirgen, die aus einem bestimmten, als ho mogen angenommenen Gestein bestehen, und durch eine senkrecht zur Kraftanwendungsrichtung und mit konstanter Kluftdichte angenommenen Kluftschar aufgeteilt werden, sind von der Versuchsfläche und der Messungsbasis unabhängig, und die entsprechenden Standardabweichungen nehmen mit wachsender Messungsbasis ab, indem sie asymptotisch auf Null zugehen.

- Die Sicherheit in Bezug auf die Verformbarkeit für Bauten, die einem gleichen Gebirge gleiche Spannungen übertragen, wächst mit der Gründungsfläche, sodass es also möglich sein wird, die Hypothese zu betrachten, bei diesen Bauten innerhalb der bestehenden Sicherheitskriterien Ersparnisse zu erreichen.

Rock mechanics has tried to characterize rock masses by means of field and/or laboratory tests. The former usually involve considerable forces and are too expensive to be carried out in such a number that their results can be representative. As to the latter, although they do not present the same disadvantages than the former ones, they cannot be considered to represent the rock mass owing to the small dimensions of the specimens tested. Therefore a law is required which will take into account the scale effect, both purely geometrical and due to the physical characteristics of the surfaces of the rock mass divided by joints.

The analysis as a whole of the results obtained in the laboratory as well as in the field is thought to be extremely convenient as it is a cheaper and easier way to characterize rock masses without impairing the accuracy of results.

Following these lines, this work is in attempt to determine the mean value and the dispersion of the modulus of deformability of a rock mass from knowledge of deformabilities of rock that forms it, of joints that divide it, as well as of the probability of their occurrence, taking into account the dimensions of the rock mass considered. Thus the problem dealt with here is a first step, still of a schematic nature, for characterizing the rock mass as concerns deformability on basis of both field determinations of jointing and laboratory determinations of deformability.

Different parameters were studied among with mention should be made to the surface of the loaded area, the volume of the specimen, gauge length, rock texture, taking into account the maximum size of the minerals forming the rock and the intensity of jointing. Three types of rock with quite different textures were tested. The joints were materialized by means of plane cuts obtained with a diamond disk, always the same, in order to maintain as much as possible the same roughness of surfaces cut.

The micropetrographic analysis of the three types of rock tested showed the following modal composition, in percentage:

- Fine-grained crystalline limestone:

calcite	≃ 100
quartz	few grains

- Medium-grained biotitic granitic gneiss:

quartz	38
sound feldspar	40
weathered feldspar	11
micas	6
other	5

- Coarse-grained alkaline granite:

quartz	29
feldspar	60
micas	10
other	1

A cube, 40 cm in edge, was cut from rock of each type. Thirty-two gauge lengths were glued on each of the four lateral faces; they were set 2 cm apart and in two parallel rows. By these means was it possible to evaluate deformations occurred in lengths from 2 cm to 30 cm, these following an arithmetic progression in which 2 cm is the common difference (photo 1). Such a cube is considered the 1st stage of the test.

From the initial cubs four prisms were cut. After they had been tested, they were transversely cut in order to obtain eight cubes, 20 cm in edge (3rd stage of the test).

By overall testing of specimens formed by the transverse cuts, deformability due to jointing could be studied, a given intensity of jointing being represented by the number of joints per meter.

By successive cuts, either vertical or horizontal, a 9-stage study could be performed on test specimens whose dimensions made it possible to test surfaces up to the ratio 1:256, volumes to 1:4096 and gauge lengths to 1:15.

The highest number of joints considered in a test was seven, which enabled us to study eight intensities of jointing ranging from zero to 23.33 joints per meter (photo 2).

Photo 1 Photo 2

In the 9th stage, 234 specimens had been formed from the initial cube.

All tests were carried out under simple compression, along the same direction in each specimen, and in such a way as to avoid possible variations due to anisotropy. Forces were applied by means of hydraulic presses with different sensitivities, depending on the specimen surfaces, so as to obtain maximum stresses of about 200 kgf/cm^2 (20 MPa).

The measurement of strains was carried out by means of Tensotast mechanical strain gauges with a precision of 0.001 mm and 2 cm gauge length. Measurement of strains corresponding to the 4 cm gauge length was carried out by adding two measurements relative to all possible groups of two consecutive 2 cm lengths, and so forth for the remaining lengths.

In the course of this study 35603 determinations were carried out, distributed as follows: 14022 for limestone, 8585 for gneiss and 12996 for granite, which were suitably grouped and processed by statistical methods. As a result, some conclusions thought relevant could be drawn.

Owing to the high number of determinations, it was possible to analyse whether unit strains or the moduli of deformability would fit a normal distribution. Histograms shown in Fig. 1 to 3, which concern a 2 cm gauge length without cuts show that tests of unit strains obtained in each one of the three types of rock tested, in determinations ranging from 1113 to 1926, fit a normal distribution curve, with a maximum variation coefficient of about 6%, and that the corresponding cumulative frequency curves present a variation coefficient of about 1% with reference to theoretical curves.

Table I shows the values of the mean $\bar{\varepsilon}$, median $\tilde{\varepsilon}$, mode $\hat{\varepsilon}$ and standard deviation $_s\bar{\varepsilon}$ of unit strains measured ε_i, as well as the values of the kurtosis $_b\bar{\varepsilon}$ and of Pearson's first coefficient of the skewness $_a\bar{\varepsilon}$, respectively given by the expressions:

$$_b\bar{\varepsilon} = \frac{\sum_{i=1}^{N} n_i(\varepsilon_i - \bar{\varepsilon})^4}{_s\bar{\varepsilon}.\sum_{i=1}^{N} n_i} - 3 \qquad _a\bar{\varepsilon} = \frac{\bar{\varepsilon} - \hat{\varepsilon}}{_s\bar{\varepsilon}}$$

where N is the number of intervals considered and n_i is the number of units ε_i in each interval. The kurtosis is the degree of peakedness of a distribution, taken relative to a normal distribution, its being said positive when the distribution is normal or mesokurtic, and negative when the distribution is flat-topped or platykurtic.

Pearson's first coefficient of skewness gives the degree of departure from symmetry taken relative to a symmetrical distribution; it said to have positive skewness if the distribution is skewed to the right and to have negative skewness if the distribution is sekewed to the left.

Table I also presents, relative to frequencies and cumulative frequencies, standard errors of estimates, $_pf^d$ and $_pf^a$, coefficients of correlation, $_rf^d$ and $_rf^a$, chi-squares, $\chi 2f^d$ and $\chi 2f^a$, respectively given by the general formulas:

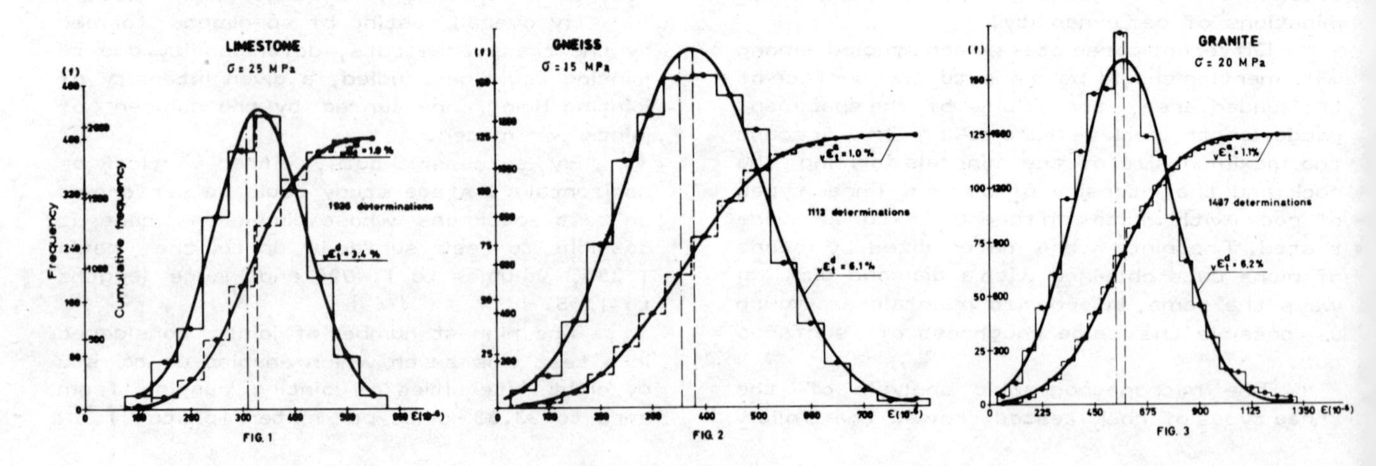

FIG. 1 FIG. 2 FIG. 3

$$ {}_{p}f = \sqrt{\sum_{i=1}^{N} (f_i - f_t)^2 / (N-1)} $$

$$ {}_{r}f = \sqrt{1 - \left(\frac{{}_{p}f}{{}_{s}f}\right)} \qquad \chi^{2f} = \sum_{i=1}^{N} \frac{(f_i - f_t)^2}{f_t} $$

where

f_i - frequency observed in the interval of order i

f_t - theoretical frequency corresponding to f_i

Values indicated in Table I, mostly the coefficients of correlation and the chi-squares, which correspond to high significance levels, plainly slow closeness of fit to normal distribution curves.

TABLE I

CHARACTERISTICS	UNIT STRAINS (10^{-6})			MOD. OF DEF. (10^2 M Pa)		
	LIMEST.	GNEISS	GRANITE	LIMEST.	GNEISS	GRANITE
MEAN	330	380	585	816	459	461
MEDIAN	310	360	555	822	427	419
MODE	350	400	570	563	313	313
ST. DEVIATION	85	135	185	226	213	215
KURTOSIS	0.03	-0.32	0.74	-2.57	-2.95	-1.31
PEARSON'S 1st COEF.	-0.23	-0.15	0.08	0.95	0.69	0.69
${}_{p}f^d$	10.1	7.08	7.06	182	123	121
${}_{p}f^a$	11.2	6.30	12.7	290	160	160
${}_{r}f^d$	0.998	0.992	0.992	0.505	0.600	0.706
${}_{r}f^a$	0.999	0.999	0.999	0.737	0.867	0.910
$\chi^2 f^d$	3.47	8.81	18.2	2845	$\simeq\infty$	$\simeq\infty$
LEVEL OF SIGNIF.	0.75	0.75	0.50	0.00	0.00	0.00
$\chi^2 f^a$	2.93	4.45	13.5	1047	921	616
LEVEL OF SIGNIF.	0.75	0.98	0.75	0.00	0.00	0.00

Fig. 4 to 6 present the histograms and most probable normal and cumulative curves for the values of the moduli of deformability corresponding to the unit strains referred to above. A complete lack of fitting is found, which is shown by high coefficients of variation.

The fact that these distributions are not normal is also plainly shown by the marked difference between the values of the arithmetical mean, median and mode, and by the high values of the kurtosis, Pearson's first coefficient of skewness, and chi-squares, as well as by the low coefficients of correlation and null levels of significance shown in Table I.

Thus the following conclusion may be drawn: as the sets of unit strains measured on a given rock are normal distributions, the inverses of the moduli of deformability will be normal distributions too, reason why their mean value $\bar{E}$ will necessarily be given by the weighted harmonic mean of the values calculated E_i, that is:

$$ \bar{E} = \sum_{i=1}^{N} n_i \Big/ \sum_{i=1}^{N} \frac{n_i}{E_i} $$

where N and n_i respectively stand for the number of intervals considered and the number of unit strains in each interval as stated hereinbefore.

As is known, if the values of E_i are not significantly different which often happens in practice, the arithmetical and harmonic means will be very alike and thus it will not matter whether to calculate the mean value $\bar{E}$ by one or other mean. The same will not occur if the values of E_i present a marked dispersion, as in the three following examples:

Rock	Means (10^2MPa)		Differences	
	arithmet. (wrong)	harmonic (right)	absolute	relative
Limestone	816	762	+ 54	7%
Gneiss	459	397	+ 62	16%
Granite	461	342	+129	38%

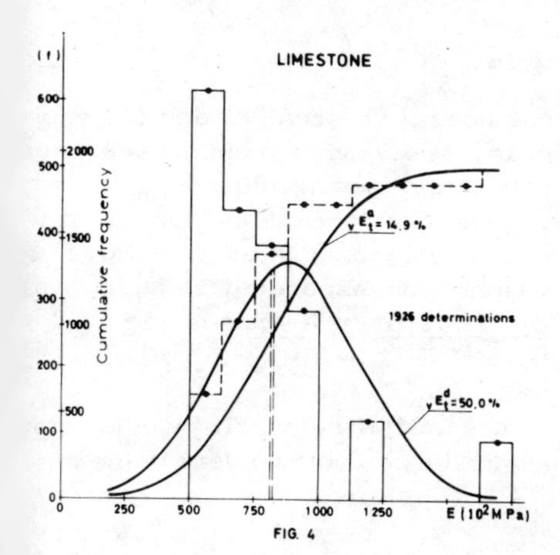

FIG. 4

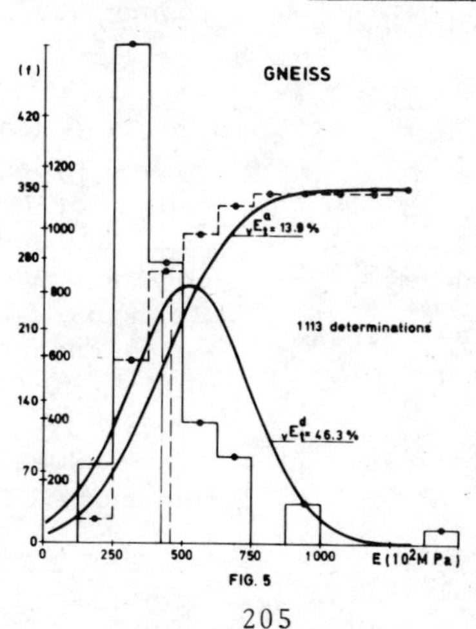

FIG. 5

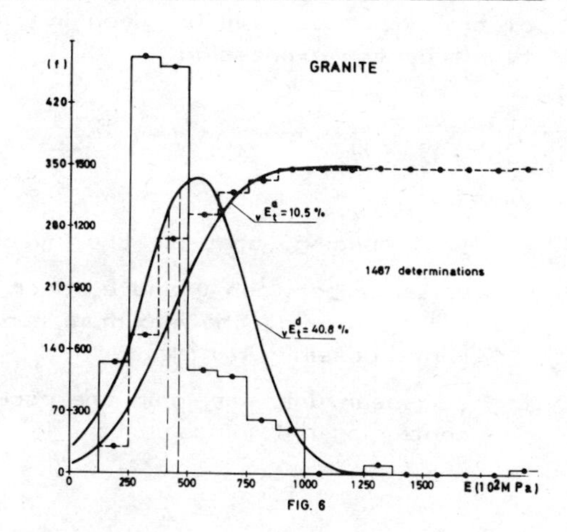

FIG. 6

In these cases the arithmetical means systematically attain higher values since their distributions (Fig. 4 to 6) necessarily always have positive skewness. The values of relative differences are in agreement with the maximum grain sizes of rock tested with reference to the gauge length of 2 cm.

In Fig. 7 to 9, mean unit strains are plotted against the gauge length for a constant number of cuts which represent joints respectively for limestone, gneiss and granite. As was proved, for each gauge length, these unit strains have normal distributions with mean values $\bar{\varepsilon}_i$ and standard deviations $_s\bar{\varepsilon}_i$.

$\bar{\varepsilon}_n$ - mean unit strain in the rock mass containing n joints in b.

In the above expression, $\frac{r}{e}$ and $\frac{e-r}{e}$ are respectively equal to the probabilities p_{n-1} and p_n of ocurrence of n-1 and n joints in the gauge length b of the rock mass considered. On the other hand,

$$_b\bar{\varepsilon}_{n-1} = {_b\bar{\varepsilon}_r} + (n-1)\,\Delta\,\sigma \qquad \text{(b)}$$

$$_b\bar{\varepsilon}_n = {_b\bar{\varepsilon}_r} + n\,\Delta\,\sigma$$

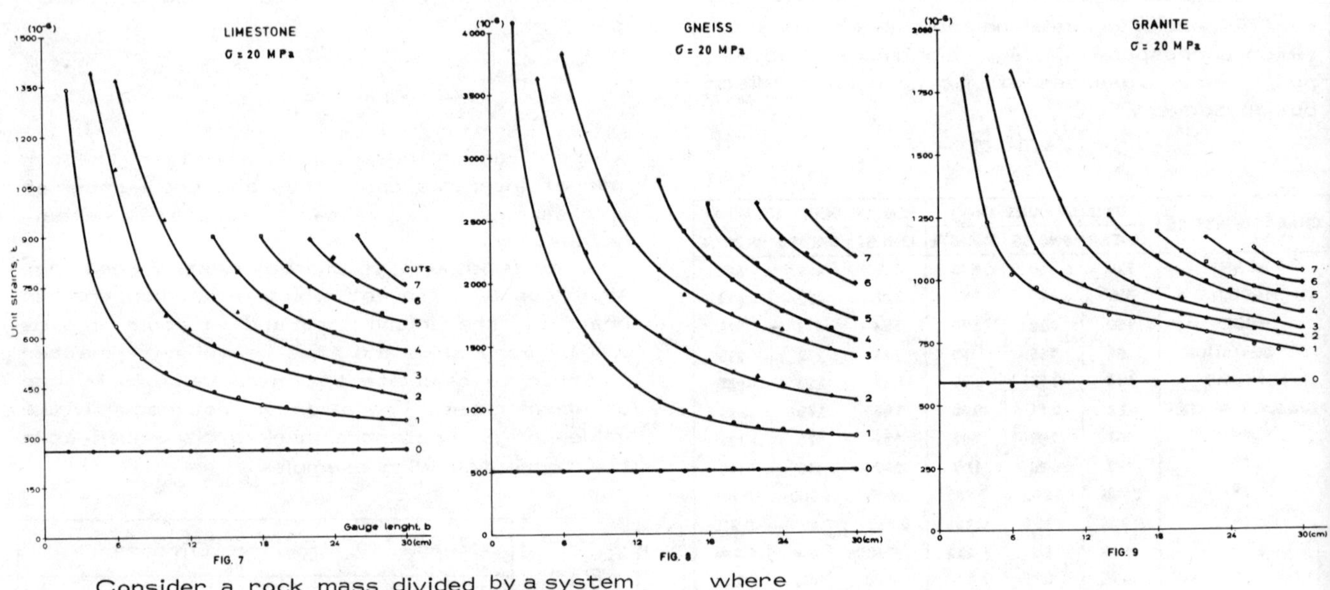

FIG. 7 FIG. 8 FIG. 9

Consider a rock mass divided by a system of joints in which the intensity of jointing is I, formed by a rock assumed to be homogeneous along a direction normal to the system and having a modulus of deformability $\bar{E}_r$. If a given gauge length b is concerned by tests carried out along that direction and if the specific strain of joints assumed to be homogeneous is denoted by Δ (that is, the strain undergone by stress unit), the most probable unit strain $\bar{\varepsilon}_{mr}$ of the rock mass will be given in probabilistic terms by the expression:

$$\bar{\varepsilon}_{mr} = \frac{r}{e}\,\bar{\varepsilon}_{n-1} + \frac{e-r}{e}\,\bar{\varepsilon}_n = p_{n-1}\,\bar{\varepsilon}_{n-1} + p_n\,\bar{\varepsilon}_n \qquad \text{(a)}$$

where

e - joint spacing, that is, the inverse of I;

r - distance between 0 and e, such as n.e = b + r, n being the maximum number of joints possible in b;

$\bar{\varepsilon}_{n-1}$ - mean unit strain in the rock mass containing n-1 joints in b;

where

$\bar{\varepsilon}_r$ - mean unit strain of the rock forming the mass

σ - normal stress applied to the mass

Consideration of (b) in (a) allows to write:

$$\bar{\varepsilon}_{mr} = \bar{\varepsilon}_r + \Delta\,\sigma\,I \qquad \text{(c)}$$

or, writing in terms of mean modulus of deformability:

$$\bar{E}_{mr} = \bar{E}_r/(1 + \Delta\,\bar{E}_r\,I) \qquad \text{(d)}$$

The expressions (c) straight and (d) equilateral hyperbolas, show what tests have proved, that is, that the mean values $\bar{\varepsilon}_{mr}$ and $\bar{E}_{mr}$ are independent of the gauge length b, only depending on the intensity of jointing I. Standard deviations corresponding to $\bar{\varepsilon}_{mr}$ were calculated on basis of the expression

$$_s\bar{\varepsilon}_{mr} = \sqrt{P_{n-1}\;{_s\bar{\varepsilon}^2_{n-1}} + P_n\,.\;{_s\bar{\varepsilon}^2_n}}$$

since values of the unit strains fit normal distributions. Thus it is possible to determine the range within which the probability of occurrence of unit strain values is 68%, or any other range.

Unit strains which are limits of the 68% probability of occurrence are

$$\varepsilon^{\pm} = \bar{\varepsilon}_I \pm {}_s\bar{\varepsilon}_I \qquad (e)$$

These two curves ε^+ and ε^- are symmetrical relative to the mean value $\bar{\varepsilon}_I$ in a unit strain gauge length representation, and results obtained have made it possible to conclude, by statistical methods, that their variation is well represented by an exponential law of the type

$$\varepsilon^{\pm} = \varepsilon_I \left[1 \pm e^{-k_1 b^2 - k_2 b - k_3} \right] \qquad (f)$$

where k_1, k_2 and k_3 are three parameters depending on the rock mass.

The analysis of expression (f) shows that the values of ε^+ and ε^- asymptotically tend to the mean value $\bar{\varepsilon}_I$ when the gauge length augments indefinitely.

By writing expressions (e) in terms of moduli of deformability one gets for their limit values:

$$E^{\pm} = \frac{\sigma}{\bar{\varepsilon}_I \mp {}_s\bar{\varepsilon}_I} \qquad (g)$$

and expressions (f) become:

$$E^{\pm} = \bar{E}_I \left[\frac{1}{1 \mp e^{-k_1 b^2 - k_2 b - k_3}} \right] \qquad (h)$$

Curves E^+ and E^- are not symmetrical relative to their mean value $\bar{E}$ but they will admit it as an asymptotical value.

Now that a rough picture of the work carried out has been given, some figures will be shown which synthetize the results obtained. Thus in Fig. 10, 11 and 12, respectively for limestone, gneiss and granite, the moduli of deformability E^+ and E^- are presented which limit the range with 68% probability of occurrence with reference to the gauge length b and for eight intensities of jointing, ranging from 0 to 23.33 m^{-1}. Values obtained from the experimental unit strains are indicated which closely fit the exponential law (h) considered as the defining law. In the tables of these figures, the notations used as well as the values of the modulus of deformability $\bar{E}_I$ and of the exponential equation parameters (h), k_1, k_2 and k_3 are indicated for each intensity of jointing.

An important conclusion developed is that the mean values of the unit strains and thus also of the moduli of deformability are independent of the gauge length and of the test area; they only depend on the intensity of jointing. What depends on the gauge length are the standard deviations of these characteristics which decrease as it augments, according to the example given in Fig. 13 for limestone in which the intensity for jointing equals 10.00 m^{-1}.

The comparative analysis of Fig. 10, 11 and 12 fairly well shows that ranges corresponding to equal probability of occurrence become narrower and tend asymptotically to the mean value as the gauge length increases, i.e. the probability of occurrence of a modulus of deformability value below the mean value decreases as the gauge length increases, reason why the safety coefficient as regards deformability of structures conveying equal stresses to the same rock mass increases with the foundation area.

Fig. 14 represents the mean values of the experimental unit strains and moduli of deformability with reference to the intensity of joint

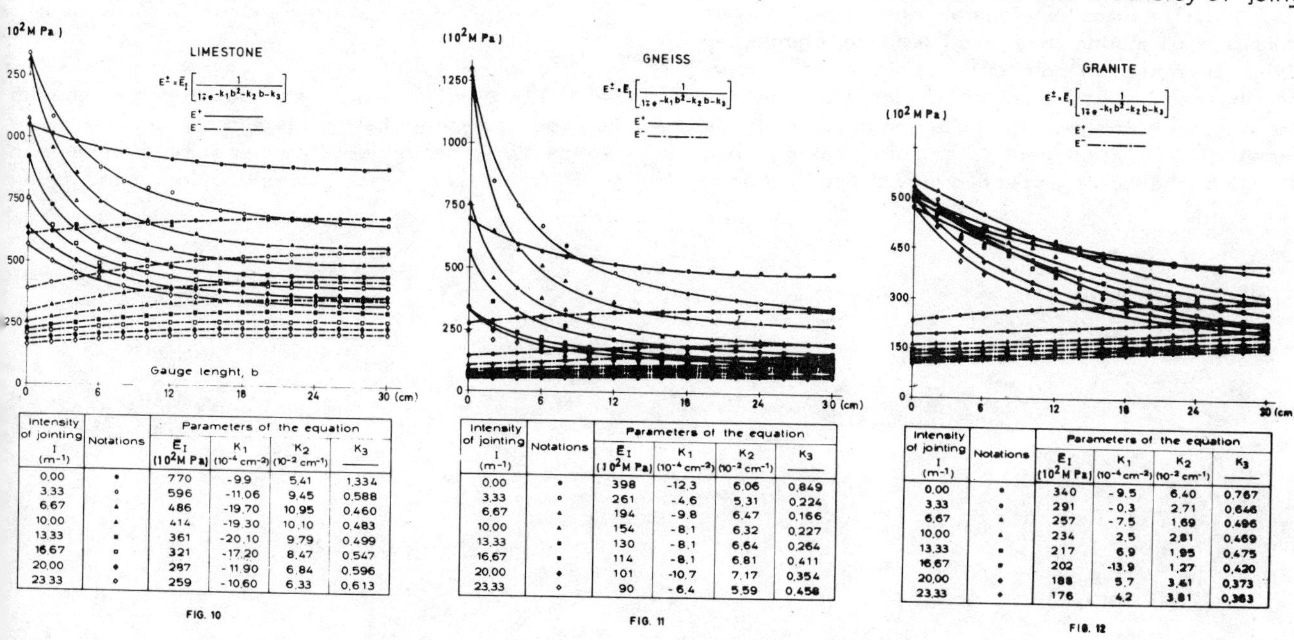

Intensity of jointing I (m^{-1})	Notations	Parameters of the equation			
		E_I (10^2 M Pa)	K_1 (10^{-4} cm^{-2})	K_2 (10^{-2} cm^{-1})	K_3
0.00	•	770	-9.9	5.41	1.334
3.33	∘	596	-11.06	9.45	0.588
6.67	▴	486	-19.70	10.95	0.460
10.00	▴	414	-19.30	10.10	0.483
13.33	■	361	-20.10	9.79	0.499
16.67	▫	321	-17.20	8.47	0.547
20.00	◆	287	-11.90	6.84	0.596
23.33	◇	259	-10.60	6.33	0.613

FIG. 10

Intensity of jointing I (m^{-1})	Notations	Parameters of the equation			
		E_I (10^2 M Pa)	K_1 (10^{-4} cm^{-2})	K_2 (10^{-2} cm^{-1})	K_3
0.00	•	398	-12.3	6.06	0.849
3.33	∘	261	-4.6	5.31	0.224
6.67	▴	194	-9.8	6.47	0.166
10.00	▴	154	-8.1	6.32	0.227
13.33	■	130	-8.1	6.64	0.264
16.67	■	114	-8.1	6.81	0.411
20.00	◆	101	-10.7	7.17	0.354
23.33	◇	90	-6.4	5.59	0.458

FIG. 11

Intensity of jointing I (m^{-1})	Notations	Parameters of the equation			
		E_I (10^2 M Pa)	K_1 (10^{-4} cm^{-2})	K_2 (10^{-2} cm^{-1})	K_3
0.00	•	340	-9.5	6.40	0.767
3.33	•	291	-0.3	2.71	0.646
6.67	▴	257	-7.5	1.69	0.496
10.00	▴	234	2.5	2.81	0.469
13.33	■	217	6.9	1.95	0.475
16.67	■	202	-13.9	1.27	0.420
20.00	◆	188	5.7	3.41	0.373
23.33	•	176	4.2	3.81	0.363

FIG. 12

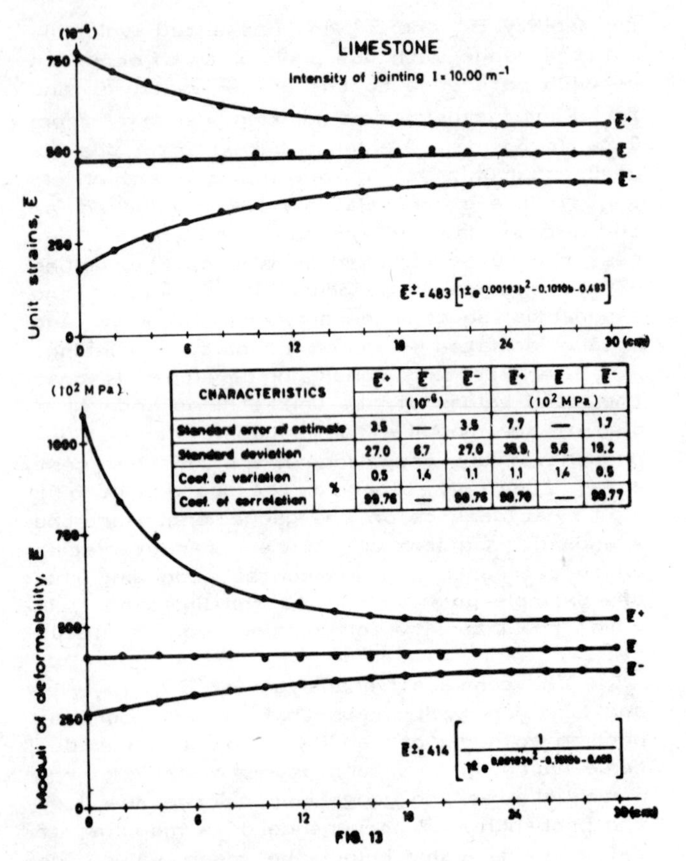

CHARACTERISTICS		$\bar{\varepsilon}^{+}$	$\bar{\varepsilon}$	$\bar{\varepsilon}^{-}$	$\bar{E}^{+}$	$\bar{E}$	$\bar{E}^{-}$
		(10⁻⁶)			(10² MPa)		
Standard error of estimate		3.5	—	3.5	7.7	—	1.7
Standard deviation		27.0	6.7	27.0	38.9	5.6	19.2
Coef. of variation	%	0.5	1.4	1.1	1.1	1.4	0.5
Coef. of correlation	%	99.76	—	99.76	99.70	—	99.77

FIG. 13

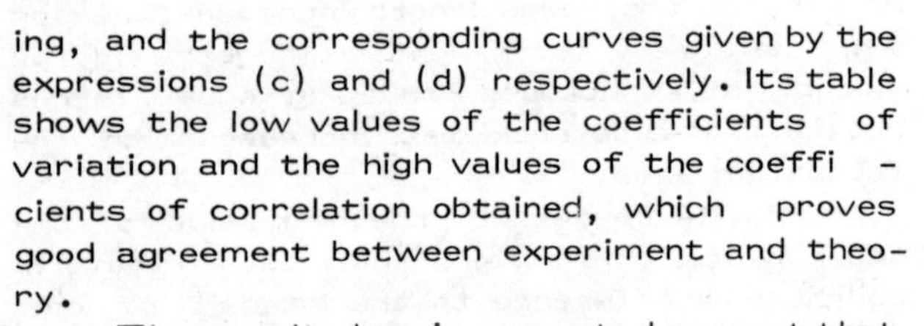

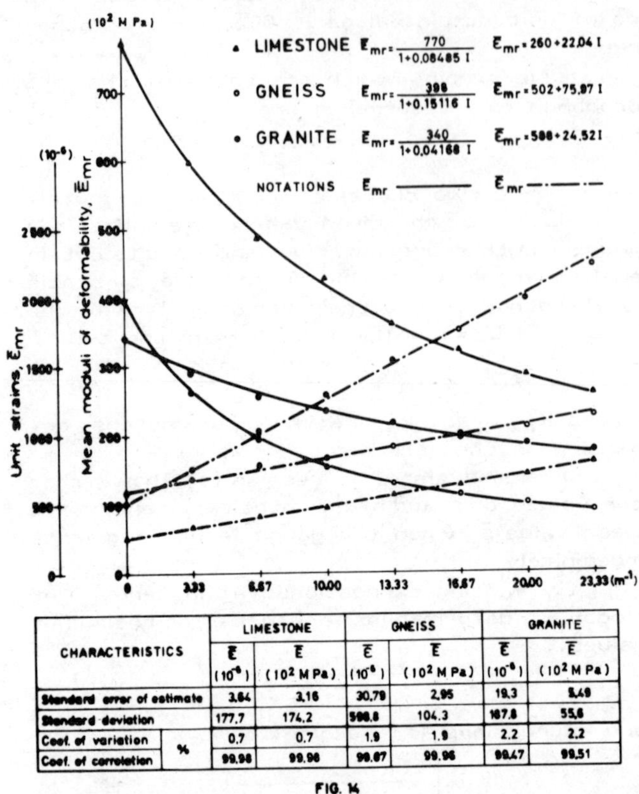

CHARACTERISTICS		LIMESTONE		GNEISS		GRANITE	
		$\bar{\varepsilon}$ (10⁻⁶)	$\bar{E}$ (10² MPa)	$\bar{\varepsilon}$ (10⁻⁶)	$\bar{E}$ (10² MPa)	$\bar{\varepsilon}$ (10⁻⁶)	$\bar{E}$ (10² MPa)
Standard error of estimate		3,64	3,16	30,79	2,95	19,3	5,49
Standard deviation		177,7	174,2	598,8	104,3	187,8	55,6
Coef. of variation	%	0,7	0,7	1,9	1,9	2,2	2,2
Coef. of correlation	%	99,98	99,98	99,67	99,96	99,47	99,51

FIG. 14

ing, and the corresponding curves given by the expressions (c) and (d) respectively. Its table shows the low values of the coefficients of variation and the high values of the coefficients of correlation obtained, which proves good agreement between experiment and theory.

The results herein presented suggest that this line of study may soon lead to characterize rock masses from other points of view, as those of rupture and of shear, through the comparative analysis of a larger number of laboratory and field tests, and by taking into account the scale effect over these characteristics.

The economy of tests and mainly the economy of large structures is one of the purposes in view which has to be attained without impairing their safety. This, however, only can be achieved by gaining a better statistical knowledge of the characteristics that govern rock mass behaviour.

The author wishes to express his thanks to the experimental assistant Manuel Reis e Sousa for the valuable cooperation in the performing of the tests, computations and drawings.

INFLUENCE OF THE SYSTEM OF STATIC LOAD ON DEFORMABILITY OF ROCKS IN FIELD TESTS

L'INFLUENCE DU SYSTÈME DE CHARGEMENT STATIQUE SUR LA DÉFORMABILITÉ DES ROCHES DANS LES ESSAIS "IN SITU"

EINFLUSS VON DAUERBELASTUNGSSYSTEMEN VON FELSEN AUF DEREN VERFORMBARKEIT IN FELDVERSUCHEN

Kazimierz THIEL
Professor
Polish Academy of Sciences
Hydroengineering Institute
Gdańsk, Poland

SUMMARY. The test covered 12 types of rock occurring in the foundations of four designed dams. The loads were applied to two surfaces: 1.96 m^2 and 0.49 m^2.

The test methodics was uniform but two load systems were used /marked as System A and System B/. In System A the load sequence included several short-lived cycles of loading and unloading, one cycles continued until the state of relative stability of deformations, one cycle with a single load-step continued for several hours /or several days/, and again, several short-lived cycles of loading and unloading. System B included several short-lived cycles of loading and unloading in successively growing load intervals.

A comparison of values of the modulus of deformation and of the modulus of elasticity determined by means of the two load systems revealed a high degree of similarity between them /differences ranging between ±10%/. There is a condition, however, that a sufficient number of the cycles of loading and unloading is performed within every load interval in System B. Since the total duration of tests in System B is about twice shorter than that of System A, the former has been approved and recommended for general use in such kinds of field tests.

The paper provides a method of selecting reliable values of the moduli in a given series of tests as well as the determined values of the moduli for the twelve types of the tested rocks.

RESUMÉ. Les essais ont été effectué sur douze roches constituant la fondation de quatre barrages projetés. La surface de chargement des roches était de 1,96 m^2; en plus de 0,49 m^2.

La méthode d'essais était uniforme mais on a utilisé deux systèmes de chargement /A et B/. Le système A comprenait quelques cycles de chargement de courte durée, un cycle en maintenant chaque palier de charge jusqu'à une stabilisation relative des déformations, un cycle en maintenant une charge pendant quelques heures ou quelques jours, et de nouveau quelques cycles de chargement de courte durée. Le système B comprenait quelques cycles de chargement de courte durée dans des intervalles de charges progressivement croissants.

La comparaison des valeurs de modules, de déformation et d'élasticité, obtenues dans les deux systèmes de chargement, a demontré qu'elles sont pratiquement identiques /la différence était de ±10%, à condition que dans le système B soit effectué un nombre suffisant de cycles dans chaque intervalle de charges. Etant donné que la durée d'essais dans ce système est deux fois plus courte que dans le système A, il a été admis à une application générale dans tous les essais effectués "in situ".

On a présenté la façon dont on fait le choix des valeurs de modules décisifs dans chaque essai ainsi que ces valeurs pour les douze roches étudiées.

ZUSAMMENFASSUNG. Die Untersuchungen wurden bezüglich zwölf, im Untergrund von vier projektierten Talsperren liegenden Felsen, durchgeführt. Die Belastungsfläche des Felsen betrug 1.96 m^2; zusätzlich 0,49 m^2.

Die Methodik der Untersuchungen war einheitlich, wobei zwei Belastungssysteme /A und B/ in Anwendung kamen. Das system A beruhte auf der Ausführung einiger Zyklen kurz dauernder Belastungen und Entlastungen, eines Zykluses bis zur relativen Stabilisierung der Verformungen, eines Zykluses bei mehrstündiger /oder mehrtägiger/ Beibehaltung eines Belastungsgrades und erneut einiger Zyklen kurz dauernder Belastungen und Entlastungen. Das System B dagegen beruhte auf Ausführung einiger kurz dauernder Zyklen von Belastungen und Entlastungen in sukzessiv wachsenden Belastungsklassen.

Die Vergleichung der in beiden Systemen erreichten Modulwerte der Belastungen und Entlastungen ergab, dass diese sich in beiden Fällen nahestehen /Unterschied ±10%/ unter der Bedingung jedoch, dass im System B eine genügende Anzahl Zyklen von Belastungen und Entlastungen im Bereich jeder Belastungsklasse ausgeführt wird. Da die Untersuchungszeit in diesen System etwa zweimal kurzer ist als im System A, wurde er zum allgemeinen Gebrauch in derartigen Felduntersuchungen empfohlen.

Die Auswahlmethode massgebender Modulwerte für eine gegebene Untersuchung wurde angegeben, und die Modulwerte für 12 untersuchte Felsen wurden festgesetzt.

INTRODUCTION

An accurate determination of values of the deformation and elasticity moduli for the rock mass is confronted with the following difficulties, to mention only the most characteristic ones:

- area of the load surfaces used in the tests is small in comparison with the actual area of the dam foundation,
- blasting of the rock in the drifts leads to a formation of a surrounding zone of strongly disturbed rocks,
- duration of loads applied in the course of tests is short in comparison with the duration of loads during the performing of the dam and throughout its operating period,
- the limited number of test /time and cost factors/ accounts for a „spot" character of the results.

In order to diminish effects of the factors given above the test are conducted of relatively large load surfaces, special blasting specifications are used to decrease the size of the strongly disturbed rock zone, and seismic tests are carried on to permit a generalization of the „spot" results of the static load tests by means of correlating the values of the static and the seismic moduli. The generalized data are then considered representative of the larger areas of the dam's foundation.

The effect of time factor may be taken into account by extending the duration of the load period, yet it makes the test procedures more complicated and burdensome, while the periods of the load applying remain too short in relation to the period of perfoming and the operation time of the dam.

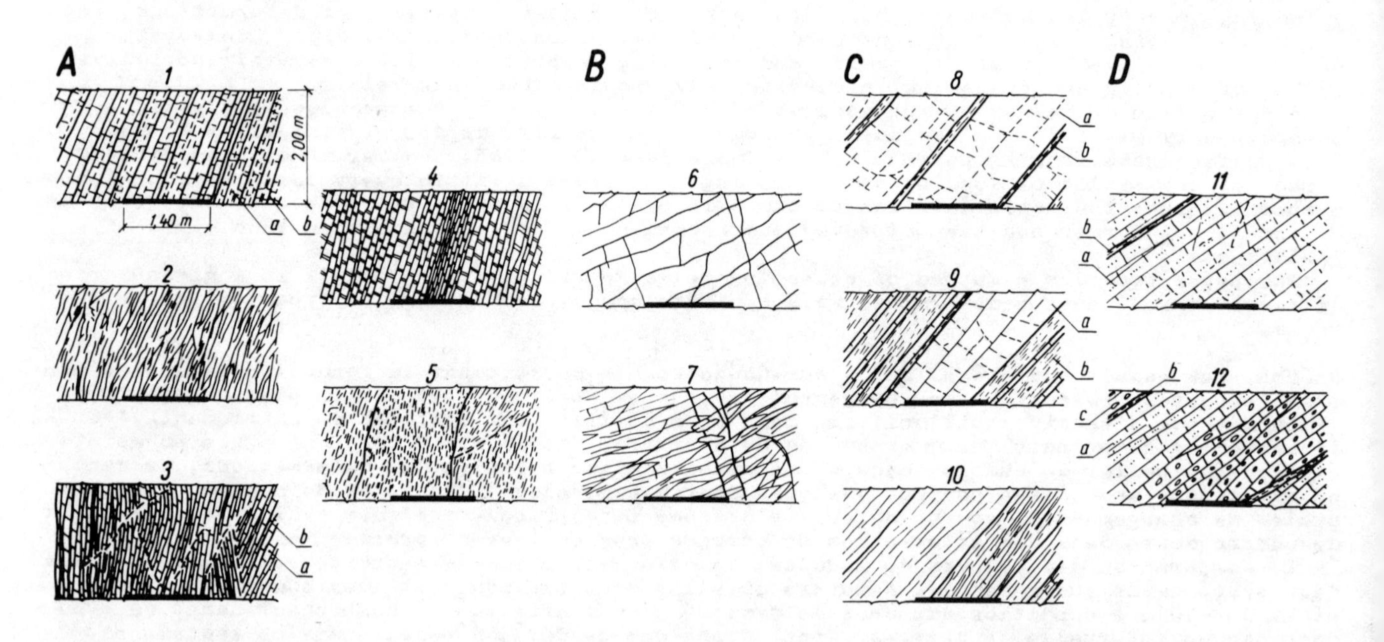

Fig.1. Geological profiles of the tested rocks. A- Dam I: 1-limestones, a-limestones, b-clay shales, 2-marly limestones, a-marly limestones, b-clay shales, 3-marls, a-marls, b-clay shales, 4-hornstones, a-hornstones, b-clay shales, 5-clay shales, B- Dam II: 6-micaceous shales, 7-micaceous shales with muscovitae supremacy. C- Dam III: 8-sandstones, a-sandstones, b-shales, 10-shales. D- Dam IV: 11-sandstones, a-sandstones, b-shales, 12-conglomerates and sandstones, a-sandstones, b-shales, c-conglomerates.

Profiles géologiques des roches. A-Barrage 1: 1-calcaire, a-calcaire, b-schiste argileux; b-calcaire marneux, a-calcaire marneux, b-schiste argileux; 3-marne, a-marne, b-schiste argileux; 4-cherts, a-cherts, b-schiste argileux; 5-schiste argileux. B- Barrage III: 6-schistes miceuses, 7-schistes miçeuses avec preponderance de muscovites. C-Barrage III: 8-grés, a-grés, b-schiste; 9-grés-schiste, a-grés, b-schiste. D- Barrage IV: 11-grés, a-grés, b-schiste; 12-conglomerats et grés, b-schiste, c-conglomérat.

Geologische Profile der untersuchten Felsen. A-Talsperre I: 1-Kalk, a-Kalk, b-Schieferton; 2-Mergelkalk, a-Mergelkalk, b-Schieferton; 3-Mergel, a-Mergel, b-Schieferton; 4-Hornsteine, a-Hornsteine, b-Schieferton; 5-Schieferton. B-Talsperre II: 6-Glimmerschiefer; 7-Glimmershciefer mit überwiegenden Muskovit. C-Talsperre III: 8-Sandsteine, a-Sandsteine, b-Schiefer; 9-Sandsteine-Schiefer, a-Sandsteine, b-Schiefer; 10-Schiefer, D-Talsperre II: 11-Sandsteine, a-Sandsteine, b-Schiefer; 12-Konglomerate und Sandsteine, a-Sandsteine, b-Schiefer, c-Konglomerate.

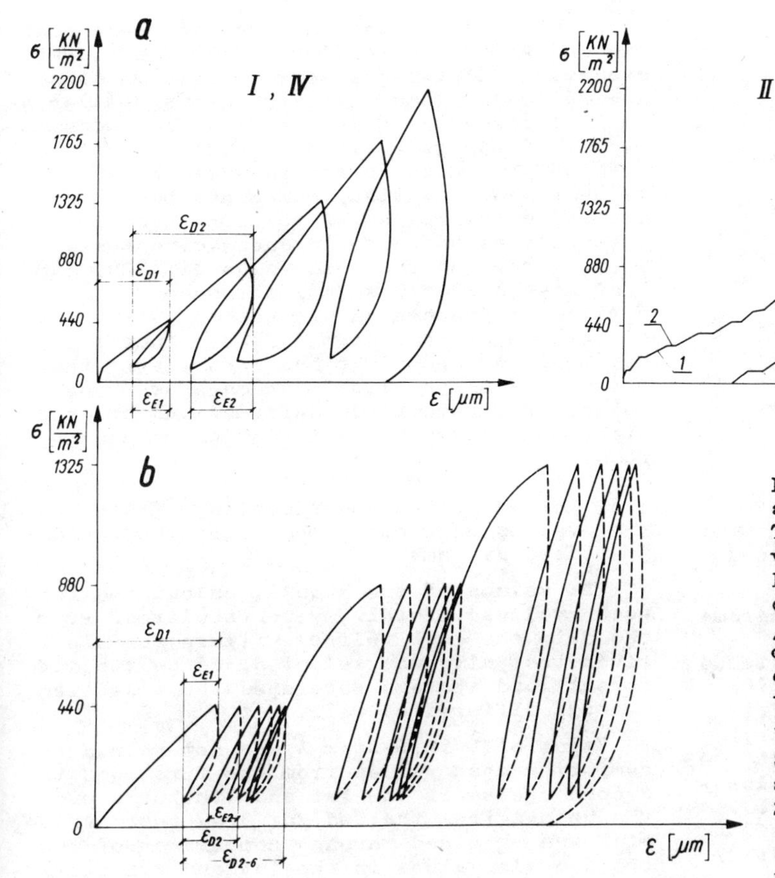

Fig.2. Diagrams of the used load systems a-System A: I and IV - Test 1 and 4, II - Test 2, III - Test 3; b-System B: ε_{D1}, ε_{D2}- values of deformations for calculating D_1, D_2; ε_{E1}, ε_{E2} -values of deformations for calculating E_1, E_2; 1-the „immediate" /180 s/ deformations, 2-deformations during the state of relative stability of deformations, 3-deformations during the several-hour or the several-day loading.

Schémas de chargement des roches a-Système A: 1 et IV - 1 et 4 essai, II - 2 essai, III - 3 essai. b-Système B: ε_{D1}, ε_{D2} - déformations pour calculer E_1, E_2. ε_{E1}, ε_{E2}-déformations pour calculer E_1, E_2, 1-déformations „instantannées /en 180 s/, 2-déformations au cour de stabilisation relative, 3-déformations au cour d'un chargement de quelques heures ou quelques jours.

Angewandte Belastungsschemas der Felsen. a-Belastungsschema A; I und IV - 1 und 4 Untersuchung, II - 2 Untersuchung, III - 3 Untersuchung. b-Belastungsschema B; ε_{D1}, ε_{D2} - Deformationsgrössen zur Errechnung, E_1, E_2. 1 - „sofort" Deformationen /in 180 s/, 2 - Deformationen in der Zeit relativer Stabilisierung, 3 - Deformationen in der Zeit mehrstündiger beziehungsweise mehrtägiger Belastung.

In order to determine the extent of impact of a given system of loading on the determining of values of the deformation and the elasticity moduli and to find out which one is the best for future purposes the author carried out a long series of tests /total of 41/ with the use of two systems of loading /A and B/. In System A a relatively low number /total of 10/ of short-lived load cycles were applied. In some of these cycles the loads were sustained until the state of relative stability of deformations, or throught several hours /some were continued for a few days/. In System B several cycles of loading and unloading were carried out in successively growing load intervals /total of about 20 to 30 cycles/.

1. CHARACTERISTICS OF THE TESTED ROCKS

The geological rock profiles are presented in Fig.1. Limestones, marly limestones, marls-all with thin clay shale interbedding /Figs.1 - 1,2,3,4/ and clay shales /Fig.1-5/ represent sedimentary rocks with many fissures, that had undergone considerable tectonic movements, the micaceous shales /Fig. 1 - 6,7/ are metamorphic rocks. The rest of rocks, sandstones, clay shales and conglomerates, the different quantities of which form the Carpathian Flysch, are of sedimentary character.

2. METHODICS OF TESTS

The most of the tests were performed with the use of 1.96 m^2 load surface; additional tests were carried on with a smaller, 0.49 m^2 load surface. The load was applied by four hydraulic jacks of 2.0 MN capacity each or by one hydraulic jack in the case of smaller load surface. A scheme of the equipment used in the tests is described by THIEL et al. /1970/.

Fig.2 shows a schematic course of the A and B load systems. The loading and unloading were executed in steps of 88.3 kN/m^2. The maximum stress of 2207.0 kN/m^2 corresponded to double or triple values of the expected stresses in the foundation of the designed dam. On the basis of deformations measured at increasing loads the modulus of deformation /D/ was determined for every cycle seperately; the modulus of elasticity /E/ was determined at decreasing loads. Values of the moduli were calculated with the Boussinesq´a formula for the homogeneous elastic half-space.

3. ANALYSIS OF THE TEST RESULTS

3.1. The behaviour of rocks under the load System A

Analysis of the load-deformation diagrams indicates that in the short-lived load cycles where every step of load was sustained for 180 sec /Test 1/ the first load of the rock generally induces rather large deformations that gradually decrease with every cycle effected subsequently. As a result the difference between deformations due to loading and those due to unloading is reduced. In the cycle continued till the state of relative stability of deformations /Test 2/ the behaviour of rocks is similar but it must be added that the increments of deformations during the stabilization time /about 1200 sec/ amount on the average to 25% /extreme values are 19% and 36%/ in relation to the „immediate" deformations, that is those resulting after 180 s duration of loads. When a single step of load was susteined through 7.2 to 14.4 ks /Test 3/ the, deformation increments was of average 10% /maximum of 32%/, while in the long-lived loads /5 days/ the increase was 20% and 36% /two tests/. Low increments of deformation in long lived loads can be accounted for by low stresses used in these tests /883.0 and 1324.0 kN/m^2/. Another factor accounting for the low increments is that in the same test sites the rocks were previously loaded with higher stresses /2207.0 kN/m^2/. During the repetition of several short lived load cycles /Test 4/ the rock behaves as in Test 1 but the deformations are smaller in the same load intervals. This is an evidence that fissures and joints in the rock close during the load cycles. That is also evidenced by the systematic decreasing of the irreversible deformations in successive cycles.

3.2. The behaviour of rocks under the load System B

The behaviour of rocks is generally similar to that under the load System A. With every first load cycle within a given load interval the deformations are relatively big and they grow smaller in the subsequent cycles; the difference between deformations due to loading and unloading grows smaller as well. Increments of deformations in successive cycles of the given load interval amount to 5 to 35% but with an increase of the load value the deformation increments become smaller. Also the values of the irreversible deformations decrease in successive tests /Test 1 reached the load value of 1324.0 kN/m^2, Test 2 - to 2207.0 kN/m^2/ although this particular phenomenon was not so easily observable as in System A, where four tests had been performed. It has been stated that regardless of the load systems A or B the values of irreversible deformations are the higher the lower the deformation modulus of rocks.

3.3. Determination and selection of the values of D and E moduli in the A and B load systems

The values of the moduli, calculated for each cycle seperately, were tabulated. From the data the most reliable figure for the given test site was selected. Since two different load systems were used the selection methods differed as well.

Value of D in System A was determined by comparing mean values from the first and the second cycles of the 1st and 4th tests and the values from the 2nd /or 3rd/ test; value of E was obtained through comparison of the third cycle values in the 1st and 4th tests and the values from the 2nd /possibly 3rd/ tests. In both cases usually the lowest values were accepted.

The course of changes in the values of the moduli for particular cycles, and for the tests, is exemplified in Fig.3 which shows the data from one of the test sites. Analysis of such diagrams for ten test sites /THIEL, 1972/ proves that following:

Values of D:

- increase in particular cycles of growing range loads /both in the 1st and the 4th tests/; the largest differences are between the first and the second cycles,
- increase in successive tests /comparison of tests 1 and 4/,
- decrease in the tests where the loads were sustained till the stats of relative stability of deformations /Test 2/ or where a single step of load was sustained for several hours /Test 3/, or for a few days,

Values of E:

- increase or remain the same in particular cycles of growing range loads,
- decrease, though very insignificantly, in successive tests /comparison of tests 1 and 4/,

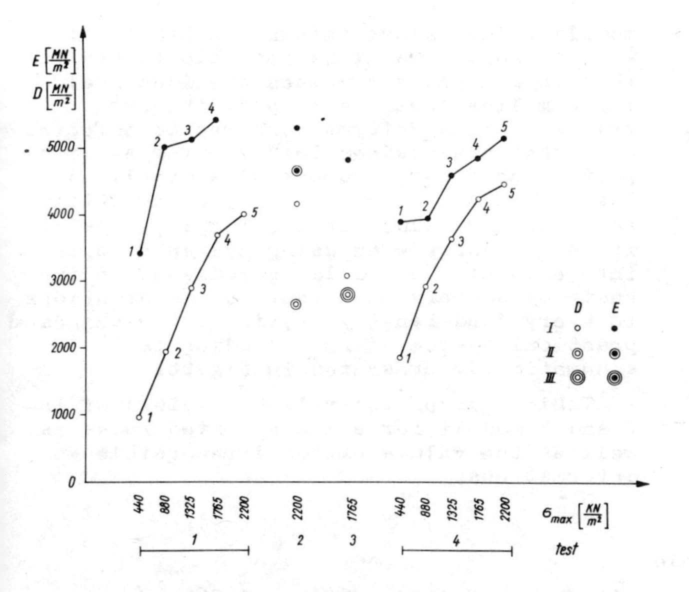

Fig.3. **Moduli of deformation /D/ and of elasticity /E/ in the successive load cycles System A. Dam I - limestones. 1,2,3,4,5,- load cycles, I - short-lived loads, II - loads till the state of relative stability of deformations, III - several-hour load.**

Modules de déformation /D/ et d´élasticité /E/ dans les cycles de chargement succecifs. Système de chargement A. Barrage 1- calcaire 1,2,3,4,5 - cycles de chargement; I - chargement de courte durée, II - chargement jusqu`à une stabilisation relative de déformations, III - chargement de quelques heures.

Deformationsmodule /D/ und Elastizitätsmodule /E/ in nacheinander folgenden Belastungszyklen. Belastungssystem A. Talsperre 1 - Kalk; 1,2,3,4,5 - Belastungszyklen; I -Kurz dauernde Belastung, II-Belastung bis zur relativen Stabilisierung der Deformationen, III-Mehrstündige Belastung.

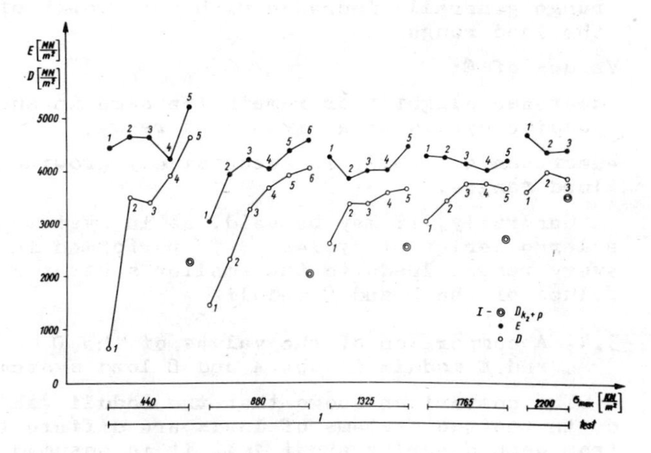

Fig.4. The moduli of deformation /D/ and of elasticity /E/ in successive load cycles. System B. Dam I - limestones. 1,2,3,4,5,6 - load cycles, I - deformation modulus, calculated for the total deformations /except of the first cycle/ of a given load range.

Modules de déformations /D/ et d´élasticité /E/ dans les cycles de chargement succesifs. Système de chargement B. Barrage 1 - calcaire; 1,2,3,4,5,6 - cycles de chargement; I - module de déformation du deuxième cycle et tenant compte de l´accroissement des déformations dans les cycles suivants du l´intervalle des charges.

Deformationsmodule /D/ und Elastizitätmodule /E/ in nacheinander folgenden Belastunszyklen Belastungssystem B. Talsperre 1. Kalk; 1,2,3,4,5 - Belastungszyklen. I - Deformationsmodule für den zweiten Zyklus unter Berücksichtigung der Deformationswächse in den übrigen Zyklen der gegeben Belastungsklasse.

-decrease at gradual unloading until the state of relative stability of deformations /Test 2/.

Generally, it may be said that the D and the E moduli values show considerable scatters yet if a large series of cycles /total of about 10/ is carried out then the scatter grows smaller and it becomes feasible to determine rather accurately the most realiable value for the given test site.

Value of D in System B was determined by taking the mean value of the modulus from particular cycles, without regard to the cycles of the first range of loads /up to 441.0 kN/m^2/ an to every first cycle of the subsequent load ranges; value of E was based on the mean value of the modulus from particular cycles for all the load ranges.

The course of changes in the values of the moduli in particular cycles is presented in Fig.4, which shows the data from one of the test sites. The D values for every load range /up to 441.0, 883.0, 1324.0, 1765.0, 2207.0 kN/m^2 / have also been plotted here. These values have been calculated with regard to the summary deformations which developed as the successive cycles were carried out in a given load range. Thus the results for the two load systems /A and B/ become more comparable since in System B only short-lived loads were applied.Analysis of such diagrams for 13 test sites /THIEL, 1972/ proves the following:

Values of D:

-increase in successive cycles of a given load range; the largest differences appear between the first and second cycles,

-even out in the successively increasing load ranges; the moduli values calculated for summary deformations in a given load range generally increase with the growth of the load range.

Values of E:

- decrease slightly or remain the same in successive cycles of a given load range,
- decrease generally in successively growing load ranges.

Generally, it may be said, as in System A, a large series of cycles /5-7/ performed in every range, leads to the smaller scatter of values of the D and E moduli.

3.4. A comparison of the values of the D and E moduli in the A and B load systems

The comparison shows that the moduli values in the two systems of loads are different from each other by about 10%. It is assumed that the accuracy of determination of the moduli values stays within the limits of ± 10 do 20%, thus it is possible to say that in general the values are identical. This implies that essentially the same values od rock deformations may be effected by either a sustained load /System A/ or by performing a large number of short-lived load cycles /System B/. In order to obtain comporable D values in the two load systems it is necessary when using Systen B to take into account the modulus calculated on the basis of summary increments of deformations in every load range / ,Fig.2b/. A suggested practical system of rock loading is schematically presented in Fig.2b.

Table 1 gives the reliable values of the D and E moduli for all the tested rocks as well as the values of the irreversible deformations.

Table 1

Values of the rock moduli /area of load surface: 1.96 m^2 /

No.	Rock	Dam	Number of test sites	D MN/m^2	E MN/m^2	Irreversible deformations mm
1	Limestones	I	12	2,100 1/	4,000 2/	1.0 3/
2	Marly limestones		1	5,100	9,500	0.6
3	Marls		1	1,600	2,300	3.0
4	Hornstones		1	900	1,600	6.0
5	Clays shales		1	400	550	14.0
6	Micaceous shales	II	1	6,500	7,500	0.3
7	Micaceous shales with muscovite supremacy		1	1,700	1,900	0.9
8	Sandstones	III	1	10,000	11,000	0.1
9	Sandstoneshales		1	3,600	4,000	0.4
10	Shales	IV	1	2,100	2,800	3.0
11	Sandstones		1	4,800	5,200	0.4
12	Conglomerates and sandstones		1	3,700	3,900	0.5

1/ extreme values: 1,200 and 8,000 MN/m^2; 2/ extreme values: 3,000 and 17,500 MN/m^2; 3/ extreme values: 0.3 and 4.5 mm

3.5. Effect of the size of the load surface upon the value of the rock modulus

In 14 test sites additional investigations were performed to determine D and E values when the load surface is reduced /0.49 m^2/. Comparison of these values with the values obtained from the surface of 1.96 m^2 shows that the moduli values from the reduced surface /0.49 m / are on the average lower by 40-45% /extreme figures: 20 - 60%/ than those from the large load surface /1.96 m^2/. This, no doubt, is related to the prosence of the zone of strongly disturbed rock around the excavation site. The influence of the zone on the modulus values is stronger the smaller the rock load surface. This is confirmed by observations of deformations measured additionally at a depth of 50 cm below the level of the load plate /the regular depth of measuring was 5 cm/. At 50 cm below the deformations were about two times smaller. The irreversible deformations at 50 cm below were also smaller than at a depth of 5 cm below the load level.

CONCLUSIONS

1. Values of the modulus of deformation /D/ show a considerable scatter in particular load cycles, yet if a sufficient number of cycles is executed /about 10 for System A and 20 to 30 in System B/ the reliable values can be determined with a satisfactory accuracy. Values of the modulus of elasticity /E/ are less scattered and the determination of the reliable figures can be done on the basis of a smaller number of load cycles.

2. Since the values of the moduli in the two load systems are very similar, and in view of the fact that the duration of test at a single test site in System A is twice as long as that in System B, it seems more practical to use the latter system. A suggested course of loads for that system is shown in Fig.2b.

3. Selection of the reliable values of the D and E moduli in a given test site can be done according to the description in 3.3.

REFERENCES

THIEL K., LINOWSKI H., ŁUKASZEK R., Etude de la déformabilité d'un massif rocheux hétérogène. 2-e Congrès S.I.M.R., Belgrad, 2-34, 1970.

THIEL K., Wpływ systemu obciążeń na odkształcalność skał /Influence of load system on the deformability of rocks - in Polish/, Rozprawy Hydrotechniczne, z.31, 1972.

THEME 1

THÈME 1

THEMA 1

C

Shear Testing

C

Essai de cisaillement

C

Scherversuche

ESTIMATING THE SHEAR STRENGTH OF ROCK JOINTS

ÉVALUATION DE LA RÉSISTANCE AU CISAILLEMENT DES FISSURES DANS LES ROCHES

BERECHNUNG DER SCHERFESTIGKEIT VON GESTEINSTRENNFLÄCHEN

N. BARTON

Norwegian Geotechnical Institute

Oslo, Norway

SUMMARY

A new criterion for the peak shear strength of rock joints is summarized. It can be used both to fit experimental data and to predict it. The predicted strength is sensitive to the following: degree of surface roughness, compressive strength of the rock, degree of weathering, mineralogy, presence or absence of water.

---ooOoo---

Résumé

Un nouveau critère pour la détermination de la résistance maximum au cisaillement dans les fissures de roches, est donné. Ce critère peut être adapté aux données expérimentales, et il peut aussi servir à prévoir la résistance au cisaillement. La résistance au cisaillement prévue est fonction des facteurs suivants: degré de la rugosité superficielle, résistance de la roche à la compression, degré d'effritement, minéralogie, présence ou absence d'eau.

---ooOoo---

Zusammenfassung

Ein neues Kriterium für die Maximalscherfestigkeit der Gestein-Trennflächen wird dargestellt, das sowohl die beste Kurvenanpassung von Versuchswerten als auch deren Abschätzung erlaubt. Die vorausgesagten Festigkeitswerte sind besonders von Folgendem abhängig: Die Rauhigkeit der Trennflächen, die Gesteinsbruchfestigkeit, der Verwitterungsgrad, die Mineralogie und wassergesättigter oder trockener Zustand des Gebirges.

---ooOoo---

An extensive review of reported shear strength investigations, combined with observation of the behaviour of rough, model tension joints has led to a new criterion for the peak shear strength of rock joints. (Barton 1973). It can be written as follows:

$$\tau/\sigma_n' = \tan\left|(\text{JRC}).\log_{10}\left(\frac{\text{JCS}}{\sigma_n'}\right) + \phi_b\right| \qquad (1)$$

where τ = peak shear strength
σ_n' = effective normal stress
JRC = joint roughness coefficient
JCS = effective joint wall compressive strength
ϕ_b = basic friction angle

The joint rougness coefficient (JRC) represents a sliding scale of roughness which varies from approximately 20 to 0, from the roughest to the smoothest end of the spectrum. The effective joint wall compressive strength (JCS) is equal to the unconfined compression strength (σ_c) of the rock if the joint is unweathered, but may reduce to approximately ($1/4\ \sigma_c$) if the joint walls are weathered. The value of (σ_c) can be obtained by performing point load tests on rock core or irregular lumps, as described by Broch and Franklin (1972). The value of (JCS) may be obtained more directly using the Schmidt hammer on exposed joint walls. The last variable, basic friction angle (ϕ_b), is obtained from residual shear tests on flat sand blasted or rough sawn rock surfaces. Its value lies between 25° and 35° for the great majority of rocks, but for mica rich rocks a value of only 22-25° is recommended.

The three families of curves given in Figure 1 relate to three classes of roughness A, B and C. The appropriate equations a, b, and c have (JRC) values of 20, 10 and 5, and for simplicity a value of (ϕ_b)=30° has been assumed throughout. Each curve is numbered 10, 100, 500, or 1000. These figures represent (JCS) or (σ_c) values and they have been plotted in units of Kg/cm^2. (1 Kg/cm^2 = 14·2 lbf/in^2). The exact shear strength of rough (class A) joints at very low levels of normal stress is uncertain. Values of the ratio (JCS/σ_n') or (σ_c/σ_n') larger than 100 are considered "very low stress", and a linear portion is suggested,

i.e. for $(\sigma_c/\sigma_n') \geq 100$, $\tau/\sigma_n' = \tan 70°$.

An example of strength prediction is shown in Figure 2. The limestone joints were described by Krsmanovic and Langof (1964) as follows; B3: very rough bedding joints, B2: rough bedding joints, D2: very rough clean joints. The compressive strength of the limestone was 1100-1600 Kg/cm^2. Equation 1 was evaluated assuming the following values: JRC = 20 (class A roughness), σ_c= 1100 Kg/cm^2 (upper bound), JCS=1100/4 Kg/cm^2 (lower bound) ϕ_b=30° . The predicted upper and lower bound curvilinear envelopes are shown in Figure 2.

The classification of roughness illustrated in Figure 1 is intended as a guide to those who might wish to use the criterion directly as above, and dispense with direct shear testing of unfilled rock joints. Since values of (σ_c) and (ϕ_b) can be measured or estimated quite accurately, the only real unknown is (JRC). It has to be estimated using engineering judgement and experience.

In addition to direct strength prediction, the criterion can be used to extrapolate shear strength data from limited numbers of tests, thereby reducing costs. All that is required is an estimate of (JCS) and (ϕ_b). The relevant mean value of the joint

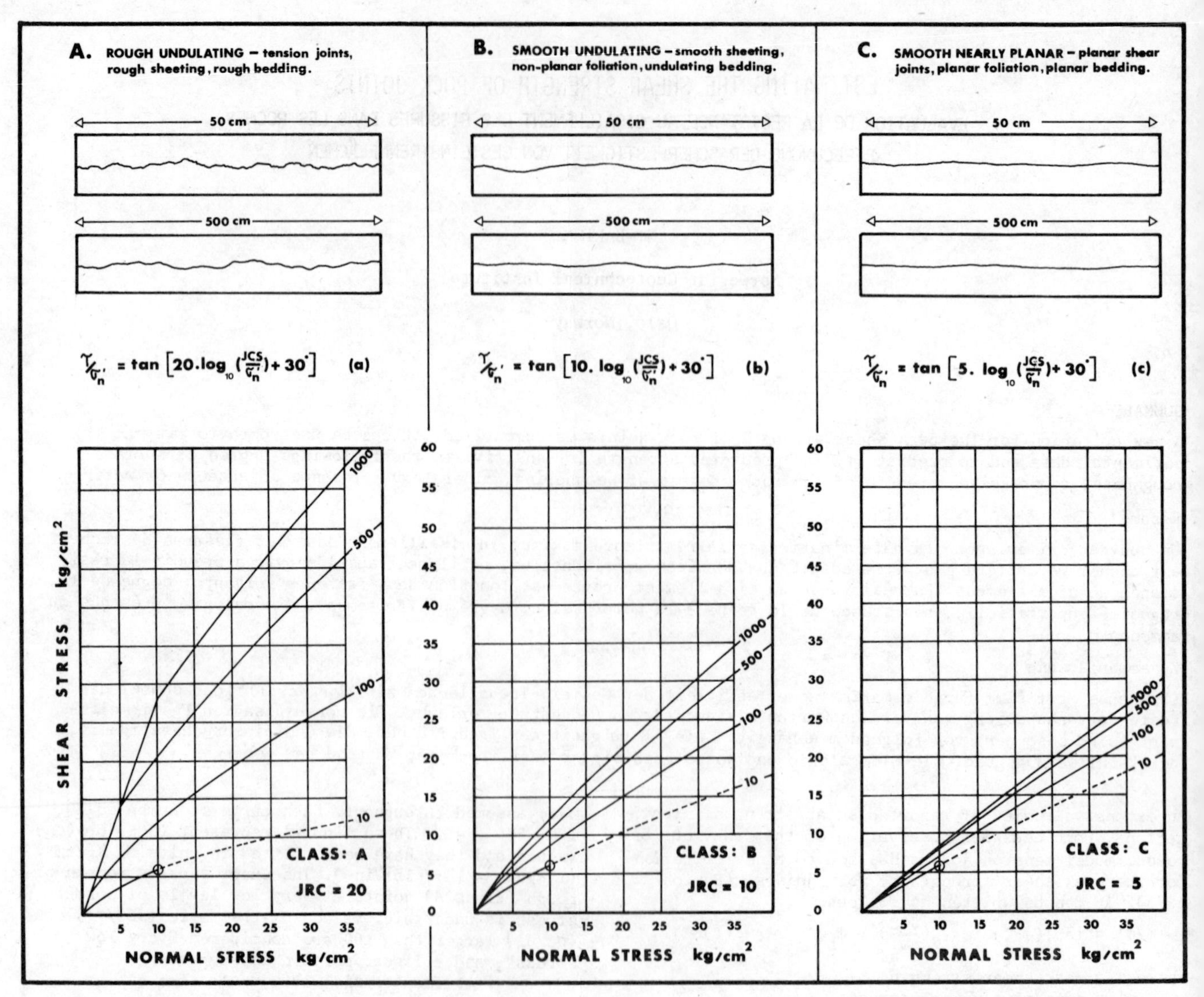

Figure 1. Classification of roughness and prediction of shear strength for non-planar rock joints.

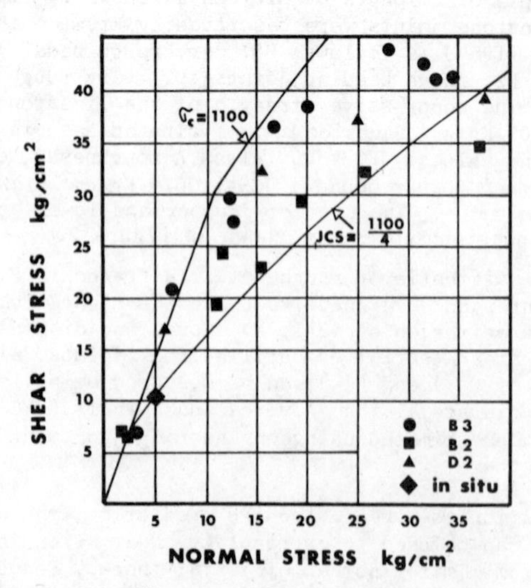

Figure 2. Experimental data for rough joints in limestone, after Krsmanovic and Langof (1964).

roughness coefficient (JCR) will be obtained by substituting the available peak strength test data (τ, σ_n') in equation 2:

$$JRC = \frac{\tan^{-1}(\tau/\sigma_n') - \phi_b}{\log_{10}(JCS/\sigma_n')} \quad (2)$$

The correct curvature for data extrapolation will thus be obtained. This should constitute a marked improvement over the linear Coulomb (c, ϕ) envelope usually employed in these extrapolation proceedures.

REFERENCES

BARTON, N. (1973), Review of a new shear strength criterion for rock joints. Engineering Geology, Elsevier, Amsterdam. (in press).

BROCH, E. and FRANKLIN, J.A. (1972), The point load strength test. International Journal of Rock Mechanics and Mining Sciences, Vol. 9, pp. 669-697.

KRSMANOVIĆ, D. and LANGOF, Z. (1964), Large scale laboratory tests of the shear strength of rocky material. Rock Mechanics and Engineering Geology, Supplement 1, pp. 20-30.

TORSIONAL SHEAR MEASUREMENTS OF THE FRICTIONAL PROPERTIES OF WESTERLY GRANITE

LES MESURES DU CISAILLEMENT TORSIONIQUE DES CARACTÈRISTIQUES DE LA FRICTION DE WESTERLY GRANIT

TORSIONSVERSUCHE ZUR ERMITTLUNG DER REIBUNGSEIGENSCHAFTEN VON WESTERLY GRANIT

R.J. CHRISTENSEN, S.R. SWANSON, W.S. BROWN

University of Utah

Salt Lake City

U.S.A.

Summary

Torsional shear tests were conducted to measure the frictional properties of ground Westerly granite surfaces under confining pressure and axial stress. A dependency of the coefficient of friction on the state of stress was established, in addition to the usual dependency on normal stress.

Zusammenfassung

Torsionsversuche dienten der Messung von Reibungseigenschaften an geschLiffenen Westerly Granitoberfláchen unter Manteldruck und Axialdruck. Zusätzlich zu dem bekannten Einfluß der Normalspannung konnte eine Abhängigkeit zwischen Reibungskoeffizient und Spannungszustand ermittelt werden.

Résumé

Les essais due cisaillement torsionique ont ete executees afin de mesurer les caracteristiques de la friction des surfaces lisses de Westerly Granit sous pression confines et force axiale. Une depandance du coefficient de friction sur l'etat de la force a ete establi, en plus de la dependance sur la force normale.

INTRODUCTION

This paper presents the results of a laboratory investigation of the strength and deformation of jointed Westerly granite torsion specimens with ground surfaces. The use of torsion specimens to investigate the properties of rock joints has been discussed by Jaeger and Cook (1969) but its implementation appears to be unique to the present investigation. The advantages of the torsional test specimens and test apparatus are that the same surfaces are in contact throughout the experiment and the effects of large amounts of sliding on the surfaces may be studied.

The laboratory study of the motion of rock joints under stress is a necessary prerequisite to determine the motion of jointed rock in field problems such as earthquakes and stress wave loadings. A knowledge of the physical properties is basic to solving these problems. The present study is limited to the response of Westerly granite with ground surfaces to different states of stress.

Properties of joints have been studied in many experimental investigations. In general, these studies can be divided into three major categories: direct shear tests, triaxial tests and in situ tests. An illustration of the specimen configurations used for the first two types is shown in Figure 1. The direct shear tests are often limited to low normal stress (usually less than 7MN/m^2). At these low stresses it is observed that the coefficient of friction is a function of surface roughness (Coulson, 1970; Hoskins et al., 1968; Byerlee, 1967a). As the surface roughness increases the joint becomes more interlocked, increasing the coefficient of friction. No general trend for changes in the coefficient of friction with changes in normal stress in all rocks can be established. For a specific rock the coefficient of friction may increase (Coulson, 1970; Pratt et al., 1972) decrease (Coulson, 1970; Pratt et al., 1972; Maurer 1965; Byerlee, 1967a; Dieterich, 1972), or stay essentially constant (Coulson, 1970; Pratt et al., 1972; Jaeger and Rosengren, 1969), with increasing normal stress.

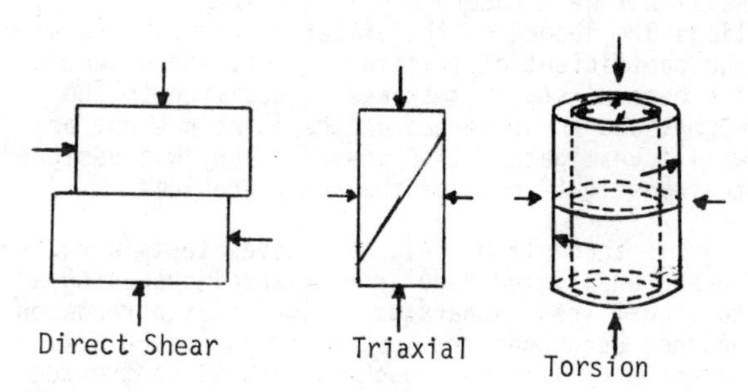

Figure 1. Rock Friction Specimens

In triaxial tests, the normal stresses are generally much higher than in direct shear tests. The stresses in the specimen can be resolved into shear and normal components along the joint to determine the coefficient of friction. At higher normal stresses the surface roughness is less important inasmuch as the rough joint becomes smoother by asperities being sheared off and the smooth joint becomes rougher as slip takes place (Byerlee, 1967b). Also, for both types of roughness, surface gouge of filler material is generated which modifies the effect of the initial roughness. Thus, the coefficient of friction tends to the same value for all surfaces, but the relative shearing displacement characteristics may be different. It has been noted that the coefficient of friction often decreases with increasing normal stress in the triaxial test (Jaeger and

Cook, 1969; Jaeger and Rosengren 1969; Byerlee; 1967b; Byerlee, 1968). Good correlation between direct shear and triaxial tests of joints has been obtained, however, by Jaeger and Rosengren (1969) for normal stresses in the range of 3 to 30 MN/m^2.

Although consistent series of tests have not been conducted using the same rock and surface condition, coefficients of friction obtained in triaxial tests at normal stresses of approximately 200 MN/m^2 and higher appear to be decreasing with increasing normal stress, and yet are higher than coefficients of friction measured with normal stresses in the range of 7 MN/m^2 (Jaeger and Rosengren, 1969; Byerlee, 1967b). This suggests that either μ (the coefficient of friction) increases and then decreases with normal stress or else the results are not compatible due to changes in the experimental conditions.

The mechanism of dry friction in metals has been postulated by Bowden and Tabor (1964) and many others to consist of the welding together of asperity tips under very large local pressures. Byerlee (1967) has concluded, however, that friction in rocks is due to the interaction of brittle asperity tips rather than plastic flow. Evidence in favor of the brittle fracture theory has been indirect, such as microscopic examination of gouge particles. The presumed very large local stresses at the points of contact in frictional sliding make it difficult to extrapolate directly from the usual laboratory studies of rock brittle fracture and plastic flow.

Although the previous investigations have contributed much to the present knowledge of rock joint behavior, a number of important areas are still not well understood. For example, clarifications are needed on the effect of normal stress on the coefficient of friction. Also, the effect of the general state of stress in addition to the normal and shear stress on the joint has not been well investigated. The present study was designed to investigate both of the above problems.

To accomplish these objectives tests were performed on jointed tubular rock specimens using a torsional shear apparatus. Since this arrangement has not been used previously, a discussion will be given here of the various features as contrasted with direct shear and triaxial compression experiments.

The direct shear apparatus is commonly used for frictional studies since it permits relatively large surfaces to be subjected to relatively large displacements. It suffers from the limitation that for practical reasons the maximum normal stress is usually not higher than 7MN/m^2. Also, the state of stress is limited to a normal and shear stress across the joint. Additionally, Kutter (1971) has indicated that in such a test the shear stress cannot be uniform across the joint. Since the joint edges are stress free, the shear must be zero at these points and then build up to a maximum in the interior of the specimen.

The triaxial compression test is often employed to obtain joint properties at high normal stresses. The specimen used is commonly much smaller than the direct shear specimen (the shear area is usually on the order of 3 to 30 square cm). Since the alignment of the specimen is disturbed when it is displaced, the joint displacement is limited. The state of stress at the joint consists of a lateral stress equal to the confining pressure, a normal stress equal to the confining pressure plus a component that is related to the axial stress and the joint angle. The state of stress can be varied a limited amount by using different joint angles.

The torsional jointed specimen (illustrated in Figure 1) has some specific advantages. The normal and shear stresses on the joint can be independently controlled, thus facilitating the study of the interaction between normal and shear loadings. Also, the state of stress can be varied by changing the superimposed axial loading and confining pressure. The amount of joint slip displacement is theoretically unlimited and in practice can be quite large.

The disadvantages of the torsional joint specimen as used in the present study are twofold; first the joint area is no larger than used in high pressure triaxial joint studies; and second, a non-uniform stress may occur over the joint area. This latter effect will be discussed in more detail in the experimental section.

EXPERIMENTS

Description of Experimental Apparatus

The torsion test apparatus consists of a hydraulic ram capable of 0.98 MN axial force, a hydraulic rotary actuator capable of applying a torque of 0.7 MN-cm, and a pressure vessel to allow confining pressure up to 345 MN/m^2 to be applied to the sample. All stress conditions can be applied independently. The hydraulic ram, rotary actuator, and the pressure intensifier were all servocontrolled so that each component of the system could be controlled by either a displacement or load type feedback.

The pressure vessel assembly was made from 4340 alloy steel with a mild steel safety ring press fit on the outside. Standard O-ring seals were used to seal both ends of the pressure vessel. The torque and axial load are transmitted to the test specimen from the piston of the hydraulic ram to the piston going into the pressure vessel.

Data Acquisition System

The data acquisition system consisted of displacement and load transducers, bridge balance unit, and recorders. Strain gage type load cells, developed specifically for this apparatus, were instrumented to measure both axial force and torque. The bridges were connected so that the axial load and torque could be measured independently.

Total specimen deformation was measured in axial and rotational directions. Two linear infinite resolution film potentiometers mounted external to the pressure vessel were used for these measurements.

Specimen Preparation

The test specimens were cored right circular cylinders 7.6 cm in length with an inside diameter of 2.54 cm and an outside diameter of 3.38 cm. To insure concentricity, both core drills were mounted in one collet allowing both the inside and outside of the sample to be cored in one operation. The samples were then cut approximately to length (3.8 cm) in a diamond saw using water as a coolant and a lubricant. The ends were ground to a parallelness of $\pm$ .0010 cm with a diamond grinding wheel. The specimen wall thickness varied less than 0.002 cm throughout each specimen. The samples were bonded into end caps with epoxy cement using an alignment jig to ensure concentricity and then jacketed both on the inside and outside by a .075 cm thick polyurethane membrane.

Description of Rock

The rock used in this study was Westerly granite obtained from the United States Bureau of Mines Twin Cities Research Center. The rock is composed of about 1/3 quartz, 1/3 potash feldspar and 1/3 plagioclase feldspar with traces of micas and other minerals (Green and Perkins, 1968). Westerly granite has a density of 2.63 gm/cm^3, a grain size of 0.8 - 1.2 mm and a porosity of 0.007 by volume. The static unconfined compression strength is 2.55 MN/m^2 (Brace et al., 1966).

Variation in Shear Stress Across Specimen Wall

As was stated previously, a major disadvantage in using hollow cylindrical samples is that the shear stress varies across the specimen wall. According to the linear theory of elasticity, the shear stress τ increases linearly with radius r as described by the equation

$$\tau = \frac{Tr}{J}$$

where T is the applied torque and J is the polar moment of inertia. According to this equation, the shear stress at the inside radius of the joint surface would be 25 per cent lower than that at the outside radius. However, the effect of joint slip greatly modifies the stress distribution and must be taken into account. Consider, for example, an idealization of joint deformation where the slip stress is constant and independent of joint slip displacement. For this ideal case the resulting stress distribution would be the same as that of a perfectly plastic material, i.e., constant shear stress across the joint of the torsion specimen. Thus, it may be concluded that once slip occurs the stress distribution across the joint in the hollow torsion specimen is more nearly uniform.

Experimental Results

Figure 2 shows the effect of normal stress on the maximum shearing stress for ground surfaces of Westerly granite. The values reported in this and other figures are the maximum value of stress obtained during a test. This value was obtained after a relatively large displacement (0.25 - .5 cm) and will be termed "residual shear stress" or "residual coefficient of friction". The shear stress then either remained essentially constant or dropped off slightly with increased displacement. The coefficient of friction, defined as

$$\mu = \frac{\tau}{\sigma_n}$$

is plotted in Figure 2 as a function of normal stress. In this figure the state of stress is indicated by σ_2/σ_n, where σ_2 is the joint lateral stress (and the intermediate principal stress). The joint lateral stress is equal to the confining pressure. The variation in the data due to varying stress conditions at a given normal stress seems to be quite significant. However, when two tests were conducted at the same stress conditions, the scatter was extremely small. A discussion of this will be given later.

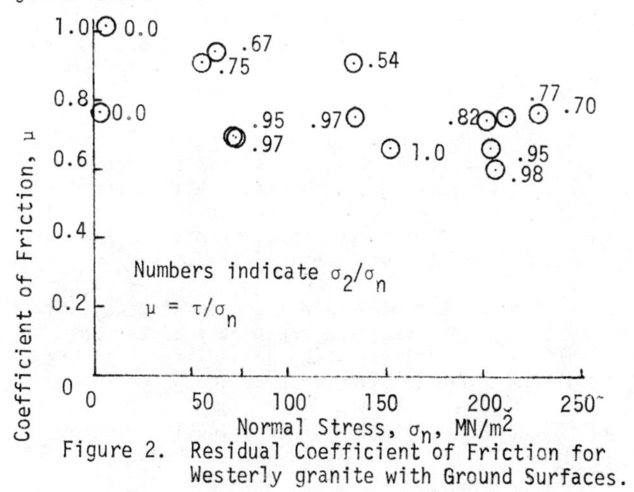

Figure 2. Residual Coefficient of Friction for Westerly granite with Ground Surfaces.

Figure 3 shows a typical plot of shear stress versus tangential joint displacement for the ground surfaces. It is apparent that large stick-slip was present at higher normal stress (above 70 MN/m^2) but not as prevalent at lower normal stress. The joint motion shown in Figure 3 indicates that a small joint displacement took place before the joint slipped. The stiffness of the joint appears to increase with increasing normal stress.

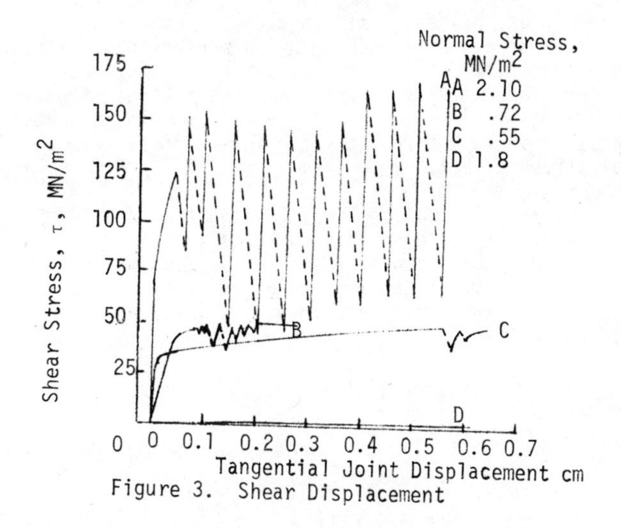

Figure 3. Shear Displacement

DISCUSSION OF RESULTS

The torsion apparatus permitted variation of the state of stress as well as the magnitude of stress. Since the lateral stress in the joint is equal to the hydrostatic pressure, and the normal joint stress is equal to the sum of the hydrostatic pressure and the superposed axial stress, it is possible to change the state of stress by simply adjusting the relative magnitudes of the axial applied load and the confining pressure. The results shown in Figure 2 indicate that tests run at identical stress conditions showed very little scatter, but that changes in the state of stress apparently affected the coefficient of friction.

The number by each data point in Figure 2 represents the ratio of the hydrostatic confining pressure (the intermediate principal stress σ_2) to the normal stress σ_n. Thus, for a ratio of 1.0 there is zero superimposed axial stress and as the numbers decrease the superimposed axial stress increases, or σ_2 decreases. As can be seen, a systematic variation with state of stress does occur inasmuch as increases in superimposed axial stress result in increases in the coefficient of friction. Also, for constant values of σ_2/σ_n the coefficient of friction decreases with normal stress.

Although not proved in the present study, it is conjectured here that the dependency of the coefficient of friction on the joint lateral stress established above involves changes in the rock behavior with the state of stress. For example, Brace et al. (1966) have shown that microcracking in Westerly granite influences the stress-strain behavior. This microcracking induced behavior may be related to changes in the real frictional contact area, and thus to the frictional behavior. The relationship of the state of stress at the joint to the stresses required for fracture of intact rock may thus be a parameter affecting frictional behavior. This "nearness to fracture" concept is discussed below.

The concept of nearness to fracture in stress space necessarily requires a description of the fracture stress locus. It is well known that the intermediate principal stress does influence the fracture strength of rock. In the present experiments on joint friction it is one of the prime test variables since it is equal to the joint lateral stress. Accordingly, a fracture criteria was used in the comparisons which incorporates the intermediate principal stress effect.

A criterion was chosen following the ideas of Mogi (1971) that represents rock fracture in the following special coordinates: $\sqrt{J_2'}$ vs. $\sigma_1 + 0.1\sigma_2 + \sigma_3$, where σ_1, σ_2, and σ_3 are principal stresses and $\sqrt{J_2'}$ is the second deviatoric stress invariant given by

$$\sqrt{J_2'} = \left\{ \frac{(\sigma_{11}-\sigma_{22})^2 + (\sigma_{22}-\sigma_{33})^2 + (\sigma_{33}-\sigma_{11})^2}{6} + \sigma_{12}^2 + \sigma_{23}^2 + \sigma_{31}^2 \right\}^{\frac{1}{2}}$$

A plot of extension, compression and biaxial fracture stress data for Westerly granite is shown plotted in these coordinates in Figure 4. The close spacing of these points indicates that a unique fracture locus is at least approximated.

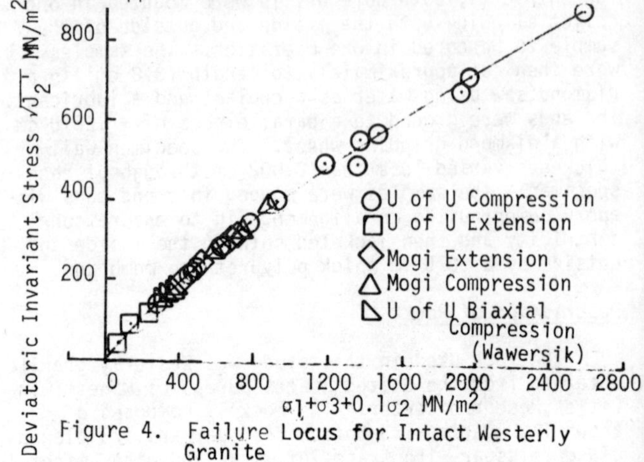

Figure 4. Failure Locus for Intact Westerly Granite

The maximum joint stresses are compared with the fracture locus for intact Westerly granite in Figure 5. It can be seen that a wide difference exists among the various jointed tests in terms of how close to fracture the jointed specimens were at the residual friction value. In fact a number of jointed specimens did fail before slip occurred, depending on the stress conditions established for the test. These latter tests are not shown, however. Again the number shown next to each data point is the ratio of the intermediate principal stress to normal stress (σ_2/σ_n). As before, a systematic variation with σ_2/σ_n is seen. Comparing Figures 2 and 5 shows that the coefficient of friction is higher for samples with states of stress closer to the failure surface.

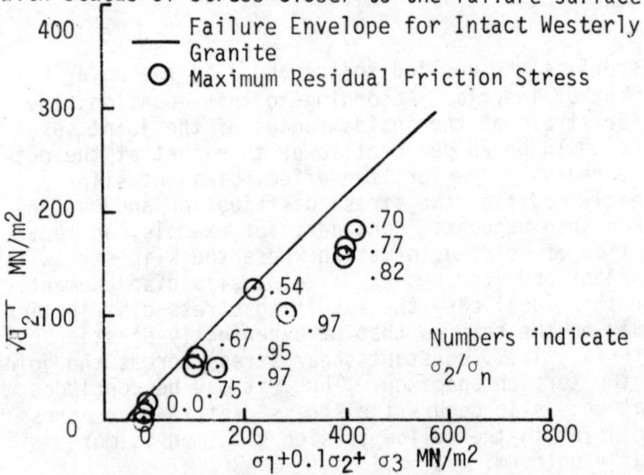

Figure 5. Comparison of Failure Locus for Intact Granite with Slip Stress.

A comparison with Byerlee's data (Byerlee, 1967b) (at approximately the same percentage of failure value of the intact rock at residual slip) on ground surfaces in triaxial tests with joint angles of 45° is shown in Figure 6. Although Byerlee's data are at higher normal stresses than the present study, the general trends in data can be compared and the agreement is quite good. The dashed line represents Byerlee's equation for coefficient of friction given by

$$\mu = 0.5 + 0.6/\sigma_n \quad \text{for } (2\text{Kb} < \sigma_n < 17\text{ kb}$$

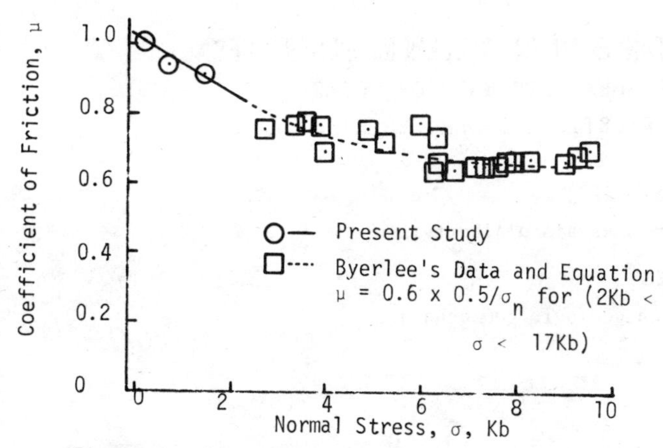

Figure 6. Comparison with Byerlee's Data

SUMMARY AND CONCLUSIONS

A laboratory investigation of the strength and deformation of jointed tubular samples of Westerly granite with ground (230 micro cm) surfaces has been completed. Special attention was given to the effect of varying the state of stress on the joint. This was accomplished by varying the lateral stress on the joint and the normal stress on the joint independently.

The following conclusions are drawn from the investigation:

1. Torsional shear loading of a tubular specimen is advantageous for joint friction studies in several respects. For example, normal stress can be varied over a wide range, large deformation can be applied, and the general state of stress can be varied. Also, both normal and tangential joint displacement can be conveniently measured.

2. The state of stress has a definite effect on joint frictional properties. This effect was correlated well by a parameter that describes the nearness of the stress state to fracture of the competent rock.

3. The mode of deformation at low normal stresses is stable sliding while at high normal stresses the mode is stick slip. The transition takes place at approximately a normal stress of 70 MN/m^2. This value may vary slightly with state of stress.

4. The stiffness of the joint before slip and during stick slip increases with increasing normal stress.

ACKNOWLEDGEMENT

This work was sponsored by the Defense Nuclear Agency through Terra Tek, Inc. under purchase order #02407. The authors acknowledge the thoughtful suggestions of the contract technical monitors, Mr. S. J. Green of Terra Tek, Inc. and Mr. C. B. McFarland of the Defense Nuclear Agency. Bryan Smith was very helpful in assisting with the experiments.

REFERENCES

Bowden, F. B. and D. Tabor, 1964, The Friction and Lubrication of Solids, Vol. 2, Claredon Oxford, p. 79.

Brace, W. F. et al., 1966, Dilatancy in the fracture of crystalline rocks, Journal of Geophysical Research, vol. 71, pp. 3939-3953.

Byerlee, J. D. 1967a, Theory of friction based on brittle fracture, Journal of Applied Physics, vol. 38;7, pp. 2928-2934.

Byerlee, J.D. 1967b, Frictional characteristics of granite under high confining pressure, Journal of Geophysical Research, vol. 72;14 pp. 3639-3548.

Byerlee, J.D. 1968, Brittle-ductile transition in rocks, Journal of Geophysical Research, vol. 73;14, pp. 4741-4750.

Coulson, J. H. 1970, The effects of surface roughness on the shear strength of joints in rocks, Technical Report MRD-2-70, Missouri River Div. Corps of Eng.

Dieterich, J. H. 1972, Time dependent friction in rocks, Journal of Geophysical Research, vol. 77;20 pp. 3690-3697.

Green, S. J., and R. D. Perkins, 1968, Uniaxial compression tests at strain rates from 10^{-4} to 10^4/sec on three geologic materials, 10th Symposium on Rock Mechanics, Austin, Texas.

Hoskins, E. R., et al., 1968, A medium scale direct friction experiment, International Journal of Rock Mechanics and Mineral Science, vol. 5, pp. 143-154.

Jaeger, J. S. and N. G. W. Cook, 1969, Fundamentals of Rock Mechanics, Methuen.

Jaeger, J. C., and K. J. Rosengren, 1969, Friction and sliding of joints, Proceedings of the Austin Institute of Mines and Metallurgy, no. 229.

Kutter, H. K. 1971, Stress distribution in direct shear test samples, Proceedings of the International Symposium, ISRM, Nancy, France.

Maurer, W. C., 1967, Shear failure of rock under compression, Journal of the Society of Petroleum Engineers, vol. 5;2 pp. 167-176.

Mogi, K. 1971, Fracture and flow of rocks under high triaxial compression, Journal of Geophysical Research, vol. 76, pp. 1255-1269.

Pratt, H. R., et al., 1972, Frictional properties of cedar city quartz diorite, Technical Report AFWL-TR-72-122, Kirtland Air Force Base, New Mexico.

L'ESSAI DE TORSION ET LA RÉSISTANCE AU CISAILLEMENT DES ROCHES

THE TORSIONAL TEST AND THE SHEAR STRENGTH OF ROCKS

DREHMOMENTVERSUCHE UND SCHERFESTIGKEIT DER GESTEINE

E. DURAND

Electricite de France - Centre d'essais d'Albertville

G. COMES

Electricite de France - Division geologie geotechnique

France

RESUME

Cette étude synthétise les résultats des essais de torsion et de torsion-compression qui ont été obtenus sur une série de roches. L'analyse se penche sur le comportement des roches soumises à un effort de torsion et sur la mesure des paramètres mécaniques de rupture. Dans un stade final, une comparaison est établie avec les essais traditionnels de laboratoire.

SUMMARY

The behaviour of different rocks, under torsional load with or without compression, is analyzed. Tests results are presented and the measurement of the mechanical parameters at fealure is emphasized. Finally, comparison is made between torsional tests and more traditional tests.

ZUSAMMENFASSUNG

Die vorliegende Arbeit fasst die Ergebnisse von Drehmoment - und Druck - Drehmomentversuche über verschiedenen Gesteine zusammen. Es wird das Verhalten durch Drehmoment beanspruchten Gesteine untersucht und der Messprozess der mechanischen Bruchkennwerte beschrieben. Schliesslich wird ein Vergleich solcher Versuche mit den üblichen Laborversuchen vorgenommen.

1 - INTRODUCTION

Jusqu'à présent, les investigations géotechniques concernant la détermination en laboratoire des caractéristiques de cisaillement des roches ont souvent été menées en utilisant des essais qui imposent un plan préétabli de rupture. Aussi a-t-il paru intéressant d'étudier un nouveau type de cisaillement (cisaillement par torsion) où la rupture se développe selon les zones de faiblesse de la roche d'une manière tout à fait analogue aux ruptures provenant de phénomènes naturels. Comme la compression monoaxiale et triaxiale classique, comme la traction directe, la torsion est, en effet, un cisaillement libre.

En outre, en lui superposant un effort monoaxial, on détermine la résistance au cisaillement de roches dans la plage de contraintes située dans le domaine des tractions-compressions. Cette plage est d'un intérêt pratique évident pour tous les problèmes de stabilité.

On peut encore élargir le domaine d'étude en y additionnant un effort hydrostatique.

L'étude a pour but de décrire l'appareillage utilisé, de présenter les résultats des essais et enfin d'établir une comparaison entre les caractéristiques mécaniques déterminées en torsion et celles obtenues habituellement en laboratoire (résistance à la traction directe, résistance à la traction brésilienne, résistance au cisaillement type Lundborg, résistance au cisaillement type Casagrande et résistance au cisaillement triaxial). Pour plus de généralités, les investigations ont porté sur une gamme très large de roches.

2 - DESCRIPTION DE L'APPAREILLAGE

Préparation des éprouvettes

Les blocs sont débités en éprouvettes tubulaires, au moyen d'une foreuse radiale équipée d'un

(+) actuellement au B. R. G. M. - France

carottier à double paroi permettant d'exécuter le double carottage simultanément. Cet équipement assure la coaxialité indispensable des surfaces latérales interne et externe du tube de roche . Les éprouvettes testées sont de deux types : 60/40 mm de diamètre pour les éprouvettes tubulaires minces et 60/30 mm pour les éprouvettes tubulaires épaisses.

Pour développer l'effort de torsion recherché un embout métallique est collé à chacune des extrémités. Le collage est réalisé à l'araldite avec précision par l'intermédiaire d'un gabarit.

La presse de torsion-compression

La presse de torsion-compression axiale qui est entièrement hydraulique peut se schématiser en 4 parties principales (fig. 1) :

- le bâti rigide formé par deux plateaux horizontaux et par quatre colonnes verticales ;
- le dispositif de compression situé sous le plateau inférieur ;
- le système de torsion situé sur le plateau supérieur et composé de deux petits vérins ;
- l'appareillage de mesure. L'équipement employé permet d'obtenir directement les courbes effort-déformation de la roche. La déformation de l'éprouvette est mesurée à l'aide de deux capteurs de déplacement venant chacun en appui sur une platine métallique collée sur une même génératrice de l'éprouvette.

La cellule triaxiale de torsion

Sur la presse de torsion, s'adapte une cellule triaxiale pouvant développer une pression de confinement de 100 MPa. L'éprouvette est placée au centre de la cellule, elle est isolée du fluide de confinement par deux membranes caoutchouc.

La déformation de torsion est mesurée par un capteur de déplacement linéaire fixé sur la cellule triaxiale et relié tangentiellement au piston.

Technique opérationnelle

Tous les essais ont été exécutés en appliquant le couple de torsion à une vitesse constante (5 m. N/s) grâce à un pupitre Mohr-Federhaff cadencé.

Les efforts axiaux ou hydrostatiques ont, au contraire, été appliqués préalablement à l'effort de torsion et maintenus constants en cours d'essais.

La fiabilité de l'appareillage a été acquise en réalisant une importante série de mesures sur un matériau très homogène : le mortier ISO. C'est seulement après cette expérimentation que les essais proprement dits ont été entrepris sur une gamme très large de roches à structures statistiquement isotropes (granite, marbre, craie, ...) et anisotropes (mortier à discontinuité artificielle, schistes...)

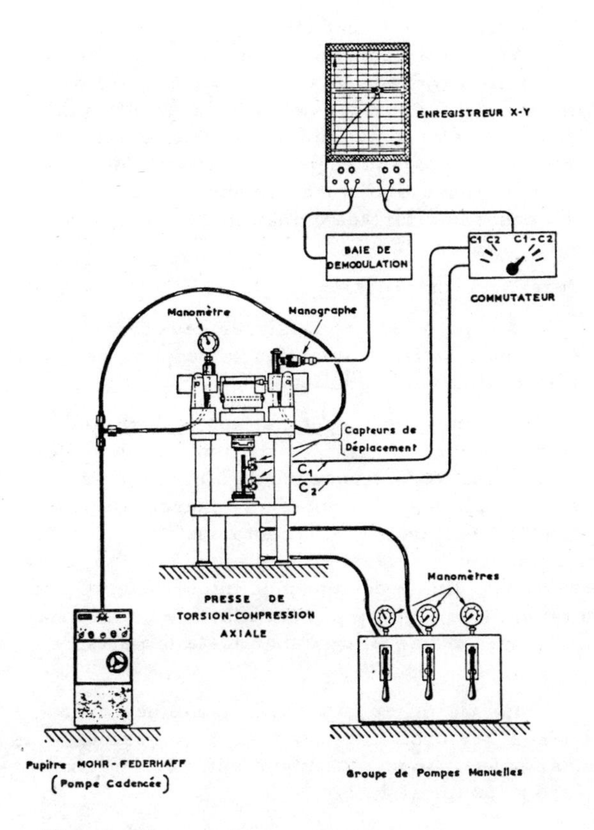

Fig. 1 - Appareillage de torsion
- Torsional apparatus
- Gerät für Drehmomentversuche

3 - COMPORTEMENT DES ROCHES A LA TORSION

Torsion simple

Les courbes effort-déformation (couple T-déformation de rotation ω par unité de longueur) obtenues au cours de l'essai de torsion simple, font apparaître trois phases distinctes dans le comportement de l'éprouvette cylindrique :

- une phase essentiellement élastique présentant assez fréquemment de l'hystérèse et de faibles irréversibilités (ouvertures de fissures sous l'effet des contraintes de traction) ;
- une phase de pseudo-écrouissage (1) toujours courte, correspondant à l'infléchissement de la courbe et au développement de la fissuration sur le pourtour de l'éprouvette ;
- une phase de pseudo-anti-écrouissage (1) difficile à contenir, où l'effort maximal que peut supporter l'éprouvette, diminue et où les irréversibilités deviennent importantes.

Pour des éprouvettes tubulaires minces, le comportement devient très fragile et la rupture apparaît brutalement. Les courbes sont linéaires pour des roches à grains bien soudés (marbre de

Vilette, anhydrite d'Echaillon, ...) et non linéaires pour des roches présentant d'importants joints intergranulaires (granite de Corbières, granite de Brommat, ...). Pour ces dernières, la déformation fissurale s'accentue vis-à-vis de la déformation matricielle lorsqu'augmente le couple de torsion. On retrouve d'ailleurs la même distinction sur les courbes effort-déformation de traction directe.

Torsion - compression axiale

Il est possible de distinguer deux types de comportement selon les matériaux auxquels ce genre de sollicitation est appliqué.

Pour un milieu poreux et non fissuré, la pente des courbes effort-déformation (couple-déformation de rotation) correspondant à différentes contraintes axiales constantes σ_a exercées sur une éprouvette tubulaire se maintient constante pour de faibles charges axiales. Elle diminue ensuite lorsque la charge axiale devient plus importante. On appellera seuil de rigidité la contrainte de compression σ_a à partir de laquelle se manifeste la perte de rigidité (2).

Pour un milieu fissuré, la pente des différentes courbes croît avec les faibles contraintes axiales, passe par un maximum (seuil de rigidité) et décroît ensuite (fig. 2).

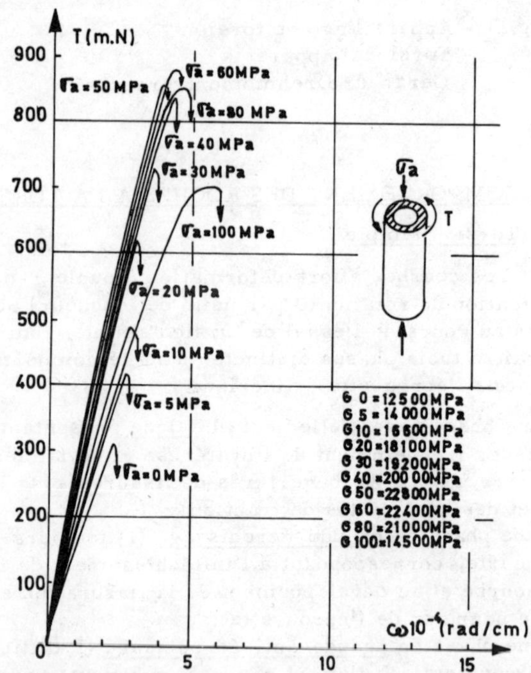

Fig. 2 - Courbes effort-déformation de torsion - Granite de Brommat
- Torsional load deformation curves for Brommat granit
- Granit aus Brommat ; Spannung-Drehverformungskurven

Ce seuil de rigidité n'est en fait que le seuil de microfissuration de la roche. Il s'identifie à la contrainte de compression à partir de laquelle la rigidité de torsion s'affaiblit.

Torsion - compression hydrostatique

L'évolution des courbes effort-déformation de torsion d'une roche sous contrainte de confinement (éprouvettes tubulaires) fait apparaître, à partir d'une certaine contrainte hydrostatique, le comportement de plus en plus plastique de la roche. Ce phénomène s'accentue nettement en testant des éprouvettes cylindriques pour lesquelles le champ de contrainte n'est pas du tout uniforme.

Les fortes contraintes de confinement peuvent même remanier la roche et provoquer une chute de sa rigidité de torsion.

Anisotropie des déformations de torsion

En réalisant des essais de torsion simple selon chacun des trois axes de symétrie d'une roche orthorhombique, on détermine les trois coefficients de cisaillement de la roche. Les mesures que nous avons faites sur les schistes du Col du Sabot dont la symétrie est de type axial déterminent des coefficients de cisaillement en torsion très voisins de ceux obtenus à l'aide d'essais clinotropes de compression monoaxiale

4 - RESISTANCES MECANIQUES DE TORSION

Les roches homogènes et isotropes soumises à un effort de torsion simple se rompent le long d'une hélice inclinée à 45° par rapport aux génératrices et orientée selon la ligne isostatique de traction (fig. 3). C'est une rupture d'extension.

La résistance de torsion à la rupture qui est une résistance au cisaillement simple non uniforme, dépend largement de la géométrie de l'éprouvette. Il a été cherché à déterminer la caractéristique mécanique de rupture qui se rapproche au maximum de celle correspondant à un champ de cisaillement simple uniforme. En réalisant des essais de torsion simple sur des éprouvettes tubulaires de même rayon extérieur R_e et de rayon interne R_i variable, il a pu être montré que la résistance au cisaillement simple uniforme R_{Tt}, c'est-à-dire la résistance à la torsion d'éprouvettes tubulaires infiniment minces, s'identifie à la contrainte de cisaillement τ_t agissant selon le rayon moyen de l'éprouvette $R_m = \frac{R_e + R_i}{2}$ à la rupture dans la mesure où le tube de roche n'est pas trop épais

$$R_{Tt} = \tau_t = \frac{T}{I} \cdot R_m$$

La mesure de cette résistance à la traction R_{Tt} par torsion nécessite cependant d'opérer sur des éprouvettes d'élancement au moins égal à 3/2 de façon à ce que la fissuration puisse se propager librement.

En torsion-compression axiale, les ruptures apparaissent comme en torsion simple, selon des hélices. Elles sont d'autant plus rapprochées des génératrices que l'effort de compression monoaxial appliqué est élevé (fig. 3). Ce sont encore des ruptures d'extension. La disposition même des ruptures et les observations faites nécessitent d'opérer sur des éprouvettes d'élancement égal ou supérieur à 5/2.

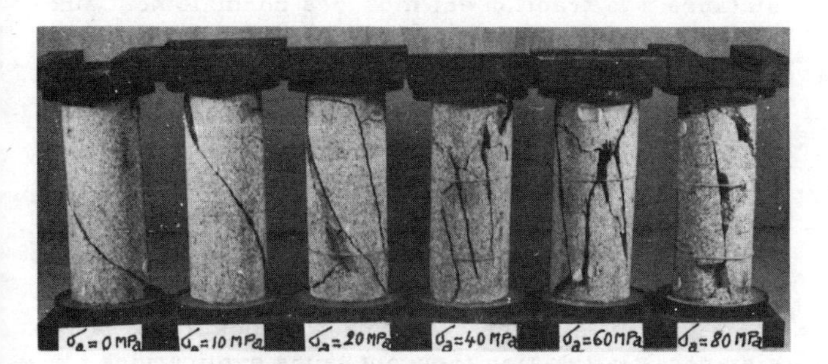

Fig. 3 - Ruptures en torsion-compression axiale. Granite de Corbière
- Failures under torsional load of an axially compressed sample of Corbiere granit
- Granit aus Corbiere ; Bruch bei Drehmomentversuchen mit einachsiger Druckspannung.

Sur la figure 4, sont reportées les résistances τ_t de cisaillement de torsion en fonction de la charge axiale σ_a appliquée à l'éprouvette. Sur cette courbe, la cohésion de la roche est représentée par l'ordonnée de son maximum et la résistance au cisaillement simple par l'ordonnée à l'origine.

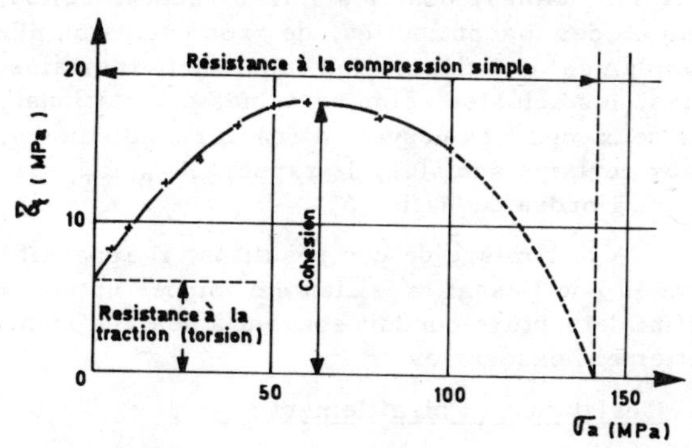

Fig. 4 - Evolution de la résistance au cisaillement de torsion en fonction de la contrainte axiale appliquée à l'éprouvette et maintenue constante en cours d'essai. Granite de Brommat
- Variation of the torsional shear strength of a sample of Brommat granit versus the axial compression, maintained constant during each test
- Granit aus Brommat ; Verlauf der Drehmomentscherfestigkeit in Abhängigkeit von der einachsigen während des Versuchs bleibenden Druckspannung

Connaissant la contrainte de cisaillement de torsion à la rupture pour différentes charges axiales constantes, on peut alors calculer les deux contraintes principales σ_1 et σ_3 du champ biaxial de contraintes :

$$\sigma_1 \text{ et } \sigma_3 = \frac{\sigma_a \pm \sqrt{\sigma_a^2 + 4\,\tau_t^2}}{2}$$

et tracer la coupe $\sigma_2 = 0$ de la surface intrinsèque.

Ce genre d'expérimentation est intéressant car il aboutit à la détermination précise de la cohésion de la roche et de la portion de courbe intrinsèque située entre le cercle de cisaillement simple et le cercle de compression monoaxiale.

En torsion sous contrainte hydrostatique, le champ d'investigation est nettement élargi du côté des compressions. Ces essais de torsion qui ont été réalisés sous des pressions hydrostatiques faibles ont abouti à des ruptures hélicoïdales orientées selon les lignes isostatiques de traction, c'est-à-dire à des ruptures d'extension. Cependant, dans le cas de roches à caractéristiques mécaniques relativement faibles comme la craie, il a été observé, outre des ruptures d'extension pour des pressions hydrostatiques faibles, des ruptures de cisaillement pour des pressions plus élevées.

Milieux à anisotropie planaire discontinue

A l'intérieur d'un bloc de mortier possédant une discontinuité planaire bien nette, des lots d'éprouvettes tubulaires ont été prélevés dans chacune des directions suivantes : $\alpha = 0°, 15°, 30°, 45°, 60°, 75°, 90°$ (3). La discontinuité est positionnée au centre du tube de roche.

Les ruptures qui ont été obtenues au cours des essais de torsion simple sont les suivantes : pour $\alpha < 70°$, les ruptures sont planes et confondues avec le plan de discontinuité (ruptures de clivage), pour un angle α supérieur, l'élancement n'est plus assez grand pour qu'elles soient entièrement contenues dans la discontinuité.

Le couple de torsion à la rupture présente une très nette anisotropie (fig. 5). La valeur minimale du couple de torsion apparaît lorsque le plan de discontinuité est incliné à 45° par rapport à l'axe de l'éprouvette.

Ainsi, la contrainte de cisaillement de torsion à la rupture correspond à la résistance à la traction normalement à la discontinuité pour une éprouvette orientée $\alpha = 45°$ et à la cohésion selon le plan de discontinuité pour une éprouvette orientée $\alpha = 0°$. Comme l'indique la figure 5, la construction géométrique de la courbe intrinsèque de clivage à partir de la courbe d'anisotropie de torsion simple est très commode.

En ce qui concerne les schistes, la dispersion des mesures est beaucoup plus importante. Les résistances de torsion sont généralement faibles, sauf lorsque la schistosité devient parallèle à l'axe de torsion. La courbe polaire prend une allure très dissymétrique. De ces mesures, il est possible de déduire non pas une courbe intrinsèque mais une zone intrinsèque.

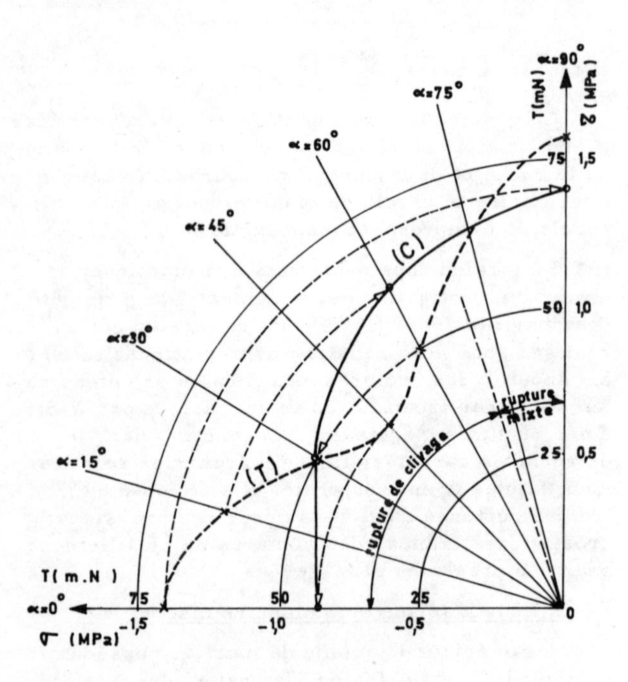

Fig. 5 - Anisotropie polaire du couple de torsion à la rupture (T) et courbe intrinsèque (C). Mortier à discontinuité
- Polar anisotropy of the torsional torque at failure (curve T) and Mohr's envelope (curve C) for a discontinuous mortar
- Polaranisotropie des Drehmoments beim Bruch (T-Kurve) und Mohr'sche Hüllkurve (C) - Bindemittel mit Trennflächen

Sur les schistes de la Coche, il a même été possible de déterminer successivement la cohésion selon différents plans de schistosité. La méthode a consisté à coller le plan de rupture et à recommencer l'essai. A chaque foi, le plan le moins résistant cède et les mesures montrent que la cohésion marque une nette progression. Dans chacun des plans de la roche, la cohésion est différente et les mesures ne reflètent que la cohésion minimale.

Ce type de cisaillement est très intéressant car il n'impose pas un plan préétabli de rupture.

5 - COMPARAISON AVEC LES ESSAIS CLASSIQUES

Jusqu'à présent, il n'a été fait état que des caractéristiques mécaniques des roches testées en torsion. Dans ce qui suit, une comparaison synthétique est établie entre ces caractéristiques et celles obtenues par les essais courants de mécanique des roches, à savoir la traction (traction directe, traction brésilienne) et le cisaillement (cisaillement Lundborg, cisaillement Casagrande, cisaillement triaxial).

Résistance à la traction

Les résistances à la traction obtenues par torsion (R_{Tt}), par traction directe (R_{Td}) et par traction brésilienne (R_{Tb}) sur une série de roches, sont regroupées sur la figure 6. Pour les schistes, la résistance à la traction est mesurée normalement aux plans d'anisotropie.

De l'examen de cette figure, il ressort que les résistances au cisaillement simple, déterminées en torsion simple, sont supérieures ou égales aux résistances de traction directe. Leurs valeurs sont cependant situées dans une fourchette relativement peu ouverte :

$$R_{Tt} \in (R_{Td}, \quad 1,3\ R_{Td})$$

Ces différences concernant la mesure de la résistance à la traction trouvent leurs explications :

- d'une part, dans la nature du champ des contraintes qui est monoaxial en traction directe et biaxial en torsion ;
- d'autre part, dans l'existence de phénomènes parasites (flexion) qui perturbent l'essai de traction directe et sous-estiment les résistances.

Sur la même série de roches, les résistances en traction brésilienne sont plus élevées que celles de traction directe. La comparaison établie avec la résistance au cisaillement simple est plus nuancée. Pour les roches très homogènes, non fissurées et à grains très fins (marbres, anhydrite, ...), les résistances de traction brésilienne et de torsion pure sont très semblables, pour les autres roches, celles présentant des discontinuités, de gros grains ou plus simplement une fissuration importante (certains granites, les schistes selon certaines orientations, ...), les deux mesures peuvent s'écarter notablement. Pour certains schistes, le rapport R_{Tb}/R_{Tt} est même de l'ordre de 7 (fig. 6).

A la lumière de ces résultats, il apparaît clairement que l'essai brésilien qui impose un plan bien défini de rupture conduit souvent à des résistances nettement excessives

Résistance au cisaillement

La figure 7 synthétise les mesures de cohésion déterminée par l'essai de torsion (C_t), par l'essai Lundborg (C_l), par l'essai Casagrande (C_c) et par l'essai triaxial (C_{tr}). Pour les schistes, la cohésion est mesurée selon les plans d'anisotropie.

- Cisaillement Lundborg

La presse de cisaillement E. D. F., type Lundborg, utilise une cellule permettant d'effectuer un double cisaillement sur des éprouvettes cylindriques de 25 mm de diamètre et d'élancement 4.

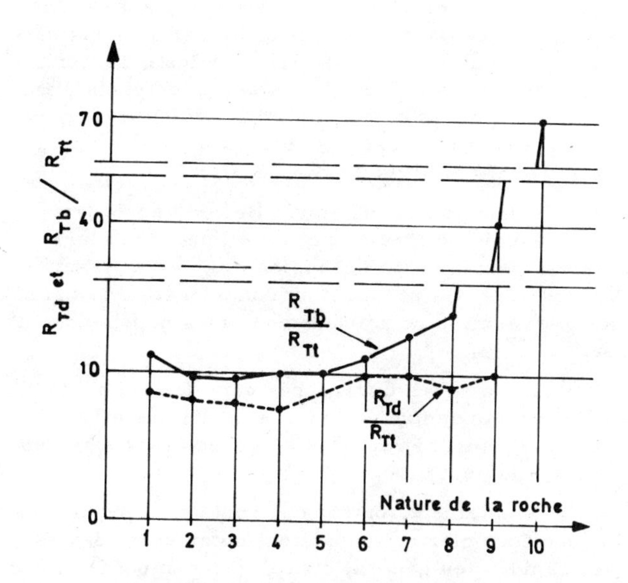

Fig. 6 - Graphique comparatif des résistances à la traction obtenues par différents types d'essais
- Comparison graph of tensile strengths obtained by different types of tests
- Vergleichende graphische Darstellung der durch verschiedene Versuchsmethoden erhaltenen Zugfestigkeit

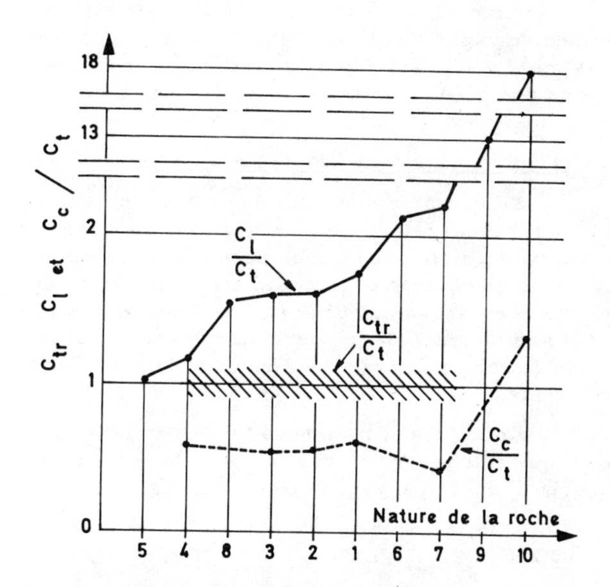

Fig. 7 - Graphique comparatif des cohésions obtenues par différents types d'essais
- Comparison graph of cohesions obtained by different types of tests
- Vergleichende graphische Darstellung der durch verschiedene Versuchsmethoden erhaltenen Kohäsion.

Fig. 6 et 7 - 1 - 2 - 3 Mortier iso saturé à 7, 28 et 90 jours - 4 Marbre de Vilette - 5 Anhydrite d'Echaillon - 6 Granite de Corbière - 7 Granite de Brommat - 8 Craie de Sancerre - 9 Schistes de la Coche - 10 Schistes du Col du Sabot.

La cohésion C_l d'une roche obtenue par le cisaillement Lundborg est systématiquement supérieure aux autres modes de cisaillement (Fig. 7). Le rapport C_l/C_t varie approximativement de 1 à 20, suivant la roche considérée. Dans cet essai, les ruptures n'affectent qu'un très faible volume de roche, si bien que c'est essentiellement la matrice rocheuse qui est sollicitée. D'ailleurs, cet aspect est nettement mis en évidence par les valeurs des cohésions mesurées sur les schistes selon les plans d'anisotropie. C'est sur ce type de roche et pour cette orientation que le rapport C_l/C_t est le plus grand.

Pour une structure statistiquement isotrope, les résultats sont très proche si la roche est bien homogène (anhydrite, marbre,... et s'éloignent dès que la roche possède une fissuration ou même une porosité (granites, craie,...).

Bien que rapide et facile à multiplier, l'essai Lundborg présente cependant l'inconvénient majeur d'imposer un plan de rupture. D'autres facteurs, tels que l'effet Poisson, l'intervalle de cisaillement, la non uniformité du champ de contrainte, en font un essai très complexe.

- Cisaillement Casagrande

L'essai type Casagrande qui impose une zone planaire de rupture (ici 1 cm d'épaisseur) et qui a été réalisé sur éprouvettes parallélépipédiques de 15x20 cm^2 de section, donne des résistances bien différentes (fig. 7). Les caractéristiques de rupture des roches dures, statistiquement isotropes ou anisotropes dans la mesure où la rupture ne se produit pas selon un plan de discontinuité, sont faibles, mais le rapport C_c/C_t est relativement constant (0,4 à 0,6). Mise à part l'incertitude qui règne au niveau de la connaissance exacte du champ de contraintes dans l'éprouvette (contraintes appliquées, contraintes induites,...), les observations conduisent à l'existence de deux phénomènes parasites bien nets : d'abord un effet de flexion sur l'éprouvette, ensuite un cisaillement progressif et non brutal. Ces phénomènes se concrétisent par des mesures de résistances relativement très faibles.

Pour les schistes dont les plans de discontinuités sont orientés parallèlement à la zone de cisaillement, les résistances mesurées par le cisaillement Casagrande sont très dispersées. En moyenne, elles sont plus élevées qu'en torsion pure. Dans ce cas, on ne sait plus très bien ce que l'on mesure car, d'une part on impose une zone relativement mince de rupture qui joue dans le sens de l'excès des mesures, d'autre part on est toujours en présence des phénomènes parasites de flexion et de cisaillement progressif qui jouent en sens inverse.

- Cisaillement triaxial classique

La comparaison entre les mesures de torsion et d'essai triaxial est très bonne. La cohésion déterminée en torsion tombe dans la fourchette de la cohésion obtenue par l'essai triaxial. Cette fourchette correspond aux deux positions extrêmes convenables du tracé de la courbeintrinsèque interpolée entre le cercle de traction directe et les cercles triaxiaux.

Enfin, il est remarquable de constater que, quel que soit le type d'essai utilisé, la pente de la courbe intrinsèque est assez constante.

6 - CONCLUSION

Les essais de torsion-compression axiale exécutés sur des éprouvettes tubulaires conduisent à la détermination des caractéristiques de rupture biaxiale pour les roches statistiquement isotropes et à la détermination des caractéristiques de clivage pour les roches à anisotropie planaire discontinue. Ce sont des essais relativement simples qui précisent les résistances d'une roche dans la partie sommitale de la courbe intrinsèque. Par contre, les essais de torsion-compression hydrostatique d'exécution longue et difficile sont avantageusement remplacés par les essais triaxiaux classiques.

Cette étude amène à distinguer deux groupes d'essais : ceux à cisaillement libre et ceux à cisaillement imposé. Ces derniers (essai brésilien, essai Lundborg, ...) reflètent les caractéristiques mécaniques correspondant essentiellement à la matrice des roches. Nous ne reviendrons pas sur le cisaillement Casagrande où se manifestent des phénomènes parasites. Néanmoins, on peut distinguer certaines nuances dans les différents cisaillements imposés. Le plan de rupture est, par exemple, davantage imposé dans l'essai Lundborg que dans l'essai brésilien et les mesures le confirment.

Si ces essais sont rapides et faciles à multiplier, ils se concrétisent par des résistances généralement excessives, et cela systématiquement dans le cas où l'on cherche à déterminer les caractéristiques mécaniques d'une roche selon les plans d'anisotropie quand ils existent. Pour ces matériaux et selon cette orientation, ces essais à plan de rupture imposé sont définitivement à écarter.

Quant aux cisaillement libres (essais triaxiaux, essais de torsion sous sollicitations pluriaxiales, essais de compression simple, de traction directe, ...), ils prennent en considération la fissuration et sont, à ce point de vue, plus proches de la réalité.

En fait, les différences dans les résultats expérimentaux entre un cisaillement libre et un cisaillement imposé reposent en grande partie sur un effet d'échelle.

Finalement, on est confronté à un problème d'ordre financier qui consiste à opter entre des essais rapides (en général cisaillement imposé) ou des essais plus longs (en général cisaillement libre). Les premiers déterminent des caractéristiques souvent surestimées, les seconds des caractéristiques plus exactes.

----

(1) Ce n'est pas un écrouissage ou un anti-écrouissage au sens classique du terme car la fissuration ne se répartit pas d'une façon homogène dans tout le volume de l'éprouvette

(2) Rigidité de torsion : $C_t = G.I = T/\omega$ où G et I sont respectivement le module de cisaillement de torsion et le moment quadratique de la section droite de l'éprouvette par rapport à son axe.

(3) α est l'angle que fait l'axe de l'éprouvette avec la normale au plan de discontinuité

REMERCIEMENTS

Nos remerciements s'adressent au B.R.G.M. pour sa contribution dans l'élaboration finale de ce document.

REFERENCES BIBLIOGRAPHIQUES

BRICE L. P. - Etude des conditions de formation des fissures de glissement et de décohésion dans les solides. Travaux, juin 1954

COMES G., MASURE Ph. - Emploi systématique du double cisaillement Lundborg pour l'étude des roches. Colloque de géotechnique, thème I, Toulouse, mars 1969

DURAND E. - Comportement des roches à la torsion. Application à l'étude de la stabilité des excavations souterraines. Thèse présentée à la Faculté des Sciences de Nancy, 1973.

HABIB P. - La résistance au cisaillement des sols. Annales de l'I T B T P, n°61, janvier 1953

HANDIN J., HIGGS D. V. and J. K. O'BRIEN - Torsion of yule marble under condining pressure. Rock Deformation, Geol. Soc. Am. Mem., 79, p. 245-274, 1960

WITTKE W., LOUIS Cl. - Quelques essais pour déterminer les caractères mécaniques des matériaux rocheux. Colloque de géotechnique, thème I, Toulouse, mars 1969.

FIELD DETERMINATION OF DIRECT SHEAR STRENGTH

DÉTERMINATION IN SITU DE LA RÉSISTANCE AU CISAILLEMENT DIRECT

IN SITU-BESTIMMUNG DER SCHERFESTIGKEIT IM EINFACHEN SCHERVERSUCH

J. FRANKLIN Consultant, Bracknell, U.K.

J. MANAILOGLOU Geoerevna S.A., Athens, Greece

D. SHERWOOD Rock Mechanics Ltd., Bracknell, U.K.

SUMMARY

The authors have based a programme of insitu direct shear tests on the recently published ISRM draft standard, 'Suggested Methods of Determining Shear Strength'. The more controversial aspects of the test method are evaluated and practical details of fieldwork discussed. The cost of testing is examined in relationship to the required number and size of specimens. An approach to data presentation is illustrated by typical test results.

RESUME

Les auteurs ont formulé un programme d'essais de cisaillement direct in situ sur la base du rapport standard provisoire récemment publié par la SIMR: "Méthodes suggérées pour la détermination de la résistance au cisaillement direct". Les aspects discutables de la méthode d'essai y sont pesés et des détails pratiques du travail sur le terrain sont considérés. Le coût des essais est examiné relativement au nombre et aux dimensions des échantillons. Des résultats typiques illustrent une forme de présentation des données.

ZUSAMMENFASSUNG

Die Autoren haben nach dem jüngst veröffentlichten ISRM Endentwurf über: "Empfohlene Methoden, um die Scherfestigkeit im einfachen Scherversuch zu bestimmen" eine Serie von am Ort ausgeführten direkten Scherversuchen programmiert. Die widersprüchlicheren Aspekte der Testmethode werden bewertet und Details aus der Praxis im Gelände diskutiert. Die Kosten des Testens werden mit Bezug auf die erforderliche Anzahl und Grösse der Proben untersucht. Typische Ergebnisse werden gezeigt, um eine vorgeschlagene Darstellung von Versuchsdaten zu illustrieren.

INTRODUCTION

The ISRM Commission on Standardisation of Laboratory and Field Tests has published a final draft standard on 'Suggested Methods for Determining Shear Strength'. Some aspects of procedure remain, however, a matter of personal preference. It is essential that test methods are regarded as evolving in spite of the production of standards from time to time.

Included in this paper are some of the more controversial topics that were discussed at length in correspondence during preparation of the ISRM document, and the authors would like to acknowledge their indebtedness to other members of the Commission. An earlier draft was put to the test during a programme of fieldwork in Greece, and we thank Geoerevna S.A. of Athens, and Rock Mechanics Limited of Great Britain, for permission to use data to illustrate the paper.

Although many tests have been described in the literature, there is little guidance on determining an appropriate test programme, specimen preparation and on the practical aspects of carrying out the test. One of the objectives of the paper is to deal with these topics in the light of experience gained during a substantial test programme involving two test specimen sizes.

In the direct shear test, as always in field testing, cost is a major factor. For some projects the benefits which may accrue by establishing more favourable parameters with field tests, are not sufficient to justify an adequate field work programme. In many cases, particularly where there is complex structure involved, a laboratory test programme may be more appropriate. This paper would be incomplete without considering these important aspects.

THE TEST SPECIMENS

Determination of the number of tests and their size

Only one peak strength can be determined per specimen, although it is possible to evaluate, with limited accuracy, a number of residual strengths at different normal loads using only one specimen block. A shear strength determination should therefore comprise several tests, preferably three or more at each test horizon.

The overall number of determinations required depends on the number of families of discontinuities (joints, bedding planes, etc) that have a bearing on rock mass stability. In some instances several determinations may be needed to account for variation in strength within a single family, for example in the case of bedding with lithological changes. Only occasionally can a stability problem be resolved to sliding on a unique and predetermined plane.

It is often helpful to run preliminary calculations of stability using approximate data, in order to find which planes are likely to be most critical. It may be necessary, depending on the particular problem, to assess only the weakest horizon of the most critical family, or alternatively to determine a range of strengths relevant to each of several families of discontinuities. It is only after consideration of the problem in hand in these terms that a proper estimate of the number of tests required can be made.

The authors suggest that it is usually better to determine the required minimum number of tests first. The size of specimen should then be assessed after study of a cost of the test programme and related benefit to the project. In some cases where the stability problem is complex, this may reveal that a laboratory test programme is more appropriate.

Size, shape and direction of shearing

The ISRM suggested size of specimen, 700 x 700mm (shear surface area approximately 0.5m^2), was selected because it is this size that is most commonly used at present. Tests on blocks as large as 5 to 10 metres in length are by no means uncommon however (Evdokimou and Sapegin, 1970; Ruiz and Camargo, 1966; Underwood, 1964) and may be appropriate if one can guarantee that the horizon to be tested is the only one of relevance to stability. Tests on 'specimens' of this size have an intrinsic problem in that the body forces acting in the full scale structure are replaced by boundary forces from jacks used in testing; this can result in an unrealistic shear displacement gradient along the base of the block (Underwood, 1964).

There is substantial if not conclusive evidence to show that the measured shear strength may be independent of the size of specimen in most circumstances, although the displacements at which this strength is mobilised are likely to be greater with larger specimens (e.g. Serafim and Guerreiro, 1968). The main problem in testing small specimens is the limited amount of shear displacement that can be achieved, usually amounting to some 10% of the specimen length. It may be impossible to reach a residual strength value if the specimen is too small. Also there is an increased probability, when small specimens are used, of individual unrepresentative results caused by peculiarities of the test horizon which are physically large when compared to the specimen size, but not when compared to the scale of the rock mass as a whole. Other factors to consider are the difficulties encountered in cutting and preserving small specimens, and the increasing importance of edge effects due to irregular geometry and to non-uniformity of stress distribution.

The choice of specimen size to some extent determines whether tests are to be made in the field or in the laboratory, although there is a considerable overlap due to the increasing size capability of laboratory equipment. Heavily fissured, swelling or water sensitive rocks are usually best tested insitu, whereas it may be economic to use laboratory tests for the more competent types of rock. Roughness of the test horizon is also a determining factor. Smooth horizons, for example slaty cleavage and some sedimentary bedding planes, lend themselves remarkably well to a laboratory evaluation.

The shape of the specimen should, within prescribed limits, be left to the discretion of the engineer in charge of the test, who should be free to use natural joints and fissures as the boundaries of the block. This not only reduces the work involved in excavation but also minimizes disturbance to the test horizon. The upper face of the block in particular is often formed by a weak horizon in the same family as the shear plane, and the ISRM suggested block thickness of 350mm should be regarded only as a guide. The minimum permissible thickness depends on the strength of rock within the specimen block, and should be such as to ensure that rock in the vicinity of the shear plane remains intact throughout the test.

It may be some advantage to test a rectangular rather than a square block, one that is elongated in the shear direction. This allows a greater shear displacement for the same contact area, so that there is more chance of reaching a residual strength. However, there may be problems in ensuring a uniform transfer of shear stress to the tested horizon if substantially elongated blocks are employed, due to elastic deformation in the block and to consequent differential movement between the front and rear faces (Underwood, 1964).

It is usually difficult to assess whether the shear strength is likely to be greater in one direction than in others so that a shear direction corresponding to that of anticipated full scale movement should be selected whenever possible. Some types of horizon, for example ripple marked strata, evidently have a strength that depends very much on the direction of shearing, although this is probably not so in full scale field behaviour.

PRACTICAL ASPECTS OF TESTING

Preparation procedure and results will be discussed with reference to insitu testing programmes for the design of dam foundations for a hydroelectric project and for analysis of reservoir slope stability.

Two "multi-stage" tests were carried out on blocks

700 x 700 mm area, using one 200 ton jack for normal loading and another for shear loading. On another site eight similar tests were carried out on specimens measuring 1000 x 1000 mm. Twin 200 ton jacks were used for applying the shear force, with flat jacks for normal load application (Fig. 1).

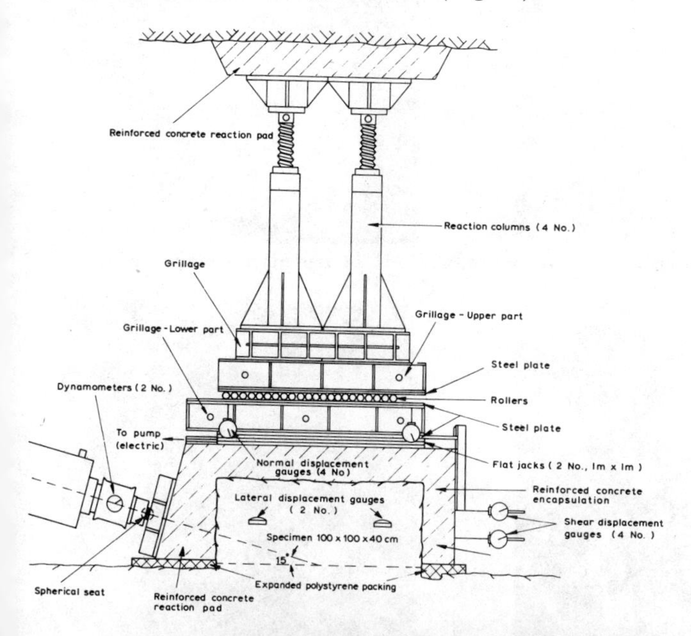

Fig. 1. Direct shear test equipment: 1m x 1m specimen

Testing was carried out in adits whose main purpose was to provide access for geological exploration and mapping. Rock at both sites comprised alternating fine sandstones, siltstones and mudstone of typical bed thickness 10-50 mm, with local occurrences of massive conglomerates and coarser sandstones. The rocks belong to the Flysch formation of Eocene/Miocene age and are characterized by an unusually pronounced stratification, with smooth and continuous bedding planes.

Excavation

Stages in preparation are illustrated in Fig. 2a to 2f. Adits were excavated at locations determined from an initial geological mapping of the ground surface. Walls of the adits were thoroughly washed to facilitate inspection, and all potential test locations were marked. The final choice of test location took into account such factors as the quality and inclination of the test horizon, the likely problems involved in cutting and preserving the specimen, and the ease with which the test chamber could be maintained and drained as well as providing the necessary reaction.

An access chamber was excavated perpendicular to the adit, of just sufficient size to expose the top of the specimen. Preliminary lighting was installed. The plan position of the specimen was selected to take advantage of natural jointing after a thorough washing of the chamber to expose the rock structure. Retaining beams, secured by four rock bolts grouted to one metre below the shear horizon, were installed to prevent relaxation of rock or sliding of steeply inclined specimens. Only then were the roof and walls of the chamber extended to their final dimensions, with rock bolts, wire mesh and plastic sheeting provided as necessary to ensure a safe and convenient working environment.

The sides of the specimen were then line drilled, followed by excavation of the floor of the chamber to the test horizon level (Fig. 2a). Shallow channels cut in the floor around the base of the specimen allow free lateral and shear movement and prevent the continuous feed of unsheared rock to the test horizon. Further channels or sumps may be needed to drain the chamber. The chamber was once more cleaned, the rock conditions recorded, and the specimen protected with damp sacking until ready for encapsultation.

During the operations a variety of problems were encountered. Precussive drilling and breaking to excavate the test chambers can be very slow in the harder rocks. One should consider the use of controlled blasting even inside the test chamber, provided that the specimen is largely protected from transmitted vibrations by line drilling. In the softer rocks much of the excavation closer to the specimen can proceed literally by hand, with only minor assistance from hand saws, hammers and chisels. In some of the softer rocks a circular saw was used for cutting the specimen, although this could only cut a shallow slot. In general, however, the method of line drilling is quickest and produces satisfactory results.

Another major problem is accurate prediction of rock conditions in the chamber. Frequently a clay filling observed in the adit will turn out to be thicker, thinner or non-existent at the location of the proposed specimen. One specimen on examination was found to contain a shear, with a throw of 8-10mm, but fortunately this could be tested by shearing in the direction of strike of the fault. The corner of another specimen had to be removed because it was constituted of a strong intact conglomerate that would probably have caused disintegration of the rest of the block during shearing; a fault had completely offset the test horizon at this location. In another case, the selected horizon was found in the course of testing to be stronger than another several centimetres deeper. The majority of shear displacement took place on the deeper horizon, so that the area of shear surface could not be defined precisely.

a) The cut specimen

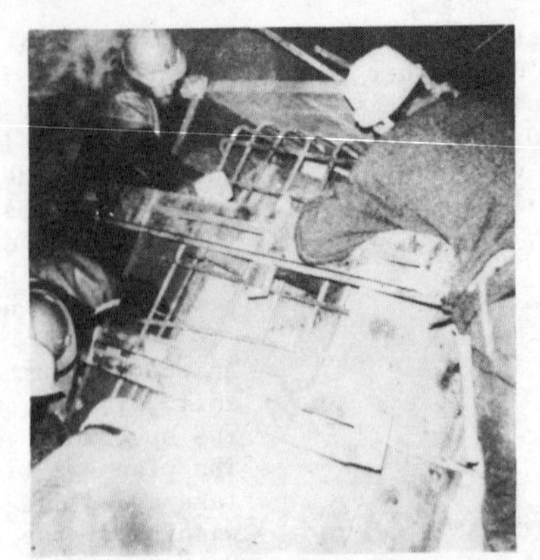

b) Fixing formwork and reinforcement

c) Completed encapsulation

d) Constructing reaction pad

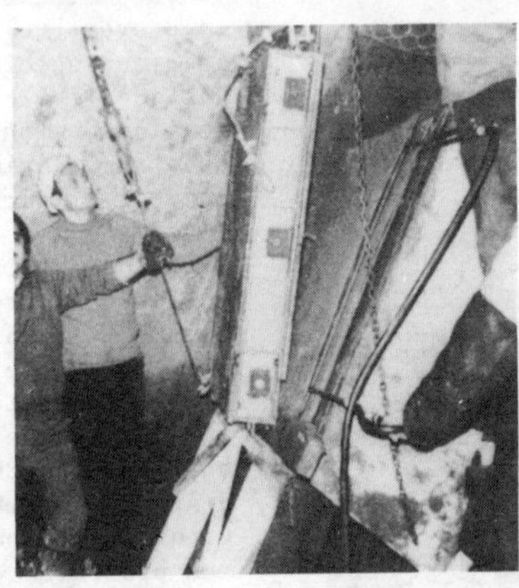

e) Positioning flatjacks

f) Assembling normal load system

Fig. 2. Stages in preparation

The test chambers themselves can give problems. In one chamber the roof that was to have provided reaction for the normal loading had to be excavated about 1m beyond its planned position and replaced with concrete. A weak layer was found during drilling for rock bolts. Further inspection revealed a lens of sand up to 400mm thick in places, which had been partially washed out to leave a void. Similar difficulties can be expected in the course of any routine field investigation, although the majority of problems can be avoided by careful inspection both before and during excavation. It is most important to ensure good lighting in the chamber, and a thorough washing down of the rock surface to reveal structures that may bé quite difficult to observe and interpret, while it may have considerable bearing on the conduct of the test.

Specimen encapsulation

Encapsulation serves the purpose of holding the specimen block intact during shearing, and also provides flat and correctly inclined bearing surfaces. The procedure used by the authors is first to place a 30-40mm layer of expanded polystyrene sheeting around the base of the block to prevent ingree of cement to the test horizon. Irregularities in the rock under this layer are filled with sand. Steel formwork, having been cleaned and greased, is bolted in position over the polystyrene, which is then adjusted to fill any substantial gaps. Reinforcing bars, bent and cut as required, are positioned inside the formwork and secured with wire (Fig. 2b). The concrete is then placed and compacted using vibration from pneumatic tools on the formwork; a high quality concrete is essential. The formwork is struck when the concrete has thoroughly set, and then the polystyrene layer is removed and replaced with damp sacking. Several specimens can be prepared in advance of testing in order to allow adequate time, preferably at least one week, for the concrete to gain strength. The retaining beams should remain in position throughout these operations, and require periodic checking to ensure that they are still tight (Fig. 2c).

Reaction pads and ties

Concrete reaction pads are usually required, for both the shear and normal load systems. These are keyed to the rock with grouted steel dowels; further rockbolts or hooks are used to hold ties for assembly and securing of the equipment. Accurate alignment and positioning are essential and it is best to mark out the positions of reaction pads and ties after the specimen has been encapsulated.

Formwork may be fabricated insitu (Fig. 2d) but is better supplied in pre-fabricated units. Again it is essential to ensure a high standard of reinforced concrete. The authors recommend that proper mix design and control procedure be used to ensure adequate strength is developed before testing.

Assembly of equipment

For safety reasons it is advisable to install the test lighting, prefereably at least 500-1000 watts per test chamber, before the start of assembly. The next step is to replace the temporary normal load provided by the retaining beams by a normal load from the test equipment itself. Particular care is needed to ensure that at no stage is the specimen left unsupported, since a shear movement of even a millimetre can invalidate the peak strength results. If assembly of the normal loading system is not possible with the retaining beams in position, these beams must be replaced by alternative supports such as screw props.

The upper surface of the encapsulation may be irregular and is smoothed by applying a thin screed of cement paste, and then a sheet of hardboard. Two flat jacks (required in this case to allow a sufficient normal displacement) are filled with oil and then placed accurately in position, followed by the plate and roller system secured by a temporary framework and wire ties. The normal load columns are installed and tightened (Figs. 2e and 2f). The pumps are checked to full pressure, connected to the flat jack, and a small normal load applied to the specimen.

The shear jacks are installed, with a spherical seat and dynamometer for each jack, and the jacks are then extended until the complete assembly is secure. Care is required in the alignment of the jacks, and also to ensure that the specimen is not sheared prematurely.

Temporary ties are removed, and those ties required to hold the normal load columns during the test are tightened and checked. The dial gauge reference beams and gauges are installed, and each dial gauge is checked for adequate and unrestricted travel. Thick glass plates may be cemented to the encapsulation using gypsum plaster, in order to provide a smooth and hard bearing surface for each dial gauge plunger. The gauges are numbered and trial readings taken to ensure that each can be read without difficulty.

TEST PROCEDURE

The direct shear test is simple in concept. In practice, however, the test procedure includes a number of precautions to ensure valid results. These are outlined in the ISRM method and some aspects will now be discussed in more detail.

Consolidation and drainage

In soil testing, consolidation behaviour is invariably noted and taken into account, whereas in rock testing it has usually been ignored. There appears to be little logic behind such a difference of approach.

Stability calculations usually call for the introduction of pore water pressure as an independent parameter in the analysis, in which case it is essential to measure shear strength under "drained" conditions with sufficient time allowed as the test proceeds for dissipation of excess water pressures. These excess pressures may be generated in the shear plane by either the application of the normal load, or by the shearing itself. Drained tests require a specification for the minimum time of consolidation before the start of shearing (consolidation time), and for the time that should elapse before peak strength is reached (time to peak).

Specification of these two time requirements introduces practical problems. In soil testing, theoretical considerations lead to a time-to-peak requirement of the order of 6 x t_{100}, where the time t_{100} to reach "100% primary consolidation" is obtained from the consolidation graph (Gibson and Henkel, 1954). If this practice is applied to tests on rock, one may find that the tests need to last many hours or even days, and it is reasonable to question whether the nature of the theory justifies the considerable expense involved.

The first problem encountered in applying the existing soils theory to field tests on rock concerns drainage conditions. One dimensional drainage is assumed, with flow from the shear plane towards the upper free face of the block. In field tests on rock the specimen is usually encapsulated with no provision for drainage from the free faces. It is doubtful whether any such provision, if installed, would serve a useful purpose; drainage in the rock specimen is likely to be greatly facilitated by the presence of fissure, and one might expect the majority of excess water pressure in the shear plane to be dissipated by flow either along the shear plane or within the 'reservoir' formed by the specimen block. The volume of water involved is likely to be very small relative to that of the specimen.

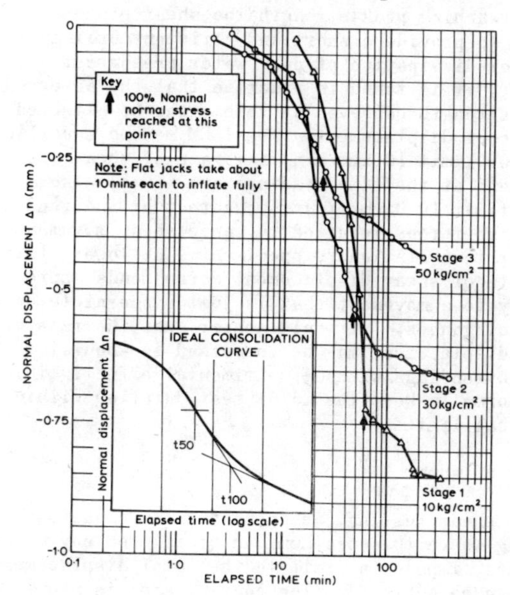

Fig. 3. Typical consolidation curves for a three stage test

A much more serious limitation is the difficulty in reliable measurement of t100. The 'consolidation' curve (Fig. 3) is in fact a record of two superimposed time-dependent phenomena, firstly consolidation in the strict sense (associated with pore water migration), and secondly 'creep' due to viscous behaviour of the rock (associated with gradual closing of fissures under frictional and high - contact - stress conditions). It is likely that in many rock tests the creep component may be significantly greater than that due to consolidation. This could lead to a considerable over estimate of t_{100} and to unreasonably prolonged tests.

It is in principle possible to use measurements of pore water pressure for control of the rate of shearing, rather than employing a theoretical criterion for this purpose. However, in practice the volumes of water involved are small, and the measurements would be excessively difficult under arduous field test conditions.

The ISRM method requires the inclusion of a consolidation stage as part of the test, with application of a $6 \times t_{100}$ criterion for clay-bearing and soil-like rocks. An empirical upper limit of 0.2mm/min is set to the rate of shear displacement before reaching peak strength; in the majority of cases this should allow sufficient dissipation of pore pressure for the test to be regarded as "drained". The authors have found the specification satisfactory as in several tests shear displacements rates were temporarily reduced substantially without any apparent increase in measured shear strength. This was taken as confirmation that near fully drained shear strengths were in fact being measured. It is however, an interim specification, and there is no doubt that the problem requires further research.

Rates of shear

After reaching peak strength the shear plane is likely to provide a short and efficient drainage path for dissipation of pore water pressures. However, it is found in practice that the observed shear strength can even at this stage be affected by rate of displacement. The ISRM method specifies an upper limit (0.2mm/min) for rate of shear displacement at the time readings are taken, also a lower limit (0.02mm/min) to ensure that the readings relate to forces required to cause shear movement and not to a stationary specimen. The lower limit for rate of shear displacement corresponds approximately to a movement that is just discernible on the dial gauges. It would appear that the rate of shear displacement may be increased to about 1mm/min between readings without detrimental effect. This will normally keep the total test duration within practical limits.

Amount of shear

Direct shear testing, as opposed to torsional shear testing where the specimen can be rotated any number of times, imposes a limit to the total displacement that can be achieved. The contact area is progressively reduced, and the normal load distribution becomes less uniform with increasing displacement (Kutter, 1971; Ruiz et al, 1968). A practical limit is usually reached at a displacement of about 10-20% of the block length, after which there is significant risk of rupture of the encapsulated block, and possibly also instability of the equipment.

The available displacement may be utilized either at a constant normal stress, with several increments of normal stress as in the 'multi-stage' test, or by a method involving cycling of normal stress (Fig. 4). In all three methods the normal stress is held constant until the peak strength has been measured (usually at a shear displacement of 1-10mm) and the methods differ only in their approach to determination of residual strength.

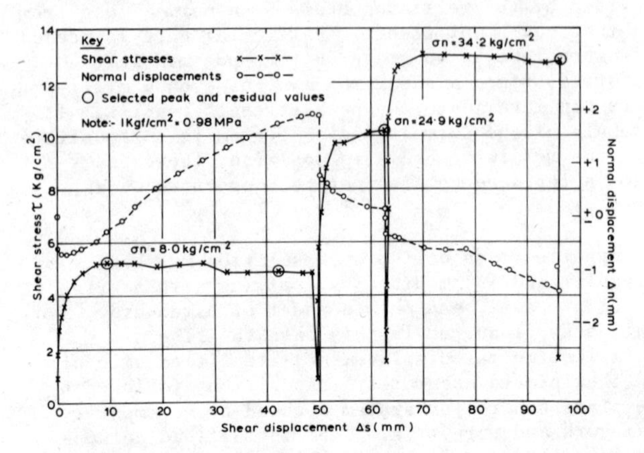

a) A typical multi-stage test

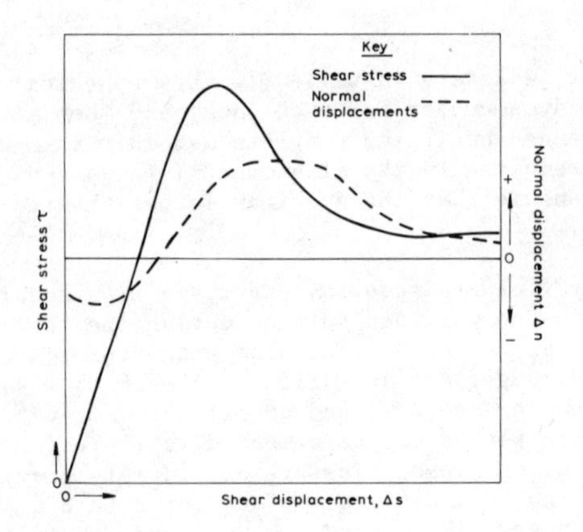

b) An ideal single stage test

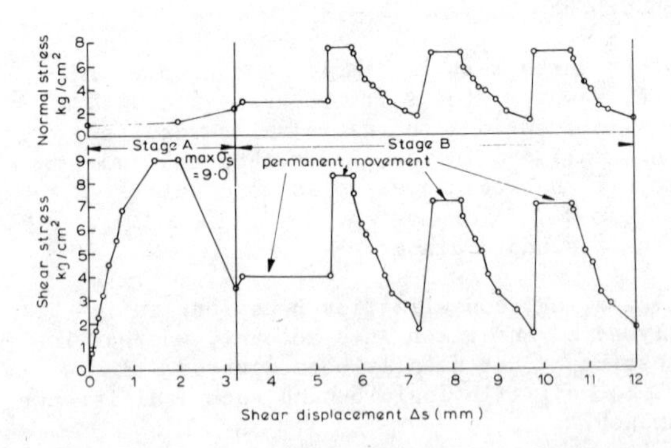

c) A test with cycling of normal load (after Drozd, 1967)

Fig. 4. Shear stress - displacement graphs

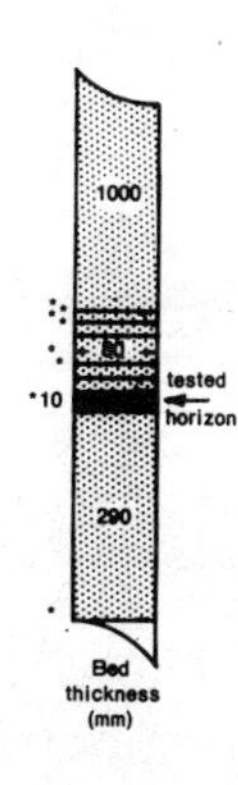

TEST BLOCK DS2

Rock Materials

SANDSTONE with SILTY MUDSTONE partings*
Sandstone beds: Light grey, medium to fine grained. Difficult to break with hammer. Bedding generally strikes N90°E, dipping 15°S.
Several sets of tight irregular joints nearly perpendicular to bedding. Fracture spacing index I_f = 220mm (range 100 – 500 mm)
Silty mudstone partings: Dark grey, slightly silty, moderately well cemented, easy to break with fingers.

Shear Surface

Type: BEDDING PLANE
Filling, weathering and alteration: tested at base of a 10mm SILTY MUDSTONE parting as above, no observed weathering or alteration.
Orientation: Bedding strike N90°E, dip 15°S (15° at 180° True North).
Direction of shear: Up dip ± 5°
Roughness: 5 mm amplitude random irregularities at 150 – 200 mm crest to crest.
Persistence: 100%
Openness: Zero
Water condition: no percolation or staining; tested with precautions to preserve natural water content.

Nature of Failure and Shear Debris

Sheared at base of the 10mm parting. Layer of blocky fragments 5mm down to fine sand size covering about 80% of the surface, layer thickness 10mm to zero. Approximately 2% of the surface polished, with very little striation.

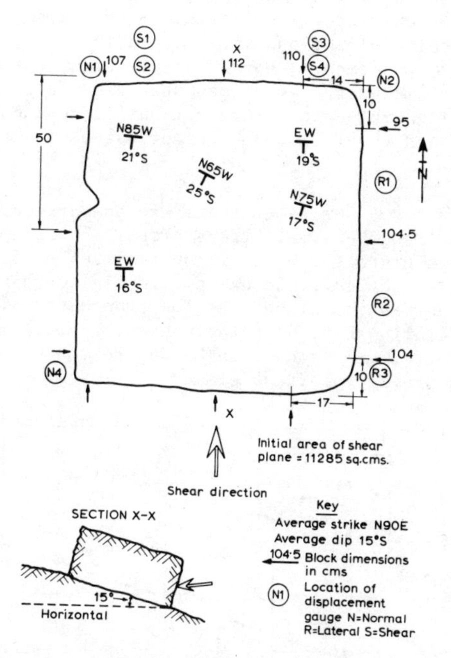

Fig. 5. Method of Specimen description

The choice is between economy and reliability, between the determination of several "residual" values at different normal stress levels on only one specimen or, continuing shear under constant normal stress to ensure that no further significant reduction in strength occurs.

In practice a "true" residual strength may only be reached after a displacement considerably greater than can be achieved in the test. For engineering purposes a residual strength reached after several metres of displacement may be less relevant to stability calculations than an intermediate strength at a smaller displacement. The programme of normal stress increments should be reviewed during the test after examining the results, rather than decided on an arbitrary basis in advance of testing. A change to a new normal stress is not advisable until a reliable strength value has been established at the original level.

A method of cycling the normal stress (Drozd, 1967) allows shear strength to be plotted, usually for three cycles of normal load, as a function of shear displacement (Fig. 4c). This approach obtains a maximum of information from a single specimen, and may be preferred to a simple multi-stage test.

However, there may be some doubt as to whether a test of this sort can be regarded as 'drained' in view of the continuously changing normal and shear stresses.

Reversals of shear direction are sometimes used in order to achieve greater magnitudes of total displacement, either with measurements during shearing in both directions, or by returning the block to its starting position and recording values for shear in one direction only. The procedure is of doubtful reliability because disturbance to the gouge or shear debris is unavoidable. No comparative work has been done on whether results after a reversal bear any relation to results for continued shear in one direction.

TEST RESULTS

Field tests are expensive and it is worth ensuring a thorough and systematic documentation of supplementary geotechnical data to allow interpretation of anomalous results and to relate test conditions to those for the site as a whole. A typical specimen description is shown in Fig. 5. This should be supplemented with laboratory data, particularly index tests, wherever possible.

Clear presentation of test results is no less important. During the test data is recorded on a suitable data sheet and is at the same time plotted graphically to allow a feedback for control of the testing programme. Examples of consolidation and shear stress-displacement graphs are given in Fig. 3 and 4.

The stress-displacement graphs obtained in this series of tests were unusual in that peak strengths were recorded for only six out of ten specimens, and even then the peak strengths were only slightly greater than residual strength values obtained. This is probably caused by the unusual smoothness of the bedding planes that were tested; also in some cases the beds had evidently been pre-sheared by tectonic folding. Residual strength estimates could be obtained with sufficient precision for practical applications after approximately 30mm of shear displacement. Normal displacements, recorded on the same graph, sometimes showed a continued dilatation throughout the test but in most cases the dilatation was followed by compression of shear debris.

Results for a series of tests are summarised on a shear strength-normal stress graph. There should be one such graph for each of the families of discontinuities tested. The example in Fig. 6 relates to tests on bedding planes and the pronounced straight line relationship, also the unusually small scatter of results, are thought to be due to the unusually smooth profile of these planes.

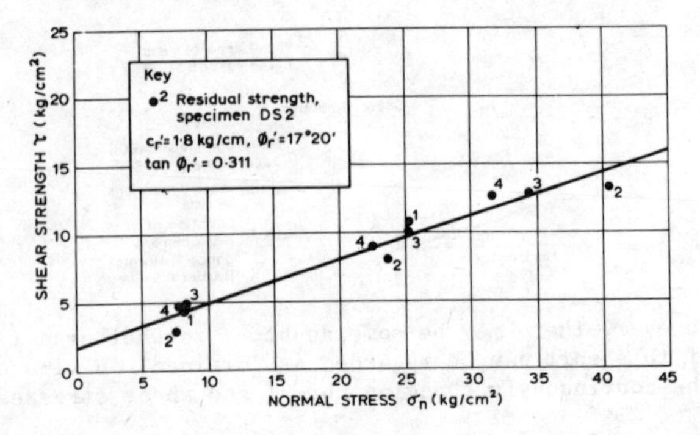

Fig. 6. Shear strength-normal stress graph: tests on Flysch bedding planes.

COST FACTORS

The main cost item in the direct shear test is excavation particularly in the careful hand excavation needed in the vicinity of the test specimen. It is relevant to note that the dimensions of a test chamber increase in approximate proportions to three times the specimen plan dimensions. The required loading capacity and therefore the bulk of testing equipment increase in proportion to the area of the shear surface. Fig. 7 shows that the overall cost increases dramatically for larger specimens. For underground tests, a major consideration must also be whether access adits are necessary for other aspects of investigation of whether their cost has to be considered as part of the overall cost of the tests.

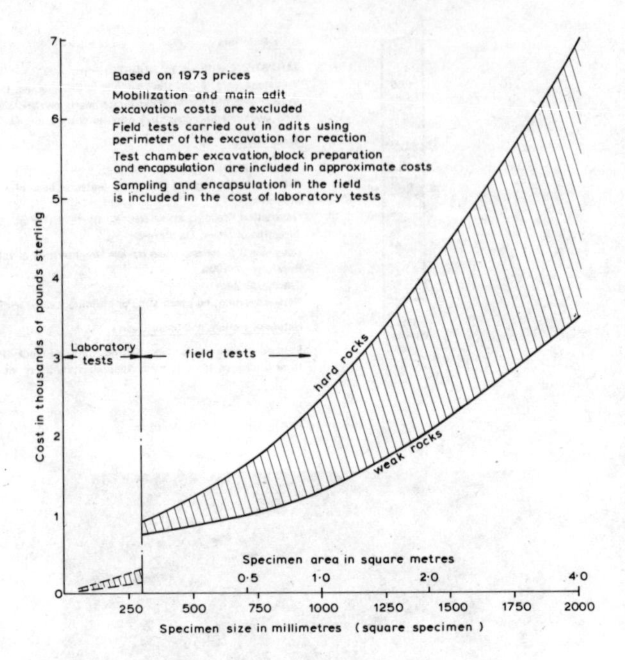

Fig. 7. Cost of testing as a function of specimen size

A multi-stage test is generally cheaper than a set of single stage tests although an attempt to squeeze the maximum of information from a single specimen block can only be to the detriment of the quality of all the data obtained. A set of three or four tests on the same horizon in a single chamber should always be considered as their cost will generally be much less than the sum of the costs of individual tests.

REFERENCES

DROZD, K., 1967, Variations in the shear strength of a rock mass depending on the displacement of the test blocks. Proc. Geotech. Conf. Oslo, 1,4/3, p. 265

EVDOKIMOV, P.D. and D.D. SAPEGIN, 1970, A large scale field shear test on rock. Proc. 2nd Cong. Int. Soc. Rock Mech., Belgrade, 2,3-17

GIBSON R.E. and D.J. HENKEL, 1954, Influence of duration of test at a constant rate of strain on measured 'drained' strength. Geotechnique, 4, p 10

KUTTER, H.K., 1971, Stress distribution in direct shear test samples. Proc. Symp. oc Rock Fracture, Nancy, II-6

RUIZ, M.D. and F.P. CAMARGO, 1966, A large scale field shear test on rock. Proc. 1st Cong. Int. Soc. Roc. Mech., Lisbon, 1, p 257

RUIZ, M.D., F.P. CAMARGO, N.F. MIDEA and C.M. NIEBLE, 1968, Some considerations regarding the shear strength of rock masses. Int. Symp. Rock Mech., Madrid, II-5, p 159

SERAFIM, J.L. and M. GUERREIRO, 1968, Shear strength of rock masses at three Spanish dam sites, Int. Symp. Rock Mech., Madrid, II-4, p 147

UNDERWOOD, L.B., 1964, Chalk foundations at four major dams in the Missouri river basin. Trans. 8th Int. Cong. Large Dams, Edinburgh, 1, R2, Q28, p 23.

UNCONVENTIONAL LABORATORY TESTS FOR THE DETERMINATION OF THE SHEAR STRENGTH OF SOIL-ROCK CONTACTS

ESSAIS DE LABORATOIRE LOIN DE ROUTINE POUR LA DÉTERMINATION DE LA RÉSISTANCE AU CISAILLEMENT DES CONTACTS SOL-ROCHE

AUSSERORDENTLICHE LABORVERSUCHE FÜR DIE BESTIMMUNG DER SCHERFESTIGKEIT DER BODENFELSEN-KONTAKTE

M. A. KANJI

Assistant Professor, University of Sao Paulo, Brazil
Chief, Rock Mechanics Division, Promon Engenharia, S.A.
Brazil

SUMMARY - When dealing with the stability of rock masses, it is important to identify the weakest planes within the rock mass, where weak layers of soil or shale intercalated between hard rock layers, or joints and faults with clay infilling is very often encountered. For this reason, drained direct shear tests on specimens of soils, soil-rock contacts of varying surface roughness, and "sandwich" or double contact with clay infilling, were carried on. The specimen preparation and testing procedures are described in detail, and the testing results are presented and discussed. The application of these tests for measurement of the residual strength of soil is also considered.

RÉSUMÉ - En étudiant la stabilité des massifs rocheux, c'est important d'identifier les plans plus faibles existant dans le massif, où les intercalations de couches de sol ou de schistes argileux entre les couches de roche dure ou diaclases et failles remplies d'argile, peuvent être souvent rencontrées. Pour cette raison, on a fait des essais drainés de cisaillement direct sur des échantillons de sol, des contacts sol-roche avec surfaces de rugositées differentes, et des "sandwich" ou double contact rempli d'argile. La préparation des échantillons et le procédé des essais sont décrit en detail: les résultats des essais sont présentés et interpretés. Il a été consideré aussi l'application de ces essais pour mesurer la résistance residuelle du sol.

ZUSAMMENFASSUNG - Bei Untersuchung der Standfestigkeit von Felsmassen ist es wichtig, die schwächsten Ebenen der Felsmasse festzustellen, wo man oft schwache Boden- oder Schieferschichten zwischen harten Felslagen oder Klüfte und Verwerfungen mit Ton gefüllt findet. Deswegen wurden drainierte direkte Scherversuche mit Bodenproben, Boden-Fels Kontakten mit verschiedenen Flächenrauhigkeiten und "Sandwich" oder Doppelkontakt mit Tonfüllung ausgeführt. Die Vorbereitung der Proben und Ausführung der Versuche sind in allen Einzelheiten beschrieben, und die Versuchsergebnisse sind angegeben und werden diskutiert. Es wurde auch die Ausnützung dieser Versuche für die Messungen der residuellen Bodenfestigkeit in Betracht gezogen.

INTRODUCTION

When dealing with the stability of rock masses, as in the case of rock slopes or dam foundations, it is important to identify the weakest planes within the rock mass, where the occurence of weak layers of soil or shale intercalated between hard rock layers, or of joints or faults with clay infilling is very often encountered. According to their position with respect to the acting forces, they may represent the potential plane of failure. It has been common practice to assume that the strength of the soil or shale represents the minimum strength present; the soil or weak infilling is sampled for testing, either on undisturbed or remolded specimens, and the strength parameters thus found are used for the stability analysis. However, it has been suggested by PATTON (1968) that such an assumption may not be valid and that lower shear strengths might be obtained along the soil-rock interface than for either material alone.

Starting with this suggestion, an investigation was carried out (KANJI, 1969, 1970) to initiate the study of the shear strength of soil-rock contacts and to compare these strengths with those obtained from the soil and rock tested alone. The investigation was afterwards extended (KANJI, 1972) to include other types of soils and rocks and to use different testing conditions to represent discontinuities with clay infilling; attention was also given to the influence of the surface roughness and the thickness of infilling.

It was assumed that very rough rock surface sheared in contact with soil could give strengths similar to those obtained for the soil itself. In Nature, the roughness of such discontinuities may vary widely, but there are many geological situations in which the contacts have small roughness, or are smooth and even polished. Examples of such conditions have been quite often referred to, as by

PATTON (1966 a, 1966 b), DEERE (1967), DUNCAN (1969) PITEAU (1970) DEERE and PATTON (1971), TULINOV and MOLOKOV (1972), and JAEGER (1972).

This paper describes tests devised for the measurement of the shear strength of soil-rock contacts and discontinuities with clay infilling, as well as summarizing and discussing results obtained. The sample preparation and testing procedures are described in detail to allow easy reproduction of the tests according to the technique achieved.

TESTING PROGRAM AND MATERIALS

The selection of materials for testing was based on confining the study to the least number of variables necessary to gain insight into the shear strength of soil-rock contacts and comparing these results with those of the soil alone. Basically, five different soils were tested alone and in contact with rock, with different surface preparations (i.e. different degrees of roughness); two rock types were used, in composite soil-rock specimens and in "sandwich" specimens. These materials were tested in such a way that the program was kept to a feasible number of tests while allowing a full investigation of the dependent variables:

- each soil or rock surface was tested alone under at least three different normal stresses;
- each soil was tested against at least two types of surface preparations of the same rock type;
- each rock type was tested against at least two different soils;
- each type of test was performed at least with two different types of soils.

In addition, some preliminary and complementary tests were performed with the purpose of characterizing or defining the shear strength of the soil or of the soil-rock contact while varying each of the following factors: initial water content of the soil, rate of shearing, amount of displacement, and reversals of movement. Several tests were duplicated to check the reproducibility of results.

Five types of soils were tested. Two of the soils, the Georgia Kaolinite and Marblehead Illite, were selected since they are relatively pure monominerallic clays.

The Goose Lake Flour is a commercially processed polymineralic mixture of sand, silt and clay particles and was used also for purposes of comparison of results, since it is a standard soil used for many researches at the Soil Mechanics Laboratory of the University of Illinois. The residual soil from basalt and the silt from discontinuities in a basaltic lava flow were chosen because they commonly occur in association with the basalt, one the rock types selected, and are found in many dam sites and other engineering works over much of Southern Brazil; they were obtained from the Ilha Solteira and the Agua Vermelha dam sites respectively. The index properties of the soils used and their approximate mineralogy from X-Ray determinations are presented in Table 1. The silt was sampled from rock cores obtained through integral sampling drilling as developed by ROCHA (1971), and due to the very limited amount of the materia it was not feasible to run index tests to control its liquid limit; however, it is estimated to be about 15%.

One of the rock types used was the so called "Bedford" limestone, from a quarry near Bloomington, Indiana, actually a Salem limestone of Mississipian age. It es light brown in color, and made of clastic particles derived mostly from a wide variety of invertebrates, and cemented with calcite. The other rock type is a fine grained, dark, dense basalt from the Agua Vermelha dam site (under construction) on the Rio Grande, and is of Mesozoic age. Both rock types were used with two surface finishes: saw cut (diamond circular saw) and polished (No. 1200 grit), but a rough natural joint of the basalt was also tested (average roughness of ca. 3 mm). Profiles of the micro-roughness of the prepared surfaces were obtained with the "Taylsurf 4" precision equipment.

EQUIPMENT AND SPECIMEN PREPARATION

To achieve the purpose of the study, a standard Wykeham-Farrance direct shear device, strain-controlled, with special provisions to allow reversals of movement was used. The rate of advancement can be adjusted from $6x10^{-1}$ to $6x10^{-4}$ mm/mm in 25 different rates of shearing within this range. All soils were tested with initial water contents at the liquid limit, i.e. liquidity index equal 1.0. No special modifications of the equipment or the shear box were needed for the soil-rock or "sandwich" specimens but a different procedure for the sample prepration and set up was employed, as shown in Figure 1.

The set up of the soil specimen in the shear box (see Figure 1a) follows the conventional procedure for testing remolded soils. To prepare the soil for the shear box, the required amount of sample for each test was completely remolded by spatula on a glass plate in a humid room. The sample was then molded in a sample trimming device, between two perforated metal plates provided with teeth. The "free" thickness of the specimens was about 5 mm for the soils of moderate plasticity and about 8 to 10 mm for the illite and the residual soil. The specimens were placed in the shear box between two saturated porous plates, to facilitate drainage.

For the direct shear testing of soil-rock

SOIL TYPES	INDEX PROPERTIES					MINERALOGY (%)										REFERENCE OR DETERMINATION BY
	W_ℓ (%)	W_p (%)	I_p (%)	%<2μ	Act. No.	Quartz	Kaolinite	Illite	Montmor.	Mix-Lay.	Chlorite	Labrad.	Augite	Goethite	Zeolite	
G.L.Flour	30	18	12	25	.48	25	30	10	-	20	15	-	-	-	-	J.L.Eades
G.Kaol.	48	26	22	54	.41	-	99	-	-	1	-	-	-	-	-	J.L.Eades
M.Ill.	104	27	77	78	.99	-	-	95	-	5	-	-	-	-	-	Gaudete et al,1965
Resid.Soil	112	38	74	66	1.12	5	10	5	70	-	-	tr.	tr.	5	-	J.E.Farjallah
Silt.	-	-	-	-	-	tr.	-	-	tr.	-	-	70	10	-	tr.	J.E.Farjallah

Table 1 - Index Properties and Approximate Mineralogical Composition (X-Ray determination)

Table 1 - Plasticité et composition minéralogique des sols utilisés (determinée par les rayons-X)

TABELLE 1-Plastizität und mineralogische Zusammensetzung der benützten Böden (Festgestellt durch Röntgen)

contacts (See Figure 1b) the following procedure was used to assemble the composite specimen. The rock slabs were cut with a diamond saw using water as the cooling medium. The polished surfaces were produced by grinding the slab surfaces with a No. 1200 carborundum grit on a rotary polishing table which had a steel surface and is commonly used for petrographic thin sections. The rock slabs used were about 5.9 by 5.9 cm, and the contact surfaces were washed with soap and detergent to clean them from any grease. A rock slab was placed in the lower shear box with its surface protruding about 0.5 to 1 mm above the surface of the box. This level was obtained by placing the slab on a filler (porous or metal plates of varying thickness), carefully controlled with a comparator. As the rock specimen was necessarily slightly smaller than the inner dimension of the shear box (6 x 6 cm), it was tightly wedged along the sides by means of metal shims. The soil sample was prepared according to the same procedure described for the testing of soil specimens, but with only perforated metal plate, and the "free" thickness was usually thinner, about 4 mm for "Goose Lake Flour" and Georgia Kaolinite, and from 5 to 8 mm for the soils of greater plasticity. The soil sample, with the perforated metal plate, was inverted (with respect to the molding position) and placed on top of the rock slab to form the soil-rock contact, or composite specimens. The "free" thickness is selected in such a way as to allow a convenient and representative thickness of the soil after consolidation. If the initial thickness of the soil is too small, the sample after consolidation may be affected by irregular stress distribution due to the presence of the teeth of the metal plate. Also, the metal plate may eventually touch the rock surface leading to erroneous results, or it may touch the opposite half of the shear box inhibiting movement, and thus damaging the equipment. On the other hand, if the initial soil thickness is too great, consolidation takes a long time to occur and a very small shear rate is needed to allow pore pressure dissipation.

The assembly of the specimen for a "sandwich" specimen (see Figure 1c) follows the same procedure as for the soil-rock contact, with the exception that an additional rock slab has to be fixed by means of metal shims or other adequate means to the upper half of the shear box. As in the case of the lower rock slab, its surface has to protude with respect to the shear box. The desired thickness of soil infilling is molded on one slab, also with the help of the trimming device. When both parts are assembled they form the "sandwich" sample.

In the case of composite soil-rock or "sandwich" specimens, an alternate procedure for the fixation of the rock slab to the shear box is the use of a cementing material, for example plaster or cement, instead of metal shims. This procedure may inhibit pore pressure dissipation particularly in the case of relatively permeable rocks but it may be necessary when testing undisturbed natural joints with infilling obtained from rock cores, or saw cut surfaces from rock cores with remolded clay infilling, as illustrated in Figure 2.

The theory developed by GIBSON and HENKEL (1954) may be used to calculate the rate of shearing for drained tests for all the test types mentioned above. For the soil-rock

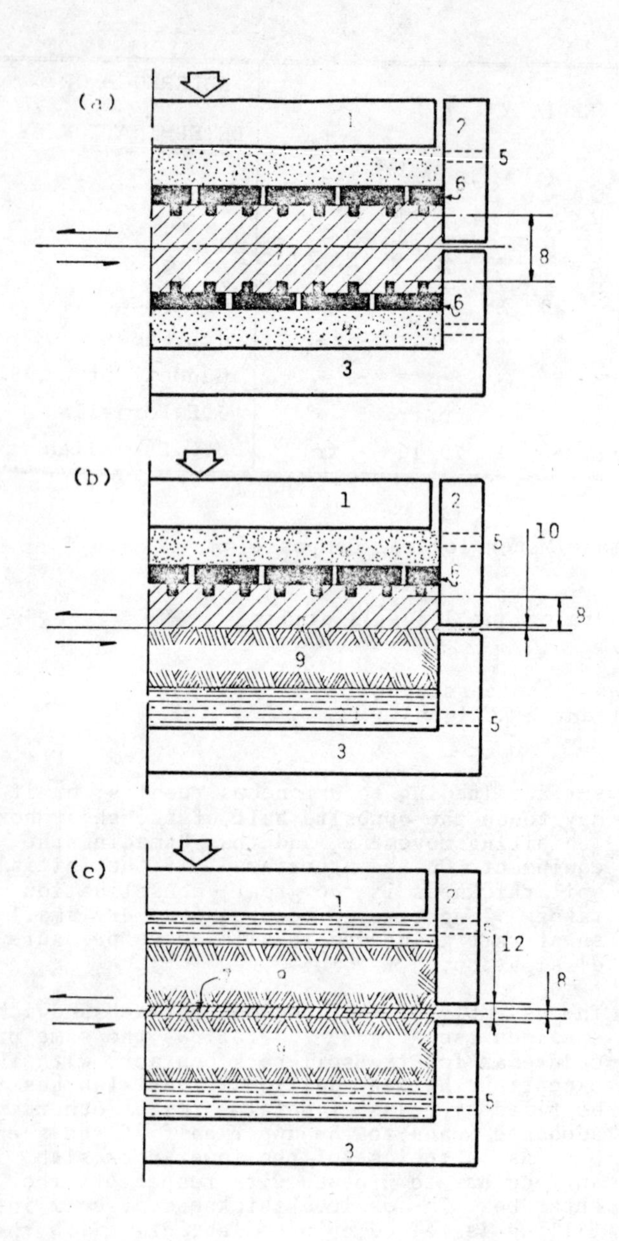

Legend:

1 cap of shear box
2 upper half of shear box
3 lower half of shear box
4 porous plate
5 drain
6 perforated metal plate with teeth
7 soil specimen
8 "free" thickness of soil specimen
9 rock specimen
10 "clearance"
11 filler: metal plates, shims, etc.
12 spacing spacing between boxes

Figure 1 - Sketches of the set up for soil (a), soil-rock contact, (b), and "sandwich" (c) specimens.

Figure 1 - Schémas d'assemblements des échantillons de sol (a), de contact sol-roche (b) et de "sandwich" (i.e. couche mince de sol entre deux surfaces rocheuses)(c).

Bild 1 - Schema der Bodeneinrichtung (a), Kontakt zwischen Boden und Felsen (b) und Doppel-Kontakt-Proben (c).

specimen, since the thickness of the soil sample is about the half of that of the soil specimen, the drainage path remains the same as well as the required rate of shearing for drained tests. For the "sandwich" specimen this path has to be considered as the semi-width of the interlayer, since drainage is only allowed laterally, in the case of impervious rock. The rate of shearing computed from the above theory is conservative, as stated by HVORSLEV (1960) but this was also confirmed experimentally in this study.

TESTING PROCEDURE

Testing procedure for the composite samples followed the same one as adopted for testing the soil alone. The soil was allowed to consolidate under incremented normal loads and the consolidation time was controlled, to ensure complete primary consolidation. Immediately before shearing the upper half of the shear box was raised by means of spacing screws so as to avoid contact between both halves of the shear box. The shearing rate used varied with the time required for consolidation. All tests were carried out in the drained condition.

As a check on the theoretical rate of shearing thus found, some tests on Goose Lake Flour were run at the computed rate and also at three other rates (the slowest being as low as 1/25 of the computed one). The peak strengths were found to be the same for all these tests. This agreement was considered to be an indication that the computed rate would assure full drainage of the specimen and avoid development of undesirable pore-water pressure

FEASIBILITY OF PORE PRESSURE MEASUREMENT

Results of the influence of the rate of shearing on the shearing strength of composite samples after large displacements (KANJI, 1970) have shown the importance of the measurement of pore water pressures at the interface, for its correct interpretation. Such technique has been satisfactorily achieved by CLARK and MAYERHOF (1972) for skin friction tests of soil and steel and, more recently, by GOODMAN and OHNISHI (1973) for sliding friction tests of rock joints.

TESTS RESULTS

The peak shear strengths and the minimum attained shear strengths at maximum displacement allowed by the equipment, for the

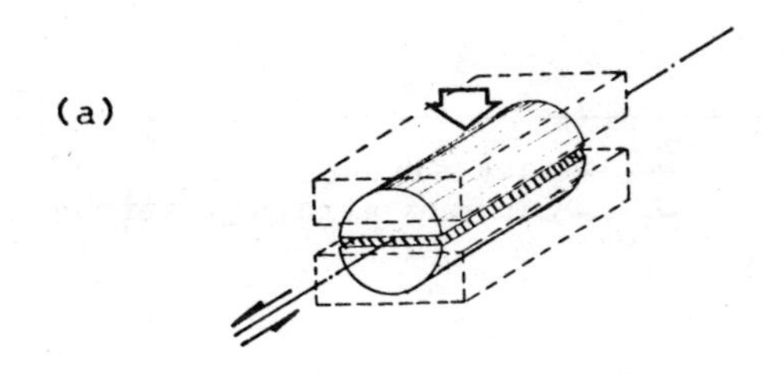

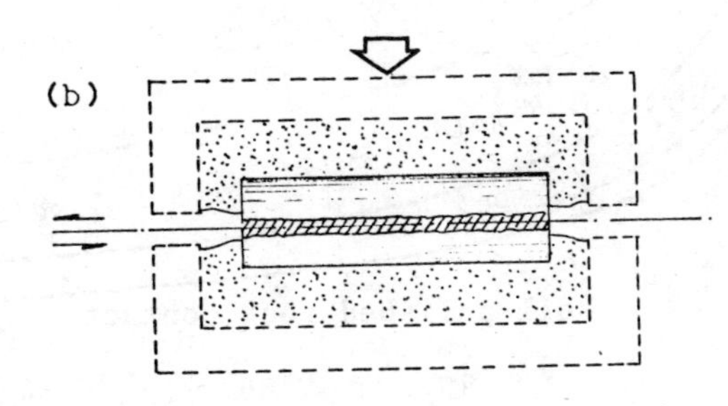

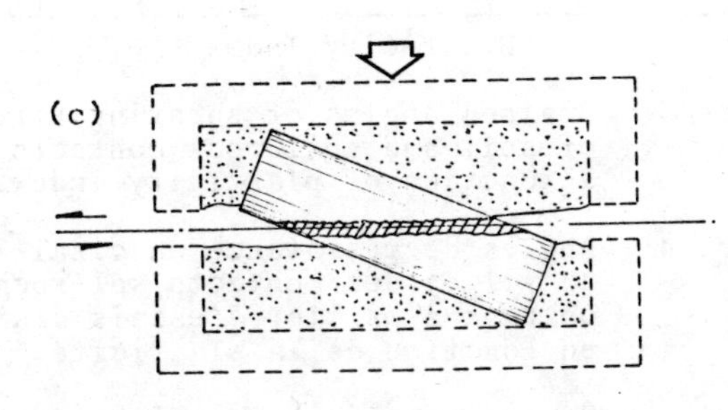

Figure 2 - Sketches of "sandwich" samples obtained from rock cores; (a) artificial cut, (b,c) natural joint.

Figure 2 - Schemas des echantillons du tipe "sandwich" obtenus a partir des carottes de forage; (a) sciees arificiellement, (b,c) diaclases naturelles.

Bild 2 - Schema von Doppel-Kontakt-Proben aus dem Felsinnern; (a) künstlicher Schnitt, (b,c) natürliche Kluft.

soils and the soil-rock contacts are shown in Figure 3. Figure 3 also shows the shear strength reduction coefficients (α) for soil-rock contacts with respect to the soil alone, for a normal stress of 1.5 kg/cm^2, about the middle of the range under which the tests were carried out. Figure 4 shows the respective maximum und minimum attained drained angles of shearing resistance for the soils and soil-rock contacts as a function of plasticity indexes of the soils tested. The test results can be summarized as follows:

(a) The maximum shear strength of soil-polished rock contacts is lower than that of the respective soil alone; the α values are usually 0.9 but in the case of basalt and its residual soil it can be as low as 0.6. For sawed rock-soil contacts the reduction is less pronounced and sometimes its shear strength equals that of the soil; some scattering for this type of surface is observed due to different geometries resulting of the saw cut from slab to slab.

(b) The minimum shear strength of the contacts, however, is much less of the corresponding to the soil alone, under the same amount of displacement; for sawed rock-soil contacts, α lies between 0.55 and 0.65, while for the contact with polished surface is usually about 0.5. The lowest α value was obtained for the "sandwich" sample, about 0.43.

(c) The drop of shear strength after the peak strength is reached is much more pronounced for the contacts than for the soil alone,and is dependent on the smoothness of the rock surface. In tests on polished rock-soil contacts where multiple reversals were employed, the drop in strength occured entirely in the first run. For tests run on "sandwich" samples under same soil and rock surface preparation as for a single contact sample, the reduction after peak strength is still greater, although the peak strengths of both types of specimens are the same.

(d) It is interesting to note that the curve shown in Figure 4 for the minimum attained strength values for polished rock-soil contacts is identical with $\phi'r$ against Ip values for the residual strength of soils measured in large displacement apparatus such as ring shear, torsional shear, multiple reversals technique, etc., and available in recent literature as, for example, BISHOP et al. (1971), TULINOV and MOLOKOV (1971) and TOWNSEND and GILBERT (1973).

CONCLUSIONS

The following conclusions can be drawn from the tests so far carried out:

(a) There are many geological situations in which smooth or even polished contacts between soil and rock may exist; therefore the shear strength of the contacts may be lower than that of the soil alone. When such a situation is encountered in the field, a testing program on soil-rock specimens should be carried out, in addition to the conventional testing of the infilling alone. Ideally it would be desirable to obtain undisturbed specimens of the contact or infilled joint. In many cases, however, the testing of the contacts using remolded soil is justified, if residual values could be achieved in the life of the rock mass, e.g. in rock slopes.

(b) The reduction in shear strengths of the contacts with respect to that of the soil

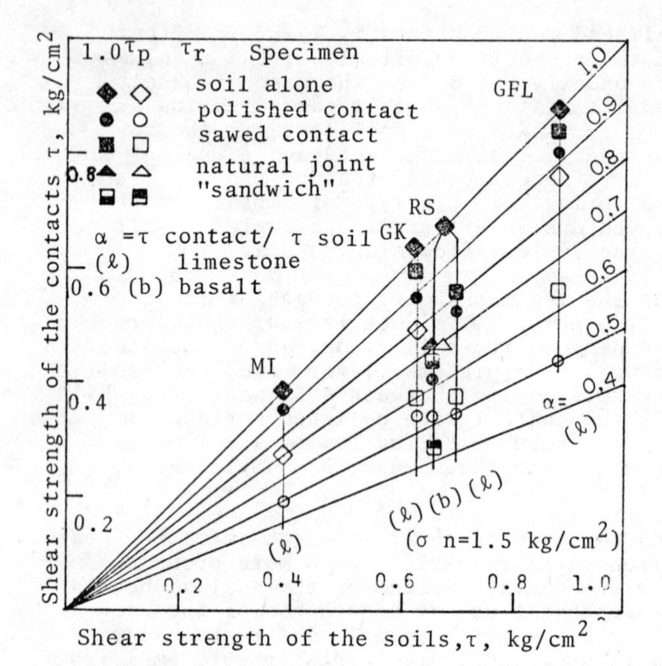

GFL - "Goose Lake Flour"
GK - Georgia Kaolinite
MI - Marblehead Illite
RS - Residual Soil (basalt)

Figure 3 - Shear strength reduction coeficients (α) for soil-rock contacts under varied rock surface conditions with respect to soil alone.

Figure 3 - Coëfficient α de reduction de la résistance au cisaillement des contacts sol-roche sur différents conditions de la surface par rapport a la résistance du sol.

Bild 3 - Reduzierung des Koeffizienten des Scherklüftungswiderstandes für Kontakte zwischen Boden und Felsen unter wechselnden Bedingungen in Verbindung mit dem Boden der Felsoberfläche.

alone may be up to 20% for peak strengths and as much as 50% for residual strengths measured in conventional direct shear equipment. The fact that the shear strength of contacts between soil or soft rocks and rock or hard materials is less than that of the soil alone, and that the failure plane develops preferably along the contact, has been also demonstrated by GUISEPPE (1970) and CHUANG and REESE (1969), the former by direct shear tests on shale, limestone and shale-limestone contacts, and the latter by tests on soil-mortar composite specimens.

(c) The drop in shear strength of a soil-rock contact occurs more sharply and at much less displacement than for the soil alone. The

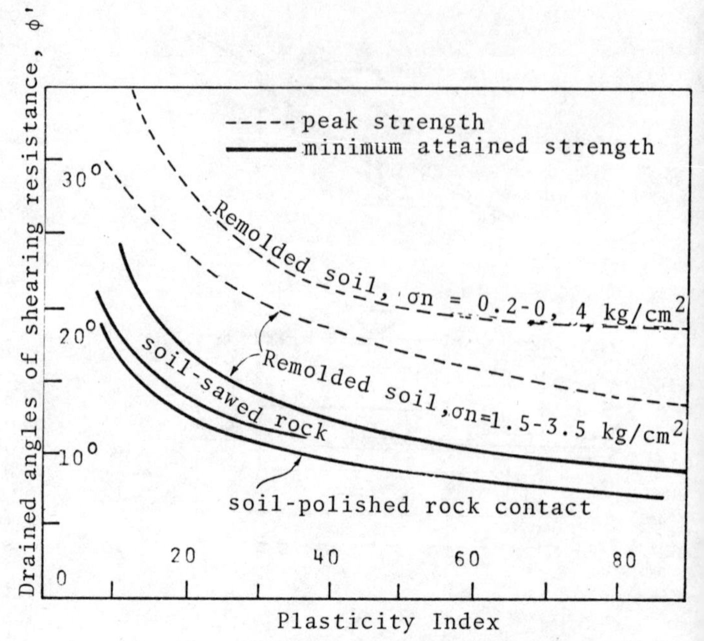

Figure 4 - Drained angles of shearing strengt of soil and soil-rock contacts as a function of plasticity index.

Figure 4 - Angles de résistance an cisailleme du sol et des contacts sol-roche, obtenns à partier d'essais drainés en fonction de la plasticité.

Bild 4 - Drainierter Friktionswinkel des Bodens und Boden-Felsen-Kontaktes in Funktion als Gestaltungsfähigkeitsanzeiger.

smoother the contact surface, the smaller is the displacement required to achieve residual strength values of the contact. This may be due to the presence of the flat, hard rock surface facilitating the orientation of the clay particles along the failure plane. It may also explain why the residual strengths of polished rock-soil contacts measured in direct shear conventional apparatus seem to correspond very closely to that of the soil alone obtained from more elaborate equipment, as ring or torsional shear, or multiple reversal technique.

(d) Finally, the rapid loss of shear strength may also lead to the possibility of premature failure, since failure may occur at smaller displacements than expected. In cases of potential failure planes in which failure may occur partly in the soil and partly along the contact, it is suspected that the differe in behavior of both materials may lead to progressive failure.

ACKNOWLEDGEMENTS

The author acknowledges the many helpful and

informal discussions with Professors Don U. Deere and F.D. Patton, formerly of the University of Illinois. Part of the study was carried out under the financial assistance granted by the "Conselho Nacional de Pesquisas", "Fundaçao de Amparo a Pesquisa do Estado de Sao Paulo", Brazil, and the University of Illinois, U.S.A.
Thanks are also due to the firm Promon Engenharia S.A., for assistance in the final preparation of this paper.

* * * * * * *

REFERENCES

BISHOP, A.W., G.E. GREEN, V.K. GARGA, A. ANDRESEN and J.D. BROWN, 1971, A new ring shear apparatus and its application to the measurement of residual strength, Géotechnique, vol. 21, No. 4, pp. 273-328.

CHUANG, J.W. and L.C. REESE, 1969, Studies of shearing resistance between cement mortar and soil, Center for Highway Research, Univ. of Texas, Austin, Res. Rep. 89-3, 74 pp.

CLARK, J.I. and G.G. MEYERHOF, 1972, The behavior of piles driven in clay. I. An investigation of soil stress and pore water pressure as related to soil properties, Canadian Geotechnical Journal, Vol 9, pp.351-373.

DEERE, D.U., 1967, Shale mylonites - their origin and engineering properties, Ass.Eng. Geologist, National Meeting, Dallas.

DEERE, D.U. and F.D. PATTON, 1971, Slope stability in residual soils, state of the Art Rep., Proceedings, 4th Pan-American Conference on Soil Mechanics and Foundation Engineering Puerto Rico, Vol. 1, pp. 87-190

DUNCAN, N. 1969, Engineering Geology and Rock Mechanics, 2 vols., Leonard Hill, London

GAUDETTE, H.E., J.L. EADES and R.E. GRIM, 1965, The nature of Illite, Proceedings, 13th. National Conference on Clays and Clay Minerals, Madison, Wisconsin, 1964, reprinted by Pergamon Press, pp.33-48

GIBSON, R.E. and D.J. HENKEL, 1954, Influence of duration of tests at constant rate of strain on measured drained strength, Géotechnique, Vol. 4, pp. 6-15

GIUSEPPE, B., 1970, The shear strength of some rocks by laboratory tests, Proceedings 2nd Congress of the International Society for Rock Mechanics, Belgrade, Vol. 5, Pap. 3-24, 8 pp.

GOODMAN, R.E. and Y. OHNISHI, 1973, Undrained shear testing of jointed rock, Rock Mechanics, Vol. 5, pp.129-149

HVORSLEV, M.J., 1960, Physical components of the shear strength of saturated clays, Research Conference on Shear Strength of Cohesive Soils, ASCE, Boulder, Colorado, pp-169-273

JAEGER, C. 1972, Rock Mechanics and Engineering, Cambridge University Press

KANJI, M.A., 1969, Resistência ao cisalhamento ao longo de interfácies solo-rocha, in Portuguese, Anais, I Semana Paulista de Geologia Aplicada, APGA, São Paulo, Vol. 3, 12 pp

KANJI, M.A.,1970, Shear strength along soil-rock interfaces, M.S. Thesis, University of Illinois, Urbana, 69 pp.

KANJI, M.A., 1972, Resistência ao cisalhamento de contactos solo-rocha, in Portuguese, Doctoral Disseration, Universidade de São Paulo, 139 pp.

PATTON, F.D., 1966 (a), Multiple modes of shear failure in rock and related materials, Ph.D.Thesis, University of Illinois, Urbana, 282 pp.

PATTON, F.D. 1966 (b), Multiple modes of shear failure in rock, Proceedings, 1st Congress of the International Society for Rock Mechanics, Lisbon, Vol.1, pp. 509-513

PATTON, F.D., 1968, The determination of shear strength of rock masses, Paper presented to the Terrametric course on Measurement Systems for Control of Construction and Mining, Denver, Col. 37 pp

PITEAU, D.R., 1970, Geological factors significant to the stability of slopes cut in rock, Symposium on Planning Open Pit Mines, Johannesburg, pp. 33-53

ROCHA, M. 1971, Método para amostragem integral de maciços rochosos, in Portuguese, Laboratória Nacional de Engenharia Civil, Mem.No. 374, Lisbon, 9 pp.

TOWNSEND, F.C. and P.A. GILBERT, 1973, Test to measure residual strengths of some clay shales, Géotechnique, Technical Note, Vol. 23, No. 2, pp. 267-271

TULINOV, R. and I. MOLOKOV, 1971, Role of joint filling material in shear strength of rocks, Symposium on Rock Fracture, Nancy, ISRM, Vol. 2, 13 pp/

PROGRESSIVE AND RETROGRESSIVE FAILURE IN DISCONTINUOUS ROCK MASSES SUBJECTED TO SHEAR LOADING

RUPTURE PROGRESSIVE ET RÉTROGRESSIVE DES MASSES ROCHEUSES DISCONTINUES SUJETTES AU CHARGE DE CISAILLEMENT

PROGRESSIVES UND RETROGRESSIVES ÜBERSCHREITEN DER FESTIGKEITSGRENZE BEI DEN ZERSCHERTEN DISKONTINUIERLICHEN FELSVERBÄNDEN

Kadri E. KASAPOǦLU

Asst.Prof. of Engineering Geology and Rock
Mechanics, Department of Earth Sciences
Hacettepe University, Ankara, Turkey

SUMMARY This paper presents a study of shear deformation which includes extensive laboratory testing, employing specimens which are geometrically analogous to 'in-situ' shear block, the use of certain dataobtained in large-scale field tests, and a theoretical approach to progresive deformation involving discontinuum and elastic-elastoplastic finite element methods. The theoretical program is accompanied by mechanical laboratory tests designed to test the reliability and applicability of conclusions suggested by the theoretical studies.

RESUME Cette étude de déformation de cisaillement que nons présentons ici comprend des essais extensifs de laboratoire faits sur les échantillons geometriquement analogues aux blocs de cisaillement 'in-situ', l'utilisation de certaines donnees obtenues des essais de terrain dans une grande échelle et une approche théorique de la déformation progressive par la méthode d'éléments finis discontinus et élastique-élastoplastique. Le programme théorique est accompagné des éssais méchaniques de laboratoire désignés pour essayer la possibilité et l'applicabilité des conclusions proposées des travaux théoriques.

ZUSAMMENFASSUNG Diese Arbeit bezieht sich auf die Untersuchung von Scherverformung und enthaelt ausführliche Laborversuche über die den 'in-situ' Scherblöcken geometrisch analogen Proben, die Verwendung von einigen Daten, die durch Grössversuche in natürlichen Verhaeltnissen erhalten sind, und eine theoretische Untersuchung der progressiven Verformung unter der Verwendung der diskontinuirlich und elastisch-elastoplastisch endlichen Elementenmethode. Gleichzeitig mit dem theoretischen Programm wurden einige entworfene mechanische Laborversuche durchgeführt, um die Anwendbarkeit und die Gültigkeit der Resultate aus den theoretischen Untersuchungen zu überprüfen.

INTRODUCTION

Direct shear tests in the laboratory and in 'in-situ' field conditions are important sources of information on strength parameters for soil and rock materials for both geologic and engineering purposes. Despite this widespread usage, the mode of deformation and the mechanism of failure involved in these tests are not well understood; as a result, important misinterpretations of the data resulting from shear testing are possible.

This work has been designed to obtain some general information on actual mechanism of shear deformation and shear failure in both laboratory and 'in-situ' shear tests, and to shed light upon some of the difficulties; in particular, the development of progressive failure in isotropic and anisotropic nonlinear materials were studied as a function of the method of application of boundary forces.

THEORETICAL ANALYSIS

The finite element method (FEM) has been employed to analyze stresses and strains in a plane-strain shear block model with three internal discontinuities labeled D1, D2, and D3 (Figure 1); where, D1 coincides with the hypothetical shear plane, and D2 and D3 coincide with potential tension fractures. The concept utilized here, as described by Wang and Voight (1969), involves the ordinary finite element partitioning of a solid model into a descrete number of two-dimensional elements with "dual nodal points" used along prescribed planes of discontinuities. A Coulomb-Navier presentation with a tension cutoff has been utilized. Dahl's (1969) finite element code with suitable modifications has been used for the elatic-elastoplastic FEM analyses. The "Torre' yield function was employed.

The physical properties of the model material (i.e., Berea sandstone) are shown in Table 1. The various force and displacement boundary conditions utilized are shown in Figure 2.

THEORETICAL RESULTS

All analytical solutions, in terms of direct-

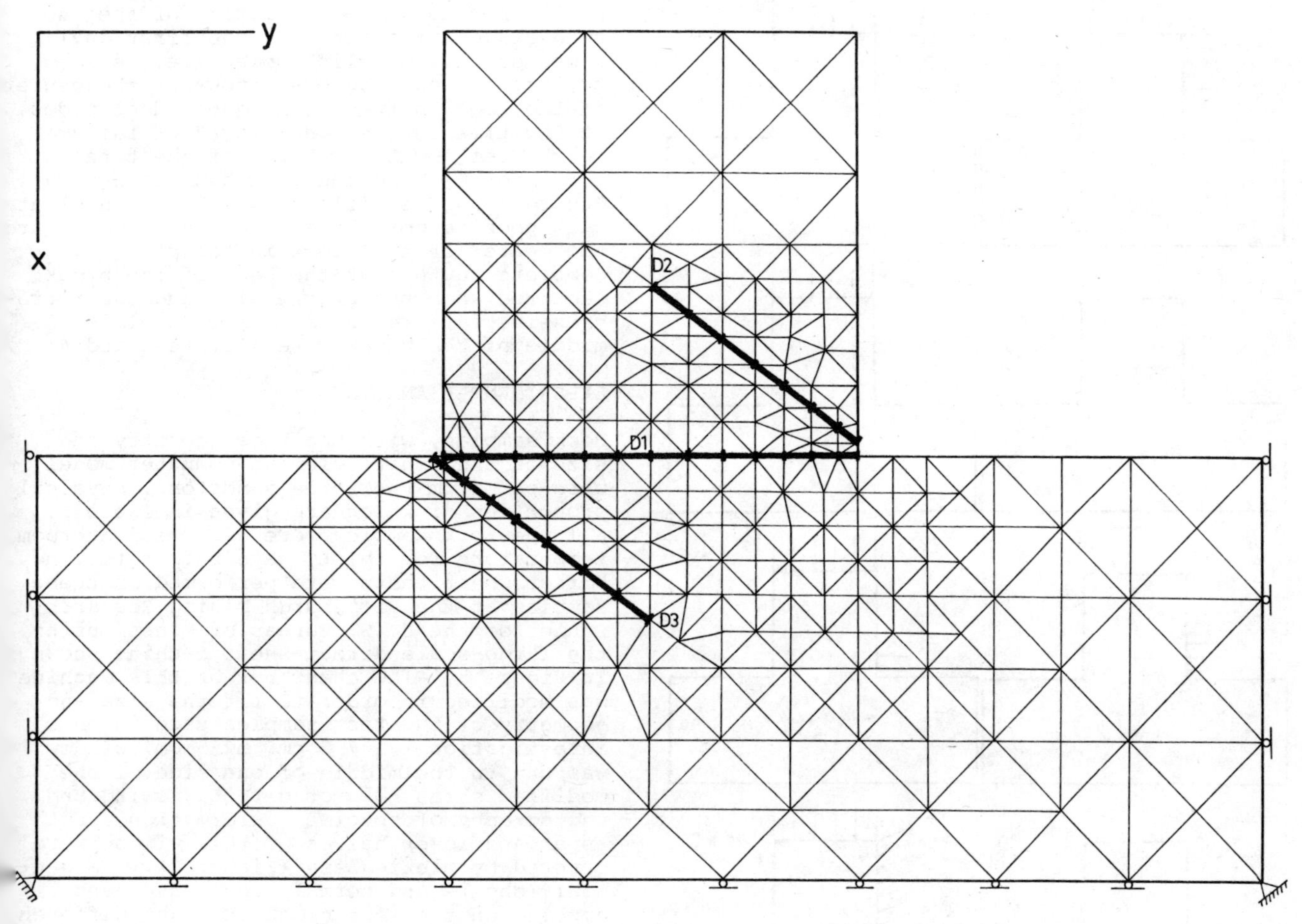

Figure 1. Finite element idealization of 'in-situ' shear block model

TABLE 1

Nominal Values of the Physical Properties of Berea Sandstone (After Khair, 1971)

Physical Property	Notation	Value
Unconfined compressive strength	σ_c	630 kg/cm^2
Unconfined tensile strength	σ_t	21 kg/cm^2
Unconfined shear strength	τ	98 kg/cm^2
Young's modulus in compression	E_c	0.81x10 kg/cm^2
Young's modulus in tension	E_t	0.41x10 kg/cm^2
Poisson's ratio in compression	ν_c	0.2
Poisson's ratio in tension	ν_t	0.1
Independent shear modulus	G	0.32x10 kg/cm^2

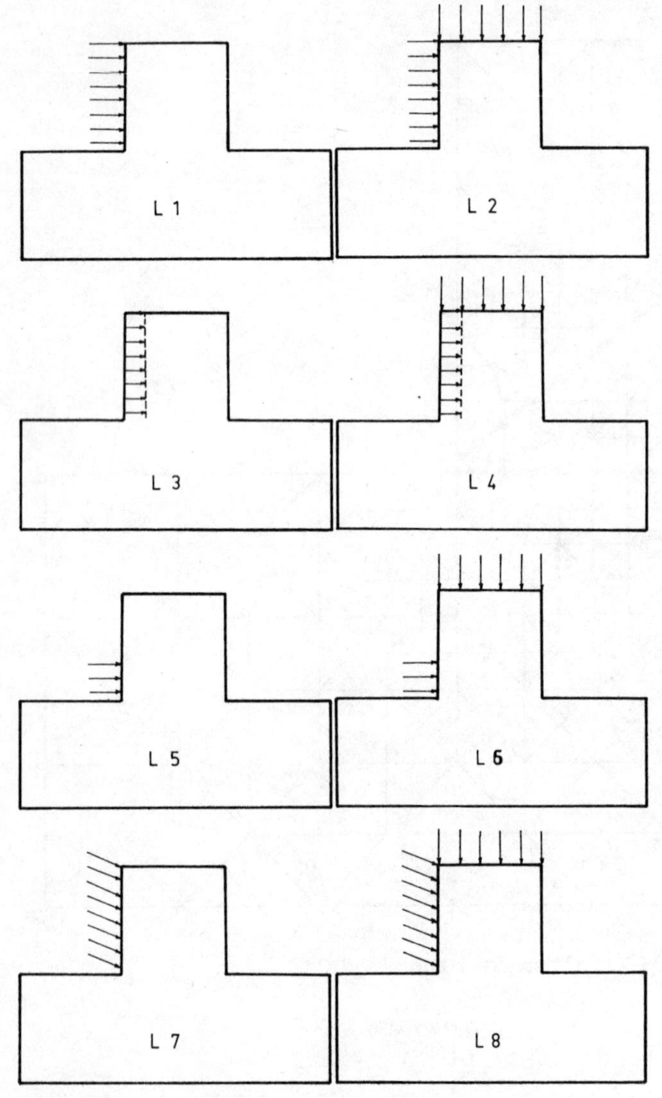

Figure 2. Boundary Conditions

ion and magnitude of major and minor principal stresses at the centroid of each triangular element and the total displacements of the nodal points, were plotted by computerized (CalComp) plotter. These theoretical results clearly show the dependence of failure mode on the boundary conditions. All boundary conditions, except for L4, resulted in initial yielding of the block at the first node of the discontinuity D1, in the form of dual node separation; with continued load application, failure was propagated along D1, in the "separation" mode (i.e., tensile failure) until complete failure occurred in the form of separation of all dual nodes on D1. For the boundary condition L4, however, yielding of the block initiated in the "separation" mode at the top of the discontinuity D3; with continued loading, failure propagated diagonally along D3, until last dual nodes on D3 became separated. This is considered to be the termination of the "first stage" of failure. Further loading, after complete opening of D3, produced the initiation of the "second stage" of failure at the first dual nodes of D1, in "slip" mode (i.e., shear failure) which progressed towards the center of the block between subsequent dual nodes. At the time the "second stage" of failure reached to about one-sixth of the total length of D1 from the left hand corner, a "third stage" of failure initiated on D1 at the opposite corner, and retrogressed toward the center of the block in "slip" mode. Complete rupture at the base of the block occurred when the progressive and the retrogressive failure surfaces met on D1 in the middle of the block base (Figure 3 and 4).

EXPERIMENTAL ANALYSIS

Rock samples, with the same geometry and size of the finite element computer model, were cut from the Berea sandstone, physical properties of which are given in Table 1. All the rock samples were air dried at room temperature for thirty days before testing. Direct shear tests were performed on these samples at the Pittsburgh Mining Research Center of the U. S. Bureau of Mines, using the large-scale direct shear machine shown in Figure 5. The shear box of this machine was modified in order to fit the size and geometry of the test samples used in this investigation. A 7.5 cm. by 5 cm. window was cut in the middle of one side of the modified shear box for direct viewing and photography of specimen deformation. Both upper and lower halves of this window were covered by plexi-glass (Figure 6). Tangential (shear) and normal loads have been applied on the test block in eight differen ways, similar to those used in the theoretical analysis (see Figure 2).

EXPERIMENTAL RESULTS

Results of about 135 direct shear tests performed on rock specimens indicated that ultimate failure of the shear block is a consequence of multiple fracture modes occurring prior to ultimate failure. Three stages have been observed:

1. Tensile fracture
2. Progressive shear fracture
3. Retrogressive shear fracture

These various modes of failure could be observed as a consequence of high speed cinematography. In the majority of the tests, the diagonal tension fracture was the first to appear. The extension of this fracture appears to be a function of the normal load applied on the shear block. At low normal loads, the diagonal tension fracture propagated entirely across and through the botto of the specimen, often splitting the sample into two pieces. In some cases, however, when the diagonal tension fracture hit a plane of relative weakness (i.e., a bedding plane), the direction of propagation diverg ed, and fracture followed the bedding plane

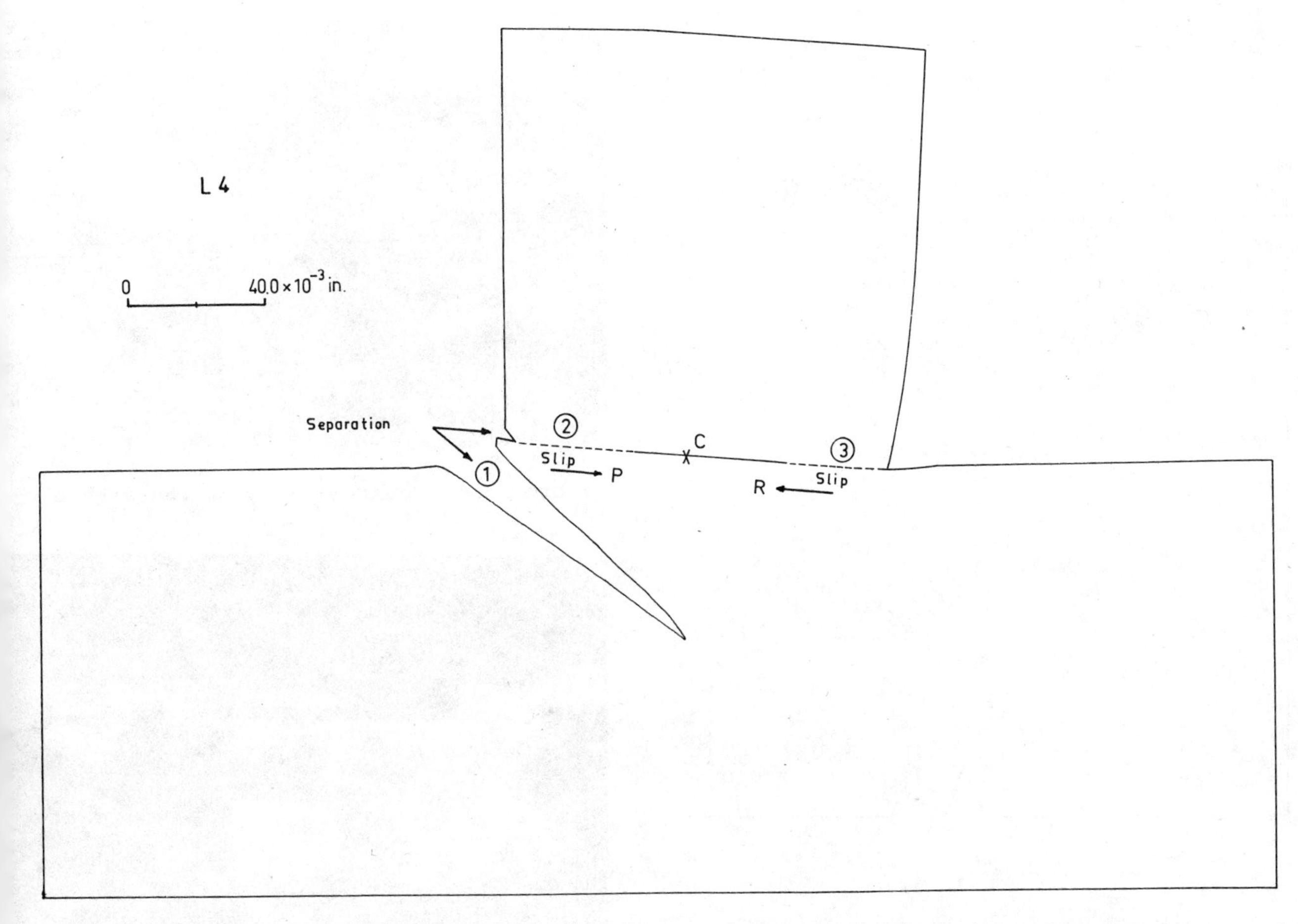

Figure 3. Three consecutive stages of failure of the shear block (arrows refer direction of fracture propagation; P implies "progressive failure"; R implies "retrogressive failure")

towards the right hand side boundary of the lower block. At high normal loads, propagation of the diagonal tension fracture typically ceased somewhere within the middle of the lower block.

The second stage, in general involved a larger displacement of the shear block in the direction of shear. Shear fracture develops in response to a reoriented field of stress set up after the appearance of the diagonal tension fracture. This shear fracture initiates at the lower left hand corner of the shear block, and propagates along the base of the shear block, parallel to the direction of the applied shear. This second stage of failure is described as "progressive shear fracture". Before this progressive shear fracture could reach to right hand boundary of the shear block, almost always a third mode of failure began as a shear fraçture at the lower right hand corner of the shear block; this fracture propagated **backward** along the base of the shear block, in a direction opposite to the direction of the applied shear. This third mode of failure, occurring in the final stage of loading, is described as "retrogressive shear fracture". Ultimate failure of the block occurred when the progressive and the retrogressive shear fractures met eachother. Figure 7 shows the photographs of the three stages of failure modes described above, as they occurred in horizontally layered rock samples tested under shear-box loading condition with normal load applied on the specimen.

DISCUSSION

In most cases of the theoretical analysis, concentration of tensile stresses occurred around the left hand corner of the shear block base. Initial fracture thus occurred at this corner, in the form of a tensile crack (the "tension cut-off" strength criterion governed), opened and propagated diagonally along the discontinuity D3. Separation along D3 releases the tensile stresses originally developed at the **lower left hand** corner of the shear block, and thus causes a redistribution of strains and stresses along the base of the block. This redistribution is responsible for subsequent failure along D1, predominantly in the "slip" mode, and associated with a frictional (Mohr-Navier) strength criterion.

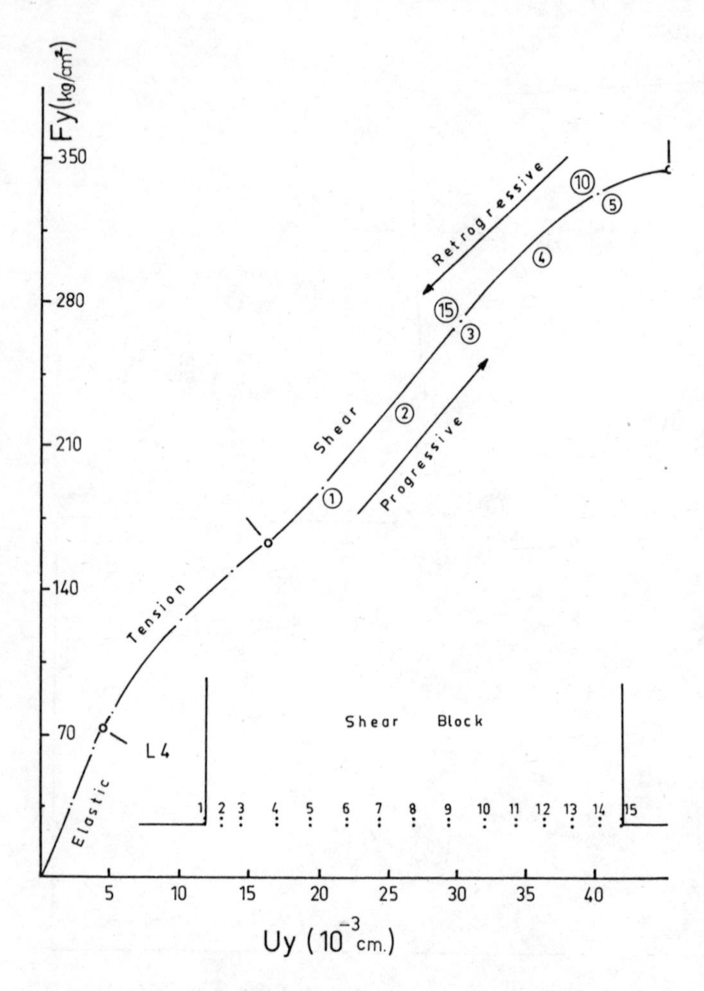

Figure 4. "progressive" and "retrogressive" failure series

Under certain "shear" test conditions, fracture propagation to a state of complete rupture can be extremely within the "separation" mode; one may question the appropriateness of a so-called "shear" test which predominantly involves a "tensile" fracture mode rather than "slip".

The multiple mode of failure described in the experimental analysis appears to be valid only for the shear-box loading condition with normal load applied on the specimen. For all the other loading conditions utilized in this investigation, failure of the shear block almost invariably occurred at the base of the shear block. Distinction between "tension" and "shear" mode, for the second stage of fracturing along the base of the shear block, was not clear even from the motion pictures taken with a high speed camera; however, a sudden small lifting up of the lower left hand corner of the shear block at the begining of the second stage of fracturing, observed in slow motion pictures taken with the high speed camera, may suggest that initiation of the second stage of fracturing is probably in "tension" mode.

In general, a remarkable agreement appears to exist between the mode of deformation and failure of the shear block as predicted from the theoretical analysis and those observed in the experimental analysis.

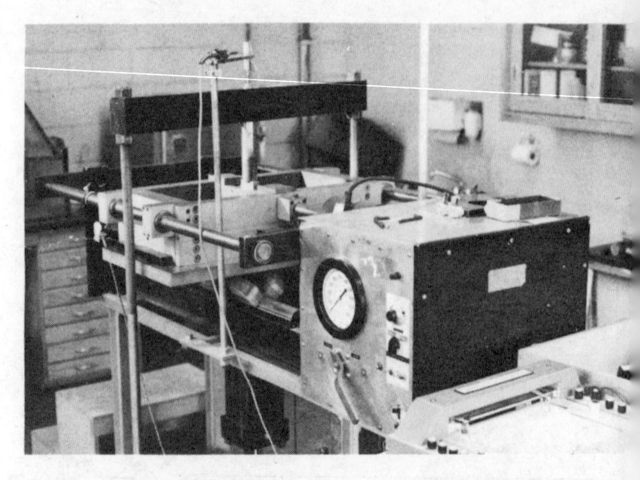

Figure 5. The overall view of the direct shear machine

Figure 6. Modified shear box

The occurrence of a diagonal tension fracture, described in an analysis of an 'in-situ' test (Voight and Kasapoğlu, 1974) differed from the laboratory model solution for somewhat similar boundary condition (c.f., Figure 2,L5), for which solution no separation on D3 occurred. This difference was attributed to the additional tensile stresses which developed around the lower left hand corner of the 'in-situ' shear block as a consequence of reaction force from the hydraulic jack to the opposite wall on the left of the shear block.

CONCLUSIONS

Results of the preceding analysis led to the following general conclusions:

Choice of boundary conditions exerts an important control on failure mechanism

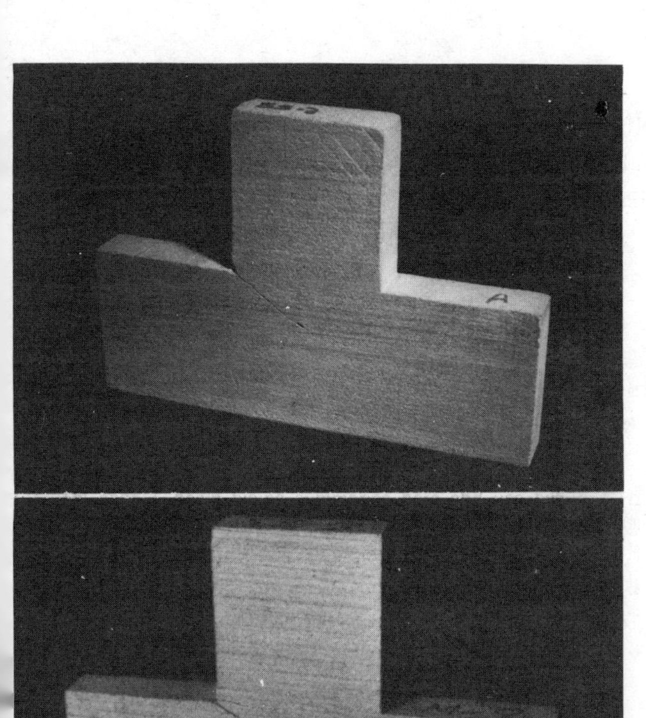

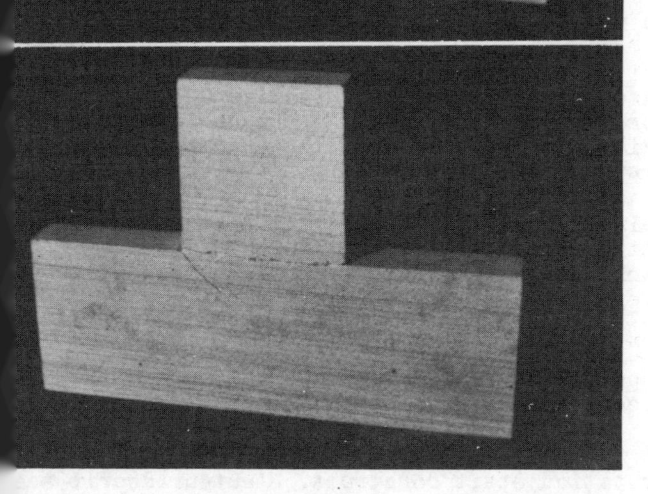

'igure 7. The three stages of failure in rock specimens

'ensile zones which develop within the test lock in response to applied shear force are f mechanical importance. Local failure hich occurs in these tensile zones, in "se- aration" mode, leads to progressive failure. nder certain boundary conditions, the ulti- ate failure of the test block is a consequ- nce of "multiple fracture modes".

In-situ' shear tests on geological materials hould be interpreted in more sophisticated erms i.e., as a consequence of variable tress states, involving inhomogeneous stress fields (with one or several of principal stresses often tensile), extensive stress re- orientation, and multiple crack propagation.

Uniform edge-displacement boundary condition (L4) produced the most consistent theoretical results in the experiments reported here; hence, loading of this type may be suggested as standard method of application of shear force to the test block both in 'in-situ' and laboratory shear experiments.

Discontinuum finite element solutions allow prediction of localized failures and analysis of progressive nature of failure mechanism. Elastic-elastoplastic solutions, on the other hand, appear to be more suitable for analysis of progressive development of yield zones in areas around the points of high stress con- centration.

The theoretical approach to the mechanism of deformation and failure characteristics of 'in-situ' shear blocks, utilizing finite ele- ment method, appears to be a valid approach for prediction of experimental results and for a more adequate understanding of field tests of rock behavior.

ACKNOWLEDGEMENT

The author most greetfully acknowledge the invaluable help of Dr. Barry Voight, of the Pennsylvania State University, Department of Geosciences. Dr. Voight provided the author encouragement, guidance, and critically re- viewed an earlier draft of this manuscript.

The assistance of Mr. Brann Johnson, graduate assistant, and Mr. E. Kimble, research aide, both of the Pennsylvania State University, and Mr. L. Marracini of the Pittsburgh Mining Research Center of the U.S. Bureau of Mines is also acknowledged.

This work was supported by the Pennsylvania Coal Research Board; the Geological Society of America; and the Society of Sigma Xi.

REFERENCES

Dahl, H.D., 1969, A finite element model for anisotropic yielding in gravity loaded rock. Ph.D. Thesis, The Pennsylvania State University.

Khair, A.W., 1971, A study of mechanical pro- perties of Berea sandstone for use in the A.G.A. large model studies. The Pennsylvania State University Internal Report RML-IR/71-20.

Voight, B. and Kasapoğlu, K.E. 1974, Progres- sive failure in a large-scale field shear test. Proc. Int. Soc. Rock Mech. Denver.

Wang, Y.J. and Voight, B., 1969, A discrete element stress analysis model for dis- continuous materials. Proc. Int. Symp. on Large Permanent Underground Openings.

ROTARY SHEAR TESTING OF ROCK JOINTS

L'ESSAI DE CISAILLEMENT DE ROTATION DANS DES ASSURES DES ROCHES

ROTATIONSSCHERVERSUCHE AN GESTEINSKLÜFTEN

H.K. KUTTER

Professor of Rock Mechanics, Dept.of Geology

Ruhr-University, Bochum

West-Germany

ABSTRACT A rotary shear apparatus provides in contrast to the conventional direct shear test the facility for unlimited shear displacement and for investigating the potential decrease of the residual shear strength with very large displacements.

A small pilot machine for rotary shear testing of joints in thick-walled rock cylinders wa built and the first results on sandstone and plaster of Paris specimens with single and double saw-cuts, sawtooth-shaped profiles, or artificially produced fractures with a rough surface are reported in this paper.

The graphs of test results reveal no pronounced decrease of residual shear strength with large displacements. However, all graphs clearly show a periodic variation of the shear strength within one rotation. These observed oscillations become more pronounced with increasing roughness and are caused by the surface geometry.

ZUSAMMENFASSUNG Ein Rotationsscherapparat ermöglicht im Gegensatz zum herkömmlichen direkten Scherversuch unbegrenzte Verschiebungen und die mögliche Abnahme der Restscherfesti keit mit sehr großen Verschiebungen.

Es wird hier über den Bau einer einfachen Ringschermaschine für dickwandige Gesteinszylinder und über die damit an Sandstein- und Gipsproben mit Klüften in Form von einfachen und doppelten Sägeschnitten, künstlich erzeugten Rissen mit rauher Oberfläche oder sägezahnähnliche Profile gewonnenen Ergebnisse berichtet.

Die Diagramme der Versuchsergebnisse zeigen keine eindeutige Abnahme der Restscherfestigkeit bei großen Verschiebungen, jedoch eindeutige periodische Schwankungen der Scherfestigkeit innerhalb einer Rotation. Diese Schwankungen nehmen mit größerer Rauhigkeit zu un sind auf die Oberflächengeometrie zurückzuführen.

RESUMÉ L'éssai conventionel de cisaillement permet seulement une déformation limitée. Ainsi la question du frottement résiduel sur des grandes déformations ne peut pas être repondue avec cet arrangement d'éssai.

C'est pour ça un appareil de cisaillement de rotation était construit. L'auteur décrit ses résultats des éssais de cisaillement de rotation avec des échantillons de grès et de gypse Les fissures étaient des coupures de scie, des fractures artificielles avec une âpre surface et une géométrie semblable celle des dents de scie.

Les diagrammes des résultats montrent que la résistance résiduelle de cisaillement ne diminue pas visiblement avec des longues déformations. Cependant il est remarquable une oscillation périodique dans chaque phase de rotation qui peut être ramené à la géométrie de la fissure.

INTRODUCTION

The failure of rock structures at the surface is generally preceeded by relatively large displacements and deformations of the rock mass involved. It is progressive and mostly initiated by shear movements along fracture planes and discontinuities such a joints and bedding planes. The relative shear displacement along these discontinuities can therefore reach a considerable magnitude before the final collapse of the rock structure occurs. In assessing the stability of a structure it is consequently essential to know in addition to the maximum or peak shear strength of the discontinuities also the variation of their strength with large shear displacements.

A rough joint reaches its peak shear strength after a rather small relative displacement, then the shear strength decreases rapidly with further displacement and approaches assymptotically a residual value after displacements of a few centimeters. The conventional type of shear test on rock samples at least indicates such a behavior, although the very limited relative shear displacement of all these test configurations does not allow an exact assessment of the shear strength at relatively large displacements. One might expect, for instance, that the rate of decrease of residual strength with increasing shear displacement is so small that it appears to be zero at the limited displacements of the conventional shear tests but that it could amount to a significant decrease after relative large deformations.

The shear strength data obtained from fractured or jointed cores in triaxial cells are only meaningful for very small shear displacements. The triaxial cell is therefore not suited for obtaining reliable measurements of the true residual strength. Much larger displacements are possible in the direct shear test, but there an ever increasing nonuniformity in the stress distribution and the restricted specimen size put still a limit to the possible amount of shear displacement. The only test arrangement which permits unlimited shear displacement is one which employs a rotary or torsional motion. A hollow cylinder of rock is subjected to a normal axial load and to an increasing torque or moment. The fracture surface, whose shear strength is to be tested, runs normal to the axis of the cylinder and divides it into two equal parts. The principal test arrangement is shown schematically in Figure 1. The cylinder

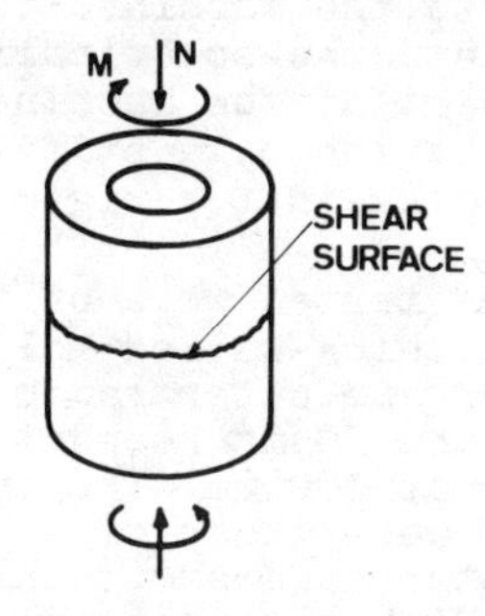

Fig. 1: The principle of the rotary shear test

is made hollow in order to avoid too large a variation in shear displacement and rate of displacement.

Torsional or ring shear tests have been used on soils to a considerable extent since the early Thirties (GRUNER and HAEFELI (1934), HAEFELI (1938), HVORSLEV (1939), HVORSLEV and KAUFMAN (1952)), and recently they have been refined and applied to detailed studies and measurements by MANDL (1971) and BISHOP et al (1971). The latter come to the significant conclusion that "in general the multiple reversal direct shear box test gives a result which in the case of clays differs very substantially from the true residual strength". The results of their ring shear test on blue London Clay, for instance, indicated that the available angle of shearing resistance varied from about 17° for small displacements to 9.4° at large displacements. The situation of a rock under shear is, of course, considerably different from that of a shear box test on clay, but in a similar way the question has to be answered for rocks, whether the strength values obtained from relatively small displacements represent the true residual strength. Torsion tests on concrete (BRESLER and POSTER (1957)) and on rock (HANDIN et al (1960)) have been so far directed towards strength evaluation of the solid continuous material, but not for the measurement and study of the shear strength of discontinuities in the solid. The only previous ring shear tests on discontinuous rock specimens are those performed at the Chamber of Mines Research Laboratory in South Africa; however no detailed results are yet available.

A pilot study of rotary shear testing of joints was initiated, whereby the primary purpose of the rotary device was of course its ability to produce unlimited shear displacements. But additional advantages are that the effective cross section of the specimen and the stress conditions do not change with increasing deformations. The normal stress stays constant and does not require constant adjustment of the applied normal load. It is furthermore reasonable (BISHOP et al 1971) to assume that the normal and shear stresses are uniformly distributed over the entire cross section.

Since there is no need for resetting the specimens during the test and no change of contact area there is little chance that fines are lost and thus the surface conditions artificially altered. The rotary shear arrangement permits furthermore the testing of different rates of displacement on the same sample under otherwise identical conditions. As a consequence of the unlimited displacements the test is, in addition to the finding of the true shear strength, extremely suitable for the study of the break and wear process of asperities, the formation of fines and the exact location of the differential shear movement. More than any other shear test the ring test allows the application of a controlled intermediate principal stress and pore pressure without too severe technical problems.

The most serious disadvantage of the rotary type test is the non-uniformity of the displacement. It certainly makes the ring shear test somewhat questionable for the evaluation of the peak strength, but for very large displacements this non-uniformity may be of less significance particularly if the ratio of outer to inner radius is not too large. The cylindrical shape of the specimens limits the size of economically and technically feasible probes, which in turn requires specimens with relatively smooth joint surfaces. Finally, the test geometry is such that under torsion tensile stresses are generated (JAEGER and COOK (1969), p. 157) which might reach the tensile strength of the solid rock if the normal load is rather small. Shear failure may therefore be preceeded by tensile failure and consequently render the test unsuitable for prolonged shear displacements.

Although the rotary shear test is mainly conceived as a laboratory test it has been proposed as a device for downhole shear testing. There is no record of a successful field application of such a device, and it would appear that serious difficulties might be encountered in adapting this technique to narrow, removed borehole conditions. But this potential use of rotary shear for field testing was one more reason to initiate this project.

TEST APPARATUS

The lack of any previous experience in using the ring shear test for rock discontinuities made it necessary to design the test apparatus as a highly simplified, relatively primitive small-scale pilot set-up.

A schematic drawing of the rotary shear device and its essential parts is shown in Figure 2. Two basically different designs are possible for a ring shear apparatus for rock: (a) The axis of both cylinder halves are fixed and consequently no relative tilt can occur between them; (b) the axis of only one of the specimen halves is fixed whereas the other is free to take up any direction and any angle with the first one. In both cases one specimen half is free to rotate around its axis, whereas the other one cannot. In effect, design (a) represents a relatively stiff testing arrangement which keeps the two specimen halves always in line but does not provide full con-

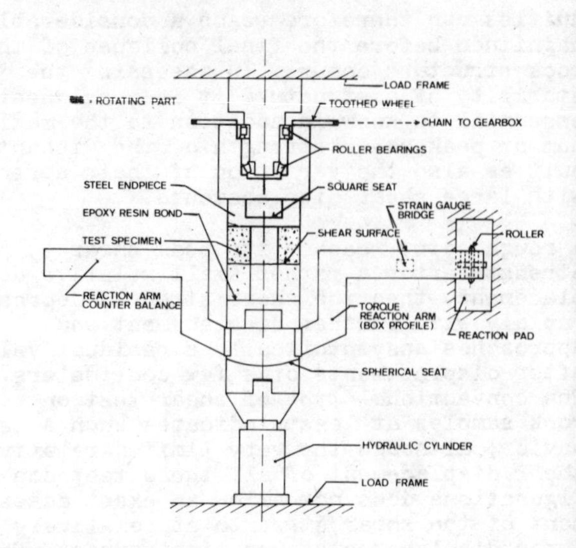

Fig. 2: Schematic diagram of rotary shear machine

tact at the discontinuity if that is not exactly normal to the axis of the cylinder A considerable amount of periodic dilation and compaction will occur during testing. Design version (b) is very flexible and thus allows full contact over the entire area of the sheared surface, eliminates excessive dilation due to an inclined discontinuity, but also leads to the introduction of additional disturbing moments. If, however, specimens are chosen whose discontinuity deviates only slightly from the plane normal to the axis, then the additional moment will be negligible and the advantage of full contact is considerable. Design type (b) was therefore chosen for the pilot rotary machine. The flexibility of the machine was achieved by adding a spherical seat (the centre of the sphere coincides with the centre of the sheared plane) to the test set-up. Figure 2 shows how the specimen is mounted into the shear frame by way of steel end pieces attached to the rock cylinder with epoxy resin. The upper end piece fits tightly into the rotating part of the machine. The rotation is generated by an electric motor and transmitted by a system of gearboxes and a chain drive to the machine. The lower end piece fits into the spherically seated stationary part of the machine which is kept from rotation by a stiff arm with a roller seated against a rigid support.

All specimens tested were of the same shape, i. e. thick-walled hollow cylinders with an inner and outer radius of nominally 50 mm and 20 mm respectively, and a total height of 100 mm. The types of surfaces tested were those of a saw cut, a tensile fracture, and sawtooth-shaped asperities. With a rotational speed of 1.6 rotations per hour the average shearing rate was 5.9 mm/min. This may be on the high side, but the preliminary nature of the pilot set-up made it necessary to build the rotary drive out of a limited number of available reduction gears and motors. A short check, however, showed that for instance a doubling of the speed would not affect the results. The normal load was induced by a hydraulic cylinder whose pressure was regulated by an Amsler valve and monitored on a dial gauge. The friction of the piston and the weight of the spherical seat with the torque reaction arm were taken into account when calculating the effective normal stress on the specimen.

The torque or shearing moment was measured by a strain gauge bridge mounted at the rotary reaction arm of the device. The rotational displacement was picked up by a spring-loaded rubber wheel which was in contact with the rotating part of the rock specimen and mounted on a 10-turn potentiometer. Shear displacement and shear torque were directly recorded on a X-Y-plotter.

The slight excentric loading which is caused by the roughness and asperities of the fracture surface leads to the build-up of even larger tensile stresses in the cylinder wall than those predicted from simple theory. In order to avoid early tensile failures (a typical example is shown in Figure 3) and a consequent change of the contact area, it was found necessary to confine those parts of the outer cylinder wall, which border on the sheared surface, with a rubber-padded steelband slightly tightened by a screw look. These steelbands can be seen on the probe shown in Figure 5. Another small device had to be installed into the centre hole of the cylinder to provide a certain rotary guidance and for keeping the two cylinder halves concentric after a large number of rotations. A slightly conical Teflon core with a diameter smaller than that of the hole and a steel rod inside it was mounted in the lower cylinder half. The Teflon cone protruded into

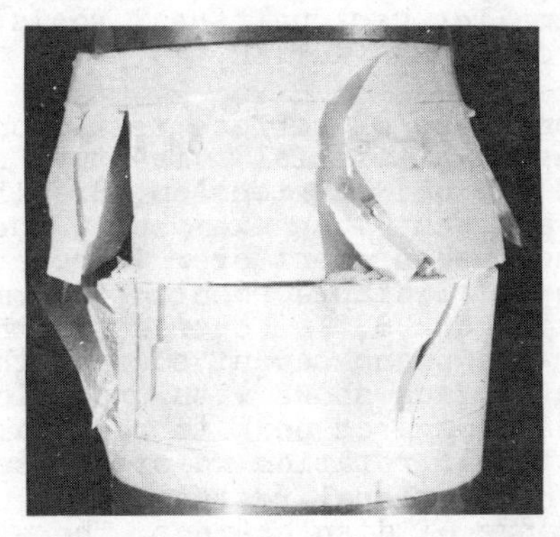

Fig. 3: Tensile failure of specimen without confinement

the centre hole of the upper half (see Figure 5) and so prohibited excessive excentricity. Teflon was chosen to keep the frictional disturbance at a minimum and the conical shape permitted the tilting of the lower specimen half.

A complete view of the rotary shear device, the conventional loading frame and the measuring equipment can be seen in Figure 4.

Fig. 4: View of rotary shear device with measuring equipment

TEST RESULTS

Rotary shear tests were performed on two materials: a high-strength plaster (Crystalax LX, with a water to plaster mixing ratio of 0.65 by weight) and the fine grained Darley Dale Sandstone. The plaster has a uniaxial compressive strength of 48 MN/m^2 and with a smooth, cast surface a coefficient of friction of 36°, as measured in the conventional shear box. The sandstone has a compressive strength of about 80 MN/m^2, an E-modulus of 1700 MN/m^2, and in the linear shear box a coefficient of friction of 37° for a rough fracture surface.

Darley Dale Sandstone

The first type of surface tested was that of a plane sawcut normal to the axis of rotation. Specimens before and after testing are shown in Figure 5. A diagram of a typical test result is given in Figure 6. There one sees how after an intial peak a small reduction in shear strength occurs during the first quarter rotation. Thereafter, however, a slow but steady increase in shear strength can be observed, on which a periodic oscillation of the shear stress is superimposed due to certain undulations in the shear surface. Only after about five full rotations, which amount to an average shear displacment of about 1.10 m, a certain stabilisation seems to set in, although a very slight increase in shear strength can still be observed. The frictional resistance has clearly reached its maximum only at the end of the test, i. e. after an average displacement of approximately 2.40 m. For

Fig. 5: Darley Dale Sandstone specimen halves with sawcut surface: a) befor and b) after rotary shear testing

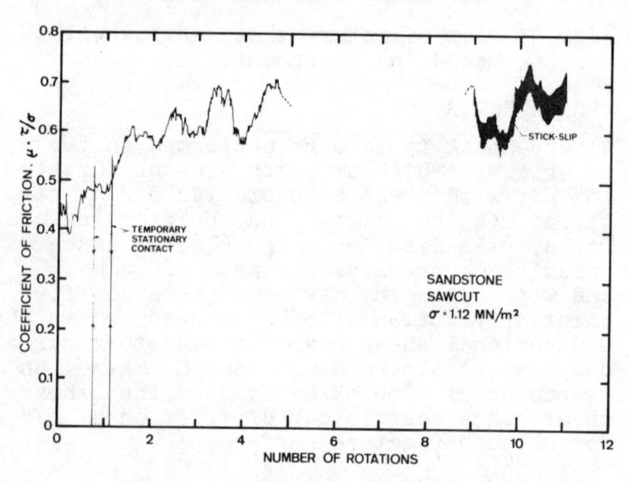

Fig. 6: Shear resistance - rotational displacement characteristic for a sawcut joint in Darley Dale Sandstone

reasons of practicality and time the test had to be terminated then. It is important to notice that for an initially smooth surface which has been roughened up and slickensided during the shear process the strength increase is not completed after a few centimeters of displacement but continues up to very large deformations.

Two other features of this particular test record are of significance: At a number of times during the testing the rotation was brought to a stop and restarted again after a pause of only one minute or two (this was found necessary to control a potential shifting of the zero of the recording device). A typical strength recording at such a temporary termination of the test is shown in an enlarged form in Figure 7. Once the rotary movement continues there is initially an increase in strength but a relatively quick return to the previous strength level after a few more millimeters of displacement. This increase of shear resistance of joints after periods of rest has been studied in great detail by DIETERICH (1972) who found that "static friction increases with the logarithm of the time that adjacent blocks remain in stationary contact". It appears that this time-dependence of friction should be a major factor in the determination of the stability of rock structures. The other significant feature of the test curve of Figure 6 is the onset of stick-slip somewhere between an average displacement of 1.20 and 2.0 m. Evidently a fairly large shear displacement is necessary before sufficient rock debries has built up for the initiation of the stick-slip process.

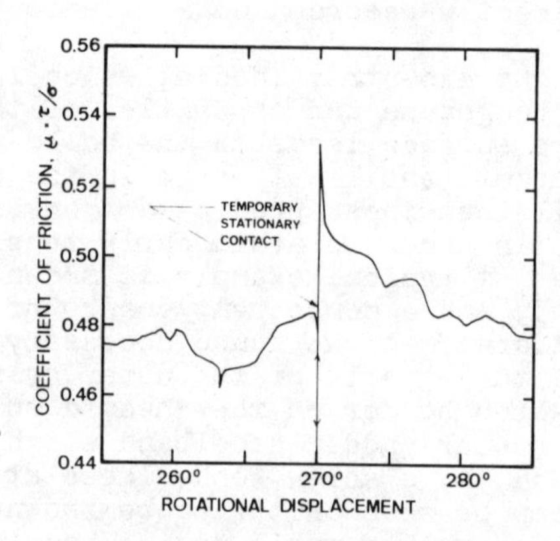

Fig. 7: Enlarged section of test record of FIGURE 6 at the point of temporary termination of rotation.

A comparison of the final coefficient of friction obtained for a sawcut surface in the rotary test with that for a rough surface in the linear shear box shows a slight difference between the two. But one would expect that a smooth surface will have a smaller residual shear resistance than a rough one (KUTTER, 1973).

The second type of surface tested on sandstone was an artificial fracture surface produced by indirect tension (Brazilian test arrangement). An example of the shear resistance measurement over 19 rotations (average total displacement = 4.20 m) is shown in Figure 8. In contrast to the findings for the plane sawcut surface the rough fracture surface shows with exception of the first drop from peak to residual after the first half rotation no significant change in frictional resistance over the entire range of displacement. There is, however, a marked periodic variation of shear resistance during each rotation. The asperities and the waviness of the fracture surface alternatively cause dilation (riding-up effect) and compaction (sliding down) and tilting of the lower specimen half, which in turn lead to an increase, respectively decrease of the effective angle of friction. These oscillations are definitely due to the unevenness of the surface since they are practically identical from one rotation to the next. Stick-slip developed after approximately four rotations but occured only intermittently during a full rotation. Taking from two specimens the mean value of the recorded resistance, in terms of the friction angle this amounts to approximately 33°, and comparing it with the value obtained on a similar surface in the linear shear test, namely 37°, it is evident that the rotary value lies lower. This is not surprising if one examines the test curve of Figure 8 where the shear resistance after the first quarter rotation (equivalent to the few centimeters of shear displacement, as obtained in the conventional shear box) is still considerably higher than the residual value.

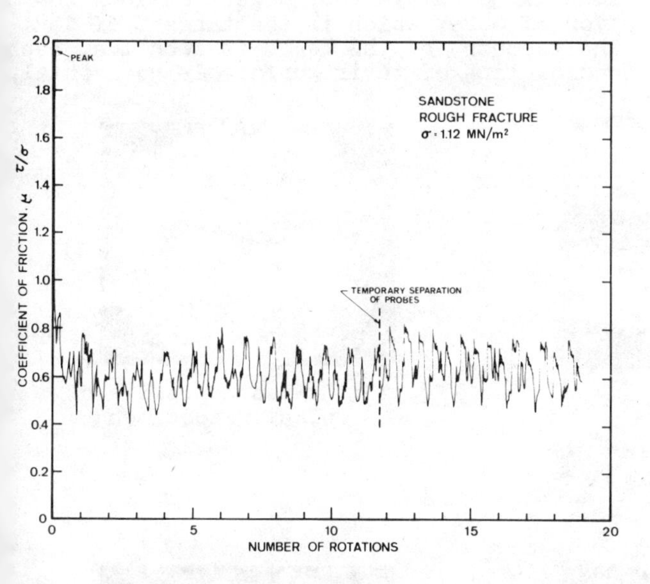

Fig. 8: Shear resistance - rotational displacement characteristic for an artificial tensile fracture in Darley Dale Sandstone

Photographs of an originally rough fracture which has been subjected to twelve rotations are shown in Figure 9. The wearing-off of asperities, the filling of gaps with compressed, fine rock debris, the general planing of the surface and the presence of pronounced slickensides are clearly visible. Most of the highly compacted fines could be easily lifted from the rough intact rock surface in the form of small plate-like pieces which exhibited slickensides on both sides. This must be taken as a proof that the differential shear movement takes place at distinct shear planes which coincide to a large extent with the boundary between the solid rock and the fines or pass partly through the layer of fines. A fluid-like simple shear deformation of the entire layer of fines does not appear to occur.

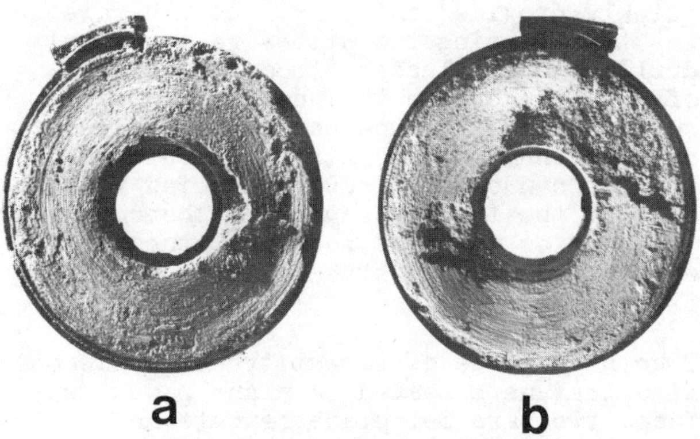

Fig. 9: Appearance of sheared rough fracture surface in Darley Dale Sandstone after twelve rotations with a normal stress of 1.12 MN/m^2. a) lower and b) upper surface

A third type of test geometry was that of two parallel sawcuts normal to the cylinder axis and 25 mm apart. This test arrangement was set up to study the interference of parallel joints under shear. The question was whether a specimen with two or more parallel joints would have the same shear resistance as one with a single joint. The result was that during the entire test (up to eight rotations) shear movement alternated from one to the other joint, but occurred never at both together. Consequently the final residual shear strength of the double-jointed specimen did not differ from that with a single joint. But, similar to the single sawcut, a steady increase of frictional resistance with increasing displacement was observed. Since the total shear movement has been distributed over two joints a longer displacement or more rotations have been necessary to reach the stable state. At those instants when the shear movement changed from one joint to the other the shear resistance dropped considerably, but this drop became smaller with further rotations. The drop in shear resistance occurs as the dynamic frictional resistance of the active joint exceeds the static time-dependent friction of the stationary joint, the roles are axchanged and the effective shear resistance drops to the dynamic friction of the previously stationary joint. As the dynamic friction slowly builds up with further displacement another reversal can take place. It is doubtful whether the same process would occur if the two joints were rough and matching surfaces. There, increasing displacement generally leads to a decrease in shear resistance and consequently a once active joint will have a high chance to remain active.

High-Strength Plaster

This material was chosen partly because a large number of cast specimens for trying and testing the rotary equipment could be quickly provided this way. The other reason was that casting the probes rather than drilling coaxial cores from rock blocks offered the chance to model any required surface geometry. One has to be aware, of course, that the results obtained from plaster cannot be directly applied to rock. Most of the fracture and wear phenomena are the same as those of rock, but they will occur at different stress levels and displacements.

Together, three different types of discontinuities were tested: A plane sawcut surface, two parallel plane sawcuts and a plane surface with sawtooth-like asperities.

The specimens with a single planar joint were rotated under a range of normal stresses up to 1.3 MN/m^2. For this entire range the angle of friction remained constant at 36° and thus agreed with the results from conventional shear box tests. No change of this value could be observed at very large displacements. The relative softness of this material and the minute particle size of the formed powder are responsible for a quick wear-down on any asperities and the true residual shear resistance of the joint is reached after a relatively small displacement.

The results from the plaster specimens with two smooth parallel joints agreed very well with those from similar tests with sandstone. The cylinders with two joints exhibited the same rotary shear resistance as the probes with a single joint and the shear deformation never occurred simultaneously at both surfaces but alternated between the two.

The third type of discontinuity is one with a sawtooth-shaped surface. Eight teeth with one vertical and one inclined face and a height of 6 mm are symmetrically arranged around the cylinder axis (see Figure 10). The angle of the inclined part of the tooth is 23° from the horizontal at the inner radius and 9° at the outer. This amounts to an average tangent of inclination of 0.29, which is the tangent of 16°. The geometry of the teeth is such that each radial line of their surface is horizontal.

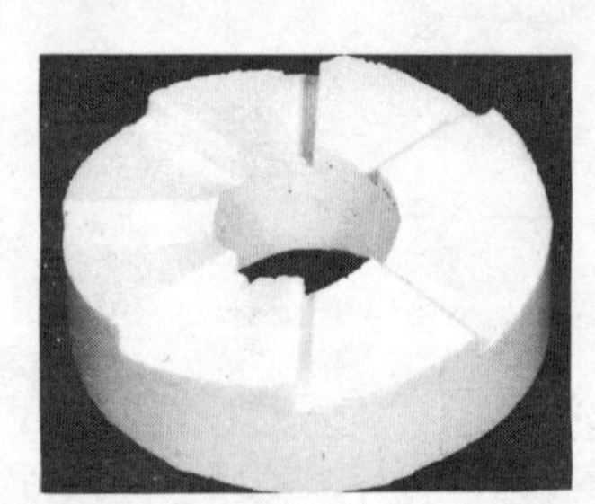

Fig. 10: Sawtooth profile of plaster specimen

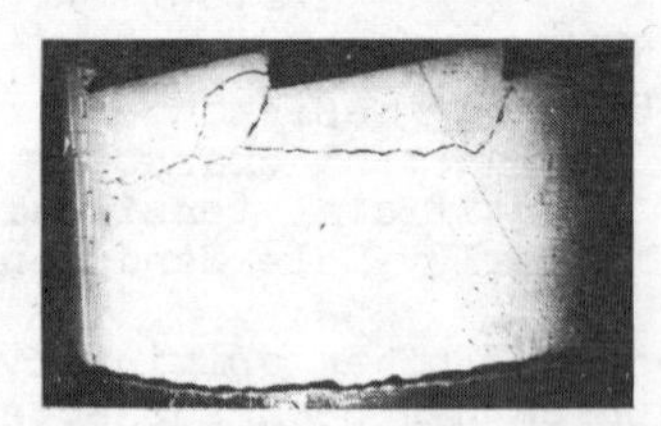

Fig. 11: Tensile fractures in sawtooth-profiled plaster specimen after rotation against the direction of the teeth.

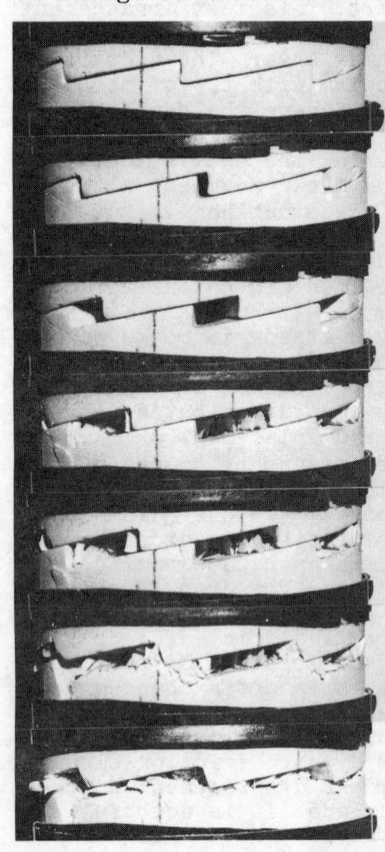

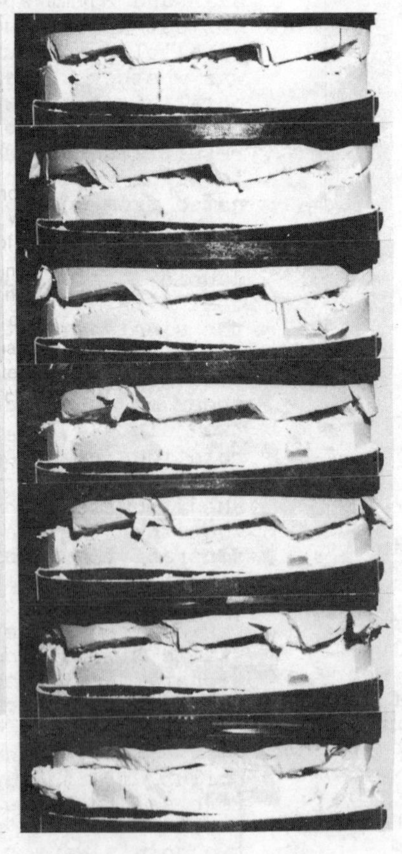

Fig. 12: Series of stages in the process of wear of the tooth-shaped asperities during rotation in the direction of the teeth

One sense of rotation leads to the riding-up of one tooth on the other, up to the point where the tooth falls into the next trough and the same process starts anew. The other sense of rotation is kinematically possible only if shear failure of the solid material, i. e. shearing off of a part of the tooth takes place. Both senses of rotation were tried, however shearing against the teeth caused at the first small displacement so severe tensile fracturing of the specimen and in some instances also failure of the epoxy resin bond at the end pieces (Figure 11) that the test had to be terminated.

Tests with rotation in the direction of the teeth were successful. A series of photographs taken at various stages during the rotation (Figure 12) show the riding-up and the wear process of the teeth. Initially only sliding takes place until at a displacement of about a half tooth length tensile failure sets in at the sharp edges of the teeth. This process accelerates as the actual contact area decreases. Then shear failure of the solid material starts. The debris gets crushed, fills the troughs, and eventually the surfaces are relatively plane and smooth. It is remarkable how small a displacement is necessary to reach the state where almost the entire tooth is worn off. Figure 13, taken at an intermediate state, shows a detailed view of the shear surface (looking in an outward, radial direction) with a shallowly inclined plateau of debris (white arrow) forming in the depression.

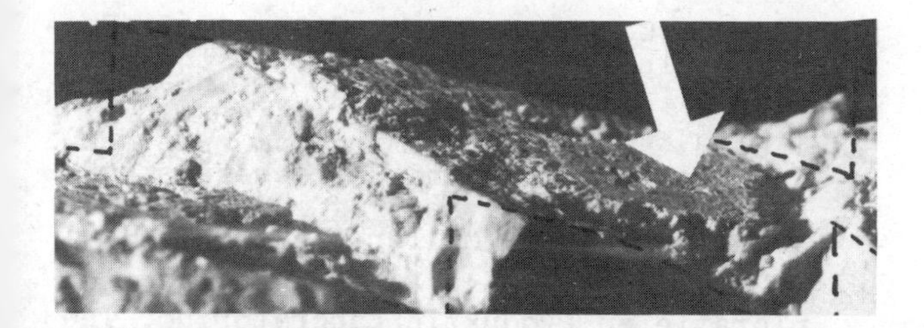

Fig. 13: Detailed view of a plateau (white arrow) of compacted debris forming between the asperities.

Finally a typical shear strength-displacement record of a sawtoothed plaster specimen is reproduced in Figure 14. The shear resistance is not, as one would expect from theory, constant during the riding-up stage, but apparently increasing steeply and dropping suddenly after each tooth length of displacement. After approximately three full rotations the effect of the asperities or teeth has completely disappeared and the shear resistance has reached a constant residual value which is the same as that of the plane sawcut.

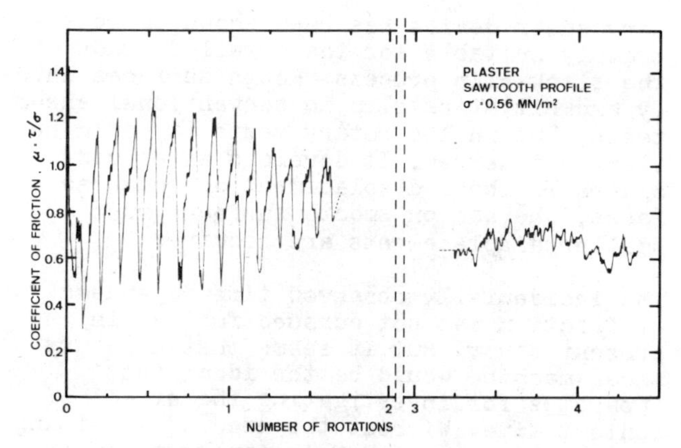

Fig. 14: Shear resistance - rotational displacement characteristic for a sawtooth profiled surface in plaster

CONCLUSIONS

It would be extremely significant for the design of rock structures if the true residual shear strength of discontinuities in the rock mass is not identical with but appreciably lower than the residual strength measured with relatively small differential displacements in laboratory and field tests. If very large displacements are required before the final and stable residual state, which represents a minimum, is established, then this would be a very relevant factor in dealing with progressive failure.

The first test results from sandstone specimens indicate, however, that, in contrast to the findings of BISHOP et al (1971) for clays, rough rock surfaces do not exhibit a clear trend of reaching the true residual state only after very large displacements. The complete absence of any change in residual shear resistance in the tests with plaster and the relatively small displacement necessary to establish the residual state for the joint in sandstone suggest that the displacement required for reaching the stable state will increase with the hardness of the rock, the roughness of the original surface, the sharpness of the debris, and the strength of the cementing material.

A pronounced displacement dependency of the residual shear strength was, however, observed for smooth sawcuts in sandstone. There the resistance increases gradually and reaches a stable state only after a displacement of a couple of meters. Results from conventional shear tests on surfaces of this type appear therefore to be rather questionable, since there the limited displacement does not permit the development of the true residual strength.

The stick-slip phenomenon has recently been considered to be a very improtant factor in the interpretation of earthquakes. The rotary shear device has been shown to be extremely suitable for the detailed study of the stick-slip process. Rough surfaces hardly exhibit stick-slip in conventional shear tests; but in the rotary tests it could be clearly observed. It develops after considerable shear displacement on rough surfaces, whereas on smooth surfaces much smaller displacements are required.

The incidentally observed time-dependence of friction was not pursued further in the present study. But it seems that a rotary shear machine would be the ideal test apparatus for investigating the effect of contact time. Without the need of resetting the samples, measurements can be taken at various normal loads and at any length of displacement at one and the same specimen. Interference due to different surface geometries can thus be eliminated. Shear tests on rock joints with control and measurement of pore water pressure should be technically easier in a rotary than in a linear shear test. It appears therefore that the rotary shear apparatus with its primary advantage of unlimited shear displacement constitutes a very promising research tool in rock mechanics. After this first trial series of experiments on a pilot machine an improved and more powerful machine would have to be used for future work.

Is a rotary shear device for rocks suited for field tests and application in boreholes? Technically, a borehole rotary shear tool would be quite feasible and certainly attractive for testing the frictional characteristics of natural fractures in situ. But the complications that enter when the fracture surface is not normal to the direction of the cylinder or borehole axis and when the non-planarity of the tested surface causes considerable variation in shear resistance during one rotation are very serious. One can imagine how ambiguous field results may turn out to be, if already controlled laboratory conditions yield shear data for rough uneven surfaces which vary at times more than 50 % during one rotation. The experience gained from this investigation certainly does not encourage the use of rotary shear devices in boreholes.

ACKNOWLEDGEMENT

This study formed part of the research program of the Rock Mechanics Project, Imperial College, London. Particular thanks are due to Messrs. J. D. Sullivan and J. Verge of Imperial College for their help and advice during the design and construction of the rotary shear machine.

REFERENCES

BISHOP, A. W., G. E. GREEN, et al, 1971, A new ring shear apparatus and its application to the measurement of residual strength, Geotechnique, Vol. 21, No. 4, pp. 273-328.

BRESLER, B. and K. S. PISTER, 1957, Failure of concrete under combined stresses, Tans. ASCE, Vol. 122, pp. 1049-1068.

DIETERICH, J. H., 1972, Time-dependent friction in rocks, Journal of Geophysical Research, Vol. 77, No. 20, pp. 3690-3781.

GRUNER, H. E. and R. HAEFELI, 1934, Beitrag zur Untersuchung des physikalischen und statischen Verhaltens kohärenter Böden, Schweizerische Bauzeitung, Vol. 103, pp. 171-174, 185-188.

HAEFELI, R., 1938, Mechanische Eigenschaften von Lockergesteinen, Schweizerische Bauzeitung, Vol. 111, pp. 299-303, 321-325.

HANDIN, J., D. V. HIGGS and J. K. O'BRIEN, 1960, Torsion of Yule Marble under confining pressure, Chapter 9, Symposium on Rock Deformation, The Geological Society of America, Memoir 79.

HVORSLEV, M. J., 1939, Torsion shear tests and their place in the determination of the shearing resistance of soils, Proceedings American Society Testing Materials, Vol. 39, pp. 999-1022.

HVORSLEV, M. J. and R. I. Kaufman, 1952, Torsion shear apparatus and testing procedures, Bulletin No. 38, USACE Waterways Experiment Station, Vicksburg, Miss.

JAEGER, J. C. and N. G. W. COOK, 1969, Fundamentals or Rock Mechanics, Methuen, London.

KUTTER, H. K. 1973, Zusammenhang zwischen Anfangsrauhigkeit und Restscherfestigkeit einer Kluft, Beitrag zur Festschrift Prof. L. Müller (in print).

MANDL, G., 1971, Koniglikjke Shell, Exploratie en Produktie Laboratorium, The Netherlands, Personal Communication.

JOINT STRENGTH CHARACTERISTICS OF A WEATHERED ROCK

PROPRIÉTÉ DE LA RÉSISTANCE DES JOINTS D'UNE ROCHE DESAGRÉGÉE

VERBINDUNGS-FESTIGKEITS-EIGENSCHAFTEN VON VERWITTERTEN STEINEN

G. R. MARTIN Senior Lecturer in Civil Engineering
University of Auckland, New Zealand

P. J. MILLAR Engineer, Ministry of Works, Central Laboratory,
Lower Hutt, New Zealand

SUMMARY

Low cost and versatile displacement controlled direct shear equipment suitable for testing weathered rock or rock joints in the laboratory is described. Results of strength tests on joints from a sandstone showing varying degrees of weathering are presented. A stage testing procedure is introduced as a means of defining peak envelopes of the various joints tested. Reductions in strength with increasing weathering are apparent and are correlated with corresponding physical and mineralogical changes in the rock. The effects of dilation on joint shear strength are examined, and a procedure for isolating the dilatant component of shear strength suggested.

RÉSUMÉ

Une installation de laboratoire à bas prix, versatile et capable de tester des roches désagrégeés ou jointeés est decrit. L'installation est controlleé par le rapport de la déformation en cisaillement directe. Des resultats des essais de résistance sur des joints d'un grès montrant des degreés variables de désagrégation sont présentés. Un procédé d'essai à étapes est introduit pour définir l'enveloppe de la résistance maximale des joints diverses essayés. Des réductions de la résistance avec l'augmentation du désagrégation sont apparentes et correspondent aux changements physiques et minéralogiques des roches. Les effets de dilatation sur la résistance au cisaillement des joints sont examinés, et un procédé isolant le composant dilatif de la résistance au cisaillement est proposé.

ZUSAMMENFASSUNG

Ein vielseitiges and billiges Schergeraet wird beschrieben. Festigkeits-Pruefungen von Sandstein-Verbindungen, welche verschiedene Grade der Verwitterung zeigen, sind dargestellt. Eine Stufen-folgende Probe, welche die Gipfel der Festigkeitskurven erkennt, wird beschrieben. Die Abschwaechung der Festigkeit mit der Vergroesserung der Verwitterung ist bewiessen, und in Wechselbeziehung mit den physikalischen und mineralischen Aenderungen des Sandstein's gebracht. Die Wirkung der Volumvergroesserung, so weit sie die Scherfestigkeit betrifft, wird geprueft. Ein Verfahren, welches den Ausdehnungs-Komponenten der Scherfestigkeit feststellt, wird dargeboten.

INTRODUCTION

Greywacke (a well indurated quartzofeldspathic sandstone) is the predominant basement rock in New Zealand, and in many regions of the country where the rock is exposed, deep, closely jointed weathered rock profiles have developed. The typical nature of the weathered rock profile may be adequately described using a previously suggested classification scheme for weathered rock (Fookes and Horswill, 1970). Table 1 shows a modified version of the scheme, where the descriptions have been written to indicate the predominant characteristics of weathered greywacke. The depth of the weathering profile (residual soil through to fresh rock) varies considerably, but may reach depths of up to 30-40 metres.

In recent years, design problems associated with large road cuttings in weathered greywacke, have highlighted the need for basic research on the physical and mechanical properties of the jointed rock, particularly problems related to slope stability. The analysis of slope stability in weathered rock leads to a multitude of difficult problems. (Deere and Patton, 1971). However, undoubtedly an understanding of joint strength characteristics must provide a better basis for improved methods of slope design.

In this paper, the results of a series of tests to obtain joint strength characteristics of greywacke showing various degrees of weathering are presented. The results were obtained using strain controlled direct shear apparatus designed specifically for the project. Design features of the test equipment are described, and test results correlated with additional physical and mineralogical characteristics of the rock.

THE DIRECT SHEAR APPARATUS

The basic principle of the direct shear apparatus developed for the experimental program is shown in Fig. 1. The principle is similar to that of the portable field equipment developed and used at Imperial College (Hoek, 1970).

Test specimens having a maximum dimension of 150 mm,

TERM	GRADE	DESCRIPTION
True Residual Soil	VI	Original rock fabric completely destroyed. Rock completely changed to soil, generally light or yellow-brown sandy clay.
Completely Weathered	V	Original rock structure completely weathered - crushable to light brown sandy silts under finger pressure. Original rock fabric still visible, with joint patterns marked by iron or black manganese dioxide stains.
Highly Weathered	IV	Original rock structure retained but generally weathered to light brown colour right through. Most of material can be crushed to silt and sand sizes under finger pressure, but harder lumps remain, Rock structure generally open and closely jointed.
Moderately Weathered	III	Original rock structure retained Brown weathering extends part way through rock fragments, leaving grey unweathered central core. Rock structure tighter. Rock fragments easily broken with light hammer blow.
Slightly Weathered	II	Hard jointed rock. Brown colour extends inwards a short distance on joint planes. Interior has colour and texture of unweathered greywacke. Separate pieces require moderate hammer blow to break.
Fresh Rock	I	Unweathered greywacke. Shows no discolouration, loss of strength or any other effects due to weathering.

TABLE I

Classification Scheme for Weathered Greywacke

are set in a quicksetting plaster or cement poured into a perspex mould. The cast sample in the form of a cube is then placed in the lower half of the shear box, and the upper half seated on top leaving the shearing plane (normally the dominant joint plane) exposed over a gap of 5-10 mm. The shear box framework is fabricated from 12.5 mm mild steel plate.

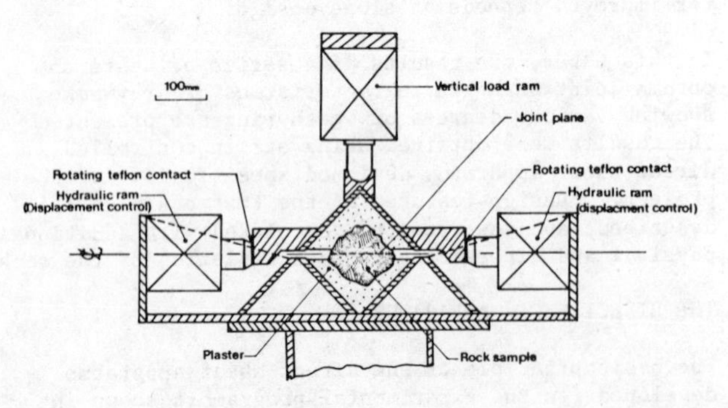

Fig. 1 Schematic Diagram of Direct Shear Apparatus

Vertical loads of up to 250 kN are applied by means of a hydraulic ram. The ram is supported by a crosshead, which in turn is held by two high-tensile rods fixed to the base of the machine as shown in the photograph of the apparatus in Fig. 2. The rods are 1.25m long, so that the effects of rotation of the vertical ram during horizontal displacement are minimized. Horizontal shearing loads of up to 250 kN are applied by means of displacement controlled hydraulic rams. Two horizontal rams are used to permit load reversals, the rams being capable of applying displacements of up to 50 mm in each direction. The ends of the rams comprise rotary conical caps (faced with teflon to reduce friction), which are seated in vertical guides in the top half of the shear box. The rams have teflon seals to minimise friction.

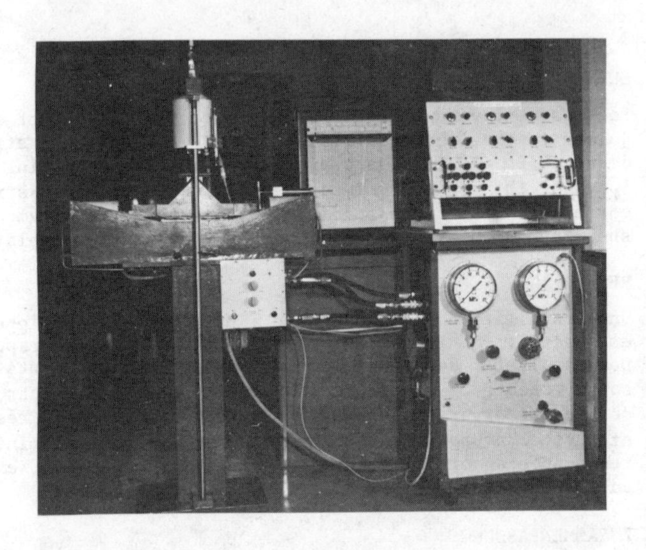

Fig. 2 General View of Direct Shear Apparatus

A three cylinder fuel injection pump driven by an electric motor is used to activate the load rams. The basic circuit diagram of the hydraulic system, which has a pressure range of 0-27 MPa, is shown in Fig. 3. A low pressure auxiliary circuit (0-4 MPa) provides improved accuracy for tests using low normal stress. Two of the pump cylinders supply oil under pressure to the vertical load ram, a constant pressure valve being used to set the required normal stress. The vertical constant pressure system incorporates a small damping chamber pressurized with nitrogen (the gas being separated from the oil by a bellofram) to reduce pressure fluctuations. This arrangement was found more convenient than a conventional large pressure accumulator. The third injection pump cylinder is used in a constant flow system which maintains a constant displacement rate of the horizontal load rams. The flow rate is accurately set using a calibrated control valve, which permits horizontal ram displacement rates of between 0-12 mm per minute. The direction of shear is controlled using solenoid valves, which can be operated manually or automatically using microswitches. The microswitches may be positioned to any required displacement limit within the maximum range of 50 mm. The use of small bore hydraulic tubing and large area rams, produced a relatively high loading stiffness of 2×10^6 N/mm. An air pressure system

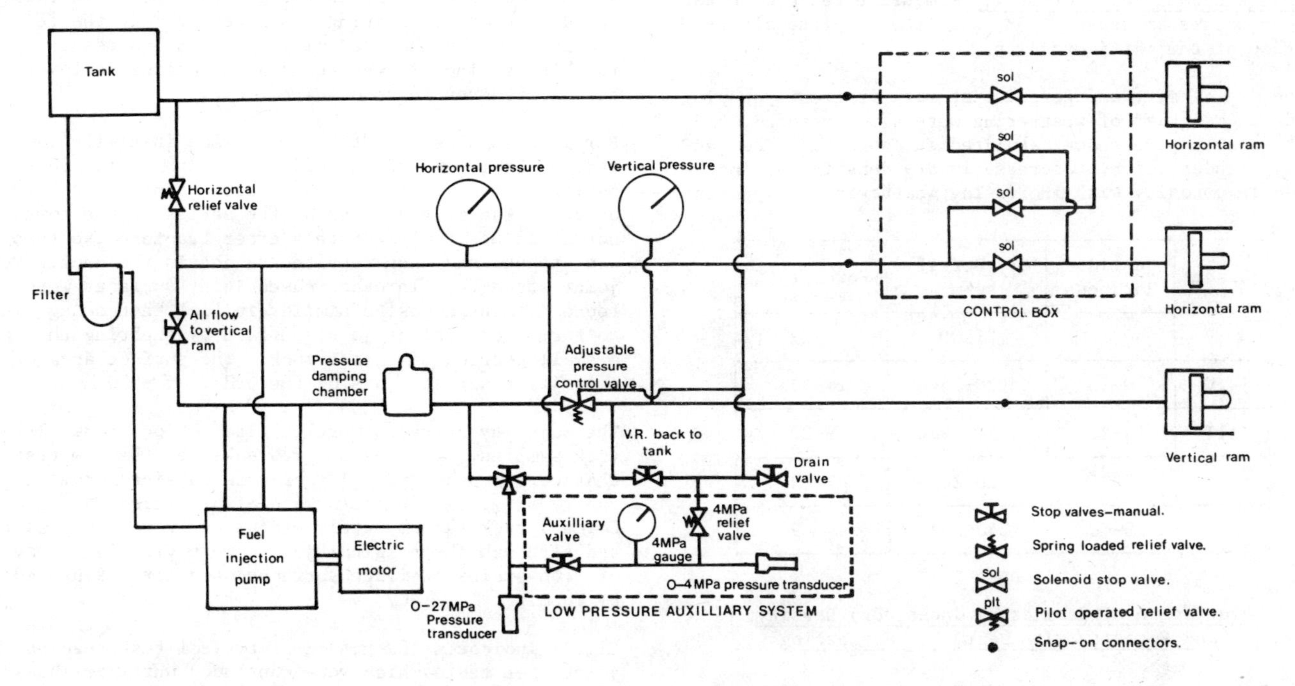

Fig. 3 Hydraulic Control System

connected to the front of all rams, enables them to be retracted at the end of a test.

Pressure in the load rams can be measured using pressure gauges, or recorded by means of pressure transducers, and a chart recorder. Transducers for high pressure (0-27 MPa) and low pressure (0-4 MPa) ranges are incorporated for improved accuracy. Vertical and horizontal displacements may be noted using dial gauges, or recorded by means of LVDT displacement transducers.

The apparatus is versatile and simple to operate, and can be constructed for a comparatively low cost. It is capable of testing most rock types at high or low pressures and high or low strain rates. The high stiffness of the loading system together with displacement controlled horizontal loading, enable the post failure load-deformation curves of brittle failures to be defined, and residual strengths to be obtained.

PHYSICAL AND MINERALOGICAL CHARACTERISTICS OF TEST SAMPLES

Greywacke rock samples for testing were carefully trimmed from a 30m high cutting in Wellington City, being formed as part of motorway development in the area. The cut exposed all grades of weathering except Grade I (fresh rock). Representative samples of each weathering grade were taken shortly after a new section of the cut was made. The rock was generally closely and tightly jointed, the selected samples being carefully extracted from the parent rock to avoid disturbance of the joints. Joint spacings were generally of the order of 25 mm and were seldom open. Thin deposits of iron oxide were common on joint surfaces. The rock samples were bound with adhesive tape, and stored in sealed plastic bags. Duplicate samples were taken to enable a detailed petrological study of thin-sections together with clay mineral analyses by X-ray diffraction and infra-red spectroscopy methods. The latter tests were carried out by the Engineering Geology Section of the New Zealand Geological Survey.

From the results of the petrological study, the unweathered greywacke rock was described as texturally poorly sorted, with an average grain size of 0.3-0.4mm. The principle minerals were noted to be feldspar (40%) and quartz (25%), (with some mica also present) cemented in a fine grained matrix (15%). Thin section studies showed that the weathering process occurs primarily in the fine grained matrix, and it is only near the ground surface in the residual soil that the rock mineral grains are significantly altered. The weathering sequence may be described briefly as follows:

Slightly Weathered Greywacke (Grade II) - thin opaque films (probably illite and iron oxide) develop at grain boundaries.

Moderately Weathered Greywacke (Grade III) - thin films are more pronounced, but no textural change.

Highly Weathered Greywacke (Grade IV) - light brown discolouration of the matrix by iron oxide more noticeable, with further development of clay minerals (illite) in the matrix. Original texture of rock well preserved, but fractures cut across individual grains.

Completely Weathered Greywacke (Grade V) - clay minerals, (primarily illite) more abundant in the matrix, but original texture of rock still mostly well preserved.

True Residual Soil (Grade VI) - massive textural breakdown occurs at depths < 3m, with the complete alteration of the matrix to clay.

The dry density and porosity of rock fragments showing varying degrees of weathering were also measured, and the results are shown tabulated in Table 2. The general tendency for a decrease in dry density and increase in porosity with increasing weathering is apparent.

Grade	Schmidt Hardness	Dry Density kg/m^3	Porosity %
V	0	1500	> 23
IV	0-10	2020-2540	17-25
III	10-20	1930-2420	9-20
II	15-25	2320-2450	7-13
I	25-40	2540-2570	< 9

TABLE 2

Variation of Schmidt Hardness, Dry Density, and Porosity with Degree of Weathering

Physical properties of the more highly weathered Greywacke grades, have been the subject of other studies (Pender, 1971).

DIRECT SHEAR TEST PROCEDURE AND RESULTS

Samples of jointed greywacke from each weathering grade were tested to failure in the direct shear equipment previously described. Samples were tested at various normal stresses ranging from approximately 0.15 to 5 MPa, although most tests were carried out at stresses less than 1 MPa, being the stress range for most slope stability problems. Tests were performed using horizontal shear displacement rates of the order of 1 - 1.5 mm/min.

As it was impossible to obtain several identical samples, the use of stage testing was necessary in order to define a peak strength failure envelope of a joint, and to allow the relative effects of dilation on joint strength to be studied. In this procedure, an initial test was performed at the lowest value of a selected normal stress range. As soon as the maximum shearing resistance was reached, the test was immediately stopped, and the sample returned to its zero displacement position. (In some cases the peak strength in the reverse direction was also obtained). The vertical stress was then approximately doubled, and the above test procedure repeated. In this way, assuming that any surface irregularities on the joint surface which were sheared off at the lower stress level would not affect the strength at the higher stress level, a failure envelope for the joint could be defined. As the failure envelopes (maximum shear stress vs. normal stress) were curved, a test sequence of repeatedly doubling the normal stress three or four times within the stress range was adopted in order to define the envelope with reasonable accuracy.

At the final normal stress value, the test was continued past the peak shear stress to define a residual strength characteristic. When the maximum shear stress had dropped off to the constant residual value, the direction of shearing was reversed, and the test continued. By then reducing the normal stress, further testing allowed residual strengths at lower normal stresses to be obtained.

For some samples, joint surfaces were initially cemented, probably due to the effects of iron oxide formation on the joint. In such cases joint fracture occurred the initial test of the series at the lowest normal stress. Immediately after fracture the test was stopped and then repeated to obtain the uncemented joint strength. In other cases joint surfaces were found discontinuous, a similar initial test being used to form a continuous joint surface by shearing through a small section of intact rock. The surface area of most joint surfaces was of the order of 9000 mm^2.

The majority of tests were carried out on Grade II-IV rock samples. Samples of greywacke for the few tests that were run on Grade I rock were obtained from a quarry site. A few tests were also carried out on Grade V rock (a completely weathered brown sandy silt). and although the original joints were visible by way of iron stains, failure surfaces were not influenced by them.

Fig. 4 indicates the nature of typical test results on joints for tests which were continued until residual strengths were obtained. Both shear stress and vertical displacement are shown plotted against horizontal displacement. It can be seen that for tests where shear displacement was reversed, the shear stress drops to zero, and then rises to the previous residual values without any marked peak. For Grades I through III, (fresh-moderately weathered rock) it was noted that considerable dilation still accompanies residual strengths, whereas for Grade V (completely weathered rock) negligible dilation occurred at residual strengths, which is characteristic of soil behaviour.

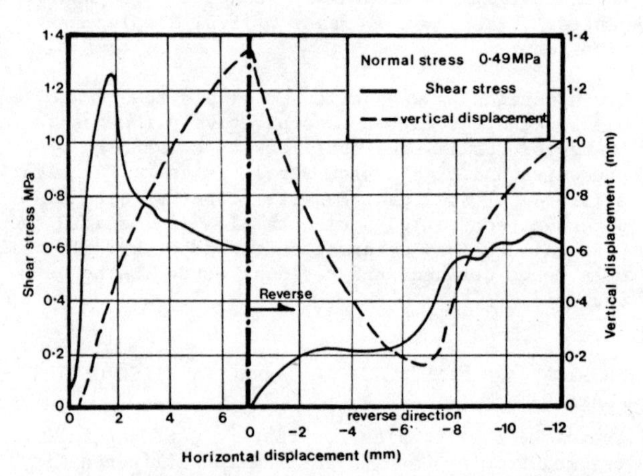

Fig. 4 Typical Results from Joint Strength Test

Test results for Grades II, III and IV rock are summarized in Figs. 5, 6 and 7 respectively. The curves show peak strength envelopes for the joints which were stage tested. It can be seen that the joint strength envelopes for Grade II and III rock cover a wide range. This might be expected in view of the variation of joint surface characteristics (which would affect the dilitant component of strength), and of variations in the degree of weathering within each grade. Variations in joint strength are somewhat less for Grade IV rock.

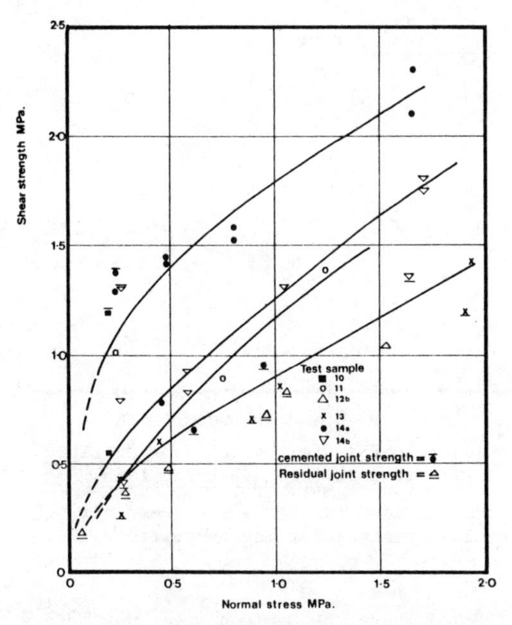

Fig. 5 Joint Strengths - Grade II Rock

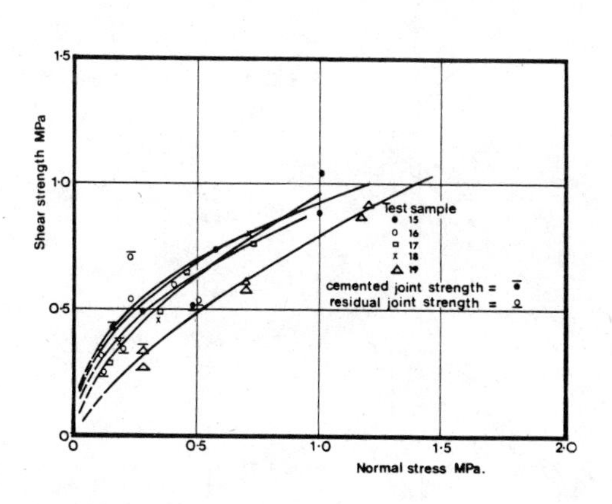

Fig. 7 Joint Strengths - Grade IV Rock

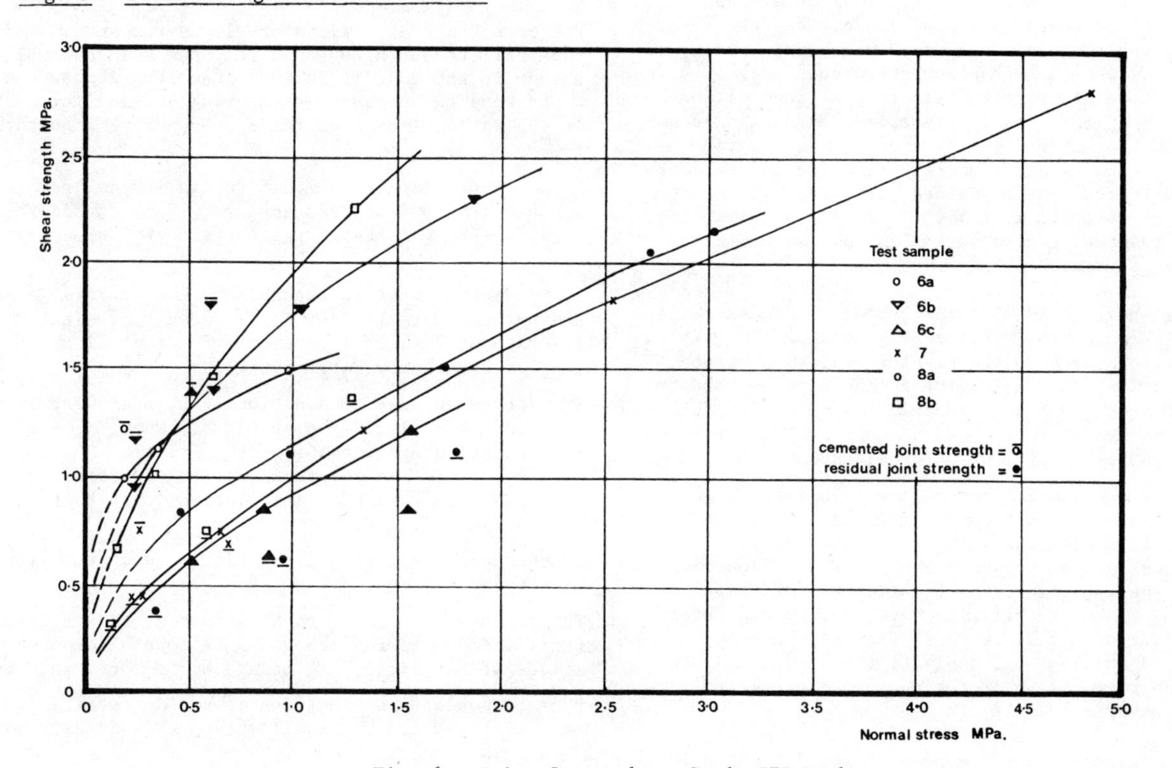

Fig. 6 Joint Strengths - Grade III Rock

The range of joint strength envelopes for the above three rock grades are compared in Fig. 8. The range of envelopes for Grades II and III are seen to overlap. This is perhaps not surprising, as the physical difference between the two grades is governed largely by the extent to which the weathering processes have penetrated the rock, (a factor which will affect comparative intact strengths), with differences in the weathering on joint surfaces being somewhat of a lesser degree. Joint strength envelopes for Grade IV rock fall in a narrow range at the lower bound of the Grade II and Grade III envelopes. Although Grade IV rock always failed along joint planes unless the orientation was unfavourable, little difference was observed between joint and intact rock strengths over the normal stress range used, whereas for Grade II and III rock, intact rock strengths were generally considerably greater than joint strengths. Hence it can be

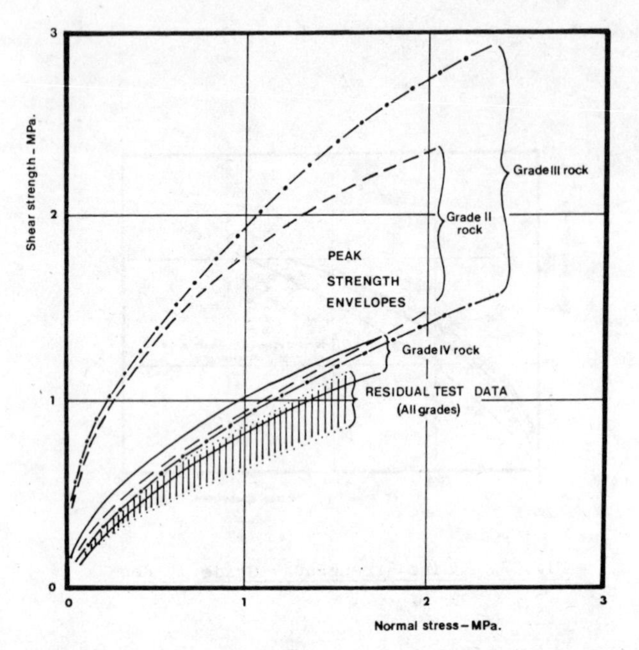

Fig. 8 Comparative Range of Joint Strength Envelopes

seen that the joint strength behaviour of Grades II and III rock represent a transition between the behaviour of fresh rock joints as an upper bound, and Grade IV joints, where the behaviour approaches that of a soil. In the latter case it is thought that although the texture of the rock is preserved, expansion accompanying the formation of clay minerals in the fine grained matrix has destroyed the frictional interlock of the unaltered coarse grained particles. The range of residual strength test data is also plotted in Fig. 8, the data showing a reduction in ϕ_r with increasing normal stress.

Following shear tests, Schmidt rebound hardness tests were performed on the surface of joints, while samples were still confined in the plaster mould. A reasonable correlation between Schmidt hardness values and the degree of weathering was obtained, as noted in Table 2.

DILATION AND ITS EFFECT ON SHEAR STRENGTH

The effects of dilation contribute to a good proportion of the shear strength of irregular joint surfaces, particularly at low confining pressure when there is little shear across projecting asperities. Two models illustrating the effects of dilation are described below, and although primarily developed to characterize the irregular failure surface of a jointed rock mass, could equally well apply to the irregular joint surface characteristic of the weathered greywacke samples tested.

A simple bilinear model has been proposed (Patton,1966) to describe the shear behaviour of a surface comprising a number of equal and regular projecting teeth. The model is shown in Fig. 9. At low normal loads, the teeth remain intact, and the shear strength of the joint may be written as -

$$\tau = \sigma_n \tan(\phi_\mu + i) \quad (1)$$

where ϕ_μ = angle of friction along the planar surface of the teeth
i = angle of inclination of teeth.

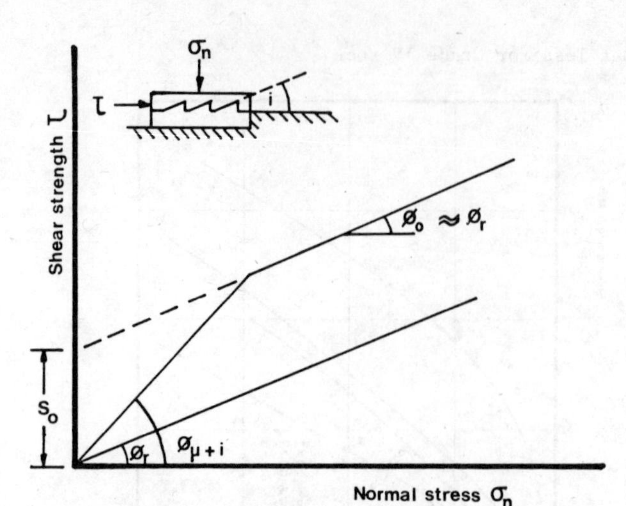

Fig. 9 Idealized Failure Envelope for Multiple Inclined Surfaces (Patton, 1966)

At high normal loads when the teeth shear off, the shear strength of the joint may be written as -

$$\tau = s_o + \sigma_n \tan \phi_o \quad (2)$$

where s_o and ϕ_o are the Coulomb shear parameters for the rock material.

Patton noted that failure envelopes for actual jointed rock failure surfaces would not show such a simple change in the mode of failure described above, but would tend to be curved reflecting varying intensities of the various modes of failure occurring simultaneously.

A more general failure model for an irregular rock surface (Ladanyi and Archambault, 1969) considers the total shearing force S as the sum of four components:

S_1 = component due to external work done in dilating against the normal force N, = $N\dot{v}$ where $\dot{v}$ = the dilation rate at failure (increment of normal disp./increment of shear disp. at failure).

S_2 = component due to additional internal work in friction due to dilatancy = $S\dot{v} \tan \phi_f$, where ϕ_f = a statistical average value of the friction angle when sliding occurs along irregularities of different orientations. (For tightly interlocked joint surfaces, $\phi_f \to \phi_\mu$.)

S_3 = component arising from friction with no dilation = $N \tan \phi_\mu$.

The components S_1, S_2 and S_3 arise due to resistance from sliding deformation only. A fourth component arises if asperities are being sheared off, that is,

S_4 = component from shearing of solid asperities = $A s_o + N \tan \phi_o$ if all shear resistance is coming from this source.

For a general failure case, both sliding and shearing of asperities may occur simultaneously. By defining a shear area ratio, $a_s = A_s/A$, where A = total projected shear area, and A_s = area over which asperities are being sheared, Ladanyi and Archambault write the total shearing resistance as:

$$S = (S_1 + S_2 + S_3)(1 - a_s) + S_4 a_s$$

$$\text{or} \quad \tau = \frac{S}{A} = \frac{\sigma_n(1-a_s)(\dot{v}+\tan\phi_\mu) + a_s(\sigma_n \tan \phi_o + s_o)}{1 - (1 - a_s)\,\dot{v} \tan \phi_f} \qquad (3)$$

The above equation reduces to equation (1) at low normal loads and for regular asperities ($\phi_\mu = \phi_f$, $\dot{v} = \tan i$, $a_s = 0$), and to equation (2) at high normal loads when all asperities are sheared off ($a_s = 1$, $\dot{v} = 0$).

Ladanyi and Archambault note that for a general case of an irregular rock surface, $\dot{v}$ and a_s may be expected to vary continuously with normal pressure in the manner shown in Fig. 10, with the result that equation (3) yields a curved failure envelope as shown.

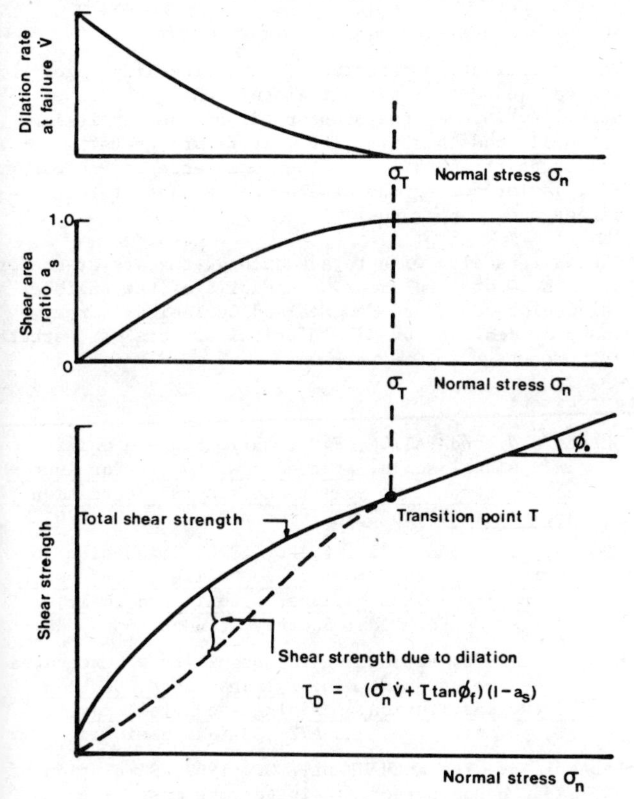

Fig. 10 Generalized Failure Envelope for Irregular Rock Surface (Ladanyi and Archambault, 1969)

It would seem reasonable to assume that on shearing dilation will occur until the internal shear strength of the asperities is less than the frictional shear strength. With reduced dilation at failure corresponding to higher normal stresses, it can be envisaged that shearing of asperities occurs at a lower level, resulting in a greater value of a_s. At normal stresses in excess of the transition point T, the rock can be envisaged as shearing through the base of asperities with no dilation.

The contribution to the shear strength arising from dilation, can be attributed to the strength components S_1 and S_2, and hence the dilatant component of shear strength may be written as

$$\tau_D = (\sigma_n \dot{v} + \tau \dot{v} \tan \phi_f)(1 - a_s) \qquad (4)$$

As a_s is difficult to measure directly, values of τ_D cannot readily be computed. However, by making several approximations, it is suggested that an estimate of τ_D can be obtained in the following manner.

The form of the functional relationships $(1 - a_s)$ vs. σ_n and $\dot{v}$ vs. σ_n would appear from Fig. 10 to be fairly similar. Hence it would seem reasonable as a first approximation, that the ratio of $\dot{v}/(1-a_s)$ for any value of σ_n could be equated to a constant K. Substituting in equation (4) we have

$$\tau_D = (\sigma_n + \tau \tan \phi_f)\, \dot{v}^2/K \qquad (5)$$

When $a_s = 0$, $K = \dot{v}$, and hence a value of K for a particular test can be obtained from the intersection of the $\dot{v}$ vs. σ_n curve with the $\sigma_n = 0$ axis. For tightly jointed rock it seems reasonable to assume that $\phi_f = \phi_\mu$. An initial value of ϕ_μ can be obtained by assuming $\phi_\mu = \phi_o$ (the asymptote of the failure envelope at high normal stresses), and hence by substituting in equation (5), values of τ_D may be computed for various values of σ_n. By then plotting the function $(\tau-\tau_D)$ vs. σ_n, an improved value of ϕ_μ may be measured from the gradient of this function at the origin (i.e., $\sigma_n = 0$). This new value can then be substituted in equation (5), and improved values of τ_D obtained. Generally, 3 or 4 iterations are sufficient to give a convergent solution for ϕ_μ.

Table 3 shows the final results for such a procedure for test data obtained from a Grade III rock joint, while Fig. 11 illustrates the proportion of strength arising from dilation at lower normal stresses. A transition from a dilatant failure mode to one involving shearing of asperities with no volume change, is clearly seen at a normal stress of 3 MPa.

Sample	Grade	σ_n(MPa)	$\dot{v}$	τ(MPa)	K	$\phi_f(=\phi_\mu)$	τ_D(MPa)
		0.29	0.4	0.450			192
		0.65	0.3	0.750			212
7	III	1.36	0.2	1.230	0.5	36°	178
		2.55	0.05	1.840			19
		4.87	0	2.780			0

TABLE 3

Calculation of the Component of Shear Strength Due to Dilation from the Expression:

$$\tau_D = (\sigma_n + \tau \tan \phi_f)\, \dot{v}^2/K$$

It should be noted that the decrease in joint dilation with increasing normal stress is also of significance with respect to the validity of the stage testing procedure adopted. Due to the reduction in dilation for stage tests at progressively higher normal stresses, asperities will tend to shear off at successively lower levels. Hence it is reasonable to assume that the effect of joint damage on measured peak strengths in successive tests, is minimal.

Also it is of importance to note that the residual strength envelopes obtained form the stage testing procedure, reflect strengths mobilized on a shearing surface having the characteristics of that generated

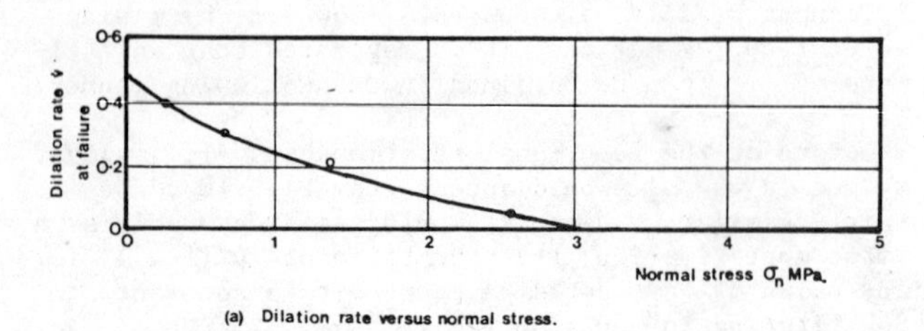

(a) Dilation rate versus normal stress.

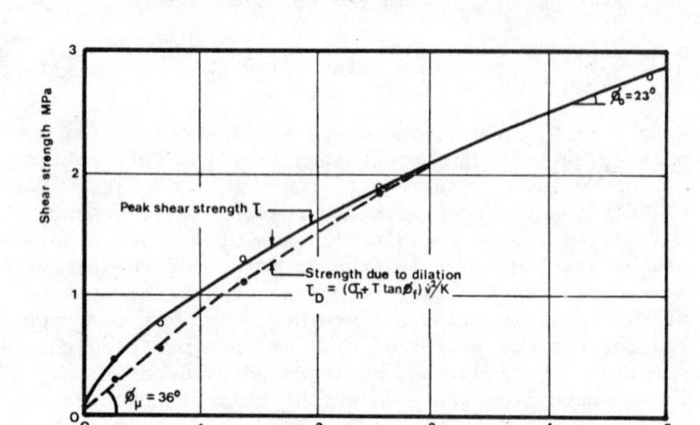

(b) Shear strength components versus normal stress.

Fig. 11 Analysis of Strength Due to Dilation (Sample 7 - Grade III Rock Joint)

in the test at the highest normal stress. Hence residual strengths measured at the lowest normal stress for example, will differ from the strength which would have been recorded if the initial test at this stress had been continued to a large displacement. For the latter test, the shearing surface would reflect a state where the asperities were sheared at a higher level. Whereas this value is of practical significance with respect to field strengths during large displacements, the stage tested residual strength can be considered a more characteristic physical parameter of the rock material. The observed non-linearity of the residual strength envelopes obtained, are felt to reflect the decrease in the dilatant component of residual strength with increasing normal stress.

SUMMARY AND CONCLUSIONS

The suitability of direct shear apparatus of the type described, for investigating joint strength characteristics of rock has been demonstrated. The hydraulic system designed to apply controlled shearing displacement, was found to be most satisfactory.

The stage testing procedure adopted as a means of defining peak strength envelopes was considered relatively successful, and overcame the difficult problem of obtaining duplicate field samples for testing.

Joint strength tests on weathered greywacke over a normal stress range of 0-5 MPa, showed a broad transition of peak strengths from an upper bound for fresh (Grade I) rock to a lower bound for highly weathered (Grade IV) rock. Both the Grade II and Grade III rock joints showed a similar range of strengths, indicating that the effects of weathering on joints was similar for both grades. Petrographic studies indicated that the weathering process occurred primarily in the fine grained rock matrix, with strength tests suggesting that for the Grade IV rock, expansion associated with clay mineral formation has broken grain interlock sufficiently to give little difference between joint and intact rock strengths at low normal stresses.

Residual strength test data was indicative of a reduction in residual angle of friction with increasing normal stress.

An approximate method of determining the dilatant component of joint strength using the general failure model for jointed rock developed by Ladanyi and Archambault, was illustrated. The transitions from a dilatant to a non-dilatant failure mode involving shearing of asperities was clearly seen.

ACKNOWLEDGEMENTS

The investigation described in the preceding pages was carried out as part of a study on "Rock Slope Stability", under the sponsorship of the New Zealand National Roads Board. The writers are grateful for this support and also for the assistance of Professor P.W. Taylor during the development phases of the direct shear apparatus.

The writers also wish to acknowledge the assistance of Mr. L.E. Oborn and Dr. B.W. Riddolls of the Engineering Geology Section, New Zealand Geological Survey, who provided data on mineralogical aspects of weathering processes in Greywacke.

REFERENCES

DEERE, D.U. and PATTON, F.D., 1971, Slope Stability in residual soils, Proceedings, Fourth Pan American Conference on Soil Mechanics and Foundation Engineering, San Juan, Puerto Rico, pp 87-170.

FOOKES, P.G., and HORSWILL, P., 1970, Discussion on engineering grade zones, Proceedings, Conference on in-situ Investigations in Soils and Rocks, British Geotechnical Society, London, pp 53-57.

HOEK, E., 1970, Estimating the stability of excavated slopes in opencast mines, Transations, Section A of the Institution of Mining and Metallurgy, Vol. 79, pp. A109-132, and A72-A83 (discussion).

LADANYI, B., and ARCHAMBAULT, G., 1969, Simulation of shear behaviour of a jointed rock mass, Eleventh Symposium on Rock Mechanics, California, Chap.7 pp 105-125.

PATTON, F.D., 1966, Multiple modes of shear failure in rock, Proceedings, First Congress of International Society of Rock Mechanics, Lisbon, Vol. 1, pp 509-513.

PENDER, M., 1971, Some properties of weathered greywacke, Proceedings, First Australia-New Zealand Conference on Geomechanics, Melbourne, pp 423-429.

CREEP AND PSEUDOCREEP OF ROCKS AND THEIR EFFECT WHEN ESTIMATING THE STABILITY OF JOINTED ROCK MASSES

FLUAGE ET PSEUDO-FLUAGE DES ROCHES ET LEUR IMPORTANCE POUR L'ESTIMATION DE LA RÉSISTANCE DES MASSIFS ROCHEUX COUPÉS PAR FISSURES

KRIECHEN UND PSEUDO-KRIECHEN VON FELSGESTEINEN UND DEREN BEDEUTUNG FÜR DIE EINSCHÄTZUNG DER STANDSICHERHEIT DES DURCH DIE SPALTEN ZERSCHNITTENEN FELSVERBANDES

N.N. MASLOV
Head, Soil Mechanics and Engineering Geology Chair, Moscow, USSR
T.V. PAVLISHEVA
Senior Eng., Soil Mechanics and Eng. Geology Chair, Moscow, USSR

SUMMARY

Microshear deformations along the joints ("pseudocreep") have been found to play a considerable part in the stability of the rock mass dissected with joints. The above deformations show themselves as consecutive shear of "projectures" over the surface of the contact joint walls and result in the cohesion of the rock soil effecting the general shear strength of the rock block.

In this case the shear strength due to cohesion depends on the amount of "projectures" on the shear area unit, the shear strength of these projectures and the shear area proper within the limits of sheared projectures.

In this sense the nature of cohesion in rocks differs greatly from that of clay soils, in which the cohesion relates to the shear area (of a sample or mass) and depends directly on its value.

In case of considerable concentration of stresses, caused by the nonuniform distribution of the shearing force along the above projectures on the wall joints, their shear can take place in rock of less strength since under such conditions the rock undergoes "true creeping" conditioned by the rheological features of the rock under question in situ and by the stress acting on it.

The creep deformation, as the "pseudocreep" display, causes a more even manifestation of the process of projectures shearing with time and therefore a build-up of the rated value of cohesion of rock along the joint.

In the above case, the value to be determined was that of possible decrease of the rock strength ("prologed strength") in case of "true creep", the initial stress conditioning the possibility of its display ("creep limit") and the features of the "pseudocreep" process.

In the paper are described the experiments aimed at determining the above indices of some varieties of rocks, experimental procedure and instruments used. The numerical data of the experiments are given as well.

RESUME

On a constaté que les déformations de microcisaillements suivant les fissures ("pseudo-fluage"), dans les conditions déterminées, peuvent jouer le rôle important pour la résistance du massif rocheux coupé par fissures. Ces déformations se produisent par rupture successive des "saillies" suivant la surface des parois se trouvant en contact des fissures et conditionnent la cohésion de rocher qui influence sur la résistance totale au cisaillement du bloc rocheux.

Dans ce cas, la valeur de la résistance au cisaillement due à la cohésion, dépend du nombre des saillis par l'unité de la superficie de cisaillement, de la résistance à la rupture de ces saillis et de la superficie même du cisaillement dans les limites des saillis à cisailler lors de la rupture.

De ce point de vue, la nature de la cohésion du rocher diffère nettement de celle des roches argileuses où la cohésion se rapporte à la superficie du cisaillement (échantillon ou massif) et dépend de sa valeur dans la proportionnalité directe.

Dans les conditions de grande concentration des tensions due à la répartition irrégulière de l'effort de cisaillement d'après les saillies susmentionnées des parois de fissures, leur rupture peut se produire quand la résistance de la roche est diminuée à cause de son "fluage réel" conditionné par les propriétés rhéologiques du matériau in situ et par une tension appliquée sur celui-ci.

La déformation du fluage, phénomène du "pseudo-fluage", mène au developpement plus régulier du processus de rupture des saillies avec le temps et, c'est pourquoi, à l'augmentation de la valeur de calcul de la cohésion du rocher suivant la fissure.

Dans le cas présent, ont été determinées la valeur de diminution éventuelle de la résistance de la roche "résistance de longue durée" aux conditions du phénomène du fluage réel et la tension initiale déterminant une possibilité de son apparition ("limite du fluage"), ainsi que les caractéristiques du processus du "pseudo-fluage".

Le rapport décrit les essais destinés à déterminer les coefficients susdits pour cer-

taines types des roches, le procédé des essais et l'appareillage. On a donné les résultats en chiffres des essais effectués.

ZUSAMMENFASSUNG

Es hat sich herausgestellt, dass die Mikroschubdeformationen an den Spalten (Pseudokriechen) bei bestimmten Verhältnissen eine wesentliche Rolle an der Standsicherheit des durch die Spalten durchgetrennten Felsverbandes spielen können. Diese Deformationen kommen dadurch zustande, dass die an den kontaktierenden Kluftflächen vorhandenen "Kämme" der Reihe nach abgeschoren werden; dadurch wird die Kohäsion des Felsgesteines bedingt, die die allgemeine Schubfestigkeit eines Felsblocks bewährt.

In diesem Fall hängt die Schubfestigkeit des Gesteins wegen der Köhäsion von der Kämmenzahl pro einer Schubflächeneinheit, der Scherfestigkeit dieser Kämme und der Scherfläche selbst im Bereich der Kämme ab.

In diesem Sinne unterscheidet sich krass der Charakter der Kohäsion in Gesteinen gegenüber dem der Kohäsion in lehmigen Böden, wo die Kohäsion auf die Schubfläche (einer Prüfprobe oder des Felsverbandes) bezogen wird und von der Grösse der Schubfläche direkt proportional abhängig ist.

Bei beträchtlichen Spannungskonzentrationen, verursacht von einer unregelmässig Verteilung der Schubkraft an den oben erwähnten Kämmen, kann das Abscheren der Kämme bei der geringfügigen Festigkeit des Gesteins auf Grund des "tatsächlichen Kriechens" zustandekommen, das von rheologischen Eigenschaften des betreffenden Materials im Felsverband und der darauf einwirkenden Spannungen bedingt wird.

Die Kriechdeformation als "Pseudokriechen" führt zu einem zeitlich regelmässiger verteilten Abscherverlauf von den Kämmen und dadurch zur Annahme eines erhöhten, in die Berechnung einzugehenden Kohäsionswertes des Gesteins in der Kluft.

Im vorliegenden Fall waren die Grösse der eventuell möglichen Abnahme der Gesteinsfestigkeit ("Dauerfestigkeit") bei dem tatsächlichen Kriechen, der Anfangsspannungswert, der das Kriechen (Kriechgrenze) bewirkt, sowie die Kennwerte des "Pseudokriechens" festzuzulegen.

Im Vortrag werden die Versuche für die Bestimmung der erwähnten Kennwerte für einige Gesteinsarten, die Methodik der Versuche und Geräte beschrieben. Es werden auch die Zahlenangaben der durchgeführten Versuche angeführt.

The construction of large projects on rocks and semi-rocks in the USSR and abroad requires rather often the estimation of the degree of stability of rock masses dissected with oriented joints with regard to the time factor.

The stability of rock masses under the aforementioned conditions is determined by the relation of passive forces, i.e. shear resistance forces acting along the joint line and preventing the reciprocal displacement of sheared rock blocks and of the active forces tending to cause the displacement of the above rock blocks along the joint line.

The angle of friction in rocks is the value studied and defined well enough in many papers.

For the cases under consideration the most serious attention should be paid to the problem of studying the cohesion of rocks, as least known and studied.

However, the problem of the relation of friction and cohesion forces at shearing of the rock block along the joint is vague from many points of view even nowdays. In our studies we assumed that the cohesion under the above conditions always displays itself in shearing of projectures and unevenesses of rock available on the surface of displacement. At the same time, unlike the clay soils the angle of internal friction of which often decreased as the normal stress grew, we registered in our tests the increase of this value as the normal stress went up. This phenomenon is in particular illustrated in Fig.1 and we shall consider it later to assess another possible phenomenon.

As may be seen in Fig.1, under conditions of conducting the test the angles of friction considerably increased at higher loads; in particular, in Test (I) the angle of internal friction made up 16°13′ at loads $0-1.2 \cdot 10^5\ N/m^2$ and it increased to $\phi = 25°$ as these loads were raised. There is every reason to suppose that in the above case the angle of friction increased as a result of some reciprocal partial intrusion of shifting rock blocks ("scratching"). The above circumstance in cirtain cases offers promise in estimating the resistance of rock blocks to shear along the joints when the rock is subjected to large loads, for exemple, at the "abutment" of arch structures or at the foundation of high gravity dams.

In any case, such a possibility should not be ignored.

It has been found out that microshear deformations along the joints ("pseudocreep") may in cirtain cases play an important part in the stability of the jointed rock mass. The above deformations result in the consecutive shearing of "projectures" over the surface of contacting joint walls and in the cohesion of the rock influencing the total resistance of the rock block to shear.

In this case the shear strength value

due to cohesion depends on the amount of "projectures" on the shear area unit, on the shear strength of these projectures and the shear area proper within the limits of projectures which shear.

In this sense, the nature of cohesion in rock sharply differs from that in clay soils, where the cohesion relates to the shear area (of the sample or rock mass)and is directly dependent of its value.

The mentioned phenomenon was evidently to be pronounced in different values of resistance of rock blocks to shear along the joint at different rate of this displacement. One could expect that at rather quick displacement the shear resistance of separated blocks primarily at the expense of the angle of internal friction would be higher than that at very slow displacement. This phenomenon many times observed in our tests in illustrated in Figs. 1 and 2.

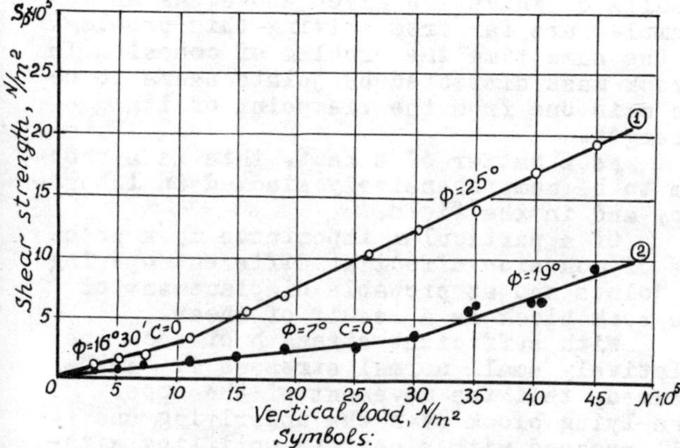

Fig.1. Shear strength versus vertical load of granite blocks with smooth surface.

As is seen, in this case depending on the type of rocks to be tested and on test conditions the angles of internal friction at slow displacements were 2-6° less than at high displacements, what is naturally rather perceptible under considerable loads. It should be also noted that at the displacement of granite blocks with even slip surface when each increment of shear load was maintained until complete damping of deformations, the angle of internal friction at loads $0\text{-}3{,}0.10^6 N/m^2$ made up $5^0\text{-}7^0$.

The nature of the above phenomenon is revealed to a certain extent in tests of artificially made gypsum test cylinders with wavy surface, at primary and successive displacement of cylinders (Fig.3).

As many be seen, the increase of the angle (α) of surface uneveness wave resulted in the increase of the angle of

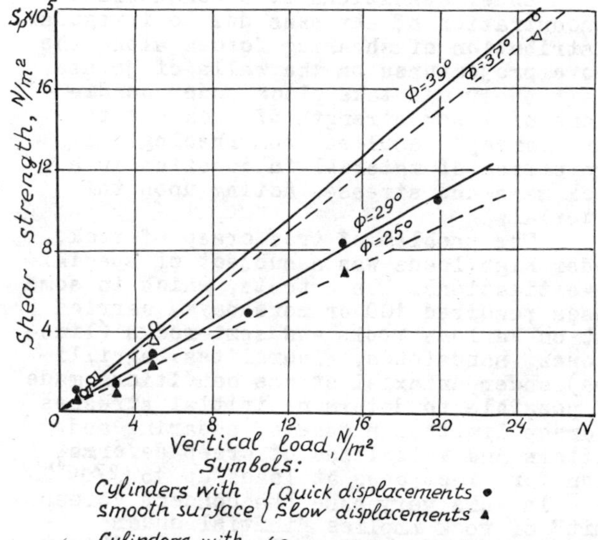

Fig.2. Shear strength versus vertical load of limestone blocks with various roughness of shear surface.

internal friction and cohesion. Along with that, at a repeated displacement, when the "flattening" of projectures to some or other degree could be expected, the angle of internal friction at loads exceeding $2{,}0.10^5 N/m^2$ sharply changed and approached the angle $\Phi = 36^0$ observed in the tests of gypsum cylinders with even surfaces (Fig.3).

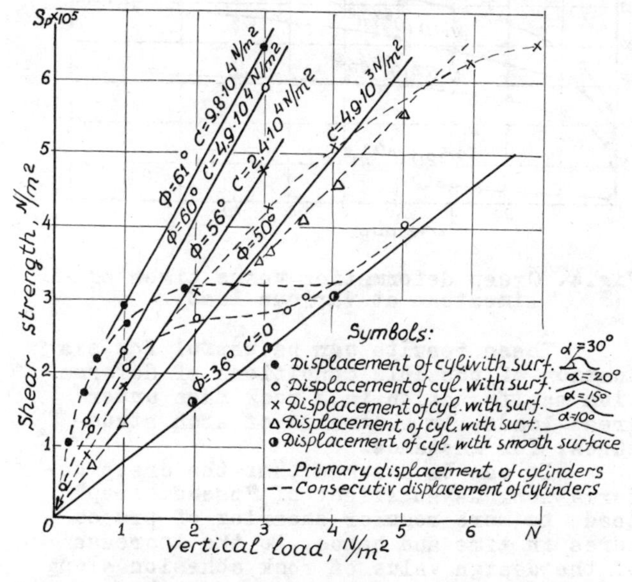

Fig.3. Shear strength versus vertical load of gypsum cylinders with various roughness of surface in case of primary and consecutive displacements of cylinders.

Under conditions of a considerable concentration of stresses due to irregular distribution of shearing forces along the above projectures on the walls of joints, their shear can take place under conditions of lower strength of rock due to "true creep" resulted from rheological properties of material in question in a rock mass and stresses acting upon this material.

The problem of true creep of rock under high loads was a subject of special investigations. These tests, which in some cases required 100 or more days, carried out on various rocks and semi-rocks (limestones, sandstones, aleurolites, agrillites) under uniaxial stress conditions made it possible to determine initial stresses ("creep limit") in case of shearing and pattern and velocities of creep deformation for limestones at loads up to $1{,}27 \cdot 10^8 N/m^2$.

In this very case the concept "creep limit" of rock implies "initial shear strength" (acc. to Bingam) corresponding to critical value of tangential stress ($\tau_{кр}$) below which there is no creeping.

The results of these tests are shown as am example, in Fig. 4. The "creep limit" for limestones appeared to be close to τ lim. $\approx 9.0 \cdot 10^6 N/m^2$; ditto for sandstones τ lim. $\approx 9.0 \cdot 10^6 N/m^2$; ditto for aleurolites τ lim. $\approx 4.5 \cdot 10^6 N/m^2$; ditto for argillites τ lim. $\approx 3.0 \cdot 10^6 N/m^2$;

This can be seen in Fig.4, where with compressive stress $N = 2.0 \cdot 10^7 N/m^2$ ($\tau = 1.0 \cdot 10^7 N/m^2$) the creep deformation occurred only to a very small extent.

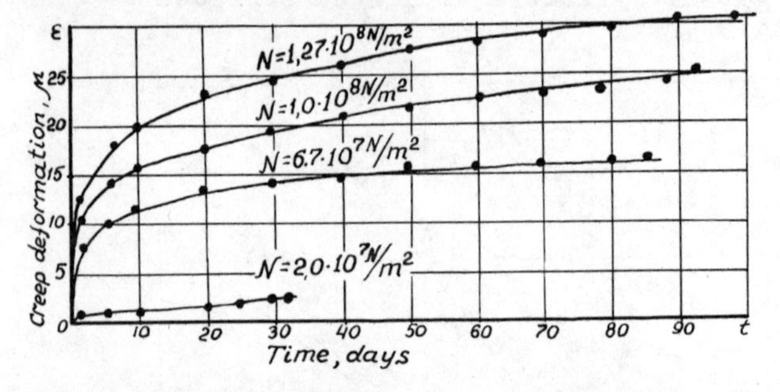

Fig.4. Creep deformation vesus times of limestone at various load

These results can be useful for evaluation of possible conditions of deformation manifestation in a rock mass under great loads, in abutments of arch structures, for instance.

It can be assumed that the creep deformation, as an effect of "pseudocreep" leads to more regular shearing of projectures in time and hence, to the increase of the design value of rock cohesion along the joint.

It stands to reason that this problem requires special study.

In case under consideration a value of possible decrease of the rock strength ("prolonged strength") under conditions of true creep effect was to be determined.

To determine the possible value of decreasing of the rock strength at high loads and under conditions of creep deformations we carried out a series of special tests of samples of various rocks. In these tests the samples under loads exceeding the inherent "creep limit" were brought to a state when the creep deformation was clearly expressed. Then the samples were subjected to crushing in uniaxial tests.

In this case the crushing strength of all samples was 15-40% lower.

So, for dolomitic limestones of Lower Cretaceous age at the Ingouri Hydroelectric Station the crushing strength decreased from $1.6 \cdot 10^8 N/m^2$ to $1.4 \cdot 10^8 N/m^2$, i.e. by 15%; while for argillites of Cretaceous and Paleogene age at the Rostokino Reservoir it decreased from $3.6 \cdot 10^7 N/m^2$ to $2.0 \cdot 10^7 N/m^2$, i.e. by 40%.

It is evident, that much attention should be paid to this phenomenon.

No doubt that a number of tests the results of which are given above, as an example, are far from solving this problem. At the same time the problem of cohesion in a rock mass dissected by joints seems to be the main one from the viewpoint of its strength.

As a matter of a fact, this is a problem to be comprehensively studied in laboratory and in the field.

Of a particular importance is a problem of cohesion effect at different opening of joints and at probable displacement of the rock block as a result of shear.

With sufficient strength of rock and relatively small normal stresses it can be assumed, that the movement of the upper free-lying block over the underlying one will proceed with a certain uplifting without shear of separate projectures of the rock on the slip surface.

In this case it can appear that resistance of displacement of one rock block over the other will be caused mainly by friction and practically in no way will depend upon cohesion. Such a situation can often occur in the zone of abutment of rock blocks in the gorge sides separated from the main rock mass by steeply dipping joints.

Failure of such blocks can occur also under the slightest seismic impacts and that is actually observed.

A comprehensive study is needed to solve this problem. It is necessary to establish the cohesion effect in rock blocks moving along the joints depending on the rock strength indices, as well as on the normal stress values, freedom of deformation of rock blocks, the value of shear shifting and at last on the amount and type of projectures on the slip surface.

The latter should establish the dependence of cohesion in rock upon the displacement area.

As was said above, it can be assumed that cohesion in rock differs from that in clay, i.e. in this case the cohesion value will not be directly proportional to the shear area that is proved by the results of the field tests.

To find this relationship a great number of tests is needed to establish the "scale effect" in this sense.

The results given above testify the possible effect of the rheological phenomena upon the decrease of the rock strength, especially on the shear of the projections over the shear surface.

These tests are to be carried on in order to find the "creep limit" values as an indication of possible conditions of creep effects and prolonged strength and first of all to find the possible concentration of shear stresses on separate projectures.

In all these cases, it is necessary to study the type and possible amount of such projectures per the shear surface unit as well as their genetic peculiarities.

The tests were carried out on a modernized shear instrument designed by Maslov-Lourié or on a 25-ton press designed by K.V.Rouppeneit, D.T.S.

T.V.Pavlisheva, engineer, carried out the above investigations and tests herself or participated in all of them.

Bibliography:

1. N.N.Maslov,
„Prolonged strength and shear deformations of retaining structures." Energia, Moscow, 1968.
2. T.V.Pavlisheva,
"True creep and pseudocreep or rock" Sbornic MARI. "Injenernaja geologiya i mechanika grountov", 1973, issue 62.
3. N.F.Renzhiglov, T.V.Pavlisheva,
"Rock viscosity" -Phisiko-techniches-kie problemi razrabotki polesnich iskopaemich, Academy of Science, USSR, Sibirskoje otdeleniye, 1970, No 5 (September, October).

EFFECT OF GEOLOGICAL FACTORS ON THE SHEARING RESISTANCE ALONG JOINTS IN ROCK

INFLUENCE DES FACTEURS GÉOLOGIQUES SUR LA RÉSISTANCE AU CISAILLEMENT SELON LES FRACTURES DANS LES ROCHES

EINFLUSS VON GEOLOGISCHEN FAKTOREN AUF DIE SCHERWIDERSTANDSFÄHIGKEIT ÜBER DIE KLÜFTE IN FELSGESTEINEN

S.E. MOGILEVSKAYA

The B.E. Vedeneev All-Union Research Institute of Hydraulic Engineering
Leningrad, U.S.S.R.

SUMMARY

Presented are experimental findings on the effect on the shearing resistance of joint separation plane morphology, saturation and clayey fillers.

The following basic regulatities were brought out by testing sandstone, granite and limestone specimens:

- Macro- and microasperities over the joint separation plane exert a marked influence on the shearing resistance parameters;
- Saturation of rock specimens affects the shearing resistance along joints in different ways. The relative reduction in shearing strength due to saturation depends on the rock type. As distinct from that of limestones, the strength of granites, and, particularly, that of argyllites drops tangibly;
- Provided the thickness of the filler exceeds the maximum height of asperities, shearing resistance depends on the properties of the filler.

RESUME

Le rapport donne les résultats expérimentaux relatifs à l'influence de la morphologie des faces de fractures dans les roches différentes, de leur saturation d'eau et des matériaux argileux remplissant ces fissures sur la résistance au cisaillement. Les recherches effectuées sur les échantillons en grès ont mis en évidence les régularités principales, à savoir:

- Les paramètres de la résistance au cisaillement sont considérablement influencés par la présence des micro et macrosaillies sur les faces des fractures.
- La saturation d'eau exerce une différente influence sur la resistance au cisaillement selon les fractures. La diminution relative de la résistance au cisaillement imputable à la saturation d'eau dépend du type des roches. Contrairement aux calcaires la résistance des granits, et surtout, des argillites, diminue considérablement.
- On a constaté aussi que si l'épaisseur du matériau argileux remplissant les fractures est plus grande que la hauteur maximale des saillies, la résistance au cisaillement dépend des propriétés de ce matériau.

ZUSAMMENFASSUNG

Im Bericht werden die Untersuchungsergebnisse über den Einfluss der Morphologie der Kluftfläche in verschiedenen felsigen Gesteinsarten, ihres Wassergehaltes und der Tonfüllung auf die Scherwiderstandsfähigkeit beschrieben. Durch die Untersuchungen an Probekörpern aus Sandsteinen, Graniten und Kalksteinen sind folgende hauptsächliche Gesetzmässigkeiten festgestellt worden:

- Die Makro- und Mikrovorsprünge auf der Kluftfläche haben einen wesentlichen Einfluss auf die Parameter der Scherwiderstandsfähigkeit.
- Der Wassergehalt von Gesteinsproben übt einen unterschiedlichen Einfluss auf die Scherwiderstandsfähigkeit über die Klüfte aus. Die relative Erniedrigung der Scherfestigkeit infolge der Wassersättigung hängt von der Gesteinsart ab. Zum Unterschied von Kalksteinen nimmt die Festigkeit von Graniten und besonders Argilliten bedeutend ab.
- Unter der Bedingung, dass die Dichte der Tonfüllung in den Klüften eine maximale Höhe der Vorsprünge übersteigt, ist die Scherwiderstandsfähigkeit von den Füllungseigenschaften abhängig.

The rock engineering conditions of rock foundations of high-head hydraulic structures are commonly characterized by complexity and diversity mainly due to tectonic phenomena which lead to fissuring and weakening of the rock mass. Various geological factors affecting the shear resistance along joints must be taken into account to permit evaluation of the shearing resistance along extended planes of weakness in the stability design of foundations of high-head hydraulic structures.

The following geological factors governing the shear resistance along joints are considered herein: morphology of separation planes, saturation, and the clayey fillers of joints.

SEPARATION PLANE MORPHOLOGY IN ROCK JOINTS

Studies conducted using procedures evolved at the Engineering Geology Laboratory of the VNIIG (Mogilevskaya, 1971, 1972) on separation plane morphology in sedimentary and intrusive rocks with reference to shearing resistance led to establishing some general regularities in the variation in space of separation plane morphology parameters. Certain regularities brought out on several types of rocks at various sites are as follows:

The complex separation plane morphology of joints of different genesis is characterized by the successive superposition of several scales of asperities complicating the roughness of a higher scale. The terms mega-asperities, meso-asperities, macro- and micro-asperities are applied to those to be measured in metres, decimetres, centimetres, and millimetres, respectively (Table 1).

Table 1

Mean parameters for different scales of roughness of joint separation planes in limestones and granites

Joint set	Roughness scale	Limestone (foundation of Toktogul Dam)				Limestone (foundation of Inguri Dam)				Granites, type I (foundation of New Konstantinovka Dam)			
		h, cm	l, cm	α, rad	α°	h, cm	l, cm	α, rad	α°	h, cm	l, cm	α, rad	α°
1 Bedding	meso	3.0	70	0.19-0.23	11-13	6	240	0,07-0.09	4-5	-	-	-	-
	macro	0.7	6.0	0.23-0.23	13-13	1.2	26.6	0.12-0.14	7-8	-	-	-	-
	micro	0.06	0.4	0.21-0.21	12-12	0.04	0.7	0.12-0.18	7-10	-	-	-	-
2 Flattened dip	mega	1000	10000	0.23-0.35	13-20	-	-	-	-	-	-	-	-
	meso	9	145	0.11-0.12	6-7	13	200	0.14-0.18	8-10	22	240	0.26-0.18	15-10
	macro	1.6	30	0.12-0.18	7-10	1.5	26.4	0.14-0.18	8-10	1.1	28	0.23-0.16	13-10
	micro	0.03	0.3	0.18-0.21	10-12	0.04	0.7	0.16-0.21	9-12	0.07	0.8	0.23-0.21	13-12
3 Steep dip	mega	1500	15500	0.16-0.23	9-13	-	-	-	-	-	-	-	-
	meso	16	440	0.07-0.07	4-4	-	-	-	-	11	230	0.18-0.15	10-9
	macro	1.0	27	0.11-0.12	6-7	-	-	-	-	1	30	0.12-0.23	7-13
	micro	0.07	0.9	0.21-0.21	12-12	-	-	-	-	0.035	0.6	0.16-0.13	9-11

Note: The values of α refer to angles measured in opposite directions along the strike.

The main parameters describing joint separation plane morphology (the angle, height and wave length of asperities designated as α, h and l, respectively) for all scales of asperities commonly vary within a wide range even along the strike and dip of one joint. Nevertheless reference areas can be singled out with parameters representative of the given joint.

Separation plane morphology within a joint set (comprising joints of identical genesis) occurring under similar structural geological conditions is characterized by approximately the same numerical values of parameters of different scales of asperities. Separation plane morphology of different joint sets is dissimilar, the higher the scale of the asperity, the greater are the differences between the morphologic parameters. The parameters of asperities may vary substantially within the same scale for joints of one genetic type in rocks of the same lithological character but occurring in different structural geological situations. Individual joint sets are characterized by somewhat asymmetrical asperity inclination angles for different asperity scales as measured in opposite directions along the dip and the strike of joints. The distribution pattern of inclination angles for different asperity scales varies from joint set to joint set. Research conducted led to the conclusion that there exist certain regularities in the variation of joint separation plane morphology in space due to the diversity of geologic factors. Hence, the specific features of joint morphology should be taken into account in seeking solutions to rock engineering problems.

SHEARING RESISTANCE ALONG A TIGHT JOINT WITH VARYING SEPARATION PLANE MORPHOLOGY

The study was aimed at elucidating the effect exerted on the shearing resistance by macro- and microroughness. The tests were performed on specimens of markedly different types of sandstones, granites and limestones varying in composition, structural-textural features, as well as in strength and strain parameters.

Shearing resistance was investigated using natural and simulated joints with different separation planes. The artificial joints simulated either maximum macro- and micro-roughness to be encountered in tension joints, or minimum roughness without any macro- and with, practically, no micro-asperities for shear joints in rock (Mogilevskaya, 1971, 1972, 1973). The roughness of natural joints was unoriented and nonhomogeneous, the macroroughness of the separation planes being characterized by α ranging from 0.35 to 0.53 rad (from 4 to 30°) and the height of the asperities fluctuating between one or two and 10 to 15 mm. Smoothed surfaces of micro-asperities over natural joint separation planes distinguish them from artificial ones. The micro-asperities over tension joint separation planes exhibit a rugged, as it were, corroded surface. Tests were also performed on cement stone specimens with simulated joints (composite specimens) of non-uniform oriented roughness. The angles of inclination at the base of the symmetrical macro-asperities amounted to 0.26 and 0.46 rad (15° and 25°). Four series of specimens with different ratios between macro- and micro-asperities were tested.

A special shearing device developed at the VNIIG was utilized in the research program to study the limit shearing resistance τ_{lim}. The values of the parameters φ and C incorporated in the Coulomb relationship were analysed together with the inclination angles of asperities measured in the direction of shear. Specimens with tensile joints were tested by repeated shearing, σ remaining constant, until a constant τ_{lim} was obtained. Subsequent shearing along joints with smoothed micro-asperities was carried out, with σ varying. Specimens with different separation planes were also tested, with σ varying.

Analysis of the above experimental findings (Fig.1) as well as of data obtained earlier from specimens of modelling materials with a homogeneous (uniform) oriented roughness (Evdokimov et al., 1970) resulted in establishing basic regularities in the effect of macro- and micro-asperities on the shearing resistance along tight joints:

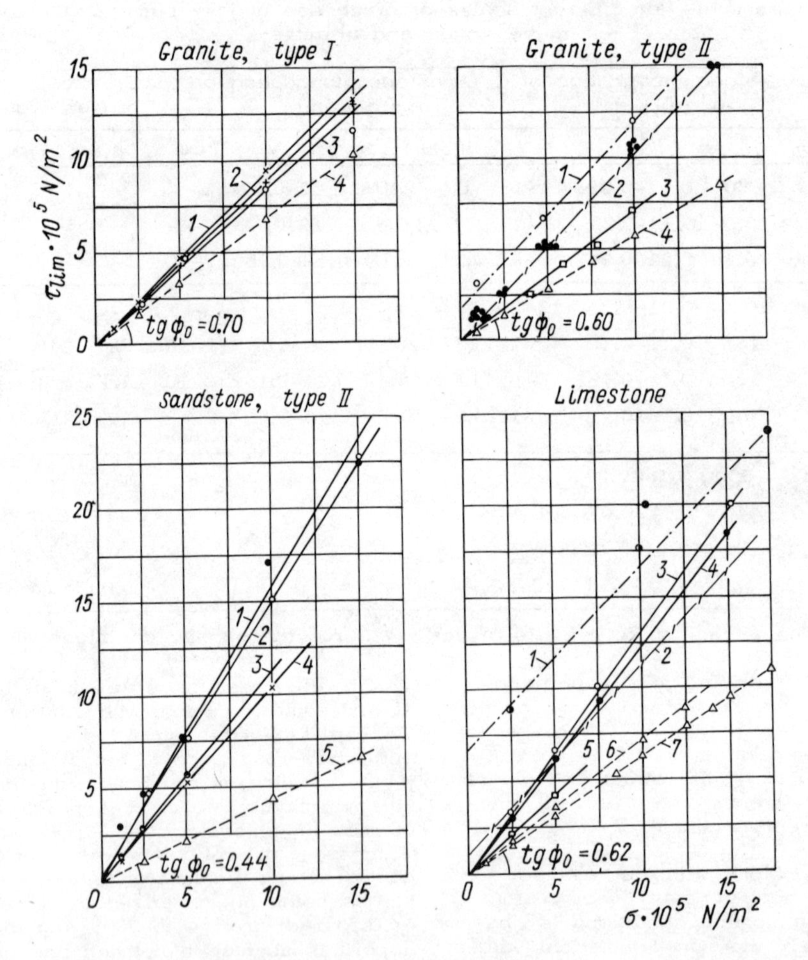

Fig.1. Data on the shearing resistance of rock along joints with varying separation plane morphology. natural joints, – – – artificial smooth joints (shear), —— artificial rough joints (tension), —/— same after repeated shearing.

In case shear occurs along a joint in a material of high strength and low deformability with a homogeneous (uniform) oriented macroroughness without crushing macro-asperities, then the shearing resistance is given by

$$\tau_{lim} = \sigma \, tg \, (\varphi_0 + \alpha) \qquad (1)$$

where α is the inclination angle of macro-asperities, φ_0 is the friction angle of a smooth joint separation plane. The relationship is found to be valid at $\alpha < \alpha_{cr}$ where α_{cr} stands for the most probable maximum angle at which sliding mechanisms transform into shearing. For non-homogeneous non-uniform macroroughness the shearing resistance may be also described by Eq.(1), either $\alpha_{pr\,max}$ or α_{med} being chosen depending on the prevailing maximum inclination angle of asperities governed by the distribution pattern and probability of occurrence of α. For instance, for granite samples (type I) and limestones the shearing resistance along joints was determined using α_{med} when the probability of occurrence amounted to more than 25%. At less than 10% probability of occurrence of α_{med} the shearing resistance was conditioned by the values of $\alpha_{pr\,max}$. Hence, in extending laboratory data to a rock mass it is recommended to obtain τ_{lim} from Eq.(1) using values of α with probability of occurrence not less than 20 to 25% obtained from field data on separation plane morphology of extended joints. Experiments showed α_{cr} to be a function of the strength of the material, the type of roughness (uniform or non-uniform) and the acting stresses. Thus for gypsum specimens of uniform roughness the inclination angle ma es up 0.09 rad $< \alpha_{cr} <$ 0.18 rad ($5^o < \alpha_{cr} < 10^o$); for cement stone specimens of similar roughness the angle is 0.44 rad $< \alpha_{cr} <$ 0.61 rad ($25^o < \alpha_{cr} < 35^o$), and for those with non-uniform roughness 0.26 rad $< \alpha_{cr} <$ 0.44 rad ($15^o < \alpha_{cr} < 25^o$).

For the rock types studied, $tg\,\phi_o$ ranged from 0.45 to 0.73 (Table 2), the value of the parameter being affected by mineral composition and rock structure. E.g. for type II sandstones represented by glauconitic quartz varieties with the interstitial and contact cements of a calciferous clayey composition with ferruginuous admixtures, $tg\,\phi$ equals 0.45, while for type I sandstones of medium-grained structure mainly composed of quartz with insignificant glauconite and mica admixtures $tg\,\phi$ is 0.60. The cement of the sandstones is argillaceous, ferruginous of the regenerative type.

Table 2

Effect of water content on the shearing resistance along rock joints with varying separation plane morphology

Rock	Characteristics of joint separation plane	Shearing resistance parameters		
		dry	saturated	relative reduction, %
Granite	plane,smooth,	0.70	0.58	17
	uneven,rough	0.93	0.81	13
Crystalline	plane,smooth	0.66	0.63	4
limestone	uneven,rough	0.9-1.04	0.9-1.07	0
Sandstone	plane,smooth	0.38-0.45	0.32-0.43	11
type II	uneven,rough	1.15-1.48	1.0-1.33	11
	same*	0.65	0.60	9
Sandstone-argyllite	plane,smooth	0.60	0.45	25
contact	uneven,rough**	0.49	0.29	41
Sandstone	plane,smooth	0.60	0.53	11
type I	uneven,rough	0.37-1.07	0.73-1.0	11
Aleurolite	plane,smooth	0.62	0.57	8
	uneven,rough	1.15	1.07	7
Sandstone aleurolite contact	plane,smooth	0.60	0.57	5

Note: *joint separation plane is weathered and ferruginous
**natural broken contact

Tests conducted on specimens with simulated or natural joints led to establishing the dependence of the parameter C in Coulomb's equation on microroughness. Shearing resistance may be defined by Coulomb's two-term equation provided ribbed micro-asperities with large inclination angles ranging from 0.26 to 1.57 rad (15° to 90°) are superposed on macro-asperities, which is characteristic for fresh tension joints. In this case micro-asperities interlock and are sheared off (Fig.1). After the asperities are ground in by shearing and their surfaces smoothed, the shearing mechanizm is transformed into rolling which occurs without any further destruction of micro-asperities, and the shearing mechanism may be described by Eq.(1). A similar shearing process is inherent to prototype joint planes whose micro-asperities are commonly smoothed due to tectonic and other secondary processes. Therefore in shear along prototype joints in high strength rock the parameter, C, usually equals zero; while in shear along fresh tensile joints its value may be rather high depending on rock composition and its properties, e.g. for type II granite specimens $C = 1.75 \cdot 10^5$ N/m^2; for crystalline limestone $C = 6.5 \cdot 10^5$ N/m^2.

The regularities established in the effect of micro- and macroroughness on the shearing resistance permit us to suggest that joint plane morphology should be used as a criterion in extrapolating to various extended joints in an in situ rock mass the data obtained by a limited number of field shearing tests. At the same time it becomes feasible to widely apply laboratory findings in assessing the shearing resistance parameters along joints and extrapolate them to in situ rock masses. Laboratory experiments being cheep and less complicated than those in the field, tests may be carried out on specimens of different composition, texture, and state of preservation (degree of weathering, water content) which will result in a fuller recognition of rock engineering features of construction sites.

THE EFFECT OF WATER CONTENT OF ROCK ON THE SHEARING RESISTANCE ALONG JOINTS

Tests were conducted on specimens of various lithological rock types incorporating plane smooth (simulated) and uneven rough (natural) joints. Specimens were water saturated in vacuum. Shearing was effected with σ values increasing from test to test. The decrease in shearing strength was evaluated by comparing the values of the parameters entering Coulomb's equation for dry and saturated specimens. Test findings on the water content effect on the shearing resistance along joints in some types of sedimentary and intrusive rock (Table 2) testify that water saturated specimens exhibit lowered shearing resistance along joints. The relative diminishing of $tg\,\phi$ depends on the mineral composition and the texture and structure of the rock. A maximum reduction in strength is observed in argillite specimens, while those of crystalline limestone display no weakening of strength whatever. ϕ was materially reduced by saturation of intrusive rock incorporating mica (granites) and sedimentary cemented rock (sandstones) containing glauconite and cements soluble in water. The cause of the dissimilar effect of water saturation on the friction coefficient in shearing of rock seems to lie in the differences in the interaction between the minerals and water due to the specific features of the crystal lattice (hydrophobic and hydrophilic minerals). No effect of joint plane morphology on the relative strength variation value was established.

Analysis of the effect of joint separation plane morphology on the shearing resistance along joints in saturated specimens indicates that Eq.(1) derived for dry specimens is valid for saturated ones as well: $\tau_{lim} = \sigma\, tg\,(\varphi_o^w + \alpha)$ where φ_o^w is the friction angle of a plane smooth joint separation plane in saturated rock.

SHEARING RESISTANCE ALONG JOINTS WITH CLAYEY FILLERS

To evaluate the effect of joint separation plane morphology on the shearing resistance of clay-filled joints tests were made on limestone and sandstone specimens with separation planes of markedly differing macro- and microroughness. The sandstone specimens had both a natural joint with macro- and micro-asperities, and an artificial one cut with a saw, the latter without any macro- or micro-asperities. The limestone specimens had either smooth natural joints without macro- or micro-asperities, or rough ones with an intricate pattern of both macro- and micro-asperities corresponding to the glide plane and the rough section, respectively. Natural fillers were used in the experiments, viz. loam with limestones and clay with sandstones.

The experimental procedure under laboratory conditions is given below. Shearing resistance along unfilled joints was tested on both dry and saturated specimens. Then a filler of a prescribed thickness was introduced into the joint. After the filler in the submerged specimen was stabilized during 30 or 40 minutes at σ_{max}, shearing tests were conducted at $\sigma = \sigma_{max}$ and $\sigma < \sigma_{max}$. The same test routine was used for specimens with unfilled joints. In sandstone specimens the prescribed thickness of the filler amounted to 5 mm, that in limestone joints to 10 mm. The experimental results go to prove that with clay-filled joints separation plane morphology (macro- and microroughness) does not affect the shearing resistance provided the maximum height of macro-asperities be less than the thickness of the filler, the shearing resistance depending in this case on the properties of the filler (Fig.2). The shearing resistance of sandstone specimens with varying separation plane morphology of unfilled joints was characterized by a cohesion parameter $C = 0$, and by an appreciable difference between the angles of friction in dry and saturated specimens, e.g. for smooth plane joint separation planes $tg\varphi$ amounted to 0.38 and 0.32, respectively, while for uneven rough ones it was 0.67 and 0.60. In clay-filled

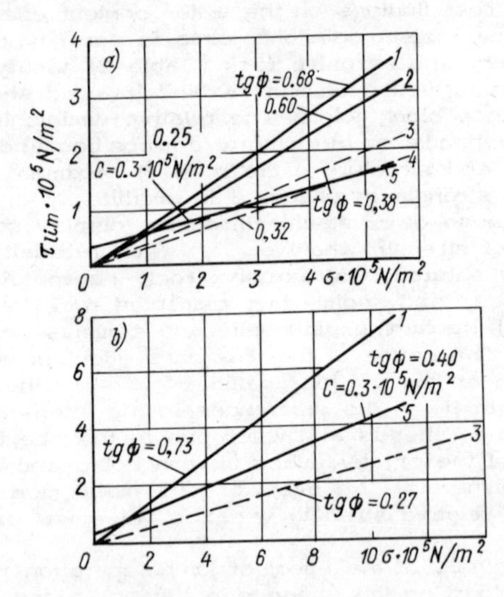

Fig.2. Data on the shearing resistance of rock specimen along joints with clayey fillers, the macro- and microroughness of the separation planes varying. a) sandstone, $h < 3$ mm; clayey filler; b) limestone, $h < 5$ mm; loamy filler; 1 - the separation plane is uneven, rough, dry, part of the joint is tight (specimen I); 2 - same, saturated; 3 - the separation plane is plane, smooth, dry with a tight joint; 4 - same, saturated; 5 - specimen 1 and 2 with a filler, saturated

joints with the water content, $W = 65\%$, the shearing resistance of plane, smooth and uneven, rough joint separation planes was equal at $tg\varphi = 0.25$ and $C = 0.3\cdot10^5$ N/m^2. The effect of joint separation plar morphology in the presence of fillers was also exar ned both in the laboratory and in the field on exter ed steeply dipping joints in limestones with meso-, macro- and micro-asperities. The analysis was con ucted by comparing the data obtained by: a) labora ry shearing tests on loamy fillers, b) specimens wi rock contacts, c) field tests on shearing rock pilla along a filled joint. The field tests were undertaker by D.D.Sapegin and A.A.Nikitin (the Rock Mechani Laboratory of the VNIIG) who sheared rock pillars a 1.2 m^2 area, with σ ranging from 0 to $12\cdot10^5$ N/m The experimental parameters of shearing resistance were as follows: $tg\varphi$ and C varied from 0.40 to 0.65 and $(0.47$ to $1.25)\cdot10^5$ N/m^2, respectively (Fig.3, lines 1, 2, 3). In the field the rock contacts under the rock pillars averaged not more than 4%, and the thickness of the filler 4 cm. Tests on a jo loam filler in a testing device with a 1 mm shear in terval at $\sigma = (0.5-12)\cdot10^5$ N/m^2 indicated that with increase in water content from 17.5% to 23%, $tg\varphi$ and C altered from 0.65 to 0.55 (33° to 39°) and from $0.95\cdot10^5$ N/m^2 to $0.20\cdot10^5$ N/m^2, respectively (Fig.3, lines 4,5).

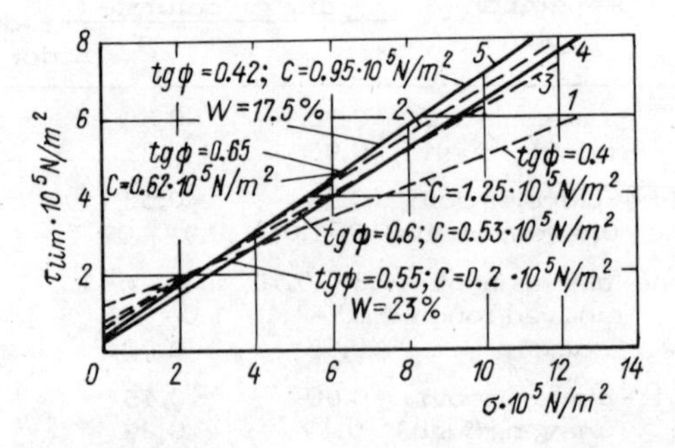

Fig.3. Field data on the shearing resistance of rc pillars with varying macro-, meso- and micro-aspe ties over separation planes; laboratory data on a my filler obtained on specimens.
1,2,3 - field tests; 4,5 - laboratory tests on loa

Laboratory tests of natural rock contacts on sp cimens obtained from the same joint revealed that was equal zero, and $tg\varphi$ ranged from 0.73 (an u ven rough joint separation plane) to 0.27 (the glic plane) (Fig.2b, lines 1,3).

Analysis of the above data suggests that with smoothed meso-macro- and micro-asperities (Tabl and with the filler thickness exceeding the height macro-asperities, the shearing resistance along joi depends mainly on the properties of the filler gove ed by density and water content.

Table 3

Parameters of the steeply dipping joint separation plane morphology measured in limestone along the strike in the direction of shear

Roughness scale	Height of asperities h, cm	Wave length ℓ, cm	Mean inclination angle of asperi ties	
	mean	mean	α rad	α_o
meso	20	$15\cdot10^2$	0.05	3
macro	1.5	75	0.05	3
micro:				
a) rough	0.05	0.60	0.31	18
b) smooth	0.01	0.80	0.05	3

CONCLUSIONS

1. Other things being equal, joint separation plane morphology is one of the controlling geological factors determining the shearing resistance along tight joints.

2. Separation plane morphology in joint sets varies under different geologic and structural conditions. This dissimilarity is due to rock composition, the kinetogenesis of joint formation and to superposed secondary processes. Definite regularities govern the variation in the principal parameters characterizing separation plane morphology in space.

3. In engineering geologic investigations on the shearing resistance along extended tight joints, their separation plane morphology should be studied with special emphasis placed on the pattern in the inclination angle distribution of the asperities, it being the main parameter determining the shearing resistance along joints provided the strength and deformability characteristics of the rock forming the joint separation plane remain constant.

4. Macro-asperities should be taken account of by Eq.(1), with φ_o assessed from dry or saturated specimens, φ_o^w depending on the object of the study. The inclination angles of the asperities should be evaluated by measurements in the direction of the probable shear of the retaining structure. In case of sufficiently uniform roughness, α_{med} is to be used, given non-uniform asperities, α values of 20 to 30% probability of occurenence are to be accepted.

5. Field data on shearing resistnace obtained from a reprerentative length of a joint may be extended to other sections of a tight joint in the same set or other sets, with their separation plane morphology included. In extrapolating experimental field data to extended joints due consideration should be given to all the scales of roughness.

6. In the early stages of engineering geological investigations approximate parameters of the shearing resistance along tight joints may be established under laboratory conditions from specimens with natural or simulated joints.

In extrapolating the experimental findings onto extended joints in the rock mass, the joint separation plane morphology in both specimens and rock masses must be made allowances for.

In examinations conducted under intricate engineering geological conditions at the later stages of the study, laboratory test findings may serve to supplement and refine field test data permitting the extension of the limited test data to joints of different genesis to be substantiated.

7. For sections of clay-filled extended joints, with the thickness of the filler exceeding the maximum height of macro-asperities no account nead be taken of joint separation plane morphology. In this case it is advisable to study the shearing resistance of the filler simulating its natural water content and density under laboratory conditions.

REFERENCES

1. Evdokimov P.D., Gouréev A.M., Moguilevskaya S.E., - Résistance au cisaillement selon les fissures dans les fondations rocheuses des ouvrages hydrauliques, Proc. of 2nd Congress of the International Society for Rock Mechanics, Beograd, 1970, v.2, 3-18, p.123-129.

2. Mogilevskaja S.E., - Proučavanje zakonitosti otpornosti na smicanje stenskih masa po pukotinama s uzimanjem u obzir morfologije nihovih Površina, Materijali i Konstrukcija, Anne XVI, N 5, Beograd, 1971, c.3-17.

3. Mogilevskaya S.E., - Laboratory Investigations of Mechanical and Physical Properties of Rock as Applied to Hydraulic Engineering Problems, "Izvestia VNIIG", 1970, v.100, p.349-365.

4. Mogilevskaya S.E., - A Criterion for Extending Shear Test Results on Long Closed Joints in Rock, "Izvestia VNIIG", 1972, v.102, p.36-47.

FRACTURED COAL SUBJECTED TO DIRECT SHEAR

CHARBON FRACTURE SOUMIS AU CISSAILLEMENT DIRECT

DAS VERHALTEN GEKLÜFTETER KOHLE IM UNMITTELBAREN SCHERVERSUCH

N.R. MORGENSTERN Professor of Civil Engineering, University of Alberta

D.K.J. NOONAN Civil Engineer, Golder Associates, Mississauga, Ont., (formerly Department of Civil Engineering, University of Alberta, Edmonton, Alberta).

Canada

SUMMARY Results are presented of direct shear tests performed in the laboratory on selected coal samples with particular emphasis on the role played by the discontinuities within the sample. The shear strength of fractur coal is anisotropic and dependent upon the orientation of discontinuities within the sample. The degrees of continuity of the jointing influences the failure mechanism and the mobilized peak strength parameters.

RÉSUMÉ Les résultats d'essais de cisaillement direct réalisés en laboratoire sur des échantillons sélectionné de charbon sont présentés ici en mettant un accent particulier sur le rôle joué par les discontinuités à l'intérieur des échantillons. La résistance à la rupture au cisaillement du charbon fracturé est anisotrope et dépend de l'orientation des discontinuités à l'intérieur de l'échantillon. Le degré de continuité des fissure influence le mécanisme de rupture ainsi que les paramêtres de la résistance maximum mobilisée.

ZUSAMMENFASSUNG An ausgesuchten Kohleproben wurden in Labor unmittelbare Scherversuche durchgeführt mit besond er Berücksichtigung des Einflusses de Klüfte in der Kohle. Die Scherfestigkeit geklüfteter Kohle ist anisotrop und hängt von der Richtung der Klüfte innerhalb der Versuchsprobe ab. Das Burchverhalten und die mobilisierten Maximalwerte der Scherfestigkeit wurden von der Kontinuitat der Klüfte beeinflusst.

INTRODUCTION

As part of a study to investigate the behaviour of fractured rock subjected to direct shear (Noonan, 1972) a detailed analysis of the strength and deformation properties of coal was undertaken. This paper presents the results of direct shear tests performed in the laboratory on selected coal samples with particular emphasis on the role played by the discontinuities contained within the samples. Coal characteristically contains systematic jointing on a fine spacing and therefore the behaviour of coal in the laboratory will reflect the behaviour of rock in the field with a broader joint spacing.

SITE AND GEOLOGY

The test samples were obtained at the Highvale Mine on the south shore of Lake Wabamun in Alberta, Canada. The mine is operated by Alberta Coal Ltd. for the use by Calgary Power Ltd. in the operation of their Sundance Power Plant.

The Wabamun Lake district is an area of low relief and belongs physiographically to the plains area of central and eastern Alberta. Rocks of late Cretaceous and early Tertiary ages constitute the bedrock of the Wabamun Lake district, and consist of sandstones, shales and coal seams deposited in a fresh water environment. Proximate coal analyses and brief petrographic descriptions indicate the coal to have a sub-bituminous B classification and to be bright and banded in nature (Pearson, 1959).

A detailed structural survey of the coal seams revealed only one set of joints (often referred to as 'cleats' in coal) with a consistent orientation. The joints were essentially planar, vertical and at right angle to the horizontal bedding planes. The average joint spacing was about 3/4 inch with most joints being continuous and closed for several feet. The bedding consisted of thin horizontal bands.

SAMPLING AND TESTING

The strength and deformation characteristics of seve different configurations containing various orientations of the joints and bedding planes were studied. The seven configurations (A to G inclusive as shown on Figure 1) can be grouped into two categories (I a II) with category I consisting of test configuratior A to C inclusive, and category II consisting of tes configurations D to G inclusive. The samples in category I share the common component of bedding pla being horizontal and shear taking place along these bedding planes. The joint planes are vertical and oriented at 0°, 90°, and 45° to the direction of the applied shear load for test configurations A, B, and C respectively.

The samples in category II share the common componer of bedding planes being vertical and oriented in the direction of the applied shear load. The joint plar dip in the direction of the applied shear load at 2C 40°, 0°, and 90° to the horizontal for test configu tions D, E, F, and G respectively.

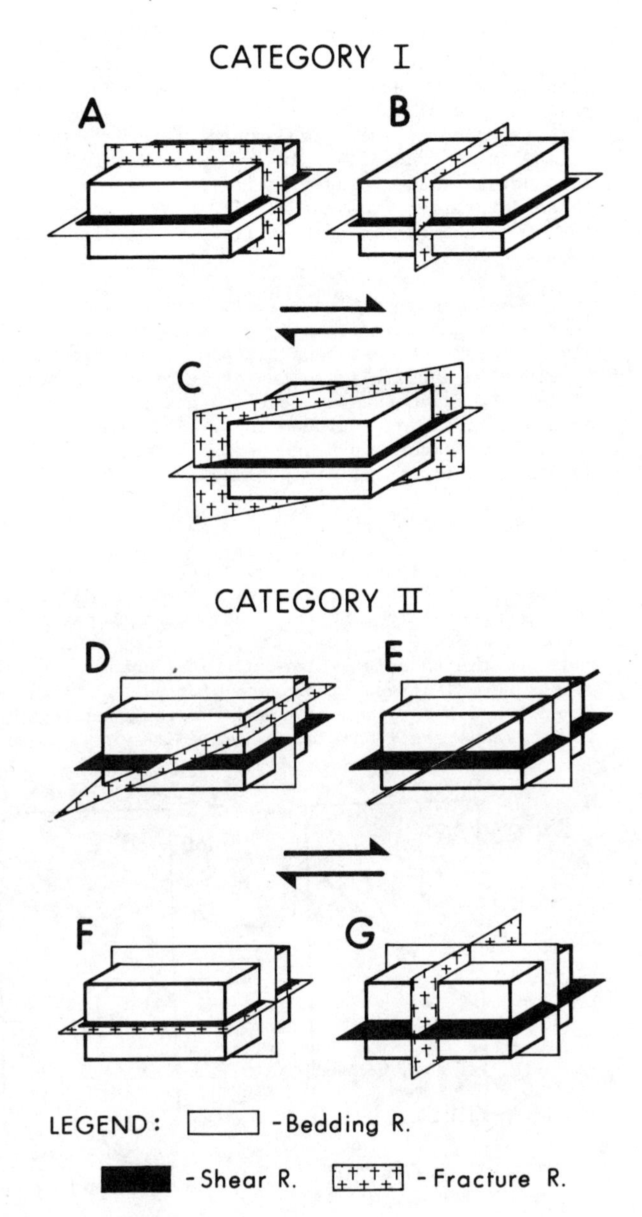

FIGURE 1 Sample Configurations

FIELD SAMPLING

Test samples were cut from blocks located near the top of a coal seam that had been loosened by blasting operations consisting of a light charge detonated about 8 feet below the top of the seam. The blasting only served to free these blocks along pre-existing planes of weakness and no evident additional fractures were induced in the sample. The samples were then cut several inches over-size on all sides using a chain saw modified to accommodate a 12 inch diameter circular rock blade.

LABORATORY PROCEDURE

The over-sized field samples were cut to about 1/8 inch under-size on all sides using a concrete saw having a mobile platform that enabled an accurate cut to be made. Although good samples of uniform dimensions were obtained, it was impossible to prevent small pieces from breaking away along the edges and especially the corners. The samples were thus brought up to final size by casting them in Devcon B plastic steel epoxy. This ensured a snug fit in the shear box and also ensured flat horizontal surfaces for seating and loading the samples. A gap of about 1/2 inch was left in the middle of the sample through which shear was to take place.

In this manner, 2, 6, 8, and 12 inches square samples were prepared for testing. The 2 inch square samples were pre-cut along the shear plane to enable the determination of the ultimate or residual angle of friction. The remaining samples were tested intact with a Wykeham-Farrance ten ton capacity direct shear machine.

During each test, the shear load versus shear displacement curve was plotted on an X-Y recorder. In addition, the vertical dilation of the samples during shear was measured and recorded by 4 linear voltage displacement transducers (LVDT) mounted on each corner.

RESULTS AND DISCUSSION

Classification Properties

A series of classification tests was carried out in order to confirm the uniformity of the test samples rather than to provide absolute values. The results of the tests yielded average values for moisture content, specific gravity and bulk density to be 24 per cent, 1.58, and 86 lbs./cu.ft. respectively with no significant deviations from these average values.

Direct Shear Tests on Pre-cut Samples

A series of 10 tests were run on 2 inch square samples with a pre-cut shear plane. The bedding planes in these samples were horizontal and the joint planes were vertical. The resulting shear stress was plotted against the applied normal stress as shown on Figure 2. The slope of this line was taken as the ultimate or residual angle of friction, ϕr, for the coal and has a value of 30°.

At very high loads the failure envelopes for most rocks becomes flatter. By considering the data points on Figure 2 a case may be made for the fact that this envelope is starting to curve above a normal stress of about 600 psi. However, for the stress range involved in the testing program, the straight line, as shown, is valid.

Direct Shear Tests on Intact Samples

(a) Before Peak

A finite element analysis of a test sample in direct shear was carried out (Noonan and Nixon, 1972). The analysis was based on the theory of linear elasticity and predicted the stresses and displacements throughout a sample of rock in direct shear before peak strength is reached. From this analysis, it is possible to estimate the Young's Modulus of the rock in direct shear. The calculated E values are plotted against normal stress on Figure 3 for each test configuration shown on Figure 1.

Bieniawski (1968) presents a complete load deformation curve recorded automatically during laboratory testing of coal specimens 2 feet cube in size in uniaxial compression. Two values of Young's Modulus of 16.7 x 10^3 and 33.4 x 10^3 psi were determined from this data. These values are in the same range as those determined from the direct shear tests. However coal in place can be much stiffer, particularly at depth.

As can be seen from Figure 3, the trend is for E to increase with an increase in normal stress. This is similar to E increasing with depth in the field. An increase in normal stress causes existing discontinuities within the sample to close and this is reflected by a corresponding increase in E. The closing of the joint is dependent upon the normal stress, and closed joints lead to a stiffer specimen.

(b) Peak Strength

For each test, the maximum shear stress recorded was plotted against the normal stress for that particular test in order to define the shear strength parameters ϕ and c, where ϕ is the angle of shearing resistance and c is the cohesion intercept. The shear stress versus normal stress graphs are plotted on Figures 4 and 5 and the values of ϕ and c determined from these graphs are tabulated in Table 1.

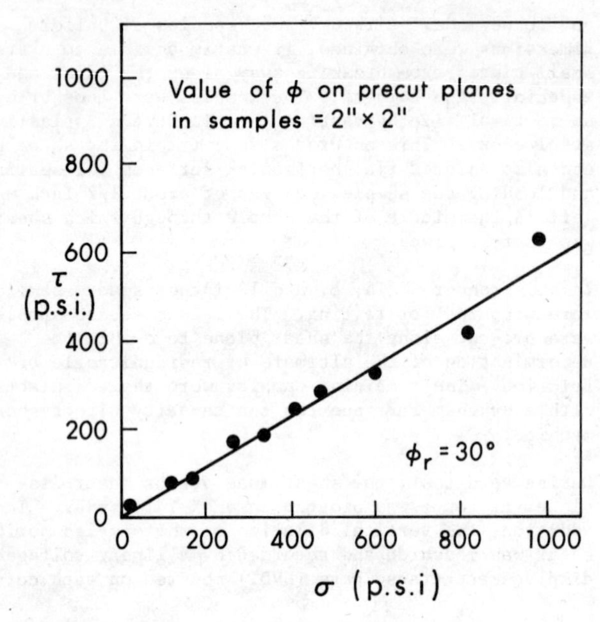

FIGURE 2 Residual Strength Envelope for Pre-cut Plane

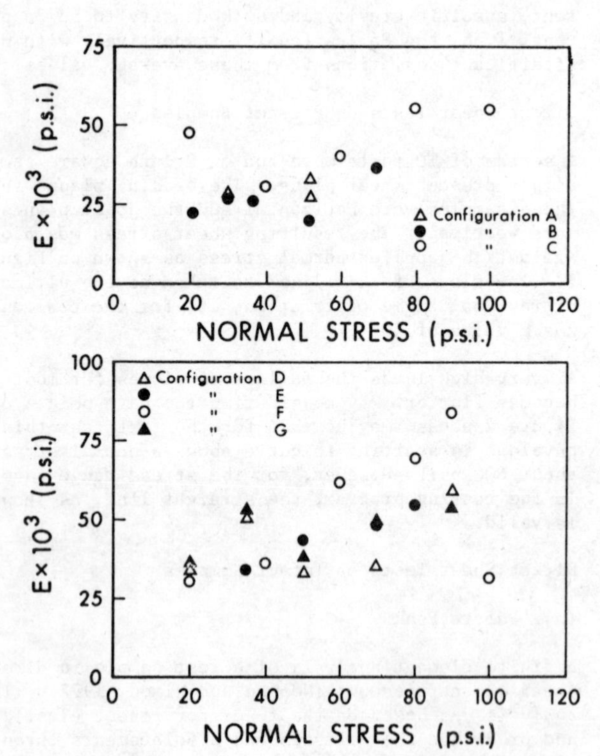

FIGURE 3 Influence of Normal Stress on Young's Modulus

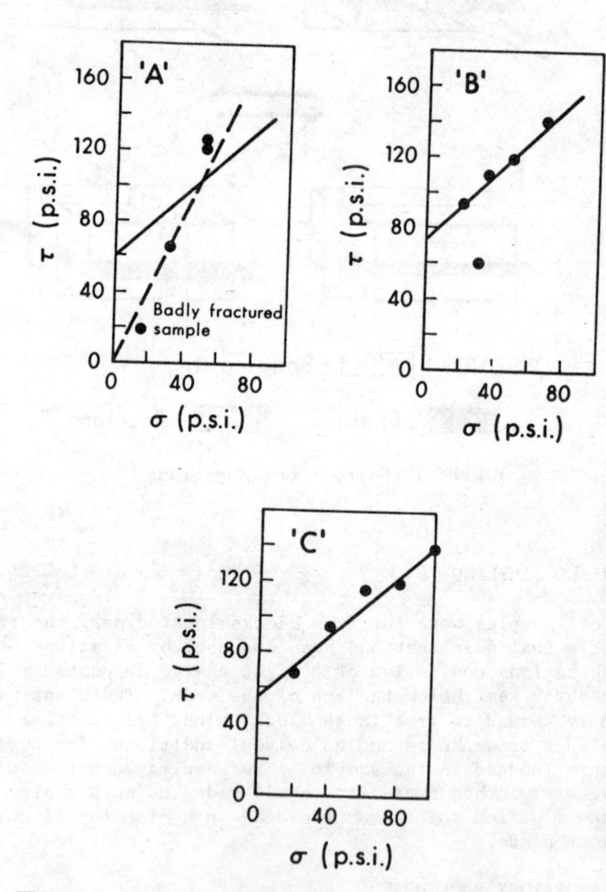

FIGURE 4 Strength Envelopes at Peak Category I

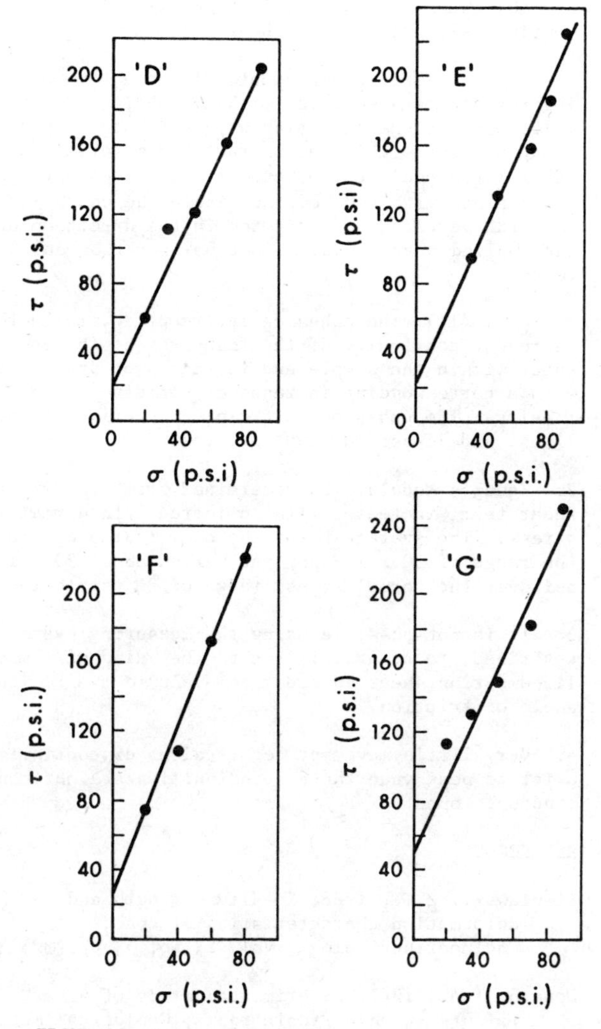

FIGURE 5 Strength Envelopes at Peak - Category II

TABLE 1

SHEAR STRENGTH PARAMETERS

CATEGORY	TEST CONFIGURATION	ϕ (DEGREES)	c (psi)
I	A	(41.5)	(60)
	B	41.7	76
	C	40.5	56
II	D	64.0	20
	E	65.5	17
	F	67.8	25
	G	65.0	50

The dashed line shown for test configuration A is the line that best fits the experimental data. However, the test indicated as being badly fractured does not reflect the strength of the material because all continuity in the zone of shear was lost during sample preparation. Also, some value of the cohesion intercept would be expected. The solid line, then will be assumed in the following discussion to be the best fit line for the valid data points assuming some cohesion intercept. Clearly the parameters found in this way are questionable and therefore they are shown in parentheses in Table 1.

The results given in Table 1 indicate that the angle of shearing resistance for category I is about 41° and for category II is about 66°. This is due to the strength anisotropy of the material and is comparable with results presented by Donath (1961) for Longwood shale tested in triaxial compression in which ϕ was found to be in the range of 20° when testing parallel to bedding and in the range of 30° when testing perpendicular to bedding.

The cohesion intercept, c, for category I is generally considerably higher than c for category II. This is due to the fact that the degree of continuity of the bedding planes is greater than that of the joint planes. This is consistent with results presented by Hobbs (1964). For Pentremawr coal he found a cohesion intercept of 400 psi when testing parallel to bedding and 700 psi when testing perpendicular to bedding.

The variation in c within category II reflects the variation in the areal extent of the joint plane with respect to the shear plane. In the case of configuration G, the joints are normal to the direction of shear and weakness along jointing does not contribute much to the overall failure in comparison with configurations D, E, and F.

In order to further explain the consistent values of ϕ for the two categories regardless of the orientation of the joint planes, the shear displacement and vertical dilation at peak were considered. The average dilation at peak was in all cases found to be very small thus clearly indicating little movement along the discontinuities up to peak. For example, in test E2, the average dilation at peak was 0.005 inches for a shear displacement of 0.163 inches. If the sample had moved along the joint plane inclined at 40°, the vertical dilation measured for a shear displacement of 0.163 inches would have been 0.137 inches. This is several orders of magnitude greater than the measured dilation. Thus, the peak ϕ angle is a function of the sample material only and not a function of the geometry of the discontinuities. This is only the case when the separation along the discontinuities is not continuous throughout the sample. When they are continuous, as is the case for models such as those used by Patton (1966) and Ladanyi and Archambault (1970), the orientation of these discontinuities plays a dominant role at peak.

After Peak

After the peak strength of the material is overcome, the shear surface becomes a continuous and open discontinuity through the sample. The geometry of this surface is dependent upon the orientation of the planes of weakness within the sample. The equation defining the failure criterion after peak may now be written as (Patton, 1966):

$$\tau = \sigma \tan (\phi r + i) \quad \ldots\ldots\ldots\ldots\ldots (1)$$

where i is the inclination of the shear surface with respect to the direction of the applied shear load. The normal stress, σ, is constant for each test and because ϕr is considered to be a constant for the material, then τ varies with changes in i.

For all values of shear displacement, the vertical movement of the sample was measured at each corner of the loading cap. Thus, for any increment of shear displacement, dx, the corresponding increments of vertical movement, dy, are known. The values of dy/dx, then give four tan i values from which four values of i can be determined.

According to Patton, the maximum value of i should govern the behaviour of the test sample. When this value of i is subtracted from $\phi r + i$, the resulting ϕr value should correspond to the independently determined value of ϕr. An investigation of the results showed that this was not generally the case. Moreover neither the average nor the minimum values of i when subtracted from $\phi r + i$ gave a resulting ϕr value corresponding to the independently determined value. In general, however, the correlation was much better for test configurations A, B, C, G, and F, where the shear surface was relatively planar.

In Patton's laboratory study, he dealt with artificially prepared samples having rigidly controlled geometry along the shear surface. The samples in this study consisted of a natural rock material taken through peak and thus no specific control was imposed on the subsequent shape of the shear surface.

Because of the irregularities on the shear surface, some rotation of the upper part of the sample about these irregularities would be expected (Goodman, 1970), and the calculated i would reflect this rotation. This rotation was more pronounced on test configurations D and E because they had the most irregular shear surfaces.

At the completion of shear displacement, the values of $\phi r + i$ obtained in test configuration D and E were seen to be consistently higher than the value of ϕr determined independently even though the value of i was on average only a few degrees. This indicates the possibility of buttressing and interlock of the irregularities during shear displacement.

Occasionally, the value of $\phi r + i$ was observed to fall below the independently determined value of ϕr. This can be explained by the presence of gouge or rounded particles on the shear surface (Patton, 1966), or by the rotation of individual blocks of coal at the shear surface (Ladanyi, 1972).

CONCLUSIONS

The following conclusions can be made concerning the behaviour of fractured coal subjected to direct shear.

1. The shear strength of fractured coal is anisotropic within the sample. The shear strength parameters ϕ and c are affected in different ways.

(a) When a continuously open discontinuity is present at the shear surface, the cohesion intercept, c, is zero and ϕ depends upon the frictional sliding resistance of the material, ϕr, and the inclination of the shear surface, i, to the direction of the applied shear load. ϕr for the coal tested is 30°.

(b) When discontinuities are present that are not continuously open at the shear surface:

(i) ϕ is dependent only upon the peak shearing resistance associated with the unfractured material. ϕ has a smaller value when shear takes place along bedding within the unfractured material (about 40° for the coal tested) and larger values when shear takes place with the bedding within the unfractured material vertical and oriented in the direction of the applied shear load, (about 66° for the coal tested).

(ii) The cohesion intercept, c, reflects the degree of continuity of the fractures at the zone of shear within the sample and increases or decreases with a corresponding increase or decrease in the continuity. The cohesion intercept, c, varied between 17 psi and 76 psi for the coal tested.

2. Young's Modulus, as determined from the direct shear test, increases with an increase in normal stress. The average E for the coal tested was in the range of 50×10^3 psi and varied about 20×10^3 psi over the normal stress range of 20 psi to 100 psi.

3. It is not possible using the measuring system described, to accurately record the value of i mobilized during shear in order to evaluate the residual angle of friction.

4. Very little movement occurs along discontinuities prior to peak when the discontinuities are not continuously open.

REFERENCES

Bieniawski, Z.T., 1968, In-situ strength and deformation characteristics of coal, Engineering Geology, Vol. 2, No. 5, pp. 325-340.

Donath, F.A., 1961, Experimental study of shear failure in anisotropic rocks, Geological Society of America Bulletin, Vol. 72, pp. 985-990.

Goodman, R.E., 1970, The deformability of joints, determination of the in-situ modulus of deformation of rock, ASTM STP 477, American Society for Testing and Materials, pp. 174-196.

Hobbs, D.W., 1964, The strength and stress-strain characteristics of coal in triaxial compression, Journal of Geology, Vol. 72, No. 2, pp. 214-231.

Ladanyi, B., Archambault, G., 1970, Simulation of shear behaviour of a jointed rock mass, 11th Symposium on Rock Mechanics, University of California, Berkeley, California, pp. 105-125.

Ladanyi, B., Archambault, G., 1972, Évaluation de la résistance au cisaillement d'und massif rocheux fragmenté, Préparé pour présentation au 24e Congres Géologique International, Montreal

Noonan, D.K.J., 1972, Fractured rock subjected to direct shear, M.Sc. thesis, University of Alberta, Edmonton, Alberta.

Noonan, D.K.J., Nixon, J.F., 1972, The determination of Young's Modulus for the direct shear test, Canadian Geotechnical Journal, Vol. 9, No. 4, pp. 504-507.

Patton, F.D., 1966, Multiple modes of shear failure in rock and related materials, Ph.D. thesis, University of Illinois, Urbana, Illinois.

Pearson, G.R., 1959, Coal reserves for strip mining, Wabamun Lake District Alberta, Research Council of Alberta, Geological Division, Preliminary Report 59-1.

INFLUENCE OF INTERMEDIATE STRESS UPON INTERNAL FRICTION IN BLOCK MASSES

INFLUENCE DE LA CONTRAINTE INTERMÉDIAIRE SUR LE FROTTEMENT INTERNE DANS UN MASSIF DE BLOCS

DER EINFLUSS DER ZWISCHENSPANNUNG AUF DEN INNEREN REIBUNGSWIDERSTAND EINES BLOCKMASSIVS

U. NASCIMENTO Research Engineer Head of Geotechnique Department Laboratorio Nacional de Engenharia Civil

C.B. FALCÃO Research Officer, Head of Special Geotechnical Studies Division, LNEC

A. PINELO Trainee Research Officer of Special Geotechnical Studies Divs., LNEC

M. MARQUES Student of Civil Engineering, LNEC

Lisbon, Portugal

SYNOPSIS - A theoretical model of the interlocking mechanism in a block mass is presented. On basis of this model, the authors quantify the dependence that exists between the internal friction in blocks, the surface friction at the contacts, the interlocking angle and the intermediate stress. Nomographs are presented which give the internal friction angle both against those parameters and the state of stress. The intermediate stress was found always to increase the internal friction angle. Lastly some comments are made on sand strength studies, which show the influence of the intermediate stress.

RÉSUMÉ – On présente un modèle théorique du mécanisme d'indentation dans un massif de blocs. Partant de ce modèle, les auteurs quantifient la dépendance, dans les blocs, entre le frottement interne, le frottement superficiel aux contacts, l'angle d'indentation et la contrainte intermédiaire. On présente des abaques donnant l'angle de frottement interne en fonction de ces paramètres et de l'état de contrainte. On vérifia que l'angle de frottement interne augmente toujours avec la contrainte intermédiaire. Finalement on fait quelques commentaires au sujet sur la résistance des sables, qui montrent l'influence de la contrainte intermédiaire.

ZUSAMMENFASSUNG – Ein theoretisches Modell des Verzahnungsmechanismus wird vorgestellt. Auf Grund dieses Modells wird der Zusammenhang zwischen dem inneren Widerstand der Blöcke, dem Reibungswinkel zwischen den Kontakten, dem Verzahnungswinkel und der Zwischenspannung quantifiziert. Es werden Abakusse vorgestellt, die jene Parameter mit dem Spannungszustand verknöpfen. Es wird festgtellt, dass die Zwischenspannung immer den inneren Reibungswinkel vergrossert. Schliesslich werden einige Arbeiten besprochen, die den Widerstand von Sanden behandeln und den Einfluss der Zwischenspannung zeigen.

INTRODUCTION

In a former work (Nascimento and Teixeira, 1971), an analysis was made of the different mechanisms that produce internal friction due to surface friction, wedge, rotation and rolling effects. For simplicity's sake, that analysis did not consider the influence of the intermediate stress, although experimental results have confirmed its importance.

In the present work, a theoretical model of the interlocking mechanism is presented.

INTERLOCKING MECHANISM

In a ground mass as mentioned above, let us consider a set of four blocks in contact, 1, 2, 3 and 4, in such a way that blocks 1 and 3 are tight into dihedral angles formed by the planes of their contacts with blocks 2 and 4 (Fig. 1 a). Be σ_1, σ_2 and σ_3 the mean principal stresses considered to be uniform in the zone of the blocks. These mean stresses, in fact, are the stresses

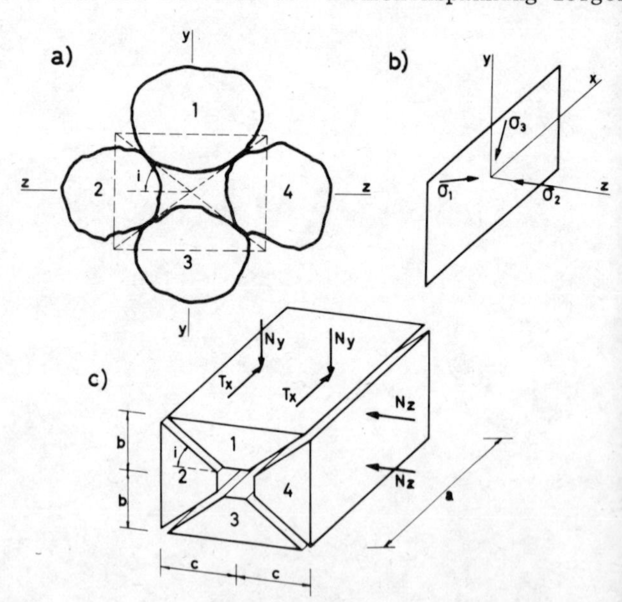

Fig. 1 - a) Blocks with interlocking
b) Directions of principal stress
c) Model of interlocking

that might exist in a portion of the continuum that would fill the whole space of that zone in replacement of the set of the blocks (Nascimento, 1973).

If the plane of the maximum (σ_1) and minimum (σ_3) principal stresses is the plane (x,y) vertical and normal to the plane of the drawing, as is schematically shown in Fig. 1 b, the intermediate stress σ_2 is thus parallel to the zz axis and acts horizontally. Let us suppose also that the planes of the contacts between the blocks have a direction normal to the plane (y, z).

In these circumstances, the model shown in Fig. 1 c satisfactorily reproduces the mechanism of failure due to shear with interlocking. Wedges 1 and 3 can slide on wedges 2 and 4 in parallel to plane (x, y). Angle i between the direction of the intermediate stress and the planes of contact will be called interlocking angle. Normal forces 2 N_y acting on wedges 1 and 3, 2 N_z acting on wedges 2 and 4, and tangential forces $2T_x$ acting on wedges 1 and 3 develop states of stress σ_1, σ_2 and σ_3. These tangential forces $2T_x$ applied to wedges 1 and 3 make them slide over wedges 2 and 4.

Fig. 2 shows projections of the planes of contact between wedges 1 and 2 on the three co-ordinated planes (x, y), (y, z) and (x, z).

Consideration of Fig. 2 a) will indicate that on the surface of contact the force resulting from the normal components N_y and N_z, represented by F_i in the figure, may be decomposed into its normal and tangential components, N_i and T_i respectively, given by the following expressions:

$$N_i = N_y \cos i + N_z \operatorname{sen} i \qquad (1)$$

$$T_i = N_y \operatorname{sen} i - N_z \cos i \qquad (2)$$

The obliquity α_i of F_i with reference to the surface of contact which we will call obliquity of interlocking will be given by

$$\operatorname{tg} \alpha_i = \frac{T_i}{N_i} \qquad (3)$$

Taking into account that

$$\sigma_y = \frac{N_y}{a\,c} \qquad (4)$$

$$\sigma_z = \frac{N_z}{a\,b} \qquad (5)$$

and that

$$\operatorname{tg} i = \frac{b}{c} \qquad (6)$$

and making

$$K_{yz} = \frac{\sigma_z}{\sigma_y} \qquad (7)$$

we obtain from (1), (2) and (3)

$$\operatorname{tg} \alpha_i = \frac{(1 - K_{yz}) \operatorname{tg} i}{1 + K_{yz} \operatorname{tg}^2 i} \qquad (8)$$

which gives the intelorcking obliquity α_i against both the interlocking angle i (an exclusively geometrical parameter) and the coefficient of pressure K_{yz} in the direction of the intermediate stress, this parameter only depending on the state of stress.

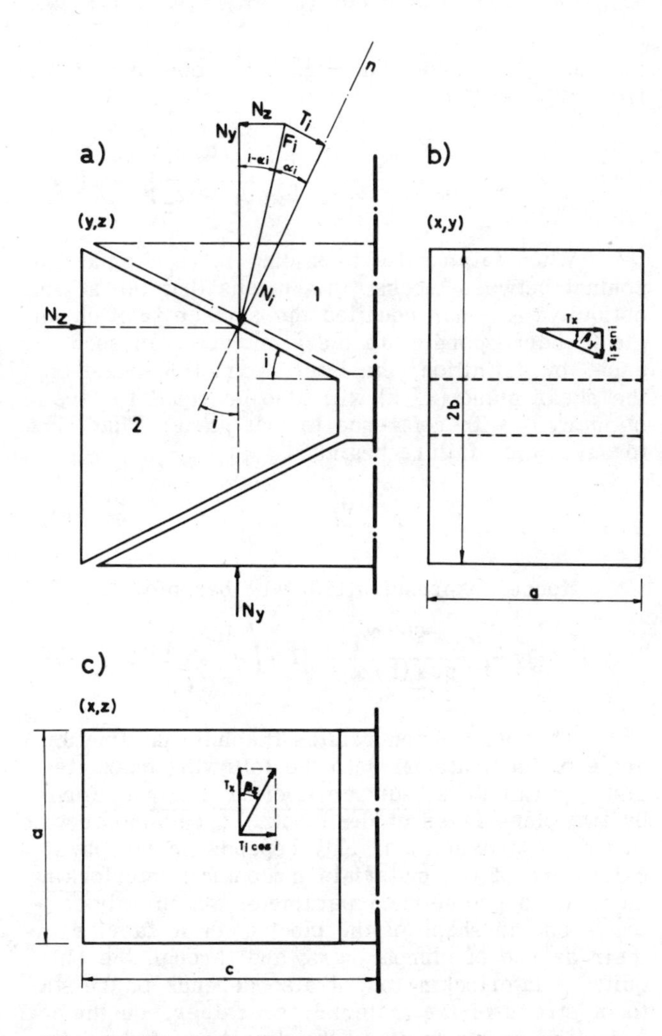

Fig. 2 - Forces acting at the contact between blocks

Nevertheless as a tangential component T_x has been assumed to exist, the true obliquity with reference to the plane of contact will be the resultant from the composition of T_x and T_i. The actual tangential force T_r on the plane of contact will then be

$$T_r = \sqrt{T_i^2 + T_x^2} \qquad (9)$$

and the actual obliquity

$$\operatorname{tg} \alpha_r = \frac{T_r}{N_i} \tag{10}$$

Writing

$$\operatorname{tg} \alpha = \frac{T_x}{N_y} \tag{11}$$

in which α is the obliquity relative to the shear plane (x, y), and taking into account that

$$N_i = N_y \frac{\cos \alpha_i}{\cos (i - \alpha_i)} \tag{12}$$

as can be deduced from Fig. 2 a), one may obtain from (9) and (10)

$$\operatorname{tg}\alpha = \operatorname{tg}\alpha_r \frac{\cos \alpha_i}{\cos (i - \alpha_i)} \sqrt{1 - \left(\frac{\operatorname{tg}\alpha_i}{\operatorname{tg}\alpha_r}\right)^2} \tag{13}$$

When failure due to sliding is reached at the contact between blocks, this means that the actual obliquity α_r has equalled the surface friction angle ϕ_f corresponding to these contacts. In such a case, by definition, the internal friction angle on the shear plane (x, z) will also be equal to the obliquity α with reference to that plane. That is to say, when failure begins

$$\begin{aligned} \alpha_r &= \phi_f \\ \alpha &= \phi \end{aligned} \tag{14}$$

Hence, expression (13) will become

$$\operatorname{tg} \phi = \operatorname{tg} \phi_f \frac{\cos \alpha_i}{\cos (i - \alpha_i)} \sqrt{1 - \left(\frac{\operatorname{tg}\alpha_i}{\operatorname{tg} \phi_f}\right)^2} \tag{15}$$

This expression relates the internal friction angle of the material ϕ to the following characteristic parameters: surface friction angle ϕ_f formed by two plane faces of the blocks, a parameter which, in first approximation, only depends on the physical nature of the materials in contact; interlocking angle i, a geometrical parameter which only depends on the shape of the blocks, their fabrics, their degree of compactness; and through the obliquity of interlocking α_i it also depends on the state of stress of the material, or rather, on the coefficient of pressure along the direction of the intermediate stress.

When $K_{yz} = 1$, that is when σ_z equals stress σ_y normal to the shear plane, expression (8) shows that the obliquity of interlocking ($\alpha_i = 0$) is null and thus expression (15) reduces to

$$\operatorname{tg} \phi = \frac{\operatorname{tg} \phi_f}{\cos i} \tag{16}$$

If $\alpha_i = 0$, also $T_i = 0$ and thus the tangential force at the contact is only T_x; wedge 1 slides horizontally on wedges 2 and 4, therefore without dilatancy (Fig. 2 b).

When $K_{yz} < 1$, that is when σ_z is lower than stress σ_y normal to the shear plane, expression (8) gives a positive α_i such as is represented in Fig. 2 a) and originates a tangential force T_i which can be expressed by

$$T_i = N_y \frac{\operatorname{sen} \alpha_i}{\cos (i - \alpha_i)} \tag{17}$$

as it follows from Fig. 2 a).

This force T_i, as fig. 2 a) shows, acts downwards the plane which makes wedge 1 go down, i. e., blocks 1 and 3 come closer whereas blocks 2 and 4 stand back. In other words, failure occurs with negative dilatancy on plane (x, y) and positive dilatancy on plane (x, z). The correspondent angles of dilatancy β_y and β_z shown in Fig. 2 will be given by the expressions:

$$\operatorname{tg} \beta_y = \frac{T_i \operatorname{sen} i}{T_x} \tag{18}$$

$$\operatorname{tg} \beta_z = \frac{T_i \cos i}{T_x} \tag{19}$$

or, taking into account (11) and (17)

$$\operatorname{tg} \beta_y = \frac{1}{\operatorname{tg} \alpha} \frac{\operatorname{sen}\alpha_i \operatorname{sen} i}{\cos (i - \alpha_i)} \tag{20}$$

$$\operatorname{tg} \beta_z = \frac{1}{\operatorname{tg} \alpha} \frac{\operatorname{sen} \alpha_i \cos i}{\cos (i - \alpha_i)} \tag{21}$$

If $K_{yz} > 1$, when stress σ_z is higher than the stress normal to the shearing plane, expression (8) gives negative α_i and the tangential force T_i acts upwards on the plane of contact. Failure will bring about the separation of blocks 1 and 3 and the approximation of blocks 2 and 4. That is to say, failure occurs with positive dilatancy on plane (x, y) and negative dilatancy on plane (x, z). The respective dilatancy angles will be given by expressions (20) and (21).

Fig. 3 shows a nomograph that gives the obliquity of interlocking α_i against the coefficient of lateral pressure K_{yz} and the interlocking angle i, in accordance with expression (8). This obliquity must be inferior to the surface friction angle ϕ_f, lest the model shall break even before the application of shear force T_x.

INFLUENCE OF THE INTERMEDIATE STRESS UPON THE INTERNAL FRICTION ANGLE

Stress σ_z may only be considered the intermediate stress if it is comprised between the extreme principal stresses, that is, if the following condition occurs:

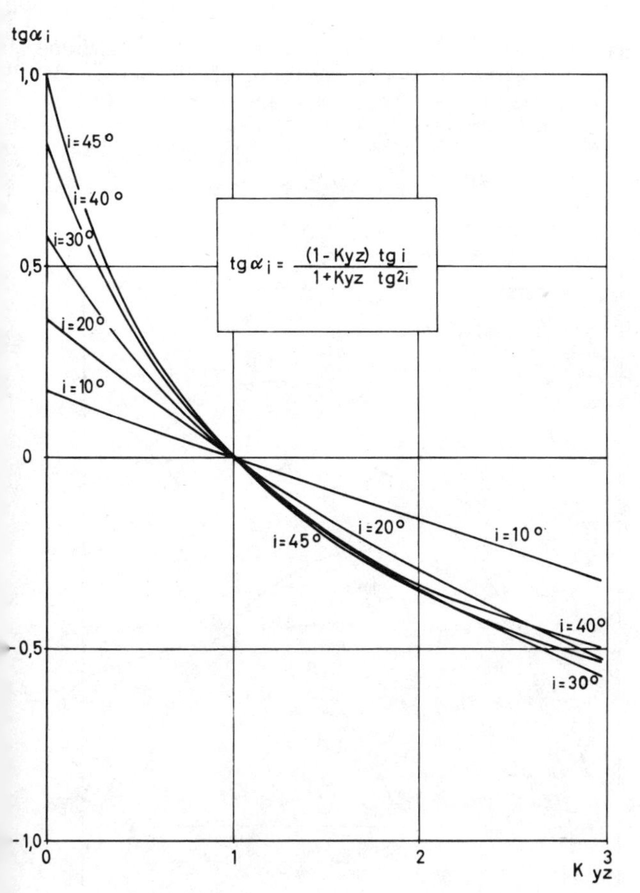

Fig. 3 - Nomograph that gives the obliquity of interlocking α_i against the coefficient of lateral pressure K_{yz} and the interlocking angle i

$$\frac{\sigma_y}{1 + \text{sen}\,\phi} \leqslant \sigma_z \leqslant \frac{\sigma_y}{1 - \text{sen}\,\phi} \qquad (22)$$

or else, by dividing by σ_y and taking (7) into account, if

$$\frac{1}{1 + \text{sen}\,\phi} \leqslant K_{yz} \leqslant \frac{1}{1 - \text{sen}\,\phi} \qquad (23)$$

At the lower limit, we shall have the state of stress corresponding to the triaxial compressive test ($\sigma_2 = \sigma_3$) and ϕ may be denoted by ϕ_c; at the upper limit we shall have the state of stress in the triaxial striction test ($\sigma_2 = \sigma_1$) to which ϕ_s will correspond.

Figs. 4, 5 and 6 show nomographs that give the values of the internal friction angle ϕ in accordance with expression (15), respectively for surface friction angles ϕ_f equal to 10°, 20° and 30°. Values of ϕ are given by a family of curves against both the parameter i - equal to 0°, 10°, 20°, 30°, 40° or 45° - and the lateral stress expressed by the dimensionless coefficient K_{yz}. In those nomographs the zone in which the lateral stress is the intermediate stress is demarcated by means of thin curves which express condition (23). Within this zone, ϕ curves are plotted in continuous lines; outside it, they are dotted lines.

Those nomographs show that the intermediate stress always increases the internal friction angle. As comparison of Figs. 4, 5 and 6 will show, for a given value of ϕ_f the wider the interlocking angle i, the bigger that increase. Likewise, for a given value of i, the wider the surface friction angle, the bigger that increase too.

Figs. 4, 5 and 6 also show that there is a maximum of the internal friction angle for a given value of the intermediate stress which increasingly exceeds the mean stress $(\sigma_1 + \sigma_3)/2$ as the surface friction angle ϕ_f and the interlocking angle i grow wider.

COMMENTS ON SOME EXPERIMENTS REFERRED TO IN THE LITERATURE

Among the abundant literature dealing with sand strength, the works by Habib (1953) and Peltier (1957) seem particularly worth an analysis in the light of the theory herein presented. These works draw attention to the difference between internal friction angles in sands, measured in triaxial compressive tests and striction tests as well as in 'triaxial' shear box tests. In this shear box the intermediate stress σ_2 may be placed at one's discretion (Peltier, 1957). The authors drew the following main conclusions from their studies: a) in triaxial tests on sands, the internal friction angle measured under compression ϕ_c is systematically wider than that measured under striction ϕ_s and the difference is about 7°; b) in tests carried out on the 'triaxial' shearing box these extreme internal friction angles ϕ_c and ϕ_s show differences of that same order of magnitude, but in the inverse direction.

Let us try to interpret these results in the light of the theory we present.

The nomograph in Fig. 6 is the nearest one to values of ϕ around 30°, as those determined by Peltier. In fact, this nomograph gives values of ϕ_c ranging from 30° to 32° 30' when the interlocking angle i varies between zero and 45°. This same nomograph will give values of ϕ_s exceeding ϕ_c in about 7° when the interlocking angle i is about 40°. That is to say the nomograph in Fig. 6 satisfactorily reproduce only the experimental results obtained with the 'triaxial' shear box in which $\phi_s - \phi_c \simeq 7^o$, under the assumption that $\phi_f \simeq 30^o$ and $i \simeq 40^o$; nevertheless, that nomograph is in full disagreement with results when ϕ_c and ϕ_s are determined following a conventional triaxial test. Why?

As it seems, such a disagreement is due to the fact that, in a conventional triaxial test, the surface elements with m a x i m u m o b l i q u i t y, c o r r e s p o n d i n g to compression and striction tests, are placed at an angle equal to the internal friction angle ϕ, in an isotropic

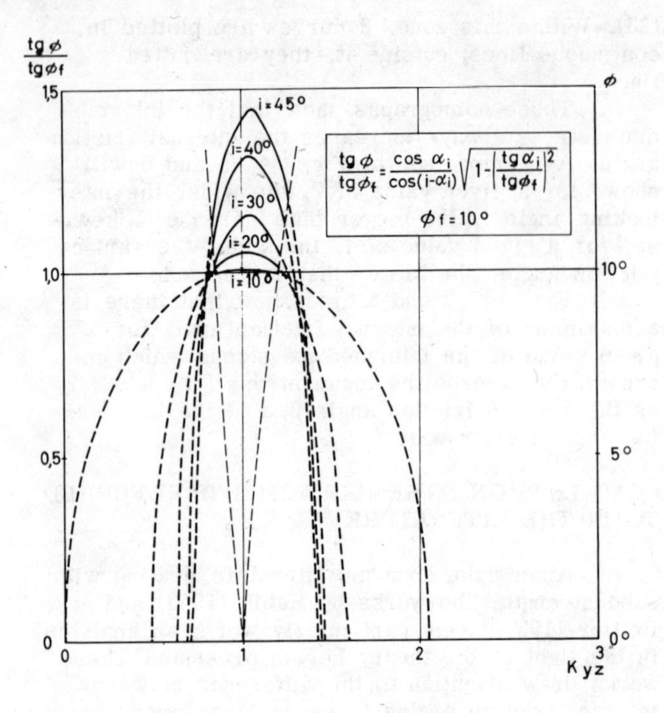

Fig. 4 - Nomograph that gives the internal friction angle $\emptyset$ for a surface friction angle $\emptyset$=10°

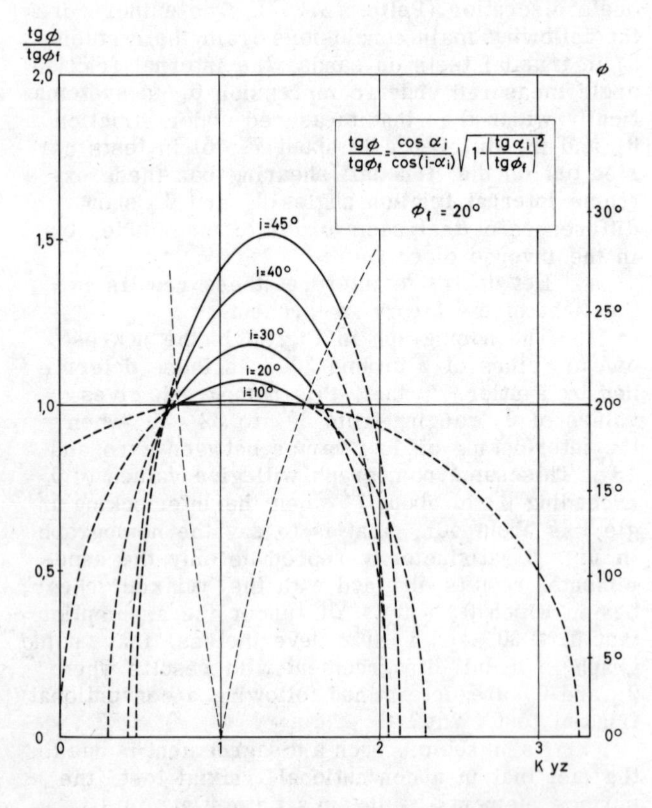

Fig. 5 - Nomograph that gives the internal friction angle $\emptyset$ for a surface friction angle for $\emptyset_f$ = 20°

material. In fact, at the compressive test, these surface elements make an angle of $45^o + \frac{\emptyset}{2}$ with the horizontal, whereas this angle equals $45^o - \frac{\emptyset}{2}$ at the striction test. Hence

$$(45 + \frac{\emptyset}{2}) - (45 - \frac{\emptyset}{2}) = \emptyset$$

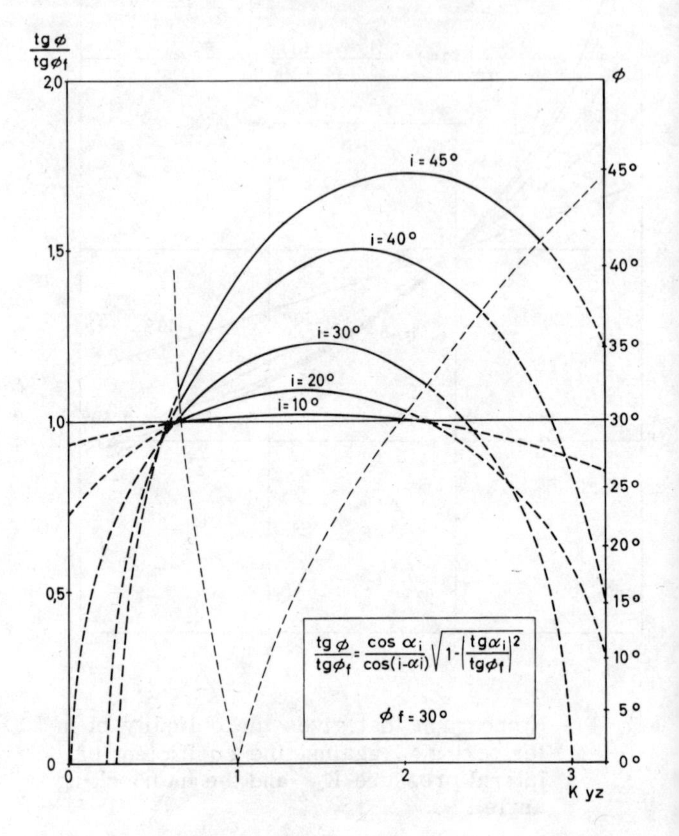

Fig. 6 - Nomograph that gives the internal friction angle $\emptyset$ for a surface friction angle $\emptyset_f = 30^o$

Therefore the conventional triaxial test would only give $\emptyset_c - \emptyset_s \simeq 7^o$ if the material were isotropic and thus if between surface elements placed at angles of about $\emptyset$ neither the surface friction angle between grains $\emptyset_f$, nor the interlocking angle i varied significantly. As regards the interlocking angle i, recent studies by Borowika Jun. (1973) have shown that there is a marked anisotropy which is displayed by a larger frequency of contacts at 0°, 60° and 90° with reference to the horizontal, the frequency of contacts at 30° being markedly lower. Therefore between surface elements of the continuum whose inclination may vary from $45 - \frac{\emptyset}{2} \simeq 30^o$ to $45 + \frac{\emptyset}{2} \simeq 60^o$, the actual interlocking angle, in accordance with the theoretical model herein presented, may also vary significantly. As concerns the actual angle of surface friction, which in the case of a real material involves other mechanisms besides friction as those of wedge or rotation, it may also be assumed to vary significantly between those surface elements of the continuum. For instance, it will be enough for ϕ_f to decrease to 20°, for the nomograph of Fig. 5 to give ϕ_s = 24°, thus about 7° lower than 31°, even if i = 40°.

With the 'triaxial' shear box, there is agreement with the theory presented, because shear of the material always occurs at the same surface element when either ϕ_c or ϕ_s is determined. Thus only the relative quantity of σ_2 varies since both ϕ_f and i are constant, regardless of their values.

Another experiment worth to be mentioned is that performed by Bjerrum and Kummeneje (1961). They showed that under triaxial tests, rectangular cross-section sand samples, intended to reproduce a plane state of deformation, present internal friction angles 3° to 4° wider than those obtained at normal triaxial tests, thus on circular cross-section samples. We believe that this increase in strength may have resulted from a stress increase along the direction of the length of the parallelipiped sample as a result of the friction developed during test between the sample and the load-plates. From this increase of stress it has resulted that the central zone of the sample is subject, not to a stress $\sigma_2 = \sigma_3$ to which would correspond $\phi = \phi_c$, but to an intermediate stress $\sigma_2 > \sigma_3$ to which, according to nomographs of Figs. 4, 5 and 6, will correspond $\phi > \phi_c$, if σ_2 is not much higher than σ_3.

CONCLUSIONS

From the above we believe the following conclusions may be drawn:

a) The theoretical model presented makes it possible to calculate the internal friction angle ϕ along a given direction and in a certain zone of a mass of blocks. The calculation is done against the surface friction angle ϕ_f, the interlocking angle i of the contacts between blocks, and the mean state of stress in this zone given only by the lateral pressure coefficient K_{yz}.

b) This theoretical internal friction angle varies when the intermediate stress σ_2 increases from the value of the minimum principal stress σ_3 to the value of the maximum principal stress σ_1. The former value corresponds to the conventional triaxial test under compression and will give $\phi = \phi_c$; the latter corresponds to the triaxial test under striction and will give $\phi = \phi_s$. The nomographs of Figs. 4, 5 and 6 give these theoretical ϕ against ϕ_f and i.

c) Supposing the internal friction angle ϕ is only due to frictional and interlocking mechanisms -which we assume in exclusion of wedge and roll mechanisms which are also present in reality - - the internal friction angle ϕ_c is always equal to or higher than the friction angle between blocks ϕ_f. However, tg ϕ_c does not exceed 1.1 x tg ϕ_f (Figs. 4, 5 and 6).

d) When the intermediate stress equals the normal stress along the direction of shear (K_{yz} = 1), shear occurs without dilatancy if the internal friction angle ϕ is such that tg ϕ = tg ϕ_f/cos i. When $K_{yz} < 1$, shear occurs with negative dilatancy on the shear plane and positive dilatancy on both sides. When $K_{yz} > 1$, shear occurs with positive dilatancy on the shear plane and negative dilatancy on both sides.

REFERENCES

1 – BJERRUM, L. and KUMMENEJ E.O. Shearing Resistance of Sant Samples With Circular an Rectangular Cross Sections, Norges Geot. Inst., Publ. No. 44, Oslo, 1961

2 – BOROWIKA JUN., H., - Rearrangement of grains by Shear Tests with sand, Eighth Int. Conf. Soil Mech. and Found. Eng., Moscow, 1973, Vol. 1.1 p 71

3 – HABIB, P. - Influence de la Variation de la Contrainte Principal Moyenne Sur la Resistance au Cisaillement des Sols Third Int. Conf. Soil Mech. and Found. Eng. Zurich, 1953, Vol. I, p. 131.

4 - NASCIMENTO, U., and TEIXEIRA, H., - Mechanics of Internal Friction in Soils and Rocks, Symposium of the Int. Soc. Rock Mechanics, Nancy, 1971. LNEC. Mem No. 398, Lisboa 1971

5 – NASCIMENTO, U. - Contribution to a Theory of Internal Friction Eighth Int. Conf. Soil Mech. and Found. Eng. Moscow, 1973, Vol. 1.2 p. 299.

6 – PELTIER, U.R. - Recherches Expérimentales sur la Courbe Intrinsèque de Rupture des Sols Pulvérulents, Fourth Int. Conf. Soil Mech. and Found. Eng. London, 1957, Vol. I p. 179

SHEAR STRENGTH OF TYPICAL FEATURES OF BASALTIC ROCK MASSES - PARANÁ BASIN - BRAZIL

RÉSISTANCE AU CISAILLEMENT DE TRAITS TYPIQUES DES MASSIFS BASALTIQUES - BASSIN DU PARANÁ - BRÉSIL

SCHERFESTIGKEIT VON TYPISCHEN GESTALTEN DER BASALTISCHEN MASSIVE - PARANÁBECKEN - BRASILIEN

Carlos NIEBLE — Head, Rock Mechanics Div., Instituto de Pesquisas Tecnologicas, Professor of Rock Mechanics, University of Sao Paulo, Brazil

Nilson Figueira MIDEA — Assistant, Rock Mechanics Div., Instituto de Pesquisas Tecnologicas

Fernando FUJIMURA — Assistant, Rock Mechanics Div., Instituto de Pesquisas Tecnologicas

Santo Bertin NETO — Assistant, Rock Mechanics Div., Instituto de Pesquisas Tecnologicas

Brazil

SUMMARY

The experience gathered in 350 direct shear tests carried out on one hundred rock blocks molded "in situ", with the purpose of characterizing the behavior of typical features of basalt masses, occurring in the Paraná Basin, such as breccia, "joint-fault" structures and contacts between lava flows is presented.

The testing techniques and the interpretative criteria as a function of the characteristics of the tested materials are discussed.

RÉSUMÉ

L'experience dans 350 essais de cisaillement direct realisés sur une centaine de bloques de roches moldés "in situ", visant caracterizer le comportement de traits typiques dans des massives basaltiques, tels que brèches, structures du type "joint-faille" et contacts entre coulées de lave est presentée dans ce travail.

On discusse la technique d'essais et les critères d'interprétation comme function des characteristiques du materiel essaié.

ZUSAMMENFASSUNG

Der Verfasser legt die bei 350 direkt durchgeführten Scherversuchen gesammelte Erfahrung vor. Die Versuche wurden auf 100 an Ort und Stelle geformte Gesteinblöcke durchgeführt und hatten den Zweck, das Verhalten der typischen Gestalten von basaltischen Massiven, wie Breccien, Kluft-Verwerfung-Texturen und Kontakte zwischen Lava-Ergussen zu charakterisieren.

Die Versuchstechniken und die Auswertungskriterien werden in Zusammenhang mit den Kennzeichnen der geprüften Materialen diskutiert.

I. - INTRODUCTION

Large Brazilian hydroelectric power plants lie on basaltic lava flows which present certain typical features which constitute "weakness zones" for the foundations, such as basaltic breccias, "joint-fault" structures and contacts between lava flows.

The shear strength of those typical features was studied in several places through direct shear tests, carried out "in situ" with different testing techniques on blocks of different sizes. This paper summarizes and analyses the results of these tests.

II. - GEOLOGY AND GENERAL CHARACTERISTICS OF

THE BASALTIC LAVA FLOWS OF THE PARANÁ BASIN

The majority of the large hydroeletric power plants in the Central Southern Region of Brazil has its foundations settled on basaltic lava flows (Fig. 1). These lava flows cover an area over one million square kilometers, with an overall average thickness of 650 m, corresponding to several individual lava flows with an average thickness of 50 m.

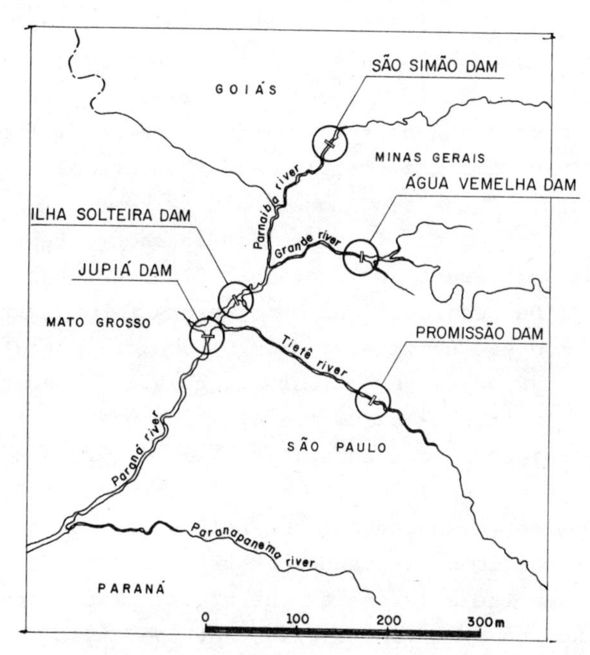

Figure 1

The individual lava flows, regardless of their geographical positions, generally present similar textural and different structural characteristics which, however, constitute typical features of fundamental importance when they affect the foundations of large structures. These features can be described as "features which, although not restricted to one place, constitute uncommon and genetically complex aspects, such as, for instance, the so-called basaltic breccias the "joint-fault" structures and the "contacts" (Fig. 2).

a. - BASALTIC BRECCIAS: "basaltic breccia" is an expression employed to describe materials situated between lava flows or supported thereupon, made up of basalt blocks intimately mixed with fines, regardless of their origin. Some typical examples are as follows:

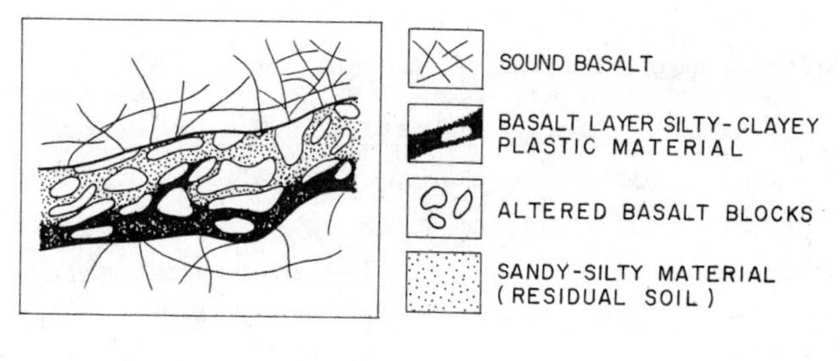

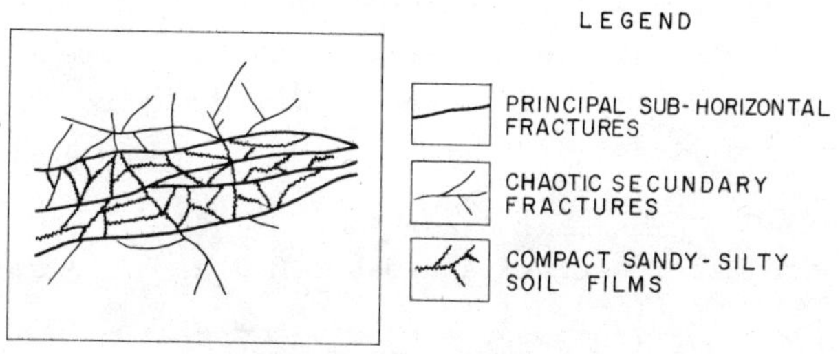

"JOINT-FAULT" STRUCTURES

Figure 2

a.1 - São Simão Breccia - It forms a layer with 5 to 15 m thickness spreading laterally all over the area of the foundations. It is characterized by a matrix of extremely variable consistence, ranging from incoherent clayey silts to silicified sandstone and siltites, and by an imbricate contact with the upper lava flow.

a.2 - Jupiá Breccia - Consisting of a quite resistant sandy matrix, and a few blocks of fairly consistent vesicular basalt. It forms a layer with few centimeters to 1 or 2 m thickness, the contact with the upper lava flow being quite plane and often open.

a.3 - Ilha Solteira Breccia - It occurs as well in the top of the lava flows as in lenses intercalated and confined within the basaltic mass. The matrix is mainly clayey, with basalt fragments, mostly quite altered, prismatic and juxtaposed.

b. - "JOINT-FAULT" STRUCTURES - Peculiar characteristics both to basaltic rock masses joints as to faults properly said, such as slickensides and infilling material (Campos and Guidicini, 1969).

b.1 - Ilha Solteira Joint-Fault - presents a variable thickness, ranging from few centimeters to over one meter, with extremely variable infilling materials, such as basalt fragments, altered sandy material and clay of the montmorilonite group.

b.2 - Água Vermelha Joint-Fault - it can be described as a sub-horizontal joint - varying from a system of 3 or 4 fractures of a few milimeters each filled by a discontinuous siltyclayey material film, to an 10 cm average thickness fracture, infilling by angular and imbricate basalt blocks and sandy-silty material originated by the decaying of the rock itself.

c. - CONTACTS - Three important contacts were observed and described as follows:

c.1 - Promissão Contact - Contact between a sandy-silty sedimentary material and the overlying basaltic lava flow presenting openings up to 2 or 3 cm with no infilling - material and quite significant lateral extensions.

c.2 - Jupiá Contact - With the same characteristics as above.

c.3 - Ilha Solteira Contact - This is the contact between the compact microcrystaline basalt of the overlying lava flow and the clayey basalt breccia (already described), found in this place.

III. - SOME CONSIDERATIONS ON TESTING TECHNIQUES

The S. Paulo Institute of Technology - (I.P.T.) has carried out 350 tests on one - hundred blocks molded "in situ" in these different places, in pits, galleries and ditches, using different testing techniques, on blocks with a base area ranging from 0,7 m x 0,7 m to 6,0 m x 6,0 m, supplied the data that are briefly analysed in this paper.

Summing up, we can classify the usual techniques for "in situ" direct shear tests into two large categories:

III.1 - Tests with loads applied in just - one direction

III.2 - Tests with loads applied in two directions

Tests with $i \neq 0$ are more frequently - used for determining the shear strength of rock masses, mainly because of greater easiness in preparing the test.

Finite element analysys shows that inclined loads improves the distribution of the tangencial stresses and reduces the concentration of normal stress at the end of the block base. The thickness and/or the - modulus of the piece used for application - and transmission of the loads plays a decisive role and certain relations between the opening for the shearing and the lateral division of the test box should be kept.

The stress distribution in shear tests with different inclinations of the lateral - load on isotropic and homogeneous bidimensional models (Ruiz, et al, 1970) showed that the maximal shear stresses generally occur outside the plane of the block base and are contained in curved surfaces whose form and position depend on the relation between the applied loads and on the inclination of the lateral load. In these author's opinion, as far as the stresses at the block base are concerned, it can be said that the most favorable angle for the tests lies at about 20°.

The distribution of stress - elasto - plastic strains in shear tests (Lorente de Nó, 1968) evidenced that in the plane of rupture, it seems to be far from uniform, principally at the beginning of the plastic zone, but the failure line obtained by the conventional method of testing using the average stresses in the plane of rupture seems to agree pretty well with the model line, and shear stresses were quite uniform.

It is logical that the above studies - were based on simplicative hypothesis, so that the model considerably departs from the actual characteristics of the prototype, considered as an anisotropic, heteregeneous, - discontinuous medium, with elastic visco -

plastic behavior. The construction of analogical models, however, has brought benefits for the testing techniques, giving the possibility of a better understanding and interpretation of those techniques. These models should be constructed, as far as possible, - using the knowledge of the characteristics - of the material under test, obtained in the "in situ" tests.

IV. - BRIEF DISCUSSION ON THE CRITERIA FOR THE INTERPRETATION OF RESULTS

There is much controversy among Rock Mechanics specialists about the following aspects:

a. - Should we carry out only a few tests on large blocks, making the largest use of results obtained in reiterative tests, or should we carry out a great number of tests on small blocks, so as to make possible the statistical analysis of the undisturbed tests.

b. - What is the influence of the geometric corrections (Patton, 1966) and studied by various other specialists (Landanyi, 1969) on the interpretation of the results?

c. - What is the best criterion of rupture to be used?

It seems that each kind of material to be tested should be studied as particular - case. This paper represents a tentative to answer some of the above questions.

V. - OBTAINED RESULTS

V.1 - Criteria of rupture used in the analysis

The results presented here were analysed in accordance with the following criteria of rupture (Fig. 3).

a. - Criterion of the limit deformation

b. - Criterion of the ultimate shear strength

c. - Criterion of the steady state of friction

V.2 - Employed test techniques

The results presented here were obtained by:

a. - Tests on small and medium size - blocks (0,7 m x 0,7 m, 1,0 m x 1,0 m and 2,0 m x 2,0 m base section), with application of loads at an angle of 20° with the horizontal.

b. - Tests on large size blocks (6 m x 6 m section base), with application of horizontal loads, parallel to the block base.

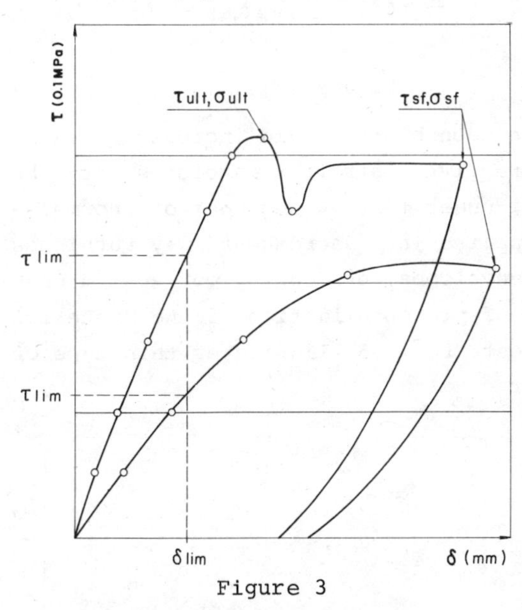

Figure 3

V.3 - Tests on basaltic breccia

This type of material behaves as a quite dense rock fill, with voids filled with - clay, silt or sandstone and altered rock. It is the maximum size of the rock fragments - that determines the minimum dimension of the test block and base opening to be left so that the shearing surface can be freely established and the appearance of apparent - cohesion, (Nieble and Cruz, 1971), will be negligible. It is suggested to use the relations recommended for granular materials - (Fig. 4).

The stiffness of the matrix determines the type of material envelopping the block. It is suggested to use the relation:

E envelopping material/$_{E}$ material under test ≥ 5

Whenever possible, the application of the normal load in the various reiterative

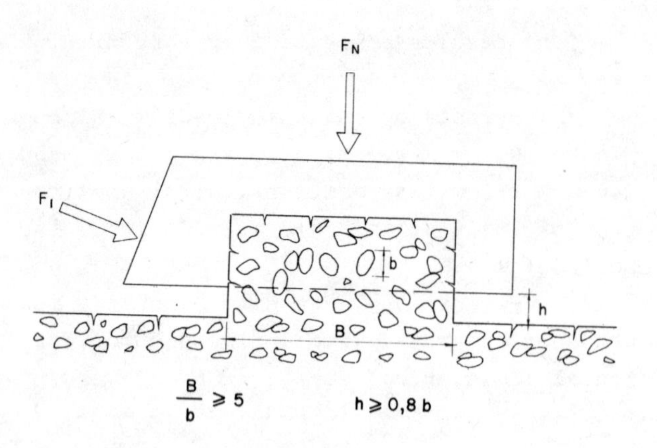

Figure 4

tests on each block should increase. This procedure gives straight envelopes for the material under test. A sequence of normal loads applied in a decrescent way furnishes curved envelopes, evidencing perhaps a phenomenon of preconsolidation of the material under test. Fig. 5 illustrates this type of behavior.

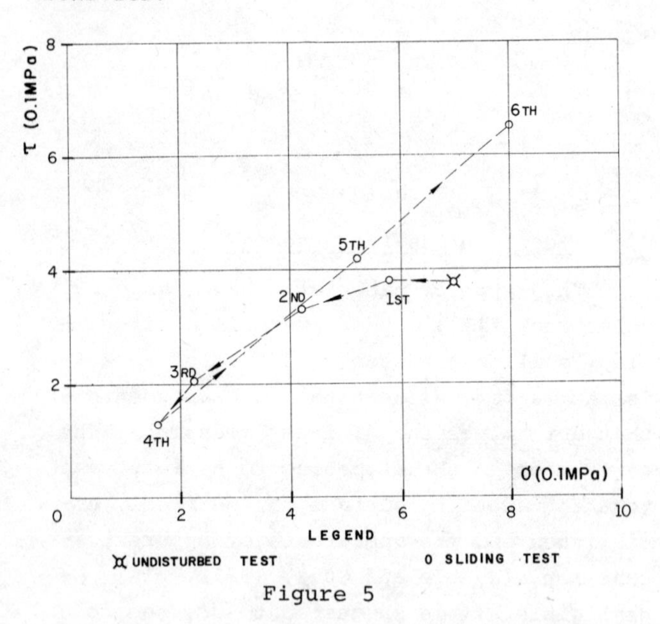

Figure 5

The interpretation of the results obtained on each single block furnishes discrepant and contradictory results, principally if the above precautions are not followed. The analysis of the results must be statistical in character, based on at least 5 test blocks. The sliding tests furnish curved envelopes and, after correction of angle α (Patton, 1966), straight envelopes with values of the friction angle about 3° to 7° lower than those obtained in undisturbed tests. Fig. 6 presents general characteristics obtained in tests carried out on this type of material in blocks with 0,7 m x 0,7 m and 1,0 m x 1,0 m base area.

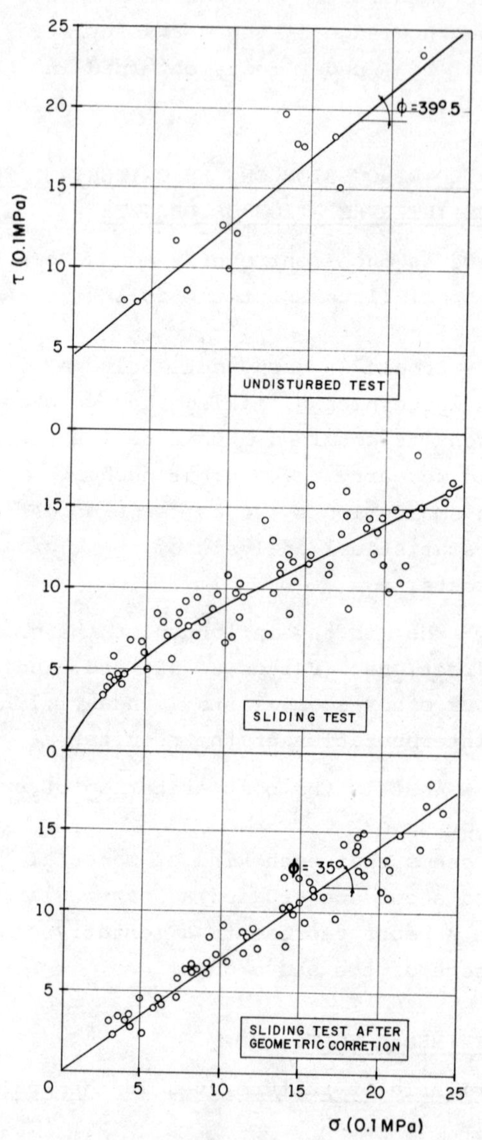

Figure 6

V.4 - Tests on contacts

These tests were performed in the foundations of Jupiá, Ilha Solteira and Promissão power plants, on rock blocks with 6 m x 6 m and 1 m x 1 m base area.

The results obtained in large scale tests were already discussed (Ruiz and Camargo, 1966 and Ruiz et al, 1968). In the first case, (Fig. 7) the tested rock presented a behavior similar to strain - hardening.

Figure 7

The large size block tested in Ilha Solteira, (Fig. 8), cut horizontally, presented a quite regular behavior as to the horizontal deformations observed.

Figure 8

The deficiency of these two tests lies in the fact that one normal stress was used (own weight of the blocks).

Besides that, the test performed in Jupiá was analysed by the criterion of limit displacement and of inversion of the downstream points. A new analysis of these results, taking into account the criterion of steady state of friction and the corrections referent to the angle α lead to more coherent results. The results obtained in Ilha - Solteira, on the other hand, clearly reflect the heterogeneity of the tested feature.

The tests performed on 1 m x 1 m blocks at the foundations of the Promissão plant, with loads applied at an angle of 20°to the discontinuity tested, presented results - within a quite narrow scattering band.

The consideration of the correction of the angle α is of fundamental importance in these interpretations; one rock block may be sufficient for characterizing the shear strength of a discontinuous geological feature under study, provided its dimensions - are compatible with the characteristics of the feature heterogeneity. During the tests, the blocks should be pushed, whenever possible, in the direction of or against the contact dip. Table 1 recapitulates the obtained results.

Table 1

SITE	DIMENSIONS OF SHEAR SURFACE (m)	TEST TYPE		$tg \frac{\tau}{\sigma}$	α	φ	TEST ARRANGEMENT
JUPIÁ	5,5 x 5,4 (30,6m²)	1st		1,14	14°	35°	5,5m 4,0m
		2nd		1,39	14°	40°	
		3rd		1,83	23°	38°	
ILHA SOLTEIRA	6,0 x 6,0 (34,9m²)	1st		2,64	39°	30°	5,5m 6,1m
		2nd		2,53	32°	36°	
		3rd		1,29	14°	38°	
PROMISSÃO	1,0 x 1,0 (2 blocks)	1st block	1st	0,54	-12°	41°	
			2nd	0,66	- 6°	40°	
			3rd	0,80	- 2°	41°	
			4th	0,93	0°	42°	
		2nd block	1st	1,12	0°	48°	
			2nd	0,99	- 1°	43°	
			3rd	0,77	- 2°	40°	
			4th	0,73	- 2°	38°	
			5th	0,70	- 3°	38°	

V.5 - Tests on "joint-fault" structures

This type of typical feature may present quite characteristic behaviors. The - tests may be performed on blocks of large (6 m x 6 m) or medium (2 m x 2 m) size (see Fig. 9); as a rule, one or two blocks are sufficient to characterize the mechanical - shear strength of the material.

Due to the indefined rupture surface,a large scattering of the angle α (average - angle of the block trajectory), measured at points disposed along the side walls of the concrete shell envelopping the masses,is to be noticed.

The tests should be performed alterna-

Figure 9

tively in the direction of or against the apparent joint dip (Ø), using whenever possible the same normal test stresses. The values of arc tan $\frac{\tau}{\sigma}$ obtained in each of these tests can be analysed in a first approach as follows:

- in the direction of the apparent dip Ø:

$$\arc tan \frac{\tau_1}{\sigma_1} = \phi - \alpha$$

- against the apparent dip Ø:

$$\text{arc tan} \frac{\tau_2}{\sigma_2} = \phi + \alpha$$

- where τ_1, σ_1, τ_2, σ_2 are the values obtained in the tests and α is an "equivalent angle of dip" of the block, supposed to be constant in the two tests, in the sense of and against the angle of dip Ø of the discontinuity, by almost equal values of normal stresses (Table 2).

As to the tests carried out in Água Vermelha, blocks with 2 m x 2 m base area were sufficient for characterizing the various types of the "joint-fault" structures described in Item 2 of this paper. Some of these tests were performed after the block had returned to its initial position, in an attempt to reduce the number of involved parameters.

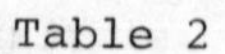

Table 2

NORMAL STRESS (kg/cm^2) (10^{-1} MPa)	TEST	ARCTG $\frac{\tau}{\sigma}$ = ($\phi \pm \alpha$)	ANGLE α
0.80	D ⟶ U	$\phi - \alpha = 50°$	4°
	U ⟶ D	$\phi + \alpha = 58°$	
1.80	D ⟶ U	$\phi - \alpha = 40°$	5.5°
	U ⟶ D	$\phi + \alpha = 51°$	
2.80	D ⟶ U	$\phi - \alpha = 36°$	5.5°
	U ⟶ D	$\phi + \alpha = 47°$	

U = UPSTREAM D = DOWNSTREAM

Fig. 10 recapitulates some of the obtained results and the parameter recommended for the project.

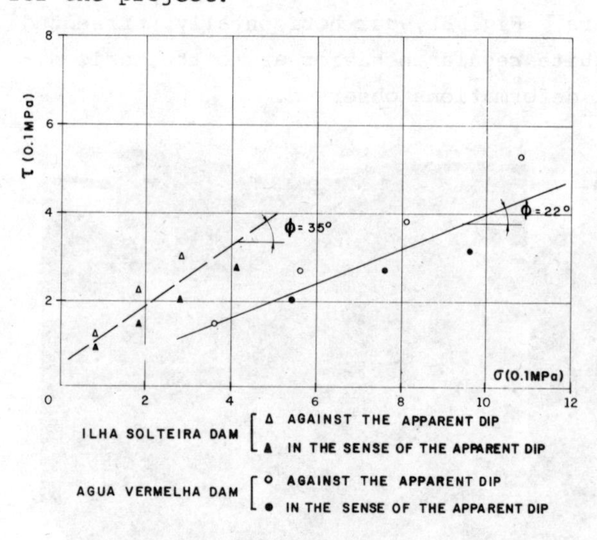

Figure 10

VI. - CONCLUSIONS

a. - The size of the blocks and the testing techniques to be used should be chosen after a detailed geotechnical and geometric characterization of the material to be tested.

b. - Basaltic breccias behave like dense rock fill. The testing technique must be adapted to each case studied and the maximum dimension of the fragments in the determining condition for the block size and the characteristics of the test. The results should be analysed statiscally.

c. - One or two tests on block of large

and medium size are sufficient for characterizing the shear strength of unbonded contacts. The average angle of the trajectory of the block α has a fundamental importance in the interpretation of these tests.

d. - A small number of tests on blocks with large or medium size base may be sufficient for characterizing the shear strength of structures of the "joint-fault" type, provided the test is performed with the intention of reducing the number of involved parameters. Tests including the application of loads in opposite senses, with almost the same normal stresses permit, in a first approach, the definition of an "equivalent angle of dip" ψ, that supplies an adequate interpretation of the results obtained.

e. - Analogical models elaborated with data obtained in "in situ" measurements and parallel laboratory tests will permit a better knowledge of the phenomenon under study.

VII. - ACKNOWLEDGEMENT

The authors thank CENTRAIS ELÉTRICAS DE SÃO PAULO S.A. - CESP and CENTRAIS ELÉTRICAS DE MINAS GERAIS - CEMIG for authorizing the publication of the data presented in this paper.

REFERENCES

GUIDICINI, G. and OLIVEIRA CAMPOS, J., Notas sobre a morfogênese dos derrames basálticos, Soc. Bras. Geol. (unpublished)

LADANYI, B., and ARCHAMBAULT, C., 1969, Simulation of shear behavior of a jointed rock mass, Proc., 11th Symp. Rock Mechs., California, p. 105-125.

LORENTE DE NÓ, C., 1968, Elasto-plastic stress-strain distribution during "in situ" shear tests, Proc., Internat. Symp. Rock Mechs., Madrid, p. 183-187.

NIEBLE, C.M. and CRUZ, P.T., 1971, An interesting case of stability in a rock fill slope, Proc., 4th Pan Amer. Cong. Soil Mechs. Found. Eng., Puerto Rico, Vol. II, p. 167-177.

PATTON, F.D., 1966, Multiples modes of shear failure in rock, Proc., 1st Internat. Cong. Rock Mechs., Lisbon, Vol. I, p. 509-513.

RUIZ, M.D. and CAMARGO, F.P., 1966, A large scale field shear test on rock, Proc., 1st Internat. Cong. Rock Mechs., Lisbon, Vol. I, p. 257-261.

RUIZ, M.D., CAMARGO, F.P., MIDÉA, N.F., NIEBLE, C.M., 1968, Some considerations regarding the shear strength of rock masses, Proc., Internat.Symp. Rock Mechs., Madrid,p. 159-169.

RUIZ, M.D., NIEBLE, C.M., TARRAN, F.C., 1970, Distribuição de tensões em ensaios usualmente utilizados em mecânica das rochas. Meios elásticos isotrópicos, contínuos,2ª Sem. Paul. Geol. Apl., São Paulo, Vol. II, p. 507-550.

SHEAR RESISTANCE OF ROCK ALONG JOINT PLANES UNDER STATIC AND IMPULSE LOADS

RÉSISTANCE AU CISAILLEMENT DES ROCHES SELON LES PLANS DES FISSURES SOUS CHARGES STATIQUES ET D'IMPULSION

SCHERWIDERSTANDSFÄHIGKEIT VON FELSGESTEINEN ÜBER DIE KLUFTFLÄCHE BEI STATISCHEN UND IMPULSIVEN BELASTUNGEN

A. A. NIKITIN

D. D. SAPEGIN

L. A. UVAROV

The B.E. Vedeneev All-Union Research Institute
of Hydraulic Engineering

Leningrad, U.S.S.R.

SUMMARY

Test results of the shear resistance of a concrete block along a rough granite plate and along a layer of loamy joint-filling material under static and impulsive loading are presented. Static tests were carried out by displacing the concrete block along the contact surface according to the well-known direct shear method. In dynamic shear tests use was made of a special experimental apparatus and procedure permitting the application of impulsive loads of up to 10^6 N to a concrete block of an area of up to 0.5 m^2. As shown by impulsive test results, the shear strength of the block along the contact surface at the moment immediately preceding initial shear displacement is higher as compared to that obtained from conventional static tests. However, in the process of dynamically-induced shear displacement of the block its shear strength decreases considerably and may become lower than the statically-obtained value.

RESUME

Le rapport contient les résultats des essais sur la résistance au cisaillement d'un bloc de béton selon une plaque de granit rugueuse et selon une couche de terre argileuse de la fissure sous charges statique et d'impulsion. Les essais statiques s'effectuaient à l'aide des méthodes de cisaillement direct bien connues par le déplacément du bloc de béton selon la surface de contact. Dans les essais de cisaillement dynamique on a utilisé une installation expérimentale spéciale et des méthodes permettant l'application des charges d'impulsion jusqu'à 10^6 N à un bloc de béton d'une surface de 0,5 m^2. Les résultats des essais montrent que la résistance au cisaillement selon la surface de contact immédiatement avant le déplacement initial du bloc est plus grande que celle obtenue par les essais statiques ordinaires. Cependant, lors du cisaillement dynamique la résistance du bloc diminue considérablement et peut devenir inférieure aux valeurs obtenues par les essais statiques.

ZUSAMMENFASSUNG

Es werden die Versuchsergebnisse der Scherwiderstandsfähigkeit eines Betonblocks über eine rauhe Granitplatte und Schicht der lehmigen Kluftausfüllung bei statischen und impulsiven Belastungen angeführt. Die statischen Versuche wurden mittels der Verschiebung des Betonblocks über die Kontaktfläche nach der bekannten Methode der direkten Scherung vorgenommen. In den dynamischen Scherprüfungen verwendete man einen speziellen experimentellen Scherapparat und eine Methodik, mit derer Hilfe ein Block mit der Fläche von bis 0.5 m^2 den impulsiven Belastungen bis 10^6 N unterworfen wird. Wie die Ergebnisse der impulsiven Prüfungen gezeigt haben, ist die Scherfesigkeit des Blocks über die Kontaktfläche direkt vor dem Anfang der Verschiebung höher, als diese bei den gewöhnlichen statischen Versuchen ermittelten Werte. Aber im Prozess der dynamischen Verschiebung des Blocks nimmt seine Scherfestigkeit bedeutend ab und kann sich kleiner als die bei den statischen Prüfungen festgestellten Werte zeigen.

INTRODUCTION

In connection with the design and construction of high concrete dams on rock foundations in seismic zones the evaluation of the shear resistance of rock subjected to impulsive-type dynamic loads has become a subject of increasing importance. At present the available data on the shear strength of rock masses under such loads are very scarce, which results in unduly conservative design and uneconomical construction of earthquake-resistant structures. Therefore, the development of experimental equipment and methods for determining the mechanical characteristics of rock, and the shear strength of rock subjected to dynamic loads in particular, as well as the accumulation of relevant data is of primary importance.

Laboratory and in-situ tests of the shear resistance of rock along joint planes under static and impulsive loading have been recently carried out using a large-scale testing apparatus developed at the VNIIG.

Laboratory tests consisted in studying the shear strength of a concrete block along a rough granite plate and a layer of loamy material taken from a fault in the rock foundation of the Toktogul dam.

In-situ tests were carried out at the Toktogul dam site on the loamy filler in the same fault.

1. EXPERIMENTAL PROCEDURE

Both in the laboratory and in-situ tests a rectangular concrete block 0.8x0.6 m was subjected to direct shear along the contact surface.

Static shear tests were carried out according to a conventional procedure by applying in increments a design normal load and then a shearing one till the limiting equilibrium of the concrete block was reached.

Similarly, in dynamic shear tests first a normal load and then a shearing load equal to approximately 80-90% of the ultimate value was applied. After the block stopped sliding, the normal load was reduced by 20-40% nearly instantaneously (within 0.005-0.05 sec). As a consequence, the ratio between the shearing and the normal loads exceeded the limit value, which resulted in the displacement of the block. As the block moved, the magnitude of the shearing load decreased and the block came to rest.

Both during static and dynamic shear tests the block was displaced repeatedly under different normal stresses. To evaluate possible variations in the shear strength of the contact upon repeated testing, check tests were carried out at the end of each test series.

2. EXPERIMENTAL RESULTS

2.1. Shearing load-displacement curves.

During static and dynamic shear tests the normal and the shearing loads applied to the test block as well as its vertical and horizontal displacements were recorded continuously by an oscillograph. By way of example, Figure 1 shows curves of the horizontal displacements of the block versus the average tangential stresses, $S=f(\tau)$, plotted from the oscillograms obtained in static (low-rate) shear tests. The scheme of loads applied to the block during dynamic tests is given in the same figure. Analysis of the $S=f(\tau)$ curves revealed several characteristic portions:

1. A portion corresponding to tangential stresses up to 70-80% of the limiting values where the curve of the displacements versus the tangential stresses actually does not deviate from linearity (the OA portion, Curve 3). The average displacement of the block observed within this portion was $5x10^{5}$ - $15x10^{-5}$ m.

2. A portion where first pseudo-plastic deformations at the contact surface due to increased tangential stresses occur (the AB portion, Curve 3). The magnitude of the displacements of the block within this portion was $5x10^{-5}$ - $2x10^{-4}$ m.

3. A portion where the block is displaced at nearly ultimate tangential stresses (the BC portion, Curve 3), with pseudo-plastic deformations at the contact surface. This portion may often be so short as to reduce to a point, in which case brittle fracture is observed, instead of shear failure (Curve 2).

4. A portion in which the shear resistance of the block decreases with its horizontal translations (the CD portion, Curve 3).

The total amount of the displacements of the concrete block in the shear tests performed ranged between $1.5x10^{-3}$ and $4x10^{-3}$ m.

2.2. Shear strength of the concrete-granite contact

The shear strength of the concrete-granite contact was studied by displacing a concrete block along a rough granite plate. Roughness elements up to 12 x $x10^{-3}$ m high were uniformly distributed all over the plate surface. The base of the test block had similar

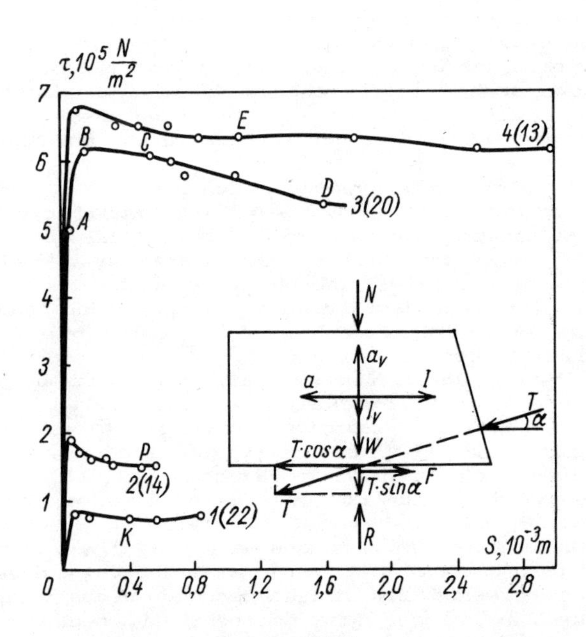

Fig. 1.

a) The scheme of loads applied to the block;
b) Typical curves $S=f(\tau)$ for displacement of the concrete block along a rough granite plate;
1...4 - Nos of curves;
(13)...(22) - Nos of test runs;
A,B...K - representative points on the curves.

irregularities. The block was simply supported by the plate, which ensured a random contact between them. Shear tests were carried out under static and impulsive load conditions.

As evidenced by static test results, the curve $\tau_{ult}=f(\sigma)$ in the range of stresses covered is almost linear (Fig.2A).

After the static tests were completed, the same pair of the test pieces (the concrete block and the granite plate) was used in a series of 15 dynamic tests. As was already mentioned, before each test run, a concrete block of a weight W was subjected to a vertical load N and a tangential load T, with the block being in a static equilibrium close to the limiting one. Then part of the normal load N was removed.

The data obtained from dynamic tests show that partial reduction (by 20-40%) of the normal load causes nonuniform displacements of the block both in the horizontal and the vertical planes occurring at different rates (a, a_v). At the first moment the block displacement is opposed by the inertia J. As the magnitude of displacements increases, acceleration decreases and becomes equal to zero at maximum rate of movement. Then acceleration changes its sign and the direction of inertia coincides with that of shearing force. A total shear strength F of the test block can be computed from a set of equilibrium equations based on the Dalamber principle.

The general implication of the oscillograms obtained in dynamic tests is that immediately before dynamically-induced shear at the moment when part of the vertical load had been removed, but the block had not yet started moving, the ratio of the tangential stresses to the normal stresses at the block base exceeded the statically-obtained shear coefficient. This is illustrated by Fig.2B showing the $\tau_{ult}=f(\sigma)$ curves of the ultimate shear strength under dynamic loading at the moment preceding the initial displacement of the block (Curve d) and of the shear strength obtained in static tests by the conventional procedure (Curve c).

However, the test results plotted in Fig.2B (Curve e) indicate also that the shear coefficients observed at maximum horizontal accelerations of the block may be lower than the statically-obtained shear coefficients by 5-8%. It is probably due to a change in the shear mechanism, the shear strength of the block being reduced as a result of sliding at high rate (sliding friction).

The average horizontal displacements of the block in dynamic tests were close to the corresponding values obtained in static tests, ranging also between 1.5×10^{-3} and 4×10^{-3} m. The average displacement of the block at maximum accelerations was 2×10^{-4} m, whereas at maximum rate of movement it varied from 7.5×10^{-4} to 2.5×10^{-3} m.

In all tests with instantaneous loading it was found that the moment of initial movement of the block does not coincide with that of initial reduction in the vertical load, the average delay time being 0.02 sec. For the contact surface considered this time interval may be referred to as a measure of delay between first shear displacements and the moment of load reduction.

The first series of static and dynamic tests was followed by check static tests which showed no significant changes in the shear strength parameters of the contact surface (Fig.2A). This permits to compare the results of static and dynamic tests without any corrections.

2.3. Shear strength of loamy filler.

Shear tests on loamy joint-filling material were also carried out both under static and impulsive loading. Test samples of fine clayey soil with natural moisture content were taken from a major fault running through limestones at the Toktogul dam site. The grain-size distribution of the loam (sandy loam) filler with a plasticity index of 14.5 is given in the table below.

Table

Grain diameter, 10^{-3} m	2-1	1-0.5	0.5-0.25	0.25-0.10	0.10
Percentage	27.40	6.60	19.80	11.50	34.70

Laboratory tests were carried out using a composite specimen 0.8x0.6 m reproducing a crack with clay filler 2×10^{-3} m thick interposed between two smooth concrete plates (the punch and the base). In field tests a block 0.8x0.6 m was concreted to the bare surface of joint-filling material. Prior to shear tests the filler was compacted under normal stresses 10^6 N/m^2.

As evidenced by static test results (Fig.3A), the shear strength characteristics obtained in the laboratory and in the field are in fair agreement. The results of check static tests also agree well with those of main tests.

A laboratory shear test (run No 23, Fig.3B) on loamy material was carried out under impulsive loading. This dynamic test illustrates shear coefficient variations in the process of the displacement of the punch.

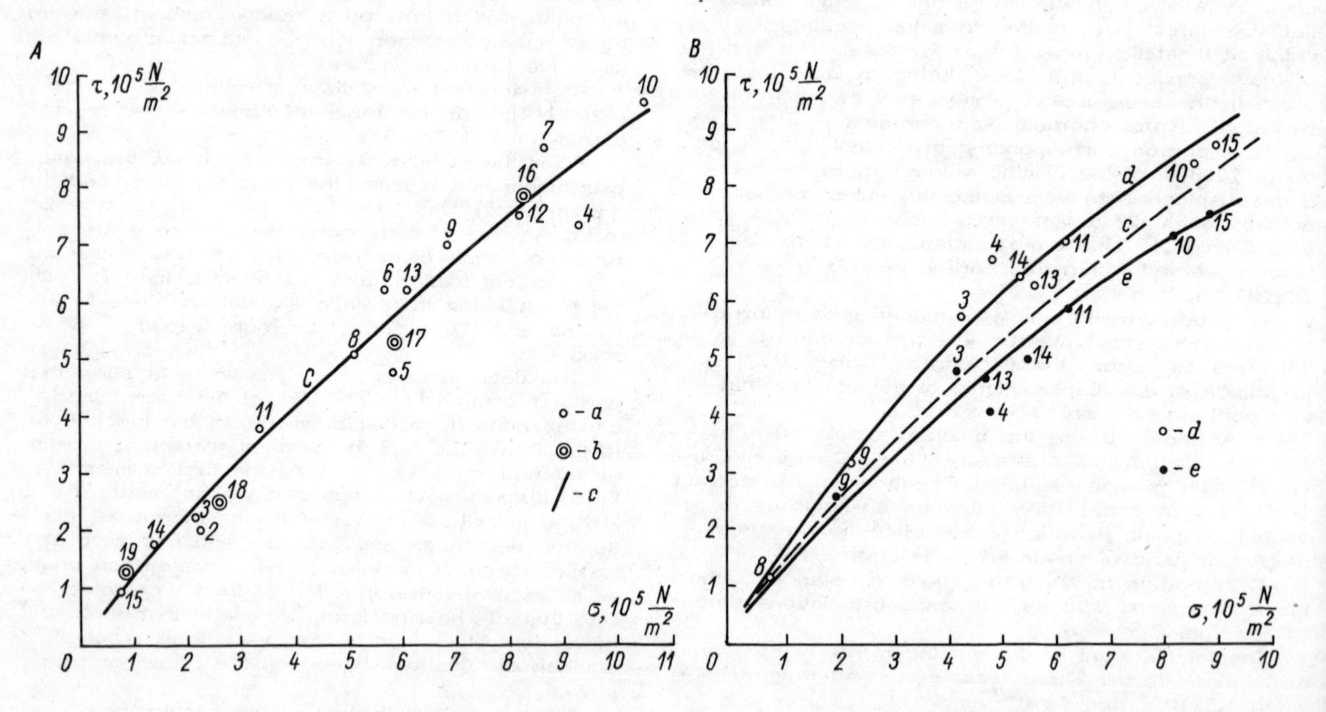

Fig. 2. Shear strength of the concrete block along the rough granite plate versus normal stresses under static (A) and impulsive (B) loading.
a - experimental points of the main test series; b - experimental points of check tests; c - regression line from experimental values of the main series of static tests; d - at the moment preceding initial shear displacement; e - at the moment of maximum horizontal accelerations.

The ultimate shear strength (point 23-1) was recorded after partial reduction of the normal load, immediately before the punch began sliding. Once the punch started moving and its movements accelerated, the shear coefficient diminished. At maximum accelerations the ratio of the tangential stresses to the normal stresses decreased sharply (point 23-2). During subsequent displacement of the punch the shear coefficient continued to decrease (point 23-3 - at maximum rate of movement; point 23-4 - at the moment immediately before the punch stopped).

As soon as the punch ceased to move, the test was resumed at increased static shearing load, the normal stress at the base of the punch remaining constant. The resulting shear coefficient value was found to be in a rather close agreement with the curve $\tau_{ult} = f(\sigma)$ obtained from the previous static tests (point 23-5). The results of the above test indicate that the shear strength of the punch decreases in the course of sliding. However, at the initial stage of shear displacement, when the punch had not yet begun moving, the ultimate shear strength of the punch was considerably higher than that obtained in conventional static tests (Fig.3, Curve e).

The in-situ test results presented in Fig.3 also point to a marked change in the shear strength of rock along joint planes in the process of impulsively induced displacements.

CONCLUSIONS

Statistical analysis of the test results obtained shows that the regression line plotted from the relation $\tau_{ult} = f(\sigma)$ by the linear approximation method is characterized by a correlation factor not lower than 0.95. This is an evidence for a very close correlation between the ultimate shear strength τ_{ult} and the normal stresses σ. The 0.99-probability values of the shear strength parameters c and μ indicate that under impulsive load conditions the shear resistance of the concrete block immediately before first displacement (at rest) is higher (by up to 16%) than that observed in conventional static tests. However, in the process of sliding the shear coefficient characterizing the resistance of the test block to sliding decreases and, as the movements accelerate, it may become lower than the statically-obtained value, this penomenon deserving careful study.

The experimental findings presented herein are, in fact, the results of first studies on the shear resistance of rock along joint planes under impulsive loading. It is apparent, therefore, that further work is to be done in order to refine methods of investigation of the shear strength of jointed rock subjected to different kinds of dynamic loads (seismic in particular), to accumulate relevant experimental data, and to utilize them in aseismic design and construction practice.

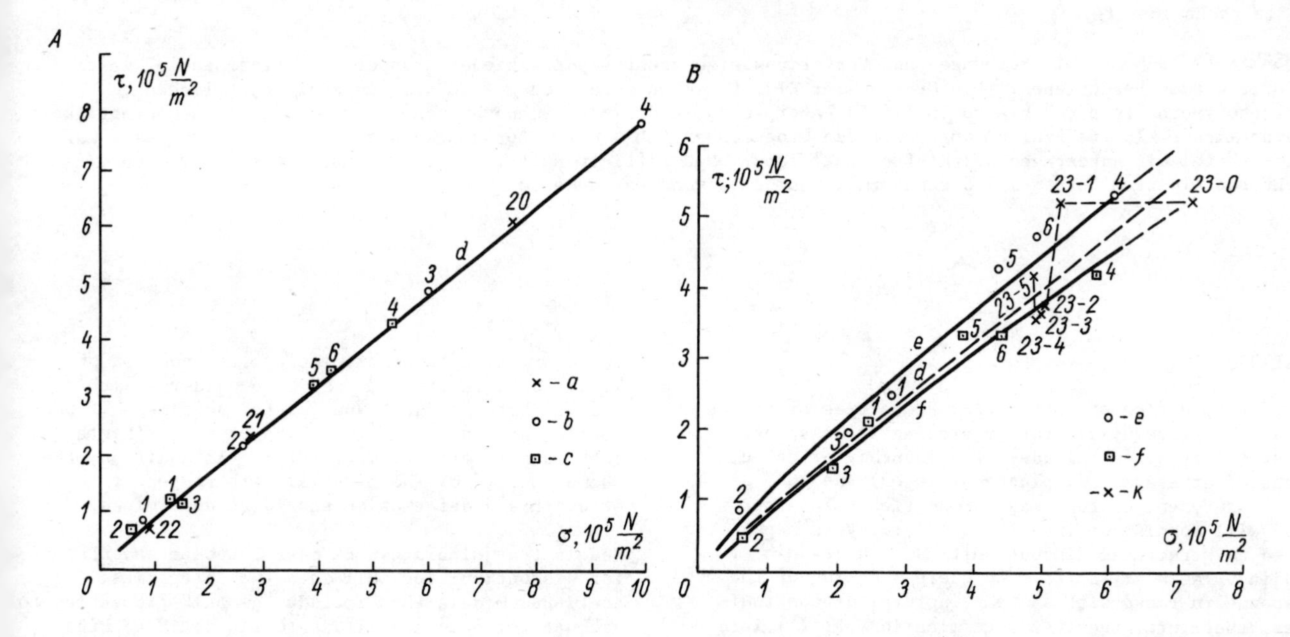

Fig. 3. Shear strength of the concrete block along the layer of loamy material versus normal stresses under static (A) and impulsive (B) loading

a - experimental points of laboratory tests; b - experimental points of in-situ tests; d - regression line from experimental values of static shear tests; e - at the moment preceding initial shear displacement; f - at the moment of maximum horizontal accelerations; k - trajectory of shear strength in test run No 23.

FRICTION AND DEFORMATION OF JOINTED QUARTZ DIORITE

LE FROTTEMENT DU GLISSEMENT ET LA DÉFORMATION DE LA JOINTÉS QUARTZ DIORITE

DIE REIBUNGS- UND VERFORMUNGSEIGENSCHAFTEN VERSCHIEDEN GROSSER KLUFTFLÄCHEN IN QUARTZ DIORIT

H.R. PRATT A.D. BLACK W.F. BRACE

Department of Earth and Planetary Sciences, Massachusetts Institute of Technology

Cambridge, Mass., U.S.A.

SUMMARY Friction and deformation of quartz diorite was studied on a scale ranging from *in situ* jointed specimens 2.0 meters in length with surface areas of a single joint of 5 x 10^3 cm^2 to laboratory shear tests on natural joints with surface areas of 60 cm^2. The shear strength of natural joints decreased by 40 percent over the range of surface areas tested and by a factor of 10 over a range of joint orientations from 30° to 60°. The average deformation modulus of *in situ* multiply-jointed specimens was a factor of 7 less than the modulus of the intact rock.

RESUME On a étudié le frottement du glissement et la déformation de la joints quartz diorite au laboratoire et "in situ" avec des échantillons jointés de 2.0 mètres de long. La surface des joints naturels variait entre 5 x 10^3 cm^2 (in situ) et 60 cm^2 (au laboratoire). La résistance au cisaillement diminuait de 40% selon la variation des surfaces examinées et diminuait d'un dixième avec une variation de l'orientation des joints de 30° jusqu'à 60°. Le module de déformation moyen des échantillons fissurés "in situ" était un septième du module de la roche intacte.

ZUSAMMENFASSUNG Die Reibungs- und Verformungseigenschaften verschieden grosser Kluftflaechen in Quartz Diorit werden beschrieben. Die Groesse der Kluftflaechen wurde von 5 x 10^3 cm^2 in zwei Meter langen Probekoerpern "in situ" bis zu 60 cm^2 in Laborproben in direkten Schubversuchen variiert. Die Schubfestigkeit natuerlicher Kluefte fiel um 40% ueber den Groessenbereich der untersuchten Kluftflaechen ab und sank auf ein Zehntel mit Aenderngen der Kluftorientierung. Der mittlere Deformationsmodul von "in situ" Proben mit mehreren Klueften betrug 1/7 des Deformationsmoduls von festem Gestein.

INTRODUCTION

The determination of the *in situ* properties of a rock mass is a prerequisite for predicting its response to static or dynamic loads. The accuracy of calculations of stress and displacement is only as good as our measurement of rock mass properties. The rock mass will consist of intact blocks or layers separated by structural discontinuities such as joints, bedding planes or faults. Adequate modeling of the response in rocks with sharp structural discontinuities, therefore, requires determination of: (1) intact properties of the rock, (2) frictional properties of the discontinuities, (3) block interaction phenomena. The methods of obtaining the required rock properties are large and small scale field tests (Wallace, *et al.*, 1970; Pratt, *et al.*, 1972), laboratory tests (Goodman, 1970; Patton, 1966; Pratt, *et al.*, 1972; Jaeger and Cook, 1969) and model studies simulating jointed rock masses (Barton, 1972; John, 1970; Rosenblad, 1970; Einstein and Hirschfeld, 1973).

In determining these properties, the concept of "scale or size effect" must be considered with respect to both "intact" and jointed specimens if properties are to be meaningful in representing the rock mass (Pratt, *et al.*, 1972). In addition, the "homogeneity" of the material with respect to strength and deformation should be determined.

Models that simulate rock mass response and account for discontinuities fall into two categories: (1) continuum models that include "global" properties to account for discontinuities (Morland, 1974; Singh, 1973) and (2) discrete models (Christiansen, *et al.*, 1971; Goodman, *et al.*, 1968; Mahtab and Goodman, 1970), for either finite element or finite difference calculations, which try to account for the strength and moduli of the rock mass by incorporating properties of joints and joint block interaction as well as "intact" properties. Each of these approaches has advantages and disadvantages depending on the scale of interest and complexity of the rock mass.

TABLE 1. *IN SITU* TEST MATRIX

Expt.	Specimen Size	Joint Area (cm^2)	α^o	τ_i kg/cm^2	E $\times 10^3$ kb/cm^2	E_d $\times 10^3$ kg/cm^2	Comment
1	1.0 x 2.2 m	7243	30	4.8	108		
2	31 x 46 cm	658	37½	18.5	58		
3	1.0 x 1.5 m	5130	45	19.1	65	48	
4	.6 x 1.0 m	2277	45	27.1	--	25	
5	15 x 31 cm	142	45	66.8	121		
6	20 x 31 cm	252	45	61.4	84		
7	25 x 46 cm	394	45	11.3	70		
8	31 x 62 cm	568	45	26.4	60		
9	1.0 x 2.0 m	5130	45	11.9	--		
10	31 x 45 cm	503	52½	47.3	--		Not gaged
11	1.0 x 1.5 m	4181	60	71.8	73	52	
12	31 x 46 cm	465	60	61.7	65		Specimen failed, no shear
13	1.0 x 1.5 m	3748	75	37.1	54	48	Specimen failed, no shear
14	1.0 x 2.2 m	Multiple joints				8	Intersecting joints
15	1.0 x 2.0 m	Multiple joints					Several parallel joints
16	1.0 x 2.1 m	Multiple joints				12	Several parallel joints

E = Young's Modulus; E_d = Deformation Modulus

Friction and deformation of quartz diorite was studied on a scale ranging from *in situ* jointed specimens 2.0 meters in length with surface areas of a single joint of 5×10^3 cm^2 to laboratory direct shear tests on natural joints with surface areas of 60 cm^2. *In situ* tests were conducted on singly and multiply jointed specimens over a range of joint areas (142 to 5130 cm^2) to investigate size effects and for several joint orientations ranging from 30° to 75° (Table 1).

EXPERIMENTAL TECHNIQUES

The *in situ* jointed specimen has the configuration of an equilateral triangular prism of constant cross-section attached at one end and loaded at the other by a calibrated flatjack package (Figure 1).

Figure 1. Specimen configuration, 1.0 x 2.3 meter specimen with a single 30° joint.

The specimen is excavated by sequentially cutting, by drilling or coring, a slot at 60° to the surface of the rock to form one side of the prism, a vertical end slot into which a flatjack package is inserted, and a second 60° slot intersecting the first slot and forming the other side of the specimen. The loading system consists of three triangular stainless steel flatjacks sandwiched between two five-centimeter thick steel plates. Details of the flatjack construction, the pneumatic-hydraulic pumping system, and methods of calibration of flatjack efficiency as a function of size, deflection and pressure are presented elsewhere (Pratt, *et al.*, 1972).

Laboratory specimens were cored from the same natural joints as were tested *in situ*. Artificial joints were prepared from NX core by either sawing or by breaking the cores lengthwise in a Brazilian tension test to provide surfaces with relief of approximately .0015 cm and .38 cm, respectively.

Measurements of the total specimen deformation, shear displacement along the joint and normal displacement across the joint were made using strain gages and DCDT's. From these data stiffnesses, deformation modulus and elastic modulus are determined.

JOINT FRICTION

The frictional properties of single natural joints depend primarily on the (1) roughness, (2) contact area, (3) asperity strength, (4) filling material and (5) the magnitude and orientation of applied stresses.

Frictional properties of interest in determining rock mass response include (1) strength, (2) shear stiffnesses and (3) normal stiffness. These properties are a function of the number and spacing of joints, the orientation of the joint sets and the interaction of joint blocks as well as the characteristics of single joints mentioned above.

Because the joint orientation is predetermined for each *in situ* test, the ratio of shear stress (τ) to normal stress (σ_n), the coefficient of friction (μ), remains constant during loading. A friction envelope is developed by conducting a series of tests at different joint orientations. These envelopes were developed over a range of joint surface areas from 142 to 5120 cm^2 (Figure 2). The *in situ* load paths

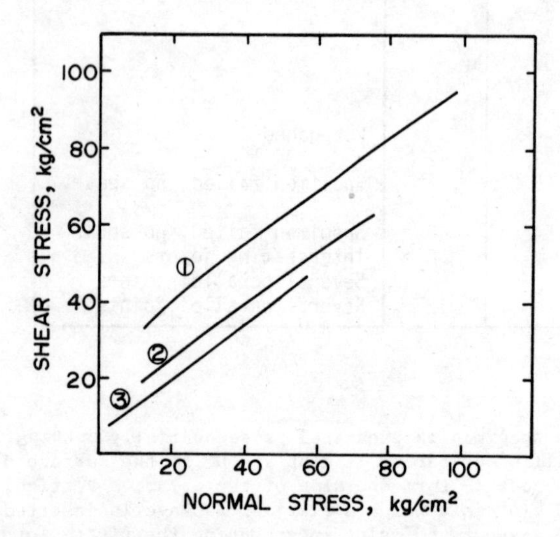

Figure 2. Friction envelopes developed from *in situ* tests on quartz diorite. Each *in situ* envelope (1, 2 and 3) represents a series of tests on specimens with different joint orientations but having approximately the same joint area. Envelope ① represents specimens with an average area of approximately 200 cm^2; ② an average area of 1500 cm^2 and ③ average area of 5000 cm^2.

are thus different from the usual laboratory direct shear test in which a predetermined normal stress is first applied and the specimen is subsequentially sheared along the plane perpendicular to the normal load. Because of this difference, a series of proportional shear tests in which τ/σ_n = constant was varied over the range 0.77 to 1.7 to simulate the field loading paths.

Shear stress-displacement data from field tests is qualitatively similar to laboratory tests over a range of surface areas and for joints with and without filling materials (Figure 3). Displacements of 3.0 cm were obtained so that residual shear stress values were reached. Over the range of surface areas tested, the shear strength of joints decreased with increasing surface area (Figure 4). It is apparent from observation of post-test surfaces of sheared natural joints that the actual joint contact area is considerably less than 100%, and may be as low as 10 to 20% depending on the wavelength and amplitude of the joint asperities and secondary modification of the joint. Stress applied to the joint during the loading phase is thus distributed only over 10 to 20%.

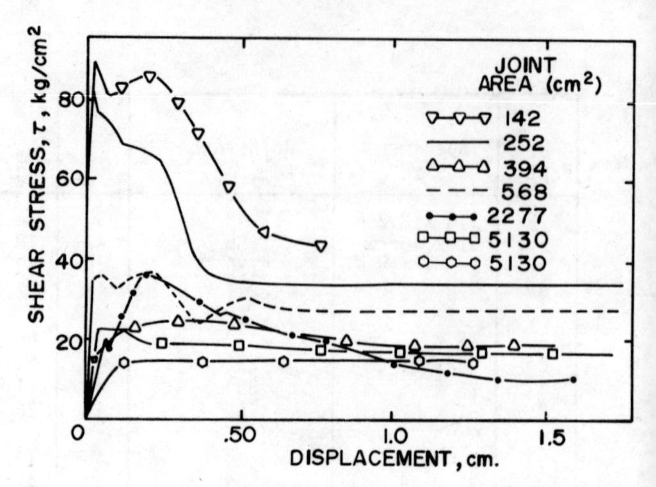

Figure 3. Shear stress as a function of displacement for joints with different surface areas. All specimens had a single joint oriented 45° to the axis of loading.

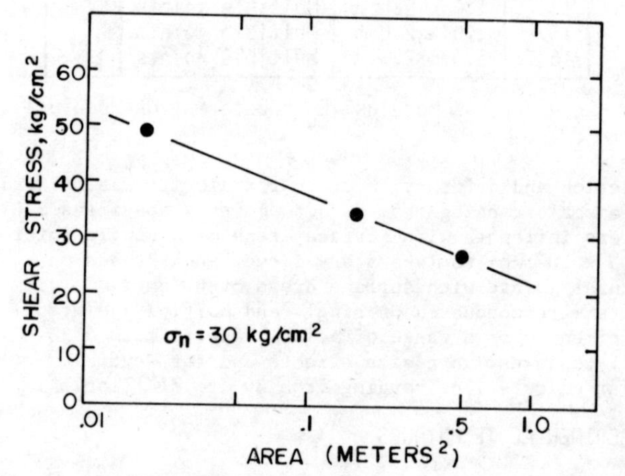

Figure 4. Maximum shear strength as a function of joint area. Specimens have a single joint.

The "true" shear stress is, therefore, considerably higher than the stress calculated from the total area of the joint. This leads to the size effect for larger surface areas with lower contact area. There would probably be no size effect if the contact areas of "large" and "small" specimens were the same. This situation could occur along fresh, smooth joints or at high normal stresses which force the asperities to mate and where joint filling would not play a major role in determining frictional properties. Laboratory shear tests on natural joints and prepared surfaces of different roughnesses indicates that shear strength is a function of surface roughness, asperity strength and the applied normal stress.

In addition, the friction angle (ϕ) is also load path dependent. A direct shear load path gave a 7° higher friction angle than specimens sheared along a proportional load path equivalent to a joint oriented 30° to the axis of loading (Figure 5). This dependence of shear strength on load path is in contrast to the failure stress of "intact" specimens which is independent of load path (Swanson and Brown, 1971).

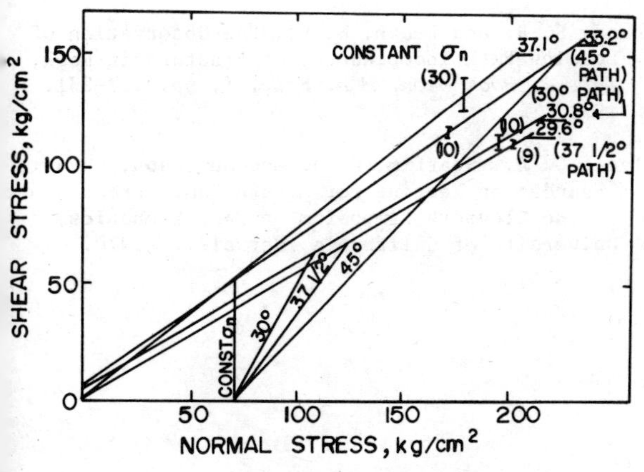

igure 5. Natural joints sheared under various load paths. The number in parentheses refers to the number of tests conducted for each load path.

s would be expected, the effect of joint orientation as a dramatic effect on the shear strength of singly nd multiply jointed specimens. A minimum shear trength was obtained for joints oriented 30° to the xis of loading and increased by a factor of 10 over range of joint orientations up to 60° (Figure 6).

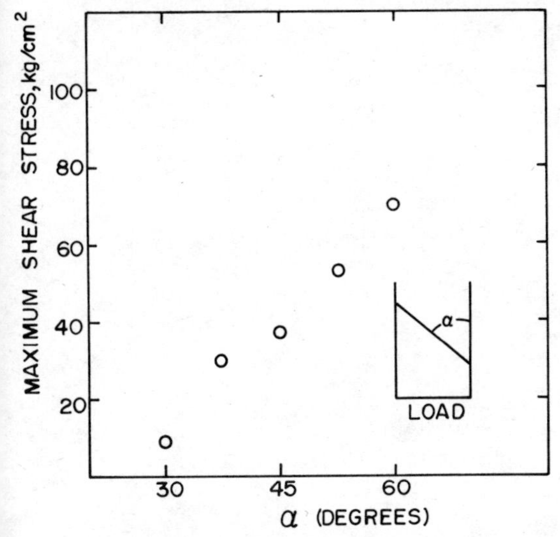

igure 6. Shear stress as a function of joint orientation.

EFORMATION

he average *in situ* elastic modulus of intact quartz iorite is 76×10^3 kg/cm^2. The *in situ* apparent oung's modulus (deformation modulus) of singly ointed specimens averaged 43×10^3 kg/cm^2 a decrease y almost a factor of 2 from the intact rock. The eformation modulus of multiply jointed specimens veraged 10×10^3 kg/cm^2, a modulus reduction by a actor of 7.6 from intact rock of comparable size. eductions in modulus between intact laboratory pecimens and *in situ* jointed rock of factors from 3 o 10 have been previously reported (Bellport, 1965; oon and Merritt, 1970; Stowe, 1972).

The shear stiffness (slope of the shear stress-displacement curve) of singly jointed specimens also exhibited a size effect with increasing surface area. The stiffness decreased with increasing surface area (Figure 7). Our results fell near the upper bound of the data compiled by Barton (1972) from laboratory tests, *in situ* tests and model studies.

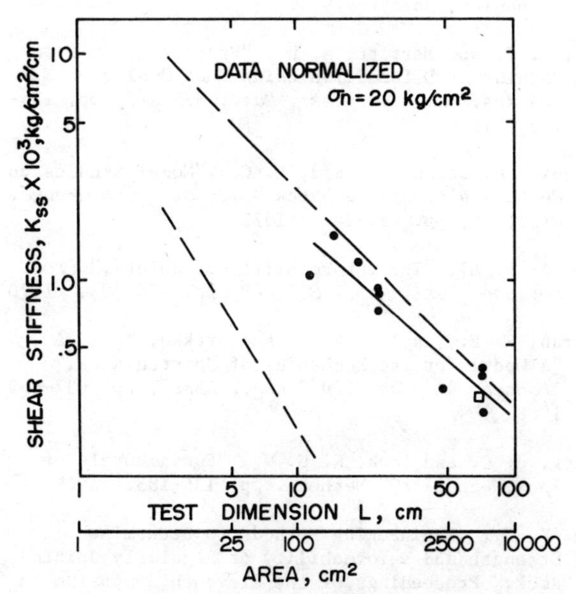

Figure 7. Shear stiffness as a function of joint surface area. Dashed line represents range of other published data (Barton, 1972).

CONCLUSIONS

Field and laboratory tests on jointed specimen indicates that: (1) The shear strength of joints decreased by 40% over a range of surface areas from 142 to 5130 cm^2. This decrease is due to the lower contact area of the specimens with large surface areas. (2) The shear strength of joints increased by a factor of 10 over a range of joint orientations from 30° to 60° to the axis of loading. (3) The average deformation modulus of multiply jointed specimens was a factor of 7 less than that of the intact quartz diorite. (4) Laboratory tests on natural joints indicates that the friction angle is load path dependent in contrast to the failure stress of intact rock which is independent of load path.

ACKNOWLEDGEMENTS

This study was sponsored by the Advanced Research Project Agency (ARPA) and monitored by the Air Force Weapons Laboratory, Air Force Systems Command, United States Air Force, Kirtland Air Force Base, New Mexico, 87115.

REFERENCES

Barton, N. R., "A Model Study of Rock-Joint Deformation," *Int. J. Rock Mech. Min. Sci.*, *9*, 5. 1972.

Bellport, B. P., "Morrow Point Dam and Powerplant Foundation Investigation," U. S. Bureau of Reclamation. October 1965.

Christiansen, L. M., Misterek, D. L. and Bowles, G.F., "Foundation Analysis of Auburn Damsite," Symposium of the International Society of Rock Mechanics, Nancy. 1971.

Coon, R. F. and Merritt, A. H., "Predicting *In Situ* Modulus of Deformation Using Rock Quality Indexes," *Am. Soc. Test. Mat., STP 477,* pp. 154-173. 1970.

Einstein, H. and Herschfeld, R. C., "Model Studies on Mechanics of Jointed Rock," *J. Soil Mech. Found. Div., 99,* pp. 229-248. 1973.

Goodman, R. E., "The Deformability of Joints," *Proc. Am. Soc. Test. Mat., STP 477,* pp.]74-]96. 1970.

Goodman, R. E., Taylor, R. L. and Brekke, T. L. A., "A Model for the Mechanics of Jointed Rock," *Proceed. Am. Soc. Civil Eng., SM#94,* pp. 637-659. 1968.

Jaeger, J. C. and Cook, N. G. W., "Fundamentals of Rock Mechanics," Metheun, pp. 136-183. 1969.

John, K. W., "Engineering Methods to Determine Strength and Deformability of Regularly Jointed Rock," Proceedings of the Eleventh Symposium on Rock Mechanics, University of California, Berkeley. 1970.

Mahtab, M. A. and Goodman, R. E., "Three-Dimensional Finite Element Analysis of Jointed Rock Slopes," Proceedings of the Second International Congress, Belgrade, 3. 1970.

Morland, L. W., "Continuum Model of Regularly Jointed Mediums," *J. Geophys. Res., 79,* pp. 357-362. 1974.

Patton, F. D., "Multiple Modes of Shear Failure in Rock and Related Materials," Ph.D. Thesis, University of Illinois. 1966.

Pratt, H. R., Black, A. D. and Bonney, F. J., "Frictional Properties of Cedar City Quartz Diorite," Air Force Weapons Laboratory, AFWL TR-72-122. 1972.

Pratt, H. R., Black, A. D., Brown, W. and Brace, W.F., "The Effect of Specimen Size on the Mechanical Properties of Unjointed Diorite," *Int. J. Rock Mech. Min. Sci. 9,* pp. 513 530. 1972.

Rosenblad, J. L., "Failure Modes of Jointed Rock Masses," Proceedings of the Second International Congress, Belgrade, 2. 1970.

Singh, B., "Continuum Characterization of Jointed Rock Masses," *Int. J. Rock Mech. Min. Sci., 10,* pp. 311-349. 1973.

Stowe, R. L., "Comparison of *In Situ* and Laboratory Test Results on Granite," *AIME Trans., 252,* pp. 195-198. 1972.

Swanson, S. R. and Brown, W. S., "An Observation of Loading Path Independence of Fracture in Rock," *Int. J. Rock Mech. Min. Sci., 8,* pp. 277-281. 1971.

Wallace, G. B., Searfim, E. J. and Anderson, F. A., "Foundation Testing for Auburn Dam," Proceedings of the Eleventh Symposium on Rock Mechanics, University of California, Berkeley. 1970.

ROCK FRICTION - A LABORATORY INVESTIGATION

ÉTUDE DU FROTTEMENT DE LA ROCHE

LABORUNTERSUCHUNGEN ZUR GESTEINSREIBUNG

H.J. SCHNEIDER

Dipl.-Geol.

Institut für Bodenmechanik und Felsmechanik

Abteilung Felsmechanik, Universität Karlsruhe

Karlsruhe, West Germany

UMMARY

nvestigations of the influence of both the surface geometry of joints as well as of material haracteristics on frictional resistance along rock joints are described in the paper. The riction tests were conducted both on rock samples as well as on models with natural joint urfaces. The models were plaster casts of rough fractured surfaces of three different rock ypes, namely granite, sandstone and limestone.

USAMMENFASSUNG

ntersuchungen über den Einfluß der Kluftflächengeometrie und der Materialparameter sind Geenstand des nachfolgenden Berichtes. Hierzu wurden Scherversuche sowohl an Gesteinsproben ls auch an Modellkörpern aus Gips mit natürlichen Kluftgeometrien durchgeführt. Diese natürichen Kluftgeometrien wurden durch Abformen von Zugklüften in Granit, Sandstein und Kalkstein ewonnen.

ESUMÉ

our étudier l'influence de la géométrie de la surface d'une fissure aussi bien que l'influnce des matériaux sur le frottement, l'auteur décrit ses recherches de frottement. Les essais e cisaillement étaient exécutés non seulement avec des échantillons de roche mais aussi avec es modèles en plâtre ayant une géométrie de surface d'une fissure naturelle. Ces modèles de lâtre possédaient la géométrie de surface d'une diaclase d'extension de granite, de grès et e calcaire.

NTRODUCTION

he solution of most of the stability probems in rock engineering is based upon the se of an angle of friction, which may be determined either from simple or cumbersome ests. As our present knowledge of friction rocess clearly shows, this relationship beteen shear and normal stresses does not sufficiently describe the complexity of the friction process and neglects the influence of arious parameters influencing this process. herefore a better understanding of friction rocesses and the development of criteria for he evaluation of friction forces on disconinuities in rock masses remains the main aim f research on friction in rock mechanics.

he investigations in the last few years have ndicated considerable difference in frictioal behaviour of different rocks and of disontinuities of various origin. It seems, herefore, necessary to examine this diffeence in behaviour more closely.

nalysing the friction process various paraeters,influencing the frictional behaviour f rocks, can be divided into three main roups as shown in Table 1.

The first group contains essentially parameters which can directly be measured in a test whereas the parameters of the other two groups depend only upon nature of the material and its discontinuities and are not test variables.

The influence of these different parameters on the frictional behaviour is very complex. The usual friction tests on rock samples give only the combined influence of the material and geometrical parameters, and it is thus not possible in such tests to study the influence of either one or a particular combination of these parameters. A test system was, therefore, chosen in which the influence of individual parameters (material and geometrical) could be investigated.

The problem of reproducing the same natural surface of the discontinuity in different tests was solved by making plaster casts from a rock sample. It was thus possible to study the roughness-dependent frictional behaviour of different joint surfaces for the same material strength and vice versa.

Table 1

mechanical parameters	material parameters	geometrical parameters
shear force	material strength	geometry of the joint surface (roughness)
normal force	mineral composition	degree of identation
normal stiffness	fabric	contact area
deformation along the direction of shearing	friction of mineral grains	
deformation normal to the direction of shearing (dilatation)	water	
	degree of weathering	
	joint filling	
shearing velocity		

Friction tests on rock samples

The model tests described later in this paper were based on friction tests made on samples of granite, sandstone and limestone. In order to obtain joints of similar origin and, for a particular rock type, joints with similar surfaces, the investigations were conducted on joint surfaces artificially produced by tensile fracture. The three rock types produced fracture surfaces of varying roughness (Fig. 1) caused by different texture of the materials.

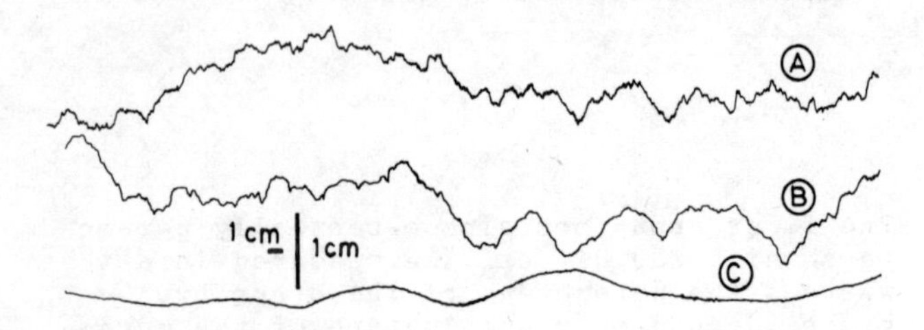

Fig. 1: Profiles of surface geometries of joints caused by tension in granite (A), sandstone (B) and limestone (C).

The essentially trans-granular fracture along cleavage planes of irregularly arranged mineral grains results in a very rough fracture surface in granite (Fig. 1 A) and thus gives a high degree of indentation, both on a microscopic as well as on the macroscopic scale. The washboard type shape of the sandstone joint surface is due mainly to the anisotropy caused by sedimentation. In contrast to granite the indentation on microscopic scale is not predominant in sandstone samples because of the point to point contact. In comparison to the above two rocks the fracture surface in limestone is relatively smooth. The indentation was only observed on a microscopic scale (Fig. 1 C).

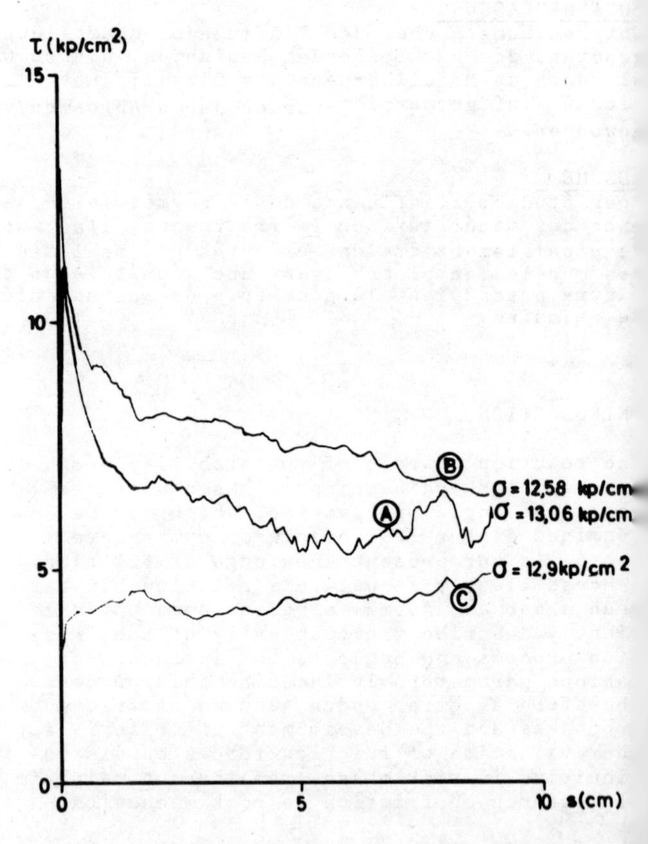

Fig. 2: Stress-strain curves of friction tests on rock samples of granite (A) sandstone (B) and limestone (C).

The shear tests were started with full indentation and the shear force was measured with increasing deformation under constant normal force. The resulting stress-strain curves (Fig. 2) are characteristically different for the three rock types. For granite the stress rises very quickly to a high peak value, and falls thereafter to a residual strength value after a small deformation. A similar rise was observed for sandstone samples. The fall to the residual strength here was, however, slower and more regular. Limestone samples show, however, no well defined peak strength. The shear stress remains more or less constant throughout the deformation.

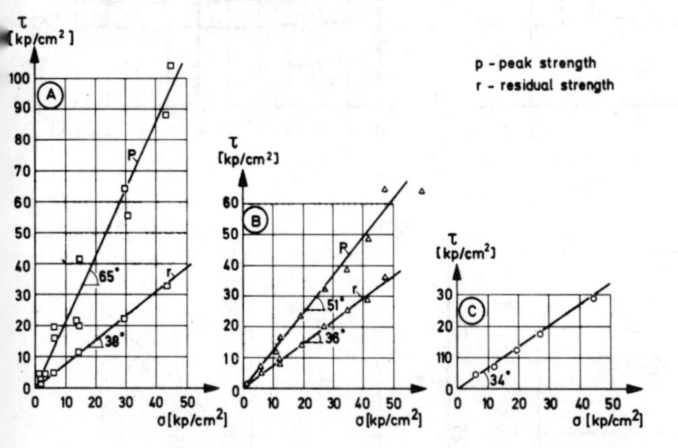

Fig. 3: τ-σ- diagrams of friction tests on rock samples of granite (A), sandstone (B) and limestone (C). (Peak friction results of Granit from Rengers (1971))

These tests gave values of peak friction angles of 65° for granite and 51° for sandstone (Fig. 3). The friction angle values corresponding to the residual strength for both (granite 38°, sandstone 36°) were, however, not very different from each other. For limestone samples a value of 34° for the angle of friction was obtained.

Friction tests on models with natural joint surface geometries

Friction tests on models (Fig. 4) formed from plaster casts of fracture surfaces of the granite, sandstone and limestone rock samples - used in the previously described tests - were conducted to investigate the influence of surface-roughness on frictional behaviour. It was thus possible to study the frictional behaviour of joints having varying surface roughnesses without having to consider the influence of material parameters.

The stress-strain curves obtained in the model tests (Fig. 5) are similar to the curves for the respective rock samples with corresponding surface roughness. The shear stress in the model of roughness corresponding to the surface of granite show a distinct peak value which falls rapidly to a residual value. The stress in the sandstone model drops slowly and more regularly after having attained a peak value. Similarly the limestone model also shows the characteristic behaviour of the limestone samples. The mo-

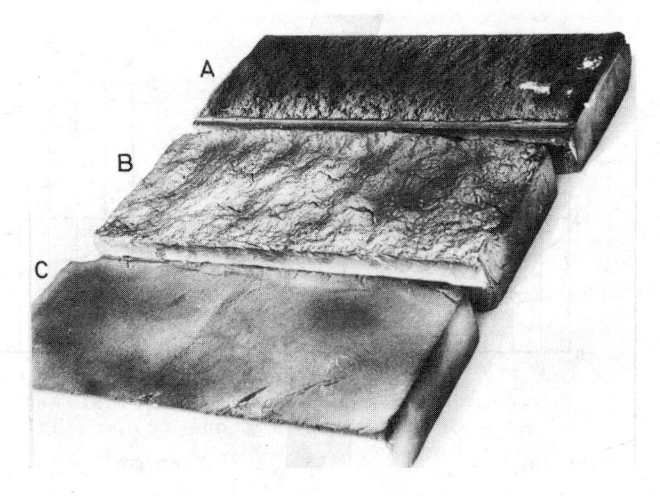

Fig. 4: Models formed from plaster casts of fracture surfaces of granite (A), sandstone (B) and limestone (C).

del tests gave a friction angle value of 51° corresponding to the peak strength in both granite as well as sandstone models, whereas the friction value corresponding to the residual strength shows a difference of 4° for the two models (Fig. 6). The friction angle in the limestone model shows a small drop of 2° from the peak value to the residual value. The peak strength is, however, smaller than the residual strength of the granite model. This difference in frictional behaviour of the models can only be explained by their different joint surface geometry as all other parameters were kept constant in the model tests. It is, therefore, necessary to measure the surface geometry quantitatively. One possible method could be the determination of the maximum dilatation under zero normal load, which means that all asperities of the two surfaces in contact slide one upon the other without any shearing of the asperities. This maximum dilatation was determined both experimentally as well as by Fourier-analysis and the inclination spectral method using surface roughness profiles (Fig. 1).

The dilatation curves (Fig. 7) so obtained show a similar behaviour for models of granite and sandstone in early stages of deformation. The constantly increasing dilatation in the sandstone model explains the slow decrease in shear strength from peak to residual value. The dilatation measurements of sandstone model under definite normal loads also confirm this behaviour (Fig. 8). As the curves in Fig. 8 show, the magnitude of dilatation for sandstone models are the largest followed by models of granite and limestone. With increasing normal stresses the dilatation decreases. This decrease in dilatation could be considered as a measure of the shearing of the asperities. The absence of large asperities in the limestone model is thus responsible for the small decrease of dilatation with increasing normal load.

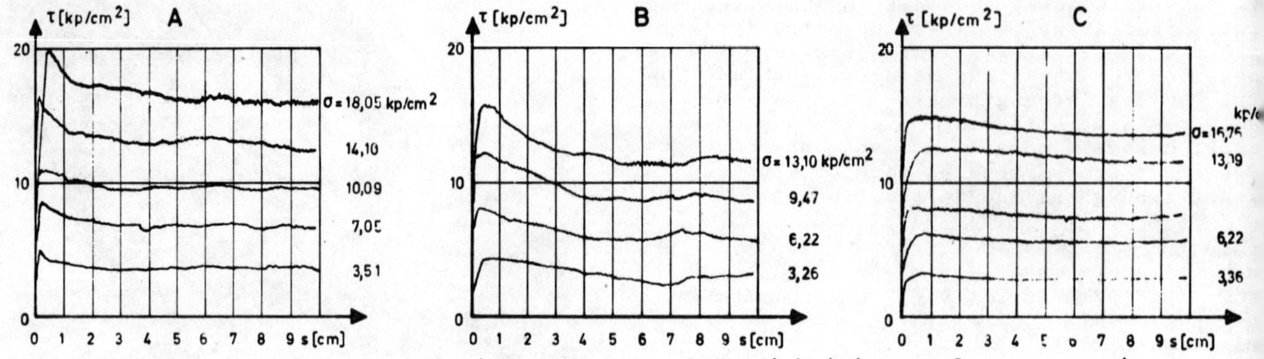

Fig. 5: Stress strain curves of friction tests on models with joint surface geometries of granite (A), sandstone (B) and limestone (C)

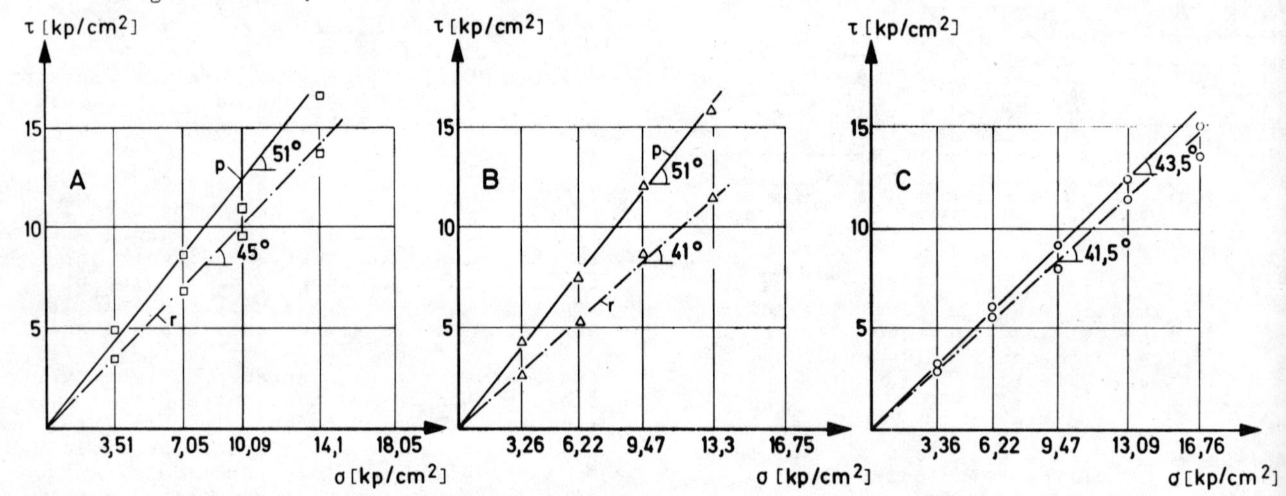

Fig. 6: τ - σ - diagrams of friction tests on models with surface geometries of granite (A), sandstone (B) and limestone (C)

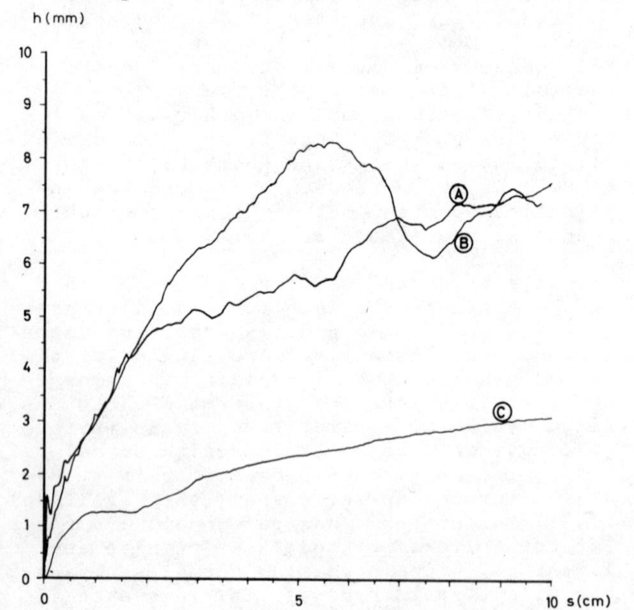

Fig. 7: Maximum dilatation at zero normal load (experim. determined) for the models with granite (A), sandstone(B) and limestone (C) surface geometry

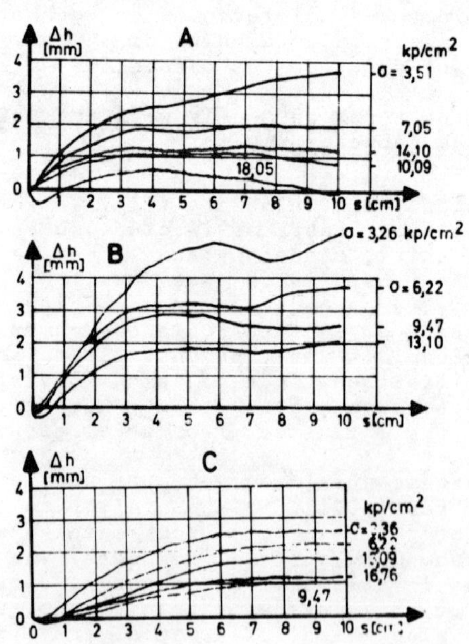

Fig. 8: Dilatation curves of the friction model tests with surface geometrie of granite (A), sandstone (B) and limestone (C)

In the tests where a normal load was applied these models have also displayed a similar shear stress behaviour during this initial phase.

CONCLUSIONS

The geometry of the joint surface influences the shape of the stress-strain curve decisively. For the curve having a peak strength value, its magnitude will essentially be determined by material parameters. The residual strength depends both upon the surface geometry of the joints as well as the material parameters. The peak friction acts only during very small deformations. It does not therefore seem reasonable to apply values of peak friction in practice, although the peak friction may contribute significantly to the safety of rock structures.

REFERENCES

Barton, N.R., 1972, A model study of rock-joint deformation.- Int. J.Rock Mech. Min. Sci., Vol. 9, pp 579-602, London.

Byerlee, J.D., 1967, Theory of friction based on brittle fracture.- J.Appl. Phys., Vol. 7, pp 2928-2934.

Coulson, J.H., 1970, The effect of surface roughness on the shear strength of joints in rock.- Tech.Report MRD-2-70 Missouri River Division, Corps of Engineers, Omaha, Nebraska, 68101.1.

Goodman, E.R., Heuze, F.E., Ohnishi, Y.,1972, Research on strength deformability - water pressure relationship for faults in direct shear.- Final Report on ARPA Contract A0210020 University of California, Berkeley.

Krsmanovic, D., 1967, Initial shear strength of hard rocks.- Géotechnique 17,2, pp 145-160.

Patton, F.D., 1966, Multiple modes of shear failure in rock.- Proc. First Congress Int.Soc. Rock Mech., Lisbon, Vol. 1, pp 509 - 513.

Rengers, N., 1971, Unebenheit und Reibungswiderstand von Gesteinstrennflächen.- Veröffentlichungen des Institutes für Boden- und Felsmechanik der Universität Fridericiana in Karlsruhe, Heft 47, Karlsruhe.

Schneider, H.J., 1974, Untersuchungen zur Gesteinsreibung.- Thesis at the University of Karlsruhe (in preparation).

Wolters, R., 1970, Reibungswiderstände auf Scherklüften - Ergebnisse von Laboruntersuchungen. - 18th Geomech. Coll. Austrian Soc. Geomech., Rock Mechan., Suppl. 1., pp 3 - 19.

THE RELEVANCE OF SIZE OF SAMPLE AND TYPE OF TEST IN DETERMINING SHEAR PROPERTIES FOR USE IN STABILITY ANALYSIS

L'IMPORTANCE RELATIVE DES DIMENSIONS DE L'ÉCHANTILLON ET DU TYPE POUR DÉTERMINER LES CARACTÉRISTIQUES DE CISAILLEMENT AFIN D'ANALYSER LA STABILITÉ

DIE ABHÄNGIGKEIT VON PROBENGRÖSSE UND VERSUCHSMETHODE BEI DER BESTIMMUNG VON SCHEREIGENSCHAFTEN ZWECKS STABILITÄTSANALYSE

B.F. WAREHAM D.E. SHERWOOD

Rock Mechanics, Ltd., Bracknell, U.K.

SUMMARY

Geological discontinuities which form the sliding surfaces relevant in rock mass movement are considerably variable. These may vary from an extremely rough interlocked surface to a wide clayey fault gouge zone in which pre-existing slip surfaces occur. The test which provides the most accurate and economic assessment of a relevant shear properties may differ depending on the nature of the surface being examined.

Three basic types of tests are described and discussed:-

1. Insitu tests:

2. Integral Sampling with laboratory tests of medium sized samples:

3. Laboratory and Field testing of small samples:

Examples of various types of tests are presented and their relevance in subsequent stability analysis considered. The structural geology, that is discontinuity type and roughness, is shown to be the major contributory factor to the choice of shear test size and type.

RESUME

Les discontinuités géologiques, qui constituent les surfaces de glissement ayant rapport aux mouvements en masse des rochers, sont extrêmement variables. On les trouve, par example, sous forme soit de surfaces fort rugueuses interdigitées soit de larges zones d'argiles de frottement dans lesquelles se presentent des plans de faille pré-existants. Ce doit être la nature de la surface à l'examen qui détermine le choix d'un essai destiné à fournir l'évaluation la plus exacte et économique des caractéristiques de cisaillement applicables.

On décrit et discute trois types d'essai basiques:-

1. Essais in situ

2. Prélèvements d'échantillons en bloc pour essais de laboratoire - échantillons de dimensions moyennes

3. Essais effectifs sur le terrain et au laboratoire de petits échantillons.

On a presenté differents types d'essais et a discuté leur importance relative dans l'analyse ultérieure de la stabilité. La géologie structurale. c.à.d. le facteur le plus significatif dans le choix d'essai de cisaillement et des dimensions des échantillons.

ZUSAMMENFASSUNG

Geologische Unterbrechungen, die die bei Massenbewegungen des Felsens vorhandenen Gleitflächen gestalten, sind höchst unterschiedlich. Sie können einerseits aus einer sehr unebenen verzahnten Fläche und andererseits aus einer breiten, fruher vorhandene Schubflachen enthaltenden Verwerfungszone bestehen. Der Versuch, der die genaueste und ökonomisch günstigste Bewertung der in Frage kommenden Schereigenschaften gibt, ist von der Beschaffenheit der zu untersuchenden Fläche abhängig.

Es werden drei Grundtypen von Versuchen beschrieben und erörtert:-

1. In Situ Versuche.

2. Ganzprobenahme mit Laborversuchen von Proben mittlerer Grösse.

3. Versuche im Labor und im Gelände von Kleinproben.

Beispiele verschiedener Versuchsarten werden dargestellt und ihre Angemessenheit mit Bezug auf eine darauffolgende Stabilitatsanalyse in Betracht gezogen. Die Geotektonik, d.h. der Typ der Scherversuche und der Probengrösseals massgebend angesehen.

INTRODUCTION

Determination of the shear properties relevant to stability analyses may vary from a full scale test (that is back analysis of a known failure) to a small scale laboratory test on drill core or hand specimen taken from a trial pit or outcrop. Although failures of natural slopes are not uncommon and details of known failures on cut slopes are available, an engineer is particularly fortunate if the back analysis of a particular failure is directly relevant to his problem. Consequently it is considered that the largest scale tests generally available are those performed on sliding surfaces of between 0.5 and 10 square metres although tests at the lower end of this range are most common. Where a construction will substantially increase the normal stresses on potential sliding surfaces, there is little alternative to tests which artificially create the modified conditions.

The behaviour of rock masses, particularly that relevant to surface and near surface constructions, is generally controlled by the number, frequency and direction of discontinuities in the rock mass and their properties when subjected to shearing. The objectives of a site investigation should therefore be to establish the structural geology and to evaluate the parameters appropriate to the critical discontinuities.

In the first instance, before any decisions are made on the testing to be carried out, a thorough study of the structural conditions relevant to the construction should be made. This may vary from a study of available literature to obtaining general information on the area, either by surface mapping, or from depth by a drilling programme or trial adits. It has become more usual of late to supplement this stage of the work with arial photogrammetry. The orientation and frequency of discontinuities together with first estimates of their likely properties when compared with the proposed construction will indicate the likely mode and scale of failure, whether it be a circular arc through highly fractured material, wedge failure, plane failure, ravelling or toppling. The economics of construction and remedial measures will then indicate an appropriate approach to testing.

Where the more likely failure modes and critical discontinuities have been identified for the chosen construction approach, detailed design procedures will call for more precise properties of the rock mass, and the scale of the testing programme can be properly assessed. The number of tests required is related to the variety of critical discontinuities which may range from clean interlocking breaks to faults which include considerable amounts of broken material or are clay infilled. In the former case both peak and residual strengths would be mobilised while in the latter the available strength may be approaching residual value due to earlier movements. In general the number of tests required is not related to test size although larger numbers of smaller tests may be necessary to reduce the risk of small features on the shear plane giving anomalous results. The cost of individual tests increases dramatically with specimen size (Franklin et al., 1974) and consequently the economics in design which larger tests may justify (e.g. possible excavation saved etc) becomes an important factor in the choice of test size. There is generally, however, a minimum specimen size which is technically acceptable for a shear surface of particular characteristic and in some cases the test size which can be justified from the economic point of view, can only be regarded as an index test in the problem.

The paper describes three of the methods which the authors use for determining direct shear strength parameters on a variety of specimen sizes. It continues to discuss both current design philosophy and other factors which influence the choice of specimen size, and the circumstances under which particular sizes are regarded as technically acceptable.

2. TESTING METHOD

2.1 Large Scale Insitu direct shear tests

The I.S.R.M standard at present under discussion suggests a shear specimen area of 0.5 square metres as this is the most commonly used size today. Franklin et al (1974) have described a series of 0.5 square metre tests carried out in connection with a dam foundation design, and of 1 square metre tests employed in a reservoir slope stability problem. They indicate that a considerable amount of the cost of insitu testing in these sizes is as a result of the excavation of a suitable test chamber and specimen. Their test set up for 1 square metre specimens is equipment has been added here.

Both gain normal reaction from columns extending to the perimeter of the excavation but normal stress is applied to the encapsulated sample in Figure 1a by direct loading using flatjacks while in Figure 1b a hydraulic jack and load spreader is used. Flatjacks have been shown by Wareham (1972) to be a simple means of applying a constant load over a given area, and by using an electric hydraulic pump and pressure maintainer unit accurate vertical stress can be maintained. The flexibility of using several flatjacks in evenly loading a considerable area and allowing large displacements has been described by Prefferle and Smith (1970). On the other hand difficulties have been experienced in obtaining equal spread of load using hydraulic jacks and load spreaders particularly with larger specimens. The flatjack method has the added flexibility that a standard set of reaction columns can be employed for a range of test sizes by the use of suitable sized flatjacks. The method does, however, require near perfect alugnment of the top of the specimen and the reaction pad because the use of a ball seating as shown in Figure 1a introduces an unacceptable risk of instability. Though the flatjacks are capable of taking up some slight misalignments, these lead to a much higher risk of rupture of the flatjacks during the test. In both of the systems illustrated, shear stress was provided by conventional hydraulic rams reacting against a block of reinforced concrete, and roller bearings were included as shown to eliminate any frictional resistance to shear.

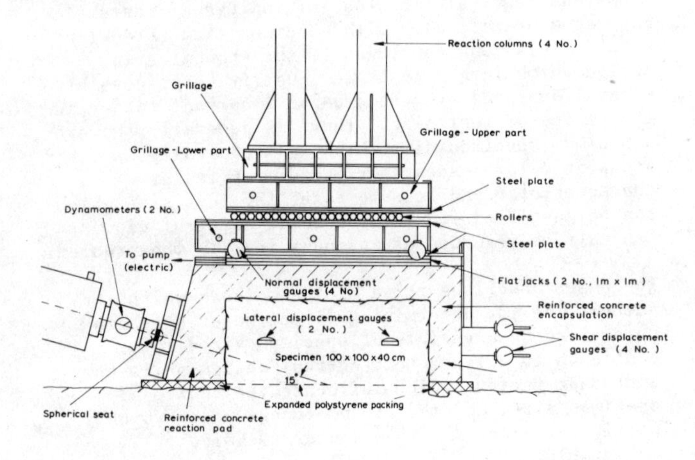

a) **Flatjacks for normal load**

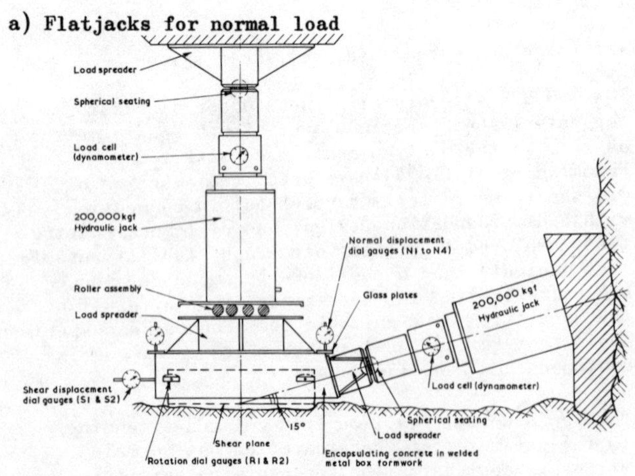

b) **Hydraulic jack for normal load**

FIG. 1 TYPICAL INSITU TEST EQUIPMENT

With this equipment multi-stage shear tests at increasing or decreasing normal load have been carried out in conditions where residual design parameters were of particular importance. No attempt has been made to return the sample to its starting position to extend the possible strain range, but in situations where this is technically acceptable, such a facility could readily be provided. Rapid cycling of normal stress is generally possible but in tests where this leads to significant normal movements the flatjack system mat restrict the rate of cycling because of the large volume changes of the jacks.

The large insitu shear test is more suited to deep underground investigations, particularly where adits will be excavated to provide access for geological study; it is doubtful whether many projects could justify the use of such tests if the complete excavation cost were set against the cost of the tests. Because of their high cost, insitu direct shear determinations are most widely used on large scale projects such as dam foundations, major slope stability problems and complex underground openings.

2.2 Integral Sampling with laboratory tests

In considering stability problems in jointed and faulted rock it is necessary to study carefully the discontinuity along which sliding is likely to take place and to determine, not only its orientation and dip, but other properties such as its roughness, the occurrence of infilling or borken material and the like. It is often the case in design of surface constructions or excavations that the relevant discontinuities are highly weathered and may contain clayey material or that faults may include a wide broken zone. These conditions may create difficulties in carrying out insitu tests (or make them unnecessary) in sampling appropriate materials for laboratory testing.

In an investigation for a motorway cut in the Old Red Sandstone near Cardiff, South Wales, the geology was shown to consist of moraine overlying interbedded sandstones and siltstones which were highly weathered in some areas. In order to obtain parameters which would be relevant forthese highly fissile and variable discontinuities the process outlined above in section 1 lead to the choice of tests on a shear surface of approximately 250mm x 250mm performed on samples taken from locations chosen by geological inspection. Test pits were therefore excavated at positions where the conditions were known from a conventional drilling programme and zones representative of the most likely failure surface were identified for sampling. Because the materials encountered were highly fissile, it was necessary to fully encapsulate the block samples in the field in such a way that subsequent preparation in the laboratory could be kept to a minimum. This was done by carefully cutting and trimming the samples to plan dimensions of nominally 260mm square with the intended plane of shear parallel to the top of the block. A steel former of identical dimensions to the 305mm square shear box apparatus was then placed over the sample and epoxy resin placed to about 10mm below the shear plane level, (Fig. 2), and the remainder of the sample then fully encapsulated with resin. Finally after the resin had set, the former and block were removed by under cutting, inverted, and the base of the block trimmed and sealed with resin. Protective reinforcement of the soft plaster filling across the shear plane was provided by steel wires spanning the shear zone, which were cut in the laboratory prior to testing. The encapsulated samples were found to travel well and were fitted directly in the shear testing machine without difficulty. The epoxy resin seal to the top of the sample was removed before locating the normal loading spreader plate.

'IG. 2 INTEGRAL SAMPLING TECHNIQUE

Cutting of the block was in this case carried out successfully using a tungsten carbide tipped chain saw but other methods are available and final choice made based on experience in similar materials. Londe (1972) has described a method using a wire saw in which a steel cable, lubricated by water flow containing carborundum as an abrasive, is used to cut the sample. Wareham (1972) has discussed various methods of cutting slots in rocks which are applicable here for preparing the block prior to sampling.

Shear parameters, both peak and residual were required at low normal stresses as the problem under consideration was the slope stability of a road cut. Consequently it was possible to provide sufficient load using the 305mm square box apparatus which relies on direct loading on the hanger principal (see Fig. 3). For tests requiring higher normal loads Hoek (1970) describes a testing machine of similar size with 00 ton capacity where normal stress is developed by hydraulic jacks against a rigid loading frame. Great flexibility is available in multi or single stage tests may be used to obtain peak parameters, and reversal of movement is available in order to determine true residual values. Rate of shearing is displacement conttolled with shear load measured and both displacement and dilation are easily measured.

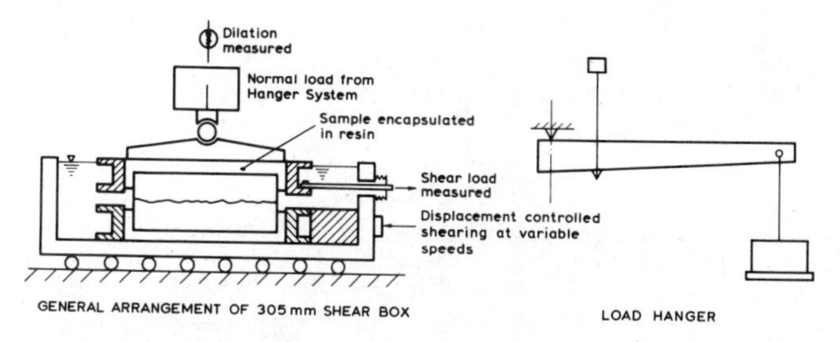

Fig.3 SHEAR TESTING APPARATUS WITH HANGER ARRANGEMENT FOR NORMAL LOAD

As this technique is used in conditions where friable and weathered materials are to be tested, it is advisable to carry out tests on material durability, so that long term degradation as a result of weathering processes, increased by the excavation of the cut, may be considered. In investigation described, Atterberg limits and slake durability indeces were determined. The apparatus, described by Franklin and Chandra (1972) indicated generally low durability and, consequently, additional protective measures to prevent percolation of surface water into and along discontinuity planes were considered in the overall drainage proposals for the works.

2.3 Laboratory and Filed Testing of Small Samples

Under certain circumstances the most appropriate and economic method of obtaining shear parameters is to test a specimen of small dimensions either in the laboratory shear box or in a portable shear testing machine. Samples may be obtained in several ways either using techniques designed to obtain samples particularly for this type of testing or by making use of cores obtained for geological investigation.

The hanger type shear testing machine already referred to is available both in 60mm and 305mm size and it is the smaller one which is generally used for this category of test. Samples from drillcore or hand picked blocks from outcrops or exploration excavations may be encapsulated in resin or plaster. If the rock material is competent they can sometimes be trimmed exactly to size using diamond cutting blades and tested in whichever manner required. Similar flexibility to that already described is available in the smaller apparatus.

A similar apparatus has been designed to be portable enabling it to be used in the field or in the laboratory. Samples tested may be up to 125mm x 125mm and are usually encapsulated in plaster. Normal and shear loads are applied by hydraulic jacks actuated by hand pumps. Shearing is consequently shear load controlled and displacement can be measured during shearing. Facility available for reversal of direction of shearing but normal displacements are generally not measured. Though the equipment is simple, the more conventional laboratory apparatus with displacement controlled shearing is to be preferred. The portable shear box is shown in Fig. 4.

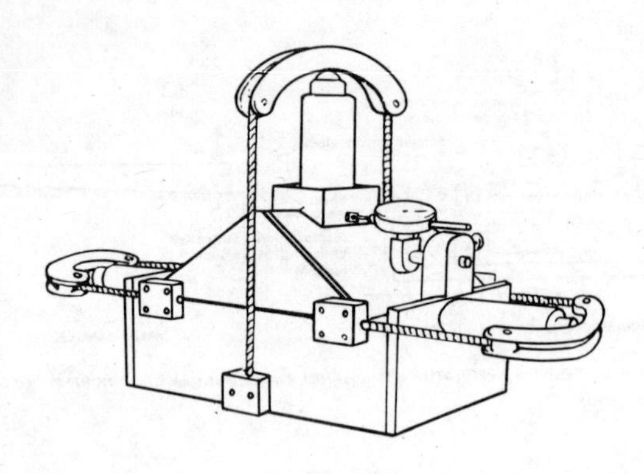

FIG. 4 PORTABLE SHEAR BOX

The advantage of small tests is their economy which allows a considerable number to be carried out for an assessment of peak and residual strength envelopes.

Drillcore is suitable for testing in the manner although drilling technique should be carefully considered as weathered or broken material within the discontinuity may be lost during the drilling process. It is advisable to use the triple tube or mylar lined core barrels in order to avoid the disturbance caused by core extrusion, particularly in soft or friable materials.

Patton (1966) and Barton (1971) have shown that the asperity angle is important in thr estimation of relevant shear properties although the size of and "wave length"of asperity should also be considered. A comparison must always be made between the sample tested and the field discontinuity as peak strengths from the test will probably depend on small scale asperities which do not affect field behaviour.

Small size laboratory tests on core samples were carried out in connection with the investigation described in section 2.2 above. The results were generally comparable with those from the integrally sampled blocks although they indicated a higher peak and residual envelope. The tested drillcore results were used largely to predict behaviour of the discontinuities where the weathering was less marked.

3. CHOICE OF TESTING METHOD

For each investigation a choice must be made on the number and type of tests which will be carried out. In most cases investigation costs and possible construction savings are the principle controlling factors although technical considerations must also be honoured. This economic approach is becoming more widespread particularly in studies where a probabalistic stability analysis is used and maintenance costs, such as disruption from and removal of a slipped mass, are often now included in the 'economic' equations'. An estimate of standard deviation about an assumed mean for a parameter will enable the probability of failure to be determined and the proper assessment of data reliability becomes essential. The effect of reliability of data on stability calculations has been discussed by Hoek (1970b) as a means of determining design levels of factor of safety.

Parameters used in stability calculations generally idealise the shear stress -normal stress relationship in terms of an angle of friction and a cohesion intercept and differentiate between peak and residual conditions. When peak parameters are employed some allowance is, in effect being made of interlocking of various sized asperities but little work has been done to establish the mechanisms which control this added strength. Consequently there is some uncertainty on whether the asperities which develop peak test strength will behave in a similar manner in the fullscale. With residual strengths, providing sufficient displacement has been permitted in testing, this problem does not apply although the condition and infilling, if any, of the discontinuity in the field is of major importance. In the use of finite element methods in which sliding may take place between blocks the full displacement strength relationship, in an idealised form, must be defined and this provides an added dimension of difficulty in interpreting test data. Again there is uncertainty as to how well test displacement-strength behaviour models field behaviour.

The philosophy of rock slope design has been discussed by Hoek and Londe in their general report to this congress and their Figure 1 summarises the overall approach to slope design problems. In the authors experience it is considered that the small scale tests described in 2.3 are suitable as index indications of shear behaviour and this type of test should be carried out at a preliminary stage of investigation on discontinuities recovered in drillcore. Conventional investigation drilling produces a core maximum diameter 100mm, often considerably less, and so the small size shear box or portable testing machine are the only possible tests. Hoek and Londe suggest that more detailed stability analyses are required for permanent slopes with high damage risk, and for temporary slopes with low damage risk where preliminary calculations indicate doubts on stability. It is suggested, however, that a further category, where improvement of cut slope angle has substantial economic advantages such as in deep open cast mining operations, should be added.

In all these cases further testing is probably necessary but this should be planned on the basis of information available from preliminary studies. As a result of the preliminary work it is probable that details of the geological trends and condition of the discontinuities, along which failure is likely to take place, will be known together with the likely modes of failure and first estimates of cut angles. This preliminary work is often used to determine the feasibility of the project. The main investigation can then largely be devoted to the insitu determination of shear parameters or of the provision of samples for suitable laboratory tests.

The size and scale of the project usually determines the methods of investigation and the scope of possible tests depends on the techniques used to gain access to the levels at which shear parameters are important. The investigation may consist of one or more of the following categories:-

1. Surface Exposure Studies on which shear test samples may be taken and tested in the portable or small laboratory shear test machines.

2. Core drilling from the surface to enable samples of limited size to be obtained from depth and again the portable or small laboratory shear box is used.

3. Trial pit or trench excavation used extensively on soil slope stability investigations and often used in rock slope investigations for shallow cuts in friable or highly weathered material. Insitu shear tests may be carried out but problems occur in providing normal loads and it is more usual to take samples and test in the laboratory.

4. Exploration adits which are used for geological investigation, instrumentation etc and due to their cost are only excavated even on major projects, after substantial field and laboratory investigations have been carried out. Samples may be taken for laboratory testing but insitu testing becomes economic.

Size of sample in all but the insitu tests is severely limited and it is considered that wherever economically possible the largest size of suitable testing machine should be used. Limitations on the size of test may also depend on a comparison between available normal load and maximum required normal stress from design considerations. Interpretation of the results should be made after a study of the relevant discontinuities in the field. As a general rule the asperities which control peak behaviour probably have a minimum wave length of about 1-10% of the total sliding surface length. Lengths are, of course, measured in the direction of sliding. A comparison between the significant asperities for the test and on the discontinuity in the field should be the first step in appraisal of test size and data. In some formations for example where rippled bedding occurs, an appraisal on these lines may suggest that the results of even the largest laboratory tests can only be regarded as an index. If insitu tests are not feasible, the engineer must rely on his experience and judgement for the choice of design parameters from the laboratory tests which may lead to a conservative design.

Some workers have suggested that measured shear strength may be independant of specimen size but have noted that displacements at which peak strengths are mobilized appear to increase with specimen size. The authors experience suggests that there is a size of specimen which this is true, and this minimum size appears to be related to asperity character according to the general rule given above. Laboratory experience bears out the dependance of displacement at peak to specimen size but the extension of this experience to field sized tests specimens suggest quite unrealistic displacements.

4. COMMENTS

The procedure generally used by the authors in determining size of test appropriate, once the likely failed mass is determined, is to estimate the relevance of peak or residual parameters to the problem, determine the significant asperity size and estimate the size of test such that these asperities are relevant to its behaviour. As a general guide asperities of wave length greater than 1 to 10% are considered as being relevant to shear behaviour and choice within this range is largely a matter for engineering judgment. In most instances economic considerations are then introduced and the test programme is designed after a proper cost-benefit analysis.

5. ACKNOWLEDGEMENTS

The authors wish to thank the directors of Rock Mechanics Limited who have given permission to publish this paper.

REFERENCES

BARTON, N.R. (1971) A model study of the behaviour of steep excavated rock slopes
Ph. D thesis University of London

FRANKLIN, J.A. and R. CHANDRA (1972), The slake durability test. Int. Jnl. Rock Mech. Min. Sci. Vol. 9 pp. 325-341 Pergamon Press.

FRANKLIN, J.A, J. MANAILOGLOU, and D.E. SHERWOOD (1974), Field determination of Direct Shear Strength 3rd International Congress Rock Mechanics, Denver (In preparation).

HOEK, E. (1970 a), Estimating the stability of excavated slopes in opencast mines. Trans. Sect. A Institution of Mining and Metallurgy, London, Vol. 79. October 1970.

HOEK, E. (1970 b), Discussion of the above. Trans Sect. A. Institution of Mining and Metallurgy

I.S.R.M. (1971), Commission on Standardisation of Laboratory and Field Tests. Suggested methods for determining the slaking, swelling, porosity, density and related rock index properties. First draft January 1971.

LONDE, P. (1972), The mechanics of Rock Slopes and Foundations.
Rock Mechanics research report No. 17, April 1972 Imperial College, London University.

PATTON, F.D. (1966), Multiple Modes of shear failure in Rock. Proc. First Congress I.S.R.M. Lisbon pp. 509-13.

PREFFERLE, W. and C.R. SMITH, (1970), Phase 1 flat-jack tests. 12th Symp. Rock Mechanics. University of Missouri Rolla Nov. 1970, A.I.M.E. New York 'Dynamic Rock Mechanics'.

WAREHAM, B.F. (1972), The use of the flatjack in Rock Mechanics with particular reference to insitu stress measurement and deformability testing. M.Sc. Thesis, University of London.

THEME 1

D

Time Dependent Deformation in Relation to Rock Strength

THÈME 1

D

La déformation sous le temps en fonction de la résistance des roches

THEMA 1

D

Zeitabhängige Deformierungen in Verbindung mit der Felsstärke

LE RÔLE DU TEMPS DANS LE COMPORTEMENT À LA RUPTURE DES ROCHES

THE ROLE OF TIME IN ROCK FAILURE BEHAVIOUR

DER ZEITEINFLUSS IM BRUCHVERHALTEN DER GESTEINE

René HOUPERT

Ingénieur

Ecole Nationale Supérieure de Géologie

Nancy, France

RESUME. Le temps joue un rôle important dans la déformation et la rupture des roches. La manière la plus simple de mettre ce rôle en évidence consiste à réaliser des essais à vitesse de sollicitation variable. Des essais de compression à vitesse de déformation constante, contrôlés au moyen d'une machine asservie et effectués sur différentes roches, montrent que la résistance ultime, la position, la pente et l'aspect de la partie des courbes contrainte-déformation située au-delà de la charge maximale dépendent de la vitesse de déformation. La variation de ces paramètres peut s'expliquer par la formation de fractures dont le développement est lié au temps. Il existe, d'autre part, un rapport étroit entre la vitesse de déformation et la relaxation des contraintes au cours de la fracturation des roches.

SUMMARY . Time has an important role in rock deformation and failure. The simplest way to make this role evident is to realise tests with various strain or stress rates. Constant strain rate compression tests by mean of a servocontrolled testing machine on various types of rocks shaw that the ultimate strength, the location, the slope and the aspect of the postfailure stress-strain curves depend on the strain rate. The variation of these parameters may be explained by formation of fractures which increasing is time-dependent. On the other hand, there is a close relation between the strain rate and the stress relaxation during rock fracturation.

ZUSAMMENFASSUNG. Die Zeit spielt eine beträchtliche Rolle in der Verformung und in dem Bruch der Gesteine. Die einfachste Art, diese Rolle offensichtlich zu machen, besteht darin,Versuche mit veränderlicher Verformungs- oder Belastungsgeschwindigkeit zu vollziehen. Druckversuche mit konstanter Verformungsgeschwindigkeit, die mit einer servogesteuerten Versuchsmachine mit verschiedenen Gesteinen vollführt wurden, zeigen,dass die Bruchlast, die Lage, der Fall und die Figur des Bereiches der Spannungs- Verformungskurve,welche ausserhalb der Maximallast liegt, von der Verformungsgeschwindigkeit abhängen. Die Änderung dieser Parameter kann durch die Bildung zeitabhängiger Brüche erklärt werden. Ferner besteht ein enges Verhältnis zwischen der Verformungsgeschwindigkeit und der Spannungsrelaxation während des Bruchvorganges.

INTRODUCTION

Les roches sont des matériaux dont le comportement mécanique dépend du temps. Parmi les manifestations les plus évidentes et les plus connues de l'influence du temps sur la déformation et la rupture des matériaux rocheux, on peut citer la déformation en fonction du temps sous charge constante, appelée fluage, la variation du module de déformation et celle de la résistance ultime avec la vitesse de sollicitation. Cette dernière manifestation est d'ailleurs liée au fluage par l'intermédiaire du phénomène de la rupture différée, c'est-à-dire de la rupture sous charge constante.

On trouve, dans la littérature, de nombreuses études concernant le fluage des roches et la variation, en compression simple, de leur module de déformation ou de leur résistance ultime en fonction, soit de la vitesse d'application des contraintes, soit de la vitesse de déformation. En ce qui concerne ce dernier point, il est bien connu que le module de déformation relatif aux sollicitations lentes (module statique ou quasi statique) est inférieur au module correspondant aux essais de chocs ou aux vibrations (module dynamique) ; de plus, la résistance ultime augmente généralement avec la vitesse de sollicitation. Remarquons cependant, que les variations du module et même celles de la résistance ultime ne sont pas toujours très apparentes pour toutes les roches, dans le domaine des sollicitations statiques (vitesse de déformation inférieure à 10^3 s^{-1}).

Le module de déformation et la résistance ultime caractérisent la courbe contrainte-déformation relative aux charges croissantes, c'est-à-dire la partie de cette courbe située avant la charge maximale. C'est la branche de la courbe que l'on obtient à l'aide d'une machine d'essai classique, pour laquelle la force constitue la variable indépendante de l'essai ; dans ce cas, l'éprouvette d'essai explose violemment lorsque la charge maximale est atteinte. Par contre, si le déplacement constitue la variable indépendante et si l'essai est réalisé à vitesse de déplacement constante par exemple, la force atteint un maximum qui correspond à la résistance ultime, et elle décroît ensuite progressivement pendant la phase de rupture ; la rupture peut ainsi être contrôlée. Ce contrôle est rendu possible par l'utilisation d'une machine d'essai munie d'un dispositif d'asservissement électro-hydraulique qui régularise la vitesse de libération de l'énergie emmagasinée dans l'ensemble machine-éprouvette. Si la rigidité longitudinale de la machine d'essai est plus grande que la valeur absolue de la pente de la courbe force-déplacement de l'éprouvette, le contrôle de la rupture est total et l'on obtient la branche de la courbe contrainte-déformation située au-delà de la charge maximale, c'est-à-dire en somme, la courbe complète. L'utilisation de machines d'essai asservies en Mécanique des Roches est relativement récente (HOUPERT, 1970 et 1972 ; RUMMEL et FAIRHURST, 1970 ; HUDSON, CROUCH et FAIRHURST, 1972). A l'heure actuelle, il n'existe que peu de données concernant l'influence de la vitesse de sollicitation sur la partie de la courbe contrainte-déformation située au-delà de la charge maximale, appelée courbe de rupture.

Nous présentons ici quelques résultats et observations concernant le rôle du temps dans le comportement à la rupture - en particulier la microfracturation - des roches, en compression simple. Cette étude est basée sur l'influence de la variation de la vitesse de sollicitation sur la courbe contrainte-déformation complète de plusieurs roches et sur des résultats d'essais de relaxation. Les essais ont été réalisés à l'aide d'une machine d'essai asservie en programmant la vitesse de déplacement axiale. Tous les essais ont, par suite, été effectués à vitesse de déformation constante.

COURBE CONTRAINTE-DEFORMATION ET VITESSE DE DEFORMATION

Nous avons réalisé des courbes contrainte-déformation σ-ε à différentes vitesses de déformation $\dot{\varepsilon}$ pour les roches suivantes : granite de Senones (fig. 1), laurvikite de Scandinavie (fig. 2), calcaire d'Euville (fig. 3) et marbre de Carrare (fig. 4). Chaque courbe représentée est une courbe moyenne obtenue à partir de plusieurs autres courbes tracées pour la même vitesse. Dans la gamme des vitesses utilisées, on n'observe que peu de changements pour le module de déformation de ces roches. Ceux du marbre,

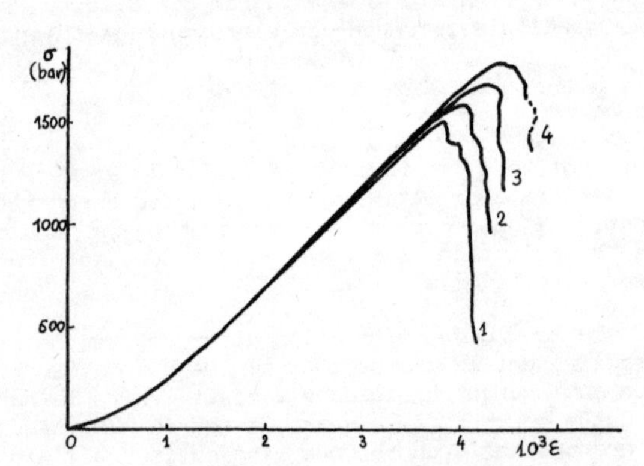

Fig. 1 - Courbes contrainte-déformation du granite de Senones pour différentes vitesses de déformation $\dot{\varepsilon}_7$;
1 : $\dot{\varepsilon} = 2{,}5.10^{-7}$; 2 : $\dot{\varepsilon} = 2{,}5.10^{-6}s^{-1}$;
3 : $\dot{\varepsilon} = 2{,}5.10^{-6}$; 4 : $\dot{\varepsilon} = 2{,}5.10^{-4}s^{-1}$.

du calcaire et de la laurvikite augmentent légèrement avec $\dot{\varepsilon}$; ceux du granite ne varient pratiquement pas. Pour le granite et la laurvikite, la pente de la partie de la courbe située après la zone linéaire et avant le maximum augmente avec la vitesse de déformation. Dans l'ensemble, pour les quatre roches, la résistance à la compression augmente avec la vitesse de déformation et les courbes relatives aux vitesses supérieures se situent au-dessus des courbes relatives aux vitesses inférieures. Pour les granites, la laurvikite et le calcaire, la déformation correspondant à la résistance ultime augmente avec $\dot{\varepsilon}$; par contre,

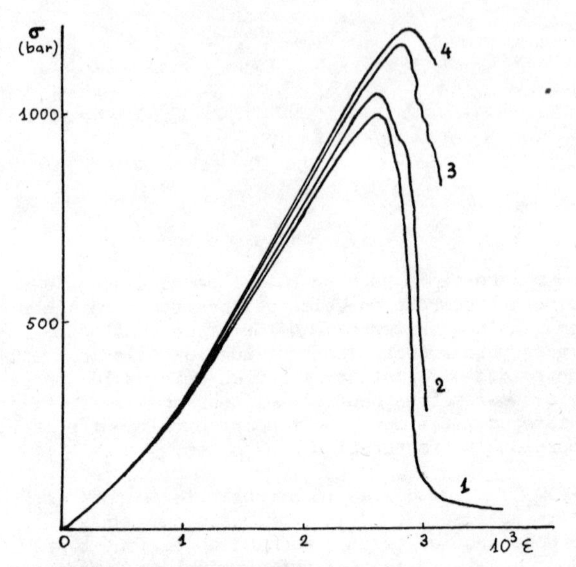

Fig. 2 - Courbes contrainte-déformation de la laurvikite de Scandinavie pour différentes vitesses de déformation $\dot{\varepsilon}$;
1 : $\dot{\varepsilon} = 2{,}5.10^{-7}s^{-1}$; 2 : $\dot{\varepsilon} = 2{,}5.10^{-6}s^{-1}$;
3 : $\dot{\varepsilon} = 2{,}5.10^{-5}s^{-1}$; 4 : $\dot{\varepsilon} = 2{,}5.10^{-4}s^{-1}$.

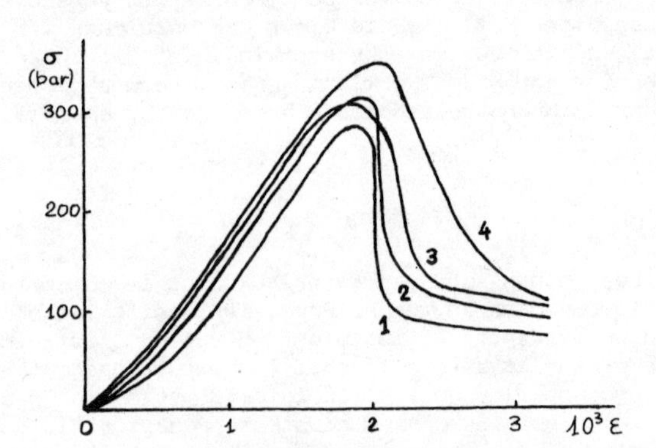

Fig. 3 - Courbes contrainte-déformation du calcaire d'Euville pour différentes vitesses de déformation $\dot{\varepsilon}$;
1 : $\dot{\varepsilon} = 2{,}5.10^{-7}s^{-1}$; 2 : $\dot{\varepsilon} = 2{,}5.10^{-6}s^{-1}$;
3 : $\dot{\varepsilon} = 2{,}5.10^{-5}s^{-1}$; 4 : $\dot{\varepsilon} = 2{,}5.10^{-4}s^{-1}$.

cette déformation décroît lorsque $\dot{\varepsilon}$ croît dans le cas du marbre. Pour le granite, la laurvikite et le calcaire, la pente moyenne de la partie de la courbe située au-delà de la charge maximale augmente (en valeur absolue) lorsque $\dot{\varepsilon}$ diminue ; dans le cas du marbre, le sens de variation de la pente n'est pas très évident ; cependant, il semble être le même que pour les autres roches. Le contrôle de la rupture n'est que partiellement possible pour le granite de Senones, quel que soit $\dot{\varepsilon}$ et la rupture est explosive pour les deux vitesses les plus élevées ; cependant, la courbe de rupture obtenue s'allonge lorsque $\dot{\varepsilon}$ décroît. La rupture de la laurvikite peut être contrôlée totalement pour la vitesse la plus faible, mais à mesure que $\dot{\varepsilon}$ croît, le contrôle devient de moins en moins possible. Pour le calcaire d'Euville et le marbre de Carrare, le contrôle est total quel que soit $\dot{\varepsilon}$. Dans le cas du marbre, la courbe est lisse pour les essais rapides, la diminution de la charge s'effectuant de manière continue, tandis que pour les essais lents, cette diminution de la contrainte est discontinue et s'effectue par paliers (courbe en escalier). Comme dans le cas du marbre de Carrare, BIENIAWSKI (1970) a observé, pour un grès, une diminution de la déformation relative à la charge maximale avec une augmentation de $\dot{\varepsilon}$. Il donne, par contre, une augmentation de la pente de la courbe de rupture avec $\dot{\varepsilon}$, contrairement à ce que nous observons pour les quatre roches étudiées. Les courbes complètes publiées par PENG et PODNIEKS (1972) pour un tuf et par PENG (1973) pour un granite, un grès, un marbre et une arkose montrent également une augmentation de la pente lorsque $\dot{\varepsilon}$ décroît.

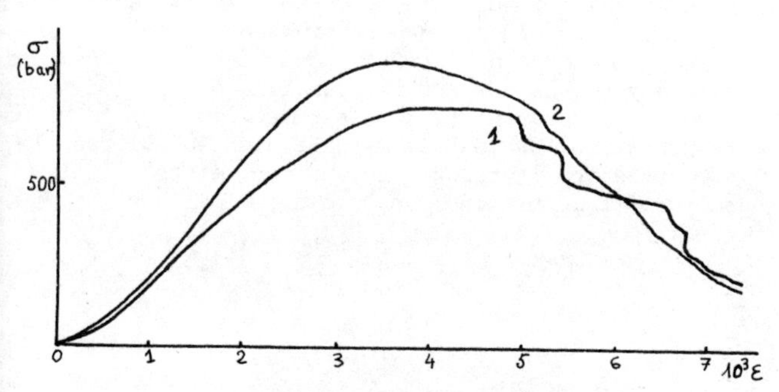

Fig. 4 - Courbes contrainte-déformation du marbre de Carrare pour différentes vitesses de déformation $\dot{\varepsilon}$;
1 : $\dot{\varepsilon} = 5.10^{-7} s^{-1}$; 2 : $\dot{\varepsilon} = 5.10^{-4} s^{-1}$.

Dans un essai de compression simple, des microfractures, orientées parallèlement à la direction de la charge, se développent progressivement dans l'éprouvette à mesure que la charge croît. Le développement de ces microfractures est d'autant plus intense que la vitesse de sollicitation est plus faible. Autrement dit, aux faibles vitesses (essais lents), les microfractures se forment bien avant le point de résistance ultime de l'éprouvette, tandis qu'aux vitesses élevées (essais rapides), ces microfractures ne se produisent pas ou précèdent de peu le point de résistance ultime. La formation d'une fracture nouvelle prélève une partie de l'énergie emmagasinée dans l'éprouvette et il en découle une réduction de la charge, ce qui correspond en quelque sorte à une relaxation des contraintes dans l'éprouvette. Par conséquent, dans le cas des essais lents, l'énergie disponible dans l'éprouvette, au moment où la charge maximale est atteinte, est inférieure à l'énergie correspondante d'un essai rapide. Comme, de plus, la quantité d'énergie emmagasinée augmente avec la vitesse de sollicitation, il en découle que le contrôle de la rupture est plus facile pour les essais lents que pour les essais rapides. Pour $\dot{\varepsilon}$ faible, la rupture est progressive tandis qu'elle a tendance à devenir explosive pour $\dot{\varepsilon}$ élevé. C'est, en particulier, le cas du granite de Senones (fig. 1) et de la laurvikite de Scandinavie (fig. 2), pour lesquels la courbe σ-ε est d'autant plus complète que $\dot{\varepsilon}$ est plus faible.

Aux faibles vitesses de déformation, les surfaces de rupture sont généralement plus rugueuses et moins lisses que dans le cas des vitesses élevées. Dans le premier cas, il se forme une grande quantité de débris lors de la rupture alors que ces débris sont moins nombreux dans le second cas. En rapprochant ces faits du développement - lié à la vitesse de sollicitation - de microfractures précédant le point de charge maximale, dont il a été question ci-dessus, on peut penser que pour les faibles valeurs de $\dot{\varepsilon}$, les défauts et les discontinuités contenus dans le matériau rocheux interviennent lors de la propagation des fractures, alors que pour les valeurs élevées de $\dot{\varepsilon}$, ces défauts et ces discontinuités n'interviennent pas dans la rupture. Aux faibles vitesses de sollicitation, des microruptures peuvent se développer au niveau des défauts et des hétérogénéités du matériau, tandis qu'aux vitesses élevées, ces microruptures ne peuvent pas s'établir. Le rôle joué par ces défauts est donc plus important dans le cas des essais lents que dans celui des essais rapides. La dispersion des résistances ultimes en fonction de la vitesse de sollicitation montre d'ailleurs que cette dispersion, donc le rôle des défauts, diminue lorsque la vitesse croît (HOUPERT et TISOT, 1969 ; HOUPERT, 1970). Par conséquent, pour $\dot{\varepsilon}$ faible, les microfractures ont tendance à emprunter les plans de moinde résistance, alors que pour $\dot{\varepsilon}$ élevé, ces plans jouent moins et les microfractures se situent plutôt dans le domaine intergranulaire, en suivant les trajectoires imposées par les conditions aux limites du champ des contraintes. WILLARD et McWILLIAMS (1969) ont d'ailleurs montré, en comparant le rapport du nombre de ruptures transgranulaires sur celui des ruptures intergranulaires, à la vitesse de mise en charge $\dot{\sigma}$, dans un granite, que ce rapport diminue lorsque $\dot{\sigma}$ croît ; ceci prouve que le rôle joué par les défauts des grains lors de la rupture tend à diminuer à mesure que $\dot{\sigma}$ croît. Ce rôle des défauts, lié à la vitesse de sollicitation, peut expliquer, du moins en partie, l'augmentation de la résistance ultime avec la vitesse de sollicitation. Pour les essais lents, les défauts et les zones de faible résistance peuvent intervenir, ce qui entraîne une diminution de la résistance ultime par rapport à celle des essais rapides, qui est plus élevée puisque les défauts interviennent moins. Pour les roches étudiées (fig.1 à 4), on observe une augmentation très nette de la résistance ultime en fonction de $\dot{\varepsilon}$. Cette augmentation est plus importante pour le granite (fig. 1) et la laurvikite (fig. 2), roches relativement hétérogènes, que pour le calcaire (fig. 3) et le marbre (fig. 4) qui sont des roches assez homogènes.

Après le sommet de la courbe contrainte-déformation, des fractures apparaissent dans l'éprouvette. Ces fractures prennent des dimensions de plus en plus grandes à mesure que la déformation axiale augmente. Chaque nouvelle fracture entraîne une réduction de l'énergie de l'éprouvette. Si l'essai est lent, les fractures se développent successivement : la charge appliquée à l'éprouvette est réduite - par l'intermédiaire de la servocommande - au fur et à mesure que les fractures se forment, par suite de la relaxation des contraintes. Il en découle un tracé vertical ou subvertical de la courbe σ-ε à chaque apparition de fissure. Ces réductions successives de la charge donnent aux faibles vitesses de déformation, une courbe en gradins. Aux vitesses de déformation élevées, cette relaxation des contraintes par fracturation n'a pas le temps de se produire. Il en résulte des courbes σ-ε dont la pente est plus petite (en valeur absolue) que celle relative aux courbes à faible vitesse ; de plus, pour $\dot{\varepsilon}$ élevé, les courbes σ-ε sont plus lisses et elles sont surélevées par rapport à celles relatives à $\dot{\varepsilon}$ faible. On observe nettement la variation de ces différents phénomènes, valeur de la pente, aspect et position relative de la courbe de rupture, sur les figures 1, 2, 3 et 4.

RELAXATION DES CONTRAINTES ET FRACTURATION

La relaxation des contraintes dans une roche soumise à une charge est une autre manifestation de l'influence du temps sur le comportement mécanique de cette roche. Par relaxation, il faut entendre ici toute diminution de la contrainte en fonction du temps (à déformation constante), quel que soit l'état du matériau. Pour réaliser un essai de relaxation à l'aide d'une machine équipée d'un système d'asservissement électro-hydraulique, il suffit d'arrêter le programme à la valeur désirée du déplacement, la vitesse de déplacement est ainsi annulée et la déformation est maintenue constante. Pendant ces arrêts, la charge décroît et cette diminution se traduit sur la courbe σ-ε par des lignes verticales. La relaxation est importante dans la phase de rupture fragile et dans cette phase, les taux de variation de la contrainte les plus importants coïncident avec la formation des grandes fractures qui affectent l'éprouvette (HOUPERT, 1972).

les arrêts, $\dot{\varepsilon}$ a été maintenu constant et égal à une valeur identique pour tous les intervalles compris entre ces arrêts. Trois séries de trois essais, chacune pour une vitesse $\dot{\varepsilon}$ donnée, ont été réalisées. La figure 5 représente les courbes moyennes obtenues pour chaque $\dot{\varepsilon}$ dont les valeurs ont été les suivantes : $1{,}5.10^{-6}s^{-1}$ (courbe 1), $1{,}5.10^{-5}s^{-1}$ (courbe 2) et $1{,}5.10^{-4}s^{-1}$ (courbe 3). On remarque immédiatement sur ces courbes que la relaxation des contraintes aux différents points relatifs à $\dot{\varepsilon} = 0$ est d'autant plus importante que la vitesse de déformation entre ces arrêts est plus élevée. La figure 6 représente les courbes de variation de la contrainte de relaxation en fonction de ε pour chaque $\dot{\varepsilon}$; ces courbes, marquées 1, 2 et 3 sur la figure 6, correspondent respectivement aux courbes 1, 2 et 3 de la figure 5. Elles traduisent bien l'augmentation de la contrainte de relaxation avec la vitesse de déformation $\dot{\varepsilon}$ utilisée entre les arrêts. Lorsque $\dot{\varepsilon}$ est faible, la relaxation a le temps de se produire au fur et à mesure que ε augmente ; il en résulte que la relaxation, lorsque $\dot{\varepsilon}$ est annulé, est faible. Par contre, lorsque $\dot{\varepsilon}$ est élevé, la relaxation ne se produit pas ou presque pas à mesure que ε croît et, par suite, aux arrêts $\dot{\varepsilon} = 0$, elle est plus importante. Pour les essais lents, la relaxation se produit progressivement, elle est donc faible au moment des arrêts : pour les essais rapides, elle est élevée aux arrêts, car elle n'a pas pu se produire auparavant ; il en est de même pour la microfracturation. Ces essais mettent bien en évidence le rapport entre la relaxation des contraintes et la rupture (fracturation) des roches, ainsi que

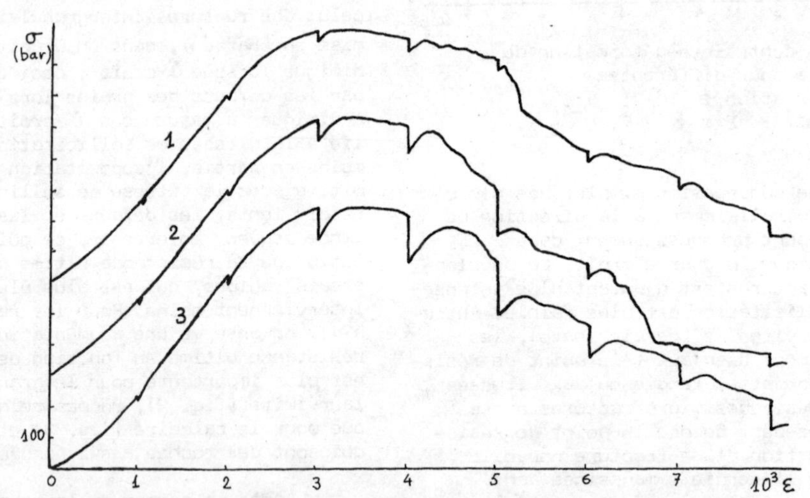

Fig. 5 – Relaxation du marbre de Carrare ; les courbes ont été réalisées à vitesse de déformation constante ($1 : \dot{\varepsilon} = 1{,}5.10^{-6}s^{-1}$; $2 : \dot{\varepsilon} = 1{,}5.10^{-5}s^{-1}$; $3 : \dot{\varepsilon} = 1{,}5.10^{-4}s^{-1}$) et à chaque accroissement de 10^{-3} de la déformation, $\dot{\varepsilon}$ a été annulé pendant 5 mn.

Les essais de relaxation permettent de mettre nettement en évidence le rapport entre la vitesse de déformation de l'éprouvette et sa fracturation au cours d'un essai de compression. Nous avons effectué, sur des éprouvettes de marbre de Carrare, des essais de relaxation au cours d'un certain nombre d'arrêts correspondant à $\dot{\varepsilon} = 0$, d'une durée de 5 mn chacun ; entre

l'influence du temps sur la formation des microfractures et des fractures relatives à la rupture : celle-ci se développent plus facilement aux faibles vitesse de déformation qu'aux vitesses élevées. Ces essais permettent également d'expliquer, du moins partiellement, l'augmentation de la résistance ultime avec la vitesse de sollicitation. Ces observations sont à rapprocher de celles de BRACE, PAULDING et SCHOLZ (1966) concernant l'influence du temps sur la microfracturation des roches, et de celles de SCHOLZ (1968) sur le rôle de la microfracturation dans les déformations non élastiques des roches, en particulier dans les déformations de fluage.

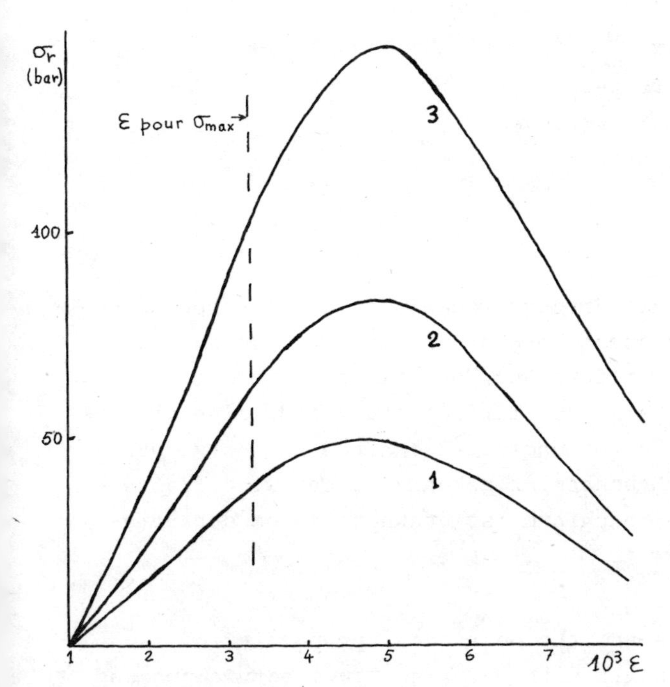

Fig. 6 - Variation de la contrainte de relaxation σ_r du marbre de Carrare en fonction de la déformation ε; les courbes correspondent respectivement aux courbes 1, 2 et 3 de la figure 5 et elles représentent la variation de σ_r relatif aux points $\dot{\varepsilon} = 0$, en fonction de ε et pour $\dot{\varepsilon} = 1{,}5.10^{-6}s^{-1}$ (courbe 1), $1{,}5.10^{-6}s^{-1}$ (courbe 2) et $1{,}5.10^{-4}s^{-1}$ (courbe 3).

CONCLUSION

Les variations de la vitesse de sollicitation ont une grande influence sur la forme de la courbe contrainte-déformation des roches, en particulier sur la partie de cette courbe située au-delà de la charge maximale et qui correspond à la phese de rupture fragile. Une augmentation de la vitesse de déformation produit les effets suivants :

- augmentation de la résistance ultime ;
- augmentation du module de déformation (la variation n'est pas très apparemte pour toutes les roches dans le domaine des $\dot{\varepsilon}$ utilisés) ;
- surélévation des courbes σ-ε;
- augmentation de la déformation relative à la charge maximale (sauf pour le marbre de Carrare pour lequel on observe l'effet inverse) ;
- diminution (en valeur absolue) de la pente de la courbe de rupture fragile ;
- aspect plus lisse et plus continu de la courbe de rupture fragile ;
- contrôle de la rupture plus difficile.

La vitesse de sollicitation joue un rôle important dans la microfracturation et la fracturation des roches. Ce rôle est mis en évidence

- par l'influence de la variation de $\dot{\varepsilon}$ sur la pente et l'aspect de la courbe de rupture fragile ;
- par la relation entre la vitesse de déformation et le taux de relaxation des contraintes.

La microfracturation (sous charge) des roches est un processus qui est essentiellement fonction du temps.

REFERENCES

BIENIAWSKI Z.T., 1970. Time-dependent behaviour of fractured rock. Rock Mech., vol. 2, p. 123-137.

BRACE W.F., PAULDING B.W., Jr et SCHOLZ C., 1966. Dilatancy in the fracture of crystalline rocks. J. Geophys. Res., vol. 71, p. 3939-3953.

HOUPERT R., 1970. La résistance à la rupture des roches en compression simple. C.R. 2e Congr. Internat. Méc. Roches, Belgrade, vol. 2, comm. 3-8, 7 p.

HOUPERT R., 1972. La rupture fragile des roches contrôlée au moyen d'une machine d'essai asservie. C.R. Acad. Sci., vol. 275, série A, p. 233-236.

HOUPERT R. et TISOT J.P., 1969. Effet d'échelle et dispersion des contraintes de rupture en compression simple dans le cas d'un granite. C.R. 2e Coll. Fissuration des Roches, Paris, Rev. Indust. Minér., n° spéc. 15 juillet 1969, p. 29-34.

HUDSON J.A., CROUCH S.L. et FAIRHURST C., 1972. Soft, stiff and servocontrolled testing machines : a review with reference to rock failure. Eng. Geol., vol. 6, p. 155-189.

PENG S.S., 1973. Time-dependent aspects of rock behaviour as measured by a servocontrolled hydraulic testing machine. Internat. J. Rock Mech. Min. Sci., vol. 10, p. 235-246.

PENG S. et PODNIEKS E.R., 1972. Relaxation and the behavior of failed rock. Internat. J. Rock Mech. Min. Sci., vol. 9, p. 699-712.

RUMMEL F. et FAIRHURST C., 1970. Determination of the post-failure behavior of brittle rock using a servo-controlled testing machine. Rock Mech., vol. 2, p. 189-204.

SCHOLZ C.H., 1968. Mechanism of creep in brittle rock. J. Geophys. Res., vol. 73, p. 3295-3302.

WILLARD R.J. et McWILLIAMS J.R., 1969. Effect of loading rate on transgranular-intergranular fracture in Charcoal gray granite. Internat. J. Rock Mech. Min. Sci., vol. 6, p. 415-421.

ZEITABHÄNGIGKEIT DER BRUCHVORGÄNGE VON GESTEINEN

TIME-DEPENDENCE OF FRACTURE PROCESSES OF ROCK MATERIALS

L'INFLUENCE DU TEMPS SUR LES PROCESSUS DE RUPTURE DES ROCHES

M. JOHN
Dipl.-Ing., Dr.techn.
Ingenieurgemeinschaft Lässer
Innsbruck, Austria

ZUSAMMENFASSUNG

Die Arbeit behandelt den Einfluß der Zeit auf die Bruchvorgänge und mechanischen Eigenschaften eines Gesteins, welches bei Belastung durch Sprödbruch versagt : Während des Bruchvorganges treten neue Risse auf, deren Ausbildung und Fortpflanzung von der Zeit abhängen; dies bedingt eine höhere Festigkeit bei schneller Belastung bzw. eine niedere Festigkeit bei langandauernder Belastung. Die Verformungseigenschaften sind erst oberhalb der Elastizitätsgrenze, welche durch den Bruchbeginn gekennzeichnet wird, zeitabhängig. Die Art des Bruches und daher auch die Bruchform ist unabhängig von der Belastungsschichte.

SUMMARY

The influence of time on the fracture processes and the mechanical properties of a material, which fails in a brittle manner, is dealt with : During the fracture process new cracks are formed; the initiation and propagation of these cracks is time-dependent resulting in higher stresses at strength failure for rapid loading and lower ones for loading over long periods of time. The deformation behaviour of the material is time-dependent starting at the elastic limit, which is brought about by fracture initiation. The type of fracturing and subsequently the mode of failure does not depend on the loading history.

RESUMÉ

Ce travail traite l'influence du temps sur les processus de rupture et sur les propriétés mechaniques des roches, qui démontrent une défaillance causée par une rupture fragile dans le cas d'un chargement. Pendant le processus de rupture des fissures nouvelles se forment, dont le développement et la propagation dépendent du temps. De ce phénomène résulte une résistance plus grande dans le cas d'une application rapide ou une résistance réduite dans le cas d'un chargement de longue durée. Les propriétés de déformation dépendent du temps seulement au delà de la limite d'élasticité, laquelle est marquée par la phase initiale de rupture. La qualité et conséquemment les formes de ces ruptures ne dépendent pas du procédé du chargement.

1. EINLEITUNG

Bei der Ausführung von Untertagebauwerken bzw. von Gründungen auf Fels kommen Belastungsänderungen mit sehr verschiedenen Geschwindigkeiten vor. Es ist daher notwendig, das Verhalten des Gesteins bzw. des Gebirges unter Belastungsbedingungen, die den tatsächlichen entsprechen, zu kennen. Weiters hat wie bei allen anderen Bauwerken die Dauerstandfestigkeit des Baummaterials - hier des Gesteins oder Gebirges - eine besondere Bedeutung.

Die Bestimmung der Gesteinseigenschaften bei hohen Belastungsgeschwindigkeiten oder bei Belastungen über lange Zeitperioden erfordert teils viel Zeit, teils hohe Kosten aufgrund von meßtechnischen Schwierigkeiten. An Hand eines Gesteinstypes - nämlich Norit - der spröd bricht, soll die Änderung des Gesteinsverhaltens unter folgenden Belastungsbedingungen in Bezug auf Zeit aufgezeigt werden :

a) kontinuierliche Belastung mit verschiedenen Belastungsgeschwindigkeiten,
b) gleichbleibende Belastung bis zum Festigkeitsversagen (Kriechversuche),
c) stufenweise Belastung : nach gleichbleibender Belastung über längere Zeit folgt kontinuierliche Belastung bis zum Festigkeitsversagen.

Weitere Versuchsergebnisse sind ausführlich an anderer Stelle (John, 1972) behandelt.

Definitionen :

Für die im weiteren verwendeten Fachausdrücke gelten folgende Definitionen, die auf den von Bieniawski (1967) im Englischen geprägten Ausdrücken beruhen :

BRUCH ist ein Vorgang, bei welchem neue Mikrorisse im Material auftreten oder bleibende Veränderungen der Materialstruktur durch Gleiten entlang von Korngrenzen oder ähnliches stattfinden.
SPRÖDBRUCH ist ein Vorgang, bei dem die im Material auftretenden Brucherscheinungen nicht unmittelbar dazu führen, daß die Festigkeit mit zunehmender Verformung abnimmt.
BRUCHBEGINN ist das Stadium, bei dem die ersten Brucherscheinungen auftreten.
BRUCHFORTPFLANZUNG ist ein Vorgang, bei welchem sich Mikrorisse im Material weiter ausdehnen bzw. weitere Brucherscheinungen hinzukommen.
FESTIGKEITSVERSAGEN ist das Stadium, bei welchem ein Material von einem Verhalten, bei dem seine Belastbarkeit mit zunehmender Verformung zunimmt, in ein Verhalten übergeht, bei dem die Belastbarkeit mit zunehmender Verformung abnimmt oder verschwindet.
DAUERSTANDFESTIGKEIT ist jene Belastbarkeit eines Materials, bei welcher es nicht versagt, wenn die äußeren Bedingungen gleichbleiben.

Das Bruchverhalten des Norit :

Bei der Belastung des Norit im einaxialen Bruch zeigt dieser anfangs linearelastisches Verhalten, da im Gestein vor der Belastung keine offenen Risse vorhanden sind. Ab einem gewissen Spannungsniveau (Bruchbeginn) treten Risse auf, die sich parallel zur Hauptspannungsrichtung in axialer Richtung fortpflanzen. Die Risse entstehen durch Zugspannungskonzentrationen an Spalten und ähnlichen Mikrohohlräumen im Material und haben daher den Charakter von Trennbrüchen. Daher ist in lateraler Richtung eine stärkere Abweichung vom linear elastischen Verhalten zu beobachten als in axialer Richtung. Bei weiterer Belastung nimmt die Dichte der Risse zu und schließlich wachsen diese zusammen und bilden die makroskopische Bruchfläche. In einer weichen Belastungsmaschine tritt unmittelbar beim Festigkeitsversagen ein plötzlicher Zusammenbruch des Norit ein, in einer sehr steifen Belastungsmaschine wird nach dem Festigkeitsversagen der Norit entlang der gebildeten Bruchfläche abgeschert.

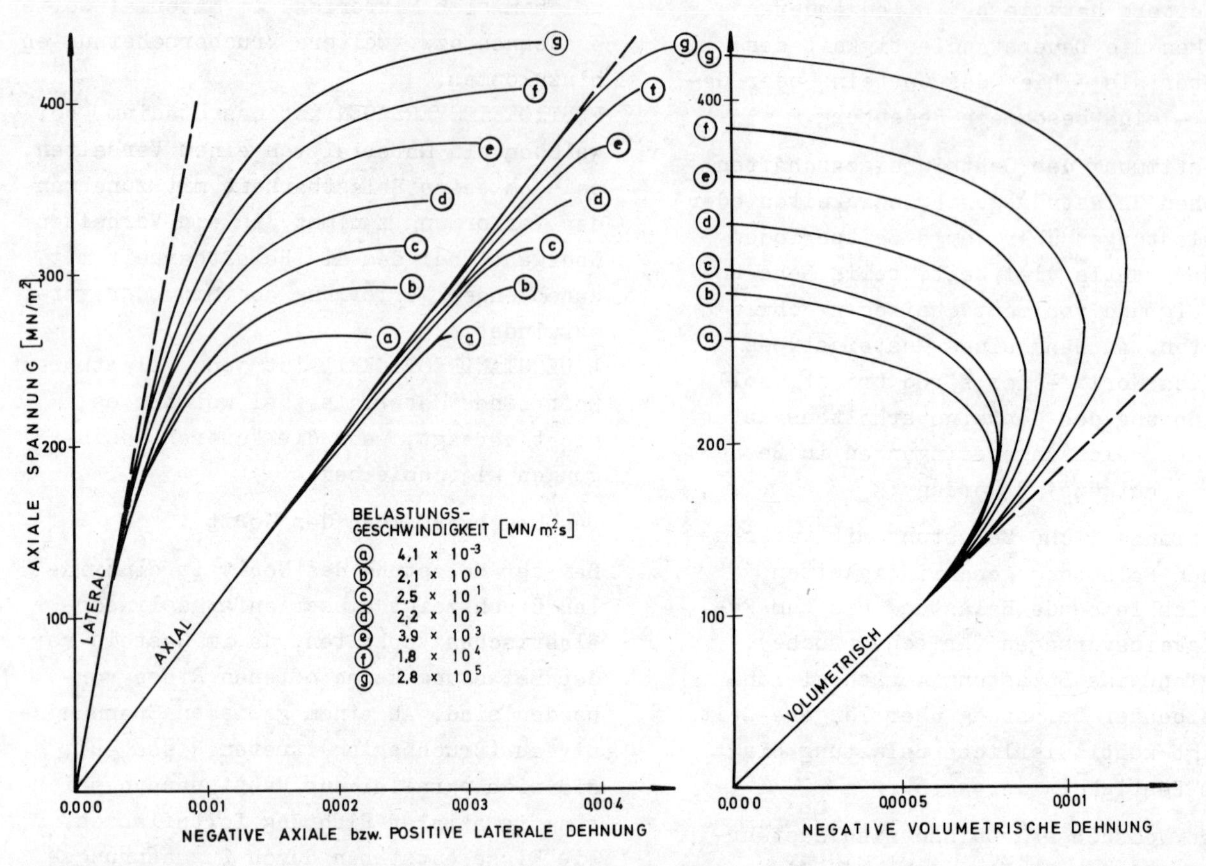

FIGUR 1: EINFLUSS DER BELASTUNGSGESCHWINDIGKEIT AUF DAS VERFORMUNGS-VERHALTEN VON NORIT IM EINAXIALEN DRUCK.

2. EINFLUSS DER BELASTUNGSGESCHWINDIGKEIT AUF DAS MECHANISCHE VERHALTEN

Aus Figur 1 ist ersichtlich, daß das elastische Verhalten des Gesteins von der Belastungsgeschwindigkeit nicht beeinflußt wird. Nach dem Bruchbeginn ist das Verformungsverhalten von der Belastungsgeschwindigkeit abhängig; das bedeutet, daß die Rißbildung und Rißausbreitung zeitabhängig ist. Je schneller die Belastung, desto weniger Zeit steht zur Rißausbreitung zur Verfügung; dies führt wiederum dazu, daß die einaxiale Druckfestigkeit mit zunehmender Belastungsgeschwindigkeit ansteigt.

Da sich die Risse vornehmlich in axialer Richtung ausbreiten ist nur ein geringer Anstieg des Verformungsmoduls zu erkennen, während das Verformungsverhalten in lateraler Richtung wesentlich stärker von der Belastungsgeschwindigkeit beeinflußt wird; die Querverformungszahl nimmt daher mit zunehmender Belastungsgeschwindigkeit ab. Das Verformungsverhalten zeigt die Tendenz, sich mit zunehmender Belastungsgeschwindigkeit elastischem Verhalten anzunähern.

Die grundsätzliche Form der Spannungs-Dehnungskurven wird von der Belastungsgeschwindigkeit nicht beeinflußt, ebenso wie das Bruchverhalten als solches; dies wird durch die Tatsache unterstrichen, daß die Bruchform - hier die eines Doppelkegels - bei allen Versuchen ähnlich ausgebildet war.

3. EINFLUSS GLEICHBLEIBENDER BELASTUNG AUF DAS MECHANISCHE VERHALTEN

Es ist bekannt (Robertson, 1964, Hardy, 1965), daß zeitabhängige Verformung, auch "Kriechen" genannt, beim Gestein in grundsätzlich derselben Form wie bei anderen Materialien wie z.B. Einzelkristalle, Metalle und Eis beobachtet wird. Wenn der Norit üben den Bruchbeginn hinaus belastet wird und die Belastung vor dem Festigkeitsversagen konstant gehalten wird, tritt zeitabhängige Verformung auf, die durch zeitabhängige Brucherscheinungen bedingt ist, da die Verformungen in lateraler Richtung viel stärker ausgeprägt sind als in axialer Richtung.

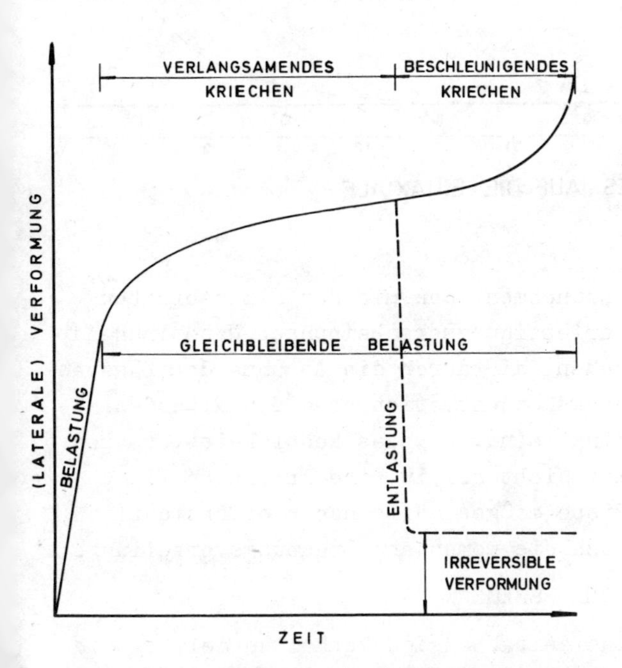

FIGUR 2: SCHEMATISCHE DARSTELLUNG DER ZEITABHÄNGIGEN VERFORMUNG VON NORIT BEI GLEICHBLEIBENDER BELASTUNG UND NACH ENTLASTUNG.

Das Verformungsverhalten des Norit ist schematisch in Figur 2 dargestellt. Interessant ist dabei, daß experimentell nur 2 Stadien, nämlich verlangsamendes und beschleunigendes Kriechen und kein Stadium mit konstanter Verformungsgeschwindigkeit festgestellt wurde (vgl. Cruden, 1971).

Bei den verschiedenen Versuchen traten besonders während des beschleunigenden Kriechens starke Streuungen im Verformungsverhalten und folglich auch in der Zeit bis zum Festigkeitsversagen auf. Dies deutet darauf hin, daß das Zusammenwachsen der Risse von der Mikrostruktur des Gesteins abhängt.

Die Verformungen während des verlangsamenden Kriechens sind teilweise reversibel, teilweise irreversibel. Die reversiblen Verformungen werden während der Entlastung zurückgewonnen; eine zeitabhängige Verformung nach vollkommener Entlastung wird nur in vernachlässigbarem Ausmaß beobachtet.

4. VERGLEICH DES MECHANISCHEN VERHALTENS BEI VERSCHIEDENEN BELASTUNGSARTEN

Bei Versuchen mit gleichbleibender Belastung werden Dehnungs-Zeitkurven (auch Kriechkurven genannt) direkt gemessen (vgl. Figur 2). Solche Kurven können jedoch auch aus Ergebnissen von Versuchen mit verschiedenen Belastungsgeschwindigkeiten ermittelt werden, indem für ein bestimmtes Spannungsniveau die Zeit und die entsprechende Dehnung bei verschiedenen Belastungsgeschwindigkeiten berechnet werden. Es zeigt sich, daß die so ermittelten Kurven denselben Charakter haben als jene Kurven, die bei gleichbleibender Belastung aufgenommen werden. Vergleicht man die Kurven beider Belastungsarten für dasselbe Spannungsniveau, stellt sich heraus, daß die Dehnungsgeschwindigkeit unter gleichbleibender Belastung höher ist. Dies führt dazu, daß die Festigkeit bei gleichbleibender Belastung niedriger ist als bei kontinuierlicher Belastung (siehe Figur 3).

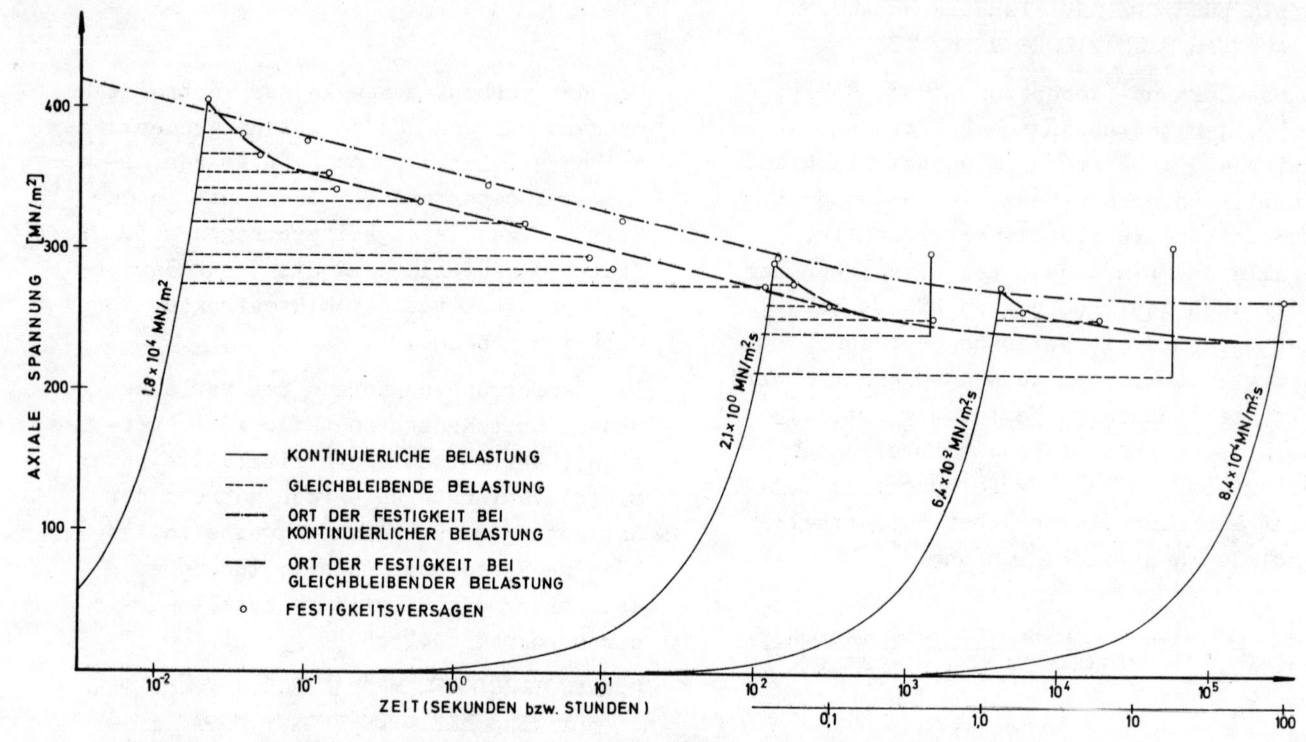

FIGUR 3: EINFLUSS DES BELASTUNGSVORGANGES AUF DIE EINAXIALE DRUCKFESTIGKEIT VON NORIT.

In Figur 3 sind die Festigkeitswerte verschiedener Belastungsarten gegen die Zeit im logarithmischen Maßstab dargestellt. Die Festigkeit bei kontinuierlicher Belastung liegt immer um denselben Wert über der Festigkeit bei gleichbleibender Belastung. Zwischen den beiden Orten der Festigkeit gleichbleibender und kontinuierlicher Belastung besteht eine Übergangszone, die sich über eine Zehnerpotenz erstreckt. Bis zu Versuchsdauern von etwa 10 Stunden sind beide Orte der Festigkeit zeitabhängig. Bei Versuchsdauer bis über 100 Stunden besteht noch immer ein deutlicher Unterschied zwischen der Festigkeit bei gleichbleibender und kontinuierlicher Belastung; das bedeutet, daß die Belastungsgeschichte für die Festigkeit entscheidend ist. Dies wird auch durch die Ergebnisse der Versuche mit stufenweiser Belastung unterstrichen, die sogar noch höhere Festigkeitswerte aufzeigen als jene bei kontinuierlicher Belastung. Es ist anzunehmen, daß mit der Rißausbreitung Verfestigungserscheinungen Hand in Hand gehen, die durch die Abnahme der Zugspannungskonzentrationen an den Rißenden bedingt sind. Für das Festigkeitsversagen ist nicht allein eine kritische Dichte der Risse maßgebend, sondern offensichtlich auch die momentane Spannungsverteilung.

SCHLUSSBEMERKUNG

Das zeitabhängige Verhalten der Gesteine kann mittels verschiedenster Belastungsarten bestimmt werden, die Ergebnisse stehen miteinander in Beziehung, da der Einfluß der Zeit bei allen Versuchen denselben Ursprung, nämlich in Brucherscheinungen, hat. Als Ursache für die Zeitabhängigkeit der Rißausbreitung werden aufgrund der vorliegenden Versuchsergebnisse Korrosionserscheinungen, die von der Spannung abhängen, (siehe auch Scholz, 1968, Cruden, 1970) vermutet.

ANERKENNUNG

Die vorliegende Arbeit ist das Ergebnis von Untersuchungen, die der Autor während seiner Anstellung im "Council of Scientific and Industrial Research" in Südafrika durchführte. Er ist Herrn Direktor Dr. H. G. Denkhaus und Dr. Z.T. Bieniawski für die Erlaubnis, die Ergebnisse der Untersuchungen veröffentlichen zu dürfen, zu Dank verpflichtet, ebenso wie allen Mitgliedern der Geomechanik-Abteilung insbesondere Herrn N. Krauland für deren Unterstützung.

AUTORENVERZEICHNIS

Bieniawski, Z.T., 1967, Mechanism of brittle fracture of rock, International Journal of Rock Mechanics and Mining Sciences, Vol. 4, p 395 - 406.

Cruden, D.M., 1970, A theory of brittle creep in rock under uniaxial compression, Journal of Geophysical Research, Vol. 75, p 3431 - 3442.

Cruden, D.M., 1971, Single-increment creep experiments on rock under uniaxial compression, International Journal of Rock Mechanics and Mining Sciences, Vol. 8, p 127 - 142.

Hardy, H.R. Jr. 1965, Inelastic behaviour of geologic materials, Ph.D.Thesis, Virginia Polytechnic Institute, Engineering Mechanics Department.

John, M. 1972, Time-dependence of mechanical properties and fracture processes of rock materials (Englisches Original mit deutscher Übersetzung), Doktorarbeit, Technische Hochschule Graz, Österreich.

Robertson, E.C., 1964, Viscoelasticity of rocks, State of Stress in the Earth's Crust, ed. W.Judd, American Elsevier Publishing Co., New York, p 181-233.

Scholz, C.H., 1968, Mechanism of creep in brittle rock, Journal of Geophysical Research, Vol. 73, p 3295 - 3302.

AUSGEWÄHLTE BIBLIOGRAPHIE

Brace, W.F. and Jones, A.H., 1971, Comparsion of uniaxial deformation in shock and static loading of three rocks, Journal of Geophysical Research, Vol. 76, p 4913 - 4921.

Griggs, D.T., 1939, creep of rocks, Journal Geology, Vol. 47, p 225 - 251, 255.

Heard, H.C., 1963, Effect of large changes in strainrate in the experimental deformation of Yule Marble, Journal of Geology, Vol. 71, p 162 - 195.

Horibe, T. and Kobayashi, R., 1965, On the mechanical behaviour of rocks under various loading rates, Rock Mechanics, reprinted from Journal of the Society of Material Science, Japan, Vol. 14, no 141.

Kumar, A., 1968, The effect of stress rate and temperature on the strength of basalt and granite, Geophysics, Vol. 33, p 501 - 510.

Maiden, C.J. and Green, S.J., 1966, Compressive strain-rate tests on six selected materials at strain rates from 10^{-4} to 10^{4} in/in/sec, Journal of Applied Mechanics, Vol. 33, p 496 - 504.

Perkins, R.D., et al., 1970, Uniaxial stress behaviour of porphyritic tonalite at strain rates to 10^{3}/second, International Journal of Rock Mechanics and Mining Sciences, Vol. 7, p 527 - 535.

Serdengecti, S. and Boozer, G.D., 1961 The effects of strain rate and temperature on the behaviour of rocks subjected to triaxial compression, Proceedings 4th Symposium on Rock Mechanics, Penn. State Univ., p 83 - 97.

ENGINEERING PROPERTIES OF YIELDING ROCK
PROPRIÉTÉS MÉCANIQUES DE LA ROCHE DÉFORMABLE
MECHANISCHE EIGENSCHAFTEN VERFORMBAREM FELSENS

R.G.T. LANE   Sir Alexander Gibb + Partners, London

J.L. KNILL   Professor of Eng. Geology, Imperial College, London, England

SUMMARY

Rock masses may exhibit long term creep when under stress or subjected to change of stress; in other cases mass movement may occur due to high shear stress at critical surfaces within the mass. The geological factors which give rise to these effects are described. Case histories are quoted which indicate the effects on engineering works and, particularly, the time scale of these movements which, according to circumstances, may have continued for several weeks - or for several years - or for several thousand years. The scope of site investigations necessary in such cases is described; the conclusions of the paper put the case for further research.

RESUME

Les massifs rocheux peuvent être susceptibles au fluage sous l'effet de contraintes suivies ou du changement de ces contraintes; dans d'autres cas des cheminements de masse peuvent se produire en raison des hautes contraintes de cisaillement existant sur les surfaces critiques à l'intérieur de la masse. Les facteurs géologiques qui produisent ces effets sont décrits. Des cas connus sont cités, où sont démontrés les effets sur des ouvrages d'art - et en particulier, l'échelonnement de ces déplacements qui, selon les conditions, peuvent avoir continué pendant plusieurs semaines - plusieurs années - ou plusieurs millénaires. L'étendue des travaux de reconnaissances nécessaires dans de pareils cas est décrite; les conclusions tirées en fin d'article font ressortir la nécessité de recherches plus approfondies.

ZUSAMMENFASSUNG

Wenn gespannt, oder wenn die Verteilung der Spannungen verändert wird, könnten sich in Felsmassen Zeichen von langfristigem Kriechen zeigen; in anderen Fällen könnten Massenbewegungen wegen hoher Scherspannungen auf kritischen Flächen innerhalb der Massen stattfinden. Die geologischen Faktoren, die diese Einwirkung verursachen, werden beschrieben. Beispiele von ausgeführten Bauprojekten werden gegeben, die im allgemeinen die Einwirkung an Bauwerken bezeichnen und insbesondere die Zeitdehnungen dieser Bewegungen, die je Umstände nach wochenlang, jahrelang oder jahrtausende lang fortgedauert haben können. Der Umfang der in solchen Fällen erfordlichen Baugrunduntersuchung wird auch beschrieben, und im Abschluss des Berichts wurde der Fall für weitere Forschung vorgelegt.

Introduction

The behaviour of large in-situ rock masses brings important problems which the Engineer will have to take into account in his design, and which the owner will have to live with, as it may be impractical to modify the natural movements of the rock mass. Many such problems are associated with long term time effects and these may include:-

(a) Yielding rocks, i.e. rocks which exhibit long term creep when under stress or subjected to change of stress.

(b) Mass movement, i.e. where the shear strength of the rock mass may reduce or the stresses may increase until the stress exceeds the strength. Although such movements are often associated with a quick event, they frequently occur as slow creep.

(c) Swelling rocks, i.e. rocks which change volume when there is a change of moisture content or porewater pressure. The special problems of swelling rock are not dealt with in this paper.

The normal geological descriptions of rock exposures and of bore-hole cores need not provide any information as to the nature or extent of these problems, but a competent geological report of the area should indicate whether such problems are likely to be met. There is no recognised systematic procedure to enable the Engineer positively to identify these effects quantitatively; and it may be difficult to initiate investigations and research when the researcher knows that the results of his work will not be available for many years.

The condition of "Yielding Rock" may be foreseen from jacking and similar tests, provided that these tests have been carried out in a standard manner with intervals at constant load after each addition or reduction of load, to record any continued creep during these periods. This paper describes several case histories which show that such a condition may be a sign that the rock under stress will continue to creep for long periods - often measured in years. These tests are also valuable in that approximate moduli of deformation can be calculated giving useful data for the design of structures supporting or supported by the rock.

Geological Factors

All geological materials when influenced by conditions of elevated stress or temperature can be subject to time dependent strain. However, at the lower stress or temperature conditions associated with normal engineering experience such continuing deformation is limited to particular geological environments. In sound rock conditions, a change of stress results in deformation which is either instantaneous or continues for a relatively short period after the stress change. Yielding rock is characterised by continuing, detectable deformation at relatively low total stress levels. The prime geological causes of yielding rock conditions may be summarised as follows:-

(i) the presence of creep-susceptible materials either as a major or minor rock-forming constituent. For example, clay minerals, micas, calcite and gypsum can all contribute to creep in a rock mass whether disseminated through the rock or actually constituting the rock material.

(ii) a change in rock properties as a consequence of mineral or textural changes. This could involve solution (e.g. calcite, rock salt), change in hydration state (e.g. gypsum/anhydrite active clay minerals) or decay (e.g. pyrite, marcasite) of the contained minerals.

(iii) the presence of voids permitting a progressive reduction in porosity as particle or grain boundaries moved and densification proceeded. Such a situation could result from a primary rock texture, such as porosity in a sandstone or vesicles in a basalt. Alternatively, secondary microscopic fracturing, stress relief or weathering might contribute to a progressive alteration in voids distribution.

In general terms, the engineer might expect to find yielding rock conditions in the following geological situations: weathered or hydrothermally altered rocks, closely sheared and fractured rocks, micaceous and argillaceous rocks, rocks with a significant porosity and soluble rocks and minerals in contact with aggressive or active groundwater flow.

Case Histories

1. Kariba South Underground Cavern Wall Movements

This case illustrates the behaviour of a rock mass which shows the usual elastic plus plastic deformation in a jack test, but with which there is no significant time effect during intervals at constant load in the test.

The Kariba dam and underground works are located on the Zambesi River between Zambia and Rhodesia. The engineering works are constructed on medium grade metamorphic rocks of Pre-Cambrian age.

At the time when the design was first prepared in 1955, knowledge of rock behaviour was based on experience without the advantage of recent research in rock mechanics. Information was available from bore hole cores and adits. The geological reports indicated that the cavern would be excavated mostly in sound massive gneiss, but with a faulted zone crossing the north-west corner. It was considered that the side walls would move inwards, during and after excavating, and as the crane beams were supported at the springing of the concrete lining of the vault, provision was made for future lateral adjustment of the crane rails. (Figure 1).

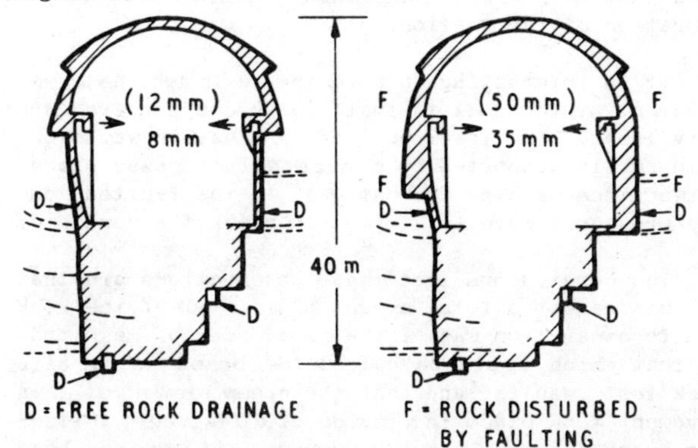

ACTUAL MOVEMENTS AT CRANE RAIL LEVEL, AND ESTIMATED ( )
CREEP TOTAL

KARIBA UNDERGROUND MACHINE HALL

FIG.1.

An approximate estimate of the magnitude of the movement was made based on the following assumptions:-

(a) Since the centre of the cavern is only 140 m below ground - and half this depth is more or less weathered - the vertical stress in the rock would be that due to the weight of the rock above.

(b) An equivalent circular excavation was assumed. At this time, the development of the finite element method of analysis was still in its infancy.

(c) The modulus of deformability for the rock had to be assumed as no test results were available at that time. Poissons ratio of 0.5 was assumed although this is probably only true at great depths.

(d) The calculated total reduction in width across the excavation was
12 mm in sound rock
50 mm in the faulted zone
corresponding to moduli of deformation of about 80,000 kg/cm^2 (8,000 N/mm^2), and 20,000 kg/cm^2 (2,000 N/mm^2) respectively.

The actual behaviour of the rock can be compared with these assumptions. Although it was impractical to carry out tests at the locations of the cavern excavation, tests were subsequently made in similar slightly weathered gneiss in adits.

The average modulus of deformation calculated from these jacking tests was 58,000 kg/cm^2 (5,800 N/mm^2), about 30% of the strain being plastic.

A typical jacking test result is shown on Figure 2. It will be seen that there was no appreciable time-strain during the intervals following increments of load. The actual inward movements recorded across the cavern were:-

8mm in the sound gneiss
33mm in the faulted zone

These movements took place during the construction contract in the period of completion of the concrete work in the powerhouse. They do not include the immediate elastic movement. There has been no recorded subsequent movement, and it has not been necessary to re-adjust the crane rails during thirteen years of operation of the station.

It is interesting to note that although the creep movement of the rock is small the forces involved are very great. The lower part of the cavern walls was temporarily supported by concrete buttresses placed between the machine foundations. In the faulted zone the pressures were sufficient to crack the concrete.

The conclusions from these observations are that in this case the total amount of movement of the rock due to excavation was of the same order of magnitude as that which would be calculated based on in-situ jack test results; and that the creep element of this movement took place in a period of a few weeks following excavation. Subsequent movement, if any, has been insignificant.

2. Farahnaz Pahlavi Buttress Dam Movements

The Farahnaz Pahlavi dam is located on the Jaj-e-Rud immediately north-east of Tehran. The dam foundations are composed of folded quartzites, sandstones and shales.

A typical result from a jack test of the foundation rock at this 105m high concrete buttress dam site is shown in Figure 2. Note the very plastic behaviour of the rock mass, and the large amount of creep which took place during the intervals after increments of load had been applied.

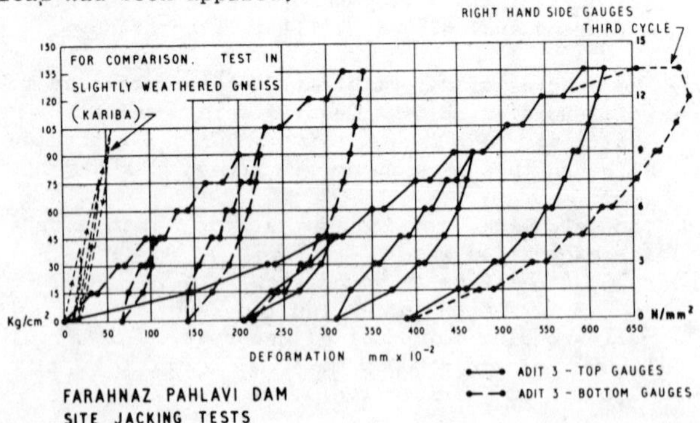

FIG.2.

Careful records have been kept of the behaviour of the dam since impounding commenced. The results for a typical buttress (No. 12) are shown on Figures 3 and 4. This buttress is 85m high and the movements are measured from a collimation line at road level, and from the deflections relative to a simple pendulum anchored in the rock 35m below the buttress foundation.

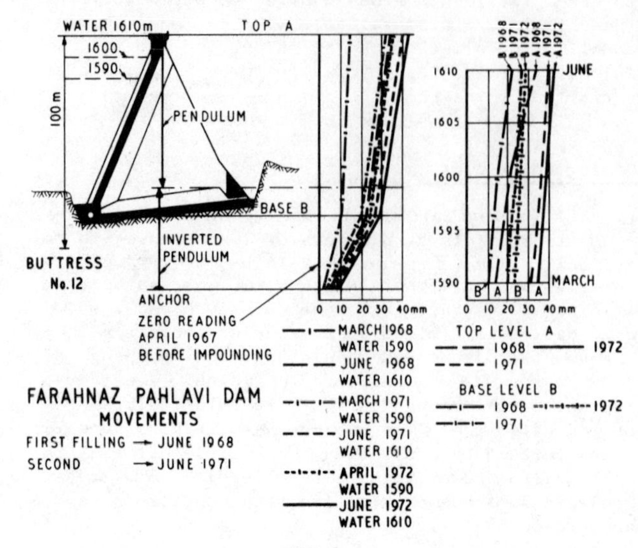

FIG.3.

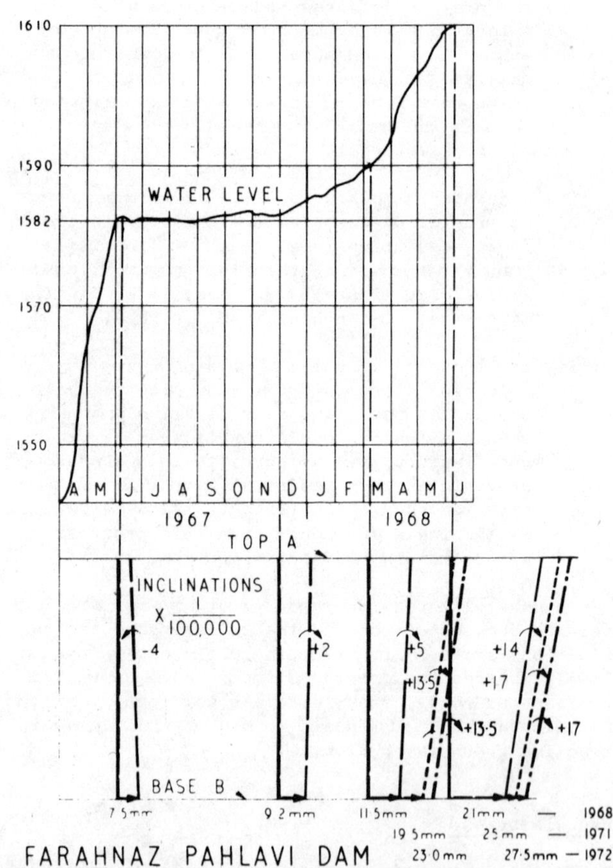

FARAHNAZ PAHLAVI DAM
DISPLACEMENTS AND INCLINATIONS BUTTRESS 12
FIG.4.

The initial impounding of the reservoir first loads the valley bottom and the heel of the buttress, thus causing an inclination towards upstream and a downstream translation. As the water pressure distribution in the rock changes, the buttress becomes inclined towards downstream and translation continues.

Note how both inclination and translation increased during the period of constant water level in 1968 and that the total deflections are greater in 1971, and further increased in 1972 compared with 1968, for the same water level.

Such behaviour could be expected in principle, based on the jack test results - but the time scale of the movements is surprising. It will undoubtedly be several more years before the buttress movements have stabilised.

A precise analysis of the movement is difficult because of complex factors which may affect it - for example, the change of water pressure distribution in the rock mass, which may take several years to stabilise. There are two effects from this cause alone - water pressure causing rock deformation and creep and water in the rock joints causing a change of strength and deformability of the rock mass. A drainage system was provided under the dam foundations.

Because of the rock conditions at this site, each buttress was built on its independent raft to allow for some differential movement.

The conclusions from these observations are:-

(a) The general pattern of behaviour of the dam and its foundations is that which would be expected from the rock type as shown by inspection and tests.

(b) The initial movements following first loading of the structure were found to be of the same order of magnitude as those which would be calculated based on the deformabilities given by the in-situ jack tests.

(c) Creep movements will continue for a long time - several years at least.

(d) Special consideration has to be given to any subsidiary works which connect between buttresses, or which may connect between rock upstream and downstream of the dam.

3. Kariba South Bank and Powerhouse Access Tunnel

A simplified geological section of the south side of Kariba Gorge below the dam is shown on Figure 5. The geological reports of Dr. L. Dubertret have described the disturbed nature of the rock near ground surface although the quartzite below a depth of 15 to 20m and the underlying gneiss remain relatively undisturbed, i.e. there is no significant displacement of a block of rock relative to adjacent rock.

It has been observed, since the original surveys, that the surface of the south bank of the gorge in this section was moving. Records showed that movements accelerated after rain, and the spray from floodgate spilling. Drainage was provided by drilling from galleries in the hillside. This immediately improved the situation, but movements continue on a reduced scale (Fig. 5). The situation has been still further improved by sealing the surface of the ground with mortar over the joints in the rock. Jack tests in the quartzite show that as a result of close clay filled joints, the rock mass has a low modulus of deformation, a ratio of plastic strain to total strain of 67 to 73% and considerable time creep during test. A finite element study showed that the pattern of surface movements is similar to that which would result from rock creeping due to the gravitational stresses in the gorge side. The main effect of rain is to add pressures due to water in the joints to these stresses, although there could also be some effect due to weakening or lubrication at the rock joints when wet, and decrease in effective stress normal to the direction of sliding.

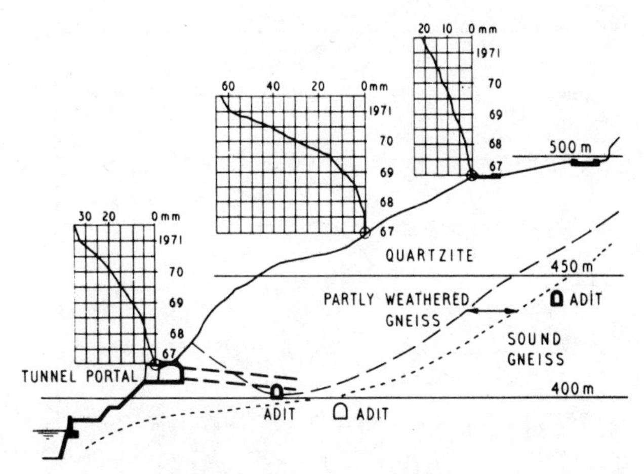

KARIBA GORGE - SOUTH SIDE

FIG. 5.

Although such movements seem small and are only shown up by instrumentation, they become significant in time.

The conclusion from these observations is that where a free surface of yielding rock exists, and that surface is not in a natural state of stress equilibrium creep will take place indefinitely. Any works passing through such creeping zones must be designed to take the movements into account as it would usually be quite impractical to try to stop the movements completely.

4. Natural Rock Slide Movements in Scotland.

The Scottish Highlands are predominantly composed of metamorphic rocks of Pre-Cambrian and early palaeozoic age. During the past 2 million years the region has been glaciated and this had contributed to oversteepening of the valley sides and consequential mass movements. A large number of natural slope failures have been identified and these appear to have occurred following the final retreat of the ice sheets some 9,000 years ago. The failures range in scale from individual joint block movements to displacements a kilometre or more across. There is evidence of continuing movement at a slide in the south-west Highlands on the eastern side of Loch Long. Here the rock consists of low grade metasediments including phyllites and some mica schists; there is a vegetated cover. The ground slope averages 32° and the regional survey has demonstrated that failures are relatively common in hillsides with slope angles of this order. The failure appears to have occurred as a translational movement in an area some 100m across, about 180m above sea level, the displacement of the slide mass being in the overall range of 50 to 100m. The failed rock mass is crossed by a railway and displacement measurements have been made in this vicinity since 1957. The observations indicate a steady downslope movement ranging between 22 and 41 mm/yr and averaging 34 mm/yr. The rate of movement as illustrated by the displacements at one location (Fig.6), fluctuates so that for a period of years the total rate of displacement may be as high as 50 mm/yr whereas for other periods the movement is markedly slower. Different observation points show a broadly similar pattern of movement indicating these responses are not randomly distributed throughout the rock but reflect a total displacement.

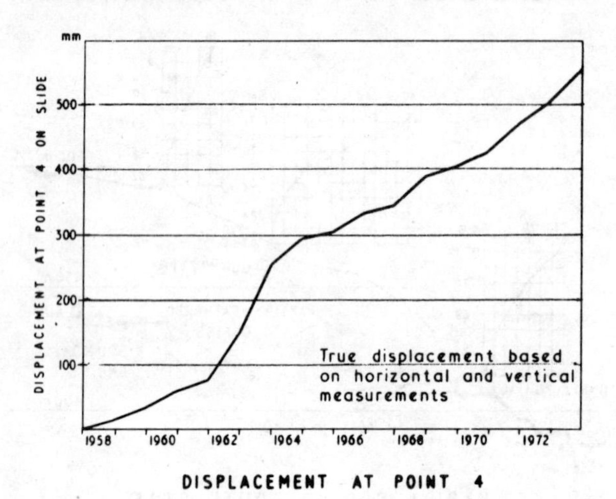

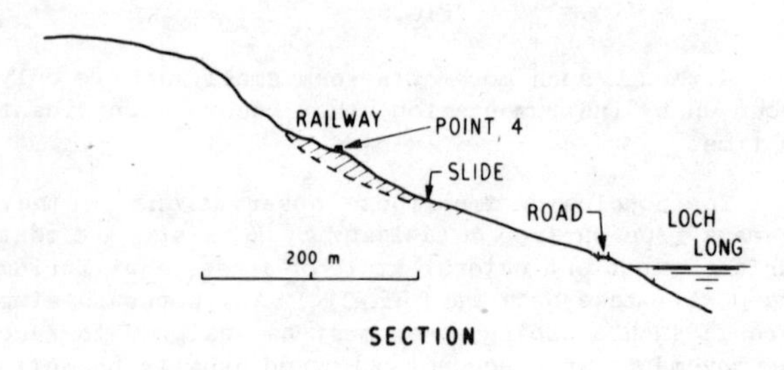

LOCH LONG

FIG.6.

Assuming that the average rate of displacement has been maintained throughout the whole history of the slide then the age of the slide is in the general range of 1,000 to 3,000 years. Although not consistent with the proposition that the slide might have occurred soon after the ice retreat, it is an indication of the order of antiquity of the movements. There are no possible artificial influences which could have induced the movement and there are few that encourage the continuing deformation, or yielding, of a rock mass along a presumed slide surface.

5. Rock Slide in the Malvern Hills

The Malvern Hills are formed by a horst like block of Pre-Cambrian rocks which divide the Palaeozoic rocks of Wales and the Welsh Borderlands from the Mesozoic sediments of central England. The Malvernian rocks are strongly deformed gneisses and granitoid rocks presumably representing an up-thrust part of the basement. The area is one of the few local sources of rock material and, in consequence, there has been an active history of quarrying. The method of quarrying adopted in the past was based upon undercutting the toe of the slope by blasting and permitting the natural weaknesses in the rock structure to assist downward displacement of the rock. In consequence, the quarry slopes have been worked at a maximum slope angle. As the quarry faces became higher, or quarries were abandonned, failures occurred primarily as a result of translational sliding or major discontinuities.

The North Quarry is a disused quarry excavated in sheared granodioritic rocks which contain abundant slickensided listric shear surfaces coated with chlorite and epidote. The main face of the quarry is 92m rising at an overall angle of 42°. Natural ground slopes are commonly in the range of 20° - 30°. The rock face (Fig.7) is about 55m in height, the lower part of the slope being mantled in scree. A rock slide developed in the top of the quarry in August 1958 and since that time movement has continued. The margin of the slide is set about 60m back from the edge of the quarry and there is now a difference of about 5m in level between the top of the slide mass and the unmoved ground behind.

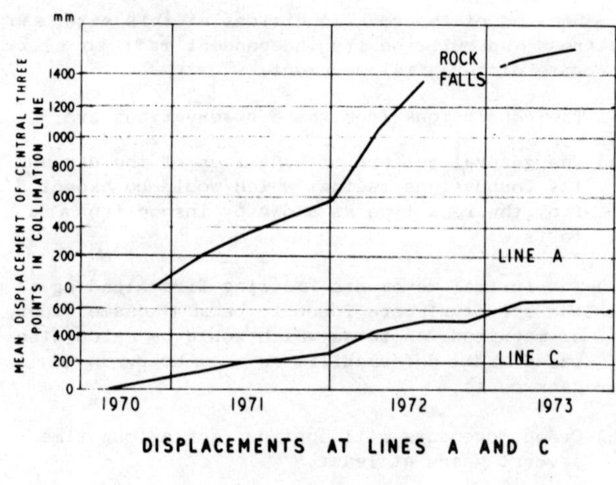

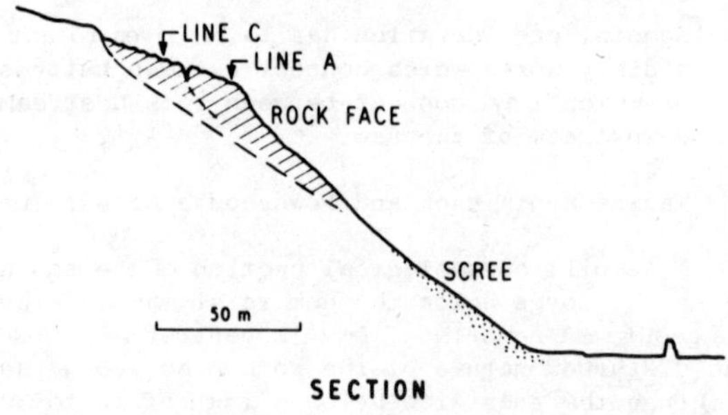

NORTH QUARRY, MALVERN HILLS

FIG.7.

Displacement observations have been made since 1970 and are based on five collimation lines set out across the upper part of the slide mass. The pattern of movement is quite characteristic in that the faster rates of movement are within the centre and towards the front of the slide mass. The mean rate of horizontal movement is 200 mm/yr although the actual rates measured range from 100 to 1,000 mm/yr. These rates, in this artificially induced rock slide, are in marked contrast to those for the Loch Long slide described previously. There is a marked seasonal influence on movement rate (Fig. 7) which is presumably a reflection of winter precipitation, although the permanent water table is well below the base of the slide surface. One aspect of interest is the extent to which the higher winter rate of deformation continued into the summer of 1972 along the edge of the quarry face (Line A). This was associated with a series of minor rock falls. This observation is of importance in that it demonstrates the consequential effects of an acceleration in movement about a limiting rate of yield.

Site Investigations

It is evident from the case histories that it is necessary to ascertain whether the critical conditions described will be met at the site of the works, and it is desirable to be able to estimate the magnitude of possible mass-rock movements as far as possible. The greatest possibility of identifying such critical conditions will be at locations where the rock mass has been over-stressed - such as in steep natural or artificial rock faces.

It is assumed that the normal inspections, exploratory works and site and laboratory tests will be made, and that no description is necessary here. Some less common, but nevertheless well-known, tests and investigations will be made according to circumstances, such as:-

(a) Recognition of specific rock types or rock conditions, as listed in Chapter 2.

(b) Existing steep slopes.

(i) Survey a number of surface targets to monitor translation and settlement with time.

(ii) Drill holes for measuring relative displacement between the bottom of the hole and higher levels. If landslide risk only is being investigated, simple holes with thin linings may be made and plumbed from time to time to find the level, and the time where and when a blockage is caused by sliding.

(iii) Slope indicators may be used to monitor creep movements. Unfortunately these may be put out of use if movement is sufficiently concentrated to cause blockage. The more satisfactory arrangement is a deep shaft within which a pendulum or inverted pendulum is installed. The shaft is lined with discrete well separated concrete rings and provided with ladder and platforms, so that measurement of the side walls relative to the pendulum can be made at right angles to each other.

(c) Yielding Rock Masses

Standard jacking tests, or various well-known alternatives such as borehole dilatometers are available to ascertain the elastic, instantaneous permanent displacement and creep characteristics of the rock. These provide the best indicator available and in common use to show the possible long-term behaviour of the rock mass. Unfortunately measurement is related to the short term time of the test, and the long term effect is inferred on the basis of experience and observation from case histories. Particularly in the case of jack tests as many as possible should be carried out as individual tests may be affected by rock disturbance during excavation.

Conclusions

The behaviour of large rock masses is a matter of observation and modern instrumentation has shown that there is a continuous movement of many natural rock masses although the visible signs, if any, may appear as a series of events. Instrumentation further shows that any action leading to a change of stress in the rock mass may initiate long term movements if the rock has yielding or swelling characteristics, or is weak at potential shear surfaces.

In the case of yielding rock, the jack or similar test provides important information in a general sense. If there is an appreciable plastic strain during the test, but with no measurable strain during the intervals after increments of load, then the ultimate strain in the rock mass following loading (or excavation) will be of the same order of magnitude as that derived from the deformability coefficient calculated from the test. This ultimate strain will not take place immediately but probably over a period of several weeks. It seems that the greater the degree of plastic strain in the test, the greater the time that stabilisation is likely to take.

In rocks which have joints at close centres, where the joints are not tight or are filled with clay or granular material, or in weathered rock, the yield tests may show creep continuing during intervals after increments of load. In such cases, the rock mass may already be slowly moving. A change of stress will initiate further movements which will continue for long periods of time - years, or even indefinitely.

It is clear that further research is necessary to enable long-term movements to be forecast on a quantitative basis. Many long-term site tests and measurements are required in conjunction with short term tests and observation of prototype behaviour. Such a programme of investigation and research would not be complete without a comprehensive geological appraisal of the site from initial site report through construction; and eventually an engineering design appraisal which separates the many cause and effect factors which influence the prototype movements.

ACKNOWLEDGEMENTS

The authors wish to record their indebtedness to the owners of schemes referred to in the paper:-

Kariba Hydro-Electric Scheme - The Central African Power Corporation

Farahnaz Pahlavi Dam - The Tehran Regional Water Board.

* * * * * * * * * * *

REFERENCES

1. Kariba Underground Works Design and Construction Methods - R.G.T. Lane & J. W. Roff Trans. 7th International Congress on Large Dams, 1961.

2. Farahnaz Pahlavi Dam at Latiyan - K.F. Scott, W.T.N. Reeve, and J. P. Germond, Proc., I.C.E. Vol.39, March 1963.

* * * * * * * * * * *

A STUDY OF ROCK CREEP UNDER LABORATORY CONDITIONS

D'ÉTUDE EN LABORATOIRE DU FLUAGE DES ROCHES

STUDIUM ÜBER DAS KRIECHEN DER GESTEINE AUFGRUND VON LABORUNTERSUCHUNGEN

B.V. MATVEYEV
Cand. of Sciences

J. M. KARTASHOV
Cand. of Sciences

VNIMI, Leningrad, USSR

Summary

The report summarizes the results of studies of rock creep. A schematic design of hydraulic installation for laboratory tests of rocks and testing techniques are reported. Experimental data are processed with the aid of equations based on the theory of linear hereditary creep. The validity of this theory for rocks is confirmed. Basic principles of program development for computer calculations of equation parameters are discussed.

Resume

Dans le rapport, on rend compte des résultats d'études des roches au point de vue du fluage. On donne le schéma d'une installation hydraulique pour les essais au laboratoire des échantillons de roches et la méthode d'essai. Le dépouillement des données d'expérience a été fait à l'aide des équations de la théorie du fluage héréditaire linéaire. On a démontré l'applicabilité de cette théorie aux roches. On a exposé les principes essentiels de l'établissement d'un programme pour le calcul sur machine des paramètres des équations.

Zusammenfassung

Im Vortrag sind die Ergebnisse der Untersuchungen der Gesteine auf Kriechen erörtert. Es wird das Schema einer hydraulischen Anlage für die Laboruntersuchungen der Gesteine und die Verfahrensmethodik beschrieben. Die Bearbeitung der Versuchsangaben erfolgte mittels Gleichungen aus der Theorie des linearen vererbten Kriechens. Es wurde die Verwendbarkeit dieser Theorie an die Gesteine bewiesen. Es wurden die Hauptgrundsätze für die Zusammenstellung eines Programmes für die Maschinenberechnung der Gleichungsparameter dargelegt.

While differing from classical elastic or friable media in their physico-mechanical properties, rocks possess some rheological features, i.e. they are opt to creeping, relaxation and strength changes under a long-term load, or as a result of the changed rate of strain.

Rheological processes occurring in rocks are described, chiefly, by analytical methods or by means of structural (rheological) models. Mathematical descriptions of rock strain with time are generally based on various theories of creep, such as the theory of hardening the theory of aging, the theory of flow and the theory of heredity (1). The theory of linear hereditary creep is widely used in the calculations of the mechanism or rock pressure and shifts. The general low of linear deformation suggested by L.Boltzmann and further developed by V.Volterra may be written as:

$$\mathcal{E}(t) = \frac{1}{E}\left[\sigma(t) + \int_0^t L(t,\tau)\sigma(\tau)d\tau\right], \qquad (1)$$

where $\mathcal{E}(t)$ and $\sigma(t)$ - strain and stress for a point on creep curve at the moment t, respectively;

E - elastic modulus of specimen material;

$L(t,\tau)$ - nucleus of integral equation.

Zh.S.Erzhanov [2] suggested the approximation of the deformation process by the law of linear hereditary creep with the Abel's (power) nucleus, such as

$$L(t,\tau) = \delta(t-\tau)^{-\alpha} \qquad \text{(Eq.2)}$$

By introducing the power function (the Abel's nucleus) into the integral equation and assuming that $\sigma(t)$ =const. in the case of creep, we obtain the following relationship for deformation of a rock specimen subjected to a long-term constant load:

$$\mathcal{E}(t)=\mathcal{E}(0)\left[1+\frac{\delta}{1-\alpha}t^{1-\alpha}\right], \quad \text{(Eq.3)}$$

where $\mathcal{E}(0)$ - deformation of specimen under a load quickly applied to reach the stress value of σ ;

α and δ - parameters of the equation.

Since at the initial moment of load application

$$\mathcal{E}(0)=\frac{\sigma}{E}$$

it may be assumed that Eq.3 involves three mechanical characteristics of rocks, i.e. $E(0)$, α and δ.

To determine the range of rocks where this theory may be applied, the authors conducted the following laboratory research which included:

(1) creep tests of different rock specimens;
(2) development of computer programs to obtain rheologic equation parameters;
(3) computation of rheological equation parameters;
(4) evaluation of results.

The following rocks: clay, coal, halite, combustible shale, limestone, sandstone and marble were selected for the tests. Cylindrical specimens were 36 mm in diameter and 70 mm in height.

The creep tests were carried on the УП-2 type hydraulic installation designed at the VNIMI (Fig.1). This installation consists of 9 test sections (two of which are shown schematically). In each section, three rock specimens 1-3 are loaded simultaneously from the compressed nitrogen cylinders 12-15 and the compressor oil cylinders 16-18. Compressor oil is fed from the cylinders 16-18 to the input of each test section, i.e. the hydraulic press, consisting of a cylinder 6 and a piston 5, and the oil transmits pressure to the specimens 1-3 via the piston 5.

The hydraulic press pistons vary in cross-section. The dimensions of the loading members of the installation conform to the different values of load applied to the specimen ranging from 10 to 90% (with 10% spacings) of the rock strength under a short-term uniaxial compression.

Beams 20-21 interconnected with bolts 8 are provided as stiffeners of the construction. Guides 4 designed as telescopic tubes mounted on coupling bolts are supplied with spherical bearings. Friction losses in the guides were found during the tests to be under 0.5%. After the failure of one of the specimens, the test load is taken up by a metal sleeve 7 and transmitted to the remaining specimens.

When pressure is applied to the test sections, a portable pressure gauge mounted on a T-piece 10 is used.

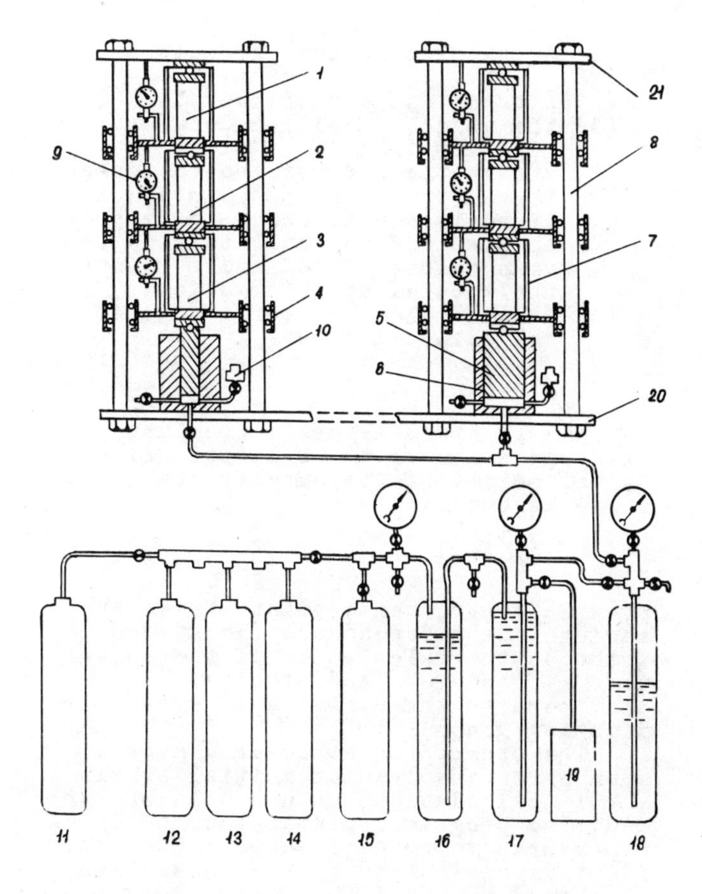

Fig.1. Type УП-2 hydraulic installation for creep tests of rocks.

With time, the pressure at the test section input diminishes due to oil leakage in the hydraulic system, but this fall does not exceed 0.5-1.0% during 2-3 days, owing to the provision of compressed nitrogen containers. If the pressure falls by more than 1%, high-pressure nitrogen is fed to the hydraulic system from the container 11 to make up for the loss and to restore pressure to the set value.

The oil in the containers 16-18 is replenished by a pump system 19. To cut friction, the hydraulic press pistons are fitted to slide and have no sealing washers or cups.

Longitudinal strain was measured by a dial indicator 9 with a graduation mark of 0.001 mm. The tests were conducted after the methods suggested in [3] and lasted from 1.5 to 2.5 months.

In order to get a comprehensive picture of relationships between stress, durations of load application and the parameters of the rheological equation (α and δ), to save time and to obtain better predictions, two computer programs were developed.

One program was intended for a case when error involved in the measurements of initial strain $\mathcal{E}_z(0)$ is negligible. This simplifies the procedures and saves time in calculating the parameters α and δ.

The basic input data include:

(1) the value of initial deformation $\mathcal{E}(o)$ at t=0;

(2) strain-times chosen on the creep curve (from 3 to 50 points); it is advisable to use as many points as possible in order to find the mean values of α and δ on the whole curve of deformation;

(3) strain values to correspond to the selected times

$$\mathcal{E}_z(t_1), \mathcal{E}_z(t_2) \ldots \ldots \mathcal{E}_z(t_n).$$

The relevant algoritm provides for the expression of the selected series "n" of points of the experimental creep curve in coordinate

$$"lg t - lg \frac{\mathcal{E}_z(t) - \mathcal{E}_z(o)}{\mathcal{E}_z(o)}"$$, the approximation of these points by an averaging linear dependence (least-square method), the calculation of the parameters α and δ and strains $\mathcal{E}_z(t)$ that permits the plotting of an approximating graph.

The other program covered a case when error involved in initial strain $\mathcal{E}_z(o)$ calculations cannot be disregarded. The program included the following procedures to be carried out after the first determination of the parameters α_1 and δ_1:

(1) calculated of standard deviation Z from the variance of the computed values of $\mathcal{E}_z(t_i)$ and the actual ones;

(2) "shuttle" search for zero deformation $\mathcal{E}_z(o)$ when the error Z is minimal, by changing the magnitude and direction of strain increment in relation to the previous values, and computation of the parameters α and δ corresponding to the minimal error;

(3) re-calculation of parameters α and δ, if required, including the rock's elastic modulus values found, for instance, by tests of a specimen under a stepped loading.

The program included data on 3-50 experimental points.

The approximation of the rock creep by linear hereditary equations was based on the assumption of the linear dependence of strains on stress with time. If the isochronic curves are found to be much like straight lines, the studied creep process follows the linear law of deformation.

Fig.2 shows the isochronic curves for halite and combustible shale. The graphs for halite show a deviation from the linear law of deformation at loads of 60-70% of the breaking values. However, the isochronic curves for combustible shale may be shown as straight lines.

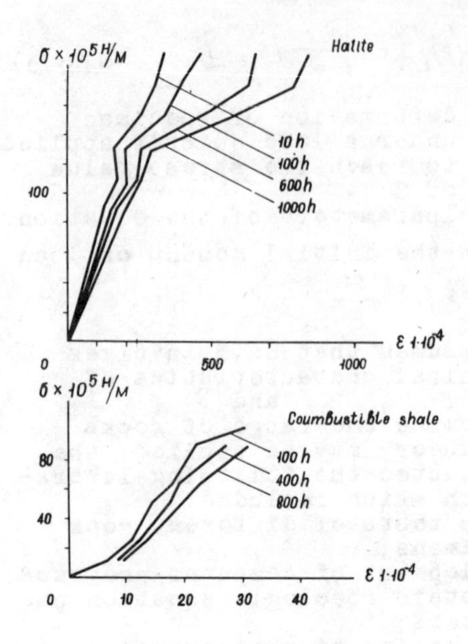

Fig.2. Isochronic curves for halite and combustible shale

Fig.2 shows the isochronic curves for halite and combustible shale. The graphs for halite show a deviation from the linear law of deformation at loads of 60-70% of the breaking values. However, the isochronic curves for combustible shale may be shown as straight lines.

Of certain interest would be a comparison of the values of α and δ included in the equation of the linear theory of heredity for both types of rocks, those which obey the linear law of deformation and those which do not. Such study would, probably, help to establish the magnitude of error involved in the approximations of processes in non-linear deformation rocks by linear hereditary equations which lie at the foundation of solutions of many engineering problems.

Moreover, it should be remembered that computation of equations of non-linear theories of the creep is a complicated and time-consuming process.

The values of α and δ found for the studied rocks from the two programs are given in Table 1.

The main findings on the approximation of the rock creep curves by linear hereditary equations may be summarized as follows:

(1) The error of initial deformation $\mathcal{E}_z(o)$ determination affects the values of α and δ parameters considerably It manifest itself in tackling engineering problems in the following manner: the error of the predictions does not exceed that of the elastic modulus determination error, when the modulus

magnitude is unjustifiably low [3].

(2) When the creep curves are shifted along the X-axis (which is the case when, fore instance, the rough ends of specimens are smashed in the course of loading), the parameter α remains unchanged, while the parameter δ varies inversely with the value of initial deformation.

(3) The parameters α and δ were calculated both for the entire creep curve (Table 1) and its separate parts; the values of α and δ for different parts were compared. The comparison showed the parameters α and δ to remain unchanged, when the shape of the creep curve and that of the curve in Eq.3 match. In all other cases, these parameters proved to be inter-dependent. To refine the findings, the experimental creep curve for halite was used in the computation many times. In doing so, the experimental points were chosen so as to enable the independent determination of α and δ for both the initial, middle and final parts of the creep curve and the whole curve. The values obtained were found to vary in the following ranges: $\alpha = 0.606 - 0.835$; $\delta = 0.0012 - 0.302\ \sec^{\alpha-1}$. The interdependence of the rheological equation parameters for halite in semilogarithmic co-ordinates is expressed by a straight line:

$$\alpha = m + n \lg \delta , \qquad \text{(Eq.4)}$$

where, unlike α and δ, "m" and "n" are constant characteristics of non-linear deformation rocks:

(4) The comoutation of the studied parameters for specimens tested at different steps of loading showed them to be a function of the load magnitude for some of the rocks. For example, in the case of halite, this relationship may be written as:

$$\alpha = 1.21 - 0.198 \frac{\sigma_z}{\sigma_c} + 0.169 \lg \delta \qquad \text{(Eq.5)}$$

(5) The dependence of α and δ on the selected part of the creep curve (test duration) and on the load magnitude seems, at first sight, to cast doubt on the validity of the theory of linear hereditary creep with respect to some rocks. However, application of the Abel's nucleus for any strain durations may be expedient, provided the accuracy of approximation fitting such durations is ensured and α and δ are properly computed. Fig.3 shows the curve of halite creep under a load of 60% of its strength in uniaxial compression. The calculations conducted under the first program, taking into account the experimental initial strain values $\varepsilon_z(0) = 105.9\ 10^{-4}$ yielded the following values for this curve:

$\alpha = 0.760$; $\delta = 0.0101\ \sec^{\alpha-1}$

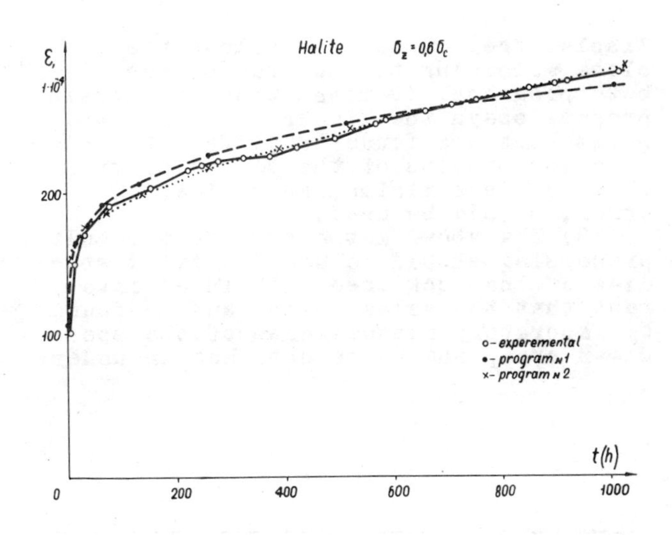

Fig.3. Creep curve for halite

The second program computations gave the following values for the curve: $\alpha = 0.496$; $\delta = 0.0002\ \sec^{\alpha-1}$; $\varepsilon_z(0) = 154.8\ 10^{-4}$.

Despite the sizable differences in α and δ values obtained from the different programs for the same creep curve, both approcimating curves are fairly close to the experimental one to a sufficient degree of accuracy, except for the initial stage of strain lasting for about 10 hours: the maximum error for the creep curve computations under the first program is 8%, while the same under the second program is 1-2%. A similar approximation was achieved in the processing of the creep curves for other rocks.

(6) The parameter α is found to vary from 0.50 to 0.96 (Table 1), depending on the rock variety and load magnitude. For some rocks, e.g. halite and coal, the parameter α falls off, as the load increases; for some others; e.g. Cambrian clay, in increases. For sandstone and combustible shale, α is independent of the load variations.

(7) The interdependence of α and δ established for some rocks is determined either by (a) the deviation of the creep curve from the linear law of deformation described by Eq.3, or (b) the error of the initial deformation measurement. At the same time, it should be noted that the use of each pair of the interdependent values of α and δ, although each value much different from the other, offers good advantage for the approximation of the creep process.

(8) To establish the validity of the linear theory of hereditary creep for some specific rock, it is recommended to use both programs for the processing of the creep curves, provided the initial deformation value obtained is re-

liable. When α and δ values are close according to the predictions of both programs, it means that the strain process obeys the linear law. When the parameters are found to differ, the computation results of the second program, which gives a minimal approximation error, should be used.

(9) The above methods of test result processing should be used in field studies of the rock creep. It is of interest that the values of α and δ found by laboratory measurements of the specimen creep and those obtained in underground tests (long-term compression of rocks prisms in mines) appear to be essentially the same for many types of rocks, e.g. sandstone, coal, halite, etc.

R e f e r e n c e s

1. Rabotnov J.N. The creep of structural elements. Nauka, M., 1966.
2. Erzhanov Zh.S. The theory of rock creep and its uses. Nauka, Akademy of Sciences of the Kazakh.SSR, 1964.
3. Kartashov J.M. Instructions on procedures for laboratory tests of rock plasticity. L., publ-d by VNIMI, 1972.

Table 1

$\frac{\sigma_z}{\sigma_c}$	First program			Second program		
	α	δ	$\varepsilon_z(0)\cdot 10^4$	α	δ	$\varepsilon_z(0)\cdot 10^4$
1	2	3	4	5	6	7
1. Halite						
0,1	0,836	0,0082	26,9	0,742	0,0020	31,2
0,2	0,843	0,0092	50,7	0,858	0,0133	46,1
0,3	0,797	0,0080	41,5	0,670	0,0012	50,9
0,4	0,797	0,0062	101,7	-	-	-
0,5	0,799	0,0100	121,6	0,848	0,0264	90,8
0,6	0,760	0,0101	105,9	0,496	0,0002	154,8
0,7	0,696	0,0067	166,0	0,537	0,0006	217,8
0,8	0,714	0,0087	201,0	0,638	0,0021	245,1
0,9	0,694	0,0071	217,0	0,641	0,0032	246,2
2. Combustible shale						
0,1	0,821	0,0048	18,0	0,923	0,0228	12,8
0,2	0,888	0,0138	20,1	0,894	0,0152	19,6
0,3	0,859	0,0223	28,5	-	-	-
0,4	0,859	0,0103	33,0	0,842	0,0079	34,5
0,5	0,879	0,0121	37,2	0,867	0,0116	37,5
0,6	0,887	0,0053	71,0	0,779	0,0013	76,4
0,7	0,848	0,0081	61,0	0,810	0,0048	64,7
3. Marble						
0,1	- -	-	-	-	-	-
0,2	0,741	0,00047	13,8	0,585	0,00006	14,0
0,3	0,963	0,00470	15,4	0,923	0,00258	17,1
0,4	0,940	0,00192	50,2	0,889	0,00099	34,2
0,5	0,964	0,00186	40,1	0,747	0,00011	42,9
0,6	0,894	0,00081	54,6	0,735	0,00011	55,5
0,7	0,906	0,00067	118,5	0,889	0,00055	118,9
0,8	0,884	0,00068	59,8	0,734	0,00011	58,4
0,9	0,855	0,00094	44,0	0,841	0,00080	44,1

Table 1 contd.

1	2	3	4	5	6	7
			4. Sand stone			
0,1	0,950	0,0030	-	-	-	-
0,3	0,941	0,0060	-	-	-	-
0,7	0,943	0,0031	-	-	-	-
0,9	0,952	0,0022	-	-	-	-
			5. Coal			
0,1	0,967	0,0040	-	0,825	0,04022	13,89
0,2	0,827	0,0016	-	0,522	0,00002	31,87
0,3	0,928	0,0038	-	0,864	0,00151	39,74
0,4	0,819	0,0039	-	0,527	0,00006	18,86
0,5	0,830	0,0027	-	0,507	0,00003	47,23
0,6	0,787	0,0021	-	0,653	0,00033	60,31
0,7	0,738	0,0023	-	0,578	0,00026	55,03
			6. Limestone			
0,1	0,822	0,0012	-	0,922	0,00474	19,22
0,2	0,889	0,0026	-	0,869	0,00202	40,41
0,3	0,855	0,0033	-	0,920	0,00841	28,65
0,4	0,829	0,0021	-	0,810	0,00161	45,53
0,5	0,710	0,0004	-	0,682	0,00027	56,17
0,6	0,937	0,0130	-	0,743	0,00082	50,99
0,7	0,782	0,0034	-	0,762	0,00266	61,66
0,8	0,906	0,0108	-	0,678	0,00063	73,11
0,9	0,818	0,0022	-	0,875	0,00428	79,65
			7. Cambrian clay			
0,2	0,629	0,0015	24,2	0,571	0,00097	23,56
0,3	0,681	0,0042	40,8	0,513	0,00035	59,71
0,4	0,800	0,0074	59,5	0,886	0,02069	55,27
0,5	0,862	0,0108	80,7	0,870	0,01390	73,21
0,8	0,882	0,0174	126,0	-	-	-

ÉTUDE COMPARÉE DES ESSAIS DE FLUAGE RELAXATION ET CHARGEMENT CYCLIQUE POUR LA DÉTERMINATION DE MODÈLES RHÉOLOGIQUES DES MARNES ET DU SEL GEMME

COMPARATIVE STUDY OF CREEP, RELAXATION, CYCLIC LOADING TESTS TO DETERMINE THE RHEOLOGICAL MODEL OF MARL AND SALT

VERGLEICHSSTUDIUM DER KRIECH-RELAXATION UND ZYKLISCHE BELASTUNGSVERSUCHE FÜR DAS BERECHNEN DES RHEOLOGISCHEN BETRAGENMODELLS DER MERGEL UND SALZPROBENSTÜCKE

J. MUSSO

G. VOUILLE

Centre de Mecanique des Roches de l'Ecole Nationales Superieure des Mines de Paris

Paris, France

RESUME

Le comportement rhéologique des roches peut être représenté par des modèles plus ou moins compliqués formés de l'assemblage en série ou en parallèle d'éléments simples tels que ressort, amortisseur et patin. On présente différents modèles permettant de rendre compte de comportements réellement observés et on expose plusieurs techniques d'ajustement permettant de déterminer à partir des courbes expérimentales les paramètres définissant les modèles théoriques.
Les essais de fluage , relaxation et chargement cyclique effectués sur des échantillons de marne et se sel gemme ont permis de déterminer le modèle rhéologique du comportement de ces matériaux. On insiste sur le fait que chaque type d'essai pris séparement ne suffit pas à caractériser complètement le comportement du matériau but ne pouvant être atteint que par la réalisation simultanée d'essais de chaque type.

SUMMARY

The rheological behaviour of rocks may be represented by more or less complicated models built from simple elements like springs, dashpots and skids. Some examples of models accounting for actual behaviours are given and several techniques are explained for computing the parameters of those models so that the theorical results follow the "best fit" to the experimental data.
Creep tests, relaxation tests and cyclic loading tests perfomed on marl ans salt samples allow the rheological model for those materials to be known. It is pointed out that doing one only kind of test is not sufficient to have a complete knowledge of the behaviour of the material: for this purpose the three kinds of test are necessary.

ZUSAMMENFASSUNG

Das rheologische Felsbetragen kann durch mehr oder weniger komplizierte Modelle beschrieben werden, die von einfachen Elementen wie: Dämpfer, Feder und Kufen gebildet sind. Es werden verschiedene. Modelle beschrieben, die reell beobachtetes Betragen schildern; es werden also mehr Methoden behandelt, die von den Experimentalkurven an die Berechnung der Parameter der theoretischen Modelle erlauben. Die von Mergel und Salzprobestücken gemachten Kriech-Relaxation und Zyklenbelastungsversuche haben die Berechnung des rheologischen Betragenmodelles dieser Materialien erlaubt. Es wird darauf hingewiesen, dass ein Versuch allein nicht ausreichend ist, um die Charakterisierung des Materialbetragen vollkommen festzustellen. Es ist unbedingt notwendig, drei Versuche durchzuführen.

MODELES RHEOLOGIQUES ENVISAGES

1) VISCOELSTICITE

Tout solide viscoélastique linéaire dont les caractéristiques ne dépendent pas du temps peut être schématisé par un assembalge fini

- de ressorts caractéristiques de l'élasticité pure $\sigma = E\varepsilon$, E module d'élasticité
- d'amortisseurs caractéristiques de la viscosité pour $\sigma = \eta\dot{\varepsilon}$, η coefficient de viscosité de Newton,

$\dot{\varepsilon} = \frac{\partial \varepsilon}{\partial t}$, ν coefficient de Poisson associé

Il est intéressant d'utiliser le calcul symbolique par la transformation de Lapla $f^*(p) = \mathcal{L} f = \int_0^\infty e^{-pt} f(t)\,dt$ qui permet de résoudre les problèmes viscoélastiques linéaires comme des problèmes d'élasticité pure, contraintes et déformations étant remplacées par leurs images par la tranformation de Laplace avec des modules transformés.

$\sigma^*(p) = E\varepsilon^*(p)$ pour le ressort

$\sigma^*(p) = p\eta\varepsilon^*(p)$ pour l'amortisseur.

On peut distinguer deux familles générales de groupement:

- Modèle de Kelvin généralisé:

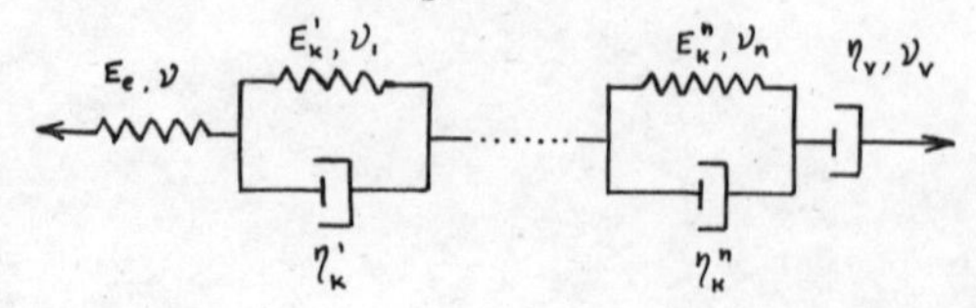

L'équation générale de comportement d'un tel modèle dans un repère principal des contraintes est:

$$[\varepsilon^*_{tot}] = \frac{1}{E(p)}\,[T_K(p)]^{-1}\,[\sigma^*]$$

$$[T_K(p)]^{-1} = \begin{bmatrix} 1 & -\nu(p) & -\nu(p) \\ -\nu(p) & 1 & -\nu(p) \\ -\nu(p) & -\nu(p) & 1 \end{bmatrix}$$

$$\frac{1}{E(p)} = \frac{1}{E_e}\left[1 + \sum_{r=1}^{n} \frac{E_e/\eta^r_K}{p + \frac{E^r_K}{\eta^r_K}} + \frac{E_e}{\nu_v}\,\frac{1}{p}\right]$$

$$\frac{\nu(p)}{E(p)} = \frac{\nu}{E_e}\left[1 + \sum_{r=1}^{n} \frac{\nu_r/\nu\;E_e/\eta^r_K}{p + E^r_K/\eta^r_K} + \frac{\nu_v}{\nu}\,\frac{E_e}{\eta_v}\,\frac{1}{p}\right]$$

La fonction de fluage monoaxial d'un tel modèle est

$$f^*(p) = \frac{1}{E_e} + \sum_{r=1}^{n} \frac{1/\eta^r_K}{p + \frac{E^r_K}{\eta^r_K}} + \frac{1}{p\,\eta_v}$$

- Modèle de Maxwell généralisé

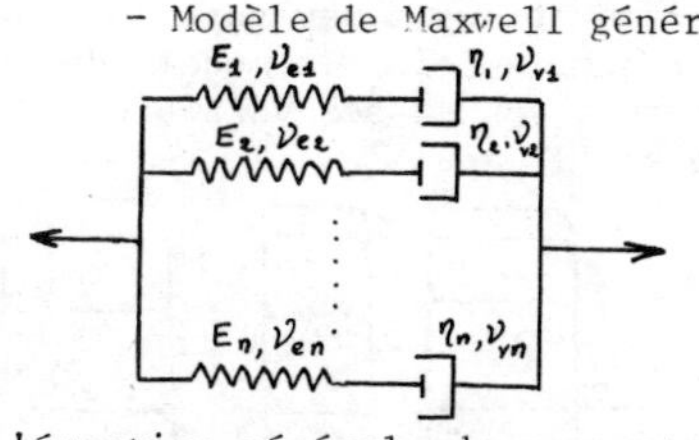

L'équation générale de comportement d'un tel modèle dans un repère principal des contraintes est:

$$[\sigma^*_{tot}] = \left[\sum_{r=1}^{n}\left[[T^r_M(p)]^{-1}\,\frac{1}{E_r(p)}\right]^{-1}\right]\,[\varepsilon^*_{tot}]$$

avec

$$[T^r_M(p)]^{-1} = \begin{bmatrix} 1 & -\nu^r(p) & -\nu^r(p) \\ -\nu^r(p) & 1 & -\nu^r(p) \\ -\nu^r(p) & -\nu^r(p) & 1 \end{bmatrix}$$

$$\frac{1}{E_r(p)} = \frac{1}{E_r}\left[1 + \frac{E_r}{p\,\eta_r}\right], \quad \frac{\nu_r(p)}{E_r(p)} = \frac{\nu_{er}}{E_r}\left[1 + \frac{\nu_{vr}}{\nu_{er}}\,\frac{E_r}{p\,\eta_r}\right]$$

La fonction de relaxation monoaxiale d'un tel modèle est:

$$r^*(p) = \sum_{r=1}^{n} E_r \frac{p}{p + \frac{E_r}{\eta_r}}$$

- Modèle quelconque

L'équation de comportement d'un groupement quelconque d'éléments linéaires est une équation linéaire de la forme

$\sigma\,(p)S(p) = \varepsilon\,(p)\;E(p)$

avec $S(p) = S_o + S_1p + \ldots\ldots\ldots\ldots S_mp^m$

$E(p) = E_o + E_1p + \ldots\ldots\ldots E_np^m$

Si $E_o = 0$ le modèle présenté a un comportement solide, liquide si $E_o = 0$.

L'équation peut s'écrire sous la forme

$$\varepsilon\,(p) = \frac{E(p)}{S(p)}\varepsilon\,(p)$$

Le mdoèle est doué d'élasticité instantanée si m=n, dépourvu si m=n-1. Les propriétés mécaniques et les énergies emmagasinées et dissipées de tout matériau viscoélastique linéaire peuvent être représentées soit par un ensemble de modèles de Maxwell généralisé ou de modèles de Kelvin généralisé.

2) PLASTICITE - VISCOPLASTICITE

Le patin de Saint Venant est caractéristique de la plasticité

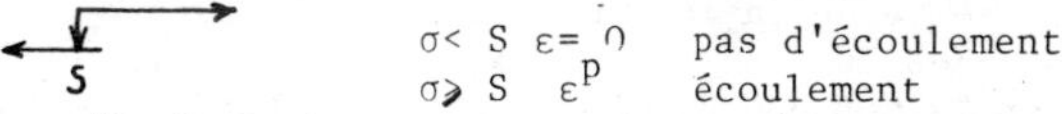

$\sigma < S$ $\varepsilon = 0$ pas d'écoulement

$\sigma \geqslant S$ ε^p écoulement

S seuil du patin.

On peut envisager d'autres modèles:

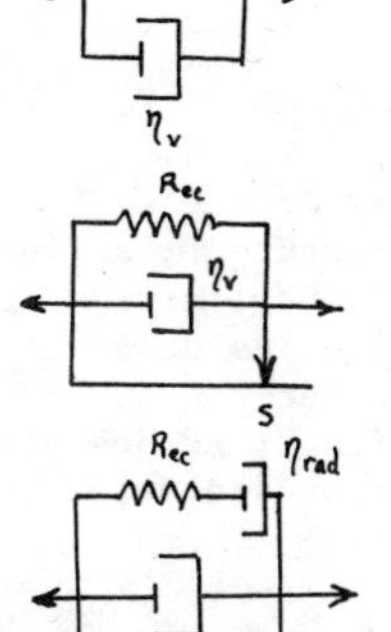

Modèle de Bingham rendant compte de la viscoplasticité: $\sigma < S$ $\varepsilon = 0$
$\sigma \geqslant S$ $\sigma^* = s + p\eta\varepsilon^*$

Modèle rendant compte de la viscoplasticité avec écrouissage grace au ressort dont l'énergie élastique emmagasinée correspond à l'énergie élastique attachée aux nouvelles dislocations créées par la déformation plastique.

Modèle rendant compte de la viscoplasticité avec écrouissage et radoucissement: l'amortisseur de caractéristique η_{rad} relache la compression du ressort, c'est le radoucissement. Le radoucissement intervient dans des essais de longue durée à déformations lentes; il explique notament l'évolution du seuil de plasticité au cours d'une période de repos, la phase de fluage à vitesse constante, l'hésitation au fluage.

3) METHODES D'AJUSTEMENT DES PARAMETRES D'UN MODELE THEORIQUE A UNE COURBE EXPERIMENTALES

D'une manière générale les modules d'élasticité instantanée sont obtenus par des essais de compression rapide; E_e est la pente de la droite de moindres carrés associée aux points expérimentaux.

La détermination des modules différés revient à ajuster une ou une famille (selon le nombre de modèles théoriques pris en compte) d'exponentielles à la courbe expérimentale.

Plusieurs méthodes ont été employées:

* raccordement de 1 modèle de Kelvin

dans un système d'axes semi logarithmiques la pente de droite de moindre carré associée aux points expérimentaux donne la constante de temps de l'exponentielle l'asymptote permettant de calculer E^1_k .

* raccordement de 1 modèle de Kelvin (ou de Maxwell) généralisé:

- méthode graphique

On compare la courbe expérimentale et la courbe théorique calculée par ordinateur sur un écran périphérique. L'opérateur modifie directement les caractéristiques du modèle théorique jusqu'à obtention d'un ajustement satisfaisant.

- modèle analytique: l'algorithme a été restreint à une estimation par moindres carrés, d'autres estimations non linéaires peuvent être envisagées du point de vu statistique.

Il existe deux méthodes générales:

1) développement en série de Taylor de la fonction

2) gradient maximum ou gradient congugé.

Ces deux méthodes échouent quelques fois (divergence pour la série de Taylor, trop lente convergence pour les méthodes du gradient). L'algorithme adopté est basé sur la méthode donnée par Marquardt (3), méthode intermédiaire entre les deux précédentes, présentant leurs avantages sans les inconvénients.
Pratiquement, toute courbe théorique est correctement ajustée par deux modèles de Kelvin en série.

ROCHE ETUDIEES

1) Marnes

Ce sont des marnes provenant des mines de fer de Lorraine (Mine de Rochonvillers) de texture très fine et assez poreuses: elles sont sensibles à l'action de l'air et de l'eau qui les altèrent si elles ne sont pas revêtues d'un enduit protecteur. Leur comportement est lié à l'élasticité et à la fragilité des pores de la texture, ce sont des roches présentant un "serrage" lors de leur mise en charge.

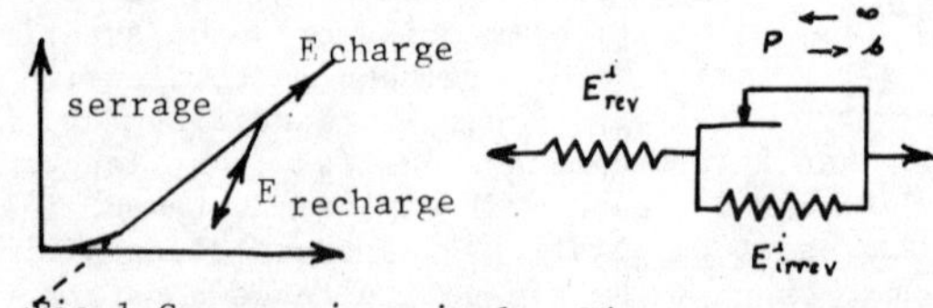

Fig.1 Compression simple   Fig.2 Interprétation Rhéoligique

Les essais de compression (fig 1) mettent en évidence un serrage initial, un module de charge et un module de recharge que l'on peut interpréter par un modèle rhéologique de la forme (fig.2)

Le patin est dissymétrique : seuil infini en extension, seuil fini ou nul en compression.

Le module irréversible est relié au comportement des pores.

Module de charge $\frac{1}{E_{ch}} = \frac{1}{E_{rev}} + \frac{1}{E_{irrev}}$

Module de recharge E_{rev}

Les essais de longue durée perturbés par un vieillissement du matériau qui affaiblit la résistance de l'échantillon nécessitent des conditions de température et d'hygrométrie parfaitement définies.

2) Sel

Les échantillons étudiés sont de diverses provenances
- sel de Varangeville (France) avec de nombreuses intercalations marneuses grossièrement cristallisé.
- sel gemme et carnalite de la mine de Saint Paul (Congo) purs et bien cristallisés.

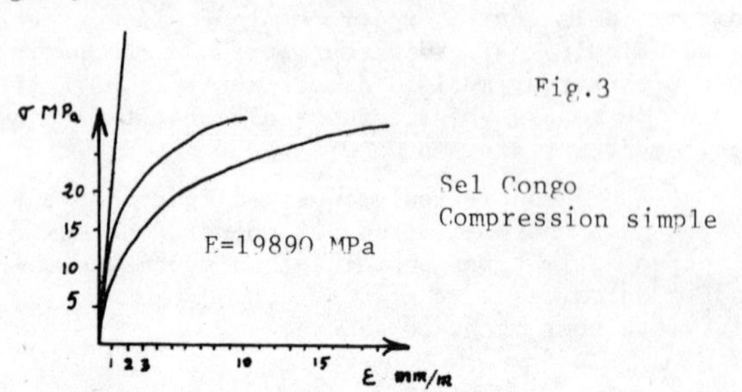

Fig.3

Sel Congo
Compression simple

Ces matériaux ont un comportement plastique: il est parfois difficile de déterminer sur un essai de compression, un module d'élasticité instantanée(Fig.3) Au delà de la limite élastique on observe un écoulement plastique qui donne une forme de tonneau à l'éprouvette avec apparition des lignes de Lüders même en compression monoaxiale pour des échantillons très purs.

FLUAGE

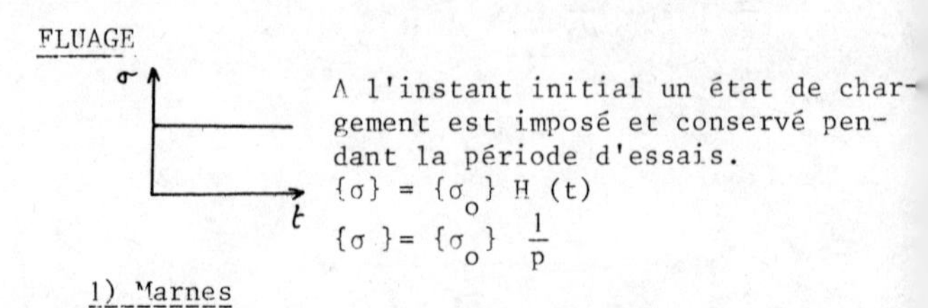

A l'instant initial un état de chargement est imposé et conservé pendant la période d'essais.

$\{\sigma\} = \{\sigma_o\}\ H\ (t)$

$\{\sigma\} = \{\sigma_o\}\ \frac{1}{p}$

1) Marnes

Pour différentes pressions (10, 15, 20, 25, 30 MPa) on observe un fluage asymptotique à asymtote horizontale, ce comportement rappelle celui du modèle de Kelvin. Les durées d'essais sont assez varaibles jusqu'à 1 an en fluage seul.

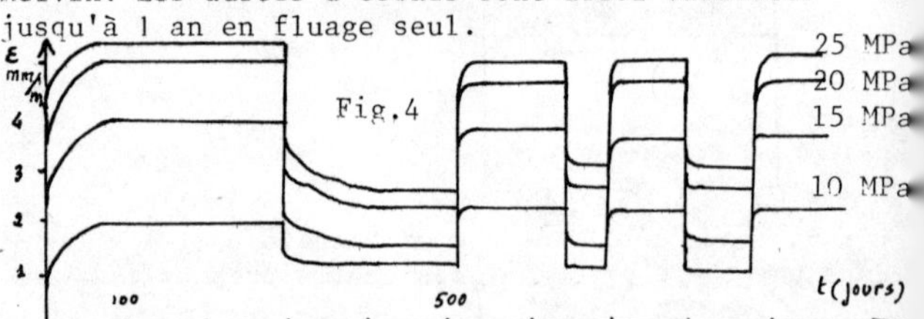

Des cycles de fluage recouvrance (relachement à 0 de la pression) ont été effectués sur de longues périodes (200 j environ) pour déterminer la part du comportement irréversible et de la plasticité (Fig.4) Après un premier cycle, tous les autres sont identiques : on observe alors le comportement de la partie reversible du matériau.
Un modèle rhéologique proposé par Morlier (fig.5) rend correctement compte des essais.

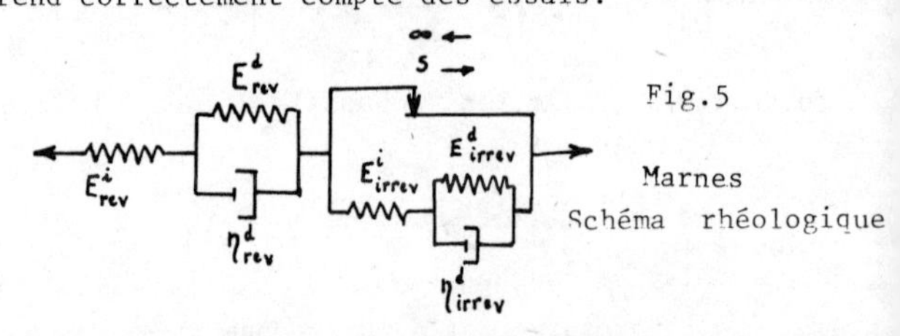

Fig.5

Marnes
Schéma rhéologique

Pour des échantillons de même provenance, on observe:
- un écart type assez faible des modules instantanés et des constantes de temps autour de la moyenne
- une forte dispersion des modules différes.

Ceci peut être relié à un vieillissement du matériau et à la difficulté de reproduire des essais de longue durée dans des conditions identiques de température et d'hygrométrie.

Les valeurs moyennes obtenues sont:

E^i_{rev} (MPa)	E^i_{irrev} (MPa)	E^d_{rev} (MPa)	E^d_{irrev} (MPa)	rev (MPa)	irrev (Mpa)
7 200	36 000	38 000	8 500	$1,14.10^5$	$2,46.10^5$

Les constante de temps en fluage sont:
3 jours pour le modèle réversible
29 jours pour le modèle irréversible.

2) Sel

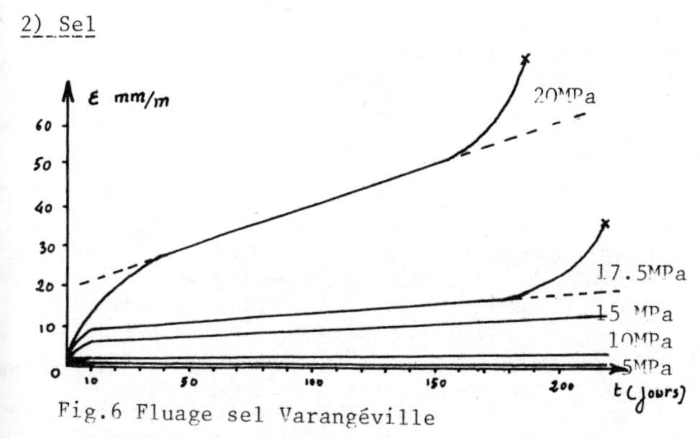

Fig.6 Fluage sel Varangéville

Selon l'état de contrainte on observe(fig.6)

- un fluage asymptotique avec stabilisation des déformations pour $\sigma < s$
- un fluage à 3 phases amenant la rupture de l'éprouvette pour $\sigma \geqslant s$
- un fluage rapide amenant aussi la rupture de l'éprouvette, l'écoulement à vitesse constante n'étant plus qu'un point d'inflexion pour $\sigma \gg s$

Un tel comportement peut être rendu par un modèle ou une chaine de modèles de Kelvin rendant compte du fluage asymptotique associé à un modèle de Bingham traduisant le fluage à vitesse constante. (Fig.8)

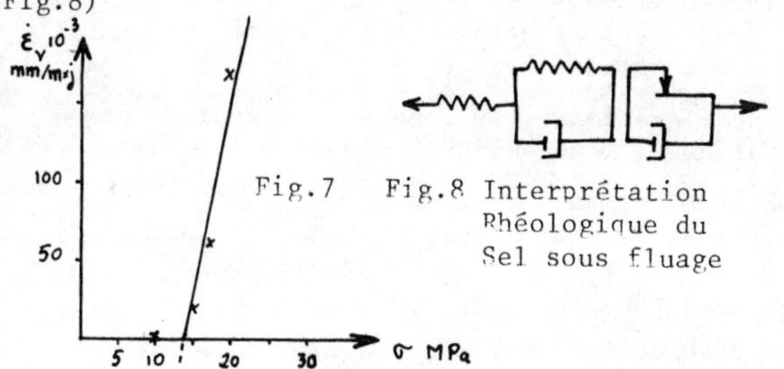

Fig.7 Fig.8 Interprétation Rhéologique du Sel sous fluage

Le seuil du patin du modèle de Bingham est déterminé sur un graphique vitesse de fluage en fonction de la constante $(\dot{\varepsilon}_{vp},\sigma) = 0$, la pente de la droite de moindres carrés associée donnant le coefficient de viscosité de l'amortisseur (fig.7)

Les valeurs moyennes obtenues sont:

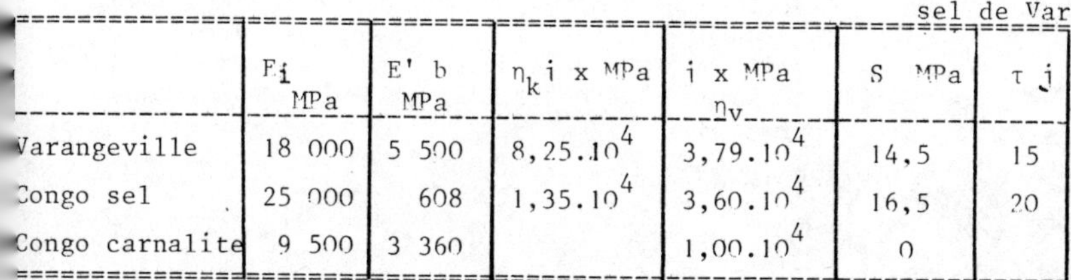

	E_i MPa	E' b MPa	η_k i x MPa	i x MPa η_v	S MPa	τ j
Varangeville	18 000	5 500	$8,25.10^4$	$3,79.10^4$	14,5	15
Congo sel	25 000	608	$1,35.10^4$	$3,60.10^4$	16,5	20
Congo carnalite	9 500	3 360		$1,00.10^4$	0	

RELAXATION

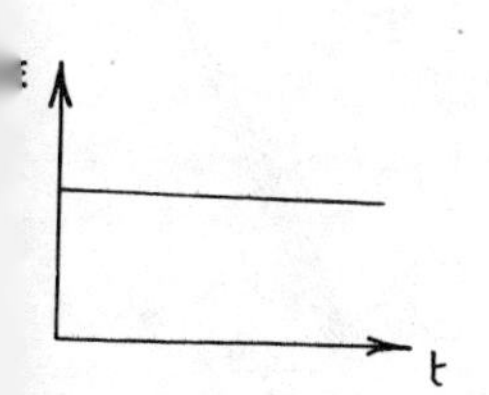

A l'instant initial un état de déforamtion est imposé et conservé pendant la période de l'essai

$\{\varepsilon\} = \{\varepsilon_o\}\ H(t)$

$\{\varepsilon\} = \{\varepsilon_o\}\ \frac{1}{p}$

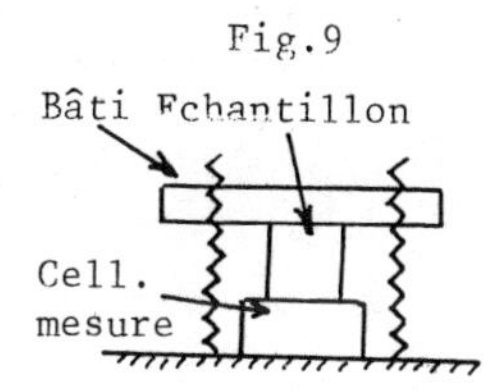

Fig.9

Ces essais ont été effectués sur une presse electromécanique à vis: c'était donc des essais à déplacement imposé et il faut tenir compte de l'élasticité du capteur de force et de la machine lors des dépouillements (fig.9)

1) Marnes

Fig.10 Relaxation des Marnes

On observe une relaxation de la contrainte qui se stabilise après une dizaine d'heures. Ce comportement rappelle celui d'un ou de plusieurs modèles de Kelvin (Fig.10). Qualitativement on obtient donc un modèle semblable à celui obtenu par un essai de fluage, cependant ce dernier soumis à ce chargement donnerait une relaxation de la contrainte dans la partie réversible du modèle, le patin étant quant à lui bloqué. Le modèle théorique relaxe suivant l'équation

$$\sigma = \frac{E^i_{rev}\,E^d_{rev}}{E^i_{rev}+E^d_{rev}}\,\varepsilon_o^{rev} + \left(E^i_{rev} - \frac{E^i_{rev}\,E^d_{rev}}{E^i_{rev}+E^d_{rev}}\right)\varepsilon_o^{rev}\,e^{-t\left(\frac{E^i_{rev}+E^d_{rev}}{\eta_{rev}}\right)}$$

avec

$$\varepsilon_o^{rev} = \frac{\sigma_{init}}{E^i_{rev}} \qquad \varepsilon_o^{irrev} = \frac{\sigma_{init}}{E^i_{irrev}} \qquad \varepsilon_o^{td} = \varepsilon_o^{rev} + \varepsilon_o^{irrev}$$

Quantitativement on voit qu'il y a peu d'accord entre la courbe de relaxation expériementale donnant un modèle à constante de temps de 0,016 jours et la courbe déduite du modèle théorique obtenu par essais de fluage à constante de temps de relaxation de 2,5 j.

2) Sel

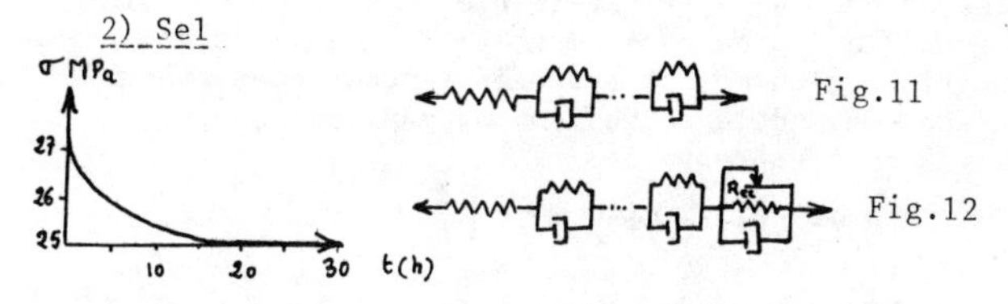

Les essais n'ont porté que sur des échantillons du sel de Varangeville. Les courbes expérimentales traduisent une relaxation de la contrainte qui se stabilise après une vingtaine d'heures quand la contrainte atteint 145.45 MPa. Ce comportement rappelle celui d'un ou plusieurs modèles de Kelvin ou d'un modèle de Maxwell (Fig.11)

Le modèle envisagé dans l'étude du fluage ne tenait pas compte de l'écrouissage du matériau. En toute rigueur il faudrait adopter comme modèle (fig.12) qui permet de rendre compte de l'écrouissage instantané grâce au ressort R_{ec}.

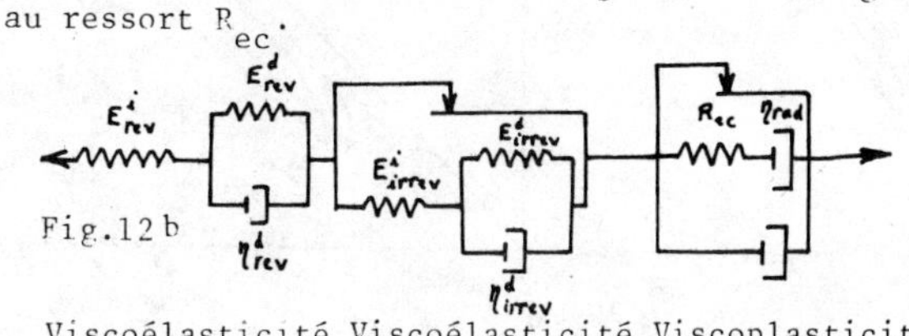

Fig.12b

Viscoélasticité Réversible — Viscoélasticité Irréversible — Viscoplasticité Ecrouissage Radoucissement

Cependant dans un essais de relaxation, essais de courte durée, le radoucissement peut être négligé. Dans ce cas, grâce à l'écrouissage, la relaxation de la contrainte n'est déterminée que par la partie viscoélastique du modèle.
Le sel de Varangeville étant formé de cristaux grossiers avec des intercalations marneuses, on peut observer un léger serrage du matériau, avec un module de recharge de 20 000 MPa environ. Le modèle rhéologique) prendre en compte serait alors (fig.12 b) avec

$E^i_{rev} = 0,2 \times 10^5$ MPa

$E^i_{irrev} = 1,8 \times 10^5$ MPa

$E^d_{rev} = 0,65 \times 10^5$ MPa

$E^d_{irrev} = 0,06 \times 10^5$ MPa

Dans ce cas la relaxation de la contrainte n'est due qu'au modèle viscoélastique réversible et effectivement la courbe théorique correspond mieux à l'expérience.

CHARGEMENT CYCLIQUE

On impose comme loi de chargement :

$$[\sigma^*] = [\sigma_M - \sigma_m] \frac{1}{T} \frac{1}{p^2} \, th \, p\frac{T}{2} + \frac{1}{p}[\sigma_m]$$

On pourrait tout aussi bien imposer une déformation cyclique. Dans un diagramme σ-ε on obtient des boucles d'hystérésis; elles se décalent les unes des autres pour deux raisons:

- fluage dû à la contrainte minimale du chargement $\frac{1}{p}\sigma_m$
- apparition de déformations plastiques

1) Marnes

Comme l'essai est répétitif, on ne pourra mettre en évidence que la partie reversible du modèle. Qualitativement la courbe expérimentale (fig.13) est caractéristique d'un modèle viscoélastique. En essayant de caler un modèle de Kelvin, donnant une courbe théorique d'expression

$$\varepsilon^*(p) = (\sigma_M - \sigma_m) \frac{1}{T} \frac{1}{p^2} \, th \, p\frac{T}{2} \left[\frac{1}{E_e} + \frac{1/\eta}{p + \frac{E_d}{\eta}} \right]$$

On obtient:

$E^d_{rev} = 0,37 \times 10^5$ MPa

$t_1 = 0,024$ j constante de temps en fluage

$t_2 = 0,0035$ j contante de temps en relaxation.

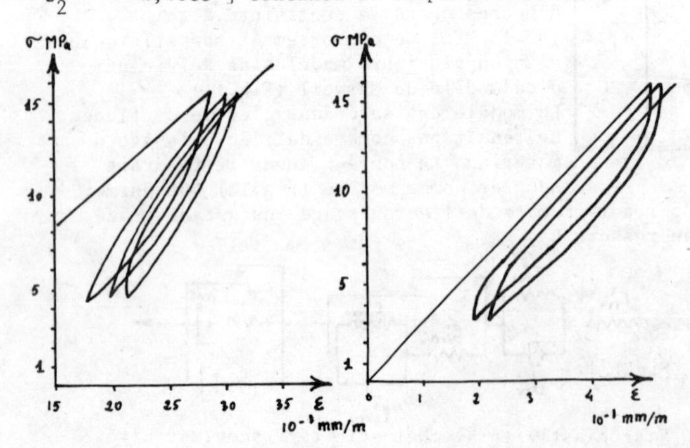

Fig.13 Marnes Cycles Fig.14 Sel Cycles

Le module différé est sensiblement le même que celui obtenu par un essai de fluage, cependant les constantes de temps diffèrent beaucoup.

2) Sel

Les essais n'ont porté que sur du sel de Varangeville (fig.14). Comme dans le cas de la relaxation on peut tenir compte de l'écrouissage en négligeant le radoucissement; d'autre part les contraintes ne dépassant pas le seuil du patin du modèle de Bingham les déformations viscoplastiques sont négligeables. Comme pour les marnes on ne pourra mettre en évidence que la partie viscoélastique réversible du modèle. Un modèle de Kelvin calé sur les courbes expérimentales donne:

$E^d_{rev} = 0,73 \times 10^5$ MPa

$\eta^k_{rev} = 4,73 \times 10^2$ J x MPa

Ce qui correspond au valeurs trouvées par les essais de relaxation.

CONCLUSION

Chacun des trois essais présentés permet d'analyser une partie des propriétés des échantillons:

- le fluage mobilise les déformations viscoélastiques réversibles et irréversibles ainsi que les déformations viscoplastiques
- la relaxation et la recouvrance mobilisent les déformations viscoélastiques réversibles
- les chargements cycliques mobilisent les déformations viscoélastiques réversibles et viscoplastiques (essais de fatigue de longue durée).

On trouve une bonne corrélation entre les caractéristiques des modèles viscoélastiques réversibles obtenus par ces trois essais.

Qualitativement pour les marnes le schéma rhéologique envisagé (fig.5) est un bon accord avec les différents essais. Le serrage des pores est un phénomène important du comportement de ces roches. Ainsi en faisant des cycles de charge décharge recharge sur un échantillon intact (fig.15), un échantillon ayant subi une relaxation et une recouvrance (fig.16) et un échantillon ayant subi 4 cycles de fluage-recouvrance (fig.17) on voit que le module de charge tend vers le module de recharge: les pores n'interviennent plus dans les déformations.

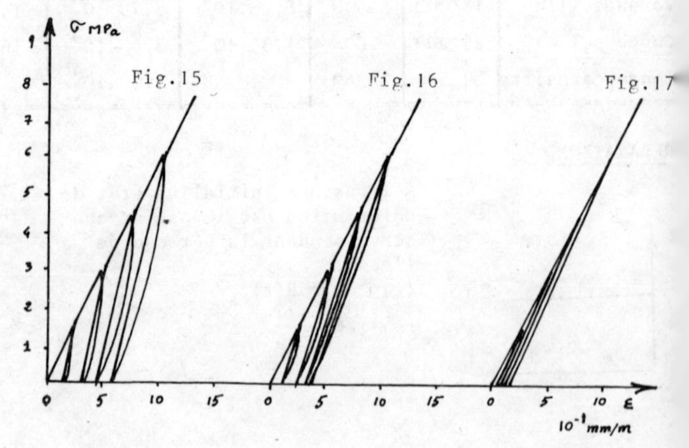

ur le sel le schéma rhéologique envisagé (fig.12)
atisfait les différents essais. Quantitativement les
aleurs des modules obtenues dans les différents
ssais se recoupent, les contantes de temps étant
uant à elles plus dispersées.
haque essai est caractéristique d'une partie du
mportement des matériaux: il faut choisir l'essai
n fonction du problème posé (un essai de fluage
ermet de rendre compte des déformations des roches
ans un pilier, un essai de recouvrance ou de relaxa-
ion de la détente des terrains dans un avancement de
alerie) et de la texture de la roche.

BLIOGRAPHIE

LAND D.R The theory of linear viscoelasticity
Pergamon Press 1960

ERSOZ B. La rhéologie. Recueil de travaux des ses
sions de perfectionnement. INSA LYON

ORLIER P.J Etude expérimentale de la déformation
des roches. Thèse de Docteur Ingénieur
Revue de l'IFP Vol. XIX n° 10-11 1964

ARQUARTD. An algorithm for least squares estimation
of monlinear parameters. J. Soc.Indust.
Appl. Math. Vol II n° 2 , 1963

TREMSDOERFER. Résolution par la méthode des éléments
finis des problèmes viscoélastiques
et élastoplastiques posés par les cavités souterraines. Thèse de Docteur
Ingénieur 1972.

ARDY . Time dependant deformation and failure of geologic material. Third symposium on rock
mechanics. Quarterly of the colorado school
of mine . Vol 54 july 1959.

ERRARD. Contribution à l'étude de la propagation
d'ondes en milieux viscoélastiques. Défini-
tions expérimentales de milieux rhéologiques.
Thèse de 3 éme cycle. Université de Grenoble
1963.

NDEL J. Cours de Mécanique des Milieux Continus .
Paris Gauthier-Villars . 1966

GENERALIZED EQUATIONS OF RHEOLOGICAL CURVES FOR ROCKS

EQUATIONS GENERALISÉES DES COURBES RHÉOLOGIQUES POUR ROCHES

VERALLGEMEINERTE GLEICHUNGEN DER RHEOLOGISCHEN KURVEN FÜR GESTEINE

M.M. PROTODIAKONOV

Honoured Scientist of the RSFSR, Professor,
Doctor of Technical Sciences

The Department of Physical and Technical Problems of Mining
in the Institute of Ears Physics, Academy of Sciences of USSR

Moscow, U.S.S.R.

SUMMARY.

Usually the rheological curves are described in parts: a) elastic deformation, b) primary creep, c) secondary creep, d) destruction.

The elastic part is described by a straight line equation. The primary creep is described by an exponential function, the secondary creep - by a straight line equation. Pre-existing imperfection and destruction are not described by any equation.

It is proposed thet all the rock deformation stages ε in time t can be described by a common equation of the following type:

$$\left(\frac{t}{t}\right)^{p} - \left(\frac{\varepsilon}{\varepsilon_1}\right)^{n} = 1$$

where t_m is the deformation time, ε_1 is the deformation corresponding to: $\frac{t_m}{t} = 2^{1/p}$; p and n are the numerical coefficient characterizing the shape of the curve.

RESUME.

Normalement, les courbes rhéologiques sont décrites par parties: a) déformation élastique, b) fluage primaire, c) fluage secondaire, d) destruction.

La partie élastique est décrite par l'équation de la droite; le fluage primaire - par l'exponentielle; le fluage secondaire - par l'équation de la droite. Le stade prédestructi[on] et la destruction - ne sont par aucune équation.

On propose de décrire tous les stades de la déformation des roches ε dans le temps t par une équation unique de la forme:

$$\left(\frac{t_m}{t}\right)^{p} - \left(\frac{\varepsilon}{\varepsilon_1}\right)^{n} = 1$$

où t_m est le temps de destruction; ε_1 la déformation correspondant à $\frac{t_m}{t} = 2^{1/p}$; p et [n] les coéfficients numériques, caractéristiques de l'allure de la courbe.

ZUSAMMENFASSUNG.

Gewöhnlich werden rheologische Kurven abschittsweise beschrieben: a) elastische Deformation, b) primärer Kriechvorgang, c) sekundärer Kriechvorgang, d) Zerstörung.

Der elastische Abschnitt ist durch die Gleichung einer Geraden darstellbar, der primäre Kriechvorgang durch eine Exponentialfunktion und der sekundäre Kriechvorgang ebenfalls durch die Gleichung einer Geraden. Der Zustand vor der Zerstörung und die Zerstörung selbs[t] können überhaupt nicht durch Gleichungen wiedergegeben werden.

Es wird vorgeschlagen, alle Stadien der Gesteinsdeformation ε in der Zeit t durch eine einzige Gleichung folgender Art zu beschreiben:

$$\left(\frac{t_m}{t}\right)^{p} - \left(\frac{\varepsilon}{\varepsilon_1}\right)^{n} = 1$$

worin bedeuten: t_m Zerstörungszeit; ε_1 Deformation, entsprechend $\frac{t_m}{t} = 2^{1/p}$; p und n Koeffizienten, die den Kurvenverlauf charakterisieren.

In studying the rock deformation in time at a constant stress, the elastic deformation is usually supposed to be practically instaneous, the remaining part of the curve is divided into three sections: 1, 2 and 3 (Fig. 1). The equation for the section 1 is generally described by an exponential function. The section 2 is taken to be linear.

he section 3 is not described by any equation.

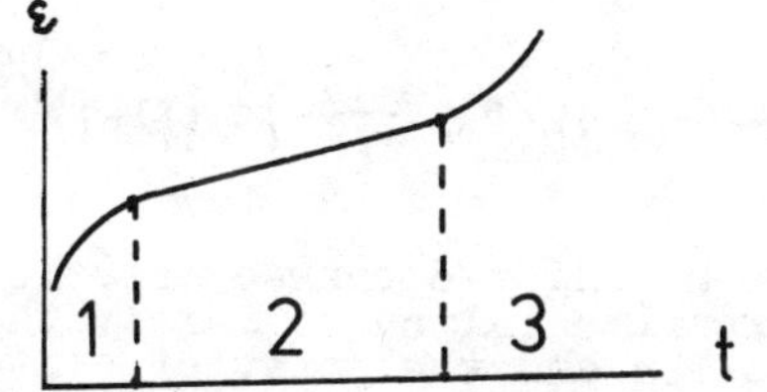

Fig. 1. Characteristic sections of the rheological curves.

Such a haphazard description makes it difficult to compare creep curves obtained under different loading conditions.

Below we propose a mutual equation for the creep curve suitable for description of all three Sections: 1, 2 and 3. In this case it is sufficient to correlate the numerical values of their coefficients only for comparing the curves.

The proposed equation is: (Fig. 2).

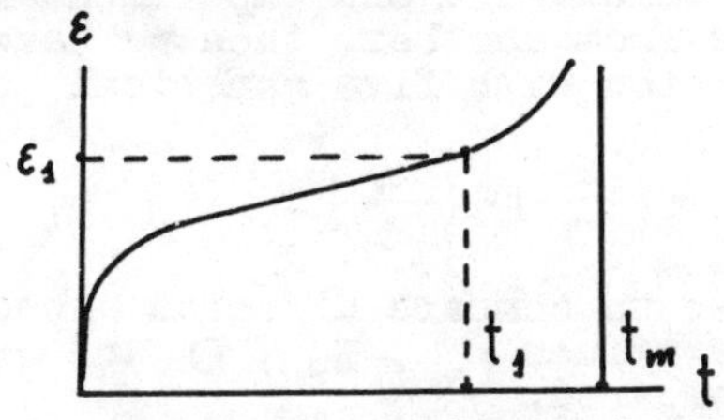

Fig. 2. Proposed rheological curve.

$$\left(\frac{t_m}{t}\right)^p - \left(\frac{\varepsilon_1}{\varepsilon}\right)^n = 1 \qquad (1)$$

There are four numerical parameters: t_m, ε_1, p and n in this equation. Therefore, to determine their values it is sufficient to have four test points on such a curve. As a rule, there are many more test points on the empirical rheological curves.

Solving equation (1) with respect to time t and deformation ε we obtain the following expressions:

$$t = \frac{t_m}{\left[1 + \left(\frac{\varepsilon_1}{\varepsilon}\right)^n\right]^{1/p}} \qquad (2)$$

$$\varepsilon = \frac{\varepsilon_1}{\left[\left(\frac{t_m}{t}\right)^p - 1\right]^{1/n}} \qquad (3)$$

At $t_0 = 0$ evidently we have $\varepsilon_0 = 0$ i.e., the curve will pass through the origin.

For smoll t and ε the ratios t_m/t and $\varepsilon_1/\varepsilon$ will be large. Thus, the 1 can be neglected with reesonable accuracy. In this case we find:

$$t \cong t_m\left(\frac{\varepsilon}{\varepsilon_1}\right)^{n/p}; \quad \varepsilon = \varepsilon_1\left(\frac{t}{t_m}\right)^{p/n} \qquad (4)$$

Such exponential equations can be easily linearized on a double logarithmic net; thus we can graphically obtain the ratio of p and n.

When $\varepsilon = \varepsilon_1$ from Eq. (1) we easily obtain following ratio for any n:

$$\frac{t_m}{t} = 2^{1/p} \qquad (5)$$

When $p = 1$ the time t will be half of t_m. The ratio will approach unity with increasing p.

If $t = t_m$ the deformation ε will tend to infinity irrespectiv of the value of p, i.e., the rock specimen is destroyed. Hence, the line $t = t_m$ is a vertical asymptote to the rheological curve. In fact, the specimen will be destroyed much before the curve reaches its asymptote.

Let us draw a line from the origin to intersect the curve under consideration (Fig. 3):

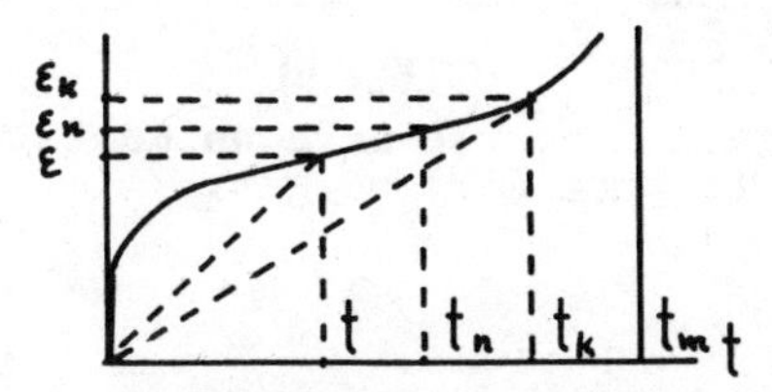

Fig. 3. Characteristic points of the rheological curve.

It is clear thet the ratio t/ε characterizes the slope of this line relative to the coordinate system.

$$\frac{t}{\varepsilon} = \frac{t_m}{\varepsilon\left[1 + \left(\frac{\varepsilon_1}{\varepsilon}\right)^n\right]^{1/p}} \qquad (6)$$

This slope is maximum when the denominator in Eq. (6) is minimum or vice versa. The situation will be the same when the expression is reised to the power p. This simplifies differentiation:

$$\left(\frac{t}{\varepsilon}\right)^p = \frac{t_m^p}{\varepsilon^p\left|1 + \left(\frac{\varepsilon_1}{\varepsilon}\right)^n\right|} \qquad (7)$$

Differentiating the denominator and equating the result to zero we get:

$$\left(\frac{\varepsilon_1}{\varepsilon_k}\right)^n = \frac{p}{n-p}; \quad \left(\frac{t_m}{t_k}\right)^p = \frac{n}{n-p}; \qquad (8)$$

Hence

$$n\left(\frac{\varepsilon_1}{\varepsilon_k}\right)^n = p\left(\frac{t_m}{t_k}\right)^p \qquad (9)$$

Differentiating Eq. (2) we obtain an expression for the tangent:

$$\frac{dt}{d\varepsilon} = \frac{t_m\, n\, \varepsilon_1^{\,n}\, \varepsilon^{\,n/p-1}}{p(\varepsilon^n + \varepsilon_1^{\,n})^{1/p+1}} \qquad (10)$$

The second derivative of Eq. (2) is:

$$\frac{d^2t}{d\varepsilon^2} = \frac{t_m n}{\varepsilon_1 p} \frac{\left(\frac{\varepsilon}{\varepsilon_1}\right)^{n/p-2}}{p\left[\left(\frac{\varepsilon}{\varepsilon_1}\right)^n + 1\right]^{1/p+2}} \times$$

$$\left[(n-p)\left(\left(\frac{\varepsilon}{\varepsilon_1}\right)^n + 1\right) - n(n+p)\left(\frac{\varepsilon}{\varepsilon_1}\right)^n\right] \qquad (11)$$

Equating it to zero we get the expression for the point of inflection:

$$\left(\frac{\varepsilon_n}{\varepsilon_k}\right)^n = \frac{n-p}{p(n+1)} \qquad (12)$$

On eliminaring two unknown quatities from Eq. (8) and (12) we get:

$$\left(\frac{\varepsilon_k}{\varepsilon_n}\right) = (n+1)^{1/n}; \left(\frac{t_k}{t_n}\right) = (p+1)^{1/p} \qquad (13)$$

Thus, having two characteristic points on the experimental curve namely the point of inflection and the point of contact of the curve with a line running through the origin, we can find p and n.

Now using the experssions (8) one may determine all four parameters in the equation (1).

However, it is not easy too properly determine the point of inflection on a flat curve. Even slight errors in its determination may significantly distort the values o the coefficients. Therefore, initial values of p and n should be varied and the best selfconsistent solution found by trial and error method.

If the calculated and experimental curve differ one from another, then we have to us a new equation with five numerical parame - ters

$$\left(\frac{t_m}{t}\right)^p - \left(\frac{\varepsilon_1}{\varepsilon}\right)^n - \left(\frac{\varepsilon_1}{\varepsilon}\right)^m = 1 \qquad (14)$$

In order to compare different rheologica curves the values t_m, ε_1, p and n must be compared.

TIME-DEPENDENT BEHAVIOR OF ROCK IN COMPRESSION

L'INFLUENCE DU TEMPS SUR LA RÉPONSE DES ROCHES SOUMISES À DES COMPRESSIONS

DAS ZEITABHÄNGIGE VERHALTEN VON GESTEINEN UNTER DRUCK

W.R. WAWERSIK

Associate Professor, Department of Mechanical Engineering
University of Utah
Salt Lake City, Utah

SUMMARY Time-dependent deformation and failure were studied in two brittle rocks at ambient temperature. Competent and jointed samples were subjected to uniaxial compression and triaxial compression up to 68.95 MN/m^2 confining pressure. Time-dependent effects in the two test rocks were noticeable, particularly in the water-saturated state. However, these effects were subordinate when compared with the instantaneous rock response. Time-dependent deformation and the likelihood of time-dependent fracture decrease drastically with confining pressure (mean stress). In detail, the observed time-dependent deviatoric (shear) strain and volumetric strain were found to be non-linear functions of deviatoric (shear) stress, mean stress, water content and time which do not obey any of numerous mathematical models published to date.

ZUSAMMENFASSUNG Zeitabhaengige Verformungen und Bruch sind in zwei sproeden Gesteinsarten bei Zimmertemperatur untersucht worden. Feste und geklueftete Proben wurden sowohl einachsig als auch triaxial bis zu 68.95 MN/m^2 Manteldruck unter Druck gesetzt. Zeitbedingte Erscheingungen waren in beiden Versuchsgesteinen merklich, besonders im wassergesaettigten Zustand. Diese Erscheingungen waren jedoch von untergeordneter Bedeutung im Vergleich mit unmittelbar auftretenden Verformungs-und Bruchmerkmalen. Zeitabhaengige Verformung und Bruch nehmen drastisch mit der Hoehe des Manteldrucks (hydrostatischer Spannungskomponente) ab. Im Einzelnen wird gezeigt, dass die beobachteten Scher- und Volumenverformungen nicht-lineare Funktionen der Deviatorspannung, der hydrostatischen Spannungskomponente, des Wassergehaltes und der Zeit sind, die keinem der zahlreichen bisher veroeffentlichten mathematischen Modelle gehorchen.

RÉSUMÉ L'influence du temps sur la déformation et la rupture de deux roches fragiles, a été étudiée à la température ambiante. Des éprouvettes soit intactes soit avec des joints ont été soumises à des efforts uniaxiaux et triaxiaux avec une pression de confinement pouvant atteindre 68.95 MN/m^2. L'influence du temps a été remarquée dans les deux sortes de roches plus particulièrement pour les roches saturées. Néanmoins, les effects etaient secondaires comparés à la reponse instantanée de la roche. L'influence du temps sur la déformation et la probabilité de son influence sur la rupture diminue énormément avec la pression de confinement (composante sphérique du tenseur de contrainte). Plus précisément, l'influence du temps sur la composante déviateur du tenseur de deformation (déformation en scisaillement) et la déformation volumétrique a été trouvée être une fonction non-lineaire du tenseur déviateur, de la composante sphérique du tenseur de contrainte, de la teneur en eau et du temps, fonction qui n'obeit à aucun des nombreux modèles mathématiques proposés jusqu'à present.

INTRODUCTION

To date no conclusive evidence exists to decide whether and under what conditions the long term stability of underground openings is time-dependent (ISRM, Committee report; Wawersik, 1973). If time-dependent effects should prove to be significant, then obviously they should be incorporated into design calculations. To accomplish this end, time-dependent constitutive relations must be established. Because the stress states encountered in situ are three dimensional for the most part, the stress strain relations needed must be three dimensional as well. Such general constitutive equations are not yet available. All existing time-dependent stress-strain equations for rock are essentially one dimensional; their form may be unsuitable for extension to multiaxial stress states, they may be based solely on uniaxial loading experiments, or they are based on measurements of only one component of the strain field.

To assess the significance and the nature of time-dependent rock behavior in engineering applications, a series of laboratory experiments was conducted. To provide grounds to predict the response of jointed rock masses in situ, tests were performed on competent as well as on jointed specimens. Both the magnitude of time-dependent deformations and the likelihood of time-dependent rock fracture was studied in uniaxial compression and in triaxial compression up to 68.95 MN/m^2 confining pressure. Axial and radial strains and, therefore, volumetric and shear (deviatoric) strains were measured on cylindrical specimens in quasi-static experiments and in creep over periods ranging from 0.1 hour to 1,300 hours. All tests were carried out at room temperature.

ROCK TYPES AND SPECIMENS

Westerly granite and a Utah (Navajo) sandstone were tested. Both rock types have been described in the literature (Brace, 1964; Brown et al 1971). Experiments were performed on competent and artificially jointed, cylindrical specimens 2.54 cm. in diameter and approximately 6 cm. in length. All specimens were ground prior to testing. Specifically, all sample ends were ground parallel to within 5×10^{-4} cm.

Cylindrical, "jointed" specimens were obtained by inducing tension fractures between line loads in rectangular granite blocks, gluing the fracture surfaces and subsequently drilling cores. The freshly cored specimens were cut and ground to length and immersed into a solvent to remove all epoxy. All joint planes were oriented at a 30° angle with respect to the sample axes. The peak amplitudes of asperities along the joints were approximately ± 0.05 cm.

For the most part, the behavior of water-saturated samples were examined. The response of air dry rock was evaluated in uniaxial compression only. Air dryness was achieved by exposing each specimen to room conditions for fixed time intervals at relatively constant humidity ratios (0.0045 to 0.0005) and temperature 21°C.

EXPERIMENTS

Apparatus

The experimental apparatus consisted of: (1) a 0.5 MN hydraulic testing machine, (2) two accumulators that were pressurized in series with the hydraulic actuator for constant force control, (3) a pressure vessel including two 2.54 cm diameter steel loading pistons, and (4) a screw-driven pressure regulator.

Both loading pistons contained two vent holes to minimize pore pressure changes in water-saturated specimens during testing. To maintain a constant confining pressure in long term creep experiments the action of the pressure regulator was servo-controlled using the output of a differential pressure gauge as the feedback signal.

All specimens were enclosed in loosely fitting jackets of polyurethane whose ends were clamped to the loading piston. Frictional end effects were minimized by matching the diameters of the samples and of the loading pistons. The experiments on jointed specimens were further aided by the use of two sets of mirror-polished, lubricated steel wafers. These wafers were placed between the loading pistons and the specimen ends and permitted joint motions to occur without significant changes of stresses on the joint plane.

Measurements

Experiments on Competent Samples

Axial sample force and confining pressure were monitored by means of a load cell and two Heise gauges. All strain measurements were made indirectly. For competent specimens the axial strain parallel to the greatest compressive stress was ascertained by means of DCDT transducers that were mounted to the loading pistons external to the pressure vessel. Lateral (tangential) strain was measured by means of SR4 strain gauges on air-dry samples subjected to uniaxial compression. In triaxial compression lateral (radial) strain was determined from measurements of the integrated sample deformation. This technique was first employed by Crouch (1970). It is based on the fact that the volume adjustments of the confining pressure medium which are needed to maintain a constant confining pressure during radial sample deformation are directly proportional to the (average) radial specimen strain. Thus for homogeneous sample deformation it has been shown elsewhere (Wawersik, 1974) that

$$\varepsilon_2 = \varepsilon_3 = \frac{\Delta V}{C_1} - C_3 F \qquad (1)$$

provided the cross-sectional areas or sample and loading pistons are equal. ΔV denotes the cumulative, incremental volume adjustments of the confining pressure medium which are proportional to the linear motion of the regulator piston. C_1 and C_3 are constants the magnitude of which depends on the sample dimensions and on the pressure vessel design.

Experiments on Jointed Specimens

Experiments on jointed specimens focused on the relationship between the average normal stress σ_n and the average shear stress τ_n on the joints on one hand and the average normal and shear displacements d_n and d_s on the other. The values of σ_n and τ_n were calculated from the applied principal stresses. The displacement d_n and d_s were evaluated from comparative deformation measurements on jointed and competent samples. If the mechanical properties of the competent rock do not vary appreciably between samples, it can be shown (Wawersik, 1974).

$$d_n = \frac{V_j}{a_j} \Delta\varepsilon \qquad (2)$$

and

$$d_s = \frac{\Delta\varepsilon_1 L_j - d_n \sin\alpha}{\cos\alpha} \qquad (3)$$

where V_j = volume of jointed sample

a_j = joint area

$\Delta\varepsilon$ = difference in volumetric strain between jointed and competent specimens

L_j = length of jointed specimen

α = smallest angle between the slip direction and the sample axis

$\Delta\varepsilon_1$ = difference in the axial strain between jointed and competent specimens.

If the sample lengths are equal, Equations (2) and (3) are more conveniently expressed in terms of the two quantities that were monitored in the experiments (1) the cumulative volume adjustments of the confining pressure medium ΔV to maintain the confining pressure constant, and (2) the axial deformation readings ΔT. Thus,

$$d_n \approx \frac{1}{a_j} [\Delta V_j - \Delta V_c) - A_c(\Delta T_j - \Delta T_c)] \qquad (4)$$

$$d_s \approx \frac{1}{\cos\alpha} [(\Delta T_j - \Delta T_c) - d_n \sin\alpha] \qquad (5)$$

where subscripts j and c pertain to jointed and competent specimens, respectively.

EXPERIMENTAL RESULTS

The experimental results are ordered in four groups: (1) quasi-static tests on both water-saturated and air-dry specimens (2) triaxial creep tests on water-saturated samples (3) uniaxial creep experiments on air-dry rock and, finally, (4) quasi-static and creep tests on singly jointed samples.

Quasi-Static Experiments on Competent Rock

Representative results of the quasi-static experiments are given in Figure 1. All stress strain

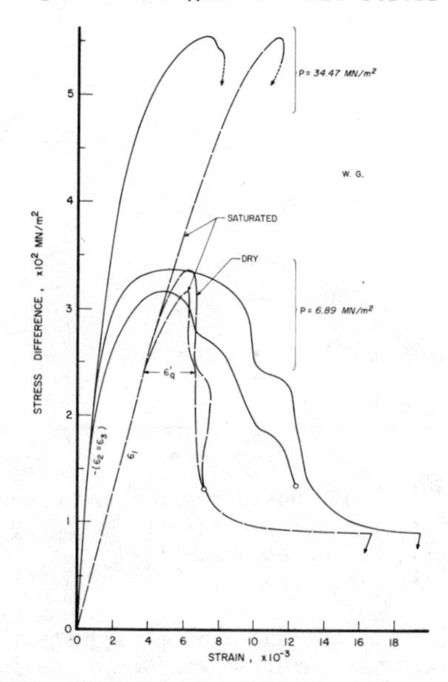

Fig. 1. Quasi-static stress strain curves for Westerly granite under confining pressure of 6.89 and 34.47 MN/m^2 (strain rate $\dot{\varepsilon}_1 \approx 10^{-5}$/sec.).

curves were ascertained at approximately constant strain rate $\dot{\varepsilon}_1 = 0(10^{-5})$/sec. Throughout, the presence of water in granite and sandstone tends to lower the strength and the principal strains to failure. The ultimate stress in water saturated Westerly granite and Navajo sandstone was 10 to 13 per cent lower than their strengths in the air-dry state regardless of the magnitude of the confining pressure. The observed decrease in the ultimate strength at the same externally imposed strain rate indicates that failure is accelerated in the presence of water. For this reason, the majority of the creep experiments were conducted on water saturated specimens to obtain a maximum number of data in the time that was available for this research.

Figure 1 shows that complete stress-strain curves were obtained at 6.89 MN/m^2 confining pressure only. However, published results for Westerly granite and the characteristics of the stress-strain curves immediately past the ultimate strength suggest a pronounced embrittlement of both rocks with increasing confining pressure which appears to be typical for so-called class II or "unstable" post-failure behavior. In all cases the stress strain curves of water saturated specimens coincided with or were bounded by the stress-strain characteristics of air-dry samples. Both observations were deemed significant for predicting the likelihood of time-dependent rock fracture.

Creep Experiments in Triaxial Compression

Creep and differential creep tests were carried out at 6.89, 34.47 and 68.95 MN/m^2 confining pressure. The applied (principal) stress difference was varied between 60 per cent and 90 per cent of the ultimate stress that was measured in quasi-static experiments at $\dot{\varepsilon}_1 = 0(10^{-5})$/sec. The duration of each creep test fell in the range of 0.1 hours to 600 hours. Sets of typical creep curves are presented in Figures 2 and 3 for two granite specimens subjected to approximately the same stress differences (0.8 times the mean ultimate strength in quasi-static compression). The data shown are representative both for the regularity of individual sets of data and for the variability of the results between tests. Throughout, it was assumed that $\varepsilon_2 = \varepsilon_3$. Given enough time, creep in ε_1 and ε_3 appeared to include primary, secondary and tertiary creep. However, tertiary creep and terminal creep fracture were actually observed in only four experiments.

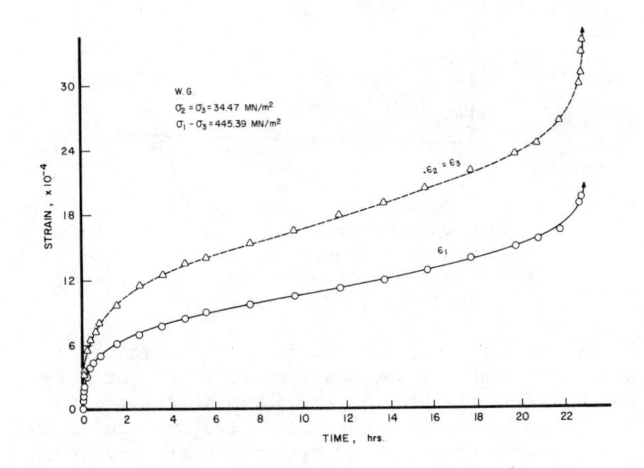

Fig. 2. Creep curves for water-saturated Westerly granite subjected to stress difference $\sigma_1 - \sigma_3 = 445.39$ MN/m^2 at 34.47 MN/m^2 confining pressure.

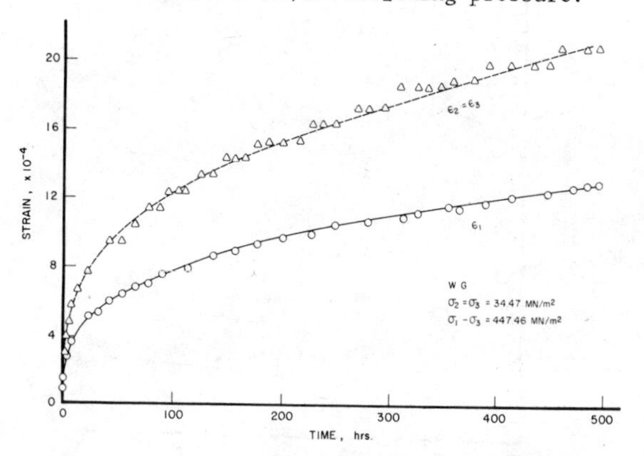

Fig. 3. Creep curves for water-saturated Westerly granite subjected to stress difference $\sigma_1 - \sigma_3 = 447.46$ MN/m^2 at 34.47 MN/m^2 confining pressure.

Primary creep was most readily described as a power function of time

$$\varepsilon_{iI} = 10^{C_i} t^{n_i}$$

Approximate values of C and n were determined from double logarithmic plots of strains versus time. Values that describe the axial strain ε_{1I} parallel to the greatest applied compression are contained in Figure 4.

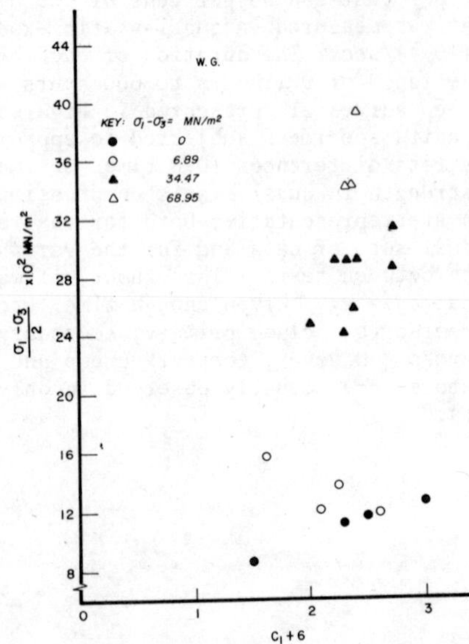

Fig. 4. Some primary creep date for water saturated Westerly granite as a function of shear stress and confining pressure assuming $\varepsilon_{1I} = 10^{C_1} t^{n_1}$; $n_1 = .28$.

Particular attention was devoted to secondary creep. All measured secondary creep rates for water-saturated Westerly granite are shown in Figures 5 through 7 which include the calculated magnitudes of the volumetric strain rates $\dot{\varepsilon}_{II}$ and shear (deviatoric) strain rates $\dot{\gamma}_{II}$. In Figure 5 the assumption was made that the secondary creep rate $\dot{\varepsilon}_{1II}$ is of the order 10^{-5}/sec in quasi-static compression experiments. Thus, the quasi-static compression data was treated here as creep data and used to supplement the results of actual creep tests. Curves that were fitted to the axial creep data in Figure 5 were cross-plotted in various ways in an attempt to relate the secondary creep rate $\dot{\varepsilon}_{1II}$ to shear stress (deviatoric stress component), confining pressure, and mean stress. For example, the results in Figure 5 were used to construct curves of constant creep rate in the spaces $\frac{\sigma_1-\sigma_3}{2}$, σ_3, and $\frac{\sigma_1-\sigma_3}{2}$, σ_m, etc. (Figure 6.)

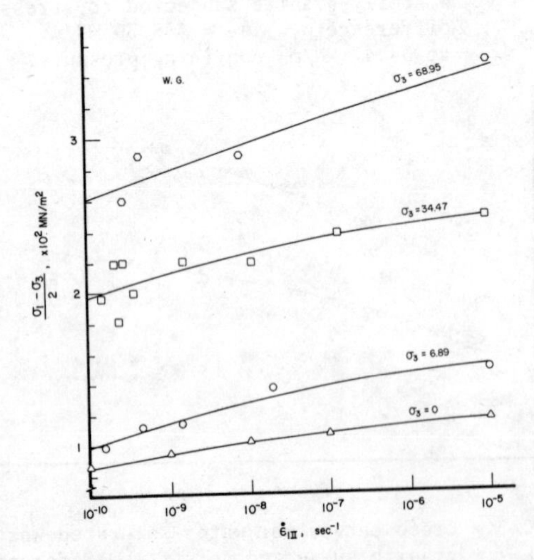

Fig. 5. Shear stress versus secondary creep rate $\dot{\varepsilon}_{1II}$ for water-saturated Westerly granite at confining pressures up to 68.95 MN/m².

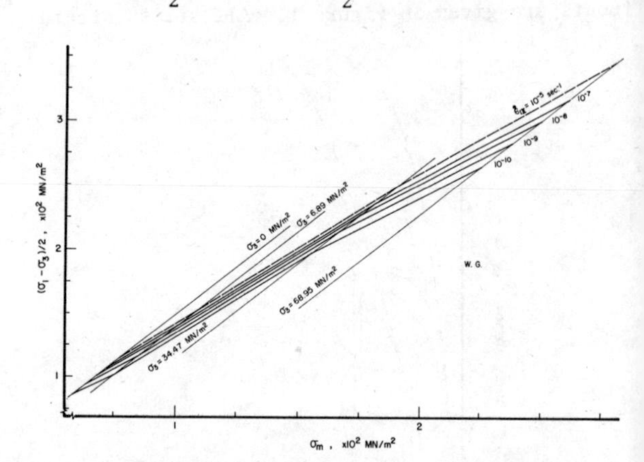

Fig. 6. Curves of constant secondary creep rate $\dot{\varepsilon}_{1II}$ for water-saturated Westerly granite in the space $(\frac{\sigma_1-\sigma_3}{2}, \sigma_m)$; $\sigma_m = 1/3(\sigma_1+\sigma_2+\sigma_3)$.

A comparison of the data above suggests that the rates of lateral, volumetric and shear (deviatoric) strains, $\dot{\varepsilon}_{3II}$, $\dot{\varepsilon}_{II}$ and $\dot{\gamma}_{II}$ in Westerly granite exhibit the same trends with changes in the above variables as the secondary axial creep rates. This is indicated in Figure 7 where the shear stress is plotted versus the secondary volumetric and secondary shear (deviatoric) creep rates.

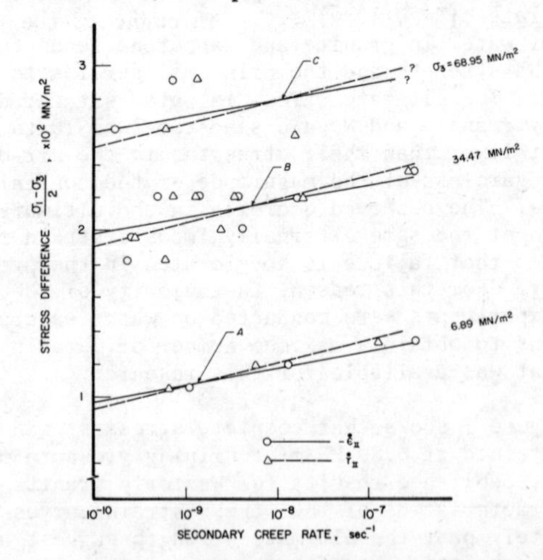

Fig. 7. Shear stress versus the time rate of change of volumetric and shear strain during secondary creep for water-saturated Westerly granite at 6.89 MN/m² to 68.95 MN/m² confining pressure.

Westerly granite is a "hard" rock of low porosity (0.9 per cent). The creep behavior of rocks of higher porosity is suggested by the creep data for Navajo sandstone (7 per cent porosity). Creep curves ε_1 and ε_3 versus time for two sandstone specimens subjected to 34.47 MN/m^2 confining pressure and to the same stress difference σ_1-σ_3 = 342.67 psi are shown in Figures 8 and 9. Obviously, the results are markedly

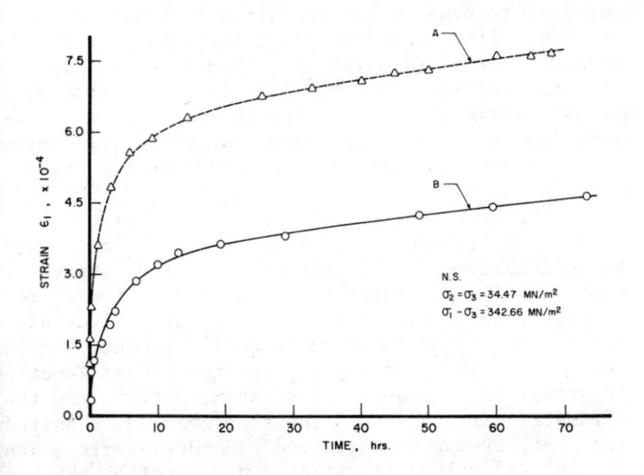

Fig. 8. Creep curves ε_1 versus time for water-saturated Nugget Sandstone at σ_1 - σ_3 = 342.66 MN/m^2 and 34.47 MN/m^2 pressure. Stress histories prior to deviatoric loading: Sample A - 34.47 MN/m^2, hydrostatic pressure for 16 hours; Sample B - 34.47 MN/m^2, hydrostatic pressure for 72 hours.

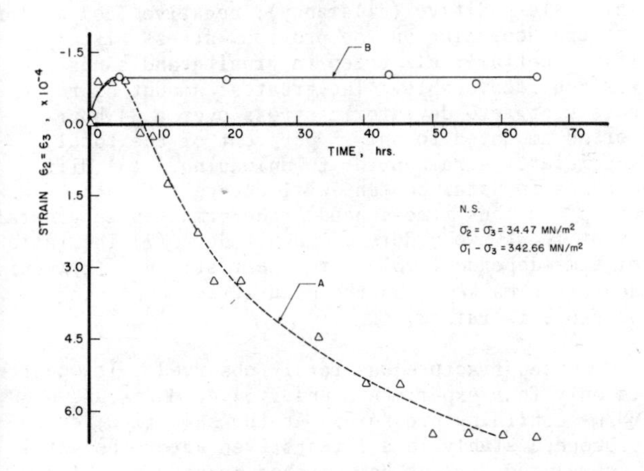

Fig. 9. Creep curves ε_3 versus time for water-saturated Nugget sandstone at σ_1 - σ_3 = 342.66 MN/m^2 and 34.47 MN/m^2 pressure. Stress histories prior to deviatoric loading: Sample A - 34.47 MN/m^2, hydrostatic pressure for 16 hours; Sample B - 34.47 MN/m^2, hydrostatic pressure for 72 hours.

different. The disparities between the two sets of curves are attributed to time-dependent compaction and differences in loading histories: prior to deviatoric loading, samples A and B were held under hydrostatic pressure for 16 and 72 hours, respectively. Very similar observations were made recently on shale and relatively porous block salt specimens.

Creep in Uniaxial Compression and the Influence of Water

Uniaxial creep experiments on air-dry granite and sandstone were carried out over periods of up to 1,300 hours. For the sake of brevity the results are not reproduced in detail. However, a comparison of air-dry and water-saturated granite is shown in Figure 10. The results of water-saturated samples

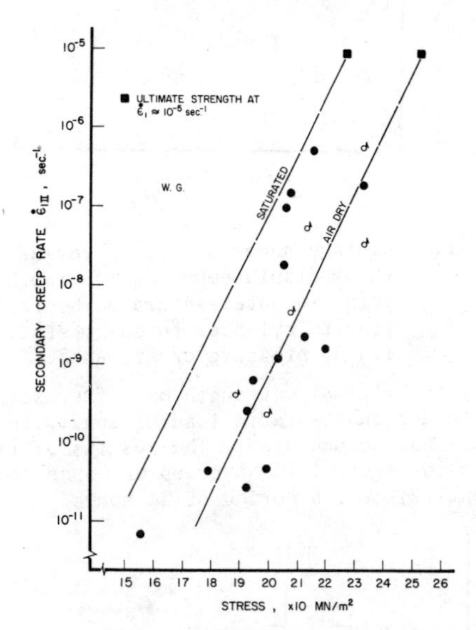

Fig. 10. Secondary creep rate $\dot{\varepsilon}_{II}$ versus stress for air-dry Westerly granite in uniaxial compression (semi-logarithmic representation).

were generated in an earlier study (Wawersik, 1973). While the semi-logarithmic plot is adequate to demonstrate the differences in rock behavior as a function of water content, it is statistically no more significant than a double-logarithmic representation. Although the form of the dependence between stress, creep and water content cannot yet be defined, Figure 11 indicates that changes in water content or, possibly, changes in (partial) pore water pressure produce significant differences in the creep rates.

Quasi-Static and Creep Experiments on Jointed Rock

Quasi-static and creep experiments were conducted on three specimens of air-dry and water-saturated Westerly granite each containing one unfilled joint inclined at 30° relative to the direction of greatest compression. The quasi-static data provided estimates of the static coefficients of friction at the onset of macroscopic sliding which are indicated in Table I. They also permitted the average normal and shear displacements d_n and d_s on the joint to be determined as functions of the average normal and shear stresses on the joint, σ_n and τ_n, respectively (Figure 11).

Creep tests on joints were carried out under 20.68 MN/m^2 confining pressure at (1) two levels of principal stress difference prior to the development of macroscopic slip and (2) at a stress difference of

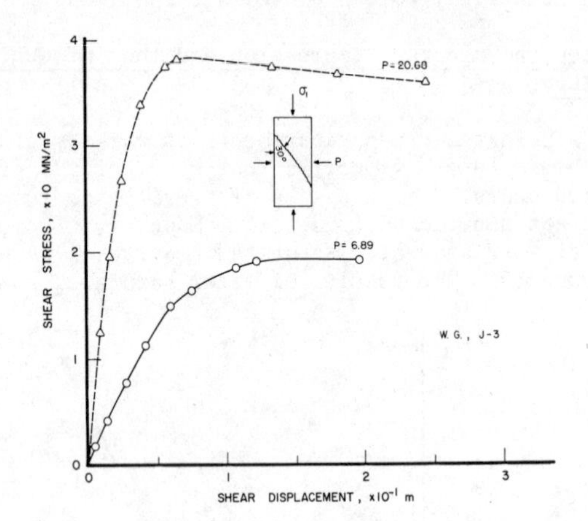

Fig. 11. Average shear stress τ_n versus average shear displacement d_s for rough tension joint in water-saturated Westerly granite cylinder in quasi-static confining pressure experiments.

0.8 times the ultimate strength but after slip had occurred under quasi-static loading conditions and some gouge had accumulated. The results of test (1) are shown in Figure 12. No creep was observed in experiment (2) over a period of 24 hours.

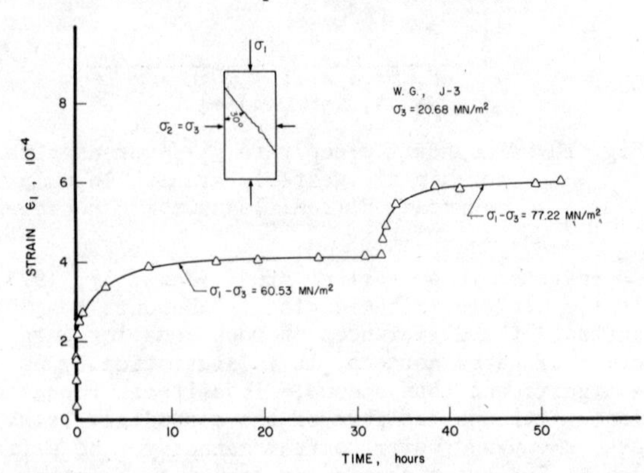

Fig. 12 Axial strain ε_1 versus time for jointed, water-saturated Westerly granite under constant principal stress diffference and confining pressure.

Sample Number	Confining Pressure $\sigma_2 = \sigma_3$ (MN/m^2)	Coefficient of Friction u_s
J-2 (air-dry)	6.89	1.00
	20.68	0.90
	34.47	0.80
J-4 (water-saturated)	6.89	1.05
	20.68	0.86
J-3	20.68	0.96

Table I. Coefficients of Friction for Joints (artificially induced tension fracture, roughness ±0.05 cm.) in Westerly granite as a function of confining pressure.

DISCUSSION

Time-Dependent Response of Competent Rock

The most significant observation here is that the time-dependent deformations in granite and sandstone are small compared with the instantaneous rock response. Moreover, the magnitude of the time-dependent response drops rapidly with confining pressure. Time-dependent fracture, which was frequently recorded in uniaxial compression, occurred in only four tests above approximately 75 per cent of th ultimate strength in quasi-static compression. Thus, as far as design work is concerned, it appears that time-dependent effects in competent rock are negligible.

What if the time scale were such that the effects of time-dependent rock behavior might have to be considered? The data of this study suggest that the time-dependent response of rock is far more complex than published accounts appear to indicate: (1) regardless of the magnitude of the creep strains for example in granite, they are non-linear function of stress (2) the deviatoric (shear) strain and the volumetric strain are of the same order of magnitude i.e. neither can be neglected, (3) deviatoric (shear strains and volumetric strains are functions both of the deviatoric (shear) stress and the mean stress. In fact, Figure 7 suggests that a change in the shea stress (deviator stress) may produce a greater change in the volume strain $\varepsilon(t)$ than in the shear $\gamma(t)$. (4) The results for sandstone indicate that creep in some rocks might be result of competing effects. In Navajo sandstone it is conjectured that effects are related to simultaneous pore collapse and micro-cracking producing net volume changes which are positive (dilatancy), negative (compaction or zero depending on the previous stress history. (5) Essentially all creep in granite and sandstone was non-recoverable. The greatest amount of recovery at zero deviatoric stress over a 54 hour period amounted to only 5 per cent of the total accumulated strain prior to unloading. (6) Differences in water content will change the rate of creep and thus time-dependent deformation in general by at least two orders of magnitude. (7) The ratio of time-dependent volume to shear strain $-\varepsilon(t)/\gamma(t)$ decreases markedly as the mean stress confining pressure is raised.

Creep fracture was rarely observed. It occurre in only four experiments under 34.47 MN/m^2 and 6.89 MN/m^2 confining pressure. At the same time, creep proceeded stably in all tests even after the total accumulated strains had reached magnitudes which were up to five times greater than the failure strains in uniaxial compression. Both of these observations corroborate the hypothesis (Wawersik 1973 that time-dependent strain at the onset of creep fracture is bounded by the difference in strain ε_q' (Figure 1) between the ascending and descending branches of the complete stress-strain curves for ai dry samples subjected to quasi-static compression. The upper bound strain is known to increase with increasing confining pressure. For example, for Westerly granite ε_q' is 6 x 10^{-4} in uniaxial compression and 6 x 10^{-3} under 82.74 MN/m^2 confining pressure. Considering that the upper bound strain becomes greater and that the creep "slows down" with increasing confining pressure (Figure 6), it is reasonable to postulate that creep fracture and time-dependent failure under time varying stress conditions are much less likely under confining pressure than the are in uniaxial compression. This reasoning might well explain why creep fracture did not occur more frequently during the course of this study.

Response of Joints

The evaluation of the influence of time on the behavior of joints in rock required first that the quasi-static joint properties be ascertained for comparison. Figures 1 and 11 show that the joints under relatively low normal stress are much weaker and more compliant than the competent rock. However, they also demonstrate that the instantaneous joint deformations exceed the time-dependent response by several orders of magnitude. For all practical purposes, therefore, the data suggest that unfilled joints at least are inactive regardless of the amount of water present. Furthermore, the observed increase in the coefficient of sliding friction along the joints during the time which the joint stresses were held fixed appears to rule out the possibility of unstable time-dependent joint slip. This latter observation confirms similar data that was presented earlier by Dietrich (1972).

SUMMARY AND CONCLUSIONS

This work had the very practical objective to evaluate whether or not time-dependent deformation and failure of rocks need to be considered in the total design of underground structures. To achieve this objective quasi-static, creep and creep-to-fracture experiments were conducted on air-dried and water-saturated Westerly granite and Nugget sandstone under uniaxial compression and compression with superimposed confining pressure. Both axial and lateral strain measurements were made in all experiments.

The results of these tests indicate that time-dependent effects of the rock types studied were noticeable, particularly in the water-saturated state. However, these effects were subordinate when compared with the instantaneous rock response. Time-dependent deformation and the likelihood for time-dependent failure decreases drastically with confining pressure (mean stress). Thus, in field situations time-dependent phenomena are considered appreciable only in the immediate vicinity of underground structures where at least one of the principal stresses is near zero. Time-dependent deformation and failure could become potentially hazardous at elevated pore pressure, i.e. if the effective mean stress is small.

Due to various constraints and because the influence of time in granite and sandstone was judged of secondary importance, no efforts were made to model the observed time-dependent response. However, all data suggests that the observed volume and shear (deviatoric) strains are non-linear functions of shear stress, mean stress and time which do not obey any of numerous published mathematical models proposed for rocks to date. Specifically, the results suggest that valid time-dependent stress-strain relations will have to be based on complete strain measurements under several different stress states. Uniaxial loading experiments and measurements of one strain component by themselves are inadequate and misleading.

It is emphasized that the above conclusions pertain to two specific rock types. While the behavior of these two rock types might be qualitatively representative for a large class of so-called hard rocks, the results presented here do not always apply, for example to shales or to rock salt. Furthermore, the data in this report are restricted to room temperature behavior and the validity of the effective stress law was implied but remains unproven.

ACKNOWLEDGEMENTS

This work was supported by the Advanced Research Projects Agency and was monitored by the U.S. Bureau of Mines, Twin Cities Mining Research Center, under Contract No. H0220007. The author wishes to acknowledge the large amount of research which constituted the basis for the present work. References to most previous research had to be omitted because of space limitations but are cited by the author elsewhere.

REFERENCES

Brace, W. F. (1964) "Brittle Fracture of Rocks," State of Stress in the Earth's Crust, W. F. Judd, ed., American Elsevier Publishing Co.

Brown, W. S., and Swanson, S. R., (1971) "Stress-Strain and Fracture Properties of Nugget Sandstone" University of Utah Final Report UTEC 71-058 to Kirtland Air Force Base, Albuquerque, NM.

Crouch, S. L. (1970), "Experimental Determination of Volumetric Strains in Failed Rocks," International Journal of Rock Mechanics and Mining Sciences, 7;6.

Dietrich, J. H., (1972), "Time-Dependent Friction in Rocks," Journal of Geophysical Research, 77;20.

International Society for Rock Mechanics (ISRM) (1971) Commission on "Definition of the Most Promising Lines of Research," Final Report.

Wawersik, W. R., (1973), "Time-Dependent Behavior of Rock in Uniaxial Compression," Proceedings of the 14th Symposium on Rock Mechanics (ASCE) - contains forty references.

Wawersik, W. R., (1974), "Technique and Apparatus for Strain Measurements on Rock in Constant Confining Pressure Experiments," submitted to Rock Mechanics.

THEME 1

THÈME 1

THEMA 1

E

E

E

Cyclic Loading and Fatigue

Renversement de charge et d'endurance

Zyklische Belastung und Erschöpfung

ROCK FRAGMENTATION BY HIGH FREQUENCY FATIGUE

FRAGMENTATION D'UNE ROCHE PAR FATIGUE À HAUTE FRÉQUENCE

HOCHFREQUENZ DURCH FELSDAUERSCHWINGZERBRECHUNG

Patrick J. CAIN Syd S. PENG Egons R. PODNIEKS

Twin Cities Mining Research Center, Bureau of Mines
Twin Cities, Minnesota

SUMMARY

The fatigue failure characteristics under high frequency (10 KHz) cyclic loading were determined for Tennessee marble, Charcoal granite, and Sioux Quartzite. The fatigue strength for each rock type shows a correlation with the static strength. The analysis of the damping and internal heat generation indicated that nearly all of the power input was accounted for as a change in enthalpy. The thermal strain was calculated and found to range up to 30 pct of the dynamic strain amplitude. The specific energy required for failure was determined and possible applications are discussed.

SOMMAIRE

Les caractéristiques de la rupture du marbre du Tennessee, du granite dit 'Charcoal' et du quartzite 'Sioux' ont été déterminées par des essais de fatigue à haute fréquence (10 kHz). Une corrélation existe entre la limite d'endurance et la résistance statique. L'analyse de l'amortissement et de la production de chaleur indique que la plus grande partie de la puissance absorbée est retrouvée comme un changement en enthalpie. Le calcul de la déformation thermale démontre que celle-ci peut monter jusqu'à 30 pour cent de l'amplitude des déformations dynamiques. Nous avons déterminé l'énergie spécifique nécessaire pour causer la rupture, et présenté des applications potentielles.

ZUSAMMENFASSUNG

Die Eigenschaften der Dauerschwingzerbrechung des 'Tennessee' Marmors, des 'Charcoal' Granites und des 'Sioux' Quarzites wurden unter Hochfrequenz (10 kHz) gemessen mittels Dauerfestigkeitsproben mit periodischer Belastung. Die Dauerfestigkeit steht in Wechselbeziehung zur statischen Festigkeit. Die Analyse der Daempfung zeigt, dass der groesste Anteil der zugefuehrten Energie in einer Enthalpie-aenderung verbraucht wird. Die Kalkulation der Waermedehnung zeigt, dass diese bis zu 30 prozent der gesammten Dehnungsamplitude reichen kann. Die spezifische Energieforderung zur Zerbrechung ist bestimmt worden, und moegliche Anwendungen werden diskutiert.

INTRODUCTION

The effect of low-frequency cyclic loading on rock is an area which has been investigated to a limited extent (Burdine, 1963; Haimson, 1972; Haimson, 1973; Peng, 1973). Also acoustic methods have been used to determine the physical and structural properties of rock. Ultrasonic devices have been frequently mentioned in discussions of novel rock fragmentation techniques (Farmer, 1965; Maurer, 1970). Past efforts to use sonic devices as cutting tools have employed a transducer driving a cutting medium such as an abrasive slurry (Goetze, 1956) or a bouncing tool (Graff, 1971). As the energy available from sonic transducers has increased, it is now important to explore the possibility of fracturing rock by sonic energy. In this program the failure of rock by the direct application of sonic energy is being investigated.

The energy required to maintain the vibrations and induce failure is primarily determined by the damping or energy dissipation. In this investigation the energy dissipation or internal friction has been used to predict the heating and the resulting thermal stresses which may influence the fracture of the specimens.

EXPERIMENTAL PROCEDURE

Three rock types, Charcoal granite, Tennessee marble, and Sioux Quartzite, were chosen to provide specimens with different ductilities and static strengths. The properties of these rocks are listed in Table 1.

The power source used in these experiments was a piezoelectric transducer connected to the cylindrical rock specimens by a transmission line as shown in Figure 1. The transducer is a high Q resonant device with a catenoidal horn for amplification and a nominal resonant frequency of 10,150 Hz. The complete system carries two standing waves and each component has free ends and the connections are only lightly stressed. This arrangement is advantageous because the maximum strain is at the center of the specimen and the end effects are negligible.

TABLE 1. - Mechanical and thermal properties of Charcoal granite, Tennessee marble, and Sioux Quartzite

Properties		Charcoal granite	Tennessee marble	Sioux Quartzite
Uniaxial compressive strength.........	$\frac{kN}{m^2}$	2.30×10^5	1.16×10^5	3.89×10^5
Uniaxial tensile strength............	$\frac{kN}{m^2}$	1.22×10^4	8.40×10^3	1.83×10^4
Young's modulus, E..........	$\frac{kN}{m^2}$	6.76×10^7	6.20×10^7	6.96×10^7
Thermal diffusivity, α.............	$\frac{cm^2}{sec}$	9×10^{-3}	10.7×10^{-3}	20×10^{-3}
Thermal conductivity, k.......	$\frac{cal}{cm\ sec\ ^oC}$	5.17×10^{-3}	6.6×10^{-3}	12×10^{-3}
Thermal expansion coefficient, α*....	$\frac{1}{^oC}$	10×10^{-6}	10×10^{-6}	15×10^{-6}

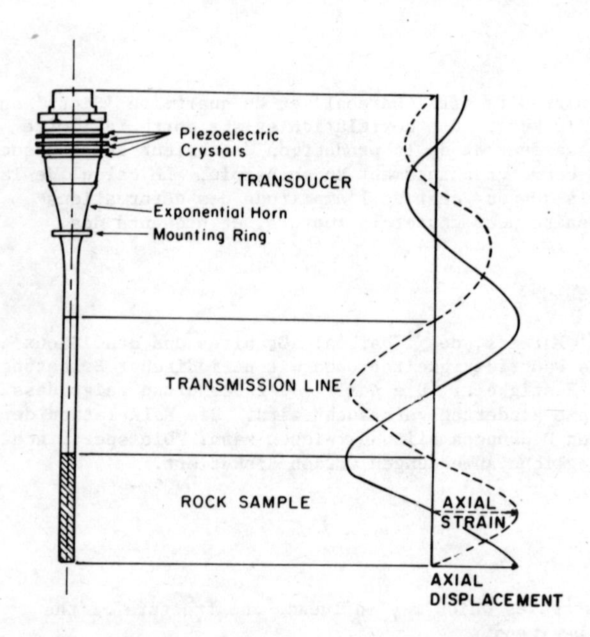

FIGURE 1. - Transducer-Specimen Assembly With Strain and Displacement Mode Shapes.

The rock specimens were cylinders 1 inch in diameter and 10 inches long. In preparing specimens for testing, a pair of strain gages were bonded on opposite sides of the midpoint of the specimen and wired in opposite sides of a wheatstone bridge to indicate axial strain. The resonant frequency of the specimen was matched to that of the transducer by trimming the ends of the specimen. To provide an indicator of specimen structural condition before and after testing, the longitudinal pulse travel velocity was determined.

The input power was provided by a 200-watt power amplifier controlled by a variable-frequency oscillator. The input voltage, input current, and strain amplitudes were monitored. The strain amplitude was recorded on a strip chart together with th temperature at the strain gage location.

During each test the input frequency was regulated to maintain resonance in the system, and the voltage was regulated to maintain constant strain amplitude in the rock specimen. The maximizing of the strain amplitude was used as the criterion for resonance. The fatigue tests were terminated when pronounced detuning or irregular input current and strain gage signals were observed. In some cases t rock specimen was broken in several parts at failur If the specimen did not fail, the test was terminat after approximately 10^8 cycles were reached.

Postfailure testing included measuring the bar resonant frequency of intact specimens and the long tudinal ultrasonic pulse travel time. The specimen were cut in half lengthwise, and the cut surfaces were ground and polished so the extent of the fatig cracks could be determined.

In addition to the fatigue test specimens, one specimen of each rock type was tested at amplitudes increasing in steps so that the rate of temperature increase as a function of amplitude could be determined for a single specimen.

EXPERIMENTAL RESULTS

The data taken in the course of the experiment included the number of cycles to failure as a function of the strain amplitude and the temperature of the specimen as a function of time. The relationsh between strain amplitude and the number of cycles t failure for Charcoal granite, Tennessee marble, and Sioux Quartzite is shown in Figure 2. The strain amplitudes at failure are small, but it must be note that rock fails in tension at low strains. The son strain amplitudes at failure are a significant fraction of the quasi-static tension failure strain (15-50 pct). However, on the compressive side of the load cycle, the strain amplitude is very small (less than 5 pct) compared with the strain at quasistatic compressive failure.

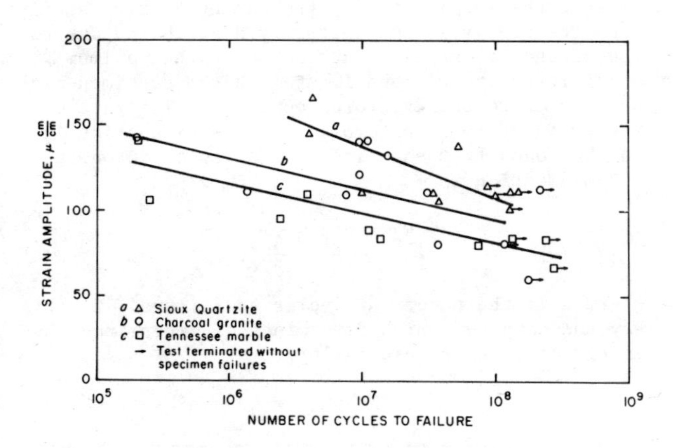

FIGURE 2. - Variation of Fatigue Life With Strain Amplitude for Tennessee Marble, Charcoal Granite, and Sioux Quartzite.

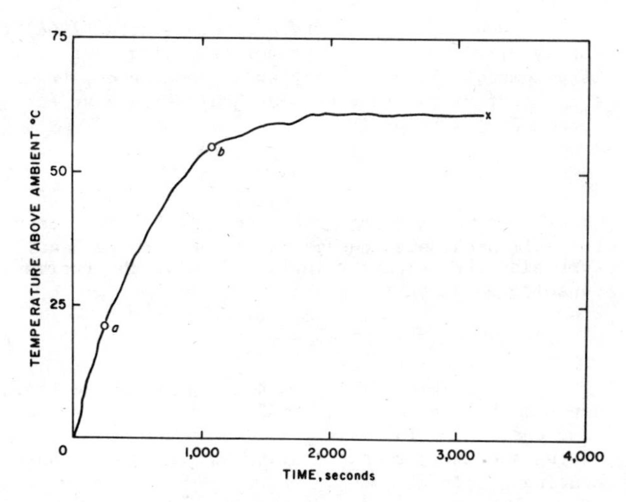

FIGURE 3. - Surface Temperature Increase Above Ambient for a Charcoal Granite Specimen With a Strain Amplitude of 140 μ cm/cm.

The three rock types tested had similar exponential relationships between the number of cycles to failure and the strain amplitude (fig. 2). The endurance limit is related to the static tensile strength, with the rock type with the highest strength, Sioux Quartzite, requiring the greatest number of cycles to failure and that with the lowest strength, Tennessee marble, requiring the least number at a given strain amplitude.

Close examination of the cracks revealed a fractured zone of less than individual grain size on either side of the crack in all three rock types. These zones were composed of small branching cracks on the planes of maximum shear at 45 degrees to the crack line. Formation of single large cracks normal to the specimen axis indicates the failure is primarily tensile. The distribution of the fracture locations in the maximum strain region indicates that fracture location depends on weak points in the rock. Both intergranular and transgranular cracking occurred in each sample.

A typical time history of the surface temperature at the center of a Charcoal granite specimen is shown in Figure 3. When loading begins at time t = o the temperature increases rapidly and almost linearly to point a, then continues to increase at a decreasing rate to point b, where it begins to approach asymptotically a steady state which is maintained until failure. Many specimens failed before steady state temperature conditions were reached. The maximum temperatures ranged up to 160° C depending on the strain amplitude and rock type. The highest temperatures were usually observed in tests of Sioux Quartzite.

The initial constant rate of temperature increase is proportional to the energy being dissipated in the specimen. The rate of temperature increase as a function of strain amplitude for single specimens of each rock type is shown in figure 4. Using single specimens reduces scatter caused by material variations and emphasizes the relationship with strain amplitude. The rate of temperature increase is approximately proportional to the cube of strain amplitude.

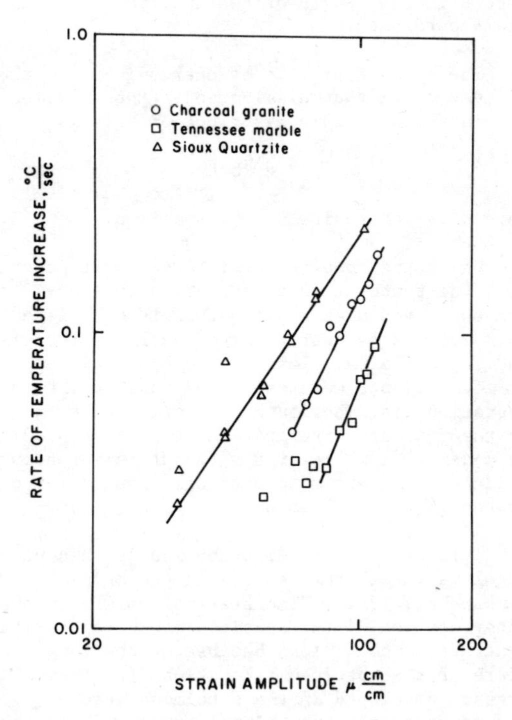

FIGURE 4. - Initial Rates of Temperature Increase for Various Strain Amplitudes.

The internal heat generation in the specimen can be expressed in terms of heat balance in midsection of the specimen during the initial loading. When the temperature is low and no heat is being lost at the boundary, the rate of internal heat generation equals the product of the rate of temperature increase, $\mathring{T}$, and the heat capacity of the material:

$$g = \mathring{T} c \rho \quad (1)$$

where c is the specific heat and ρ is the density.

In a material property approach (Lazan, 1964) the energy dissipation per unit volume during each cycle is assumed to have a power law dependence on strain ε_o; therefore the rate of heat generation g at the specimen midsection is

$$g = d\varepsilon_o^{\,n} f \qquad (2)$$

where f is the loading frequency. It has been assumed that all dissipated energy is in the form of heat. Combining the damping relation (2) with the thermodynamics equation (1) gives

$$\overset{o}{T} = \frac{d\varepsilon_o^{\,n} f}{\rho c} \qquad (3)$$

From the experimental data (Figure 4) the exponent can be evaluated as n = 3 and if it is assumed that the same relationship holds for the entire volume of the specimen, then the distribution of internal heating, G, is

$$G = df\varepsilon_o^{\,3} \sin^3 \frac{\pi Z}{L} \qquad (4)$$

where L is the length of the specimen and Z is the axial coordinate.

The power P or rate of energy input to the specimen must equal that dissipated in the specimen. From the sinusoidal strain distribution this is

$$P = \frac{4}{3} b^2 L g \qquad (5)$$

where b is the radius of the specimen.

Using the theoretical internal heat generation rate, the temperature distribution in a solid cylinder with outer radius b and length L is calculated by the usual methods of heat transfer analysis (Ozisik, 1968). In the calculation, the boundary heat transfer coefficients were estimated and the internal heat generation distribution was determined by equation 4. The theoretical temperature distribution predicted the measured temperatures with sufficient accuracy to validate the assumption that all input power was dissipated in the form of heat.

This temperature distribution is then used to calculate the thermal stress in the specimen (Timoshenko, 1951). The state of stress in the center section of the specimen can be approximated by plane strain conditions because of the long slender nature of the specimen. Equations for thermal stresses developed in the specimens were derived and used to determine the thermal stress values for the three rock types tested (Cain, 1974).

The cyclic strain is axial and the fractures are formed normal to the axis; thus, only the axial thermal strains affect fracture. The results showed that the axial thermal strain is compressive in the specimen center and tensile at the outer surface. The peak tensile stress which is the sum of the alternating strain amplitude and the thermal strain at the outer edge can be expected to control failure. To evaluate the contribution of the thermal strain to the peak tensile strain, the maximum tensile stress is shown as a function of time in Figure 5.

The specific energy for fatigue failure, E_v, is defined as the total energy input per unit volume to the specimen before failure and is a parameter used to evaluate the fragmentation efficiency. In the case of the longitudinally resonating fatigue specimens the energy is not uniformly distributed due to the sinusoidal strain distribution. The maximum specific energy will be located at the specimen midsection where the fractures occurred. The rate of energy input to a unit volume at the midsection, g, can be found from equation 5. The specific energy at the midsection is

$$E_v = g \frac{N}{f} = \frac{P}{\frac{4}{3} b^2 L} \frac{N}{f} \qquad (6)$$

where N is the number of cycles to failure. In this way the damping, which determines g, determines the energy consumed before failure.

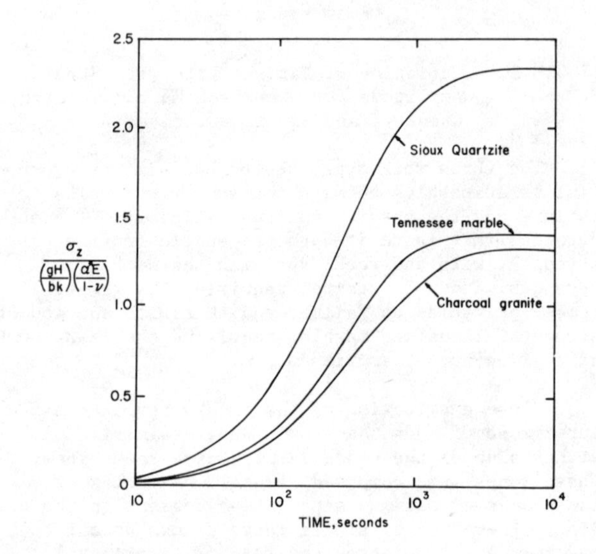

FIGURE 5. - Variation of Maximum Axial Tensile Thermal Stress With Time.

DISCUSSION OF THE RESULTS

The ratio of thermal to vibrational strain will increase with time because the thermal strain increases while the vibrational strain amplitude is constant. The dependence of the ratio on the strain amplitude is controlled by two opposing trends. Increasing the strain amplitude rapidly decreases the number of cycles, or time, before failure while increasing the heating rate and equilibrium temperature.

These two effects combine so that for extremely high and low strain amplitudes the thermal strains are small. The peak thermal strains experienced by any rock type are on the order of 30 pct; although this is not large enough to cause fracture, it is too large to neglect and must be considered as a contributing factor.

The specific energy, E_v, requirements are shown as a function of the number of cycles to failure in Figure 6. The dominant factor in determining the specific energy is the number of loading cycles. From

Figure 2, the change of strain amplitude is quite small compared with the change in the number of cycles to failure. At first it appears that the most efficient process from specific energy considerations is to fracture the rock with the least number of loading cycles. However, the principal advantage of a vibratory or oscillatory load is that it can form tensile fractures, which requires lower stresses than compressive fractures.

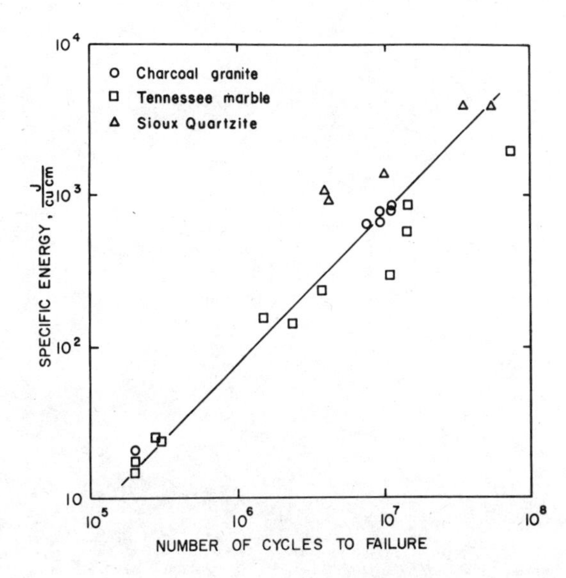

FIGURE 6. - Variation of Specific Energy With the Number of Cycles to Failure for Fatigue Fracture.

An important point of interest is the comparison of fatigue failure of rock under high (10 KHz) and low (1-4 Hz) frequency loading. Since different rock types have been investigated, the tests must be compared on the basis of the ratio of the applied stress to the static strength. By this method the effect of tensile and compressive loading can be compared. Peng (1973) and Haimson (1973) also tested rock under alternating tension-compression loading and reported that rock could be fatigue fractured with peak tensile loads as low as 40 pct of the tensile strength. Although in both cases the amplitude of the compressive portion of the load cycles exceeded the tensile by a factor of approximately 10, the tensile load amplitudes are similar to the tensile and compression load amplitudes used in this work. The results in terms of fatigue limit for both high-frequency and low-frequency alternating compression-tension tests are similar except that rock could be fragmented by load amplitudes as low as 30 pct of the static strength with the high-frequency loading. The important point is that the fatigue failure is reached in much less time with high-frequency loading. The fractures produced by both high- and low-frequency alternating tension-compression loading were of tensile nature. The heating effects were not observed in low-frequency fatigue (Haimson, 1973) because at the low rates (1-4 Hz) any heat generated by internal friction can readily dissipate.

In evaluating the potential application of high-frequency fragmentation methods, there are two modes to consider, i.e., breaking rock from the free face of a semi-infinite rock mass, or fragmenting rock with finite dimensions. The criterion to be used for such an evaluation is the comparison of the energy consumption and wear of the tools and equipment. If a vibratory tool is acting on a free rock face of a semi-infinite body and the mechanical impedance of the device and the face is matched, the stress waves can be transmitted into the body. However, if the impedance is mismatched, energy transfer will be inefficient and high interface stresses will be generated. To meet the goal of low tool wear, an impedance-matched system is necessary. The problem of energy being carried from the face into the rock mass by stress waves decreases with higher frequency vibrations, since the vibrations are rapidly attenuated by damping and the input energy will remain near the face in the form of thermal or strain energy. The energy losses can be minimized further if the amplitude is sufficiently high to cause failure in a short time. This does not necessarily imply that a single-cycle static loading is optimum, because the advantage of achieving tensile fracture (through dynamic loading) would then be lost.

On the other hand, in a rock mass of finite dimensions the stress waves are continued within the body and if the loading frequency is matched to the natural frequency, determined by the rock properties and dimensions, a resonant state of vibration can be achieved. When the high-frequency loading is applied in this manner, large amplitudes can be built up with a minimum of stress on the interface between the tool and the rock. This concept can be used to design a crusher to handle very hard rocks.

CONCLUSIONS

1. The endurance in high-frequency fatigue was related to tensile strength; rocks with higher static tensile strengths require more load cycles to be fractured at a given load amplitude.

2. Rock can be fatigue-fractured by high-frequency load amplitudes as low as 30 pct of the static tensile strength.

3. The fractures observed under high-frequency alternating tension-compression loading were tensile in nature.

4. Nearly all of the energy transferred to the specimen was accounted for as heat generated in the specimen.

5. For the rocks tested it was observed that, based on energy consideration, the most efficient cyclic fragmentation method is that requiring the least number of loading cycles to fragment rock at resonance.

6. At this time it appears the most promising immediate application of high-frequency fatigue will be in the fragmentation of large pieces of hard rock.

REFERENCES

Burdine, N. T. Rock Failure Under Dynamic Loading Conditions. Journal of Soc. of Petroleum Engr., March 1963, pp. 1-8.

Cain, P. J. Private Communication, 1974. Available on request from R. A. Friedel, Bureau of Mines, Minneapolis, Minn.

Farmer, I. W. New Methods of Fracturing Rocks. Mining and Minerals Engineering, January 1965, pp. 177-184.

Goetze, D., and G. E. Miller. An Investigation of the Ultrasonic Disintegration of Solids. WADC Tech. Rept. 55-277, June 1956.

Graff, K., et al. Fundamental Studies in the Use of Sonic Power for Rock Cutting. Annual Technical Report, for ARPA Contract No. H0210010 monitored by U.S. Bureau of Mines, The Ohio State University Research Foundation, December 1971, pp. 18-27.

Haimson, B. C. Mechanical Behavior of Rock Under Cyclic Loading. Annual Report for ARPA Contract No. H0210004 monitored by U.S. Bureau of Mines, the University of Wisconsin, Madison, Wis., March 1972, p. 92.

Haimson, B. C. Mechanical Behavior of Rock Under Cyclic Loading. Annual Report for ARPA Contract No. H0220041 monitored by U.S. Bureau of Mines, the University of Wisconsin, Madison, Wis., April 1973, p. 88.

Lazan, B. J. Damping Studies in Materials Science and Materials Engineering. ASTM, STP 378, June 1964, pp. 1-20.

Maurer, William C. Potential Application of Novel Rock Disintegration Techniques in Mining. 31st Annual Mining Symposium, Duluth, Minn., January 1970, p. 187.

Ozisik, M. N. Boundary Value Problems of Heat Conduction. Internat. Textbook Co., 1968, p. 150.

Peng, S. S., E. R. Podnieks, and P. J. Cain. Study of Rock Behavior in Cyclic Loading. Presented at the 6th Conference on Drilling and Rock Mechanics at Austin, Tex., January 22-23, 1973, SPE preprint No. 4249, pp. 181-192.

Timoshenko, S., and J. N. Goodier. Theory of Elasticity. McGraw-Hill Book Co., 2nd ed., 1951, p. 406.

MECHANICAL BEHAVIOR OF ROCK UNDER CYCLIC LOADING

COMPORTEMENT DES ROCHES SOUMISES À DES EFFORTS CYCLIQUES

MECHANISCHES VERHALTEN VON GESTEIN UNTER ZYKLISCHER BELASTUNG

B.C. HAIMSON

Associate Professor

Rock Mechanics, University of Wisconsin

U. S. A.

SUMMARY The cyclic fatigue phenomenon in four hard rock types has been investigated by subjecting 2.5cm dia. x 6.3cm specimens to uniform cyclic loading (1 cps, < 10^6 cycles) in uniaxial compression, tension, tension-compression and triaxial compression. Results show that hard rocks are significantly weakened or fatigued by cyclic loading. In uniaxial tension and in uniaxial compression the fatigue strength is 60-80% of the monotonic strength. In triaxial compression the fatigue strength rises as the confining pressure is increased. By far, the most damaging cyclic load is the tension-compression type, its fatigue strength reaching 30%. In load-control tests the strain-time behavior is not unlike that observed in creep with transient, steady state, and accelerated stages. The accumulated permanent strain for different upper peak cyclic stresses was found to always be bounded by the complete-stress-strain curve. The volumetric strain undergoes cyclic dilatancy, the onset of which decreases with cycling. Acoustic emission and specimen photomicrography suggest microfracturing as the principal mechanism of fatigue failure.

RÉSUMÉ Le phenoméne de fatigue pour quatre types de roches dures a été étudié en soumettant des échantillons de 2.5 x 6.3 cm ā des efforts de compression uniaxiale, tension, tension et compression et compression triaxiale. Les résultats montrent que les roches dures sont sensibles aux effets de fatigue. Pour les tests en tension ou compression uniaxiale la contrainte de rupture après fatigue n'est que de 60 a 80% de la contrainte de rupture originale. La contrainte de rupture après fatigue augmente quand la pression est augmentée dans le test triaxial. La condition de chargement la plus défavorable est obtenue par une suite de tensions et compressions: la contrainte de rupture n'est que de 30% de la contrainte originale. Certains phénomènes observes ressemblent au fluage. Des émissions acoustiques et des microphotographies suggèrent que le phenomène de fatigue est due essentiellement ā des microfractures.

ZUSAMMENFASSUNG Die zyklische Ermüdung in vier Hartsteintypen wurde untersucht. 2.5cm ϕ und x 6.3cm Probestücke wurden einer uniformen Belastung (1 Hz, < 10^{-6} Perioden) uniaxialer Kompression, Spannung, Kompression-Spannung, oder triaxialer Kompression ausgesetzt. Resultate zeigen, dass Hartsteine bei zyklischer Belastung bedeutsam geschwächt oder ermüdet werden. Bei uniaxialer Spannung oder uniaxialer Kompression ist die Dauerfestigkeit 60-80% der monotonen Festigkeit. Bei triaxialer Kompression steigt die Dauerfestigkeit mit zunehmenden Druck. Die schädlichste zyklische Belastung ist die Spannung-Kompression, wo die Dauerfestigkeit nur 30% erreicht. Das Verhalten der Überlastung mit Zeit in Belastungskontrolltests errinnert an Resultate von "creep" Messungen, mit kurzflüchtigen, konstanten, und beschleunigten Zuständen. Die angesammelte permanente Überlastung für verschiedene Maximal-stresse ist immer von der kompletten Überlastungs-Stress-Kurve begrenzt Die volumetrische Überlastung zeigt zyklische Erweiterung, dessen Anfang mit den Zyklus abnimmt. Akustische Emission and Probestück Photomikrographie deuten auf Mikrobruch als der Hauptmechanismus des Ermudüngsversagen.

INTRODUCTION

Rock formations as well as rock structures are subjected to both static and dynamic loads. Static loads result from such sources as tectonic and gravity forces. Small dynamic loads are continually propagated through natural vibrations of the earth's crust. Large dynamic forces are intermittently applied through major earthquakes, rock blasting, drilling, traffic, etc. The mechanical behavior of rock under static loading has been thoroughly investigated. However, rock reaction to the cyclic, repetitive stresses resulting from dynamic loads has been generally neglected with the exception of a few rather limited studies. It is a known fact that cyclic loading often causes a material to fail prematurely at a stress level lower than its determined strength under monotonic conditions. This phenomenon is commonly termed "fatigue". Faults, joints, bedding planes, tunnel walls, excavation roofs and ribs, bridge abutments, dam and road foundations are only a few of the natural and manmade rock structures that can be weakened by repetitive loading. Better understanding of cyclic fatigue could assist the engineer in preparing a more rational design that will eliminate premature failures. It could aid in earthquake prediction and control research. Knowledge of fatigue characteristics could also help improve rock breaking methods. It is, therefore, imperative that the effects of cyclic stresses on rock are fundamentally studied with the ultimate goal of deriving practical applications.

Among the first comprehensive studies of rock cyclic fatigue was Burdine's (1963) investigations of Berea sandstone strength under uniaxial and triaxial compression. He found that the monotonic compressive strength could be weakened by as much as 24% due to repetitive loading. Hardy and Chugh (1970) detected a cyclic fatigue effect in three hard rock types tested in uniaxial compression. Saint-Leu and Sirieys (1971) and Attewell and Farmer (1973) concentrated their efforts in understanding the deformational behavior of rock under uniaxial cyclic compression.

Independently of the aforementioned work a comprehensive study of the major aspects of cyclic loading in hard rock has been underway at the University of Wisconsin since 1969 (Haimson and Kim, 1972, Haimson, 1972, 1973, Tharp, 1973, Kim, 1973). The effect of repetitive stresses on strength, deformation and fabric were investigated in four rocks under four major loading configurations. The purpose of this paper is to present some of the principal results obtained and to point out practical applications.

RESEARCH PROGRAM

Four hard rock types (Tennessee marble, Indiana limestone, Berea sandstone, Westerly granite) were thoroughly tested under uniaxial cyclic compression and uniaxial cyclic tension; one rock type (Westerly granite) was also tested under triaxial cyclic compression and uniaxial cyclic tension-compression; a fifth rock type (Georgia marble) was selectively used in some uniaxial compression tests. In each rock specimens were cored in the same direction out of the same block. They were then cut and surface-ground to yield parallel plane surfaces to within .002cm. Specimen size was kept at 2.5cm diameter and 6.3cm long.

Wide scatter of results often accompanies cyclic testing of most materials. To prevent unnecessary variability special attention was given to careful specimen preparation and installation into the loading machine. In uniaxial cyclic compression tests specimens were mounted in a special jig consisting of a lower platen rigidly attached to the hydraulic ram of the loading machine and an upper platen which was part of a swivel head mechanism. Once the alignment between platens and specimen was established the swivel head was locked in position for the duration of the test. In uniaxial cyclic tension and in uniaxial cyclic tension-compression tests specimens were first glued with epoxy to threaded end-caps, carefully maintaining concentricity. The top end-cap was rigidly attached to the crosshead of the loading machine, the bottom end-cap fit loosely into a pot filled with "woods-metal", a material whose melting point is 160°F. By keeping the woods-metal in the liquid state when installing the specimen and then freezing it in position, alignment was ensured. Results indicate that very little bending took place since in most of the tests tensile rupture occurred away from specimen ends. The triaxial cyclic compression tests were run in a pressure-cell which enabled the confining oil to maintain its volume approximately constant throughout the vertical load fluctuations, thus keeping the horizontal pressure within $\pm$ 5% of its predetermined value. Specimens were kept dry using heat-shrinkable-tubing jackets.

In each of the four loading configurations the basic cycle was stress-controlled (i.e. stress was the independent variable), triangular in shape, and had a frequency of 1 cps (equivalent to the frequency of large events in earthquakes and blasting). The lower-peak-stress was kept constant throughout the testing, at approximately 600 bars compression in the cyclic tension-compression tests, and near zero in the other loading configurations. The upper-peak-stress was varied from test to test. The number of loading cycles per test was limited to 10^5-10^6. Strain was measured using strain gage instrumented cantilevers, L.V.D.T.'s or strain gages bonded directly to specimens.

The general objectives of the research program were to (a) determine the mechanical behavior of rock under cyclic loading and provide data that are both fundamental and useful in scientific and engineering practice, and (b) study the internal mechanism that results in cyclic fatigue.

ROCK STRENGTH UNDER CYCLIC LOADING

The effect of repetitive loading on the strength of rocks was determined by testing a series of 40 to 80 specimens for each rock type and loading configuration. The upper peak was varied from specimen to specimen in the following manner. First the stress level was determined at which only one cycle was sufficient to cause failure (equivalent to the compressive strength-C_0, or the tensile strength - T_0, depending on the loading type). Then the upper-peak-stress was decreased by 5% and the number of cycles to failure determined. The process was continued until no fatigue effect was obtained within the limit of cycles tested. The results are best illustrated by S-N plots showing the number of cycles (N) required to fail a specimen loaded to a certain upper-peak-stress (S). Average curves representing the drop in strength with the number of cycles for the four loading types used in these tests are given in Figs. 1 and 2. The respective values for the monotonic strengths of the different rocks and loading conditions are given in Table 1.

Table 1

Compressive and Tensile Strengths of Tested Rocks at Loading Rates Equivalent to 1 cps.

Rock Type	Compressive Strength C (bars)	Tensile Strength To (bars)
Indiana limestone	740	45
White Tennessee marble	1600	110
Berea sandstone	880	26
Westerly granite	3200	110
W. G. at 70 bars conf.	4120	
W. G. at 170 bars conf.	4850	

It is clear from the S-N curves that all the tested rocks exhibited fatigue characteristics, i.e., were weakened by cyclic loading. The fatigue strength for the number of cycles tested varied between 60 to 80% of the respective monotonic compressive strength for all the rocks tested in cyclic uniaxial compression. The fatigue strength in cyclic uniaxial tension was approximately equal for all rocks at 65% of the monotonic strength. It is interesting to note that in

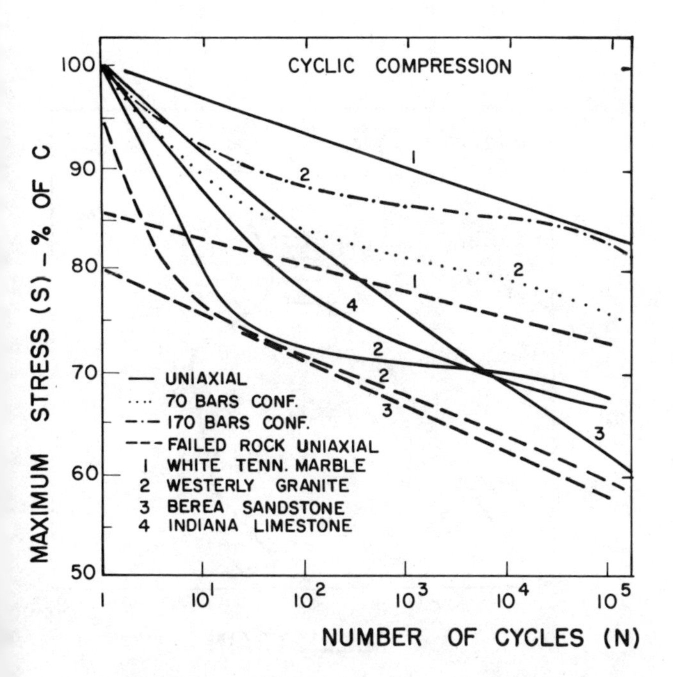

Fig. 1 S-N Curves in Uniaxial and Triaxial Compression in Terms of Percentage of Respective Monotonic Compressive Strengths (C).

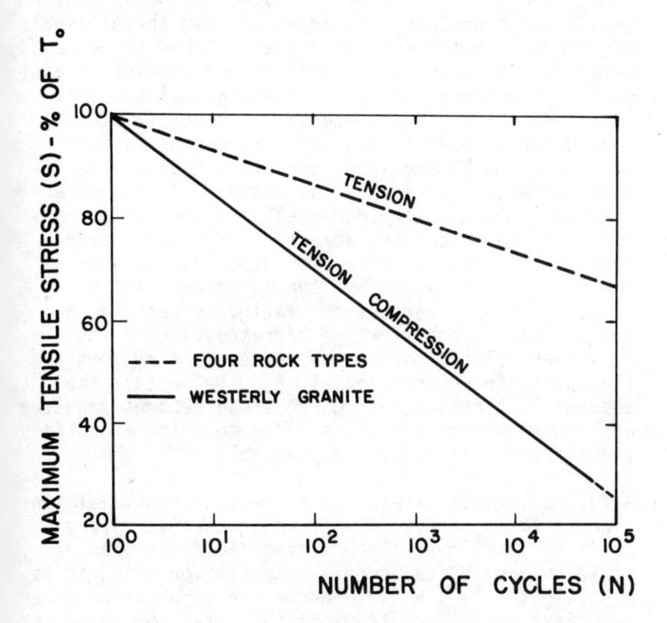

Fig. 2 S-N Curves in Uniaxial Tension and Tension-Compression in Terms of Respective Monotonic Tensile Strengths (T_0).

cyclic tension all S-N curves were linear, and represented by the equation S = 100 - 7logN. In cyclic triaxial compression (Fig. 1) the fatigue strength of Westerly granite increased with the confining pressure from 65% at zero confining to 75% at 70 bars, to 80% at 170 bars. In tension-compression, however, (Fig. 2) the fatigue strength was considerably lower than in tension only, reaching about 30% of the monotonic strength. The S-N curves indicate, in general, that the value of the monotonic strength, which is often used in the design of hard rock structures, may not be the relevant strength parameter since it ignores the effect of repetitive loading. Rather the fatigue strength as determined by the reported tests could be used as the rock effective strength that can withstand static, dynamic and cyclic loadings. The extremely low value of tensile fatigue strength in tension-compression suggests that this type of loading is most damaging and could be employed to advantage in rock breaking.

Cyclically compressed Georgia marble, that had been previously 'failed' by deforming it into the descending portion of the complete stress-strain curve, exhibited substantial fatigue endurance (Fig. 3). S-N curves of rock specimens first deformed to levels corresponding to their compressive strengths, unloaded and then cyclically loaded in stress-control, similarly showed considerable fatigue strength (Fig. 1). These results could be useful in the design of structures where rock might have previously been deformed to beyond the limit corresponding to its compressive strength. Failed pillars, ribs or other structural components could resist cyclic loading to an extent determined by appropriate S-N curves.

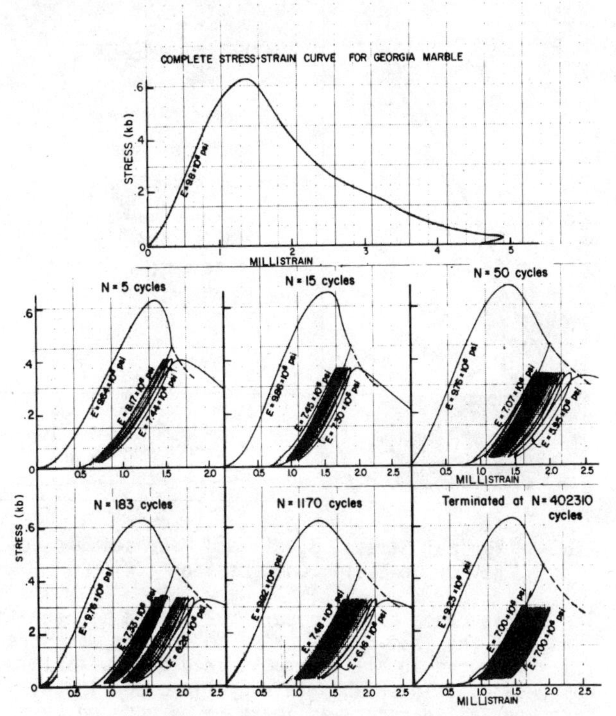

Fig. 3 Stress-Strain Curves Representing Compressive Cyclic Loading in Failed Georgia Marble. Dashed Lines are Expected Continuations of the Complete-Stress-Strain Curves.

CYCLIC DEFORMATION

The cyclic stress-axial strain behavior has been recorded in all the rocks and loading types. A feature common to all stress-strain curves is the phenomenon of a rather large hysteresis in the first cycle, followed by decreasing loops in the next few cycles, a narrowing of the loops to an almost constant shape and size in the following group of cycles, and a reopening in the last several cycles prior to failure. In very short life tests (1-20 cycles) only the first and the last stages are apparent. Also, the phenomenon of cyclic creep is generally observed in all rocks and loading types, i.e. for every stress level within the stress range of the repetitive loading the strain increases with each cycle. Three cyclic creep stages are observed, directly related to the hysteresis loops: a primary stage in which the strain increases from cycle to cycle at a decelerating rate, followed by a steady stage of linear strain increase, and culminating in an accelerated strain increase stage up to failure. The line connecting all the peak strain points in a strain-time plot closely resemble that of a static creep curve, (Fig. 4). The lower peak strain points define the amount of permanent deformation after each cycle. It is interesting to note that the permanent deformation after the first cycle is often 30 to 70% of the total permanent deformation just before failure. Hence, by loading a given rock through one cycle only, a fairly good estimate can be made of the total permissible permanent deformation. This could be used in conjunction with changes in rock structures to obtain a precursor of impending failure.

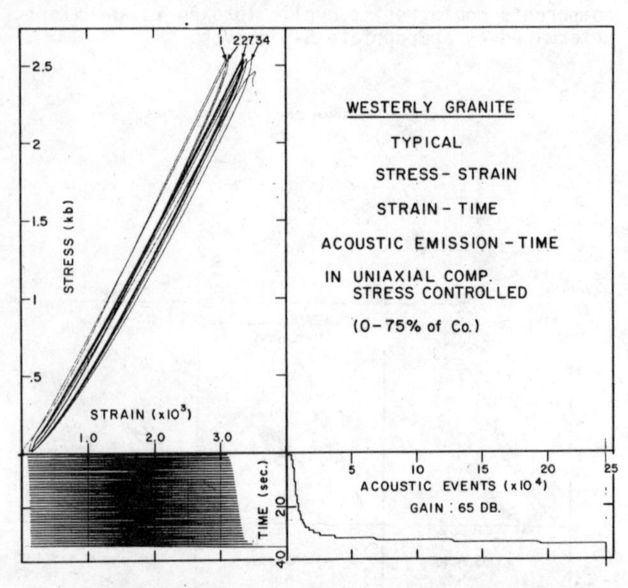

Fig. 4 Typical Stress, Strain and Microseismic Behavior in Cyclic Compression.

The cyclic creep of the upper peak strain between the first and the last cycles prior to failure was carefully measured in all the rocks loaded in uniaxial compression. Invariably this cyclic creep in both intact and failed rock, was found to be bounded by the complete stress-strain curve of the respective rock, (Figs. 3, 5). This result is significant in that it reinforces the suggestion that the complete stress-strain curve defines for any stress level the minimum (ascending part) and the maximum (descending part) allowable strain. This important conclusion could be used in structure design as well as in geophysical applications.

Determining the complete stress-strain curve for a rock is considerably less time consuming than preparing an S-N curve. Monitoring the amount of ac-

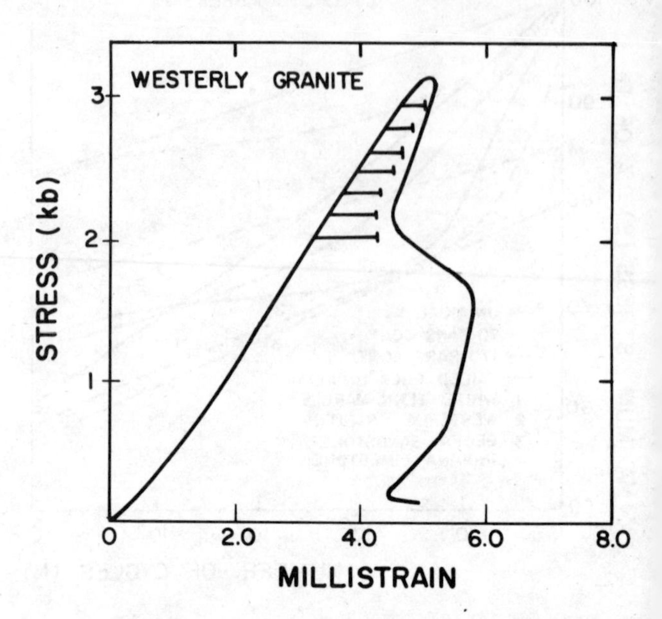

Fig. 5 The Complete-Stress-Strain Curve for Westerly Granite in Uniaxial Compression and the Average Cyclic Creep of Upper Peak Strains Under Cyclic Loading.

cumulated permanent deformation at a particular stress level (whether in a laboratory specimen or an underground structure) and comparing it with the allowable magnitude from the complete stress-strain curve could establish the stability condition and provide an estimate of the amount of cyclic loading that the rock can still withstand. The shape of the complete stress-strain curve could indicate the ranges of maximum stress for which the rock is more susceptible to fatigue effects. These are the regions of minimum allowable permanent strain, usually caused by the portions of the descending stress-strain curve having positive slopes. Such is, for example, the case of Westerly granite whose S-N curve for uniaxial compression shows a very strong fatigue effect in the top 30% of the stress range corresponding to its positively sloped portion of the descending complete stress-strain curve (Figs. 1, 5). Below this the descending stress-strain curve slope becomes negative and the number of cycles required to bring about fatigue failure increases considerably.

A typical stress-strain curve in cyclic uniaxial tension is shown in Fig. 6. Its characteristics are a strongly non-linear slope during the first loading cycle (except White Tennessee marble for which it is a straight line), a large permanent deformation after the first cycle (about 50% of the total permanent set a straightening of the loading portion of the following cycles, and little change prior to final rupture.

The stress-strain curve in tension-compression (Fig. is useful in understanding the different effects that tension and compression have on rock. As the load shifts from compression into tension there is a sharp drop in modulus indicating the opening of the heretofore closed microcracks. The additional drop in the tensile modulus between first and last cycles is around 30%, considerably higher than in other loading types, and it is perhaps this excessive 'softening' which makes tension-compression the most damaging cyclic loading.

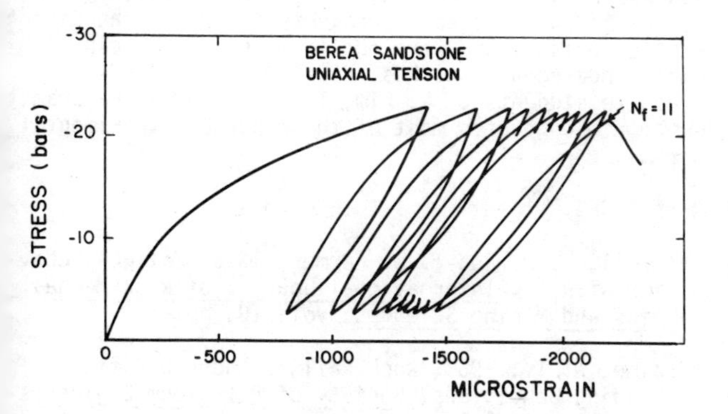

Fig. 6 Typical Stress-Strain Curve in Cyclic Uniaxial Tension-Berea Sandstone.

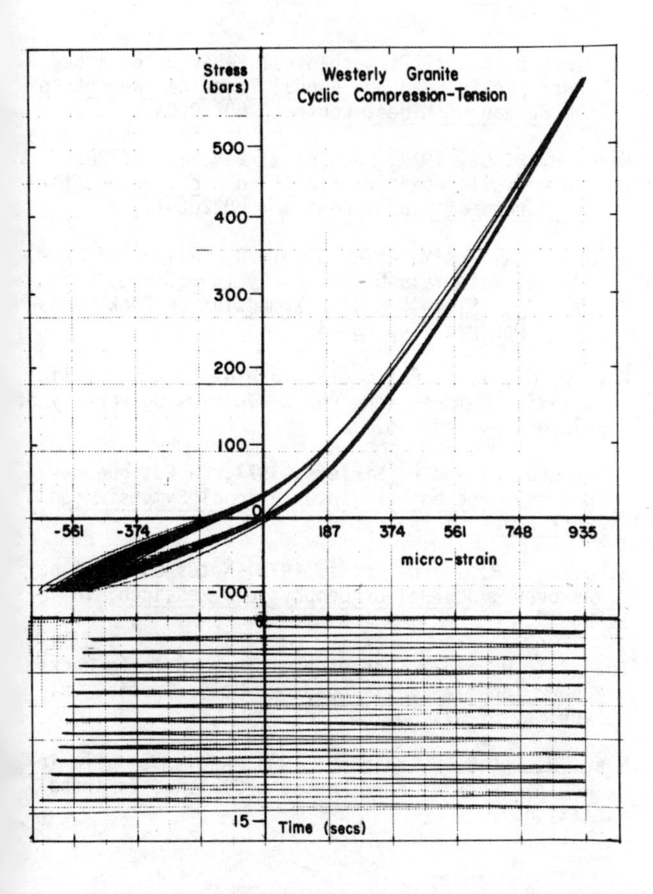

Fig. 7 Typical Stress-Strain and Strain-Time Curves Recorded During Tension-Compression Cycling.

The volumetric strain was calculated in uniaxial and triaxial compression tests from direct axial and lateral strain measurements. Typical examples are shown in Figs. 8 and 9 for uniaxial and triaxial compression. The trend is similar in both loading types. In each loading cycle dilatancy is clearly observed. A phenomenon noticed in most cases, and first identified by Scholz and Kranz (1973), is that the onset of dilatancy shifts with each cycle to a lower stress. Each cycle results in an increased amount of dilatancy. At the end of each cycle there is a net gain in the volume of the specimen. The first cycle and the last cycles before failure end in large permanent volume gains. During the steady state stage of the loading the volume increase is reduced but continues. The result is that typically during the latter part of the cyclic life the volume of the rock will be larger than the original amount throughout each loading cycle.

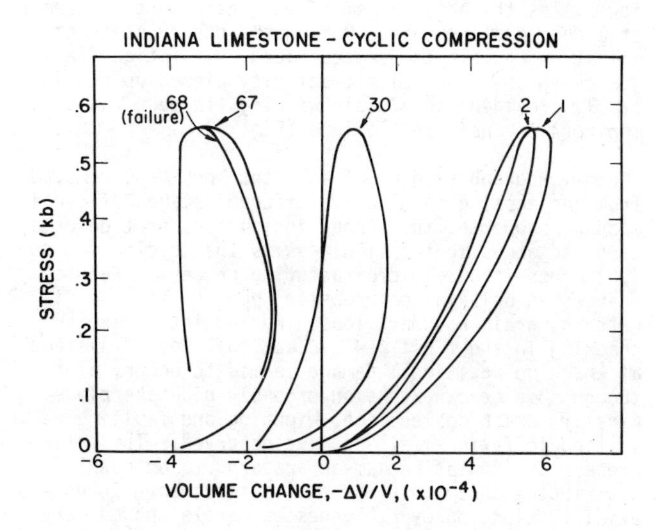

Fig. 8 Typical Stress-Volumetric Strain Behavior in Cyclic Uniaxial Compression-Indiana Limestone.

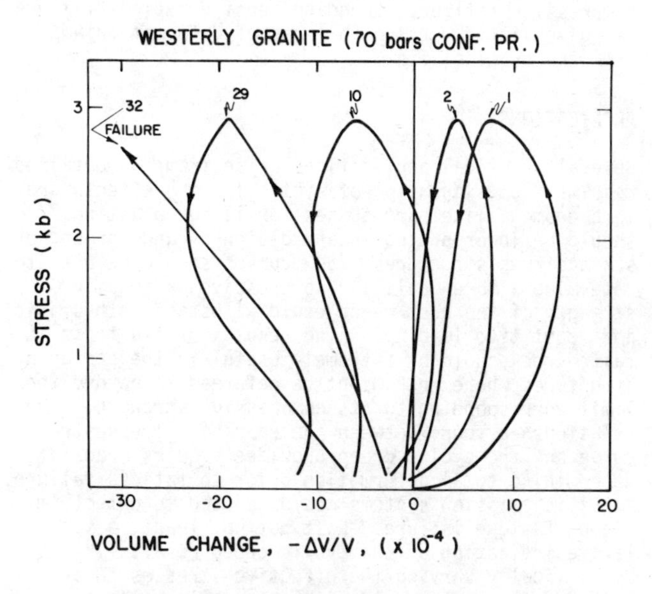

Fig. 9 Typical Stress-Volumetric Strain Behavior in Cyclic Compression Under Static Confining Pressure of 70 Bars-Westerly Granite.

FATIGUE MECHANISM

Acoustic emission and photomicrographic studies were used to complement the strength and deformation data in analyzing the internal mechanism that resulted in premature failure under cyclic loading. An acoustic emission system consisting of a crystal pick-up, a preamplifier, a totalizer, an audio monitor, and a time-base plotter, was used to record the cumulative number of seismic events above a certain threshold emanated from the cyclically loaded specimens. Seismic activity was usually detected in the very first loading cycle since the upper peak load was always above the region of linear elastic behavior. In the next few cycles the acoustic emission continued to increase at a decelerating rate. During the steady state stage almost no new events were recorded. As fatigue failure was approached the seismic activity picked up considerably providing a valuable warning (through the audio monitor) of incipient failure (Fig. 4).

Photomicrograph studies of selected specimens removed from the testing machine at different stages of cyclic loading supported the strong indications from deformation and acoustic emission results that cyclic fatigue is the result of a microfracturing process. Fabric changes in uniaxial compression appeared to be dominated by grain boundary loosening and intergranular cracking in the first few cycles, followed by a stage at which no additional damage seemed to occur, although some crack extension probably did take place. Finally, crack coalescence, widening and faulting resulting in fatigue failure were observed. The entire process of cumulative damage appeared to be evenly distributed throughout the entire specimen. In uniaxial tension, however, Tennessee marble showed very localized fabric changes. A few of the more crucial existing microcracks slowly enlarged until one gained on the others, propagated and split the specimen. Other than the very close vicinity of the rupture plane no changes were observed in the internal structure of the rock. The implication here is that, unlike compression fatigue, impending tensile fatigue failure may give little warning in terms of deformation away from the critical flaw.

APPLICATIONS

Several practical applications arise from the obtained results. Consideration of cyclic loading effects due to phenomena like earthquakes, drilling, blasting, should be incorporated in any design of underground or surface rock structures. S-N curves should be used to determine a more realistic compressive or tensile strength of the rock which could withstand both static and repetitive loadings. The results of the tests in failed rock could be extremely useful in the design of structures where rock might be deformed to beyond the limit corresponding to its compressive strength. The relationship found between the complete stress-strain curve and the cyclic creep provides a quick means of determining total deformation prior to fatigue failure. Acoustic emission systems could be used to detect imminent fatigue failure. Last but not least, a speculative indication of the cyclic creep results is that by cyclically varying the effective stresses in a locked fault it may be possible to relieve the accumulated strain without risking large seismic events (Wang and Haimson, 1974).

ACKNOWLEDGEMENTS

Cyclic loading experiments were started by the author in 1969. Subsequently they were supported by the Wisconsin Alumni Research Foundation (1970-1971), and by the Advanced Research Projects Agency of the Department of Defense and were monitored by the Bureau of Mines under contracts Nos. H0210004 and H0220041. Graduate students C. M. Kim, T. M. Tharp, V. Rajaram, and K. Kim conducted most of the reported experimental work.

REFERENCES

Attewell, P. B. and I. W. Farmer, 1973, Fatigue Behavior of Rock, International Journal of Rock Mechanics and Mining Sciences, vol. 10, pp. 1-9.

Burdine, N. T., 1963, Rock Failure under Dynamic Loading Conditions, Society of Petroleum Engineers Journal, pp. 1-8.

Haimson, B. C. and C. M. Kim, 1972, Mechanical Behavior of Rock Under Cyclic Fatigue, Proceedings, Thirteenth Symposium on Rock Mechanics, ASCE, pp. 845-864.

Haimson, B. C., 1972, Mechanical Behavior of Rock under Cyclic Loading, Annual Technical Report to the Bureau of Mines, Contract H0210004.

Haimson, B. C., 1973, Mechanical Behavior of Rock under Cyclic Loading, Final Technical Report to the Bureau of Mines, Contract H0220041.

Hardy, H. R. and Y. P. Chugh, 1970, Failure of Geological Materials Under Low-Cycle Fatigue, Proceedings, Sixth Canadian Symposium on Rock Mechanics, Montreal, pp. 33-47.

Kim, C. M., 1973, Fatigue Failure of Rock in Cyclic Uniaxial Compression, Ph. D. Thesis, University of Wisconsin, Madison.

Saint-Leu, C. and P. Sirieys, 1971, La Fatigue des Roches, Proceedings, International Symposium on Rock Fracture, Nancy.

Scholz, C. H. and R. Kranz, 1974, Notes on Dilatancy Recovery, Journal of Geophysical Research, Vol. 79 No. 9.

Tharp, T. M., 1973, Behavior of Three Calcite Rocks Under Tensile Cyclic Loading, M. S. Thesis, University of Wisconsin, Madison.

Wang, H. and B. C. Haimson, 1974, Aseismic Slip in Faulted Rock by Pore Pressure Cycling, in preparation.

FATIGUE IN ROCKS: FAILURE AND INTERNAL FISSURATION OF BARRE GRANITE UNDER LOADS CYCLICALLY APPLIED

FATIGUE DES ROCHES: RUPTURE ET FISSURATION INTERNE DU GRANITE DE BARRE SOUS CHARGES APPLIQUÉES CYCLIQUEMENT

BEANSPRUCHUNG DER GESTEINE: BRÜCHE UND INNERE SPALTUNGEN IN BARRE GRANIT DURCH PERIODISCHE BELASTUNGEN

M. MONTOTO

Head, Dpt. of Petrology, Univ. of Oviedo

Oviedo, Spain

Summary

The "weakness" that Barre Granite shows when cyclically stressed under uniaxially compressive loads may be explained in terms of petrographic considerations.
If cyclic stresses below its static strength are applied, it is possible to observe intracrystalline slips and deformations througout the rock. The application of consecutive loads cycles tends to concentrate the deformation action in some areas and then intragranular submicroscopic microcracks start to develop.
Successive load cycles increase these above mentioned phenomena in number of importance and the rock interior becomes seriously damaged. Microcraks tend to spread and interconnect thus causing the final sudden failure.
Polarizing microscopy and S.E.M. has been employed for fractographic studies and the interpreting of failure mechanism.

Resumé

La "faiblaise" que le granit de Barre montre quand il est soumis cycliquement à des charges uniaxiaux peut être expliquée par des considérations pétrographiques.
Si on lui applique de charges cycliques en dessous de la résistence statique, on peut observer des glissements intracristalins et des déformations dans la roche. L'application de cycles de charge consécutifs tend à la concentration de l'action déformante dans certaines zones, et alors il commence a se developper de microfissures intragranulaires submicroscopiques.
Les cycles de charge succesifs accroissent en nombre et en importance les phénomènes surmentionés, et l'interieur de la roche en resulte serieusement endomagé. Les microfissures tendent à s'etendre et s'interconecter provocant ainsi la soudaine fracture finale.
On a utilisé la microscopie polarisante et S.E.M. pour faire des études fractographiques et pour l'interprétation du mécanisme de fracture.

Zusammenfassung

Die geringe Festigkeit des Barre Granits, sobald er periodischen einachsigen Drucklasten unterworfen wird, vom petrographischen Gesichtspunkt aus erklärt werden.
Bei periodischem Druck unter seiner statischen Krafteinwirkung ist es möglich, durch das ganze Gestein intrakristalline Verwerfungen und Verformungen festzustellen. Nach weiteren Druckperioden, neigt die deformierende Wirkung dazu, sich an einzelnen Stellen zu konzentrieren, und es entwickeln sich allmänhlich intergranulare submikroskopische Mikrorisse. Durch nachfolgende Druckperioden nimmt die oben erwähnte Erscheinung, sowie an Anzahl als auch an Wichtigkeit zu, und das innere Gefüge der Gesteine wird dadurch ernsthaft geschädigt. Die Mikrorisse dehnen sich aus, verbinden sich untereinander und bewirken auf diese Weise den endgültigen plötzlichen Bruch.
Polarisationsmikroskopien und S.E.M. sind für fraktographische Studien und zur Auswertung des Bruchmechanismus bisher zur Anwendung gekommen.

Introduction

The term "fatigue" is used to refer the reduction in strengh of materials subjected to cyclic loads.
It is a very important fractographic phenomenon in material technology and has been increasingly studied during this century especially in the field of metallurgy. In the field of Rock Mechanics these studies are very recent. They were initiated in the 60's, from a scientific point of view in the "Pennsylvania State University" (U.S.A.). The work of Hardy and Chugh (1970), carried out on specimens of Barre Granite, Indiana Limestone and Tennessee Sandstone, proved definitively that geological materials are influenced by cyclic loads. Limestone and sandstone exhibit an apparent fatigue limit, as the authors show by means of appropriate S-N curves.
This paper intends to contribute to a better knowledge in rock fatigue failure processes

by means of scanning electron microscopy (S.E.M.) studies on the fatigue failure surfaces combined with polarizing microscopy observations using oriented thin section from different areas of the specimen apparently unbroken.

Fatigue tests

The first fatigue tests in this research were carried out using cylindrical samples. These were of 50 mm. in diameter 120 mm. long and perfectly homogeneous. They all had the same orientation to the original block of Barre Granite used for these tests.
Loads were applied under uniaxial compression. It was inmediately apparent that this process would not give us "clean" fatigue failure surfaces, because the shearing effect present at failure would completely crush the rock all along the failure planes. So any fractographic structures developed during the application of cyclic loads would disappear through microgranulation at failure.
For these reasons, both the form and size of samples and the load application method were changed. The new samples were in the form of beams with the approximate following dimensions: lenght 23 cm., witdh 2,3 cm. and height 3,8 cm.
Beam (tensile) test was the loading method used, with two upper central and two lower lateral side knives. The whole was symmetrical about the central vertical of the samples. In this way a "clean" crack surface is produced at failure, without microcrushing developing along it. This allows the fatigue failure surfaces first to be studied directly with common binoculars and then under S.E.M. Further thin sections for polarizing microscopy studies were obtained.
Due to the exclusively fractographic character of this paper we avoid detailing all the numerical data corresponding to the different tests. A short description of then is presented. Different frequencies were applied: 0.5, 1 and 2 c.p.s., but in each test it was maintained constant. The number of cycles necessary to reach the final failure was very variable, ranging from 413 to 8225. To summarize the values of minimum and maximum load Fmin and Fmax. applied along each test is practically impossible. In general during the first cycles of the different tests, the values of Fmin. and Fmax. were 72-164 Kg. They were successively changed during the test up to the final failure; values at that moment were: Fmin. = 50-119 Kg. and Fmax. = 180-330 Kg. Many variations in the values of Fmin. and Fmax., related to the number of applied cycles, were programmed for each test. All of them aimed at provoking some differences in the fractographic structures developed on the fatigue failure surfaces. Unfortunately the were unobserved by us.
Those mentioned differences are very noticeable in the fatigue failure of metals. In them, it is possible to correlate their characteristics with the load conditions and especially with the number of applied cycles. This has been unquestionably demostrated by McMillan, and Pelloux (1967) in a very interesting work on alluminium alloys.

Scanning Electron Microscope studies

The first aspect apparent in the studied fatigue failure surfaces was their brittle nature with sharp edges, microfaulted craks, fissures, etc. This has currently been noted by other authors, and given the conditions under which the cyclic load experiments were undertaken a different result could not be expected.
On the failure surfaces visible under "moderate" enlargements (about a thousand times) it is possible to observe some open cracks in intergranular or intragranular positions. Obvious in both cases are the brittle nature of the cracks and the numerous fractographic structures simultaneously developed during the Barre Granite beams failure. Also visible on these surfaces are a variable number of pores of very differing sizes, which range from 10 to 0.3μ. Usually, though, they tend to be between 2 and 6μ.
As further optical polarizing microscropy shows, microcracks develop in the initial failure stages. Using either the electron or the optical microscope, it is often apparent how they use the pores, inclusions, etc. to nucleate and grow, spreading from these points or from their surroundings.

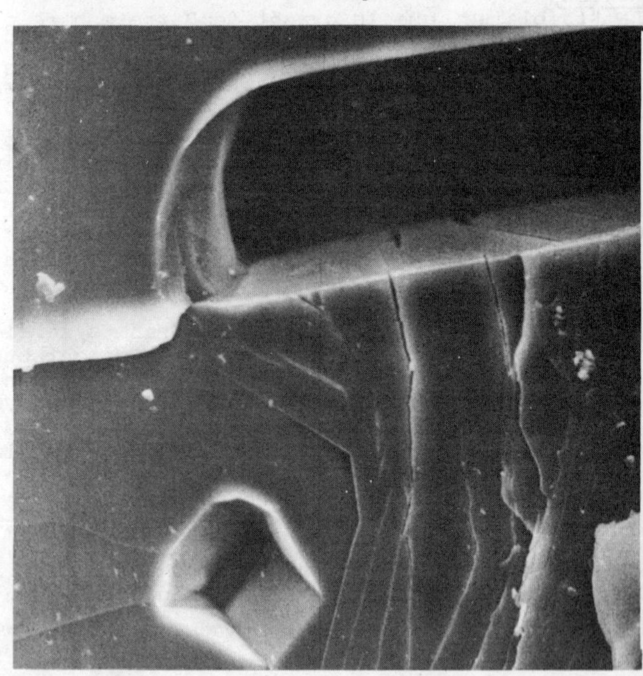

Fig. 1.- Microcracks easily develop in points of physical discontinuity (SEM, x 1000).

Such is the case in the hole in a feldspar crystal in Fig. 1, that could correspond to an apatite inclusion which came away at failure. A well defined group of intragranular microcracks radiate from it.
Those pores are without doubt important in

the rock failure and fractographic structures development. So they are sometimes clearly related to failure surfaces and the development of cleavage steps, cracks with clear tendencies toward rivern patterns, etc. Nevertheless contrary to what might be expected we could observe some aligned pores no linked by a crack developed along them. Amongst the typical fractographic strctures which develop in granitic rocks, stand out those which occur most often and easily in well cleavaged rock-forming minerals such as feldspars. In these there very often develop cleavage microcracks. Seen in space they are made up of two or even three cleavage directions. As such they can be termed "cleavage steps" because of their particular morphological aspects (Fig. 2).

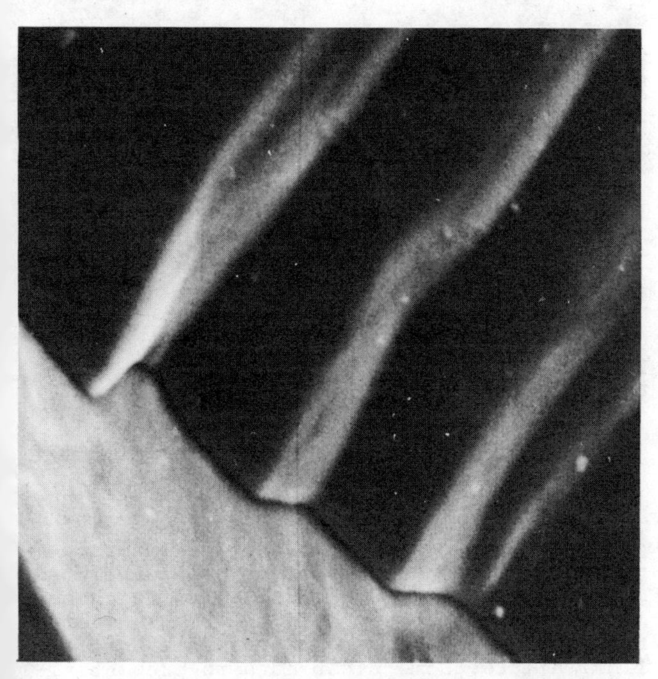

Fig. 2.- Well formed "cleavage steps" developed in a feldspar failure surface (SEM, x 1000).

Sometimes it is very interesting to be able to identify submicroscopy steps on those which can be observed more easily.
The steps can interconnect giving rise to the well-known "rivern patterns".Using them it is possible to deduce the direction of the advancing crack.
It is more than likely that some of the structures identified here as "cleavage steps" may in fact be "striations", a very important and the most characteristic structure developed on fatigue failure surfaces (Fig. 3). Striations have been extensively studied by a great number of authors dealing with fatigue failure problems in metallurgy. Even so this author has no available references of them in rocks. They have been defined as curved marks on fatigue failure surfaces which are: a) more or less parallel and normal to the local direction of the advancing crack, b) variable in width depending on the applied load values, c) equal in number to the number of applied cyclic loads, and d) more or less concentrated in zones. It was very difficult to be sure if all the structures identified as striations were in fact so. Perhaps some of them were smoothly curved cleavage steps, and the perspective may be the reason for this confusion.

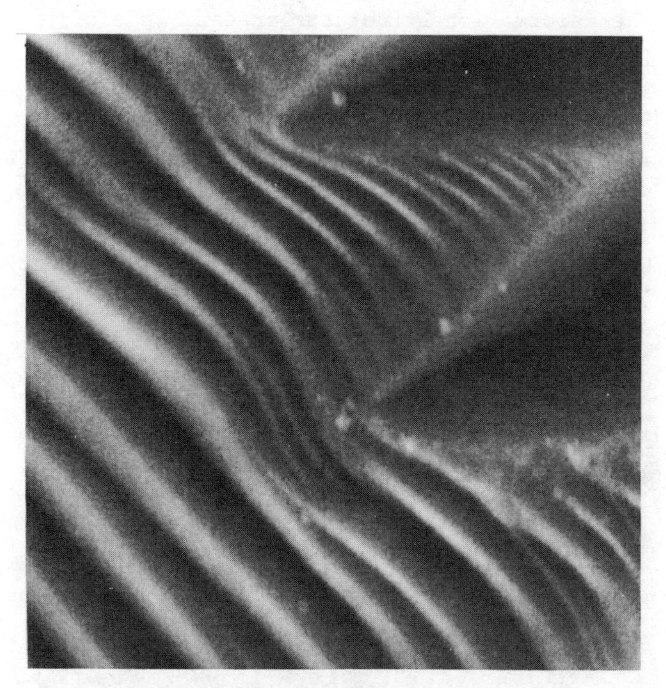

Fig. 3.- Striations: morphological aspect presented by the most characteristic fatigue fractographic structure (SEM, x 10.000).

Optical microscopic study

The last section presented those fractographic characteristics produced during the applied load cycles, and visible on the failure surface of Barre Granite.Here examples of the development of cracks, microcracks, morphological and crystalline network deformations, etc. are presented. These occur inside the rock, be it near or far from the failure surface.
They are really interesting fractographic structures since they allow us to recognize the succesive stages followed by the rock during fatigue process up to the final failure. Structures such as "cleavage steps", so well recognized under SEM, can be followed in their development under optical microscopy; it can be clearly noticed how they spread through the mineral grains where they form. These studies show the very wide crack distribution inside the rock. Thus it is apparent that the final failure is not caused by a single crack, but by a very complicated network of internal cracking, as some other authors have before pointed out.

It can also be seen that intense deformation takes place in the crystalline networks of rock forming mineral grains. This occurs before microcracks begin to form, and very often brings on the development of "extinction bands" and "deformation bands" quite visible under optical microscopy. Inside quartz grains these structures are very often quite noteworthy. Sometimes "extinction bands" tend to develop under a more or less crystallographic concordant disposition, in other cases their development can be observed from initial blurred models to real, well-formed and individualized bands. Those initial blurred forms are between wavy extinction and faint crystalline mosaics. In later deformation stages, in the sense of an increasing deformation intensity, "deformation bands" are developed.

The deformation structures present in biotite are also very interesting. The mineral plasticity is outstanding very often undergoing intense fractureless bending especially when grains are located in interstitial positions.

The interior cracking in feldspars illustrates very well the Barre Granite failure process: Intracrystalline microcracks mainly tend to appear along the clavage planes, some of them interconnect across the crystal "jumping" from one cleavage plane to another, tacking advantage of another oblique cleavage (Fig. 4). In a more advanced stage of the

Fig. 4.-These intracrystalline "cleavage steps" show the first stages of the failure process (C.N., x 60)

Fig. 5.- As microcracking develops all through the rock, major cracks forms affecting larger areas of it.(C.N.,x100).

process cleavage steps made up of interconnected microcracks, producing well developed cracks, which extend themselves to neighbouring grains can be seen(Fig. 5). This scheme repeats itself all through the rock until the finalfailure. Some other authors present similar ideas to interpret rock failure, Hoshino and Koide (1970), Bieniawski (1967).

Quartz grains use to present numerous and well formed allineations of inclusions. In a previous paper Montoto and Esbert (1971) we thought that in general they constitute mechanical weakness planes, along which cracks would be developed easily. Nevertheless this is not the case in Barre Granite fatigue cracking. Here different sets of inclusions are very well-defined, they spread through out the quartz and forming a perfectly parallel series. No crack or microcrack was possible to identify along them, despite the fact that many of failure planes are subparallel to the lines of inclusions.

Everything mentioned up to now supports the idea that despite the fact that final failure always occurs instantaneously, the fractographic structures which cause this failure have been developing "in their own time". So the development of these structures could be fairly slow, following the weaker petrofabric and

crystallographic directions present in the rock.
During the period leading up to the final failure extensive surface cracking did no seem to appear. Rather, numerous very short microcracks which have been interconnecting leading to the final failure of the rock formed. This explains so many of the inter an intragranular cracks, incipient and well developed cleavage steps, and many other different fractographic structures.
Those structures will have to be revised in later research, branching out to other types of rock of geotechnical importance. Now we are trying to apply new research techniques, especially stereo-fractography and we hope that an appropiate specimen preparation will allow the application of fluorescent microscopy to automatic scanning microfotometry or quantitative microscopy electronically controlled for automatic stereometric analysis. This is with a view to resolving some important problems like the present confusion between some "cleavage steps" and "striations" and the automatic measurement of microcracks in their length and orientation.

Conclusions

The "weakness" showed by Barre Granite under fatigue may be explained in terms of petrographic considerations. In this sense it is obvious that rocks contain many inhomogeneities that locally lower their resistance to mechanical stresses.
Tha most important of them are:

a) Random agglomeration of anisotropic crystals of wide variation in size an shape.
b) Mixed minerals of different elastic characteristics.
c) Inclusions, crystal imperfections, original microcracks previous to testing deformations, and many other petrographic discontinuities.

Our interpretation of the fatigue failure process for Barre Granite is the following:
1) When stresses below the static strength of the rock are applied, crystalline deformations can be produced in those areas of greatest stress concentration. These areas are defined by means of theoretical mechanic considerations and through the intrinsic petrographic heterogeneities of the rock.
2) Such deformations are readily visible in quartz and basically consist of oriented bands of anomalous extinction. Many of them are also apparent in feldspars and biotite.
3) At first these deformations seem to be localized in relatively few minerals grains.
4) The applications of consecutiva load cycles tends to concentrate the deformation action in various areas in an accumulative and progressive way.
5) Thus initial intracrystalline microcracks start to develop. In feldspars initial microcracks easily spread along cleavage planes. Typical "cleavage steps" are produce as microcracks join parallel cleavage planes on their way, jumping from one plane to another.
6) More important cracks appear as a result of the coalescence of the initially formed microcracks which grow and develop with more load cycles. The repetition of this simplified scheme accelerates the failure process of the rock. The final failure is never progresive but occurs suddenly and unexpectedly.
Thus it can be staid that: The succesive load cycles increase in number and importance the crystalline deformations created during the first cycles. In this way microcracks are initiated which then spread and interconnect causing the final sudden failure.
The final failure occurs at relatively low stress levels, compared to those causing failure under static processes, Hardy and Chugh (1970). This can be explained in terms of the accumulative and progressive nature of this kind of deformation, peculiar to cyclic processes.
In our opinion three stages can be recognized in this process:

Stage 1 Intracrystalline slips and deformations develop, as well as slight and very localized microcrushing. Depending on the applied load this stage can be reduced to a few cycles.

Stage 2 When the applied stresses are high enough to overcome the strong crystalline bonds, the crystal tattice is broken and intragranular submicroscopic cracks start to develop.
These microcracks grow and interconnect causing important cracks in the rock. Thus the internal constitution of the material becomes seriously damaged.
We think that this stage takes up almost all the load application time prior to failure.

Stage 3 When some of these important cracks interconnect the final failure occurs in a violent, sudden and unpredictable way.

Acknowledgments

We would like to express our sincere gratitude to "Juan March" Foundation (Spain) which has supported this research in "The Pennsylvania State University" and specially to Dr. H.R. Hardy, Director of the Laboratory of Rock Mechanics in P.S.U.
The S.E.M. studies were carried out in the "Materials Science Laboratory" in P.S.U., where Dr. White and coworker's kindness were so appreciated. Dr. R.Y. Kim and Mr. E. Kimble's aid, in the Lab, of Rock Mechanics, was decisive in our research.

****

References

BIENIAWSKY, Z.T., 1967, Mechanism of brittle fracture of rocks, Int. J. Rock Mech. Min. Sci., Vol 4, p 395-423.
HARDY, H. and Y.P. CHUGH, 1970, Failure of

geologic materials under low-cycle fatigue, Sixth Canadian Symposium on "Rock Mechanics", Ecole Polytechnique, Montreal, Canada.

HOSHINO, K. and H. KOIDE, 1970, Process of yielding and the macroscopic fractures in the rocks, Rock Mech. in Japan, Vol. 1, p 41-43.

McMILLIAN, J.C. and M.N. PELLOUX, 1967, Fatigue crack propagation under program and random loads, in "Fatigue crack propagation", ASTM STP n° 415, p 505-532.

MONTOTO, M. and R. ESBERT, 1971, Deformación y rotura de rocas: criterios petrográficos para su estudio, I Congreso Hispano-Luso-Americano de Geología Económica, Madrid-Lisboa, Sec. 5, p 129-148.

****

RHEOLOGICAL PROPERTIES OF ROCKS UNDER THE PULSATING LOADS

COMPORTEMENT RHÉOLOGIQUE DES ROCHES SOUS LES CYCLES DE CHARGEMENT

RHEOLOGISCHES VERHALTEN EINIGER GESTEINE BEI SINUSFÖRMIGEN WECHSELSPANNUNGEN

Yuichi NISHIMATSU Associate Professor, Department of Mineral Development Engineering, Faculty of Engineering, University of Tokyo, Tokyo, Japan

R. HEROESEWOJO former student of Graduate School of University of Tokyo, Chief Engineer, P.N. Aneka Tanbang, Tjikotok, Jawa, Indonesia

Summary

This paper deals with the rheological behavior of several rock samples under the pulsating stress, frequencies of which range from 3×10^{-3} to 5 Hz. The stress-strain hysteresis loops under the sinusoidal compressive stress are observed with the cathode ray oscilloscope, and classified into three different types, i.e.; (i) linear type or perfectly elastic body, the rheological model of which is given by a spring, (ii) elliptical type, or linear visco-elastic body, the rheological model of which is given by a combination of springs and dash-pots, (iii) crescent type, or non-linear visco-elastic body, the rheological behavior of which could not be represented by any combinations of springs and dash-pots.
The dog-bone shaped rock specimen is loaded in tension with the pulsating fatigue testing machine and the tension test device. The stress-strain hysteresis loops under the sinusoidal tensile stress are classified into either of Type (i) or (ii). However, the crescent shaped stress-strain hysteresis loop is not observed under the action of tensile stress. This result is explained with a rheological model which contains a new element of model named "Stopper".

Zusammenfassung

Der vorliegende Aufsatz beschreibt das rheologische Verhalten einiger Gesteine bei sinusförmigen Wechselspannungen, deren Frequenz zwischen 3×10^{-3} und 5 Hz liegen. Die Spannungsdehnungs-Hystereseschleife bei sinusförmigen Druckspannungen wird mittels Kathodenstrahlenoszillographen beobachtet, und zwar in folgenden drei Typen: (i) linearer Typ oder elastischer Körper, deren mechanischen Modelle mittels einer Feder gezeichnet sind; (ii) elliptischer Typ oder linearer viskoelastischer Körper, deren mechanischen Modelle mittels einer Kette der kelvinischen Körper gezeichnet sind; (iii) sichelförmiger Typ oder nicht-linearer visko-elastischer Körper, deren mechanischen Modelle nicht mittels Verbindungen der Federn und Kolben gezeichnet werden können.

Die mantelförmige Gesteinsprobe ist mittels Dauerschwingungsdruckprüfungsmaschinen und eines Zugversuchsgerätes beansprucht. Die Spannungsdehnungs-Hysterese-Schleife wird entweder im Typ (ii) oder (i) einklassifiziert. Doch bei Dauerschwingungszugversuch wird die sichelförmige Hysterese-Schleife nicht beobachtet. Diese Ergebnisse werden mittels einer neuen Einheit der mechanischen Modelle dargestellt.

Résumé

L'essai rapporte le comportement rheologique des roches sous les cycles de chargement. Cette frequence varient entre 3×10^{-3} et 5 Hz. Les cerceaux d'hysteresis d'effort-deformation sous l'effort compression sinusoidal sont measués par l'oscilligraphe à rayons chathodiques, et classèrent à les trois types; (i) type lineaire, ou corps elastique. Ce modèle mecanique est un ressort. (ii) type elliptique, ou corps visco-elastique lineaire. Ce modèle mecanique est une chaine de corps de Voigt. (iii) type de croissant, ou corps visco-elastique nonlineaire. Ce modèle mecanique n'est pas reprêsent par quelque combinaison des ressort et amortisseur de choc.
L'éprouvette en forme de hartére est en charge de tension par machine d'essai de fatigue et l'instrument d'essai de tension. Les cerceaux d'hysteresis d'effort-deformation avec contrainte de tension sinusoidal sont classés à quelque type (i) ou (ii). Le cerceau de hysteresis en forme de croissant n'est pas observé sous le chargement de tension. Les resultats des essais sont expliqués par le modèle mecanique qui contient une nouveau élément de modèle.

1. Introduction

It is well known that the rock is not a perfectly elastic body, but a visco-elastic body. Therefore, the mechanical behavior of rock should be discussed from the view point of rheology.

There are some papers (Terry and Morgangs, 1958; Ito and Terada, 1962; Woehlbier, et al., 1969) on the rheological model for the propagation and attenuation of sonic wave or vibra-

Table 1. Dimensions and strengthes of sample rocks

	Compression test				Tension test			
	compressive strength (kg/cm²)	dimension mmφ x mm	stress level (%Sc)		tensile strength (kg/cm²)	dimension mmφ x mm	stress level (%St)	
			σm	σa			σm	σa
Granite	1,600	22.6 x 48	32.5	30	55	33 x 70	22	16
Marble	1,100	28.0 x 60	30.5	27.5	65	33 x 70	23.5	18.5
Andesite	910	30.0 x 66	36	33	50	33 x 70	23	16
Sandy tuff	419	30.0 x 60	33.5	28.5	60	33 x 70	27	21
Tuff	625	28.2 x 57	26.5	22.5	60	33 x 70	20	14

tion of rock samples. Furthermore, there are some papers (Hiramatsu and Nishihara, 1957; Price, 1964; Kiaybinski, 1966) on the rheological model, which describe the creep behavior of rock samples. However, there are few paper dealing with the rheological properties of rock samples under the cyclic load, the frequency of which ranges from 10^{-3} to 10 Hz.

In this paper, the authors discuss on the rheological behavior of rock samples under the pulsating load and try to determine the rheological model for each of rock samples.

2. Experimentals

2.1. Rock samples and preparation of test piece.

The rock samples used in this experiment are a granite, a limestone, an andesite and two tuffs.

The cylindrical specimens are cored and cut from a block of each rock sample. The both end faces of the specimen are ground on the grinding table, and furnished to be normal to the cylindrical axis and parallel with each other within the accuracy of ±25/1000 mm. The furnished test piece for compression test has the height-diameter ratio of 2 :1.

The both parallel ends of rock specimen for tension test are glued to the steel end pieces by means of an alignment jig (Nishimatsu,1970) as shown in Fig. 1. After drying out the adhesive, the section of specimen is reduced and

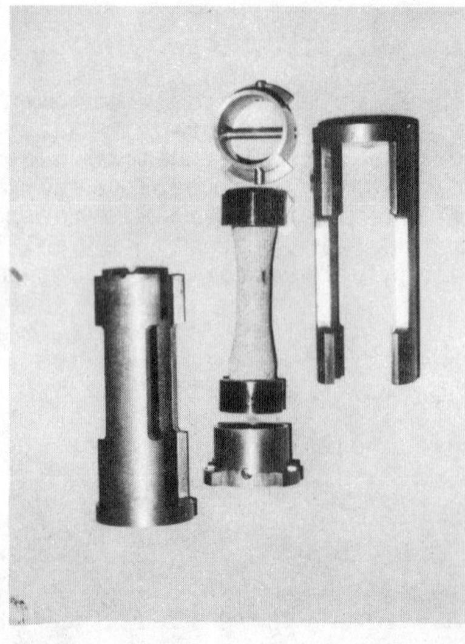

Fig. 2 Illustration of the tension test device.

Fig. 1 The alignment jig for the preparation of test pieces used for the uniaxial tension test.

aligned over about three quarters of its length by means of grinding lathe.

The dimension and strength of furnished tes piece are shown in Table 1.

2.2. Test apparatus and procedure

The testing machines used in this experiment are a Losenhausen type pulsating compression fatigue machine for the test in the upper range of loading frequency and a servo-control type fatigue testing machine for the test in the lower range of loading frequency. Therefore, the tension test is carried out by means of a particular tension test device (se Fig. 2) which transduces the compressive load to the tensile load (Nishimatsu and Heroesewojo, 1972).

The load is measured by a wire resistance strain gage type load cell, and the strain is measured by 2 pieces of wire resistance strai gages glued symmetrically parallel to the axi of cylindrical test piece. Out put of both gages are amplified by the dynamical strain meter to feed into a cathode ray oscillograph or X-Y recorder, where the stress-strain hysteresis loops are observed and recorded.

The test piece set on the testing machine i loaded by the sinusoidal pulsating load with the designated stress level (see Table 1). The loading frequency used in this experiment ranges from 0.003 to 5 Hz.

3. Three types of stress-strain hysteresis loop.

The stress-strain hysteresis loop is ob-

Table 2. The dynamic and static Young's modulus of rock samples of the firstgroup

	compression ($\times 10^5$ kg/cm^2)		tension ($\times 10^5$ kg/cm^2)	
	static	dynamic	static	dynamic
Marble	7.30	7.30	8.80	8.30
Granite	5.53	5.60	(3.20)*	(3.30)*

* Granite shows an elliptical hysteresis loop in tension

served and recorded after the repeatation of a few thousands cycles of loading. Then, the hysteresis loop does not change its shape and position during the observation.

Examples of hysteresis loops observed are shown in Fig. 3. As known from these diagramms, there are three types of hysteresis loop as follows:

(i) linear type such as the hysteresis loops of granite and limestone.

(ii) elliptical type such as those of tuffs.

(iii) crescent type such as those of andesite under pulsating compressive stress.

Fig. 4 shows schematic pictures of these three types of hysteresis loop.

Based on the type of hysteresis loop, the sample rock could be classified into three groups.

The first group of rock has a linear stress-strain loop under either of pulsating compressive and tensile stress. The dynamic Young's modulus coincides approximately with the static Young's modulus, as shown in Table 2.

However, there is a little difference between the behaviors of limestone and granite. The stress-strain diagramm of granite under the compressive load opens slightly upwards. This phenomena would be discussed later in detail.

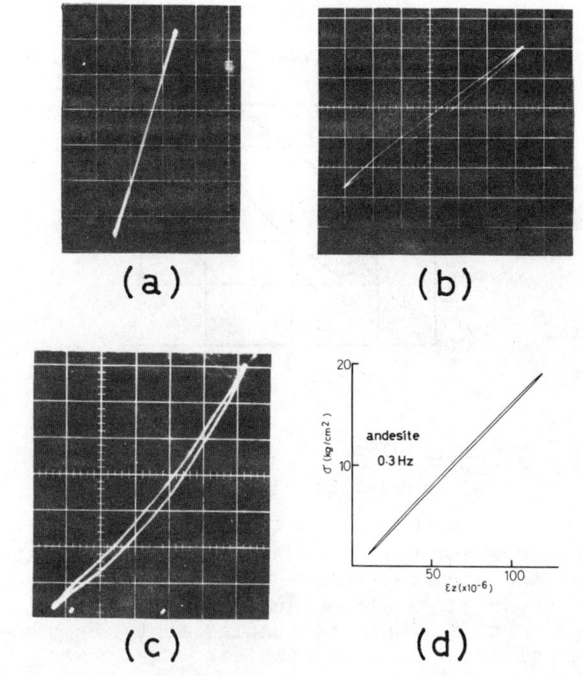

Fig. 3 Examples of hysteresis loops.
(a) Marble in compression test. (5 Hz)
(b) Sandy tuff in compression test. (0.1 Hz)
(c) Andesite in compression test. (5 Hz)
(d) Andesite in tension test. (0.3 Hz)

The second group of rocks has an elliptical hysteresis loop, the rheological model of which could be expressed as a combination of spring and dash-pot.

The third group of rocks shows a crescent shaped hysteresis loop under the pulsating compressive stress, but an elliptical hysteresis loop under the tensile stress. The crescent shaped hysteresis loop can not be explained by any combinations of spring, dash-pot and slider. Therefore, it needs some new concepts or model element to express such a behavior of rock.

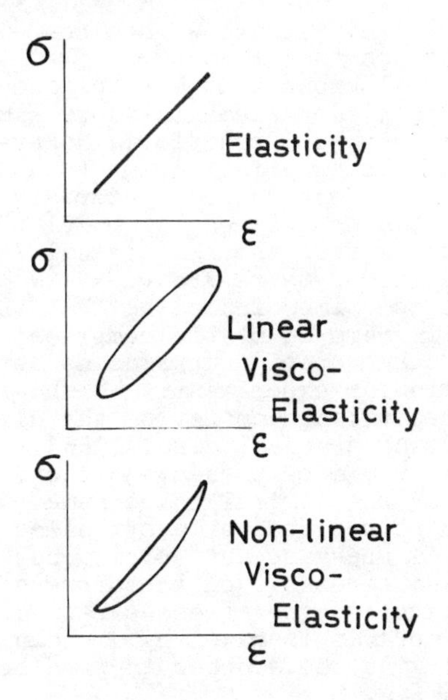

Fig. 4 Schematic diagramms of three types of hysteresis loop.

4. Rheological model of rock

4.1. Linear visco-elastic model

Under the action of cyclic stress given by

$$\sigma = \sigma_a \cdot \sin \omega t \qquad (1)$$

the linear visco-elastic body shows an elliptical stress-strain hysteresis loop as shown in Fig. 4, where the strain is given by

$$\varepsilon = \varepsilon_a \cdot \sin(\omega t - \delta) \qquad (2)$$

However, the pulsating load dealt in this report, is given by

$$\sigma = \sigma_m + \sigma_a \cdot \sin \omega t \qquad (3)$$

where σ_m is the mean stress which is larger than the stress amplitude σ_a.

This mean stress would initiate a delayed strain in the rheological body. However, if the rheological model of this body consists of spring and Voigt model, the creep or delayed strain would approach asymptotically

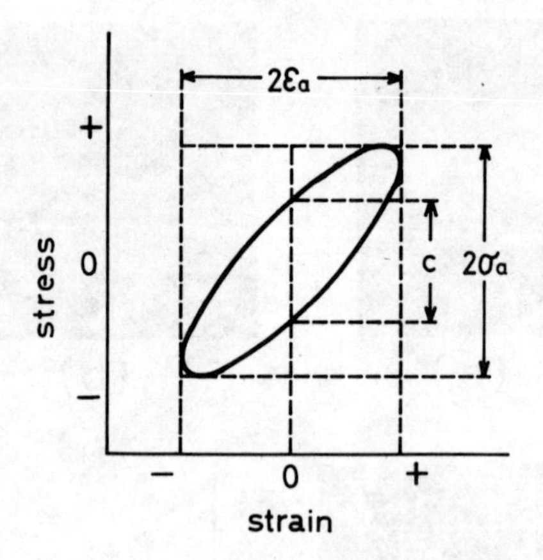

Fig. 5 Elliptical hysteresis loop of linear visco-elastic body.

to a constant value. It was already indicated that the stress-strain hysteresis loop does not change its position during the observation. Therefore, it would be assumed that the rheological model of rock sample of the second group consists of spring and Voigt models, and the hysteresis loop depends upon the cyclic parts of stress i.e. the second term of Eq. (3).

Based on the theory of linear visco-elasticity, we get (see Fig. 5)

$$|E^*| = \sigma_a / \varepsilon_a \quad , \quad \sin\delta = c/2\,\sigma_a \qquad (4)$$

$$E' = |E^*| \cdot \cos\delta \, ,$$
$$E'' = \omega \cdot \eta' = |E^*| \cdot \sin\delta \qquad (5)$$

where E^* : complex modulus expressed as $E^* = E' + iE''$
E' : dynamic modulus
η' : dynamic viscosity
δ : phase angle
ω : angular velocity

The complex modulus is independent of time elapsed and level of applied stress, but

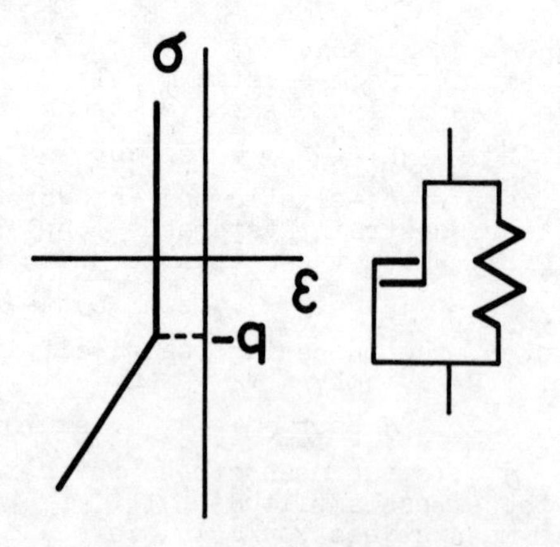

Fig. 7 A mechanical model consisted of a stopper and a spring (right), and its stress-strain diagram (left).

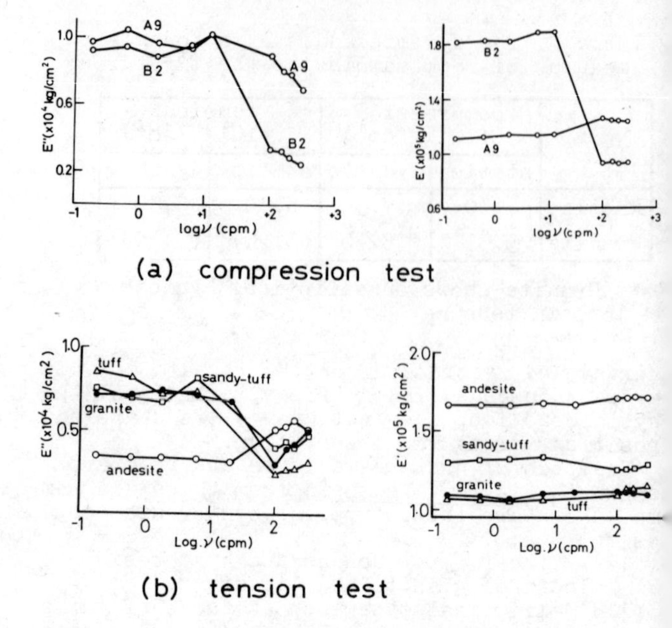

Fig. 6 The dynamic modulus and viscosity of rock samples of the second group as a function of the loading freq..

dependent upon the frequency of loading cycles.

Using Eqs. (4) and Eqs. (5), we can calculate the dynamic modulus and viscosity for each hysteresis loop of rock samples of second group in the wide range of loading frequency. The results are shown in Fig. 6.

There is no remarkable peak in these diagramms. It means that the rheological behavior of these rock sample is rather complicated and could not be expressed with such a simple model as Zenner model or Voigt model.

4.2. Non-linear model with a new element of model "Stopper"

It is well known that a rheological model containing slider elements shows some non-linear rheological behavior. However, the model containing slider elements could not give the crescent shaped hysteresis loop. Therefore, a new element of model would be needed to express the rheological behavior of rock samples of third group.

It was sometimes indicated that the stress-strain diagramm in static compression test shows a curve opening upwards as obtained for granite in our experiment. Walsh explained this curve taking account of the closing of pre-existing cracks (Walsh, 1965).

Now, it would be presented a concept of new element of rheological model named "Stopper" which is represented by a symbol as shown in Fig. 7, and behaves as a rigid body over the designated stress level in compression.

For examples, the stress-strain diagramms opening upwards is given by a chain of spring combined with the stopper in parallel as shown in Fig. 8.

Furthermore, the chain of model unit which consist of spring, dash-pot and stopper combined in parallel would show a crescent shap-

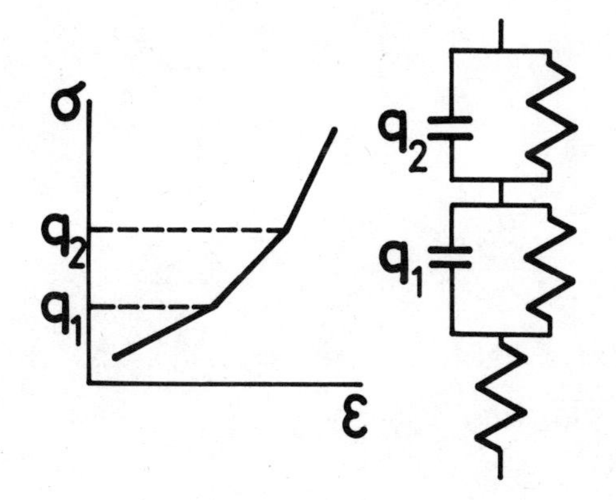

Fig. 8 The stress-strain diagram opening upwards and the mechanical model consisted of a few units which contains a stopper and a spring in parallel.

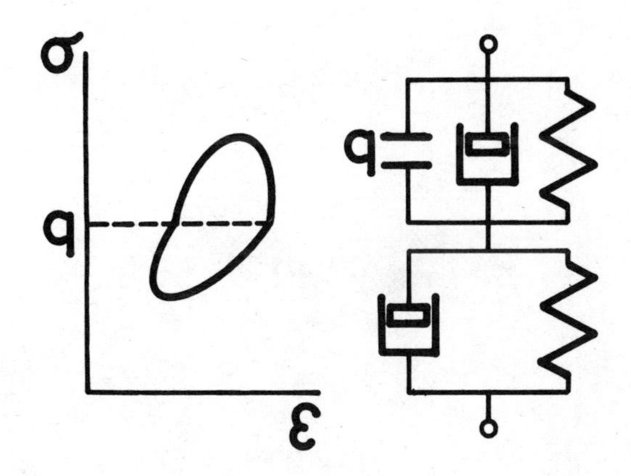

Fig. 9 A crescent shaped hysteresis loop and a mechanical model consisted of a few units which contains spring, dash-pot, and stopper in parallel.

ed hysteresis loop as shown schematically in Fig. 9.

It would be noticed that the stopper has nothing to do with the mechanical behavior under the stress below the designated level. Therefore, the rheological model containing some stopper shows a linear visco-elasticity for the tensile stress as observed in our experiment.

5. Conclusion

In oder to present a rheological model of rock samples, the stress-strain hysteresis loop of rocks is observed under the pulsating loads.

The hysteresis loop is classified into three types i.e. (1) linear type, (2) elliptical type, and (3) crescent type.

Based on some theoretical analyses on the hysteresis loop observed, it is indicated that the model of rock sample showing an elliptical hysteresis loop is expressed with a chain of Voigt model in series.

Furthermore, in oder to explain the crescent shaped hysteresis loop of some rocks under the compressive stress, a new element of rheological model is presented.

It is indicated that this new element named "Stopper" behaves as a rigid body over the designated stress level in compression, but has nothing to do with mechanical behavior under the stress below a designated level.

It is claimed that the rheological model containing stoppers would be able to express not only a crescent shaped hysteresis loop but also other complex rheological behaviors of rocks.

References

Hiramatsu, Y. & Nishihara, M.: On the creep of some sedimentary rocks, J. Min. & Met. Inst. Japan, 73(1957) p.493/7

Ito, I. & Terada, T.: A rheological study on the dynamical behavior of rocks, J. Min. & Met. Inst. Japan, 78(1962) p.723/30

Kidybinski, A. : Rheological models of Upper Silesian Carboniferous rocks, Int. J. Rock Mech. Min. Sci., 3(1966), p.279/306

Nishimatsu, Y. : The torsion test and elastic constants of the orthotropic rock substance, Proc. 2nd Congr. I. S. R. M., Vol.1, p.479/84 (1970)

Nishimatsu, Y. & Heroesewojo, R. : The fatigue failure and fractography of the rock under the pulsating tensile stress, Proc. 15th Japan Congr. Mat. Res., 1972, p.141/4

Price, N. J. : A study of time-strain behavior of coal measure rocks, Int. J. Rock Mech. Min. Sci., 1(1964) p.277/303

Terry, N. B. & Morgangs, T. A. : Studies of the rheological behavior of coal, Mechanical Properties of Non-metallic Brittle Materials (ed. by W. H. Walton), 1958, p. 239/58

Walsh, J. B. : The effect of cracks in the uniaxial elastic compression of rocks, J. Geophys. Res., 70(1965) p.399/411

Woehlbier, H., et al. : Neue Ergebnisse über den Einsatz des Ultraschallimpulsverfahrens in der Gebirgsmechanik, Bergb.-wiss., 16(1969), s.177/80

THEME 1

THÈME 1

THEMA 1

F

Dynamic Strength, Elastic Properties, and Wave Propagation

F

Résistance dynamique, propriétés élastiques, et propagation d'ondes

F

Dynamische Stärke, elastische Eigenschaften, und Wellenverbreitung

METHODS FOR DETERMINING THE AVERAGE DYNAMIC ELASTIC PROPERTIES OF A FRACTURED ROCK MASS AND THE VARIATIONS OF THESE PROPERTIES NEAR EXCAVATIONS

MÉTHODES POUR LA DÉTERMINATION DES CARACTÉRISTIQUES ÉLASTIQUES DYNAMIQUES MOYENNES DES MASSIFS ROCHEUX ET DES VARATIONS DE CETTES CARACTÉRISTIQUES PRÉS DES EXCAVATIONS

MÉTHODEN FÚR DIE BESTIMMUNG DER DURCHSCHNITTLICHEN ELASTISCH-DYNAMISCHEN EIGENSCHAFTEN VON GESTEINSAUFSPEICHERUNGEN UND DER VERÁNDERUNGEN DIESER EIGENSCHAFTEN IN DER NÁHE VON STOLLENWÁNDE

M. BERNABINI G.B. BORELLI
Institute of Mining Geophysics
University of Rome
Rome, Italy

SUMMARY Some techniques and methods for determining the average dynamic elastic properties of a rock mass, through velocity measurements between pairs of holes, are described. The measurements must be as numerous and differently oriented as possible. To obtain characteristic values of the average elastic properties and of the non-homogeneity of the rock statistical methods are used. The seismic refraction method with geophones spaced 0,5-2 m apart is suggested for determining the variation of elastic properties near the excavation surfaces. The suggested method has given good results. Some exemples are reported.

RESUME On décrit des techniques et des méthodes pour la détermination des caractéristiques élastiques moyennes des massifs rocheux au moyen de mesures de vitesse entre des couples de sondages. Ces mesures doivent être les plus nombreuses possible et différemment disposées. On a utilisé la méthode statistique pour tirer des index des caractéristiques élastiques moyennes et du manque d'homogénéité des roches. Pour la détermination de la variation des caractéristiques élastiques près de la superficie d'une excavation on utilise des mesures de vitesse entre des sondages de carottages soniques et la méthode sismique à réfraction avec des sismographes à un intervalle de 0,5 à 2 m entre eux. Cette dernière méthode a donné des bons résultats. On reporte les techniques utilisées et on donne des exemples.

ZUSAMMENFASSUNG Es werden einige technische Verfahren und Methoden fuer die Bestimmung der durchschnittlichen elastischen Eigenschaften der Gesteinsaufspeicherungen durch zwischen Bohrungspaare durchgefuehrte Geschwindigkeitsmessungen beschrieben. Diese Messungen muessen so weit wie moeglich zahlreich und verschiedentlich orientiert sein. Zur Bestimmung der Indices der durchschnittlichen elastischen Eigenschaften und der Unhomogoenitaet des Gesteins werden statische Methoden angewendet. Fuer die Bestimmung der Aenderungen der elastischen Eigenschaften in der Naehe einer Ausgrabungsoberflaeche, werden Geschwindikeitsmessungen z ischen Bohrloecher, Schallkernbohrmessungen und Refraktions-Seisikmessungen mit in Abstaenden von 0,5 bis 2,0 m angesetzte Geophone durchgefuehrt. Diese letzte Methode hat gute Ergebnisse gebracht. Man gibt die verwendete Technik an und man beschreibt einige Beispiele.

INTRODUCTION

The Institute of Mining Geophysics of Rome University has applied seismic methods to study problems of rock mechanics for over 10 years. In this paper some of the methods and results already presented in Italian journals together with more recent results and new methods developed during the last few years are described.

The first group of methods refers to the evaluation of the average dynamic elastic properties of a rock mass through velocity measurements taken between pairs of boreholes, especially for non-homogeneous rocks. The second group refers to the evaluation of the same properties near the surface of an excavation.

METHODS FOR THE EVALUATION OF THE AVERAGE DYNAMIC ELASTIC PROPERTIES OF A ROCK MASS

In order to evaluate the average dynamic elastic properties, the longitudinal elastic wave velocity is determined between several pairs of points inside the rock mass to be examined. Such velocity is that obtained from the ratio between the emitter-receiver distance and travel time. The location of the holes is chosen according to the shape of the mass under examination, the receivers and the source are then lowered at various depths. Generally the distance between receivers in the same hole and the distance between two subsequent positions of the emitter are chosen to be of the same order of magnitude (or at least equal to 1/2-1/3) as the distance between the holes, in order not to have equivalent paths. The receivers, the subsequent positions of the emitter at different depths and the hypothetical rectilinear paths between emitter and receivers are shown in Fig. 1 for a pair of holes. An example of a hole arrangement relative to the investigation of a rock mass on which foundations of a viaduct were to be made is shown in Fig. 2.

The area to be investigated to a depth of 50-80 m (dashed area), the hole location and the sections between the various pairs of holes along which tests have been

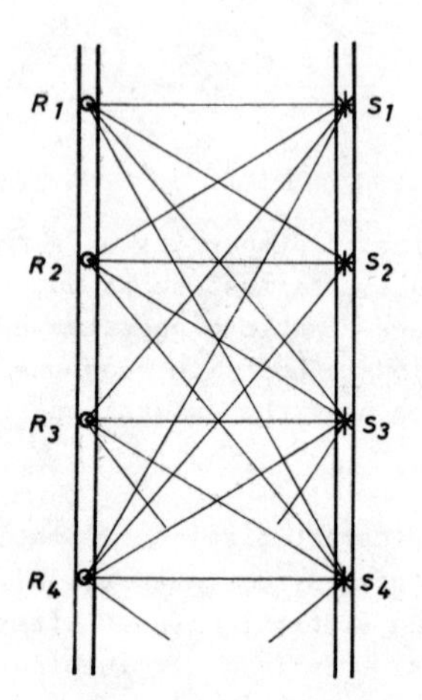

Fig. 1 Positions of receivers R and source S for a pair of holes.

carried out in accordance with the scheme shown in Fig. 1 are reported in fig. 2. The test began by placing geophones in holes 2 and 3 and shooting at various depths in hole 1. The geophones were taken out of hole 2 and put in holes 4 and 5 and shots were made in hole 2 of hole 3 and so on. Each rock prism so formed (e.g. F1-F2-F3; F2-F3-F4-F5; etc) was analysed separately.

The speed values determined along the various emitter-receiver paths are normally scattered, and statistical

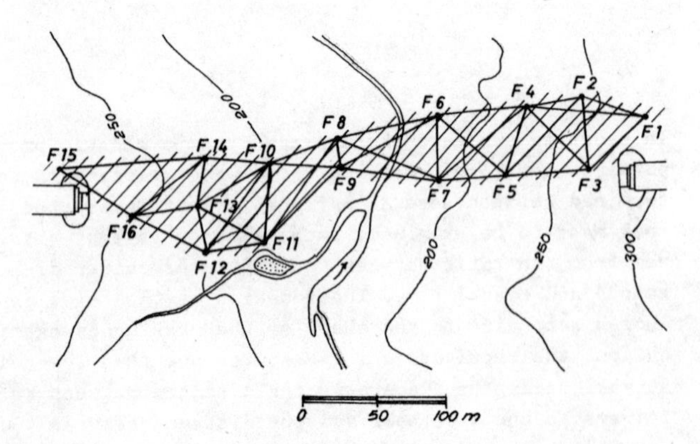

Fig. 2 Hole arrangement used for a survey.

methods are therefore needed to obtain average parameters characteristic of the rock.

For each rock prism the average speed is calculated as the arthimetic mean of the speeds relative to all the paths considered. This mean value is considered as the characteristic average parameter of that rock prism to be used for comparison with the speed of other rock prisms or with the speeds determined from laboratory tests.

As and index of the average scattering of values and, therefore, as a parameter to evaluate the average non-homogeneity of the portion of rock, we consider the standard deviation S and the standard deviation percentage S% given by:

$$S = \sqrt{\frac{\sum_{i=1}^{n} (V_i - V_m)^2}{n-1}} \qquad S\% = \frac{S}{V_m} \cdot 100$$

with V_i single value and V_m mean speed.

The analysis of the variance S^2 enables one to judge whether two portions of rock can be considered elastically similar or not (the two means are - or are not - significantly different) and to distinguish parts having significantly different elastic characteristics within one portion of rock.

It is evident that in this type of analysis, which is extremely useful particularly in the case of rocks with a low quality index, it is very important to have a high number of measurements covering as many as possible different paths. In these cases it may be convenient to use an apparatus having as many channels as possible (though very precise) rather than an extremely precise apparatus having only one or two channels. For example, if the scattering S% exceeds 10% and the travel times are at least 10 milliseconds even normal seismic refraction apparatus having 12 channels with reading approximation of $\pm$ 0,2-0,3 milliseconds may be used successfully. In this way a large number of measurements can be obtained with few shots in a short time.

In the case of layered rocks, when analysing the speed values and their variance, the ratios between the seismic wavelength utilised, the thickness of the layers, the distance between the source and the receiver and their reciprocal position are all very important. These factors, the influence of which has been analysed in a previous paper (Bernabini,1969), determine in a non-fractured rock a normal scattering of speed values. In fractured layered rocks the scattering due to stratification is superimposed on the normal scattering of values. In order to evaluate, at least in part, the normal scattering due to stratification, we use a correlation analysis (linear or of the second order) between the speed values and the angles formed between the strata and the emitter-receiver path. Once the variance due to the correlation has been eliminated, the residual scattering gives the maximum possible values of the "anomalous" scattering due to the existing fractures.

Among many practical cases studied since 1958, Table 1 shows the results of tests carried out on a portion of stratified rock before and after cementation.

TABLE 1

	Before cementation	After cementation
Number of values	44	45
Mean value of speed V_m	1.965 m/s	2.645 m/s
Standard deviation S	355 m/s	350 m/s
Standard deviation percentage S%	18	13

It can be noted that the cementation caused a sharp increase (34,6%) in the mean value, but not a similar decrease in the scattering. Regression analysis was carried out between the speed values and the angle between the strata and the emitter-receiver path. The results are shown in Table II.

TABLE II

	Before cementation	After cementation
Total standard deviation	355 m/s	350 m/s
Correlation coefficient	0,205	0,566
Regression standard deviation	73 m/s	198 m/s
Residual standard deviation	348 m/s	289 m/s

It can be seen that before cementation the correlation is not significant, whereas it is so after cementation (See Fig. 3). The residual standard deviation, that in the first case remained practically unchanged, decreased in the second case with respect to the intial value. As a consequence of cementation the rock resumed its anisotropic character due to stratification.

METHODS FOR THE DETERMINATION OF ELASTIC CHARACTERISTICS IN A ROCK NEAR AN EXCAVATION SURFACE

Various methods were applied to determine the variations of the elastic characteristics of a rock mass near an excavation surface: - 1) Direct measurement of speed between pairs of holes, drilled normally to the surface and at a short distance from one another (2-10 m): 2) sonic log with one emitter and two receivers spaced 0,5-1 m: 3) Microseismic refraction along the walls.

While the first two methods are widely used and well-known the third is rarely or never applied elsewhere as far as we know.

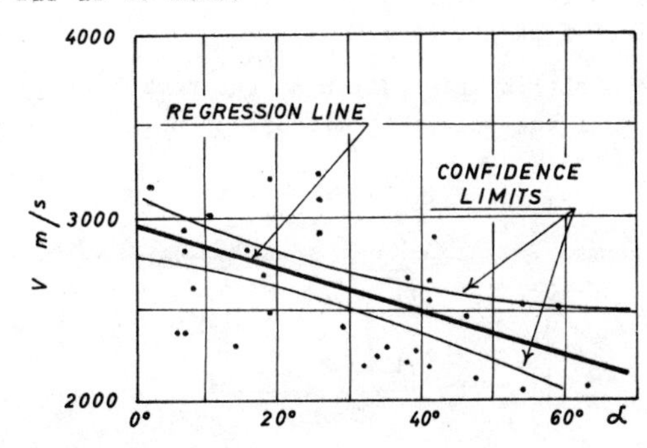

Fig. 3 Correlation analysis between velocity values V and angles α between strata and emitter-receiver path.

Instead it is well-known that the seismic refraction method enables one to determine the increase in speed on increasing distances from the surface. Therefore, this system can be used to determine the properties and the thickness of the rock zone that has been loosened or fractured because of the excavation and presents therefore a lower seismic speed than the deeper part of the rock mass not affected by the excavation.

The method proposed consists of executing a normal refraction profile with geophones very close to one another (0,5-2 m) and with maximum distances of 4 to 30 m between the source and the geophones. Since the travel times are small the use of a cathode ray oscilloscope with recordings on polaroid film is required. The apparatus scheme used is shown in fig. 4. The vibrations are produced by a hammer on which a piezoelectric transducer is mounted. The impulse of the transducer triggers the oscilloscope by means of an amplifier. This instrumentation was set up in order to obtain repeatable travel times of ± 10 microseconds with piezoelectric transducers and ± 50 microseconds for electromagnetic transducers, at least in hard rocks. To originate vibrations in very fractured rocks electric detonators placed in holes made using a small hand drill, were used.

For distances of 2 m between the geophones, 4 horizontal electromagnetic transducers fixed to the wall were used as receivers, while for distances of 0,5 m only two piezoelectric transducers were used.

Once the transducers are fixed to the walls, hammer blows are struk on pre-arranged spots, then the transducers are moved and other hammer blows are struck on the same spots, and so on until the established programme is completed.

Spreads of 18-22 m (10-12 transducer positions)were generally chosen using electromagnetic transducerc while the vibrations were originated at 3 points - 2 at the extremities of the spread and 1 in the middle in order to obtain 3 reciprocal time-distance diagrams. Spreads of 4 m were instead chosen for piezoelectric geophones, with 2 points of vibration situated at the extremities of each spread.

In order to obtain information on the rock farther from the wall the scheme of measurements is completed

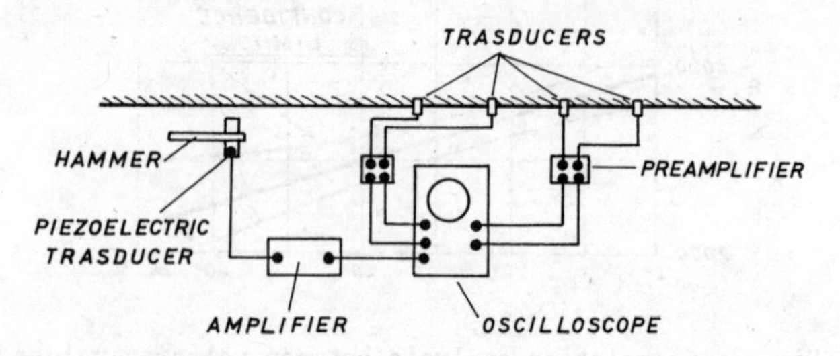

Fig. 4 Apparatus scheme for seismic refraction profiles.

by making two recordings on the same basis with 4 transducers 6-8 m apart, the vibration source placed 5-10 m from the extremities. The space-time diagrams obtained using the above scheme are shown in Fig. 5. Normally also seismic spreads are carried out with geophones spaced 10 m apart to gain information on the rock at a greater depth.

Some results obtained from tests carried out in 1970 and 1972 on some stretches of two tunnels excavated for the Alto Gesso plant (Entracque-Cuneo) are reported. Generally each stretch showed 4 lines, 2 at about 0,5 m from the floor on the right and left wall and two near the roof - one on the right and one on the left wall. One 18-22 m spread and two 4 m spreads were carried out along each alignment. A seismic survey was also carried out with geophones every 10 m along the floor of the tunnel. The interpretation of the

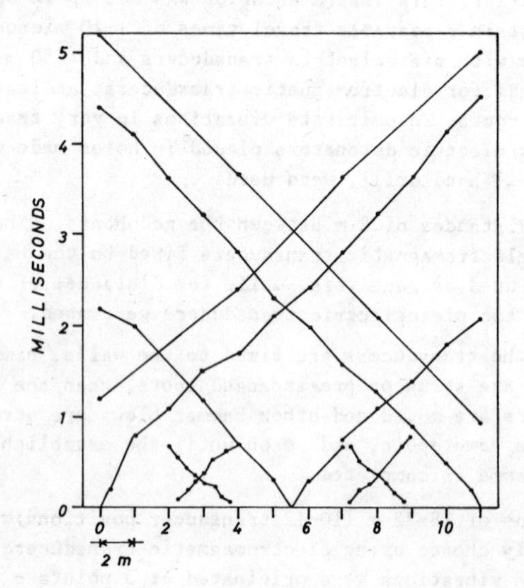

Fig. 5 Time-distance diagrams obtained from a refraction test

values measured was made using the delay-time method (Gardner, 1939) (Bernabini, 1965).

In the first tunnel excavated in gneiss, it was possible to determine the presence of a lower speed zone around the tunnel. This zone presented greater thickness and lower speed along the roof lines; than along the floor lines the speed increased as the distance D from the entrance increased (See Fig. 6). An analogous test, carried out in a drift where a system of presplitting excavation had been used, showed, instead, that the loosened zone had very small thicknesses (from 0 to 20 cm), thereby demonstrating the different

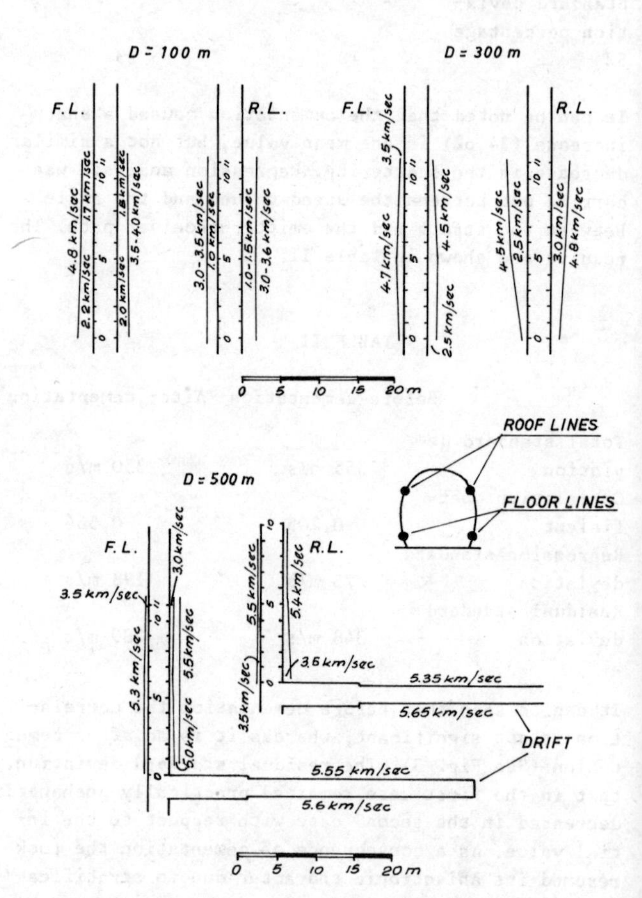

Fig. 6 Results obtained with refraction tests in a tunnel excavated in gneiss.
D - distance from the tunnel entrance
F.L. - Results along floor lines
R.L. - Results along roof lines

effects due to the two systems of excavation used.

In the second tunnel excavated in granite, with the normal volley system, it was found (See Fig. 7) that the zone around the excavation was not very thick (0,2-0,6 m) but had a low speed (1-2 km/s).

Therefore, this method has shown a great difference

in the behaviour of the two type of rock after excavation. In the gneiss, probably because of its schistocity and of the presence of microfractures, the disturbance due to the excavation spread widely around the excavation itself and the more the rock was fractured the greater it was. Instead in the granite there was only a limited fractured zone.

This method has been experimented in many cases, also in connection with loading tests and tests for determining static moduli and it has always proved useful for judging the reliability of such tests. This method is also rapid; in fact, only 2 to 3 hours of field work are needed to carry out a complete profile.

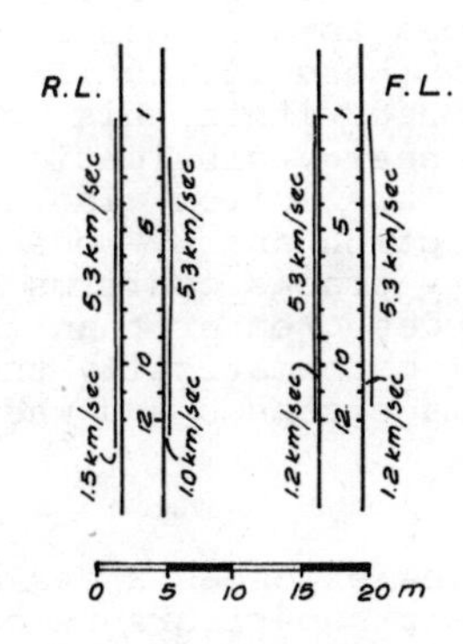

Fig. 7 Results obtained with refraction tests in a tunnel excavated in granite
F.L. Result along floor lines
R.F. Result along roof lines

ACKNOWLEDGEMENTS

The authors would like to thank ENEL and in particular Ing. Motta, Director of the Centro Nazionale Studi e Progetti of Turin, for the help given and for the authorisation to publish data on the Alto Gesso plant survey.

REFERENCES

Bernabini, M. and M. Beomonte, 1965, Un esempio di controllo con il metodo sismico delle caratteristiche di una roccia consolidata, Geotecnica, n. 2.

Bernabini, M., 1965, Alcune considerazioni sui rilievi sismici a piccole profondità, Bollettino di Geofisica Teorica e Applicata, Vol. VII, n. 26.

Bernabini, M., 1969, Sulle determinazioni dirette delle onde elastiche longitudinali in rocce stratificate, Riv. It. di Geotecnica, n. 3.

Gardner, L.W., 1939, An areal plan of mapping subsurface structure by refraction shooting, Geophysics, Vol. IV, n. 4.

DYNAMIC STRENGTH OF IN SITU ROCK

RÉSISTANCE DYNAMIQUE DES ROCHES IN SITU

DYNAMISCHE FESTIGKEIT VON IN SITU FELS

Charles GODFREY
Chief Scientist
Physics International Company
San Leandro, California
U. S. A.

SUMMARY

Pre- and post-shot examination of jointed granitic rock exposed to underground explosions shows no observable damage occurring at radii beyond that where the peak stress has dropped to $\sim 7 \times 10^8$ N/m^2 (7 kilobars). An analysis of seismic signals, however, indicates that elastic behavior does not begin until the peak stress has dropped to a stress slightly larger than the overburden stress [$\sim 10^7$ N/m^2 (100 bars)]. In between these limits lies a substantial region of inelastic response. It is postulated that response within this region is dominated by relative motion across the joints with consequent energy dissipation by frictional losses and plastic deformation at joint intersections. This motion also causes a redistribution of the energy in the incident stress wave by reflection and by mode conversion. An analysis of stress waves impinging on both lubricated and dry cracks confirms that such motion is to be expected for stress waves having stress amplitudes greater than the overburden stress. Some headway is being made in attempts to model mathematically the response of jointed rock between the limit where observable physical damage ceases and where elastic response begins.

RÉSUMÉ

L'examen avant et après le coup de roches granitiques jointes exposées à des explosions souterraines indique l'absence de dommages apparents à des rayons supérieurs aù point où la force de pointe où la force maximum est tombée à $\sim 7 \times 10^8$ N/m^2 (7 kilobars). Toutefois, l'analyse des signaux séismiques indique que le comportement élastique ne commence qu'au moment où la force maximum est tombèe á une force légèrement supérieure à la force de surcharge [$\sim 10^7$ N/m^2 (100 bars)]. Entre ces limites, il existe une région substantielle de réponse inélastique. On pose en postulat que la réponse dans cette région est dominée par le mouvement relatif en travers des joints avec dissipation de l'énergie conséquente par pertes de friction et déformation plastique aux intersections des joints. Ce mouvement provoque également une redistribution de l'énergie de l'onde de force incidente par réflection et par conversion de monde. L'analyse des ondes de force se heurtant á la fois aux fentes lubrifiées et aux fentes sèches confirme qu'on doit s'attendre à un tel mouvement pour les ondes de force ayant une amplitude supérieure à la force de surcharge. On est parvenu à certains progrès dans les efforts faits pour définir mathématiquement la résponse des roches jointes entre la zone où les dommages physiques observables cessent d'exister et celle aù la résponse élastique commence.

ZUSAMMENFASSUNG

Die vorherige und spätere Untersuchung von gegliedertem Granit, der unterirdischen Explosionen ausgesetzt war, zeigt keinerlei sichtbare Beschädigung bei Radii j enseits des Punktes, an dem der Spitzendruck auf $\sim 7 \times 10^8$ N/m^2 (7 Kilobar) abgefallen ist. Eine Analyse von seismischen Signalen ergibt jedoch, das elastisches Verhalten nicht einsetzt, bevor die Spitzenbelastung auf einen Grad abgefallen ist, der etwas höher ist als der Überlastungsdruck [$\sim 10^7$ N/m^2 (100 Bar)]. Zwischen diesen Grenzbereichen liegt ein substantieller Bereich von unelastischer Reaktion. Es wird vorausgesetzt, dass Reaktionen innerhalb dieses Bereichs von relativer Bewegung quer durch die Spalten beherrscht werden, was einen Energieverlust durch Reibung und plastische Deformation an den Verbindungsschnittpunkten zur Folge hat. Diese Bewegung verursacht auch eine Umverteilung der Energie in der einfallenden Druckwelle durch Reflexion und Umwandlung. Eine Analyse von Druckwellen, die sowohl auf geschmierte als auch auf trockene Spalten einwirkten, bestätigt, das eine solche Bewegung bei Druckenwellen zu erwarten ist, die grössere Amplituden als der Überlastungsdruck aufweisen. Gewisse Fortschritte sind erzielt worden bei den Versuchen, ein mathematisches Modell für die Reaktion von gegliedertem Fels zu erstellen, und zwar für die Reaktion zwischen den Grenzbereichen, wo sichtbare physische Beschädigung aufhört und wo eine elastische Reaktion eintritt.

INTRODUCTION

During the ban on nuclear surface explosions, free-field calculations have to be relied upon to predict the environment to which various structures would be subjected by nearby nuclear explosions. The most compelling argument for this technique is that it uses explicitly measured properties of materials and solves the dynamic equations of motion uniquely. Yet measurements of the free-field motion generated by contained nuclear explosions in the granitic rock of the Nevada Test Site (PILEDRIVER, HARDHAT, SHOAL events) have shown peak displacements which have been difficult to reproduce in calculations. Material models based on static or dynamic tests performed on laboratory-size samples give displacements which are much too small. It was demonstrated (Godfrey, 1969) that much of the initial discrepancy could be accounted for by assuming that the joint patterns inherent to all in-situ rock would decrease the effective strength of the rock substantially compared to that of laboratory samples. Subsequent laboratory static tests employed prefactured samples, but even these exhibited strengths that did not seem compatible with the large displacements observed in large-scale explosions. The following discussion attempts to show that the effective yield strength for in-situ rock under dynamic loading is roughly equal to the overburden stress at that location.

UNDERGROUND EXPLOSIONS IN ROCK

An analysis will now be made from data derived from Nevada Test Site underground explosions in granitic rock. The region of interest is traversed by systems of joints and fractures. As many as eleven sets of joints and fractures have been recorded along the HARDHAT 1500 tunnel (Bowers and Emerick, 1963) and nine sets within approximately 70 m of the PILEDRIVER CR drift (Goodman, 1968). Blocks having dimensions greater than 30 cm in this formation are rarely observed without microscopic fracturing of some sort (McArthur and Mixz, 1960). It is also recognized that water will usually fill the pores and joints in rock formations at depths below a few tens of meters. It was estimated that the rock at the HARDHAT, PILEDRIVER, site had roughly 1 percent by weight of combined water and 2 percent free water in small-scale fractures and pores (Houser and Poole, 1961). The role of this water and the joints and fractures during the free-field motion is unknown. Qualitatively, the presence of joints is known to reduce the ability of rock to sustain shear. The presence of water in a joint further reduces the shear stress which that joint can sustain (Heard, 1970).

A petrographic study of the pre- and post-shot fracture density of HARDHAT and PILEDRIVER granodiorite (Borg, 1973) found that observable microfractures first increased above preshot (i.e., background) levels at a radius where the peak radial stress was $\sim 7 \times 10^8$ N/m^2 (7 kilobars).

A marked increase in fracturing began where the peak stress reached $\sim 40 \times 10^8$ N/m^2 (40 kilobars); above 50×10^8 N/m^2 (50 kilobars), the medium was intensely fractured.

An analysis was made by Mueller (1969) of the radius and corresponding peak stress at which the stress wave from the SHOAL event in NTS granodiorite became elastic. The analysis is based on Sharpe's (1942) displacement potential for a spherically symmetric outgoing wave in an elastic medium. Using this analysis and the observed free-field data Mueller derived an elastic radius of 477 meters for SHOAL and a corresponding peak radial stress of 145×10^5 N/m^2 (145 bars). Thus the material apparently responded inelastically to a peak stress greater than 1.6 times the overburden stress.

Mueller applied the same analysis to buried explosions in other media and determined that the elastic transition stress (σ_{el}) could be approximated by

$$\sigma_{el} = 1.5\,\sigma_{ob}$$

where σ_{ob} is the overburden stress (Mueller and Murphy, 1971). This would indicate that the hypothesis proposed herein is valid for more than granitic rock.

Cooper and Brode (1972) plotted experimentally derived stress data from HARDHAT (yield = 4.9 kt), PILEDRIVER (yield = 61 kt), SHOAL (yield = 12.5 kt) and French data from explosions of 13 to 177 kt in granite. These data overlapped reasonably when scaled by the cube root of the yield. One can therefore compare the scaled radius derived from SHOAL for the transition from inelastic to elastic response with the scaled radii corresponding to various damage levels observed in HARDHAT and PILEDRIVER (Table 1).

TABLE 1

PHENOMENA OCCURRING AT VARIOUS RADII OF HARDHAT AND PILEDRIVER EVENTS

Scaled Radius (m/kt$^{1/3}$)	Peak Stress 10^8 N/m^2 (kilobars)	Damage Level or Response
> 10	> 50	Intensely fractured
10 to 12	40 to 50	Slightly fractured to highly fractured
12 to 30	7 to 40	Microfracturing
30 to 200	0.145 to 7	Inelastic response but no observable effect on internal structure
> 200	< 0.145	Elastic response

A noteworthy feature of this table is the fact that within a scaled radius extending from 30 to 200 meters/kt$^{1/3}$ the medium behaves inelastically, but there are no observable fractures or internal changes.

The inelastic response of a fractured granite medium in the stress regime above 10^7 N/m^2 (100 bars) is further evidenced by measurements of the risetime of the stress wave. For HARDHAT and PILEDRIVER the risetime increased over ten-fold as the stress dropped from 7×10^8 N/m^2 (7 kilobars) to 10^7 N/m^2 (100 bars) (Perret, 1963; Perret, 1968). For a shock wave in a truly elastic medium the increase in risetime over this stress regime would be very small.

DYNAMIC RESPONSE OF CRACKS TO STRESS WAVES

An analysis of the dynamic response of a crack to an impinging stress wave shows that relative motion across the crack can be expected for very low amplitude stress waves.

Knopoff (1957) derived the response of a plane lubricated crack to incident stress waves. The analysis below will draw on his results and extend them to a non-lubricated crack. Let us consider a plane dilatational wave impinging on a fracture plane or crack in an otherwise elastic medium. Two specific cases will be considered: (1) a perfectly lubricated crack [i.e., the coefficient of friction (μ) = 0] and (2) one with a coefficient of friction of 0.6. Case 1 is the limiting case of a plane crack filled with enough fluid to separate the two sides of the crack. Case 2 represents a dry planar crack with the two sides in intimate contact. A μ of 0.6 is typical for day competent rock. In between Case 1 and 2 lies a whole range of cracks partially filled with fluid and/or debris or having weathered faces. For completeness, it should be pointed out that some cracks can have such large geometric interference that the effective μ is greater than 0.6.

Assume a dilatational elastic wave (P-wave) to impinge on the crack at any angle of incidence (α). It will be assumed that the wave does not put the crack into net tension. By specifying the boundary conditions at the crack one can solve for the amplitudes of the reflected and transmitted P-waves and the reflected and transmitted distortional waves (S-waves). One can also get the corresponding amplitudes for the tangential motions of both surfaces and amplitude of relative motion. This was done for a Poisson's ratio (ν) of 0.2 and plotted in Figures 1 and 2. For Case 1 there is relative tangential motion at all values of α. For Case 2, substantial relative motion across the crack occurs for α between 45 degrees and 75 degrees. For Case 1, an overburden stress would have no effect, since the crack surfaces cannot sustain shear no matter what the normal stress. For Case 2, an overburden stress would be expected to result in a normal stress across the crack. If this normal stress was the order of the stress amplitudes in the incident wave, the ranges of non-elastic response and their amplitudes shown in Figure 2 (and cases intermediate to Case 1 and Case 2) would be reduced substantially. Where the overburden stress was much less than the incident stresses, however, the analysis would be valid. If the crack was near the surface, the analysis would be valid to very low stress levels. For a crack at a depth of 300 m, where the overburden stress might be $\sim 10^7$ N/m^2 (100 bars) relative motion would occur for stress waves having stress amplitudes greater than this value. It is of interest to point out that the above analysis is all independent of wavelength and the results will therefore apply whatever the shape of the wave.

A similar analysis has been carried out for a plane S-wave impinging on a crack. In this case, the direction of vibration of the incident S-wave must be specified (or reduced to its two components). For vibrations or components parallel to the plane of the crack, there is no motion normal to the crack and no P-waves are reflected or transmitted. For the perfectly lubricated crack, the S-wave must be completely reflected and there is no transmitted S-wave. For a dry crack having a finite coefficient of friction the normal stress is still zero and hence the crack can transmit no shear. Thus these S-waves would be completely reflected for any value of α. Here again the existence of an overburden stress would affect the transmission of stress across the crack. If the net shear stress (the shear wave amplitude plus the appropriate component of static shear loading) exceeds the product of the coefficient of friction and the normal component of the overburden stress, then there will be relative motion across the crack for all angles of α.

For S-waves having vibrations in the plane defined by a perpendicular to the plane of the S-wave and a perpendicular to the plane of the crack, the situation is more complicated. For an S-wave which does not put the crack in net tension the response to a perfectly lubricated crack is shown in Figure 3. A similar analysis for a dry crack with a coefficient of friction of 0.6 is shown in Figure 4. For $\alpha > 38$ degrees, total internal reflection of the P-wave occurs. Instead of a reflected or transmitted P-wave, a disturbance is set up which decays exponentially with distance from the crack. Since these damped waves do not carry away energy from the crack, the energy of the incident wave is divided between the reflected and transmitted S-waves. The presence of these damped waves does, however, result in a change in phase in the S-waves. In Figures 3 and 4, the relative tangential amplitude plotted for $\alpha >$ 38 degrees is that of the S-waves only.

The magnitudes of the amplitudes shown in Figure 2 and Figure 4 for the dry crack cannot be used rigorously. The equations used to derive them assumed an elastic response of the crack. As soon as relative motion takes place, however, frictional energy would be dissipated in the crack. This in turn would affect the distribution of energy to the reflected and transmitted waves. The angles at which relative motion would begin, however, are valid. The analysis would also imply that, for a stress wave which increased to some peak value and then returned to zero, the final net displacement of

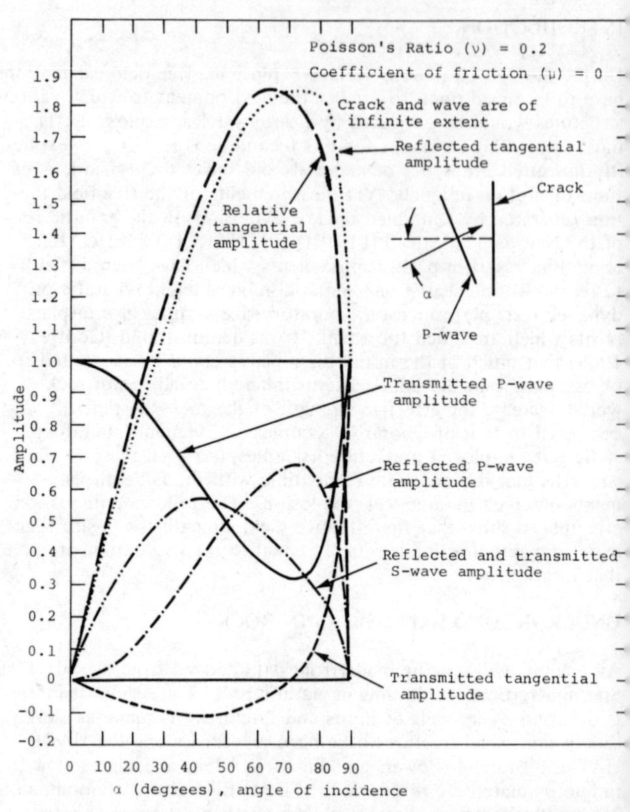

Figure 1 Effects of a plane crack on an elastic wave (Case l).

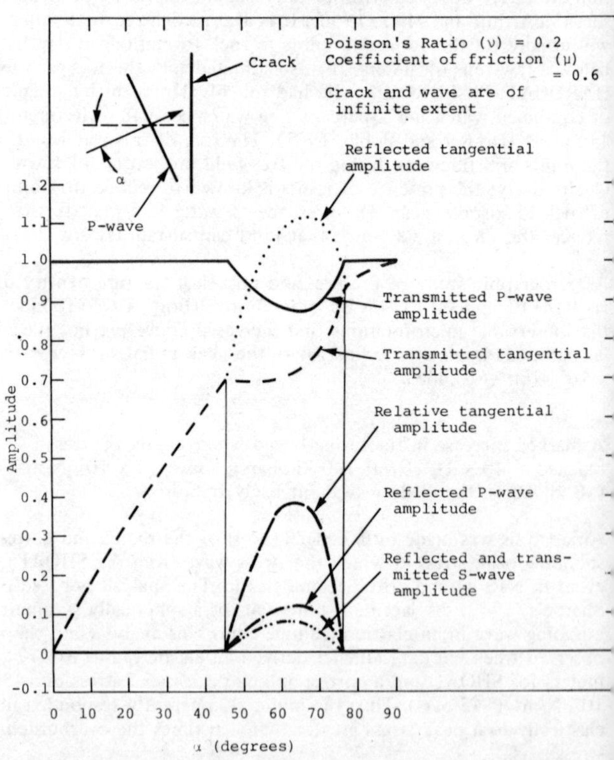

Figure 2 Effects of a plane crack on an elastic wave (Case 2).

the crack would be zero. Because of the dissipation of energy, however, the net displacement would not be zero. Even in the case of the lubricated crack, there would still be the reduction of energy in the transmitted wave due to reflection and mode conversion.

The above analysis is applicable only when the crack is not subjected to net tension. If and when this occurs, the crack opens up and presents a free surface to the stress wave. As long as the crack remains open it can transmit no stresses.

In the above discussion, the overburden stress has been suggested as an approximate threshold criterion for the initiation of relative motion across a crack. It is pointless to try to refine this threshold. The overburden stress as generally employed is the approximate weight per area of the overburden. It is not the overburden stress per se which controls the normal stress across an underground joint; it is the appropriate in situ stress across the joint. Except at very large depths, the in situ principle stresses are found to vary from a value roughly equal to this overburden stress to half of this value.

APPLICATION TO PRESTRESSED FRACTURES OR FAULTS

The crack analysis employed above assumed a dry crack with a coefficient of friction of 0.6. At certain angles of incidence, the shear stress applied by an incident stress wave is greater than 0.6 of the normal stress applied by the wave and relative motion across the crack is assumed to occur. By superposition, one can apply the same reasoning to a prestressed crack. Assume that the above crack had a normal stress of 1.6×10^7 N/m^2 (160 bars) and a shear stress of 1.0×10^7 N/m^2 (100 bars) across the crack; theoretically the results shown in Figures 2 and 4 would still be valid, i.e., stress waves impinging on the crack would cause relative motion for the incident angles shown. If the crack in question were a fault, its effective coefficient of friction would be considerably less than 0.6. In this case, the range of incident angles which would cause relative motion would be increased. It is not clear how this relative motion, if it really occurred, might affect a prestressed fault. Some earthquake models attempt to explain the unstable nature of fault slippage by assuming that sliding is characterized by a "dynamic" coefficient of friction that is less than the "static" coefficient which defines the frictional resistance before sliding. If this is so, the triggering of a prestressed fault by an incident stress wave would appear to be quite understandable. Assume the fault to be prestressed to the maximum shear stress compatible with the static coefficient (the fault might even be creeping). Then a stress wave, of any amplitude, which met the criteria (i.e., the appropriate μ, ν and α) for relative motion, would cause the fault to slip and bring about the applicability of the dynamic coefficient. Motion would continue until the shear stress fell to a value compatible with the dynamic coefficient. The triggering concept outlined above does not explain how the first slippage in an otherwise static environment takes place. It may, however, provide a useful model in understanding how the energy released by an epicenter is instrumental in releasing the energy stored in an entire fault.

Toksöz and Kehrer (1971), by an analysis of observed surface waves, calculated the tectonic strain energy released by the SHOAL, HARDHAT and PILEDRIVER events. The energy in the waves appeared to be released essentially simultaneously with the propagation of the shock wave from the explosion and to come from the immediate vicinity of the explosive source. The ratio of calculated tectonic energy in the surface wave (W_{tect}) to the surface wave energy of the explosive source (W_{exp}) for the three shots is shown in Table 2. Toksöz postulated that the stress relaxation occurred primarily due to cracking. It seems more logical, however, to assume that the primary cause of the release of energy is the mechanism described herein. The stress waves moving out from the source initiate motions along prestressed joints or faults.

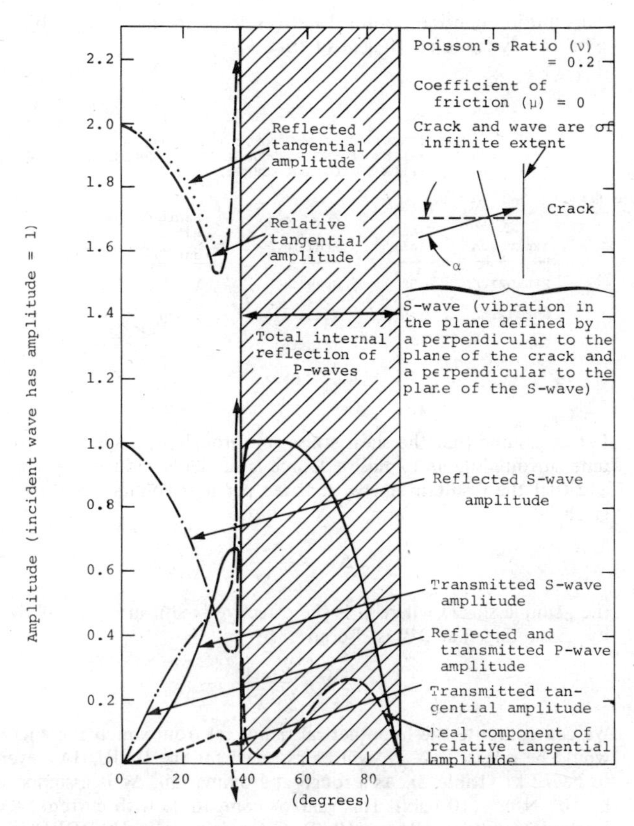

Figure 3 Effects of a plane crack on an elastic wave (Case l).

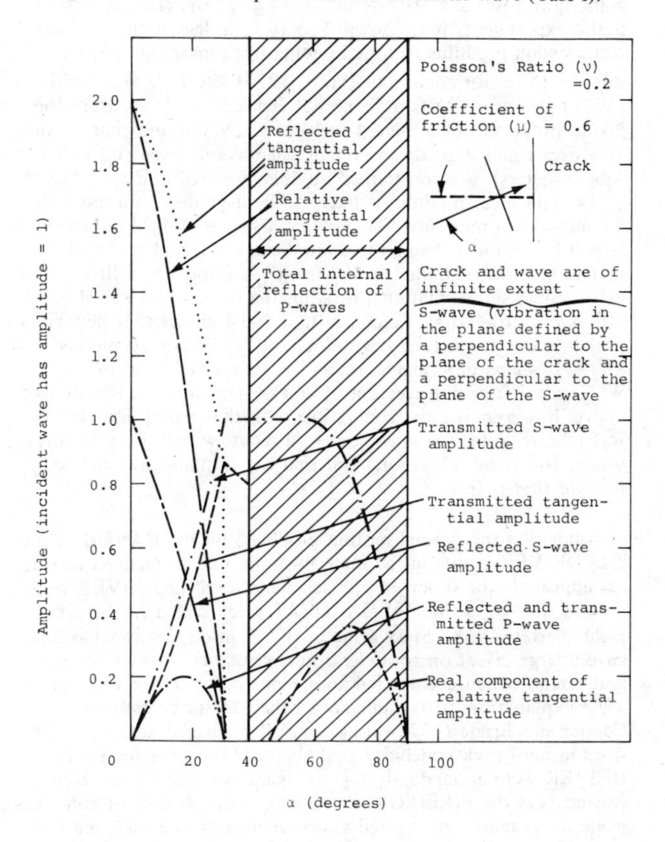

Figure 4 Effects of a plane crack on an elastic wave (Case 2).

This motion continues until the stress drops to that compatible with the dynamic coefficient of friction.

TABLE 2

CHARACTERISTICS OF TECTRONIC STRAIN RELEASE FROM A SAMPLING OF UNDERGROUND NUCLEAR EXPLOSIONS (FROM TÖKSOZ AND KEHRER, 1971)

Explosion	Yield (kt)	Medium	Energy Ratio (W_{tect}/W_{exp})
PILEDRIVER	58	Granite	13.65
HARDHAT	6	Granite	12.00
SHOAL	12.5	Granite	1.05

Let us assume that the shear stress (τ) throughout a spherical volume surrounding an explosive source is suddenly reduced by $\Delta\tau$ and that the resultant energy radiated per unit volume ($\Delta\tau$) is given by

$$\Delta W = \frac{(\Delta\tau)^2}{2G}$$

(i.e., simple shear) where G is the effective in-situ modulus of rigidity. Assuming that ΔW is also given by

$$\Delta W = \frac{W_{tect}}{4/3\ \pi r^3}$$

We can compute the hypothetical radius (r) from which the energy would be released. W_{tect} will be assumed for the HARDHAT event to be 72 kt (Table 2). As a rough approximation, $\Delta\tau$ is assumed to be 10^6 N/m^2 (10 bars). This value is compatible with current earthquake models (Brune, 1970). G for competent HARDROCK granodiorite is 3.2 x 10^{10} N/m^2 (0.32 megabar) (Holzer, 1965). Static experiments have shown 2 to 10 fold degradations in the compression modulus of rock in going from intact laboratory samples to in-situ conditions (Pratt, 1973). Pfefferle and Smith (1971) performed tests utilizing flat jack devices to measure the in-situ properties of a jointed rock mass. They found that, as the area over which the jacks were applied was increased (up to 10 square meters), the constrained modulus was reduced by a factor of 14. The shear modulus is likely to be degraded even more than a compression modulus. For our calculation a 10-fold reduction in G will be assumed. Using these numbers, r is found to be 815 meters or a scaled radius of 450 m/kt$^{1/3}$. Cooper and Brode (1972) data shows that at this radius the peak stress was about 10^7 N/m^2 (100 bars). Reference to Table 1 shows that new cracks probably did not extend beyond a scaled radius of 30 meters/kt$^{1/3}$. It seems improbable, therefore, that a major portion of W_{tect} came from the creation of cracks. The crude radius derived above, however, is quite compatible with the assumption that there was relative joint movement out to a radius where the peak stress was ~ 10^7 N/m^2 (100 bars) and that the response was elastic beyond that radius.

In comparing the ground motion produced by the HARDHAT and PILEDRIVER events in the same medium, one anomalous feature has appeared: the observed displacements for PILEDRIVER were roughly 2.5 times those of HARDHAT when scaled to the same yield (Perret, 1968). Since a factor of 2.5 in displacement would have a large effect on an underground structure, it is important to understand which event acted anomalously and to see whether some explanation of its anomalous behavior can be assumed. Cooper and Brode (1972) in plotting all published data on explosions in hard rock concluded that the displacements for PILEDRIVER were anomalously high. It is known that a fault zone existed near the PILEDRIVER working point. This fault zone was made up primarily of sheared and broken rock and included very little, if any, clayey gouge. Particle velocity gages were placed on both sides of the fault to see what its effect would be on the ground motion. They were placed at 155 m and 172 m respectively on a horizontal line from the working point. The readings of these two gages are shown in Table 3.

TABLE 3

PEAK VELOCITY MEASUREMENT FOR PILEDRIVER EVENT (FROM PERRET, 1968)

Distance From Source (meters)	Gage Designation	Component Measured	Peak Particle Velocity (m/sec)
155	F-SL-1 RUR	Radial	14.6
	RUV	Vertical	18.6
	RUT	Tangential	26.8
172	F-SL-2 RUR	Radial	Signal saturated at 65.0
	RUT	Tangential	3.6

A quantitative interpretation of these data would be very difficult to make. Some qualitative conclusions, however, can be made. The fact that the vertical and tangential peak velocities of F-SL-1 are both larger than the radial velocity shows that the wave motion is far from one-dimensional. Non-uniformity of the medium could account for some activity of the vertical and tangential gages. For a passive medium, however, it is difficult to imagine how such motions would exceed the radial motion which was driving them. It is also difficult to see how the radial velocity can increase dramatically just by traversing a fault. If, however, there were a large amount of strain energy stored in the volume surrounding the fault and the incident stress wave triggered its sudden release, the observed motions become more credible. The plane of the fault zone was not at right angles to a radius from the working point. It is quite possible, therefore, that relative motion across the fault introduced a negative component to the radial velocity of F-SL-1 and a positive component to the radial velocity of F-SL-2. The observed radial displacements on which the anomalous behavior of PILEDRIVER was based were all at radii beyond F-SL-2. They could therefore have been increased a substantial amount by the mechanism hypothesized.

MODELLING OF JOINTED ROCK

Calculational techniques employing finite difference or finite element codes are quite successful in solving the equations of motion for the free field motions produced by an explosion. At high stress levels, the equations of state and constitutive models employed in these codes, however, have not included any physical description of the in situ effect of the joints. Holzer (1965) compares calculations of explosions with experimental data. He concludes that "experimental confirmation of this (calculational) method is most convincing in the region above 10^9 N/m^2 (10 kilobars)." The data presented herein would indicate that in the region where the peak stress was above 10^9 N/m^2 (10 kilobars), the fracture of the rock probably dominates the effects of the joints. There has also been reasonable success in predicting the propagation of stress waves at stress levels below 10^7 N/m^2 (100 bars). (See for example Mueller, 1970 and Andrews and Shlien, 1972). Here the response is considered to be nearly elastic. It is the region in between that is still causing trouble. An understanding and modelling of the joint motion may provide the link required to allow a calculation of an explosive source to be carried out to a point where elastic theory is valid. Holzer does show calculations in salt which were carried out successfully to a point where the calculated and observed reduced displacement potentials showed reasonable agreement. Salt however, is not a jointed medium. Its resistance to deformation is so low that it finds plastic flow more acceptable than the creation of fractures. It is comforting but not surprising, therefore, that the above calculation can be performed successfully.

It is quite possible to calculate the response of a spherically divergent wave upon impinging on a plane crack in an otherwise infinite homogeneous medium. The addition of even one more crack complicates the problem considerably. The interaction of each P-wave or S-wave with a crack can make four new waves. Between the two cracks, an infinite number of waves would be generated. In the real situation, several major fracture systems (and some minor ones) normally break up any geologic formation into blocks whose major dimensions rarely exceed a meter. A rigorous solution would require the use of a 3-dimensional code in which the calculational zone sizes were a fraction of the joint spacing and all the interfaces between blocks were represented by slide lines. This approach may someday be possible, but with present day computer technology is quite impractical.

The alternative to the modelling of jointed rock by specifically including the joints in the calculation is to determine equations of state and constitutive models which effectively average out the effects of many joints on the passage of the stress wave. The equation of state (i.e., the dependence of pressure on the volume and internal energy) is not drastically affected by the presence of joints. It is the constitutive relations which cause the problems. The hypothesis in this paper is that the yield stress for large scale in situ motion is roughly equal to the overburden stress. This hypothesis does not, however, define what is the effective strength of a jointed formation for the inelastic motion which occurs after the yield stress is exceeded. Nor does it specify the reflection of energy, its mode conversion or its irreversible transformation to heat in traversing the joints.

Physically the situation is quite complicated. Relative motion along a joint will be interrupted when that joint ends at some intersecting joint plane. There will be large stresses (and local plastic deformation) developed at such intersections. The natural orientation of blocks is highly efficient. A reorientation of the blocks would be resisted even if all of their joints were perfectly lubricated. Such reorientation can only be accommodated by local plastic distortion at intersections, fracture of the blocks and/or dilation of the volume occupied by the blocks. Intuitively one would expect the resistance to reorientation to increase as relative displacements between blocks increased until these displacements reached magnitudes comparable to the dimensions of the blocks.

Reorientation of the blocks often leads to an increase in the effective strength of the medium. Reorientation of the blocks from their natural orientation is usually accompanied by an increase in volume and a consequent opening up of the joints. If the joints are filled with fluid, the pore pressure drops and the effective strength of the joint increases. This phenomenon was first recognized by Frank (1965) and named "dilatancy hardening."

Reaugh (1973) has been attempting to model some of these effects by employing a material with a hysteretic shear modulus. This gives an irreversible transformation of stress wave energy into heat for a cycle of compressions and relaxation. Initial results indicate that the calculated dispersion and attenuation of the stress wave in the region of interest can be matched reasonably well to experimental data by using this approach. Consideration is also being given to employing a variable shear modulus. The results of this study will be reported at a later date.

Acknowledgments. The work reported herein was carried out under the sponsorship of the Defense Nuclear Agency.

REFERENCES

Andrews, D. J. and Shlien, S., 1972, Propagation of Underground Explosion Waves in the Nearly Elastic Range, Bulletin of the Seismological Soc. of America, Vol. 62, No. 6, pp. 1691-1698.

Borg, I. Y., 1973, Extent of Pervasive fracturing around underground nuclear explosions, International Journal of Rock Mechanics and Mining Sciences, Vol. 10, p. 11-18.

Bowers, W. E. and Emerick, W. L., 1963, Supplementary geologic mapping in the 1500 reentry tunnel, area 15, NTS, Nye Co., Nevada, USGS Tech. Letter, Area 15-4.

Brune, James N. Tectonic stress and the spectra of seismic shear waves from earthquakes, J. Geophys. Res., Vol. 75, No. 26.

Cooper, H. F. and Brode, H. L., 1972, Ground shock and the survivability of deep underground superhard facilities, R&D Associates RDA-TR-128-DNA (draft).

Frank, F. C., 1965, On Dilatancy in Relation to Seismic Sources, Rev. Geophys., Vol. 3, pp. 484-503.

Godfrey, C. S., 1969, Calculations and experiments on the dynamic properties of rocks, Proceedings: Strategic Structures Research Vulnerability/Hardening Long Range Planning Meeting, Vol. I, DASIAC Special Report 85, DASA 2288-I.

Goodman, R. E., 1968, Effects of joints on the strength of tunnels, research on rock bolt reinforcement, Omaha District, Corps of Engineers, Dept. of Army, Rept. 5.

Heard, H. C., 1970, The influence of environment on the inelastic behavior of rocks, Presented at the Symposium on Engineering with Nuclear Explosives.

Holzer, F., 1965, Calculation of Seismic source mechanisms, University of California, Lawrence Radiation Laboratory, UCRL-12219.

Houser, F. N. and Poole, F. G., 1961, Summary of physical and chemical nature of granitic rocks at the U-15a site, climax stock, NTS, USGS Tech. Letter, Area 15-1.

Knopoff, L., et al., 1957, 2nd Annual Report, Seismic Scattering Project, Chapter 12, Institute of Geophysics, UCLA.

McArthur, R. D. and Mixz, J. B., 1960, Geology of the granite site, area 15, NTS, Preliminary Rept. GN-7-60.

Mueller, R. A., 1969, Seismic energy efficiency of underground nuclear detonations, Bull. Seismological Soc. America, Vol. 59, No. 6, p. 2311-2323.

Mueller, R. A., 1970, Prediction of Seismic Motion from Contained and Excavation Nuclear Detonations presented at the Symposium on Engineering with Nuclear Explosives, 14-16 January.

Mueller, R. A. and Murphy, J. R. 1971, Seismic Characteristics of underground nuclear detonations, part I. Seismic spectrum scaling, Bull. Seismological Soc. America, Vol. 61, No. 6, p. 1675-1692.

Perret, W. R., 1968, Free field ground motion studies in granite, HARDHAT event, operation nougat, POR 1803, Sandia Laboratories.

Pfefferle, Warren and Smith, Craig R., 1971, Phase I Flat Jack tests, Dynamic Rock Mechanics, Twelfth Symposium on Rock Mechanics, Chap. 21.

Pratt, H., Private communication, Terra Tek Inc.

Reaugh, J., 1973, Private communication, Physics International Co.

Sharpe, J. A., 1942, The production of seismic waves by explosion pressures. I. theory and empirical field observations, Geophysics, Vol. 18, p. 144-154.

Toksöz, M. Nafi and Kehrer, Harold H., 1971, Underground nuclear explosions: tectonic utility and dangers, Science, Vol. 173.

ULTRASONIC TESTING OF FOUNDATION ROCK

APPLICATION DE LA MÉTHODE ULTRASONIQUE SUR LA FONDATION ROCHEUSE

UNTERSUCHUNG DES GRŰNDUNGSFELSES MIT DER ULTRASCHALL-METHODE

Nikola GRUJIĆ

Institute for Geological and Geophysical Research

Belgrad, Yugoslavia

Summary

The paper deals with testing of foundation rock by means of impulse ultrasonic method. Two procedures are used: a) determination of longitudinal wave velocities c through the rock mass around hydraulic jacks; b) determination of longitudinal wave velocities along gallery walls. In both cases the length of basis was 4-5 m. In Triassic limestones of the Mratinje dam site (Montenegro, Yugoslavia), by measurements under a) a close correlation between c and modulus of deformation D and between c and elasticity E was found out. Measurements under b) were used to delineate sound and weakened rock parts.

Résumé

Dans cette publication est décrite la procédure pandant les recherches des masses rocheuses du basement par la méthode ultrasonique. Deux procédés ont été appliqués: a) la détermination des vitesses de propagation des ondes longitudinales c dans les masses rocheuses qui entourent le vérin plat; b) la détermination de c le long des parois des galleries. En tous les deux cas le longueur de la base des mésures était 4-5 m. Dans les endroits de l'emplacement de barrage de Mratinje (Montenegro, Yougoslavie), situé dans les calcaires triassique, une correlation étroite entre c, le module de déformation et le module d'élasticité a été obtainu par le procédé a). D'après les résultats obtainu par le procédé b) les parties des masses rocheuses solides ont été separées des parties moins solide.

Zusammenfassung

In dieser Arbeit ist das Untersuchungsverfahren der Gesteinsmassen durch die Impuls-Ultraschall-Methode beschrieben. Dabei wurden zwei Vorgänge angewandt: a) die Bestimmung der Fortpflanzungsgeschwindigkeiten der longitudinalen Wellen c durch die Gesteinmasse, die die hydraulischen Druckkissen umgibt; die Bestimmung der c entlang der Wände der Galerien. In beiden Fällen beträgt die Länge der Messbasis 4-5 m. An der Wasserdammstelle Mratinje (Montenegro, Jugoslawien), in den triassischen Kalken, ist bei dem in a) angegebenen Vorgang eine enge Korrelation zwischen c, dem Verformungsmodul D und dem Elastizitätsmodul E festgestellt worden. Der in b) angegebene Vorgang ermöglichte die Absonderung der härteren Gesteinmassen von den schwächeren.

1. Introduction

Rock testing by ultrasonic impulse methods was first applied in Yugoslavia in 1962. Only two years later it had gained its place among the standard investigation methodes, and found particular application in water engineering projects (Trebinje, Đerdap, Mratinje, etc.). Ultrasonic testing was developed because of a number of reason. One of these was the requirement for detailed data about rock quality. It was also required to develop a dynamic method which would involve a volume of rock comparable with that investigated by static testing so as to provide a sounder basis for comparison of the velocity of propagation of longitudinal sound waves c with the modulus of deformation D and the modulus of elasticity E. It was hoped that if a sufficiently high degree of correlation could be found between c and the two moduli it would be possible, at least for some types of rock, to get D or E by measuring c (Kujundžić and Grujić, 1966). No less an impetus for the application of ultrasonics was the knowledge that seismic method with profile or base lengths of, say, 3o to 1oo meters usually give an excessively averaged velocity value.The resulting velocities are usually in effect apparent velocities because of the impossibility of tracing the ray paths through an inhomogeneous or quasi-homogeneous formation. The shorter measuring base used in ultrasonic methods renders the identification of ray geometry possible. from other data, e.g. that obtained by detaled geological mapping.

2. Equipment

We use an L.E.A. Ausculteur Dynamique, type BC-4. Energy pulses are generated in the rock by 1 c/s blows of an 8oo W electrodynamic hammer. A magnetostriction detector operating at the lower end of the ultrasonic range pick up the arriving pulses which are fed finally to a cathode ray tube where they are displayed as a seismogram. A separate reference signal is adjusted to coincide with the first arrival by means of a graduated potentiometer, whose scale reading then gives the pulse travel time.

3. Purpose and Procedure

As a rule the ultrasonic pulse method is applied in situ for:

a) obtaining correlations between c and D or between c and E,

b) detailed, step-by-step examination of rock in exploratory adits or tunnels,

c) cheking consolidation grouting.

The principle of the methode is the measurement of the velocity of proragation of longitudinal pulses generated in the rock by repeated impacts. The length of the base on which the velocities are determined ranges from 2 to 5 meters.

Ultrasonic testing around hydraulic jacks (a). Moduli of deformation and elasticity are determined by jacking tests, usually employing a flat hydraulic jack (Kujundžić, 1965). The jack is a hollow disk of diameter 2 m., with a toroidal perimeter to ensure uniform stress distribution. It is inserted into a carefully prepared slot in the rock, of dimension depth 4 m, length 3.6 m, width o.6 m. Deformation is measured in terms of the volume of fluid pumped into the jack.For deriving desired correlations, longitudinal wave velocities are determined in the rock which will surround the jack, before it is inserted in the slot. The procedure developed is adapted to the facilities provided by the slot and to the available equipment.

An inclined borehole (Ø 32-36 mm) is drilled on either side of the slot, to a depth such that its bottom lies on the axis of the jack about 5 m from the mearer wall of the slot. A steel rod is inserted, long enough to reach to the bottom and just project from the mouth of the hole. The wall of the slot is divided up into a grid of measuring points, five points each on a vertical line, usually three verticals. The magnetostriction detector is applied at each of these points. Thus, for example, 3o measurements are made. This number is sufficient to justify statistical treatment of the velocities (mode, arithmetic mean, deviation, etc.). The mode or arithmetic mean velocity together with the modulus of deformation or elasticity constitute a pair of values for the scatter diagram.

The only preparation necessary for the ultra sonic test is the pneumatic drilling of the lateral holes, the slot being made primarily for the hydraulic jack test. Testing the rock in the neighborhood of the one slot takes 4 to 6 hours.

Ultrasonic logging (b). The procedure is similar to that of acoustic well-logging that it is performed in a horizontal adit or tunnel instead of a well. The measuring profile is marked along the adit wall by points every 2 meters at a height of 1 m. Pulse energy is transmitted to the rock at one point and the time taken for the pulse wave to arrive at a neighboring point is measured. Logging is performed with an overlap, that is to say for the next measurement the impact and pick-up points are displaced along the wall by only half the distance between neighboring points. Therby the average velocity is determined with a constant base length of 4 meters. Results are plotted on a velocity-distance graph, the velocity point being plotted abo the center of the corresponding distance interval. Ultrasonic logging of an 8o-1oo long adit can be done in 6-7 hours.

4. Results of Ultrasonic Testing on the Mratinje Dam Site

Mesozoic limestones and dolomites are the foundation rock of a number of dams in Yugoslavia. Due to their brittleness and monominaral constitution they exhibit dama

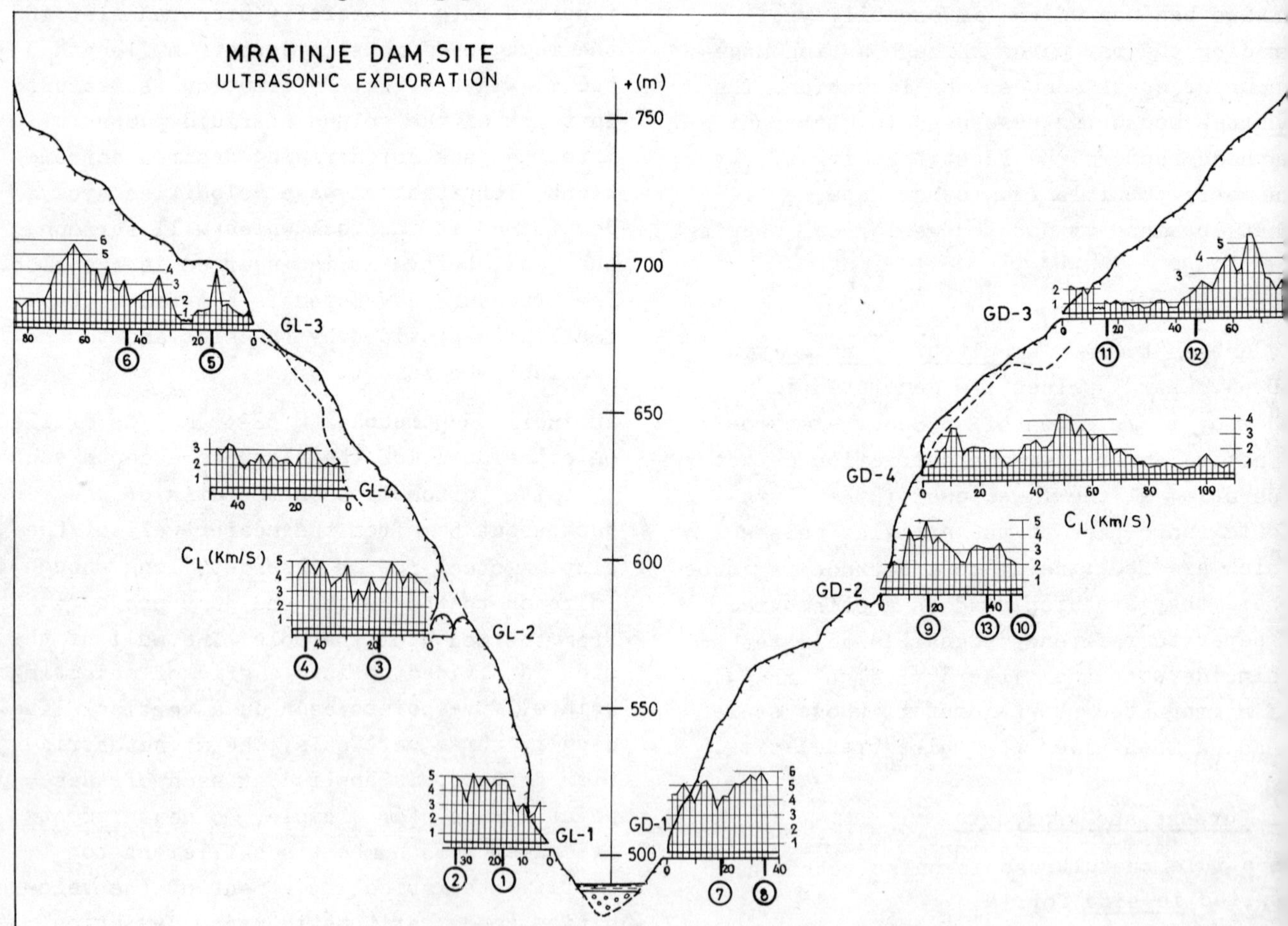

Fig.1. Cross section of the dam site profile

n the form of jointing and also often of .issolution processes. True mineral decompo- ·ition is absent. The sound rock is compact,+ o that the pulse propagation velocity .epends on the degree of fissuring and the tate of the joints (gap width, nature of 'ill if any, natural stresses, etc.). These bservations also apply to the Mratinje dam ite in Montenegro, Yugoslavia. The Mratinje rch dam, now under construction, is situ- ted in the deep and narrow gorge of the iver Piva. The gorge sides are built by assive Triassic limestone. The degree of ock damage is greater higher up in the rofile. Four exploratory adits were driven n each of the gorge sides, distributed rom near the valley floor to the height of he crest of the dam. Ultrasonic logging was arried out in all of them, and the rock in he neighborhood of 13 flat hydraulic jacks as tested by the method described above.

,D and c,E Correlations. The jacking test ocations are shown on the cross section of he dam profile in Fig.1., denoted by ircled numbers. The jacking test were per- ormed by the "Jaroslav Černi" Institute of ater Resources Engineering, and the ultra- onic testing by the Institute for Geologi- al and Geophysical Research, Belgrade. he field data from static and ultrasonic ests were processed independently before inal comparison. The measuring configura- ion for the ultrasonic tests around the draulic jacks and polar velocity graphs re shown in the plan and cross section in g.2., on the exemple of jack No.4.

very $\underline{c}_{HJ}$ (Table I and Fig.3,) is the arith- etic mean of the 24 to 30 measurements made or a given jack. $\underline{D}$ and $\underline{E}$ were determined rom the volumetric deformation values tained with pressures between 2 and kp/cm^2. The ranges of $\underline{c}_{HJ}$, $\underline{D}$ and $\underline{E}$

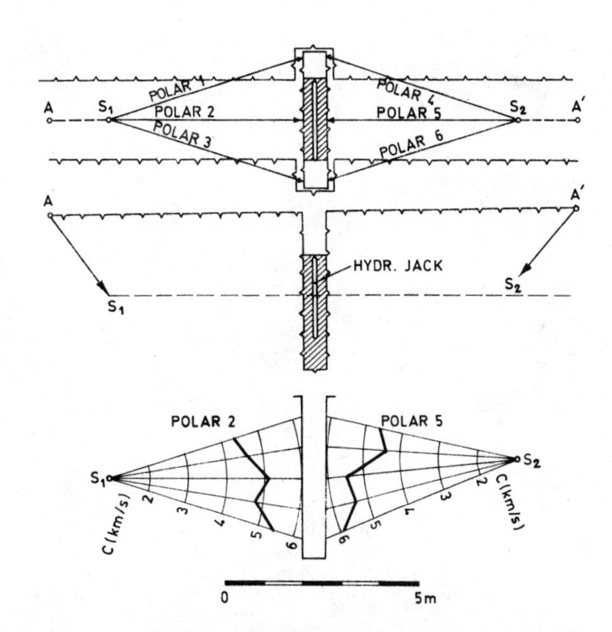

Fig.2. Ultrasonic testing around jack No.4

found were: $\underline{c}_{HJ}$ from 1.78 to 4.95 km/s, $\underline{D}$ from 10,000 kp/cm^2 to 160,000 kp/cm^2 and, $\underline{E}$ from 20,000 to 250,000 kp/cm^2. It may be seen that these ranges are almost as wide as the extreme limits to be expected in a limestone formation. Corresponding values of $\underline{c}_{HJ}$, $\underline{D}$ and $\underline{E}$ are given in Table I.

Table I
Corresponding Values of c_{HJ}, D and E

Jack No.	c_{HJ}(km/s)	D(kp/cm^2)	E(kp/cm^2)
1	4.95	140,000	210,000
2	4.20	130,000	225,000
3	4.67	150,000	210,000
4	4.86	150,000	230,000
5	2.43	45,000	90,000
6	3.46	75,000	145,000
7	4.63	160,000	250,000
8	4.50	130,000	200,000
9	3.33	70,000	120,000
10	2.03	20,000	50,000
11	1.78	10,000	20,000
12	3.04	50,000	90,000
13	2.94	55,000	-

The regression lines calculated from the data in the Table I are:

$$D = 91,000 + 47,800(c_{HJ} - 3.60) \quad kp/cm^2$$

$$E = 153,000 + 65,900(c_{HJ} - 3.66) \quad kp/cm^2$$

+ Longitudinal wave velocities were deter- mined in the laboratory on 95 core samples from Mratinje, and gave $\underline{c} = 5.76 \pm 0.59$ km/s.

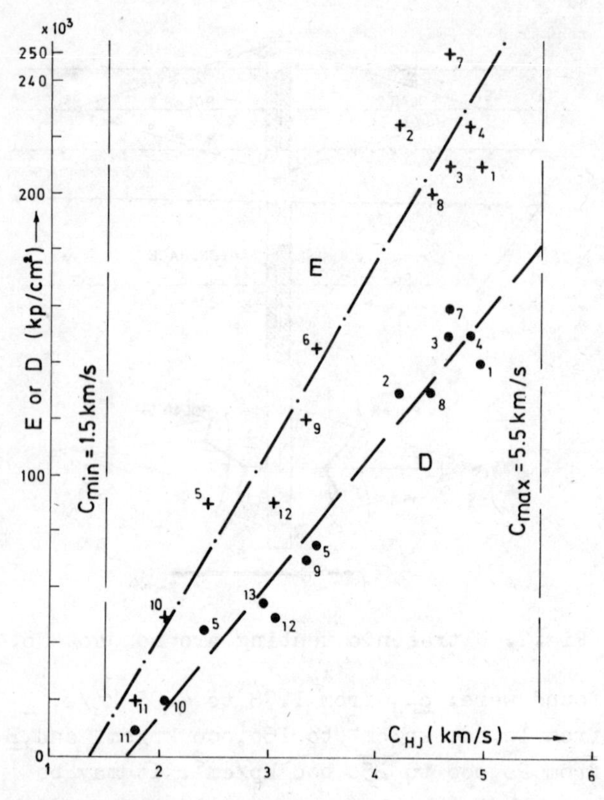

Fig.3. Scatter diagrams

The correlation coefficients are r(D)= o.98 and r(E)= o.96. The scatter diagrams are shown in Fig.3. The correlations are obviously high enough to allow satisfactory conversion of velocities into moduli, and this was utilized at Mratinje.

Ultrasonic logging. Ultrasonic logging was carried out in all the adits with a base length of 4 meters and an overlap of 2 meters. The logged velocities c_L confirm that lower in the dam profile (adits GL-2, GD-1 and GD-2) the rock mass is firm and coherent while higher up (GD-3,GD-4 and GL-3) there are compact blocks with intervening crushed zones. The adit logs are shown in Fig.1. Geological observations in adits were consistent with the ultrasonic exploration although they did not reveal so markedly the difference in rock quality. In fact, at Mratinje and elsewhere ultrasonic logging has proved very sensitive for detecting differences in rock fissuring, enabling accurate delimitation of sound rock zones and damaged, less coherent ones.

The velocities determined in this mode of logging are influenced to a certain exten by the presence of a stress release zone around the adit. It may be taken, however that the logged velocities give a suffici ently reliable indication of the quality the rock beyond the stress release zone. This may be concluded from Fig.4 where me velocities measured through the rock arou the jacks and mean velocities from a numb of en surface measurements in the vicinit of the same jacks are compared.The former are slightly higher than the later, especially at the lower end of the range.

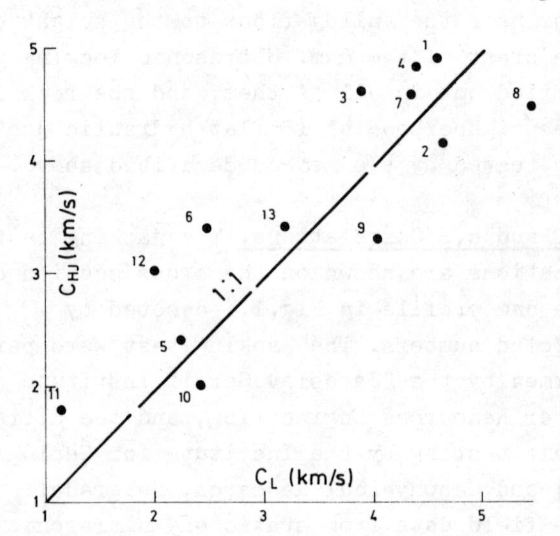

Fig.4. Velocities determined by surface logging (c_L) compared with velocities determined through the rock (c_{HJ})

5. Rock Quality Estimation

The geological report described the ro around jack No.11 (c_{HJ}=1.78 km/s, D = =1o,ooo kp/cm^2, E= 2o,ooo kp/cm^2) as broc breccoidal limestone with cracks up to 2c mm wide containing a clay fill. The rock around jack No.1 (c_{HJ}= 4.95 km/s, D = =14o,ooo kp/cm^2, E= 21o,ooo kp/cm^2) is de scribed as massive and sound limestone with a sparse network of joints which are either tight or filled with calcite.Rock quality assessment between these two extremes took into account longitudinal ave velocity, modulus of deformation, and ossibilities of improvement by consolidaion grouting. Intense fracturing together ith appreciable quantities of clay fill - elocities in the range c = 1.5 to 2.5 km/s limits the consolidation effect of grouting since it is difficult to wash out the ill. Judging by experience on Yugoslav onstruction sites (e.g. Trebinje dam site), ffective consolidation in limestone can be ounted on if the velocities are in the nterval 2.5- 3.5 km/s. To check the success f grouting, measurements can be repeated fterwards: if the velocities are not lower han 3.0 km/s, consolidation may be consiered satisfactory. Let us note that veloities above 4.0 km/s are not generally inreased by grouting. Thus, a longitudinal ave velocity of 3.0 km/s figures as a criical value in rock quality estimation of imestone rock mass. Below this value the ock mass is evaluated as poor or marginal.

s a generalization of the above considerations we may introduce a quality index q, ith a range of 0-1, defined as:

$$q = (c - c_{min})/(c_{max} - c_{min})$$

here c_{min} and c_{max} are the upper and lower imits of the longitudinal wave velocitiy easured in situ. For the Mratinje limestone t was taken that c_{min}= 1.5 and c_{max}= 5.5 m/s as determined through the rock around he jacks, and c_{min}= 0.7 and c_{max}= 5.5 km/s s determined by surface logging. The resuling quality indexes and classes are given n Table II.

Table II
Rock Quality Classification
Mratinje Dam Site

q, Quality class	c_{HJ}/c_L km/s	Predicted D modulus kp/cm^2
0.00-0.25 poor	1.5-2.5 0.7-2.0	<40,000
0.25-0.40 marginal	2.5-3.0 2.0-2.5	~ 50,000
0.40-0.50 satisfactory	3.0-3.5 2.5-3.0	~70,000
0.50-0.75 good	3.5-4.5 3.0-4.3	~110,000
0.75-1.00 very good	4.5-5.5	≥150,000

We have observed that the improvement in rock quality, in terms of longitudinal wave velocity, achieved by consolidation grouting can be expressed as follows:

poor → marginal, satisfactory (?)
marginal → satisfactory, good
satisfactory → good

\+ + + + +

References

KUJUNDŽIĆ, B., 1965, Experimental Research into Mechanical Characteristics of Rock Masses in Yugoslavia, International Journal of Rock Mechanics and Mining Sciences, Vol.2, pp. 75-91, Pergamon Press

KUJUNDŽIĆ, B. and GRUJIĆ, N., 1966, Correlation Between Static and Dynamic Investigations of Rock Mass "in Situ", Proc. of the First Congress of the ISRM, 3.56, pp. 565-570, Lisbon

EINE NEUE ULTRASCHALLBOHRLOCHSONDE FÜR DIE BESTIMMUNG DER GEOTECHNISCHEN EIGENSCHAFTEN VON INTAKTEM FELS

A NEW ULTRA-SONIC BOREHOLE-METER FOR MEASURING THE GEOTECHNICAL PROPERTIES OF INTACT ROCK

UNE NOUVELLE SONDE ULTRASONIQUE POUR LA MESURE DES PROPRIÉTÉS GÉOTECHNIQUES DES ROCHES

D. MEISTER

West - Germany

Zusammenfassung

Ein neues Ultraschallbohrlochverfahren für die Messung von P-Wellengeschwindigkeiten und Schwächungskoeffizienten wird vorgestellt. Der Bohrlochsender ist als Hochleistungsultraschallwandler ausgebildet. Die Verstärkung der Meßeinrichtung beträgt 12o db.

Am praktischen Beispiel eines Untertageeinsatzes wird die Bestimmung von P-Wellengeschwindigkeiten und Schwächungskoeffizienten erläutert und der Zusammenhang zwischen den seismo-akustischen Kenngrößen und den geotechnischen Eigenschaften des untersuchten Gebirges aufgezeigt.

Summary

The cross-hole ultra-sonic-pulse technique is presented as a means of measuring P-wave velocities and amplitude The apparatus makes use of a high-powered ultra-sonic transmitter and has an amplification factor of 12o db.

An example of an underground measurement illustrates P-wave velocities, energy attenuation and the relationship between the seismo-acoustic and the geotechnical parameters.

Résumé

Une sonde ultra-sonique pour des mesures de la vélocité des ondes "P" et de l'affaiblissement relatif de l'énergie séismo-acoustique entre deux trous de forage est présentée. L'appareil fonctionne à base d'un émetteur ultrasonique de puissance. L'amplification de l'appareil-electronique s'élève à 12o db.

Un exemple pratique d'une mesure "in situ" illustre la vélocité des ondes "P", l'affaiblissement relatif de l'énergie et la relation entre les caractéristiques séismo-acoustiques et les propriétés géotechniques du terrain exploré.

1. Einführung in die Problematik

Der Einsatz seismischer Untersuchungsmethoden beim Tunnel-, Stollen- und Kavernenbau ist im Vergleich zu Verformungsmessungen heute noch in der BRD relativ unbedeutend. Das liegt einerseits daran, daß die Zusammenhänge der seismischen mit den geomechanischen und den ingenieurgeologischen Parametern zu wenig erforscht sind. Andererseits haben sich die Schwierigkeiten bei der Verwendung von seismischen Verfahren für Gebirgsdruckuntersuchungen hemmend auf die Verbreitung dieses Meßverfahrens beim Untertagebau ausgewirkt.

Die Problematik bei der geotechnischen Interpretation der gemessenen seismischen bzw. seismo-akustischen Parameter darf aber nicht dazu führen, dem Tunnel- oder Stollenbauingenieur den geomechanischen Informationsgehalt seismo-akustischer Messungen vorzuenthalten. Die Bedeutung dieses Verfahrens beispielsweise als Entscheidungshilfe bei der Felsankerung oder für die Beurteilung der Standfestigkeit im Untertagebauwerk sollte nicht übersehen werden.

Die Hauptaufgabe der ingenieurgeophysikalischen Arbeit muß zunächst darin bestehen, die Zusammenhänge zwischen den seismo-akustischen Parametern einerseits und den ingenieurgeologischen bzw. geomechanischen Parametern andererseits zu erkunden. Aus dem letzteren lassen sich dann erst die bautechnischen Rückschlüsse ziehen.

Wie sich die einzelnen Parameter im wesentlichen zusammensetzen geht aus der nachfolgenden Zusammenstellung hervor:

A. Seismo-akustische Parameter:

1. P-Wellengeschwindigkeit v_p
2. S-Wellengeschwindigkeit v_s
3. Amplitudenspektrum $A(\omega)$
4. Schwächungskoeffizient α
5. Divergenzkoeffizient n
6. dynamische Moduln E, G, ν

B. Ingenieurgeologische Parameter:

1. Gesteinsart
2. Schichtung
3. Schieferung
4. Klüftung (Klüftigkeitsziffer k, Durchtrennungsgrad, Kluftintensität K)
5. Porosität und Korngrößenverteilung
6. Auflockerung infolge von Schießarbeit
7. Auflockerung infolge von Spannungsumlagerung

C. Geomechanische Parameter:

1. Spannungszustand des Gebirges
2. Festigkeitsverhalten des Gebirges
3. Verformungsverhalten des Gebirges

Selbstverständlich erhebt die Aufzählung der Parameter nicht den Anspruch auf Vollständigkeit. Immerhin verdeutlicht sie aber, wie komplex der Zusammenhang der seismo-akustischen mit den ingenieurgeologischen und den geomechanischen Parametern ist.

2. Geotechnische Grundlagen

In verschiedenen Arbeiten wurde versucht, Einzelabhängigkeiten der o.g. Parameter zu erforschen. Verständlicherweise beruhen die erzielten Ergebnisse überwiegend auf Laboruntersuchungen.

Die umfangreichsten Untersuchungen beziehen sich auf das Problem der Abhängigkeit der Schallgeschwindigkeit von der Porosität und der Korngröße von Sedimentgesteinen. Durch die Arbeiten von BIOT (1), WYLLIE, GREGORY und GARDNER (14) kann dieser Komplex als abgeschlossen angesehen werden. Als Beispiel sei nachfolgend die Gleichung von WYLLIE et al. erwähnt:

$$n = \frac{v_{por} \; (v_{Mat} - v_p)}{v_p \; (v_{Mat} - v_{por})} \qquad (1)$$

Es sind:

v_p = Wellengeschwindigkeit im Sedimentgestein
v_{Mat} = Wellengeschwindigkeit der Gesteinsmaterie
v_{por} = Wellengeschwindigkeit der Porenfüllung
n = Porosität

Die obige Gleichung haben verschiedene Autoren benutzt, um den Klüftigkeitskoeffizienten eines Gebirges zu ermitteln, in dem sie anstelle der Porosität den Klüftigkeitskoeffizienten eingeführt haben. Die Richtigkeit der Analogie zwischen Porosität und Klüftigkeit muß aber stark bezweifelt werden.

Für den Untertagebau ist weniger die Porosität als die Klüftigkeit des Gebirges eine entscheidende Einflußgröße. Hier haben In-situ-Untersuchungen von BRÜCKL u. FÜRLINGER (2) dazu geführt, daß erstmalig eine Abhängigkeit der seismischen Wellengeschwindigkeit von der Klüftung eines Gebirges aufgestellt werden konnte. Für den stark geklüfteten Dachsteinkalk im Bereich des Hochkönig-Massivs wurden folgende Beziehungen zwischen der Kluftintensität K und der Laufzeit T hergeleitet:

$$K = a_1 + a_2 \frac{T}{T_B} \qquad (2)$$

Die Größen a_1 und a_2 müssen durch Messungen ermittelt werden. Sie sind von Kluftkörperbereich zu Kluftkörperbereich verschieden. T_B wird aus Mittelwerten von T für verschiedene Werte von K gebildet. Innerhalb des Meßgebietes konnte der Einfluß der übrigen ingenieurgeologischen und geomechanischen Parameter als vernachlässigbar klein angesehen werden.

Von geophysikalischer Seite ist dem Problem der Gebirgsdruckabhängigkeit der seismischen Wellengeschwindigkeit größte Aufmerksamkeit gewidmet worden. Die Arbeiten von OBERT (8), BUCHHEIM (3) und RÖSLER (11) müssen in diesem Zusammenhang als grundlegend angesehen werden. Ihre Untersuchungen gingen von dem Gedanken aus, mit Hilfe an Gesteinskernen aufgenommener Eichkurven (Wellengeschwindigkeits-Druckdiagramme) und durch In-situ-Messungen den Gebirgsdruck zu ermitteln. Dieses Verfahren mußte angesichts der komplexen Abhängigkeit der seismischen Wellengeschwindigkeit von den Gebirgsparametern sehr bald auf Schwierigkeiten stoßen. Zwar führten einige wenige Versuche zu gewissen Erfolgen (SAVICH und KOPTEV (12), UHLMANN (13), aber es darf als sicher gelten, daß das Problem der Bestimmung des Gebirgsdruckes mit Hilfe seismischer oder seismo-akustischer Wellen heute noch nicht gelöst ist.

Einen Überblick über die Beziehungen zwischen relativer Schallgeschwindigkeitsänderung und Prüfdruck gibt Abb.1.

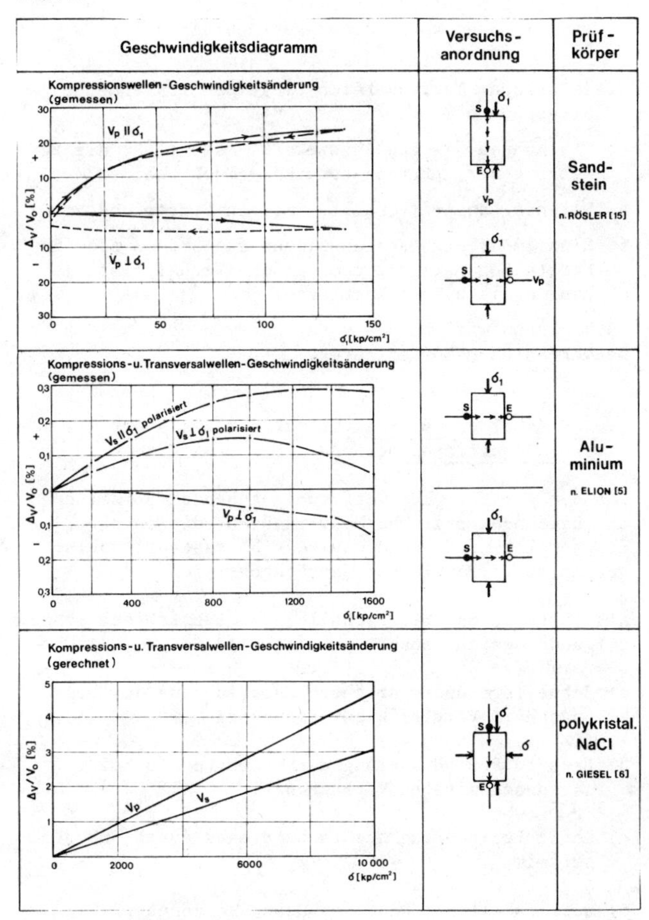

Abb.1: P- und S-Wellengeschwindigkeit in Abhängigkeit vom statischen Druck

P- and S-wave velocities as a function of statical pressure

Vitesses des ondes "P" et "S" en fonction de la pression statique

Die für die Bau- und Bergbautechnik bisher wenig befriedigenden Ergebnisse der seismo-akustischen Untersuchungsmethodik werfen die Frage auf, wie dieses Meßverfahren für die Praxis nutzbringender zu erschließen ist. Da der Einsatz des Meßverfahrens im Verlauf der Planungs- und der verschiedenen Bauphasen eines Bauwerkes möglich ist, muß zwecks Beantwortung der aufgeworfenen Frage zunächst eine Abgrenzung erfolgen. Das nachfolgend diskutierte Verfahren soll sowohl während der Erstellung von Probestollen als auch bei der Ausführung des endgültig-Bauwerkes zur Anwendung gelangen.

Erste Voraussetzung für eine erfolgreiche Messung ist eine gründliche ingenieurgeologische Untersuchung des Meßbereiches. Von der berg- bzw. bautechnischen Seite werden nun folgende Fragen an den Messenden herangetragen:

1. Wie mächtig ist die Zone der Gebirgsauflockerung infolge von Schießarbeit?
2. Wie tief dringt der Bereich der Gebirgsauflockerung infolge von Spannungsumlagerungen ins Gebirge hinein?
3. In welchem Teufenbereich liegt das tragende Gebirgsgewölbe?
4. Wie können die Ergebnisse der Messung für die Bemessung der Ankerung zunutze gemacht werden?
5. Welches Langzeitverhalten zeigen Firste und Stoß?
6. Sind im Gebirgsbereich hinter den Stößen oder der Firste ungünstigere geologische Verhältnisse vorhanden als bisher kartierte?

Nachfolgend wird zunächst das angewandte Bohrlochmeßverfahren näher erläutert.

3. Das Bohrlochmeßverfahren auf der Basis der Ultraschallimpulsmethode

Von den generell zur Verfügung stehenden seismischen und seismo-akustischen Meßverfahren, die in Abb.2 dargestellt sind, wurde auf das Ultraschallimpulsverfahren in Bohrlöchern zurückgegriffen.

Als Vorteile des Ultraschallbohrlochverfahrens können folgende Gesichtspunkte genannt werden:

a) Schnellere und einfachere Durchführung der Messungen im Vergleich zur Sprengseismik

b) Bessere Reproduzierung der Meßwerte als bei sprengseismischen Versuchen

c) Keine Behinderung des Baubetriebes durch Sprengseismik

d) Möglichkeit für Dauerversuche ist gegeben

e) Geschwindigkeitsprofile können in jeder beliebigen Richtung, auch parallel zur Stoßoberfläche, gelegt werden

f) Für die Messungen können vorhandene Ankerbohrlöcher ausgenutzt werden.

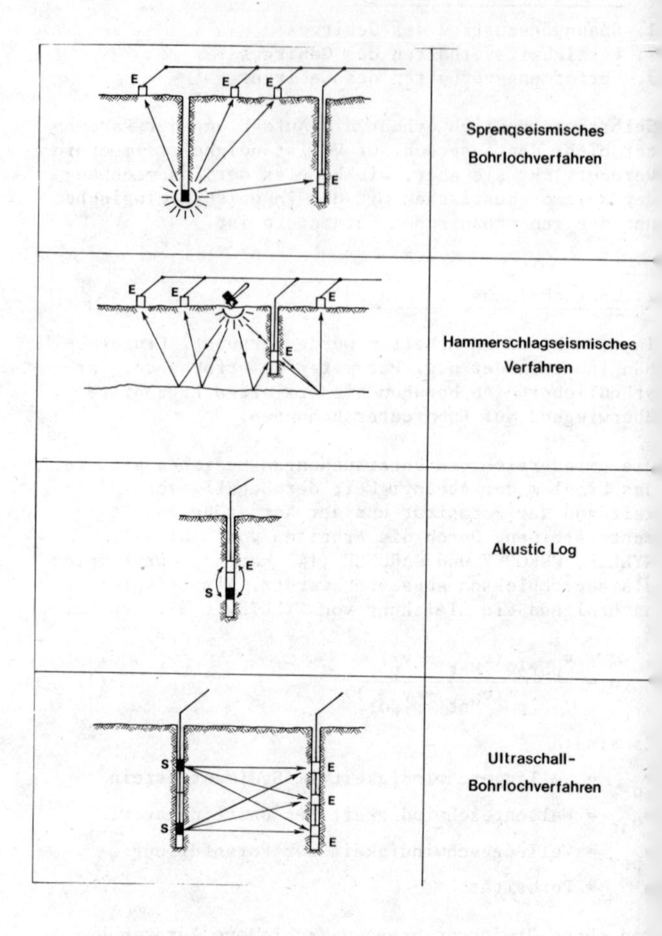

Abb.2: Seismische und seismo-akustische Verfahren beim Untertagebau
Seismic and seismo-acoustic methods in underground engineering works
Méthodes séismiques et séismo-acoustiques dans les travaux souterrains

Nachteile des Verfahrens sind:

a) Kleinere Reichweite gegenüber Spreng- und Hammerschlagseismik

b) Falls keine Ankerbohrlöcher vorhanden sind, entstehen zusätzliche Kosten für Meßbohrungen

Ausschlaggebend für den erfolgreichen Einsatz der Ultraschallsonde ist die Lösung folgender, technischer Probleme:

a) Bereitstellung ausreichender seismo-akustischer Energie

b) Verwirklichung eines hohen Verstärkungsfaktors der Meßapparatur

c) Optimale Ankopplung der seismo-akustischen Wandler im Bohrloch

d) Festlegen einer optimalen Untersuchungsfrequenz.

Von der Lösung dieser Fragen hängt die Reichweite des Meßverfahrens entscheidend ab.

Bei der angewandten Bohrlochmeßmethode wurde auf eine Anordnung von Schallquelle und -empfänger zurückgegriffen, die UHLMANN (13) auf Vorschlag von BUCHHEIM (3) für sprengseismische Versuche benutzt hat. Bei dieser Meßmethode wurden in zwei benachbarten Bohrlöchern Schallquelle und Schallempfänger untergebracht, so daß die seismo-akustischen Eigenschaften des zwischen den Bohrungen befindlichen Gebirges ausgemessen werden können. Die möglichen Schallsender- und Schallempfängerpositionen im Bohrloch sind in Abb.2 dargestellt.

3.1 Zur Frage der Reichweite der Ultraschallsonde

Nach RISNITSCHENKO (1o) kann für die Amplitudenschwächung bei der Ausbreitung seismo-akustischer Wellen im homogenen und isotropen Raum geschrieben werden:

$$\frac{A_{i+1}(r,\omega)}{A_i(r,\omega)} = \left(\frac{r_i}{r_{i+1}}\right)^n \exp - \alpha\ (\omega)\ (r_{i+1} - r_i) \qquad (3)$$

Es sind:

$\alpha(\omega)$ = Schwächungskoeffizient oder auch Dissipationskonstante
ω = Kreisfrequenz
n = Koeffizient der Schallfelddivergenz
r = Entfernung von der Schallquelle
$A(r,\omega)$ = Verschiebungsamplitude bei der Frequenz ω

Der Ausdruck $f(r) = \left(\frac{r_i}{r_{i+1}}\right)^n$ bestimmt die Amplitudenabnahme, die durch die geometrische Divergenz bedingt ist. Der Exponent hängt vom Wellentyp ab. Zum Beispiel gilt für:

Kugelwellen: $n = 1$
Zylinderwellen: $n = 0.5$
Ebene Wellen: $n = 0$

Breitet sich die Welle im anisotropen Medium (z.B. Gestein) aus, so haben die obigen Zahlenwerte für n keine Gültigkeit mehr. Die Divergenzfunktion f(r) ist für diesen Fall weitgehend unbekannt.

Der Schwächungskoeffizient α ist sehr stark frequenzabhängig. Um dieses zu verdeutlichen, wurde der in einem Frequenzbereich von 5o Hz bis 2o kHz und in einem feinkörnigen, homogenen Granit von NICHOLLS et al. (7) gemessene Schwächungskoeffizient in Abb.3 dargestellt.

Zur Abschätzung der Reichweite der Ultraschallbohrlochsonde wurden die Amplitudenverhältnisse $A_{i+1}(r,\omega)\ /\ A_i(r,\omega)$ nach Gleichung (3) berechnet. Dabei wurden n zwischen o.5 und 2.1 und α zwischen 1o db/m und 9o db/m variiert. Diese Wertespanne dürfte für eine Meßfrequenz von ca. 3o kHz annähernd zutreffen.

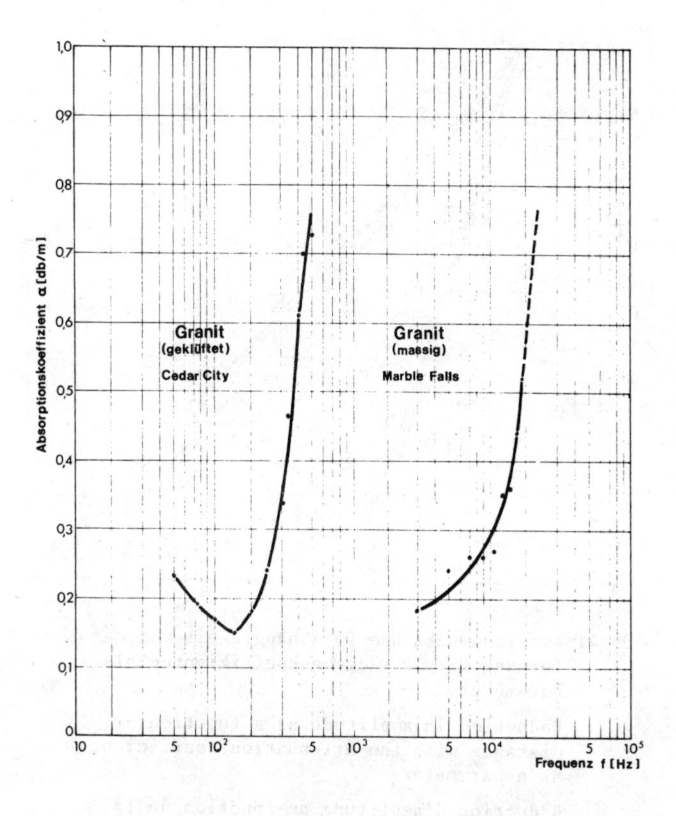

Abb.3: Abhängigkeit des Schwächungskoeffizienten von der Frequenz

Attenuation coefficient as a function of frequency

Le coefficient d'affaiblissement sur la fréquence

Abb.4 zeigt die Ergebnisse dieser Untersuchungen. Die auf der Ordinate abgetragenen Amplitudenverhältnisse geben direkt die Größe der jeweils erforderlichen Spannungsverstärkung der Meßapparatur an. Die Schwächungskurven zeigen, daß der Einfluß des Schalldivergenzkoeffizienten mit zunehmendem α-Wert geringer wird. Bei kleinem Schwächungskoeffizienten bestimmt demnach die Form der Wellenfrontausbreitung den Schwächungsvorgang entscheidend mit. Geht man bei der Abschätzung der Reichweite der Meßapparatur von einem technisch realisierbaren Verstärkungsfaktor von 10^6 aus, so könnte man bei sehr starker Amplitudenschwächung (α = 9o db/m) eine Reichweite von ca. 2,25 m erzielen. Weist das Gebirge einen geringeren Schwächungskoeffizienten auf (z.B. α = 3o db/m), so können Sender und Empfänger ca. 4,5o m voneinander entfernt sein. Das bedeutet z.B., daß es im kompakten Gebirge möglich ist, Ankerbohrlöcher für Schallsondierungen zu benutzen.

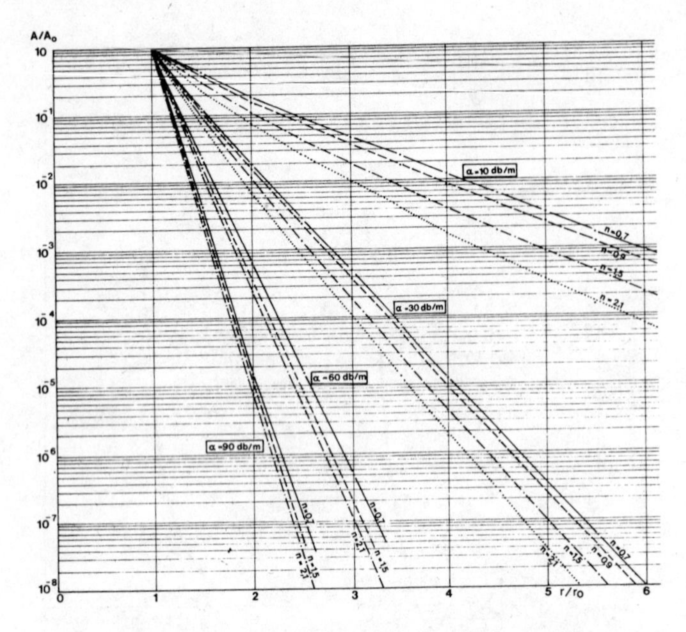

Abb.4: Amplitudenabnahme in Abhängigkeit von der Entfernung mit Schwächungskoeffizienten als Parameter

Reduction in amplitude as a function of distance with the attenuation coefficient as a parameter

Réduction d'amplitude an fonction de la distance avec comme paramètre, le coefficient d'affaiblissement

3.2 Die Versuchsapparatur

Die wesentlichsten Bestandteile der Ultraschallmeßapparatur sind:

a) elektrische Sendeeinrichtung
b) Bohrlochschallsender
c) Bohrlochschallempfänger
d) pneumatisches Ankopplungssystem
e) elektronischer Empfangs- und Registrierteil

Aus Abb. 5 geht das Blockschaltbild der Meßeinrichtung hervor.

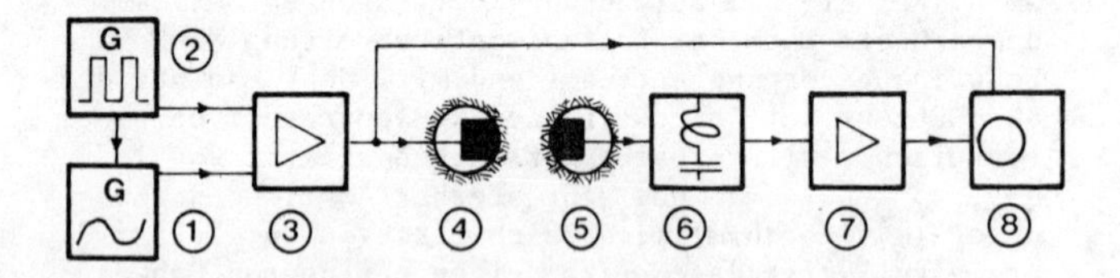

Abb.5: Blockschaltbild der elektronischen Meßeinrichtung

Block diagram of the electronic measuring equipment

Schéma en boites de l'installation de mesures électronique

Hauptbestandteil der elektrischen Sendeeinrichtung ist ein tastbarer Ultraschalleistungsverstärker. Die zu verstärkende Spannung wird einem RC-Generatur entnommen. Die Meßfrequenz beträgt 3o kHz. Zur Tastung des Leistungsverstärkers wird ein Rechteckgenerator benutzt. Die Tastfrequenz beträgt 77 Hz. Am belasteten

1. Piezoelektrische Ringe	5. Dichtungsringe
2. Elektroden	6. Stahlbolzen
3. Alu-Körper	7. Kunststoffgehäuse
4. Stahlkörper	8. Kabel

Abb.6: Bauteile des Ultraschallsenders

Component parts of the ultrasonic transmitter

Éléments constitutifes de l'émetteur Ultrasonique

Ausgang des Leistungsverstärkers steht ein impulsförmi ges Meßsignal zur Verfügung. Als elektromechanischer Wandler im Bohrloch dient ein keramischer piezoelektr scher Schwinger. Es wurde ein Hochleistungsultraschallsender entwickelt, der für Bohrlocheinsätze in ein Kunststoffgehäuse eingebaut wird. Der Wandler ist aus zwei Piezoxide-Ringen zusammengesetzt, die abstrahlseitig von einem zylindrischen Aluminiumkörper und rückseitig von einem zylindrischen Stahlkörper ab geschlossen werden. Sämtliche Teile sind mittels eine Stahlbolzens mechanisch vorgespannt. In Abb.6 sind di einzelnen Bauteile des Wandlers veranschaulicht.

Die vom Sender ausgestrahlten akustischen Signale pas sieren die Meßstrecke und werden vom Bohrlochempfänge wieder in elektrische Signale umgewandelt. Den aktive Teil des Empfängers bildet ein in einer Aluminiumkaps untergebrachter piezoelektrischer Körper. Die Kapsel wiederum ist für Bohrlochmessungen in einem Kunststoffgehäuse untergebracht. Um für Messungen in größe ren Bohrlochteufen eine optimale Spannungsübertragung zu gewährleisten, ist im Kunststoffgehäuse des Empfän gers ein Impedanzwandler untergebracht.

Entscheidend für den Erfolg der seismo-akustischen Me sungen ist die Ankopplung des Schallsenders und des Schallempfängers an die Bohrlochwandung. Die von der Bundesanstalt für Bodenforschung entwickelten Schallsonden sind derart konstruiert, daß der akustisch aktive Teil aus dem Kunststoffgrundkörper ausgefahren, die Bohrlochwand angedrückt und nach Beendigung der M sung wieder in das Kunststoffgehäuse zurückgefahren werden kann. Der Anpreßdruck wird pneumatisch erzeugt Dieses Verfahren der Ankopplung hat gegenüber der Kop lung mit Wasser den Vorteil, daß auch in First- und Kämpferbohrlöchern Messungen möglich sind.

Die von dem Bohrlochempfänger abgegebenen Meßsignale passieren zunächst einen Bandpaßfilter und werden dar verstärkt. Die Verstärkung beträgt 12o db. Die Registrierung der Meßsignale erfolgt mittels eines Oszilloskops und Polaroidkamera. Für Untertagemessung ist die elektronische Meßeinrichtung in einem Meßwage untergebracht.

Die mit der beschriebenen Apparatur durchgeführten Zeit- und Amplitudenmessungen haben eine Genauigkeit von $\pm$ 3 %.

4. Untertagemessungen

4.1 Meßort und geologische Verhältnisse

Ultraschallsondierungen wurden im Stoß eines Stollens mit 6 m Durchmesser durchgeführt. Der Stollen war in einem Gebirge bestehend aus Wechsellagerungen von sandigen Schiefertonen und Grauwacken aufgefahren worden. Für die Messungen standen 3 horizontale Bohrungen von 8 m Teufe zur Verfügung. Der Abstand zwischen Bohrung 1 und 3 betrug 1,54 m, zwischen Bohrung 3 und 2 3,17 m. Bohrung 3 mit einem Durchmesser von 66 mm diente zur Aufnahme des Empfängers; in die Bohrungen 2 und 1, die einen Durchmesser von 86 mm hatten, wurde der Ultraschallsender eingebaut.

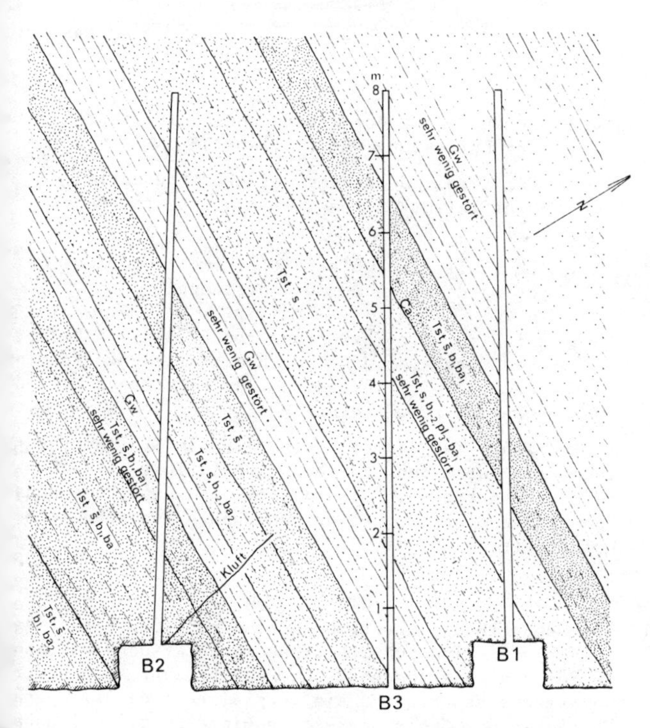

Abb.7: Geologische Verhältnisse in der Ebene der Meßbohrungen

Geological situation in the plane of the boreholes

Conditions géologiques au plan des trou de forage pour les mesures

Die geologischen Verhältnisse am Stollenstoß sind in Abb.7 dargestellt. Die Meßbohrungen durchörtern Schieferton- und Grauwackenbänke. Zwischen den Bohrungen 1 und 3 stehen 3 sandige bzw. stark sandige Schiefertonbänke an. Im stoßnahen Bereich verläuft B 3 ca. 1,5 m in einer wenig geklüfteten Grauwackenschicht (0 - 5 Klüfte/m). Eine geringe Klüftung weist auch die mittlere der angefahrenen Schiefertonbänke zwischen B 1 und B 3 auf. Im Bohrlochtiefsten verläuft B 1 in einer mächtigen Grauwackenbank.

Zwischen den Bohrungen B 2 und B 3 stehen 7 Schieferton- und 2 Grauwackenbänke an. Die Schiefertonbänke sind zum Teil wesentlich dünnbankiger als die zwischen B 1 und B 3. Im stoßnahen Bereich wurden die Schichten von einer Querkluft durchsetzt. Außerdem liegen B 2 und B 3 zumindest im stoßnahen Bereich in einer Faltenachse.

4.2 Meßergebnisse

Die Sondierungen erfolgten in 5o cm Abständen bis zu einer Teufe von 8 m. Die Ergebnisse der Messungen sind in Abb.8 dargestellt. Diese Abbildung zeigt von oben nach unten die Verteilung der Kompressionswellengeschwindigkeiten, der Amplituden und des Schwächungskoeffizienten längs der Bohrlochachse.

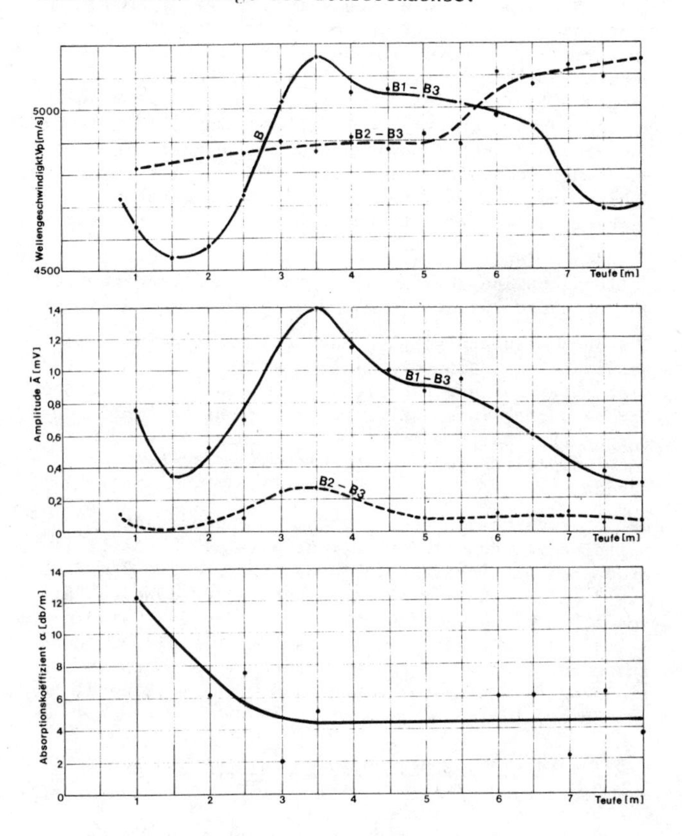

Abb.8: Wellengeschwindigkeit, Amplitude und Schwächungskoeffizient in Abhängigkeit von der Bohrlochteufe

Wave-velocity, amplitude, and attenuation coefficient as a function of borehole depth

La vitesse d'amplitude et le coefficient d'affaiblissement sur la profondeur de trou de forage

Die Amplitudenwerte sind Mittelwerte aus der ersten negativen und der darauffolgenden positiven Amplitude.

Der Schwächungskoeffizient wurde nach folgender Gleichung ermittelt:

$$\alpha = \frac{n \left(\ln \frac{r_i}{r_{i+1}}\right) - \ln \frac{A_{i+1}}{A_i}}{r_{i+1} - r_i} \cdot 8{,}7 \qquad (4)$$

Es sind:

r_i = Abstand zwischen B 3 und B 1

R_{i+1} = Abstand zwischen B 2 und B 3

A_i = Amplitude bei der Entfernung

A_{i+1} = Amplitude bei der Entfernung

Bei der Berechnung der Gl.4 wurde für n der Wert 0.9 zugrunde gelegt.

Das Beispiel der Messungen von B 1 nach B 3 zeigt, daß die gemessenen Geschwindigkeits- und Amplitudenextremwerte in der gleichen Entfernung vom Stoß anzutreffen sind. Bei 3,5o m Teufe liegt ein Geschwindigkeits- u. Amplitudenmaximum. Der Geschwindigkeitsanstieg vom Minimalwert (v_p = 454o m/s) bei 1,5o m Teufe bis zum Geschwindigkeitsmaximum (v_p = 516o m/s) beträgt ca. 14 %. Noch deutlicher tritt der entsprechende Amplitudensprung hervor: er beträgt 3oo %. Die von 1,5o m Teufe zum Stoß hin größer werdenden Wellengeschwindigkeiten und Amplituden sind durch Betonierungen im Bereich des Bohrlochmundloches verursacht worden. Sie haben geomechanisch keinerlei Bedeutung.

Von 3,5 m Teufe bis zu 7,8 m Teufe fallen sowohl die Wellengeschwindigkeits- als auch die Amplitudenwerte ab, um danach wieder etwas anzusteigen.

Bei den Messungen von B 2 nach B 3 konnte ein Geschwindigkeitssprung von 4 % zwischen 5,5o und 6,o m beobachtet werden. Parallel dazu wurde ein Amplitudensprung nachgewiesen. Ein zweiter, größerer Amplitudensprung trat bei 3,3 m Teufe auf. Ein paralleler Geschwindigkeitssprung konnte hier nicht beobachtet werden.

Der aus den Messungen B 1 nach B 3 und B 2 nach B 3 ermittelte Schwächungskoeffizient α (s.Abb.8) fällt im stoßnahen Bereich stark ab und zeigt von ca. 3 m Teufe bis 8 m Teufe kaum veränderte Werte. Der α-Wertabfall von 1,5 m bis 3,o m Teufe fällt mit dem Geschwindigkeitssprung und dem Amplitudensprung bei dieser Teufe zusammen. Eine ähnliche Teufenabhängigkeit des Absorptionskoeffizienten wurde auch von OELSNER (9) und MÜLLER et al. (6) beobachtet (s.Abb.9)

4.3 Interpretation der Meßwerte in bautechnischer Hinsicht

Wichtigstes Ergebnis der In-situ-Messungen mit der Bohrlochsonde ist das spezifisch seismo-akustische Verhalten des Gebirges in 2 bis 3,5 m Entfernung vom Stollenstoß. Da in diesem und dem benachbarten Teufenbereich keine auffallenden Veränderungen des Gebirges bezüglich Lithologie, Klüftung und Schichtung vorliegen, dürfte der Geschwindigkeits- bzw. Amplitudensprung und der Abfall der Dämpfungswerte geomechanisch bedingt sein und ein deutlicher Hinweis dafür sein, daß hier die Grenze zwischen dem entspannten Teil des Stollenstoßes und dem tragenden Gebirgsgewölbe ist. Für diesen Befund sprechen insbesondere die Ergebnisse der Amplitudenmessungen. Die stoßnahen hohen Dämpfungswerte charakterisieren die Zone der Gebirgsauflockerung. Für den untersuchten Stollen mit ca. 6 m Durchmesser reicht die Auflockerung infolge von Spannungsumlagerungen bis in eine Teufe von ca. 2,5 m. Der Auflockerungsbereich infolge von Schießarbeit konnte wegen der Betonierungen am Bohrlochmund nicht nachgewiesen werden. Die Stützlinie des Gewölbes verläuft in einer Teufe von ca. 3,5 m. Danach beträgt das Verhältnis von Stollendurchmesser D zur Stützlinienteufe S:

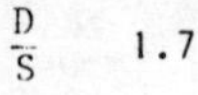

$\frac{D}{S}$ 1.7

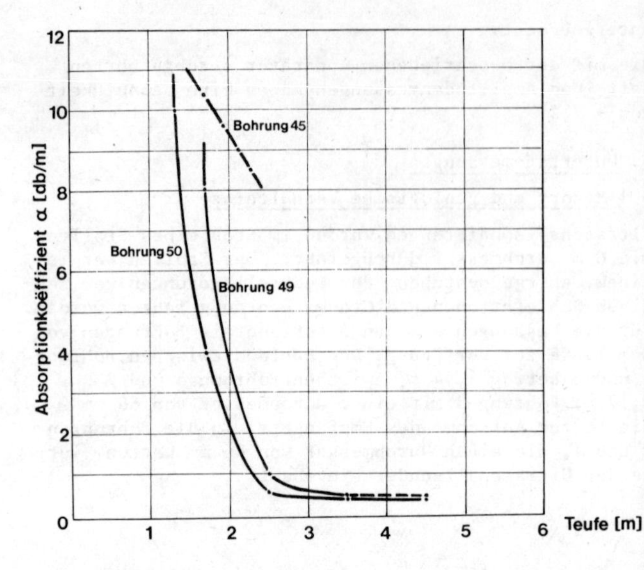

Abb.9: Abhängigkeit des Absorptionskoeffizienten von der Entfernung vom Stollenstoß

Functional dependence of the attenuation coefficient on the distance from the tunnel wall

Le coefficient d'affaiblissement en fonction de la distance du rein de tunnel

Im Hinblick auf die Verwendung von Felsankern bedeutet dieses Ergebnis, daß die Ankerkräfte etwa in eine Teufe von 3,5 - 5 m in das Gebirge abgetragen werden müßten. Daraus resultieren Ankerlängen von 4 - 5 m.

Ab 5 m Teufe ist der Gebirgsbereich im Stollenstoß kaum noch durch den Stollenbau beeinflußt. Danach noch erkennbare Geschwindigkeits- und Amplitudenabnahmen sind geologisch bedingt und haben geomechanisch keinerleit Bedeutung.

5. Ausblick

Ultraschallbohrlochmessungen sind nach den bisherigen Erfahrungen eine äußerst wirksame Untersuchungsmethode für den Untertagebau. Zur Zeit erlaubt kein anderes Untersuchungsverfahren ein vergleichbar detailliertes Sondieren des Gebirgsbereiches hinter der Stollenoberfläche. Gegenüber Verformungsmessungen haben Schallmessungen den Vorteil, daß sie direkt Rückschlüsse auf die Tangentialspannungsverteilung am Stollenrand erlauben. Der ungewisse Umweg, aus Verformungen meist mit Hilfe im Labor gemessener Verformungsmoduln Spannungen zu ermitteln, kann hier vermieden werden.

In wirtschaftlicher Hinsicht ist das Ultraschallbohrlochverfahren durchaus konkurrenzfähig. Die Sondierung eines 1o m tiefen Bereiches mit Messungen im Abstand von 5o cm ist in 1 1/2 Stunden zu bewältigen. Bei Verwendung von Extensometern z.B. liegen brauchbare Ergebnisse erst nach Tagen vor. Insbesondere bieten sich bei vorgesehener First- und Stoßankerung Ankerbohrlöcher für die Ultraschallsondierung an.

Die Möglichkeit der Steigerung der seismo-akustischen Sendeleistung bietet weiterhin die Chance, die Reichweite der Sonde zu erhöhen, so daß noch größere Gebirgsbereiche sondiert werden können.

Literatur

(1) BIOT, M.A.: Theory of propagation of elastic waves in a fluid saturated porous solid, Part 1 und Part 2. J.Acoust.Soc.Amer.,28(1965), S. 168 - 191

(2) BRÜCKL,E. u. FÜRLINGER,W.: Ein Vergleich von geologischen Gefügeaufnahmen mit seismischen Messungen. Z.Geophysik, 39(1973) S.291 - 3o2

(3) BUCHHEIM,W.: Zum Problem der Drucksondierung in Gesteinen auf akustischer Basis. Freib.Forschungshefte C 7(1953) S. 41 - 47

(4) ELION,H.A.: Recent advances in stress measurement by ultrasonics. Proc. 3.Intern.Congr. Acoust.1959 Stuttgart,Elsevier Publishing Company 196o, Amsterdam

(5) GIESEL,W.: Geschwindigkeiten elastischer Wellen und Wärmeleitfähigkeit im Steinsalz. Z.Geophysik 33(1967), S. 9 - 33

(6) MÜLLER,G., MÜLLER,L. u. H.P.GÖTZ: Messung der Spannungs- u.Materialumlagerungen in geklüftetem Fels. Proc. 2.Congr.Intern.Soc.Rock Mech. Beograd 197o, Vol.III

(7) NICHOLLS,H.R., SCHMECHEL,F.W. u.R.D.MUNSON: Strength properties of the Phillipson, Storke, and Ceresco Ridge levels as determined by seismic absorption techniques. U.S.Department of the Intercor Bureau of Mines,November 197o

(8) OBERT,L.: Measurement of pressures on rock pillars in underground mines. Part I and II. Rep. of Invest., U.S.Department of the Interior Bureau of Mines 1939,Nr.3444 and 3521

(9) OELSNER,CH.: Hammerschlagseismische Untersuchungen im Hinblick auf zeitliche Veränderung der Standfestigkeit von Magazinbauen. Freib. Forschungshefte C 225, 1967

(1o) RISNITSCHENKO,J. und SILAJEWA,U.: Die Fortpflanzungsgeschwindigkeit der elastischen Wellen in Gesteinsproben bei Druckbeanspruchung (russ.). Iswestia Akademii Nauk SSSR, Geophys.Serie 3 (1955), S. 93 - 97

(11) RÖSLER,R.: Experimentelle Untersuchungen zur Abhängigkeit der Schallgeschwindigkeit von der Druckbeanspruchung bei Gesteinen. Freib. Forschungshefte C 12, 1954

(12) SAVICH,A.J., V.J.KOPTEV u. E.A.GRIGORIANTS: Study of natural stress distribution in rock massifs with the help of seismic-acoustic methods. Proc. 2.Congr.Internat.Soc.Rock Mech., Beograd 197o, Vol. I

(13) UHLMANN, M.: Über die Erkundung der Spannungsverhältnisse in Stützpfeilern des Kali-Steinsalzbergbaus auf akustischer Basis. Freib. Forschungshefte C 36, 1957

(14) WYLLIE,M.R., GREGORY,A.R. u. L.W.GARDNER: Elastic wave velocities in heterogenous and porous media. Geophysics 21(1956), S. 41 - 7o

IN SITU ULTRASONIC INVESTIGATION OF FAILURE OF LIMESTONE

ÉTUDE DE PHÉNOMÈNE DE RUPTURE DES CALCAIRES AU GISEMENT NATUREL PAR LE PROCÉDÉ ULTRASONORE

IN SITU UNTERSUCHUNGEN DES BRUCHVERLAUFES VON KALKSTEIN DURCH ULTRASCHALLVERFAHREN

A.I. SAVICH Candidate of Phys.-Math. Sciences, Chief Expert
V.I. KOPTEV Candidate of Techn. Sciences, Chief Expert
A.M. ZAMAKHAIEV Senior Engineer
Hydroproject Institute, Moscow, USSR

SUMMARY

Study of large rock masses failure nature under the action of various external loads plays an important part in the solution of many problems of rock mechanics, mining, seismology ets. Investigation of failure process in the interior zones of rock masses,inaccessible for direct measuring of deformation, is of particular interest. Topics reviewed include procedures and results of ultrasonic method survey which has been used for investigation the development of deformation and failure process in rock mass sections under load plates. Described and discussed herein are the laws of changes of elastic wave characteristics in deformable media and seismic criteria indicating the beginning of failure process are established as well.

RÉSUMÉ

L'étude du phénomène de rupture aux grands massifs rocheux sous l'effet de différentes sollicitations extériures est de grande importance pour la résolution de nombreux problèmes existant dans la mécanique des roches, dans les travaux de mines, dans la séismologie, etc.
Les études du mécanisme de rupture dans les points intérieurs du massif, inaccessibles aux mésures directes des déformations, présentent un intérêt tout particulier. Le rapport décrit la méthode et les résultats d'utilisation du procédé ultra-sonore pour l'étude de la dynamique de déformation et de la rupture des zones rocheuses locales sous l'effet des vérins. On examine et traite les régularités principales de la modification des caractéristiques des ondes élastiques dans le milieu de déformation et on définit aussi les critères séismiques caractérisant le début de la rupture.

ZUSAMMENEASSUNG

Die Untersuchung des Bruchverlaufs eines grossen Felsverbandes unter der Einwirkung von Aussenbelastungen spielt bei der Lösung der Probleme in Bodenmechanik, Bergbauwesen, Seismologie u.s.w. eine wichtige Rolle. Besonderes Interesse stellt dabei die Untersuechung des Bruchverlaufs in den Punkten innerhalb des Felsverbandes, die für unmittelbare Messungen von Verformungs - erscheinungen unzugänglich sind. Im Vortrag werden die Methodik und Ergebnisse bei der Anwendung des Ultraschallverfahrens für die Untersuchung der Dynamik der Verformung und des Bruchs der Felsabschnitte unter Druckplatten bechrieben. Es werden die Hauptgeschwindigkeiten bei der Änderung der Kennwerte von elastischen Wellen in Deformationsmedien dargelegt, sowie seismische Kriterien, die vom Anfang des Bruchverlaufs zeugen, festgestellt.

INTRODUCTION

Study of rock masses failure process under external loads plays an important part in the solution of many problems of rock mechanics, engineering geology, mining and seismology (Müller 1971, Maslov 1968, Sadovsky 1969). The experimental investigations of rock masses interior zones, inaccessible for measuring the deformation with the help of available instruments, are of particular interest. It is of great importance to locate the most "dangerous" rock mass zones, to study the development of deformations with time, to define the criteria of the beginning of failure. The solution of the problems is neccessary for predicting the earthquakes and developing the methods of long-term and current control of the stability of the rock foundations of large structures.

The geoacoustic method is of great promise for investigation of deformation processes in internal zones of rock mass (Riznichenko 1967, Savich 1969, 1970). Nevertheless, until recently the method has been mainly used for in-situ studies of the rock deformation process under the action of loads much less the breaking ones and to some extent - for rock samples failure tests (Riznichenko 1967).

Practically, there are no data on elastic wave parameters variations in case failure of rock masses takes place; the above reason does not allow for development of the geoacoustic method of rock mass failure investigation.

For this reason the "Hydroproject" Institute performed in 1970-1973 ultrasonic investigations at the Inguri arch dam site with the aim:

- to study the elastic wave parameters (velocities, damping) changing in natural rock masses under the loads close and equal to the breaking ones;
- to study particular features of the deformation development with space and time under large loads;
- to determine the seismic criteria of the beginning of the failure process;
- to search the possible methods of geoacoustic prediction and location of the most "dangerous" zones of possible failure in rock masses.

This paper presents the main results of the investigations effected.

1. INVESTIGATION PROCEDURES.

To solve the tasks put forward a complex of ultrasonic measurements of elastic wave parameters changes under the load plates, loaded progressively up to rock failure, was used.*

Ultrasonic sondes, each with seven piezoelectric detectors (Savich, 1969) spaced on 0.1-0.2 m centers (Fig. 1) were fixed in two bore holes, bored up to one meter in depth, at points diametrically opposite, close to the load plate edges.

The rock was loaded with the help of circular rigid load plates of 0.06-0.15 m^2 area (0.28-0.45 m in dia). The load plates were installed in special chambers arranged in the rock mass at various depths from the rock surface. The rock mass was subjected to increments of loads by 0.98-3.9 MPa. Each increment of load was maintained for several days up to stabilization of the deformation processes with time. The process was controlled by observing the bench marks vertical movement and by the shape of curves $\epsilon = f(t)$ (deformation versus time). The moment of change of damped deformations into the sustained ones as well as the moments of the rock upheaval around the load plates and of the plastic deformations occurence indicating the beginning of the failure process were determined by the above curves (Ukhov, 1972). On the basis of the above said data, the long-time ultimate strength σ_{cst} of the rock zone under investigation was evaluated and compared with the ultrasonic measurements data. Seven tests were performed; maximum load, applied to the load plate, was 49.0 MPa. Intensively and medium jointed limestones of Lower Cretaceous age (Cr_1), with modulus of deformation varying from 980 to 15700 MPa were investigated.

Ultrasonic measurements (profiling along holes and sounding between holes) were made at certain time intervals for recording elastic waves propagating in the vertical and horizontal directions under the load plate for each load increment. The ultrasonic equipment employed (ИПА-59 and P-5-5 ultrasonic impulse seismoscopes) and adopted observation procedure allowed for defining relative changes of velocities with error no more than ± 0.5 %. The predominant frequentcy of longitudinal waves recorded was f =30-50 kHz.

2. TEST RESULTS

Comprehensive data of the changes of kinematic and dynamic elastic wave parameters in the deformed zone under each load plate was obtained due to detailed recording of all waveforms at every fixed position "transmitter-receiver" system, at various loads and at different moments of time. The most steady correlations were obtained for the velocities of longitudinal elastic waves (v_p) and that was the reason for a more detailed analysis of the change of this particular parameter. This investigation was based on examination of the wave velocity (v_p) and pressure (p) relation curves at each observation interval (Fig.1), determining the general pattern of velocity (v_p) changes within the entire deformed rock mass section, correlating these changes with the shape of the deformation curves $\epsilon = f(p)$. On the basis of the totality of data obtained from a group of load plates the following general regularities of wave velocity (v_p) change in a rock mass under great and breaking loads were found:

1) elastic wave velocities increase smoothly as loads increase up to breaking ones. Under loads close to the breaking ones abrupt wave velocity changes take place which, as a rule, are followed by a general sharp decrease of wave velocity value (Fig.1);

2) particular features are revealed in $v_p = f(p)$ curves for rocks of different degrees of preservation. Intensively jointed rock with low values of initial velocities v_{p_0}* feature sharp velocity increase at

* geotechnic testes were headed by Yu.A. Fishman and S.B.Ukhov (S.B.Ukhov, 1972).

* Vp_0 is velocity at p =0.

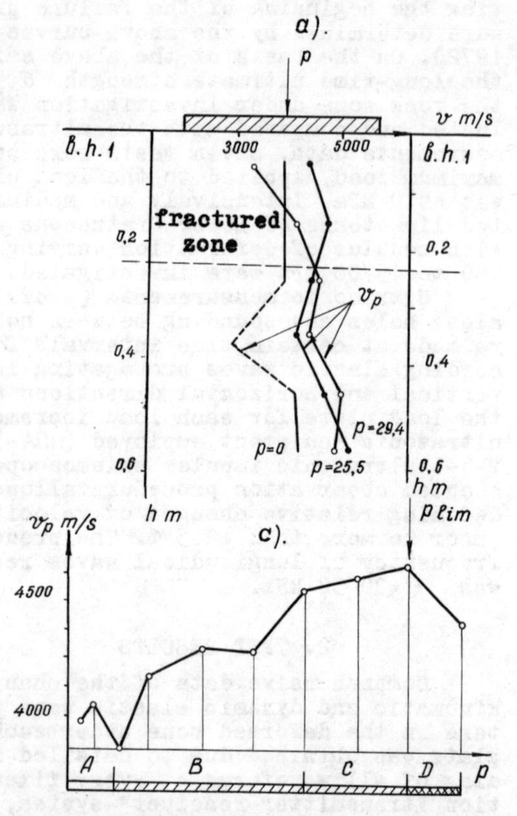

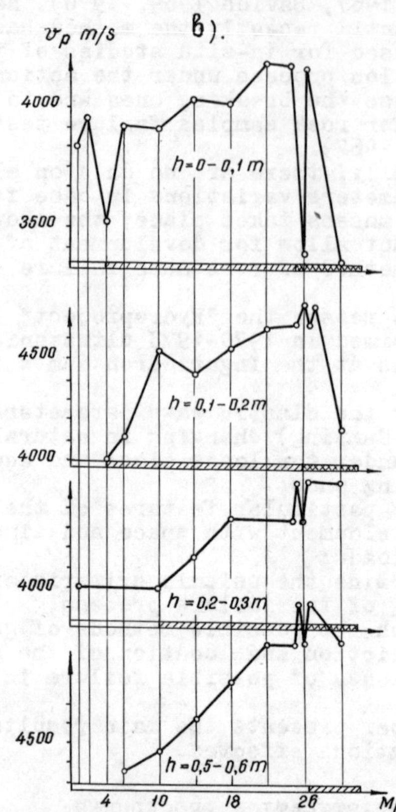

Fig.1. Change of longitudinal wave velocities v_p in rock mass under the load plate a) test arrangement and $v_p=f(h)$ curves at various pressures; b) $v_p=f(p)$ curves at bore-hole I for various depth intervals (h); c) $v_p=f(p)$ summary curve for bore-hole I; A,B,C,D - failure stages after Pacher.

Fig.1. Variation de vitesses des ondes longitudinales V_P au massif des roches sous l'effet du verin lors du chargement a) schéma de l'essai et les diagrammes $V_P=f(h)$ avec pressions différentes; b) courbes $V_P=f(P)$ suivant le trou I pour les profondeurs différentes h ; c) courbe récapitulative $V_P=f(P)$ suivant le trou I; A,B,C,D - étapes de rupture d'après Pakhere.

Bild.1. Geschwindigkeitsänderung von Longitudinalwellen im Felsverband unter der Druckplatte bei der Auflast a) Versuchsanordnung und Abhängigkeiten $V_P=f(h)$ bei verschiedenen Drücken; b) Kurven $V_P=f(P)$ für das Bohrloch I für verschiedene Intervalle von Tiefen h ; c) Allgemeine Kurve $V_P=f(P)$ für das Bohrloch I; A,B,C,D - Stadien des Bruches nach Pacher.

low pressures and gradual reducing of (v_p) at moderate pressure (p) values (Fig.2a). In medium and slightly jointed rocks the $v_p=f(p)$ curve shape is more complicated. The following principal cases of changes of the v_p value are considered below:

a) continuous velocity increase at variable values of gradient dv_p/dp (curve 2, Fig.2b);

b) v_p increases up to some ultimate value $v_{p\,lim}$ with further sharp reducing of velocity (Curve 3, Fig.2b);

c) alternation of intervals of velocity increase and decrease at continuous increase of pressure (Fig.2b). This type of curves is usually observed while loading the rock mass containing great local heterogeneities.

In relatively strong rocks, an interval characterized by the velocity reducing corresponds to the interval of sharp reducing of intensity of vibration recorded. As a rule, the phenomenon takes place in weak rock varieties too, nevertheless, the decrease of intensity is usually much slower;

3) a pronounced variability in the pattern of curves $v_p=f(p)$ are observed in the space under the load plate. As in case of moderate pressure not reaching the ultimate values (Savich, Koptev, 1970) there are zones in rock mass under load plates which significantly differ in their ability to withstand additional loads depending on various block structures and jointing degree ofrocks.

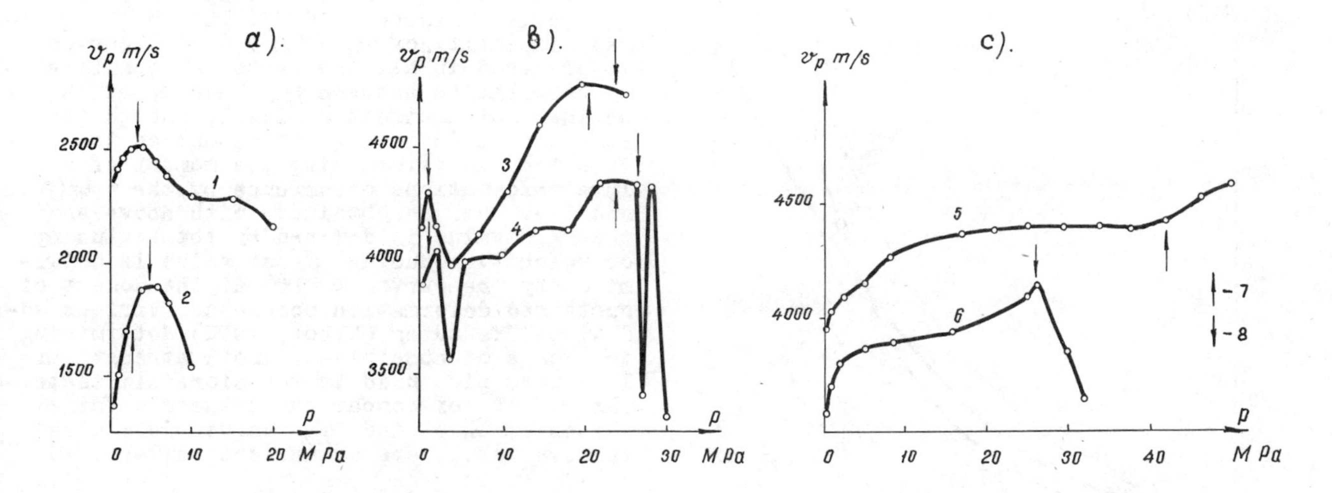

Fig.2. Various types of $v_p = f(p)$ curves for various cases of failure of rock test blocks a) failure of weak, intensively jointed rocks $v_p < 2000$ m/s ($< 0.4\, v_{p\,max}$); b,c) failure of medium jointed rocks ($v_p > 3500$ m/s or $v_p > 0.5\, v_{p\,max}$); b - failure of relatively homogeneous, uniformly jointed rock blocks; c - failure of rock blocks with large local heterogeneities; 1. - Test N 4, h = 0.2-0.3 m; 2. Test N 3, h = 0.55-0.65 m; 3. Test N 7, h=0-0.6 m; 4. Test N 6, h = 0.6-0.7 m; 5. Test N 4, h = 0.3-0.4 m; 6. Test N 1, h = 0-0.1 m. 7.8 - points of failure beginning obtained from static (7) and ultrasonic (8) measurements.

Fig.2. Types différents des diagrammes $v_p = f(P)$ lors de la rupture des massifs de la roche a) rupture des roches faibles, fortement fissurées $v_p < 2000$ m/s ($< 0,4\ v_{p\ max}$); b,c) rupture des roches de fissuration moyenne ($v_p > 3500$ m/s ou $v_p > 0.5\ v_{p\,max}$); b - rupture des blocs relativement homogènes et réguliérement fissurés; c - rupture des blocs avec de grandes hétérogénéités locales; 1. - essai N 4 h = 0.2 à 0.3 m; 2. - essai N 3 h = 0.55 à 0.65 m; 3. - essai N 7 h = 0 à 0.6 m; 4. - essai N 6 h = 0.6 à 0.7 m; 5. - essai N 4 h = 0.3 à 0.4 m; 6. - essai N 1 h = 0 à 0.1 m; 7,8 - point du début de rupture d'après les données de mésures statistiques (7) et ultra-sonores (8).

Bild 2. Verschiedene Abhängigkeiten $v_p = f(P)$ beim Bruch der zu untersuchenden Gesteinspfeiler a) Bruch von lockeren, stark klüftigen Gesteinen, $v_p < 2000$ m/s ($< 0.4\ v_{p\,max}$); b,c) Bruch von Gesteinen miltleren Klüftigkeit ($v_p > 3500$ m/s bzw, $v_p > 0.5\ v_{p\ max}$); b) Bruch von relativ homogenen Blöcken mit einer regelmässigen Klüftigkeit; c) Bruch von Blöcken mit lokaler grosser Inhomogenität . 1.-Versuch Nr.4 h = 0.2-0.3 m; 2.-Versuch Nr.2 h = 0.55-0.65 m; 3.-Versuch Nr.7 h = 0-0.6 m; 4.- Versuch Nr.6 h = 0.6-0.7 m; 5.- VersuchNr.4 h = 0.3-0.4 m; 6.- Versuch Nr.1 h = 0-0.1 m; 7,8 - Punkt des Bruchanfangs nach Angaben von statistischen (7) und Ultraschallmessungen (8).

It is interesting to note that the drop-down of curves $v_p = f(p)$ at great "p" values in some cases is observed only after prolonged action of load (3-4 days), although the reducing of velocity v_p is more often observed just after some ultimate value of $P = P_{lim}$ is reached.

3. DISCUSSION OF RESULTS

The general pattern of velocity v_p change with variation of pressure in some sections of rock mass under the load plates is similar to a great extent to the pattern of well-known curves $v_p = f(P)$ obtained from breaking the rock samples in laboratory tests (Riznichenko, 1967). To determine more safely the reasons of one or another velocity variations in rocks under the load plates the experimental curves $v_p = f(p)$ were compared with the correspondent stress-strain curves $\epsilon = f(P)$. The results of the comparison showed that intervals of velocity change with pressure in all cases practically comply with four stages of deformation by Pacher (1970), (see Fig.1b,c).

I. Zone of initial deformations (section A) features either approximately constant v_p or sharp variations of the v_p value of small amplitude, resulting from microdestructions of weak material filling the joints.

II. Zone of elastic deformations (section B) which features smooth increase of velocity v_p that corresponds to compression of rock as of a jointed aggregate.

III. In the transition zone (section C)

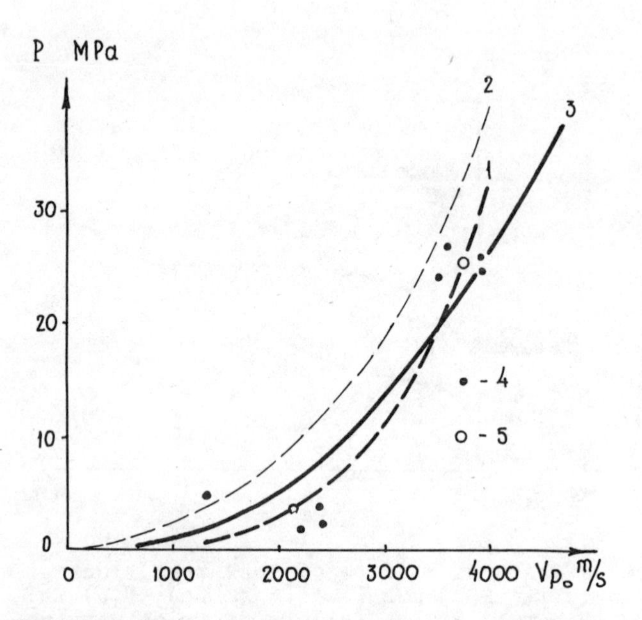

Fig.3. Relation between initial longitudinal wave velocity v_{p_o} in rock mass, breaking stress P_{lim} and compressive strength σ_c st values
1) experimental v_{p_o} and P_{lim} relation curve; 2-3) v_{p_o} and σ_c relation curves, computed by the formula (2) at: 2- $\sigma_{c\,max}$ = 19,6 MPa; $v_{p\,max}$ = 6800 m/s; 3- $\sigma_{c\,max}$ = 13,7 MPa; $v_{p\,max}$ = 6900 m/s; 4) results of measurements; 5) mean values.

Fig.3. Rapport entre les valeures de vitesse des ondes longitudinales au massif v_{p_o} et les valeurs des tensions de rupture P_{lim} et la valeur de résistance à la compression σ_cst
1) diagramme (expérimentale) de liaison entre v_{p_o} et P_{lim} ; 2 à 3) diagrammes de liaison des valeurs v_{p_o} et σ_c calculées d'après la formule (2) où: 2- $\sigma_{c\,max}$ = 19,6 MPa; $v_{p\,max}$ = 6800 m/s; 3- $\sigma_{c\,max}$ = 13,7 MPa; $v_{p\,max}$ = 6900 m/s; 4) résultats des mesures unitaires; 5) valeurs moyennes.

Bild.3.Verhältnis zwischen den Geschwindigkeiten "v_{p_o}" von Longitudinalwellen im Felsverband und Bruchspannungen" P_{lim} " sowie der zeitlichen Druckfestigkeit "σ_c St"
1) Experimenteller Verlauf der Abhängigkeit "v_{p_o}" von "P_{lim}"; 2-3) Abhängigkeiten "v_o" von "σ_c" nach der Formel (2) bei: 2- $\sigma_{c\,max}$ = 19,6 MPa; $v_{p\,max}$ = 6800 m/s; 3- $\sigma_{c\,max}$ = 13,7 MPa; $v_{p\,max}$ = 6900 m/s; 4) Ergebnisse von einzelnen Messungen; 5) Mittelwerte.

visco-elactic deformations distinctly show up and micro-fracturing is occuring resulting in deceleration or stopping of velocity v_p increase under pressure.

IV.Zone of velocity drop-down (section D, Fig.1,2) corresponds to the interval of sustained creep. This is indicative of appearing and developing substantial irreversible changes in the structure of the tested rock block resulting in its failure (stage IV by Pacher, 1970). Though the general similarity of $v_p=f(p)$ and $\epsilon=f(p)$ curves is observed in all the tests the quantitative correlation between P_{lim} and σ_c st is sometimes not manifested clearly enough (Fig. 2). It depends to a great extent on the difficulties in determining the moment of failure deformations occurrence by the $\epsilon=f(p)$ and $\epsilon=f(t)$ curves obtained. With above said the P_{lim} value is defined by the beginning of velocity reducing; σ_c st value is determined by the curves $\epsilon=f(t)$ at the moment of sustained deformation occurence. Various additional features (Ukhov, 1972) determining the range of possible ultimate strength values were also used in the aforesaid tests. The results of comparison between obtained values of σ_c st and P_{lim} values determined in five tests, are summarized in Table 1.

Table 1.
Comparison of σ_c st and P_{lim} values

Sl nos	No of test	Characteristics of rock of the test site: D MPa	v_p km/s	Variation limits: σ_c st MPa	P_{lim} MPa
1	1	3.4×10^3	3.6-3.8	22-23	22-23
2	3	0.9×10^3	1.3-2.2	2-3	4-6
3	4	2.8×10^3	3.6-3.9	19-24	21-24 (1)
4	6	1.0×10^3	2.2-2.4	3-5	2 (2)
5	7	15.4×10^3	3.9-4.2	42-78	>50

Notes:(1) P_{lim} value is determined by the nature of v_p variation just under the load plate (h = 0-0.2 m). At depths more than 0.5 m considerable values of v_p (>3600 m/s) are typical of and velocity stall is stated at p = 25.5-26.5 MPa (curve 2, Fig. 2b); (2) at P_{max}= 49.8 MPa obtained at tests no stall of $v_p=f(p)$ curve was observed.

As one can see from the data in Table 1 the quantitative correspondence between σ_c st and P_{lim} values is stated. The ultimate P values determined at the sections close to the load plate (at 0.5 m depth), at which the velocity reducing begins (P_{lim}), coincide apparently with the σ_c st long-term ultimate strength values and adequately well fix the moment of beginning of failure. Hence, sharp drop-down of velocity and anomalous elastic waves damping are reliable means in indicating the beginning of rock mass failure.

To aid in predicting the possible ways of σ_c st limit values determination, the nature of dependence of P_{lim} on initial v_o values was analized. Comparison of experimental P_{lim} and v_{p_o} values showed that with increase of initial velocities v_p the ultimate breaking stresses P_{lim} increase as a rule (Fig.3). For the rocks under consideration the dependence between v_{p_o} and P_{lim} in the first approximation may be described by the equation:

$$\lg P_{lim} = -10{,}6 + 3{,}3 \lg v_o \qquad (1)$$

where v_{p_o} is measured in m/s, and P_{lim} - in MPa.

The obtained experimental relation (1)

was compared with well-known generalized designed relation curve of $\mathcal{V}$ and σ_c parameters, determined in laboratory tests (Shaumian, 1972):

$$\left(\frac{\sigma_c}{\sigma_{c\,max}}\right) = f\left(\frac{\mathcal{V}_p}{\mathcal{V}_{p\,max}}\right) \qquad (2)$$

The best agreement of curves (Fig.3) is observed at $\mathcal{V}_{p\,max}$ = 6900 m/s and σ_c = 1370 MPa which are determined as mean-maximum values obtained from over 100 samples taken in the sites of load plate tests. Thus, in the observed range of $\mathcal{V}_p$ and P_{lim} variations, P_{lim} values determined by the relation (1) correspond sufficiently to values of compression strength σ_c defined by the "generalized" curve (2).

The agreement between the experimental data and the design curve proves that the P_{lim} value and consequently the σ_c st value may be estimated from the initial $\mathcal{V}_{p_o}$, $\mathcal{V}_{p\,max}$ and $\sigma_{c\,max}$ values. Accuracy of such calculations(with small $\mathcal{V}_{p_o}$ and P_{lim} values especially) is sufficient apparently only for the approximate evaluation of rock strength characteristics. Nevertheless in many cases these data are proved to be of great interest from the point of view of practice, because they enable the quantatative characteristics of strength of the rock mass tested "in-situ".

The analysis of relation between $\mathcal{V}_o$ and P_{lim} based on the experimentally obtained curves $\mathcal{V}_p = f(P)$ showed, that failure at ultimate values of pressure for the given $\mathcal{V}_{po\,lim}$ value did not take place in all points of rock mass where $\mathcal{V} < \mathcal{V}_{lim}$(3). As a rule, failure occurs only in the points where inequality (3) comes into effect parallel with a considerable velocity increase with pressure. For instance the failure of rocks with $\mathcal{V}_{po} \approx$ 3600-3900 m/s is observed only in case $P \geqslant$ 25.5 MPa and the velocity increment is about 18-20%, i.e. great deformation of rock mass has taken place. In rocks with $\mathcal{V}_{p_o}$ = 2000 m/s the velocity increment more than 30-35% is needed for rock failure. On account of heterogeneity and complicated nature of stress distribution the process of deformation in actual rock mass runs unevenly. Various degree of $\mathcal{V}_p$ change and local nature of failure affirm the above statement. Proceeding from the above said seismic criteria of the beginning the process of failure of some sections of the limestone mass under investigation are as follows:

1) at the given P values the failure is possible in the rock mass zones where initial values of velocity $\mathcal{V}_{p_o}$ are less than a certain ultimate value determined from the curve in Fig.3 at the given value P_{lim} ;

2) if the conditions described in item 1 come into effect, failure takes place only in case a certain ultimate value of $\mathcal{V}_p$ change with pressure is attained.

The aforesaid criteria are supposed to be used in the geoacoustic methods of current control of the rock dams foundation behavior.

REFERENCES

1. MASLOV N.N. Soil Mechanics and Engineering Geology Fundamentals. "Vysshaya Shkola", Moscow, 1968.
2. MÜLLER L. Engineering Geology. Rock Mass Mechanics."Mir", Moscow, 1971.
3. PACHER F. General Report of Theme 2 "Deformability of Rock Massives". Proc. of the II nd Cong. of the Int.Soc. for R. Mech., Beograd, 1970.
4. RIZNICHENKO U.V. Rock Pressure Investigation by Geophysical Methods."Nauka", Moscow, 1967.
5. SADOVSKY M.A., NERSESOV I.L. Earthquake Prediction, Problem in Question. "Vestnik Akademii Nauk USSR", N 4, 1969, Moscow.
6. SAVICH A.I., KOPTEV V.I., NIKITIN V.N., YASHCHENKO Z.G. Seismic-Acoustic Methods of Investigation of Rock Masses. "Nedra", Moscow, 1969.
7. SAVICH A.I., KOPTEV V.I., GRIGORIANTS E.A. Study of Natural Stress Distribution in Rock Massives with the Help of Seismic-Acoustic Methods. Proc. of the II nd Cong. of the Int.Soc. for R.Mech.,Beograd, 1970.
8. SHAUMIAN L.V. Physico-Mechanical Properties of Rock Masses. "Nauka", Moscow, 1972.
9. TOMASHEVSKAYA I.S., HAMIDULLIN Ya.N. Presades of Rock Samples Failure. "Izvestia Acad.Nauk "USSR", "Physics of Earth" Series, N 5, 1972.
10. UKHOV S.B., KUBETSKY V.L., FISHMAN Yu.A., LAPIN L.V. Field Investigations of Rock Foundations Bearing Capacity. "Discrete Medii in Hydraulic Engineering" - Transactions of the Coordination Conference on Hydraulic Engineering, v.77, 1972.
11. VINOGRADOV S.D., MIACHKIN V.I. Seismic Refraction Methods of Rocks Stressed State and Failure Investigation. "Geoacoustics", "Nauka", Moscow, 1966.

ELASTISCHE EIGENSCHAFTEN VON FELSGESTEINEN UNTER MINUSTEMPERATUREN

ELASTIC PROPERTIES OF ROCKS AT SUB-ZERO TEMPERATURES

PROPRIÉTÉS ÉLASTIQUES DES ROCHES AUX TEMPÉRATURES AU-DESSOUS DE ZERO

O. K. WORONKOW Kand. der geol.-minerl. Wissenschaften

G. I. NOZDRIN Ingenieur

W. I. MAROW Ingenieur

B.E. Wedenejew--Allunionsforschungsinstitut für Hydrotechnik

Leningrad, USSR

ZUSAMMENFASSUNG

Es sind die Geschwindigkeiten von longitudinalen (C_p) und transversalen (C_s) elastischen Wellen, die Poissonzahl ν_d , die dynamischen Elastizitäts- E_d und Schermoduln G_d als Funktionen der Temperatur (von +20°C bis -30°C) in verschiedenen trockenen, feuchten und wassergesättigten Felsgesteinen untersucht worden. Die Empfehlungen zur Bewertung von C_p , C_s , E_d , G_d und ν_d werden bei Temperatur- und Feuchtigkeitsvariationen gegeben.

SUMMARY

The velocity of longitudinal (C_p) and transverse (C_s) elastic waves, Poisson's ratio ν_d , the dynamic modulus of elasticity E_d and that of shear G_d , were studied as functions of temperature (from +20° to -30°) in dry, humid and water saturated rocks. Methods for evaluation of C_p , C_s , ν_d , E_d , and G_d varying with temperature and humidity are recommended.

RESUME

La vitesse des vagues élastiques longitudinales C_p et transversales C_s , le coefficient de Poisson ν_d , les modules dynamiques d'élasticité E_d et de cisaillement G_d , sont étudiés comme fonction de la température (de +20°C à -30°C) dans les roches sèches, humides et saturées d'eau. On propose des méthodes pour évaluer la variation de C_p , C_s , ν_d et G_d avec la température et l'humidité.

Im Zusammenhang mit der Anwendung der seismischen und akustischen Methoden zur Bestimmung der Klüftigkeit und baulichen Eigenschaften von Gesteinen in Felsmassiven in den Gebieten des hohen Nordens und ewigen Frostbodens ist es wichtig, die Temperatur - und Feuchtigkeitseinflüsse auf die Geschwindigkeiten von longitudinalen (C_p) und transversalen (C_s) elastischen Wellen, die Poissonzahl ν_d , die dynamischen Elastizitäts - E_d und Schermoduln G_d festzustellen.

Über 200 Proben und klüftige Blockmodelle von Felsgesteinen sind von den Verfassern geprüft worden. Diese Modelle bestanden aus einer Gruppe der aus Felsgesteinen ausgeschnittenen Platten von ca. 1 cm Dicke. Für die Kluftausfüllung wurden Wasser, Eis, Ton, Lehm, Sand verwendet. Die Kluftporosität wurde bei den Versuchen von 0 bis 100% variiert. Es waren vulkanische (Basalte, Andesite, Bimssteine, Schlacken), intrusive (Granite unterschiedlicher Zusammensetzung und verschiedenes Alters, Diorite, Gabbro u.a.), metamorphe (kristalline Orthoschiefer, Gneise, Marmore) und Sedimentgesteine (Sand- und Kalksteine) untersucht worden. Für die Ultraschallmessungen im Frequenzbereich von 100 bis 150 kHz wurden folgende Einrichtungen verwendet, und zwar: 1) Ultraschall-Seismoskop vom Typ IPA-59 mit einer zusätzlichen Abtastung zu genaueren Messungen von Zeitabständen und mit einem vergrösserten Verstärkungsfaktor; 2) Sender aus der Bleizirkonattitanatkeramik und Empfänger mit bimorphen Elementen aus desselben Materials; 3) spezieller Kernhalter für die Profilierung.

Die Beobachtungen wurden durch die Durchschallung und Profilierung ZZ (vertikale Ausstrahlung und vertikaler Empfang) bei einer Temperaturänderung t von +20 bis zu -30°C durchgeführt. Das Wellenbild wurde vom Seismoskopschirm photographiert. Die Geschwindigkeitsmessungen von C_p und C_s wurden an Proben mit einer Länge von 10 cm und mehr erfolgt, wobei ein Messfehler 2-4% betrug. Für das Gefrieren wurden die Proben bei vorgegebenem Wassergehalt und in den eng anliegenden Gummiüberzügen in einem Kühlraum mit t = -55°C untergebracht, wo sie sich im Laufe von 5 Stunden befanden. Darauf wurden die gefrorenen Proben in einen Kühler mit der automatisch regelbaren Temperatur hinübergetragen, wo sie bei jeder fixierten Temperatur t im Laufe von 4-5 Stunden ausgehalten wurden.

§1. GESCHWINDIGKEITEN VON LONGITUDINALEN (C_p) UND TRANSVERSALEN (C_s) ELASTISCHEN WELLEN

Die vorgenommenen Untersuchungen über die Geschwindigkeiten von longitudinalen (C_p) und transversalen (C_s) elastischen Wellen in Abhängigkeit von t bei vorgegebenen Werten des Wasser- und Eisgehaltes erlaubten folgende Schlüsse zu ziehen:

1. Während des Gefrierens von lufttrockenen Felsgesteinen mit kleinem Wassergehalt in Gewicht und Volumen verändern sich C_p und C_s praktisch nicht. Sowohl das gebundene Wasser, als auch das Kristall-

wasser im Fels üben also beim Übergang zu Minustemperaturen (bis -30°C) keinen Einfluss auf die Fortpflanzungsgeschwindigkeiten der Wellen in den gefrorenen Gesteinen aus.

2. Beim Gefrieren von feuchten und wassergesättigten eruptiven und metamorphen Gesteinen nehmen C_p und C_s bei einer Temperatur von 0 bis -2°C bedeutend zu. Bei der weiteren Kühlung dieser Gesteine ändern sich C_p und C_s gering. In einigen Fällen wird eine allmähliche Zunahme von C_p und C_s im Temperaturbereich von -2°C bis -30°C beobachtet. Der Übergang des freien (kapillaren und gravitativen) Wassers zum harten Zustand verursacht also eine scharfe Veränderung von C_p und C_s.

3. In fast allen Sedimentgesteinen (Sand- und Kalksteine) vergrössern sich C_p und C_s während des Gefrierens im weiten Temperaturbereich von 0 bis -15°C und sogar bis zu -20°C, wobei in einigen Fällen eine Anfangsgefriertemperatur (t_{AGt}) zwischen 0 und -0,5°C liegt.

4. Die Veränderungen von C_p und C_s in den feuchten und wassergesättigten Eruptiv-, metamorphen und einigen Sedimentgesteinen in Abhängigkeit von t lassen sich durch die Formel berechnen:

$$c = c_0 e^{\frac{a t}{b+t}}.$$

In der Formel bedeuten: c_0 - eine experimentell ermittelte Wellengeschwindigkeit im aufgetauten Fels; a und b - Koeffizienten, die von einer Gesteinsart abhängig sind.
Die Mittelwerte der Koeffizienten a und b sind sowohl für $C_p(t)$, als auch für $C_s(t)$ gleich: $a = 0,4$ und $b = 0,3$ für die wassergesättigten (eisgesättigten) Intrusiv- und vulkanischen Gesteine; $a = 0,15$ und $b = 0,7$ für die wassergesättigten (eisgesättigten) metamorphen Gesteine.

5. Die Änderungen von $C_p(t)$ und $C_s(t)$ in feuchten und wassergesättigten felsigen Sedimentgesteinen werden nach der Gleichung $c = c_0 e^{\frac{a\theta}{b+\theta}}$ bestimmt, wobei $\theta = t - t_{AGt}$ (Aptikajew, 1964). Bei einigen Versuchen mit den Sand- und Kalksteinen erhielt man $t_{AGt} = -0,5°C$.

6. Für die eruptiven und metamorphen Gesteine kann man den Übergang von C_p und C_s im aufgetauten und wassergesättigten Fels (Man bezeichnet sie als $C_{p(wss)}$ und $C_{s(wss)}$) zu diesen Geschwindigkeiten im eisgesättigten Zustand (Bei $t \leq -2°C$ bezeichnet man sie als $C_{p(gefr)}$) und $C_{s(gefr)}$) nach folgenden empirischen Formeln erfüllen:

$$\frac{\Delta C_p}{C_{p(gefr)}} = 0,73 - 0,112\, C_{p(wss)} \qquad (1)$$

$$\frac{\Delta C_s}{C_{s(gefr)}} = 0,80 - 0,231\, C_{s(wss)}, \qquad (2)$$

wobei $\Delta C_p = C_{p(gefr)} - C_{p(wss)}$, $\Delta C_s = C_{s(gefr)} - C_{s(wss)}$ (C wird in km/s angegeben). Man muss annehmen, dass die Werte bei $C_{p(wss)} \geq 6,5$ km/s und $C_{s(wss)} \geq 3,5$ km/s Null gleich sind. Die Korrelationskoeffizienten der Formeln (1) und (2) sind entsprechend gleich 0.93∓0.01 und 0,96± 0,006.

7. Für die felsigen Sedimentgesteine lässt sich der Übergang von C_p und C_s im aufgetauten und wassersättigten Fels zu diesen Geschwindigkeiten im eisgesättigten Zustand (bei $t = -20°C$) nach folgenden Gleichungen errechnen:

$$\frac{\Delta C_p}{C_{p(gefr)}} = 0,735 - 0,111\, C_{p(wss)} \qquad (3)$$

$$\frac{\Delta C_s}{C_{s(gefr)}} = 0,938 - 0,280\, C_{s(wss)} \qquad (4)$$

Dabei muss man annehmen, dass die ΔC -Werte bei $C_{p(wss)} \geq 6,65$ km/s und $C_{s(wss)} \geq 3,4$ km/s Null gleich sind. Die Korrelationskoeffizienten der Gleichungen (3) und (4) sind gleich 0,96±0,01 bzw. 0,99± 0,003.

8. Die Gleichungen (1) und (3) sind einer früher für die Proben verschiedener Felsgesteine und das Felsmassiv ermittelten Formel (Woronkow und Michailowsky, 1972) (Bild.1) ähnlich und präzisieren sie in bezug auf die felsigen eruptiven, metamorphen und Sedimentgesteine. Zum erstenmal sind die Gleichungen (2) und (4) zur Umrechnung von C_s für die Felsgesteine beim Übergang vom aufgetauten Zustand zum gefrorenen (oder umgekehrt) erhalten.

9. Der Temperatureinfluss auf einen Anisotropiekoeffizienten der Geschwindigkeit elastischer Wellen in den lufttrockenen Gesteinen ist noch nicht festgestellt. Die Gesteine, die eine bedeutende Anisotropie der Geschwindigkeiten im trockenen Zustand haben, besitzen in den wassergesättigten und gefrorenen Zustanden eine weniger ausgeprägte Anisotropie der Geschwindigkeiten.

10. Für die wassergesättigten klüftigen Blockmodelle, in denen als Kluftausfüllung Wasser, Lehm, Ton, Sand benutzt wurden, ist der Übergang von C_p und C_s im aufgetauten Zustand zu diesen Geschwindigkeiten im gefrorenen Zustand (bei $t = -8°C$ und niedriger) folgenden Gleichungen untergeordnet; und zwar: den Gleichungen (1), (2) für die Granitblöcke, den Formeln (3), (4) für die Sandsteinblöcke.

11. Zwischen den Reziprokwerten der Geschwindigkeiten $1/C_p$ und $1/C_s$ in den obengenannten eisgesättigten gefrorenen Blockmodellen (bei einer fixierter Temperatur) und der Kluftporosität n_{kl} existiert eine lineare Abhängigkeit:

$$1/C_p = \alpha_p \cdot n_{kl} + \beta_p; \quad 1/C_s = \alpha_s \cdot n_{kl} + \beta_s,$$

wobei n_{kl} in % angegeben wird.
Die Koeffizienten α und β sind bei $t = -3,4°C$ in Tafel 1 angeführt.

Tafel 1

Gesteine für die Block-modelle	Kluftaus-füllung	$\alpha_p \cdot 10^7$	$\beta_p \cdot 10^4$	$\alpha_s \cdot 10^7$	$\beta_s \cdot 10^4$
Granit	Eis	9,8	2,21	26	3,17
-"-	Sand	6,4	2,11	12	2,94
-"-	Lehm	11,0	2,17	21	3,49
-"-	Ton	11,0	2,19	37	3,2
Sandstein	Eis	9,9	2,34	-	-
-"-	Sand	1,1	2,24	5,1	3,56
-"-	Lehm	10,0	2,24	20	3,52
-"-	Ton	11,0	2,24	32	3,72

Die Koeffizienten α und β nehmen um ca. 10-15% bei höheren Temperaturen bis -0,4°C zu und vermindern sich um 5-10% bei niedrigeren bis -16°C (im Vergleich zu $t = -3,4°C$).

12. In Abhängigkeit von einem Kluftausfüllungstyp ist ein Charakter von $C(t)$ -Kurven verschieden. Die Geschwindigkeiten in den gefrorenen (vorwassergesättigten) klüftigen Blockmodellen sind von t praktisch nicht abhängig, d.h. bei niedrigeren Temperaturen als -4°C (mit Sand gefüllte Klüfte), -9°C (mit Lehm gefüllte Klüfte), -10°C (Tonklüfte), -7°C (mit Eis gefüllte Klüfte).

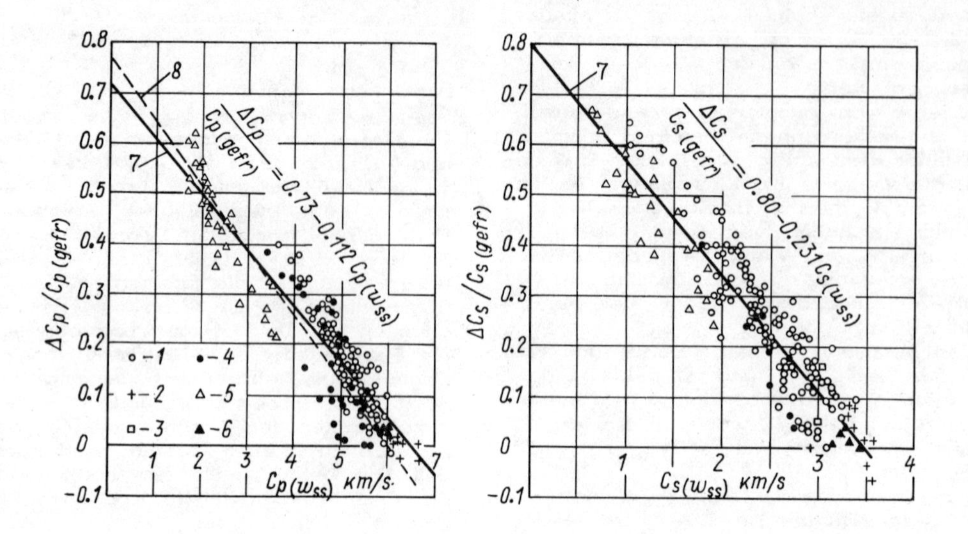

Bild.1. Relative Geschwindigkeitsveränderungen von C_p und C_s in den Proben der eruptiven und metamorphen Gesteine beim Übergang vom wassersättigten Zustand zum gefrorenen in Abhängigkeit von C_p und C_s in den wassergesattigten Gesteinen.
1 - Granite verschiedener Art, Gneise und Gneise-Granite; 2 - Metamorpher Schiefer; 3 - Marmor; 4 - Basalte, Andesite, Mikrodolerite; 5 - Schlacken, Schlackenlaven, Bimssteine; 6 - Diabas, Gabbro, Porphirit; 7 - Regressionslinie für eruptive und metamorphe Gesteine; 8 - dasselbe für verschiedene Felsgesteine nach den Angaben der Arbeit von Woronkow O.K., Michailowsky G.W. (1972).

§ 2. EINFLUSS DER TEMPERATUR-WASSERGEHALTSVERHÄLTNISSE AUF DIE POISSONZAHL

Die Poissonzahl ν_d wurde mit Hilfe des Nomogramms von L.Knopow nach den Beziehungen C_s/C_p oder C_R/C_p bestimmt. In unseren Untersuchungen waren folgende Fehlergrenzen von ν_d : a) bei $\nu_d \leq 0{,}2$ betrug ein absoluter Fehler $\Delta\nu_d = 0{,}03$; b) bei $\nu_d > 0{,}2$ $\Delta\nu_d / \nu_d = 10\%$. Die Analyse der experimentellen Werte, die für die Felsgesteine bei verschiedenen Temperatur- und Wassergehaltsverhältnissen (Eisgehalt) festgestellt worden waren, erlaubt folgende Schlüsse zu ziehen:

1. Die Poissonzahl verschiedener Felsgesteine hängt von t praktisch nicht ab, wenn ihr Wassergehalt (Eisgehalt) während der Versuche konstant ist. Nur in den wassergesättigten Graniten und Sandsteinen vermindert sich ν_d im Mittel um 0,05-0,07 (nicht verwitterte Gesteine) und 0,1-0,13 (verwitterte Granite) beim Übergang von den positiven Temperaturen zu den negativen.

2. Einen wesentlichen Einfluss auf die Poissonzahl ν_d der Felsgesteine üben ein Wassersättigungsgrad S_r und ein Grad der Porenfüllung mit Eis S_{ri} (Bild.2). Dieser Einfluss ist um so stärker, je kleiner ν_d im trockenen Fels ist.

Die kleinen Poissonzahlen haben, zum Beispiel, die trockenen Granite, Sandsteine und andere Gesteine mit grossem Quarzgehalt ($\nu_d = 0{,}08$ für Quarzgesteine). Zur Bestimmung von ν_d in Abhängigkeit von S_r und S_{ri} wurden folgende Gleichungen bei der Veränderung der Wassersättigung und des Grades der Porenfüllung mit Eis im Bereich von 0 bis 100% verwendet:

$$\nu_d = \nu_{d_0} + B_1 \cdot S_r^2 \tag{5}$$

$$\nu_d = \nu_{d_0} + B_2 \cdot S_{ri}\ , \tag{6}$$

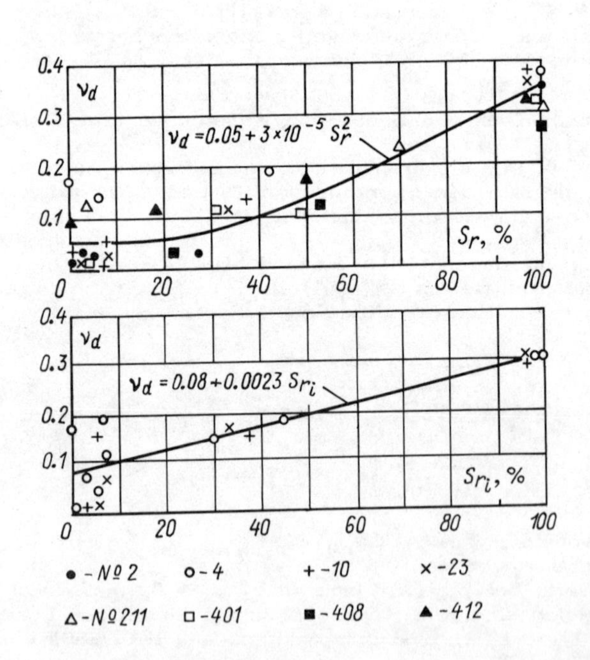

Bild.2. Beispiel der Abhängigkeit der dynamischen Poissonzahl ν_d für Granite vom Wassersättigungsgrad S_r und Ausfüllungsgrad S_{ri} der offenen Poren mit Eis. NN 2,4,10,123 - Quarzplagioklasgranite; N 211 - Orthoklasplagioklasgranit; NN 401,408,412 - Mikroklingranite.

wobei ν_{d_0} einem absolut trockenen Gestein entspricht. S_τ und $S_{\tau i}$ werden in % angegeben. B_1 und B_2 bedeuten die von einer Gesteinsart abhängigen Koeffizienten. Die Mittelwerte für ν_{d_0}, B_1 und B_2 sind in Tafel 2 zusammengestellt.

Tafel 2

Gestein	ν_{d_0}	$B_1 \cdot 10^5$	$B_2 \cdot 10^3$
nicht verwitterte Granite verschiedener Art	0,05-0,08	3,0	2,3
verwitterte Granite	0,23-0,26	2,2	0,6
Gneis und Gneis-Granit	0,03-0,04	2,6	2,8
Schiefer und Marmor	0,2	1,2	1,1
vulkanische Gesteine	0,14-0,18	-	1,5
Arkosesandsteine	0,01	3,4	2,6
Quarzsandsteine	0,03-0,05	2,2	1,9
Marmorkalksteine	0,27-0,28	0,7	0,7

Bei der Variation von S_τ von 0 bis 40-50% (Das entspricht einem Zustand des Massivs über einen Grundwasserspiegel) verändert sich ν_d klein, aber bei S_τ= 50-100% nimmt ν_d intensiv zu. Die relativ hohen Poissonzahlen können also bei Vorhandensein von wassergesättigten Zonen (oder Zonen mit grossem Eisgehalt) im Felsmassiv zeugen.

3. Die vulkanischen halbfelsige Gesteine (Schlackenlaven, Schlacken, Bimssteine) und einige Kalksteintype beweisen bei den Variationen der Temperatur, der Feuchtigkeit und des Eisgehaltes keine gesetzmässigen Veränderungen von ν_d. Die hohen Poissonzahlen für solche Gesteine können als Kennzeichen der wasser- oder eisgesättigten Zustände nicht dienen.

§ 3. EINFLUSS DER TEMPERATUR-WASSERGEHALTSVERHÄLTNISSE AUF DIE DYNAMISCHEN ELASTIZITÄTS- UND SCHERMODULN

Die Elastizitäts- E_d und Schermoduln G_d wurden nach den entsprechenden Formeln $E_d = 2 \rho \cdot C_s^2 (1+\nu_d)$, $G_d = \rho \cdot C_s^2$ errechnet, wo ρ eine Gesteinsdichte bedeutet. Bei der Bestimmung von E_d und G_d betrugen die Fehlergrenzen 5-7%. Als Ergebnis des Studiums über den Einfluss der Temperatur und Feuchtigkeit auf E_d und G_d sind folgende Schlüsse:

1. Bei voller Wassersättigung von Eruptivgesteinen werden die Granite bei positiven Temperaturen durch die grössten Veränderungen von E_d und G_d gekennzeichnet (die Mittelwerte für $E_{d(wss)}/E_{d(tr)}$ = 1,3-1,4; $G_{d(wss)}/G_{d(tr)}$ = 1,13). Das kann man auf eine kleine Zunahme von C_s und eine wesentliche Vergrösserung von ν_d (um 2-3 mal) bei der Wassersättigung zurückführen.

2. Für die vulkanischen Gesteine erhielt man folgende mittlere Werte: $E_{d(wss)}/E_{d(tr)}$ = 1,2; $G_{d(wss)}/G_{d(tr)}$ = 1. Bei der Wassersättigung dieser Gesteine ist ein Zuwachs von E_d nur durch eine Vergrösserung von ν_d bedingt, während C_s praktisch unveränderlich ist.

3. Bei der Wassersättigung der metamorphen Felsgesteine (kristalline Schiefer, Marmor), die im trockenen Zustand E_d= 70000-80000 MN/m^2 haben, verändert E_d sich nicht. Aber G_d vermindert sich um 5-10%. Die Gneise zeigen bei der Wassersättigung eine Vergrösserung von E_d um 1,1-1,16 mal und eine Zunahme von G_d um 1,1 mal.

4. Bei der Wassersättigung der felsigen Sedimentgesteine waren folgende Mittelwerte der Elastizitäts- und Schermoduln ermittelt worden: $E_{d(wss)}/E_{d(tr)}$ = 1,14, $G_{d(wss)}/G_{d(tr)}$ = 0,9 für Sandsteine; $E_{d(wss)}/E_{d(tr)}$ = 1,15, $G_{d(wss)}/G_{d(tr)}$ = 1,08 für Marmorkalksteine. Die Mittelwerte von E_d und G_d blieben für Kalksteine unverändert.

5. Beim Gefrieren der trockenen Felsgesteine bis zu -30°C ändern sich E_d und G_d praktisch nicht.

6. Beim Gefrieren der feuchten und wassergesättigten Gesteine nehmen E_d und G_d stark zu (Bild.3), besonders im Temperaturbereich von 0 bis -2°C für die eruptiven und metamorphen Gesteine und von 0 bis -4°C für die Sedimentgesteine. Bei niedrigeren Temperaturen sind E_d und G_d in den eruptiven und metamorphen Gesteinen praktisch konstant, aber in den Sedimentgesteinen wachsen diese Moduln bei den Temperaturen bis zu -20°C allmählich. Die Abhängigkeit der Elastizitäts- E_d und Schermoduln G_d von t kann man wie folgt ausdrücken: $E_d = E_{d_0} \cdot e^{\frac{a_1 t}{b_1 + t}}$, $G_d = G_{d_0} e^{\frac{a_1 \cdot t}{b_1 + t}}$, wo E_{d_0} und G_{d_0} diese Moduln bei positiver Temperatur bedeuten. a_1 und b_1 sind Koeffizienten, die von einer Gesteinsart und ihres Wassergehaltes (Eisgehaltes) abhängen. Für die eisgesättigten Felsgesteine sind also folgende Mittelwerte der Koeffizienten a_1 und b_1 ermittelt: a_1 = 0,7, b_1 = 0,3 für Granite; a_1 = 0,3, b_1 = 1,3 für Gneise; a_1 = 0,57, b_1 = 0,4 für vulkanische Gesteine; a_1 = 1,1, b_1 = 0,3 für Quarzsandsteine; a_1 = 0,2, b_1 = 2,1 für Kalksteine; a_1 = 0,37, b_1 = 1,4 für Marmorkalksteine.

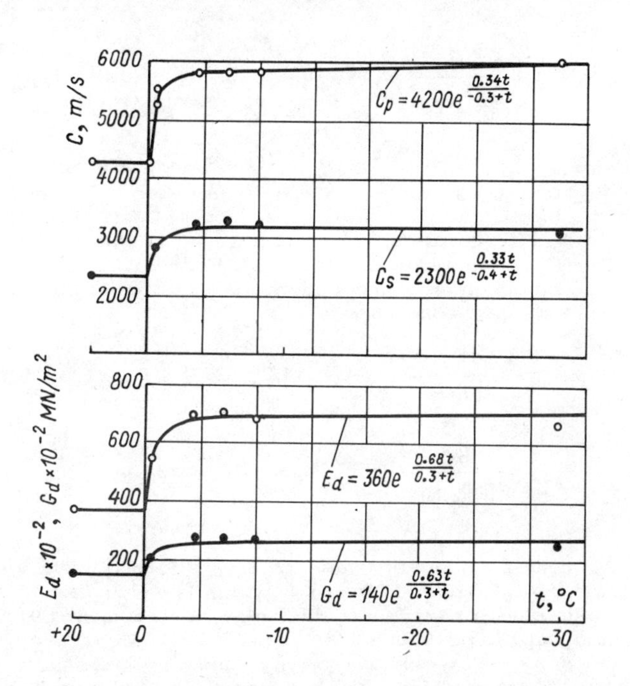

Bild.3. Beispiel der Abhängigkeit der longitudinalen (C_p) und transversalen (C_s) Wellengeschwindigkeiten, der dynamischen Elastizitäts - E_d und Schermoduln G_d in einer wassergesättigten Probe aus Orthoklasplagioklasgranit von t.

7. Eine Zunahme von E_d und G_d sind beim Gefrieren der Felsgesteine um so intensiver, je grösser ihr Wassersättigungsgrad, ihre Porosität und Klüftigkeit sind. Der Übergang von $E_{d(wss)}$ und $G_{d(wss)}$ zu $E_{d(gefr)}$ und $G_{d(gefr)}$ für die eisgesättigten Felsgesteine kann man mit Hilfe der Kurvenbilder (Bild.4) oder Formeln

(7) -(10) erfüllen.

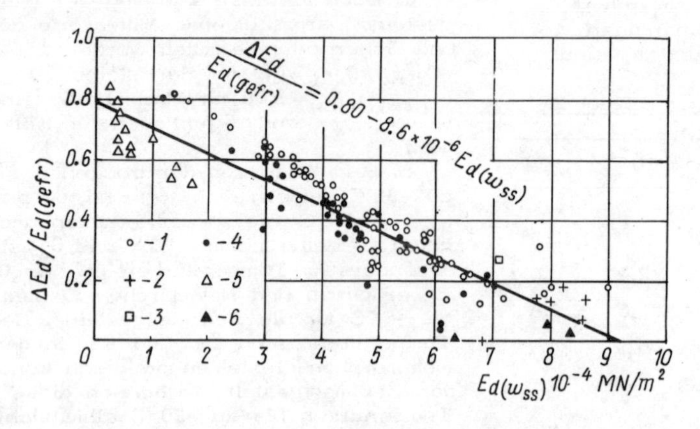

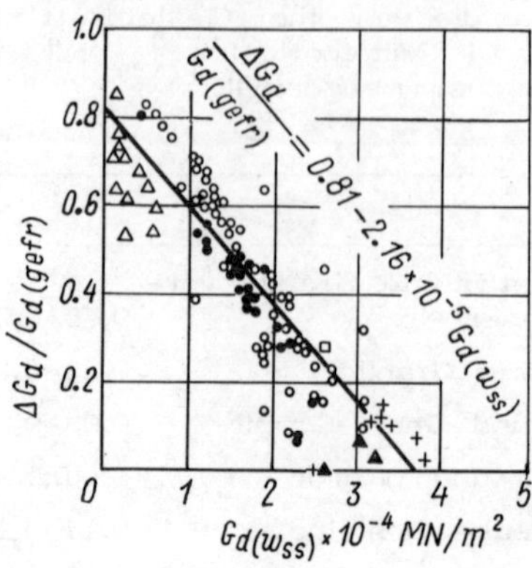

Bild. 4. Relative Veränderungen der dynamischen Elastizitäts - E_d und Schermoduln G_d für die Proben der eruptiven und metamorphen Gesteine beim Übergang vom wassergesättigten Zustand zum gefrorenen in Abhängigkeit von E_d und G_d in den wassergesättigten Gesteinen.
1 - Granite verschiedener Art, Gneise, Gneise-Granite; 2 - metamorpher Schiefer; 3 - Marmor; 4 - Basalte, Andesite, Mikrodolerite; 5 - Schlacken, Schlackenlaven, Bimssteine; 6 - Gabbro, Porphirit, Diabas.

Für eruptive und metamorphe Felsgesteine:

$$\frac{\Delta E_d}{E_{d(gefr)}} = 0{,}8 - 8{,}6 \cdot 10^{-6} E_{d(wss)} \qquad (7)$$

$$\frac{\Delta G_d}{G_{d(gefr)}} = 0{,}81 - 2{,}16 \cdot 10^{-5} G_{d(wss)}, \qquad (8)$$

wobei $\Delta E_d = E_{d(gefr)} - E_{d(wss)}$, $\Delta G_d = G_{d(gefr)} - G_{d(wss)}$
E_d und G_d werden in MN/m^2 angegeben. Man muss annehmen, dass bei $E_{d(wss)} \geq 92000$ MN/m^2 und $G_{d(wss)} \geq 37500$ MN/m^2 ΔE_d und ΔG_d Null gleich sind. Die Korrelationskoeffizienten der Formeln (7) und (8) sind entsprechend gleich $0{,}90 \pm 0{,}02$ und $0{,}85 \pm 0{,}03$.
Für felsige Sedimentgesteine:

$$\frac{\Delta E_d}{E_{d(gefr)}} = 0{,}92 - 11{,}2 \cdot 10^{-6} E_{d(wss)} \qquad (9)$$

$$\frac{\Delta G_d}{G_{d(gefr)}} = 0{,}93 - 2{,}96 \cdot 10^{-5} G_{d(wss)} \qquad (10)$$

Man muss annehmen, dass bei $E_{d(wss)} \geq 82000$ MN/m^2 und $G_{d(wss)} \geq 31500$ MN/m^2 ΔE_d und ΔG_d Null gleich sind. Die Korrelationskoeffizienten der Formeln (9) und (10) sind $0{,}989 \pm 0{,}004$ bzw. $0{,}986 \pm 0{,}005$ gleich.

8. Zur Berechnung von E_d und G_d muss man eine Gesteinsdichte ρ bei jedem untersuchten Zustand (trockenen, wassersättigten u.a.) berücksichtigen. Die ungenügende Bewertung dieses Faktors gibt ergänzende Fehler. Diese Fehler sind um so bedeutender, je grösser die Porosität und Klüftigkeit des Felsens sind. Die obendargelegten Untersuchungsergebnisse über den Einfluss der Temperatur- und Wassergehaltsverhältnisse auf die elastischen Eigenschaften der felsigen eruptiven, metamorphen und Sedimentgesteine zeigen, dass eine weitverbreitete Meinung, dass "die Einwirkung der Verfrostung auf die Felsgesteine immer letzten Endes zu ihrer Zerstörung führt unabhängig davon, wie lange sie im gefrorenen Zustand blieben" (Popov, 1969), etwas einseitig ist. Die Felsmassive, die in ihrem oberen Teil einer Schnittes eine Zonen - Block - Struktur haben (Gurejew, 1972) werden im gefrorenen Zustand dank dem Eis-Zement in Klüften und Poren zum Monolithen. Dabei nehmen ihre Elastizitäts - und Verformungsmoduln zu, die Durchlässigkeitszahl nimmt ab, die Festigkeit des Massivs (Koeffizient "c") steigert um 2-3 mal im Vergleich zum aufgetauten Zustand (Ermakow und Kozlow, 1966).

SCHLUSSFOLGERUNGEN

1. Es ist den Temperatureinfluss auf die Geschwindigkeiten elastischer Wellen in Felsgesteinen untersucht worden. Beim Gefroren der trockenen Felsgesteine verändern sich C_p und C_s praktisch nicht. Während des Gefrorens der feuchten und wassergesättigten eruptiven und metamorphen Gesteine nehmen und C_s im Temperaturbereich von 0 bis -2°C scharf zu, bei niedrigeren Temperaturen bleiben die Geschwindigkeiten praktisch unverändert. In den felsigen Sedimentgesteinen vergrössern sich die Wellengeschwindigkeiten meistens bei einer Temperaturabnahme von 0 bis -20°C allmählich. Es wurden die Empfehlungen zur Umrechnung von C_p und C_s in verschiedenen Felsgesteinen beim Übergang vom aufgetauten (wassergesättigten) Zustand zum gefrorenen (eisgesättigten) und umgekehrt gegeben.

2. Es ist den Einfluss der Temperatur- und Wassergehaltsverhältnisse auf die dynamischen Elastizitäts- E_d und Schermoduln G_d und Poissonzahl ν_d für die Felsgesteine erforscht worden:

a) Bei der Wassersättigung der aufgetauten Felsgesteine steigert sich E_d hauptsächlich infolge des Zuwachses von C_p bzw. von ν_d (in einigen Fällen um einige Zehner %). Der Wassersättigungseinfluss auf G_d ist gering.

b) Es ist festgestellt worden, dass E_d und G_d beim Gefroren der feuchten und wassergesättigten Felsgesteine nach einem der Funktion $c(t)$ analogen Gesetz stark zunehmen. Es wurden die Empfehlungen zur Umrechnung von E_d und G_d vom wassergesättigten Zustand zum eisgesättigten und umgekehrt gegeben.

c) Die Zunahme der Poissonzahl ν_d in den Felsgesteinen hängt vom Wassersättigungsgrad und Porenausfüllungsgrad mit Eis ab. Die hohen Poissonzahlen ν_d in den gefrorenen Felsgesteinen wie Granite, Quarzite, Sandsteine u.a., die im aufgetauten Zustand die niedrigen Werte von ν_d haben, können nach den Angaben des seismischen Schürfens als Kennzeichen des grossen Eisgehaltes im Felsmassiv dienen.

LITERATURVERZEICHNIS

1. Aptikajew F.F., - Einfluss eines Temperaturfeldes auf die Verteilung von seismischen Geschwindigkeiten in einer Zone von vieljährigen gefrorenen Gesteinen, Sb. "Teplowye prozessy w merzlych gornych porodach", Verlag "Nauka", 1964, S.190-199.
2. Woronkow O.K., Michailowsky G.W., - Geschwindigkeiten von Longitudinalwellen in den gefrorenen porigen und klüftigen Felsgesteinen (Proben und Massiv), Geologiia i Geophisika, SO AN UdSSR, 1972, N 1, S.82-85.
3. Gurejew A.M., - Ein Ingenieurgeologisches Modell des Felsmassivs als Untergrund, eines Wasserbauwers, Trudy koordinazionnych sowetschanij po hydrotechnike, Verlag "Energiia", 1972, N 77, S.5-14.
4. Ermakow I.I., Kozlow J.S., - Festigkeit eines klüftigen Massivs unter Bedingungen der vieljährigen Verfrostung, Trudy WNIIG, 1966, Sb.LX, S.187-193.
5. Popow A.I., - Ein Gegenstand und Inhalt der Kriolithologie als eine Lehre über die Lithogenese und Zonen der stabilen Kühlung der Erde, Problemy Kriolithologii, Verlag MGU, 1969, N 1, S.7-12.

THEME 1

THÈME 1

THEMA 1

G

Measuring Devices

G

Appareils de mesure

G

Messungsgeräte

MESURES DES CONTRAINTES AU VÉRIN PLAT - NOUVELLES POSSIBILITÉS

NEW DEVELOPMENTS IN THE FLAT JACK TEST

SPANNUNGSMESSUNGEN MIT DRUCKKISSEN - NEUE ANWENDUNGEN

Jack BERNEDE

Directeur de la Société d'Études Industrielles en Laboratoire
France

RESUME

La méthode du vérin plat est bien connue. Elle présente le gros avantage d'être directe et de ne nécessiter qu'un minimum d'interprétation, fournissant par ailleurs des résultats quasi immédiats.

Il y a surtout lieu de la rendre extrêmement facile et rapide d'exécution. Dans ces conditions on peut procéder à des mesures nombreuses et économiques.

Si la mesure est intéressante par elle-même, c'est surtout le fait de pouvoir la répéter de nombreuses fois et de fournir un lot important de résultats provenant d'essais exécutés dans des conditions diverses.

Si la méthode a des avantages elle a aussi ses limites que nous avons tenté de reculer à la fois par une analyse des causes de perturbation d'une part,et en tentant des opérations qui présentent une certaine originalité d'autre part. Les causes de perturbation principales sont la non-reversibilité des déformations sous charges et l'existence de cisaillements dans la zone expérimentale. Pour ce qui est des applications particulières, citons la mesure des tractions, le contrôle des variations de contrainte, enfin la répartition des contraintes en profondeur par l'emploi simultané de plusieurs vérins plats.

SUMMARY

The flat jack test method is well known. It has the great advantage of being a direct method requiring only a minimum of interpretation, and yielding almost immediate results.

The test must be kept brief and easy to perform, so that large numbers of tests can be done cheaply. While individual measurements are instructive, the main value of the test is that it can be repeated many times to provide a large set of data obtained under different conditions.

The test has limitations as well as advantages, which we have attempted to overcome by examining the causes of error and by introducing some new features. The main causes of error considered are non-recoverability of strains under load and shear stresses in the test area. Special applications include measurement of tensile stresses, monitoring of stress level changes and investigation of stress patterns deeper in the rock by using several jacks simultaneously.

ZUSAMMENFASSUNG

Das wohlbekannte Druckkissen. Messverfahren bietet den Vorteil, dass es rasch direkte Engebnisse liefert, die nur wenig verarbeitet werden müssen.

Es ist vor allem wichtig, das Verfahren leicht und schnell einsatzfähig zu machen, so dass zahlreiche Messungen ohne grosse Kosten durchgeführt werden können.

Aufschlussreicher als eine einzelne Messung ist die Möglichkeit, sie mehrmals zu wiederholen und eine grosse Zahl von Versuchsergebnissen unter verschiedenen Bedingungen zu gewinnen.

Trotz seiner Vorteile hat jedoch das Verfahren ein begrenztes Anwendungsgebiet, das zu erweitern wir uns bemüht haben, indem wir einerseits die Störungsursachen untersucht,andererseits neuartige Messvorgänge unternommen haben. Die wesentlichsten Störungsursachen sind die Tatsache, dass die Verformungen keine Umkehrfunktion der Kräfte sind und das Vorhandensein von Schubspannungen in der Messzone. Als besondere Anwendungen seien erwähnt : Zugspannungsmessungen, Kontrolle der Spannungsveränderungen und Feststellung des Spannungsverlaufs in der Tiefe durch gleichzeitigen Einsatz mehrerer Druckkissen.

1. RAPPELS

Bien que la méthode du vérin plat soit fort connue et déjà décrite de très nombreuses fois, nous allons citer à nouveau ses caractéristiques, en appuyant particulièrement sur ses limites face aux grands avantages qu'elle présente par ailleurs.

Outre que l'essai procure un résultat immédiat et dont l'interprétation est réduite au minimum, c'est, à notre connaissance, la seule méthode directe de mesures de contraintes; mais si elle permet d'ignorer les coefficients de déformation du matériau, une interprétation correcte des résultats nécessite, sinon l'élasticité, du moins la réversibilité des relations entre déformation et charge.

Aussi a-t-on, d'une part, intérêt à prévoir une mesure rapide pour éviter des effets différés et, d'autre part, à procéder à une décompression aussi réduite que possible compte tenu de la précision possible dans le contrôle des déformations.

Cette décompression intéresse une plage de rocher située à la paroi d'un ouvrage : roche ou béton. Très souvent ce genre de mesure intéresse la paroi d'une excavation souterraine. Elle s'effectue en pratiquant une fente étroite à l'aide d'une scie au diamant. Il s'agit là d'un perfectionnement énorme dans la pratique de la mesure et qu'on doit à M. le Professeur ROCHA.

Des bases de déformation disposées à l'entour de cette fente et préalablement au sciage (Figure 4) permettent de suivre le comportement de la face rocheuse durant la décompression puis le gonflement d'un vérin plat glissé dans la saignée. Ce gonflement, contrôlé, étant poussé jusqu'à annuler les déformations de décompression on adopte a priori cette pression d'annulation comme valeur de la contrainte qui agissait, avant saignée, normalement au plan de celle-ci.

2. EXTENSION DU DOMAINE D'APPLICATION

Toutefois l'interprétation des résultats nécessite l'adoption de certaines hypothèses que bien souvent la nature ne respecte pas et parmi lesquelles nous citerons :

- la réversibilité des déformations sous charges,
- la contrainte à mesurer, normale au plan de la saignée, est principale.

Si la seconde n'est pas respectée, les contraintes tangentielles perturbent la mesure car le vérin plat ne rend pas le cisaillement.

Enfin cette mesure a toujours été associée d'une part à l'auscultation d'un matériau comprimé et, d'autre part, limitée à des zones très superficielles.

Nous examinons ici les effets résultants de la *non-réversibilité* et des *contraintes de cisaillement*. Nous présentons ensuite nos idées et réalisations dans le cas d'auscultation d'un matériau *tendu* et pour des mesures en profondeur destinées à tenir compte de la dimension de l'*hétérogénéité* ou encore à apprécier le *gradient* des contraintes.

2.1 Non-réversibilité

2.1.1 Phénomène d'hystérésis

Considérons un matériau soumis à une contrainte de compression uniforme σ_n. La fente f (Figure 1-a) normale à la contrainte crée une décompression partielle (Figure 1-b) qui s'inscrit dans la concavité de la courbe de mise en charge naturelle du matériau réellement soumis à σ_n. Selon la dimension de σ_n par rapport aux caractéristiques de rupture du matériau, le résultat σ_m obtenu par mise en pression du vérin plat sera mesuré par défaut.

En tout cas, et par précaution, on opère généralement en évitant de dépasser σ_m puis en vérifiant par des cycles ultérieurs la marge du domaine de réversibilit[é] existant et la fermeture des boucles d'hystérésis.

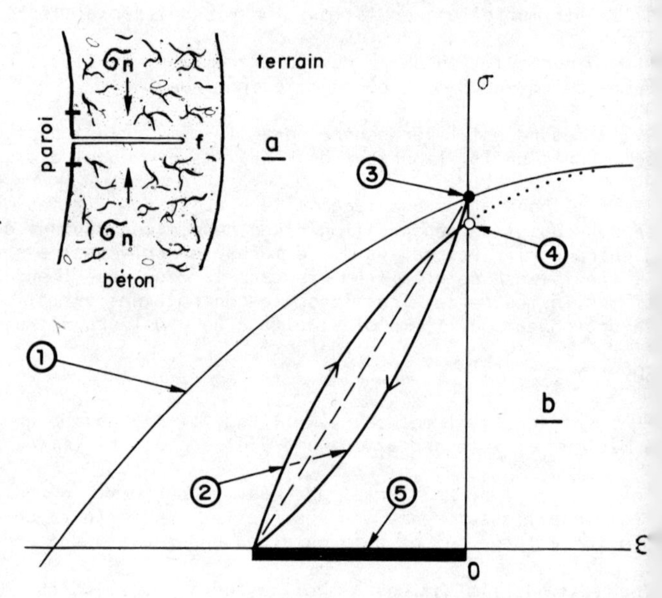

Figure 1 Effet de la non-réversibilité des déformations sous charges
Non-reversibility effect of the deformation under load
Wirkung der nicht umkehrvaren Verformungen

1 Courbe des déformations
Curve of deformation
Verformungskurve

2 Cycle d'essai
Test cycle
Ebtlastung und Lastanstieg

3 Contrainte à mesurer σ_n
Stress to be measured σ_n
Gemessene Spannung σ_n

4 Résultat σ_m
Results σ_m
Ergebnis σ_m

5 Déformation ε_m
Deformation ε_m
Verformung ε_m

Cette erreur (σ_n-σ_m) reste malheureusement difficile à estimer mains on peut admettre qu'en comparaison de l'incidence du cisaillement (§ 2.2) elle est d'un ordre de grandeur acceptable compte tenu de la précision qu'on demande à de telles mesures sur le chantier. A ce sujet il faut signaler que cette précision s'est vue approcher le bar dans des cas où les conditions de présentation des parois et de qualité de la roche étaient bonnes.

2.1.2 Réduction de la profondeur de la fente

Une solution pour minimiser le phénomène précédent consiste à pratiquer la fente la moins profonde possible compte tenu, évidemment, de la bonne présentation des parois. On y arrive aisément en dosant la pénétration de la scie diamantée. En général les quelques 23 à 25 cm de flèche peuvent être considérés comme un minimum par rapport à la dimension des ouvrages auscultés. Il y a lieu cependant de relater une expérience réalisée à l'aide de vérins plats dont la flèche allait de 15 à 25 cm et qui a donné des valeurs de contrainte mesurées se classant en raison inverse des flèches. Cette expérience a pu être complétée en augmentant par ailleurs la dimension de l'excavation, laquelle présentait il faut le préciser une géométrie parfaitement circulaire. Le changement du rapport flèche/diamètre de la galerie a agi dans le même sens que précédemment.

2.1.3 Rapidité d'exécution

Pour accélérer les opérations il y avait lieu d'adopter un matériel alliant la puissance à la légèreté. Il est à présent possible d'obtenir des durées d'exécution de saignées courantes inférieures à 60 minutes en roche très dure et tombant même à 5 minutes en roche de dureté courante. On a ainsi une réduction maximale des effets différés.

2.2 Incidence des contraintes de cisaillement dans le matériau ausculté

Cette incidence est plus malaisée à estimer que le défaut de réversibilité; d'ailleurs les deux phénomènes peuvent aller de pair. Présentement il ne sera question que des précautions à prendre, plus exactement de s'assurer qu'on n'est pas en présence d'une sollicitation de cisaillement importante.

Pour ce faire on suit, tout au long de l'essai, la déformation des diagolanes du parallèlogramme formé par quatre plots encadrant la saignée (Figure 2). On sait ainsi s'il y a ou non cisaillement, le résultat restant purement qualitatif mais l'indication étant précieuse dans le cas où on n'observe aucune déformation autre que celle consécutive à la décompression normale seule. Si par contre on décèle une déformation de cisaillement, on n'est pas encore armé pour déterminer la contrainte exacte, mais une étude en cours, tant théorique qu'expérimentale, est sur le point d'aboutir.

2.3 Matériau tendu

L'application de la méthode à la mesure des contraintes de traction nécessite une hypothèse supplémentaire à savoir l'adoption d'un module de déformation unique pour le matériau tendu ou comprimé. Cette hypothèse est d'autant moins hardie qu'il ne s'agit bien sûr que de la mesure de contraintes de traction relativement faibles telles que celles intéressant précisément les roches ou mêmes les ouvrages en béton.

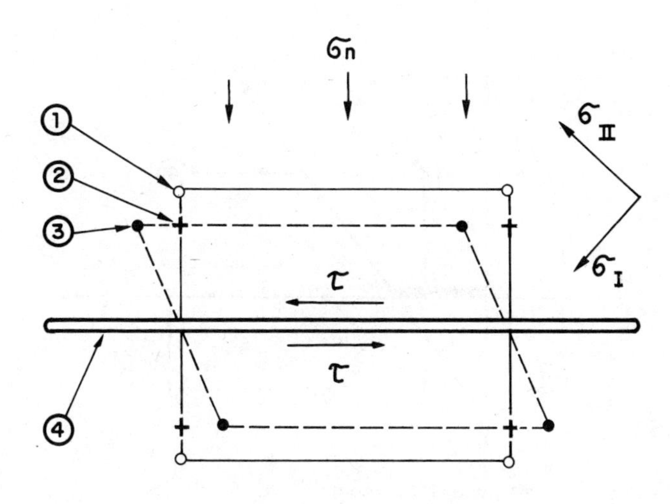

Figure 2 Effet dû au cisaillement
Shear stress effect
Wirkung der Schubspannung

1 Avant saignée
Before slot
Vor Ausfürhung des Schlitzes

2 Effet de σ_n
Effect on σ_n
Wirkung von σ_n

3 Effets de σ_n et τ
Effects of σ_n and τ
Wirkung von σ_n und τ

4 Saignée
Slot
Schlitz

Dans un matériau tendu la saignée provoque évidemment des déformations de signes opposés aux précedents (Figure 3). Il y a lieu alors de solliciter le matériau en compression à l'aide du gonflement du vérin plat mais de la quantité juste suffisante (quelques bar) pour déterminer la pente de la droite des déformations sous charge. A partir de là, on obtient la contrainte σ_t par extrapolation.

2.4 Contrôle de la variation de la contrainte provoquée par des changements de sollicitations du prototype

Sans fluctuations thermiques et dans le cas où il est possible d'en tenir compte, on peut suivre les variations de la contrainte à partir du dispositif expérimental courant. Par exemple il nous a été loisible d'obtenir les incidences du niveau de la retenue sur les valeurs de contraintes le long du parement aval d'un barrage (Figure 4). Il suffit, pour ce faire, et une fois la mesure faite, de contrôler la déformation des bases et de tracer la parallèle à la droite des déformations sous charge déterminées au cours de la mesure proprement dite (Figure 5).

Aucun contrôle de ce genre n'a encore été fait sur un rocher, mais il lui est bien entendu directement applicable. Il est extrêmement facile à réaliser mais nécessite que le rocher présente de bonnes qualités, ne soit pas soumis à des contraintes trop élevées, qu'en tout cas il ne puisse être l'objet de déformations de fluage.

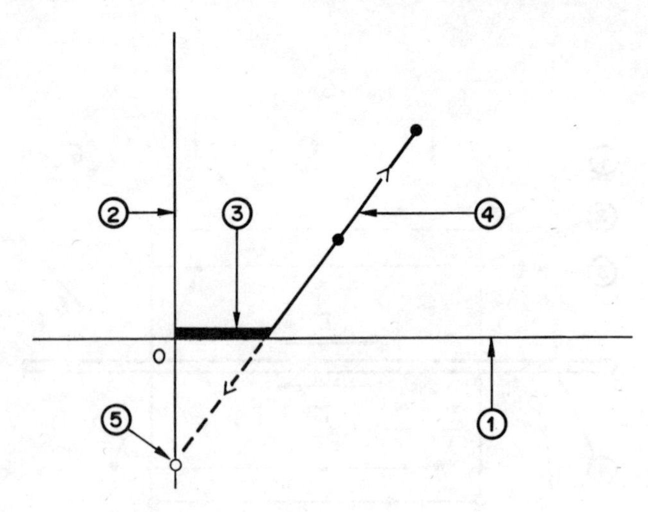

Figure 3 Mesure d'une contrainte de traction
Tensile stress measurement
Messung einer Zugspannung

1 Déformation
Deformations
Verformung

2 Pression dans le vérin
Jack pressure
Druck im Druckkissen

3 Détente par la saignée
Relief by the slot
Entspannung nach Ausführung des Schiltzes

4 Gonflement du vérin
Expansion of the jack
Füllung des Druckkissens

5 Traction (par extrapolation)
Tension (by extrapolation)
In situ Zugspannung (extrapoliert)

2.5 Saignée de grande surface

Si la saignée peu profonde est une bonne solution de la contrainte à la paroi elle n'est pas pour autant la solution optimale lorsque les dimensions de la maille de la fissuration ou de l'hétérogénéité du massif rocheux sont grandes.

On est donc obligé, dans certains cas, d'utiliser des saignées de grande surface, lesquelles ne sont généralement pas disproportionnées aux ouvrages étudiés dont les dimensions sont également grandes : centrales souterraines, conduites en charge de très grand diamètre, tunnels à plusieurs voies.

Un impératif a néanmoins été conservé à tout prix : celui de la maniabilité du matériel. Ainsi, avec un ensemble des plus légers, de transport, mise en position et fonctionnement faciles, il est possible de réaliser des saignées de 1 m2, toujours en 4 mm d'épaisseur (Figure 6).

Figure 4 - Mesure sur un béton de barrage
Measurement in concrete of dam
Messung an der Oberfläche einer Staumaue

2.6 Répartition des contraintes en profondeur

Par l'opération précédente il n'est question que d'accroître les dimensions de la saignée. Le même dispositif est aussi utilisé pour déterminer, au cours d'un même essai, la répartition des contraint en profondeur, en procédant à des mesures en plusie points à l'aide de vérins en série.

Jusqu'à présent aucun essai n'a cependant été réali sable avec plus de deux vérins (Figure 6-a) du fait que les déformations ne sont repérées qu'en surface Toutefois, nous élaborons actuellement une méthode permettant de mesurer les déformations induites loc lement par chaque vérin.

On obtient un diagramme d'essai comme celui de la figure 7 sur lequel on peut suivre les effets des phases successives de l'opération décrites ci-après

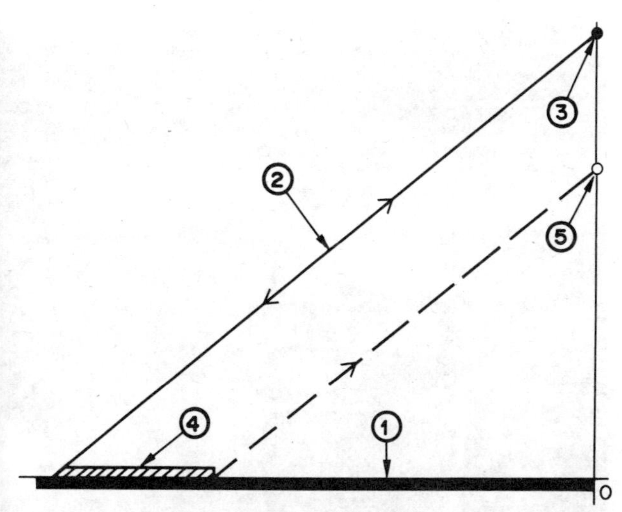

Figure 5 - Variation d'une contrainte de compression
Variation of compressive stress
Variation der Drucksspannungswerte

1 Effet de la saignée
Effect of slot
Wirkung der Schlitzesausführung

2 Essai
Test
Versuch

3 σ_n barrage plein
σ_n *full reservoir*
σ_n bei Vollstau

4 Effet de la vidange
Effect of drawdown
Wirkung der Entleerung

5 σ_n après vidange
σ_n *after drawdown*
σ_n nach Entleerung

- exécution de l'essai A (aboutissement à p_1)
- prolongement de la saignée de (A) et (A+B)
- introduction des vérins A et B
- mise à la pression p_1 du vérin A
- gonflement du vérin B, la pression p_1 étant maintenue dans le vérin A (aboutissement à p_2).

3. RESULTATS COMPARES AVEC L'HYPERCAROTTAGE

Des essais par hypercarottage ont été réalisés dans des forages, évidemment très courts, dont le fond était au droit de celui de la saignée des vérins plats.

On sait que l'interprétation de l'essai par hypercarottage est rendue délicate par la difficulté d'appréhender la contrainte σ_z qui s'exerce selon l'axe du forage.

Dans le cas présent les essais ont été forcément exécutés très près de la paroi de la galerie; aussi a-t-on pu considérer $\sigma_z = 0$. En outre le module d'élasticité du rocher avait pu être obtenu avec une bonne précision. Dans ces conditions on est arrivé aux valeurs suivantes, correspondant à la contrainte σ_n dirigée normalement au plan de la saignée du vérin plat et mesurées en deux points différents :

- vérin plat = 260 et 440 bar
- hypercarottage = 260 et 450 bar.

Il est encourageant de constater que les deux résultats se recoupent bien, obtenus pourtant par des méthodes fort différentes mais dans un rocher à résistance et module élevés.

Figure 6 - Grande saignée (largeur : 1 m - longueur : 1 à 1,5 m)
Large slot (width : 1 m - length : 1 to 1.5 m)
Groper Schlitz (Breite : 1 m - Lünge : 1 m/1,5 m)

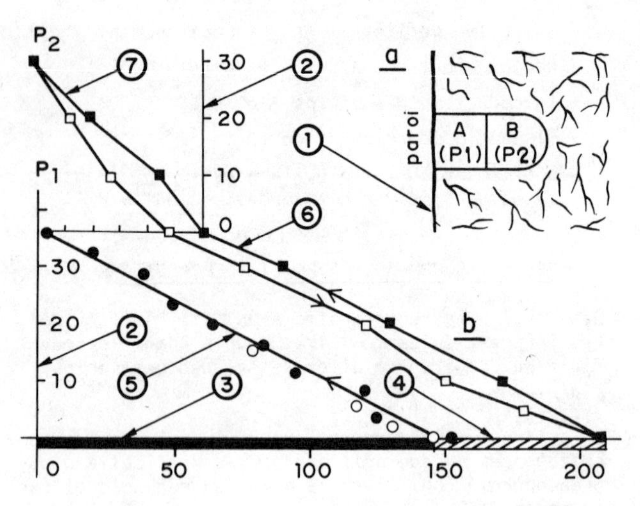

Figure 7 Essai à 2 vérins
Test with 2 jacks
Versuch mit 2 Druckkissen

1 Paroi
Wall
Oberfläche

2 Pressions dans les vérins plats
Jack pressures
Drücke in den Druckkissen

3 Déformation par la saignée A
Deformation by slot A
Verformung durch Ausführung des Schlitzes A

4 Déformation par la saignée (A+B)
Deformation by slot (A+B)
Verformung durch Ausführung der Schlitze (A+B)

5 Essai A
Test A
Versuch A

6 Deuxième gonflement vérin A
Second expansion of jack A
Zweite Füllung des Druckkissens A

7 Gonflement vérin B
Expansion of jack B
Füllung des Druckkissens B

4. QUELQUES APPLICATIONS PARTICULIERES ET ACTUELLES

Les différentes expériences qui ont été relatées dans ce compte rendu illustrent bien le domaine des possibilités d'utilisation de la méthode.

Ce type de mesure entre évidemment pour le plus grand nombre de cas, dans des études d'ouvrages souterrains. On y réalise des séries d'essais réparties en différents points et dans plusieurs sections. A partir des résultats de l'ensemble on tente de remonter par le calcul au système des contraintes règnant au sein du massif, plus précisément à l'endroit de l'excavation et préalablement à son creusement. La méthode s'adapte donc parfaitement au cas de galeries forées en roches résistantes, puisqu'on marie la réversibilité et la géométrie parfaite.

Toutefois, même en roches médiocres, les conditions sont quelquefois meilleures qu'on ne pouvait le supposer a priori, en ce sens qu'on constate la plupart du temps une amélioration sensible des caractéristiques du rocher par suite d'un durcissement consécutif à la concentration des contraintes le long des parois.

Figure 8 Mesure dans la maçonnerie d'un ancien tunne
Measurement within the masonry of an old tunnel
Messung im Mauerwerk eines alten Tunnels

Ont aussi été évoquées par le jeu des figures :

- Figures 3, 4 et 5, des mesures dans le béton d'un barrage à l'occasion d'une vidange.
- Figure 6, saignée de grande dimension dans une galerie forée en 8 m de diamètre dans une roche très dure.
- Figure 7, répartition des contraintes dans le revêtement en béton d'un tunnel à circulation.
- Quant à la figure 8 elle évoque un cas d'applicatic dont le nombre devient chaque jour plus important e qui consiste à examiner l'état actuel de tunnels anciens. Elle représente une mesure de la contrair te de la voûte en maçonnerie d'un tunnel fluvial ancien de 22 m de portée.

Citons également les mesures dans des bétons de fonda tions profondes d'une part et, d'autre part l'auscultationsoit de mines profondes (parois ou piliers) soi surtout de carrières souterraines, cette dernière aus cultation étant liée le plus souvent à des questions d'urbanisation.

REMERCIEMENTS

Nous ne saurions terminer ce rapport sans remercier Monsieur V. Mladyenovitch, Ingénieur en Chef au Bureau d'Ingénieurs Conseils COYNE et BELLIER, pour les avis autorisés et les idées intéressantes que lui ont suggérées certains résultats de nos essais.

THE VIBRATING WIRE STRESSMETER
L'ENREGISTREUR DECONTRAINTES À FIL VIBRANT
DAS SCHWINGUNGSSAITENSPANNUNGSMESSER

Ivor HAWKES

U.S. Army Cold Regions Res. and Eng. Lab.,
Hanover, NH

V.E. HOOKER

Bureau of Mines, U.S. Dept. of the Interior,

Denver, Col.
U.S.A.

UMMARY This paper describes an elastic inclusion type gauge developed to monitor stress changes around under-
round excavations. Deformation of the gauge body resulting from changes of stress in the surrounding rock mass
s measured as a change in the vibration period of a highly tensioned wire strung diametrically across the body.
t is shown that the gauge readings are relatively unaffected by rock modulus. Techniques for evaluating unixial and biaxial stress changes are described.

USAMMENFASSUNG Ein elastischer Einbaufühler wird beschrieben, der zur Überwachung von Spannungsänderungen um
nterirdische Aushube herum entwickelt wurde. Verformungen des Fühlers durch Spannungsänderungen in dem
mgebenden Gestein werden als Änderungen in der Schwingungsperiode einer stark gespannten Saite gemessen, die
iagonal durch den Fühlerkörper läuft. Es wird gezeigt, dass die Fühlerlesungen relativ einflussfrei sind vom
lastizitätsmodul des Gesteins. Methoden zur Beurteilung von ein - und zweiachsigen Spannungsänderungen werden
eschrieben.

ESUMÉ Il s'agit d'une jauge de type à inclusion elastique elaborée des changes des contraintes en cavité
outerraine. Les deformations du corps de la jauge provenant des transformations des contraintes escercées sur
a masse rocheuse sont enregistrées comme une altération des temps de vibration d'un fil haute tension traver-
ant diamétralement la jauge. It est prouvé que les modules d'elasticité de roches n'affectent que trés peu
es releves de la jauge. Les techniques destinées à fournir l'estimation des variations des contraintes uni-
xiales et bi-axiales sont décrites.

NTRODUCTION

he Vibrating Wire Stressmeter has been developed with
.S. Bureau of Mines funding to fill the need for a
ow cost gauge to monitor long term stress changes
round underground excavations. The gauge was
equired to be stable, have adequate resolution and be
asy to set and read at depths to 120 ft in boreholes
rilled by equipment readily available in mines. An
dditional requirement was that the gauge be intrin-
ically safe (incapable of igniting methane gas) for
se in coal mines.

ow cost is essential for any gauge intended for long
erm stress change monitoring. There is little point
n developing an ultra precise gauge with a cost that
nly permits it to be used in small numbers. With
ew exceptions the need is to obtain an overall
icture of any stress changes rather than a limited
umber of highly precise values. Thus the emphasis
uring the development of the Vibrating Wire Stress-
eter has been on trying to achieve the required
erformance at minimum cost.

he initial development work was divided into three
ain areas: gauge, readout meter and setting equip-
ent. Later, the gauges and equipment were evaluated
in the laboratory and in field trials in two underground mines. To December 1973, around 200 gauges had
been built and tested.

This paper describes the basic design of the gauge
and the theory of its use. Details of the setting
equipment and results obtained in the laboratory stability tests and field trials are presented in a
separate publication (Hawkes and Bailey, 1973).

VIBRATING WIRE STRESSMETER

The Vibrating Wire Stressmeter consists of a hollow
steel cylinder which, in use, is preloaded diametrically across the sides of a 1 1/2-in (38-mm)
diameter borehole by means of a sliding wedge and
platen assembly (Fig. 1). Stress changes in the
surrounding rock cause small changes in the diameter
of the cylinder. These are measured in terms of the
natural frequency of vibration of a high tensile
steel wire stretched diametrically across the cylinder
walls in the preload direction.

By calibration, changes in the wire period (time for
one cycle of vibration) have been related to the
magnitude of stress change for a range of rock types.
Because the presence of the stressmeter modifies the

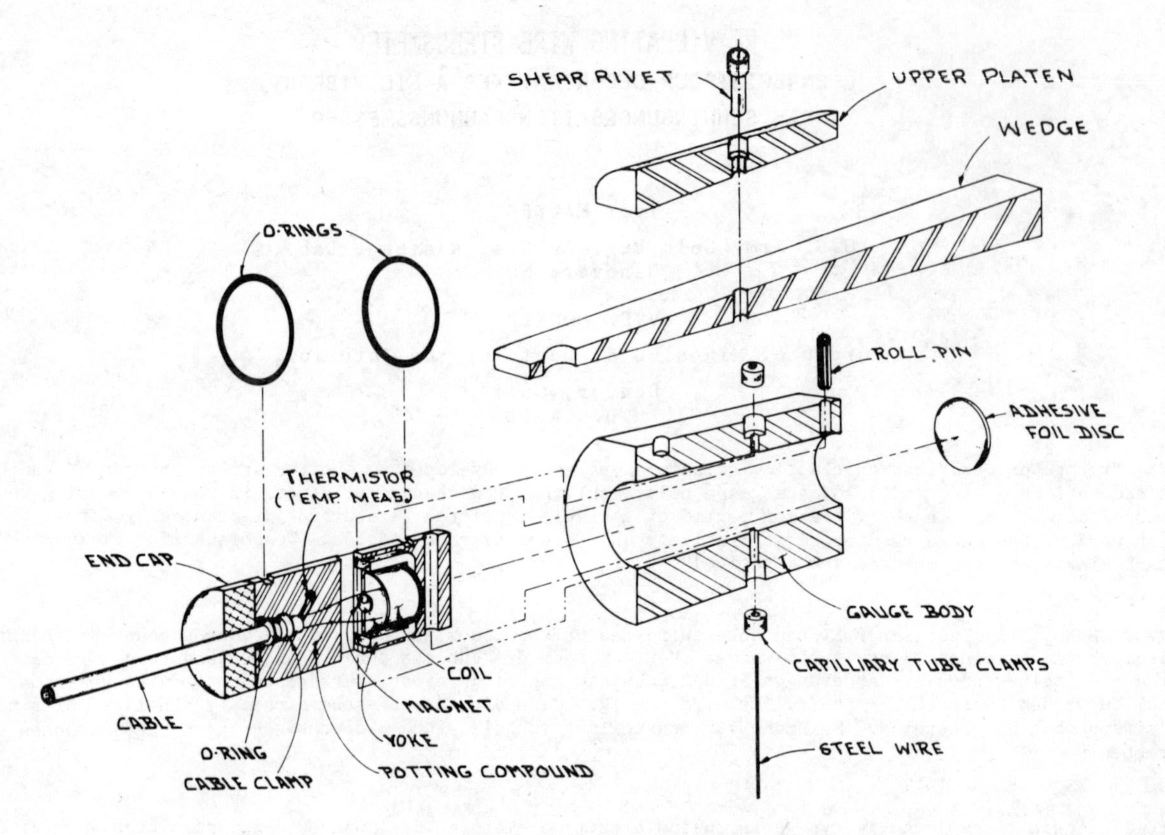

Figure 1. Exploded View of the Vibrating Wire Stressmeter

deformation of the borehole when the stress in the surrounding rock changes, conversion of the gauge readings to rock stress values does not require an accurate knowledge of the rock modulus; hence the use of the term stressmeter.

The stressmeter is unidirectional, and to completely evaluate the stress change in the plane of the borehole the readings of three stressmeters, set at specific angles to each other in the same or parallel boreholes, are required. However, in many cases, particularly when making measurements in pillars, it is probable that the stress change will be uniaxial and in a predictable direction, in which case only one gauge will be necessary for its evaluation.

Referring to Figure 1, the main element of the stressmeter is a cylindrical body, which is hardened and heat treated to 2×10^5 psi (1.38×10^6 kPa) yield strength. The high tensile steel wire (over 4×10^5 psi (2.76×10^6 kPa) tensile strength) is clamped into the body at a predetermined tension during manufacture by extruding stainless steel capillary tubes over the wire ends. The wire thus forms an integral part of the cylinder and adjustments to its tension other than by preloading are not possible. The wire tension, set during manufacture, is decreased when the gauge is preloaded in a borehole, and further decreased when compressive rock stress changes occur. This and the fact the wire tension never exceeds 20% of the ultimate strength of the wire contribute to ensuring long-term stability.

The coil, magnet and yoke (Fig. 1) are used to vibrate the wire at its natural frequency so that the distortion of the gauge body, produced by changes of rock stress, can be precisely determined in terms of the vibration period (time for one vibration cycle). A thermistor can be incorporated into the gauge to measure the rock temperature. All the electrical components are encapsulated in reinforced epoxy resi to protect them from damage, and O-rings are used to seal the encapsulated unit (gauges can be set in vertical, water filled boreholes).

No special terminals are required for the gauge cables as the wire vibration signals are not affecte by cable contact resistance. Gauge readings can be taken through cables over a mile long without error and the readout meter need only be coupled to gauges by simple clips when readings are required.

Gauge setting is accomplished using a setting tool that pulls the wedge member through a hole in its leading edge, relative to the platen and gauge body and thus preloads the gauge and platen against the borehole walls at diametrically opposite points. Under favorable conditions it is possible to recover the gauge body after use by hammering on the wedge t separate the three components.

MB3 VIBRATING WIRE READOUT METER

Difficulties were encountered in the development of suitable readout meter because of the need to pluck a short (0.78-in. or 21.4-mm) and highly tensioned (8×10^4 psi or 5.5×10^4 kPa) wire with the limited power called for by the intrinsic safety requirement

The MB3 Vibrating Wire Meter finally evolved is battery-powered with solid state electronics to produce a compact, portable meter. A digital array displays the wire vibration period (inverse frequency) to 10^{-7} sec and its accuracy is ensured by a high frequency (10^5 Hz) quartz oscillator, accurate to 0.002% over an operating range of 32° to 140°F.

The meter operates by feeding AC voltage pulses to the coil in the stressmeter, each pulse consisting of 32 cycles at a frequency selected randomly by the operator through a tuning knob. If the frequency is within a few percent of the natural frequency of the wire, then the wire will vibrate as a result of the forces set up in it by the changing magnetic field around the coil. Once excited, the wire continues to vibrate after each pulse, and, because there is still a magnetic field from the permanent magnet, an AC voltage signal at the wire vibration frequency will be generated in the coil. The meter then amplifies this signal and feeds it back to the coil as the next pulse. Once a signal has been received back from the stressmeter, the readout meter logic takes over from the operator for the fine tuning. In this manner, the meter locks onto the natural frequency of the wire. When the meter senses that the wire is oscillating at constant frequency, 100 cycles of the wire vibration are timed and then the count of the 10^5 Hz oscillator over the same time period is displayed on the digital array. The four digit display on the meter face gives the period of the wire vibration to 10^{-7} sec and is referred to as the meter or gauge reading (symbol T). The reading range is from 1500 to 4500 units, which actually represents a period change of the vibrating wire from 1500 x 10^{-7} to 4500 x 10^{-7} sec.

The various elements in the readout unit are shown schematically in Figure 2. The complete operation to take a reading only takes a few seconds and very little skill is required.

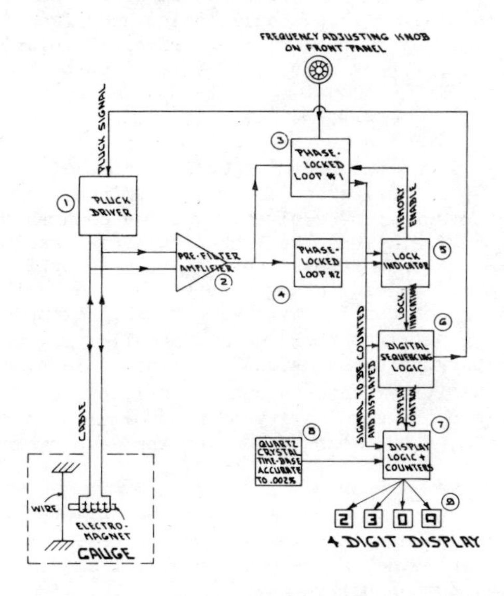

Figure 2. Schematic of Electronics of MB3 Vibrating Wire Meter

GAUGE STRAIN SENSITIVITY

The basic relationships between the natural frequency f (or period T_p) of a tensioned wire and its stress σ and strain ε are given by:

$$f = \frac{1}{T_p} = \frac{1}{2\ell}\sqrt{\frac{\sigma g}{\rho}} = \frac{1}{2\ell}\sqrt{\frac{E\varepsilon g}{\rho}} \quad (1)$$

where ℓ, E and ρ are the length, modulus and density of the wire respectively and g the gravitational constant. From Eq. (1) the wire deformation Δ is given by:

$$\Delta = \frac{4\ell^3 \rho f^2}{Eg}$$

For the Vibrating Wire Stressmeter, in English units, $E = 30 \times 10^6$ psi, $\ell = 0.780$ in, $g = 386$ in/sec^2 and $\rho = 0.283$ lb/in^3 and so the deformation is:

$$\Delta = 4.639 \times 10^{-11} f^2 = \frac{4.639 \times 10^3}{T^2} \text{ in.} \quad (2)$$

(T is the four digit meter reading; the period is T x 10^{-7} sec.) Figure 3 shows the theoretical gauge deformation plotted against meter reading and also experimental results taken with the gauge body and wedge assembly mounted in a steel test fixture having a platen radius, 3/4 in (19 mm). The difference between the experimental and theoretical deformations is attributed to the stiffness of the wedge assembly and flattening of the platen/body/wedge assembly contact points. Over a meter reading range of 1500 to 4500 units the overall deformation is of the order of 0.003 in. (0.075 mm).

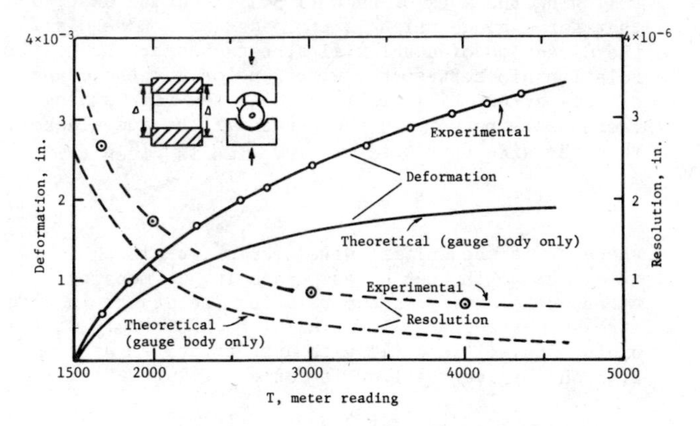

Figure 3. Gauge strain sensitivity

From Eq. (2) the gauge sensitivity to deformation, δΔ, can be obtained by differentiation:

$$\delta\Delta = \frac{9.278 \times 10^3}{T^3} \text{ in.} \quad (3)$$

The theoretical gauge body sensitivity and the measured values for the body and wedge assembly are also plotted in Figure 3 against period. At the higher period readings it is possible to resolve deformation changes of the gauge body of the order of 0.1 x 10^{-6} in. (2.5 x 10^{-6} mm). This is reduced in practice to a sensitivity of around 0.5 x 10^{-6} in. (12.5 x 10^{-6} mm) because of deformation of the wedge assembly and platen contact points.

The overall gauge stiffness was measured at 5.7 x 10^6 lb/in. (10^7 N/cm). Increasing the contact area of the platens increases the value slightly to the order of 6 x 10^6 lb/in. (1.05 x 10^7 N/cm).

GAUGE STRESS SENSITIVITY

Most of the gauges that have been developed for the evaluation of stress fields in rock masses are unidirectional, and the Vibrating Wire Stressmeter is no different in this respect. It is therefore inevitable that the bulk of the measurements made with the gauge will be aimed at evaluating an assumed uniaxial stress change. In many cases, particularly for measurements in pillars in flat sedimentary type rocks, the direction and uniaxial nature of the stress change can probably be assumed without significant error.

It is anticipated that the main use of the Vibrating Wire Stressmeter will be as a stability gauge to provide information as to whether or not the rock or coal around a given excavation is undergoing stress changes. Absolute magnitudes of stress change may not be as important as rates of change or relative changes in different regions, particularly as the absolute stress levels will not usually be known and cannot be obtained by the Vibrating Wire Stressmeter.

Uniaxial Stress Changes

The relationship between the gauge readings and the stress change in any particular rock is a function of the gauge preload setting (initial gauge reading), the orientation of the gauge relative to the principal stress directions and to some extent the rock modulus. Following the work of Hast (1958) it can be assumed that for a gauge which is preloaded in a borehole in the direction of a uniaxial stress change, the relationship between the wire tension and the change of rock stress will be linear. As the rock stress increases, the wire in the gauge will become slacker; thus the wire tension σ_w at any time is given by:

$$\sigma_w = \sigma_o - \sigma_r \alpha \qquad (4)$$

where σ_o is the initial wire tension, σ_r is the uniaxial change in rock stress and α is a dimensionless stress sensitivity factor relating the change in wire stress to the change in uniaxial rock stress. Combining Eqs. (1) and (4) with appropriate values for ℓ, E and ρ given earlier it can be shown that:

$$\sigma_r = \frac{1}{\alpha}\left[1 - \left(\frac{T_o}{T}\right)^2\right]\left[\frac{422400}{T_o}\right]^2 \text{ psi}^* \qquad (5)$$

where T_o is the initial meter reading and T the reading after the stress change. Figure 4 shows the results of calibration tests made to determine the uniaxial stress sensitivity factor, α, as a function of rock type. The tests were made under plain stress loading conditions in 2 x 8 x 16 in. (50 x 200 x 400 mm) slabs. The experimental points at the lower stress level changes were obtained with gauges set with an initial meter reading (T_o) around 1600 units. The experimental points at the upper stress level changes for Barre granite and Lucite were obtained using gauges set with an initial meter reading (T_o) of around 2200 units. These latter results have been fitted to the extrapolated graphs of the results obtained with the gauges set at the lower readings. This procedure was necessary to check the α values at high meter readings without risking failure of the test slabs.

*To convert to kilopascal multiply by 6.89.

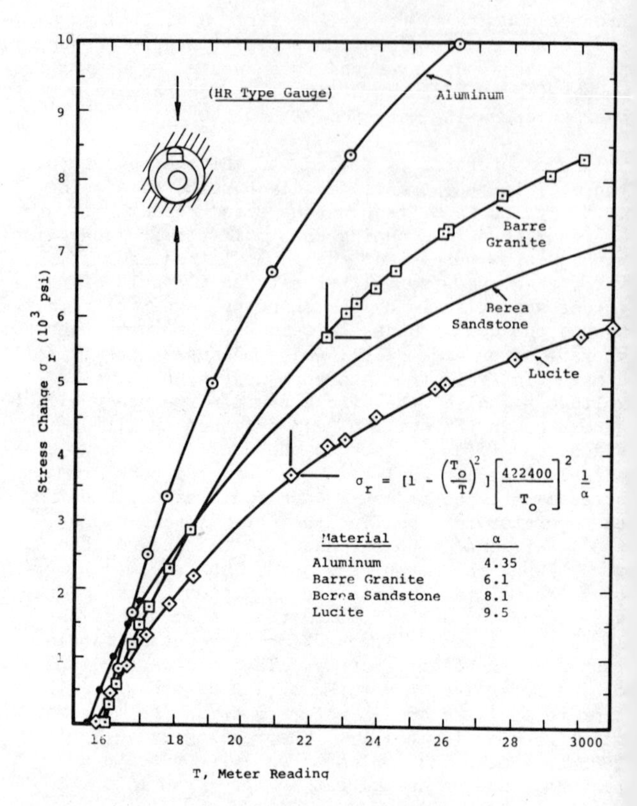

Figure 4. Uniaxial Calibration
(Solid lines through data points are plots of equation 5 with appropriate stress sensitivity factor, α)

Figure 5 is a plot of the uniaxial stress sensitivit factor α against rock modulus calculated from the da presented in Figure 4. The experimental relationshi between α and rock modulus, E_r, is given by:

$$\alpha = 9.4 - 0.5 \times 10^{-6} E_r \qquad (6$$

where E_r is in psi units*. Over a range of moduli, 4×10^5 psi (Lucite) to 10^7 psi (aluminum), a factor of 25, the stress sensitivity factor α changes only b a factor of 2. Thus the Vibrating Wire Stressmeter, while not a true stressmeter, is relatively insensitive to the modulus changes that would cause large errors in deformation type gauges. For example, wit the gauge set into rocks having moduli lying betweer sedimentary Berea sandstone and igneous Barre granit the sensitivity factor α changes only by 20%. For comparison the sensitivity of a deformation meter would change by around 250% over the same range of rock types.

Combining Eqs. (5) and (6) gives the relationship between a change in uniaxial rock stress, σ_r, the initial and final gauge readings T_o, T and the rock modulus, E_r (in psi units):

$$\sigma_r = \frac{\left[1 - \left(\frac{T_o}{T}\right)^2\right]\left[\frac{422400}{T_o}\right]^2}{9.4 - 0.5 \times 10^{-6} E_r} \text{ psi}^* \qquad (7$$

While Eq. (7) can be solved with a hand calculator, it is cumbersome. Possibly a better way of converting gauge reading to uniaxial rock stress is to determine the average gauge sensitivity over the

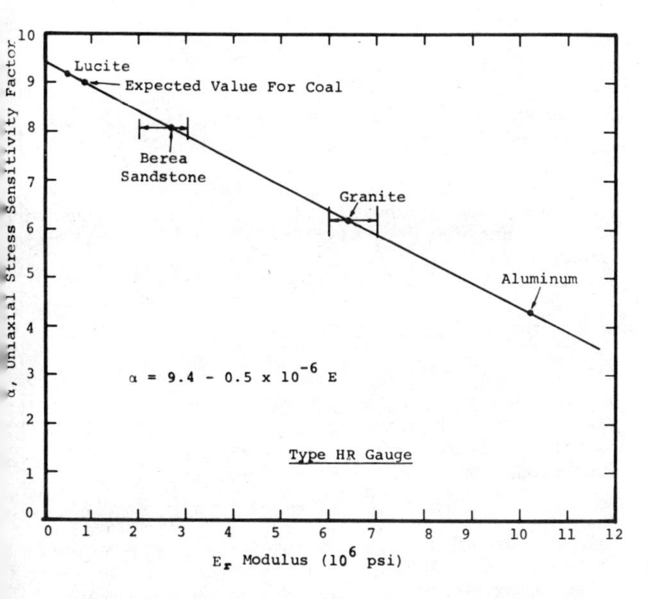

Figure 5. Relationship between the Stress Sensitivity Factor, α, and Rock Modulus

ange of readings and then multiply the change in ;auge reading by the gauge sensitivity to obtain the tress change. To do this it is necessary to calcuate the gauge uniaxial sensitivity, S.

ifferentiating Eq. (7) with respect to T, the unixial stress sensitivity, S, is given by:

$$S = \frac{3.568 \times 10^{11}}{(9.4 - 0.5 \times 10^{-6} E_r)\, T^3} \quad \text{psi*/unit meter reading} \qquad (8)$$

igure 6 is a plot of S, the gauge sensitivity gainst T, the meter reading for a range of moduli nd rock types. The sensitivity is as high as 2 psi 14 kPa) uniaxial stress change for the higher meter eadings, decreasing to the order of 10 psi (70 kPa) t lower readings. Thus with the same basic gauge esign, by setting the initial wire tension within ifferent predetermined ranges during manufacture, t is possible to have either a highly sensitive auge with a limited range or a less sensitive gauge ith a wide range.

o demonstrate the use of Figure 6 a simple example an be described. Suppose that a gauge set in Barre ranite changes from an initial preload reading of 200 to 2800 units in what is assumed to be a uniaxial tress field in the direction of gauge preload. The verage gauge reading is 2300 units and from Figure this corresponds to a uniaxial stress sensitivity f 4.8 psi (33 kPa)/unit meter reading. Thus the tress change is 200 x 4.8 = 960 psi (6600 kPa).

Biaxial Stress Changes

o resolve the magnitudes and direction of the econdary principal stress changes in the plane of a orehole three gauges are required set at specific ngles to each stress.

To convert to kilopascal multiply by 6.89.

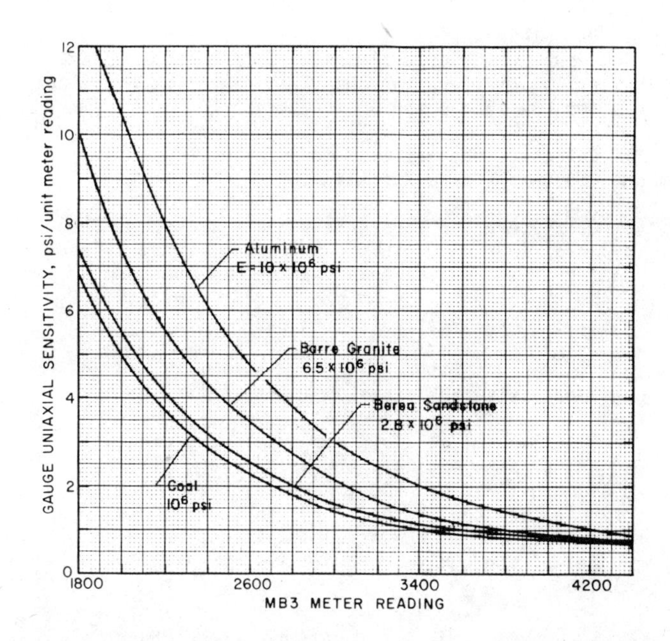

Figure 6. Gauge Uniaxial Sensitivity

It has been shown by Hast (1958) and confirmed by Hawkes (1972) that the stress change σ_θ in any direction θ (θ measured counterclockwise from the direction of σ_1) is given by:

$$\sigma_\theta = \frac{1}{3}(\sigma_1 + \sigma_2) + \frac{2}{3}(\sigma_1 - \sigma_2)\cos 2\theta \qquad (9)$$

where σ_1 and σ_2 are the secondary principal stresses in the plane of the borehole.

From this relationship it can be deduced that if three uniaxial stress change measurements are made, one vertical, one horizontal and one at 45° to vertical (σ_V, σ_H and σ_{45}), then the secondary principal stresses σ_1, σ_2 and the angle θ are given by:

$$\sigma_1 = \frac{3}{2}a + \frac{3}{4}b \qquad (10)$$

$$\sigma_2 = \frac{3}{2}a - \frac{3}{4}b \qquad (11)$$

$$\theta = \frac{1}{2}\sin^{-1}\frac{a - \sigma_{45}}{b} \qquad (12)$$

where

$$a = \frac{\sigma_V + \sigma_H}{2} \qquad (13)$$

$$b = [(\sigma_{45} - a)^2 + (\sigma_V - a)^2]^{1/2} . \qquad (14)$$

The proposed technique is as follows:

1. Set three gauges in one or more boreholes so that the first gauge is set vertical, the second at 45° to the first (counterclockwise looking down the borehole), and the third horizontal.

2. Calculate the total uniaxial stress change for each gauge as described earlier. Denote the uniaxial stress changes: σ_V for the first gauge (set vertical), σ_{45} for the second and σ_H for the third.

3. Calculate the value of constant a from Eq. (13) and constant b from Eq. (14).

4. Substitute the constants a and b into Eqs. (10), (11) and (12) to obtain the magnitude of the stress changes of the two secondary principal stresses σ_1 and σ_2 and the orientation of the principal stress σ_1, relative to the vertical.

To illustrate the technique a specific example can be considered with the stresses in psi units.

Three gauges are set in a borehole. The first, No. P106HR, is set vertical; the second, No. P107HR, at 45° to the first counterclockwise looking down the borehole; and the third, No. P108HR, horizontal (90° to the first). As the stress builds up the readings change and the equivalent uniaxial stresses are calculated.

Gauge No.	Uniaxial stress change Symbol	Value (psi)
P106HR	σ_V	667
P107HR	σ_{45}	814
P108HR	σ_H	267

Calculate value of constant a

$$a = \frac{\sigma_V + \sigma_H}{2} = \frac{667 + 267}{2} = 467 \text{ psi.}$$

Calculate value of constant b

$$b = [(\sigma_{45} - a)^2 + (\sigma_V - a)^2]^{1/2}$$
$$= [(814 - 467)^2 + (667 - 467)^2]^{1/2}$$
$$= 400 \text{ psi.}$$

Calculate secondary principal stress change σ_1:

$$\sigma_1 = \frac{3}{2}a + \frac{3}{4}b = \frac{3 \times 467}{2} + \frac{3 \times 400}{4}$$
$$= 1000 \text{ psi.}$$

Calculate secondary principal stress change σ_2:

$$\sigma_2 = \frac{3}{2}a - \frac{3}{4}b = \frac{3 \times 467}{2} + \frac{3 \times 400}{4}$$
$$= 400 \text{ psi.}$$

Calculate orientation of σ_1 relative to setting direction of gauge No. P106HR (σ_θ uniaxial stress change)

$$\sin 2\theta = \frac{a - \sigma_{45}}{b} = \frac{467 - 814}{400} = -0.868$$

$$\theta = -30° .$$

The negative sign means that vertical (σ_V direction) is clockwise from the σ_1 secondary principal stress direction.

In summary the secondary principal stress changes are 1000 psi and 400 psi, with the direction of the major change at an angle of 30° counterclockwise from vertical.

LABORATORY AND FIELD TESTS

A discussion of the laboratory and field trials is beyond the scope of the paper. But briefly, fourteen gauges have been tested in steel, aluminum and a variety of rock blocks under adverse environmental conditions for a period of 6 months without any failures or significant changes in readings.

Prior to December 1973, seventeen gauges have been set in two mines with only one failure due to the lead wires being cut by the borehole crushing. The gauges are functioning as expected and readings will continue to be taken over the next year or so.

ACKNOWLEDGEMENTS

The work reported here was carried out at CREARE Inc. Hanover, NH, under U. S. Bureau of Mines Contract H0220050.

REFERENCES

Hast, N., 1958, The measurement of rock pressure in mines. Sur. Geol. Unders. Afh, 52, Series C, 3, pp. 12-16.

Hawkes, I., 1972, Photoelastic Unidirectional (PU) Stress Meter - A Borehole Rock Stress Gage. Proc. Tenth Sym. on Rock Mechs., Univ. of Texas, Austin, 1968 (pub. 1972), pp. 503-521.

Hawkes, I. and Bailey, W. V., 1973, Low Cost Cylindrical Stress Gauge, CREARE Report No. TN-167, 90 p.

DISPLACEMENT MEASUREMENTS OF HIGH ACCURACY IN UNDERGROUND OPENINGS

MESURES DE HAUTE PRECISION DES DÉFORMATIONS D'OUVRAGES SOUTERRAINS

DEFORMATIONSMESSUNGEN HOHER GENAUIGKEIT IM UNTERTAGEBAU

K. KOVARI — Dr. sc.techn. Dipl.Ing.

Ch. AMSTAD — Dipl.Ing.

H. GROB — Professor, Dipl. Ing.

Institut für Strassen- und Untertagebau an der Eidg. Technischen Hochschule Zürich, Switzerland

JMMARY Simple and reliable displacement measurements, as a means for the continuous obser-
ation of the behaviour of underground works during every construction phase, provide an in-
spensable help for a safe and economical execution. The displacement measurements enable to:
immediately verify the adequateness of the selected construction method and of the safety
measures adopted
determine, at an early stage, possible instabilities which cannot be detected visually
draw conclusions about the overall rock quality with help of a stress analysis based upon
an estimated or measured primary state of stress.
rticularly useful information is obtained from the measurements of the displacements resul-
ng from the excavation. The present paper deals with the problem of the practical execution
convergence measurements and also describes a recently developed precision instrument,
e ISETH-DISTOMETER, which is particularly adequate for use in underground works. Due to
s simple operation, solid construction, reduced possibility of errors and adaptability to
e difficult underground working conditions, this instrument has been successfully used in
ny instances.

SAMMENFASSUNG Die laufende Beobachtung des Verhaltens von Untertagbauten in jeder Kon-
ruktionsphase durch einfache, aber zuverlässige Deformationsmessungen bietet ein unentbehr-
ches Hilfsmittel für die sichere und wirtschaftliche Bauausführung. Aus den gemessenen De-
rmationen kann man:
die Richtigkeit der gewählten Baumethode und Sicherungsmassnahmen unmittelbar bestätigen
die ev. nicht sichtbare Instabilität bestimmter Felspartien rechtzeitig feststellen und
mit einer rechnerischen Spannungsanalyse bei Abschätzung oder Messung des primären Spannungszustandes die Qualität des Felsens im Grossbereich kennzeichnen.
e gemessenen Verschiebungen, die sich durch den fortschreitenden Ausbruch ergeben, stellen
sonders gut verwertbare Informationen dar.
e folgende Arbeit befasst sich mit dem Problem der praktischen Durchführung von Konvergenz-
ssungen und berichtet über das neuentwickelte Präzisionsinstrument, "ISETH-DISTOMETER",
lches in der konstruktiven Ausbildung den besonderen Gegebenheiten des Untertagbaues Rech-
ng trägt. Einfache und rasche Bedienung, robuster Bau, geringe Fehleranfälligkeit und An-
ssungsfähigkeit an die erschwerten Arbeitsbedingungen des Untertagbaues haben den Erfolg
r Messungen bei zahlreichen Anwendungen gesichert.

SUME L'observation du comportement des ouvrages souterrains pendant chaque phase de
nstruction par des mesures de déformation simples mais sûres est le moyen le plus effi-
ce pour garantir une exécution correcte et économique des travaux. A partir de la mesure
s déformations, il est possible de:
confirmer immédiatement le propre choix de la méthode de construction et du procédé de
soutènement,
localiser les zones éventuelles de roche instable qui ne peuvent pas être détectées à
l'oeil nu,
déterminer la qualité du massif de roche par une analyse numérique des contraintes, l'état
primaire étant soit estimé, soit défini sur la base de mesures.
étude présente traite du problème de l'exécution pratique des mesures de convergence et dé-
it le DISTOMETRE-ISETH, un instrument de précision développé récemment. Par sa conception,
instrument est bien adapté aux circonstances particulières de la construction souter-
ine. Un maniement simple et rapide, une construction robuste, un fonctionnement peu sus-
tible d'erreurs et une grande adaptabilité aux conditions difficiles du travail en souter-
in ont contribué au succès des mesures.

1. Introduction

Inherent uncertainties in the numerical analysis of underground structures and the inadequacy of subjective decisions based upon experience generally raise the need for rock mechanic measurements on the site. The observation of deformations and movements is of particular interest, since displacements can be measured in a simple and accurate way and the results easily interpreted. Based upon the displacements corresponding to the different construction stages and varying in time, it is possible to draw conclusions regarding the rock quality and the development of rock loads. Since this information is quantitative, important engineering decisions may be taken on a rational basis. The measurement of convergences, i.e. of the changes in the distance between two points of the excavation or lining surface, is one of the simplest and least expensive operations. In the following, a description of the construction, operation and error analysis of a recently developed instrument for such measurements - the ISETH-DISTOMETER - is given (Fig.1). This device is particularly adequate for use in underground construction since it meets at a high level the requirements of difficult working conditions.

2. Description of the ISETH-DISTOMETER

The following important aspects were aimed at during the development and construction of the apparatus:

a) The average error m of a measurement should not exceed m=±0.02 mm for a measuring distance of l=5.0 m.

b) The need for carrying out such measurements quickly in order to avoid disturbance of the circulation or construction activity in the best possible way.

c) straight forward handling of the apparatus enabling these measurements to be carried out by site supervision personnel

d) sturdy construction in order to reduce the risk of damages

A high accuracy in the measurements is often required in practical situations, especially when the movement of a point can only be determined by indirect measurements with an unfavorable error propagation, or when the velocity of creep has to be determined in a short time. The best solution under such partly contradictory requirements was found on the well known base of the tensioned invar steel wire. With respect to the little space available in the majority of the underground works it was clear at once that a solution with pulleys and a weight for tensioning the wire could not be considered. The traction therefore has to be produced with great accuracy by a mechanical device. This is only possible by using a light but highly accurate dynamometer. The elastic deformation of a 1.0 mm diameter wire with a length of L_{AB}= 5 m and a tension of F=8.0 kg is Δ l= 2.4 mm. Since the required accuracy of a single measurement is ± 0.02 mm, the force has to be reproduced with an accuracy of ± 0.5 % to ± 0.8 % which corresponds to tolerance of approx. 50 grams. A special gadget is used for the precision tensioning of the wire. This is, fortunately, only required over a narrow range close to the get value of F=8 kg. The tensioning device moves the end of the wire towards the micrometer with the help of a precision thread.(Fig.2) A longitudinal bearing and a spring are used for the unrestrected precision setting of the instrument.

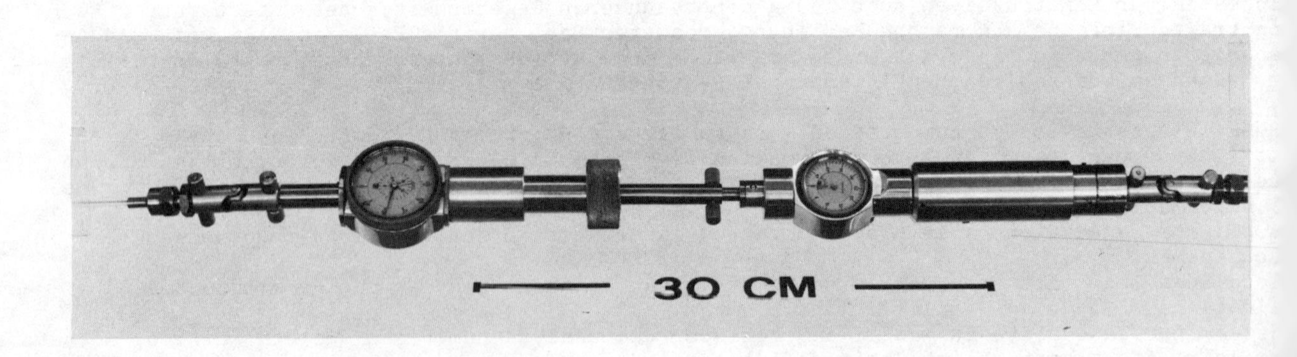

Fig. 1 The ISETH-DISTOMETER. The instrument is connected to the invar wire (left) and to a setting bolt (right).

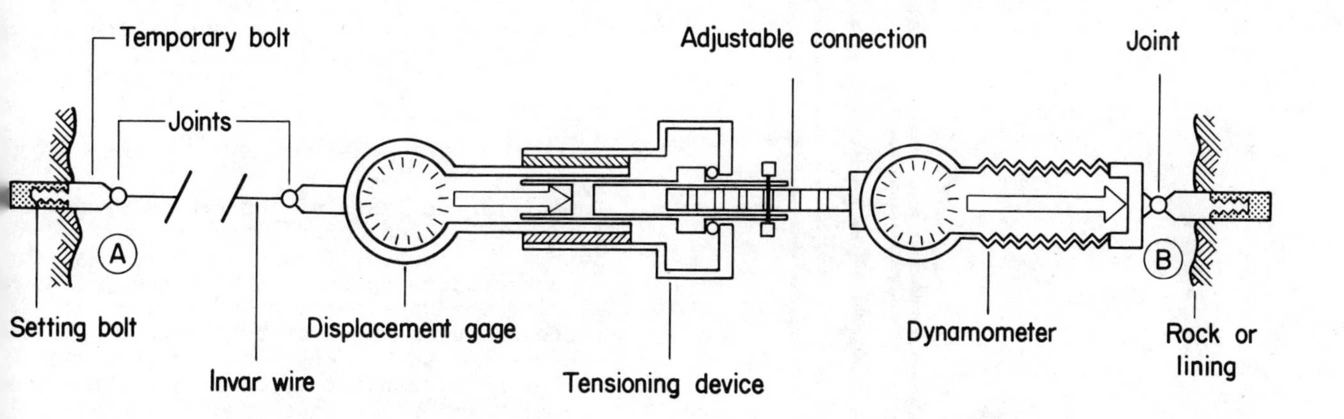

Fig. 2 Principle of the ISETH-DISTOMETER. The instrument is used for the determination of the changes in the distance between points A and B (L_{AB}).

ıe micrometer scale has divisions correspon-
.ng to 0.01 mm and a range of 25 mm. The
ınge of the instrument, however, is 100 mm
nce the connection between dynamometer and
ensioning device is adjustable (position
oles 10 mm apart).
weight is used for the control of the
'namometer which is calibrated at the be-
.nning of each series of measurements. A
.uge made of invar rods is used for the
ntrol of the instrument length (Fig. 4).
th this procedure it is possible to compen-
.te any temperature effect.

e wire is held by conical clamps construc-
d in such a way that no bending of the
re ends or an eventual rupture by fatigue
y occur. All connections are simple bolts.
iversal joints make it possible, to keep
static equilibrium of the system (instru-
nt + tensioned wire) completely free of
nstraints.

ere are setting bolts shown in Fig. 3
ich define the fixed points A and B. They
n be inserted either permanently into
illholes in rock or concrete or temporar-
y into little base plates welded on to
eel members, where they can be removed
ch time after measurements. In such a way
l permanent protrusions apt to be damaged
e avoided. For each basis length L_{AB} (Fig.
a separate wire with corresponding length
prepared. After use, the wire is rolled
over a spool for protection against any
ssible damaging or bending (Fig. 4).

2.1 Error analysis

The random and systematic errors as well as the possibilities of influencing these errors have to be analysed separately.

Random errors:
They are caused by friction at the joints, dispersion of the dynamometer readings and the possible inaccuracy of the connection bolts. In order to analyse the average error of a measurement, series of 20 measurements of various distances were carried out in an air conditioned room. Prior to each individual measurement, the instrument was unhooked from the setting bolts, the wire was wound up and unwound again, the instrument

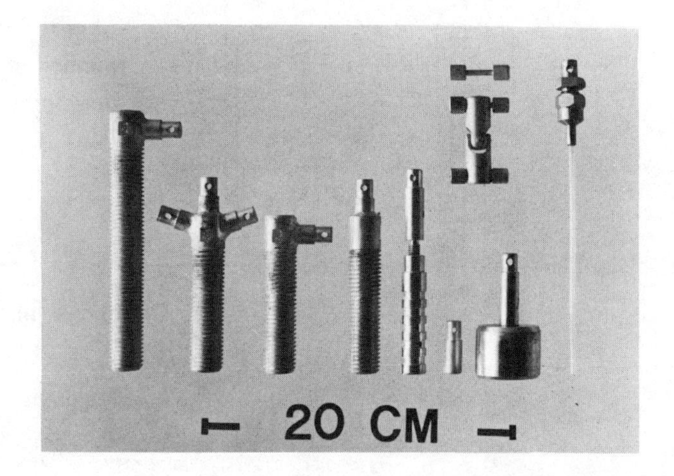

Fig. 3 Different types of setting bolts, joint and clamp for the invar wire.

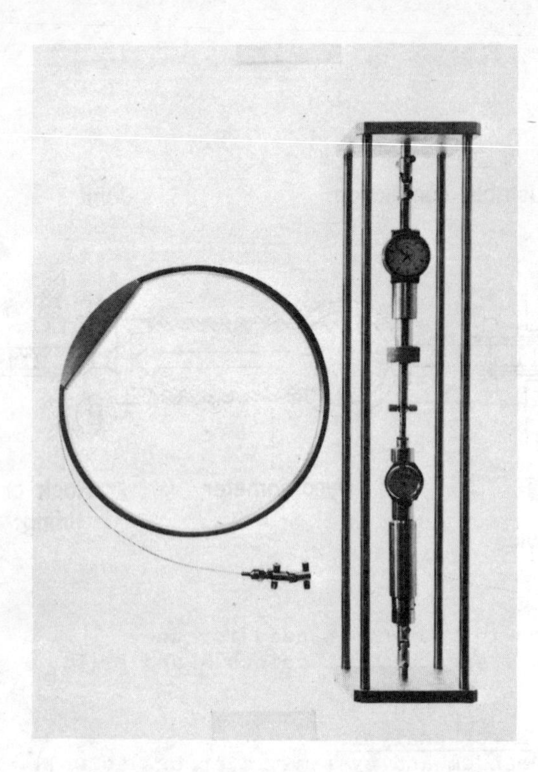

Fig.4 Spool for the invar wire and gauge made of invar rods used for the control of the instrument length.

hooked in, tensioned and the reading carried out. For each one of the series of 20 readings the mean values were determined. The distribution of the deviations about the mean are shown in Fig.5. The standard error of the mean value increases with the length measur as shown in Fig.6. For distances above 10 m the standard error of the mean of single readings is $10^{-6} \times L_{AB}$ approximately. In reali the movements of the fixed points are given by the difference of two readings. In order to receive their standard error the values indicated in Fig.6 have to be multiplied by $\sqrt{2}$.

Systematic errors:
During the analysis of the random errors ar interesting phenomenon, unknown to the authors, occurred. It was verified that due to consecutive operations of winding and ur winding the wire, it's modulus of elasticit increased by as much as 7 %. However, after a number of such operations a stable value of the modulus was reached. Fig.5 shows tha the high accuracy required could not be attained without "calming" the wire prior t measurement by a number of these handling operations. The results of Fig.5 were obtained with "calmed" wires and show that sy tematic errors may be eliminated. In cases in which a high accuracy is not necessary, this source of errors, naturally, becomes irrelevant.

3. Examples of actual measurements:

Among the numerous measurements already carried out with the ISETH-DISTOMETER, a few typical examples are described.

3.1 Determination of the contraction of a tunnel section due to the progress of the excavation front

The results of measurements are particular easy to interpret when the tunnel is excav ted by means of a tunnel boring machine.

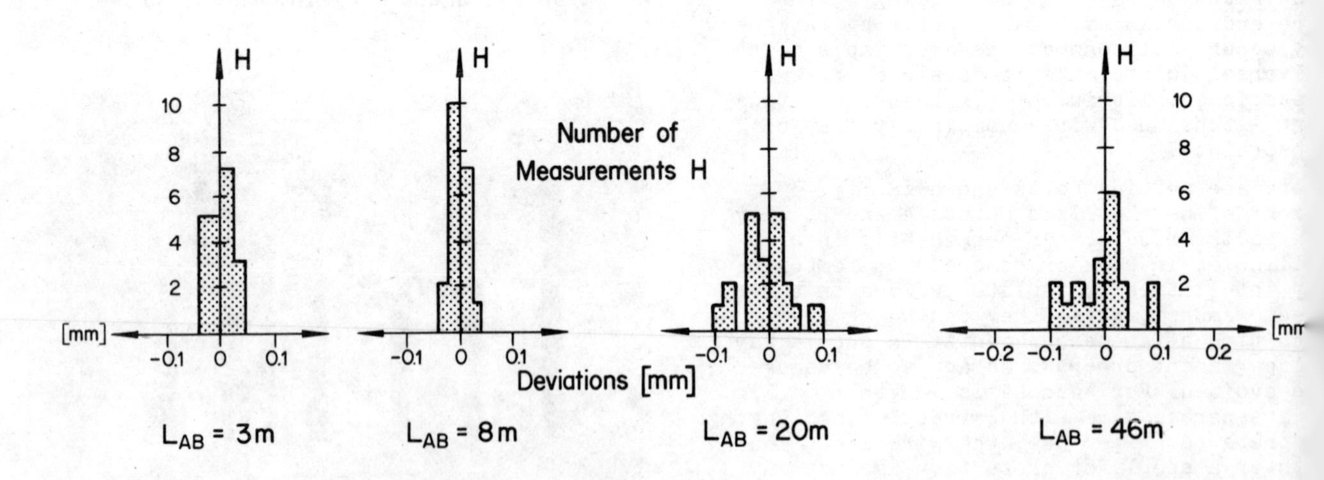

Fig.5 Hystogramm of the deviations of individual measurements from the arithmetic mean value for different distances L_{AB}.
After each measurement the instrument was removed and repositioned.

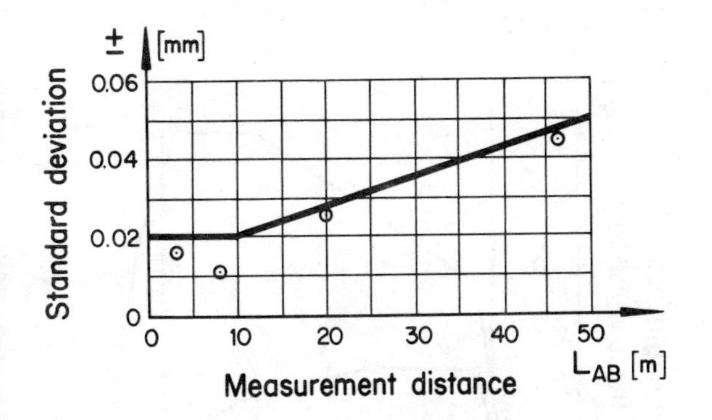

Fig.6 Standard error of the mean of measured values as a function of the distance L_{AB}. Results obtained using the distributions of Fig.5.

The rock remains practically undisturbed in the zone adjacent to the circular profile. A larger degree of loosening only occurs in the case of poor quality rock. After pulling back the machine the setting bolts can be installed in a section immediately adjacent to the excavation front and the first readings carried out (Fig.7). The second measurement is taken after some advance of the front. In this manner the tunnel profile deformation Δd which results from the elimination of the supporting action of the tunnel front (Fig.8) can be determined. If an elastic isotropic behaviour is assumed, the primary state of stress can be determined with the numerical analysis method of de la Cruz and Goodman (1). In the following the numerical determination of the ideal deformation modulus E of the rock, developed by these authors is utilised. As a first approximation we may assume that the primary state of stress is hydrostatic with an intensity p given by the height of the overburden and the specific weight of the rock. The modulus of elasticity E results from the formula:

$$E = 2k \frac{r \cdot p}{\Delta d} \qquad (\nu = 0.3)$$

$\frac{z}{r} = 0$ $k \simeq 0.95$

$\frac{z}{r} = 0.125$ $k = 0.61$

$\frac{z}{r} = 0.25$ $k = 0.47$

r: tunnel radius
Δd: measured change of diameter d (mean value)
z: distance between tunnel head and section S-S at the time of the first reading
k: dimensionless number

In general a variation of values Δd is obtained in the different directions. As long as the differences are relatively small an average value can be used for computation purpose. In spite of the simplified assumptions, the value of E provides valuable information regarding the global quality of the rock. Further periodic measurements provide information regarding the creep effects. A quick increase of deformations may indicate impending falls of material or complete failure of the surrounding rock.

The procedure described above was used in two tunnels excavated by tunnel boring machines. In spite of the limited space between machine and tunnel head and the short time available, adequate results could be obtained.

3.2 Deformation of a tunnel lining

In the Bächwald tunnel located along the Simplon highway (Kanton Wallis, Switzerland) at several locations, deformation measurements were carried out during construction. As the tunnel is following a steep slope consisting of talus and material with little

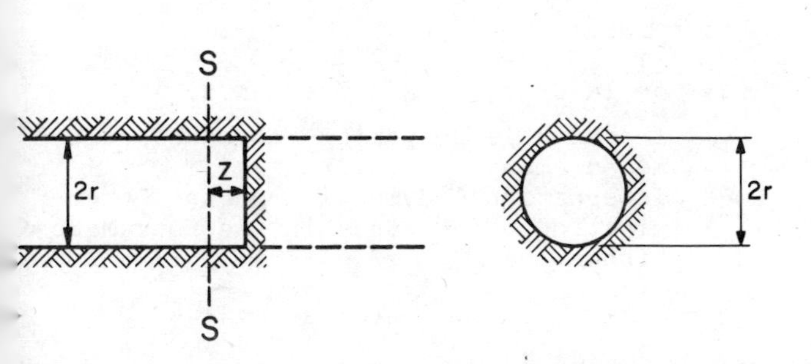

Fig.7 Location of section S-S for the determination of the tunnel contraction due to the excavation front progress.

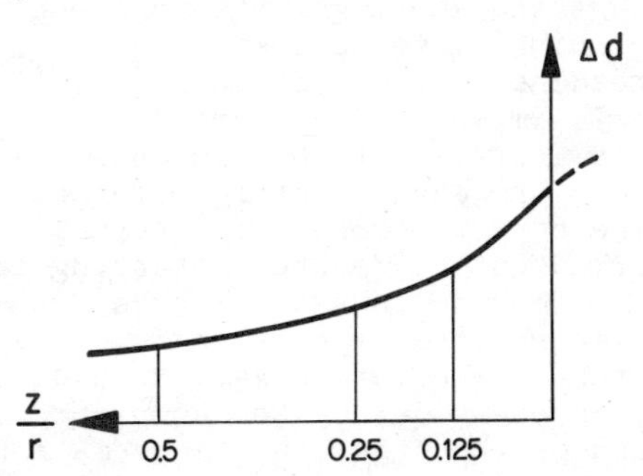

Fig.8 Measured reduction of the tunnel diameter Δd as a function of the distance between the measuring section and the excavation front.

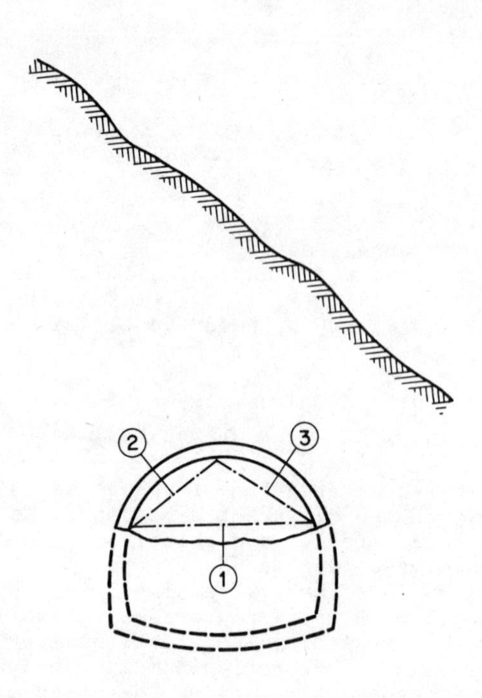

Fig.9 Bächwaldtunnel: Disposition of the control lengths (1), (2) and (3) on the vault.

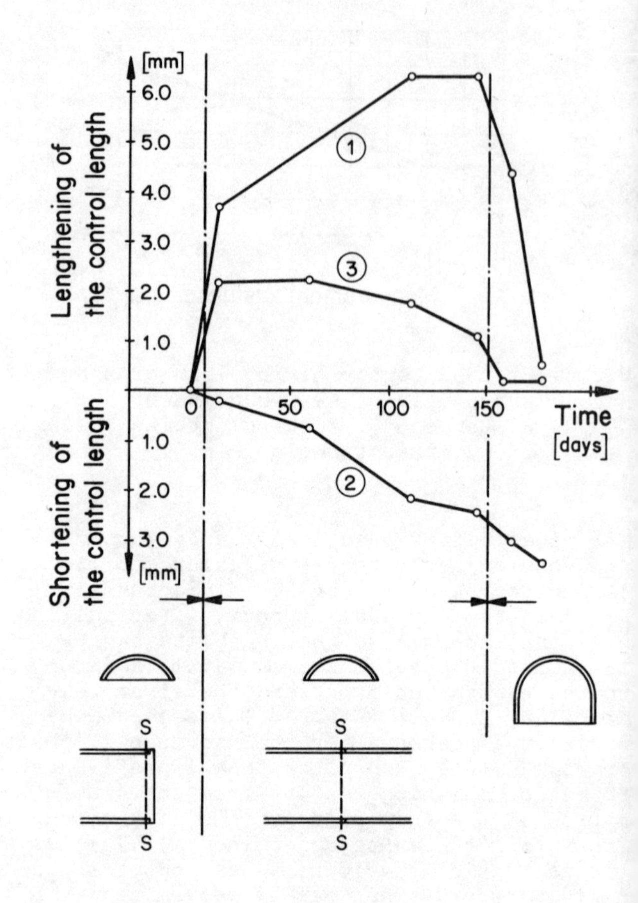

Fig.10 Bächwaldtunnel: Variations of the control lengths at different stages of construction.

cohesion, there was a fear of slides at the time of construction. However, observations during the construction and the results of measurements showed that the initial qualification of the rock was too pessimistic. The measured deformations of the lined vault resulting from the works progress provided reassuring information. During the first stage of construction only the head was excavated and the lining cast immediately. In this stage the setting bolts were embedded in the lining close to the tunnel head and a first reading of the distances (1), (2) and (3) (Fig.9) immediately recorded. Fig.10 shows the rapid increase of the distances (1) and (3), i.e., the advance effect of the tunnel head. The construction of the tunnel core was carried out by reaches, starting from the portal and moving inwards. The core was excavated over reaches of 8 m length, in such a manner that the concrete vault could be supported, on one side, by the completed lateral walls and on the other, by the remaining part of the core.

* * * * * * *

Literature:

(1) de la Cruz, R. and Goodman R.
The borhole deepening method of stress measurement,
International Symposium on the Determination of Stresses in the Rock Masses
Lisbon 1969

OBSERVATIONS ON THE PROCEDURES AND ON THE INTERPRETATION OF THE PLATE BEARING TEST

QUELQUES OBSERVATIONS SUR LES MÉTHODES D'EFFECTUATION ET SUR LES CRITÈRES D'INTERPRÉTATION DES ESSAIS DE CHARGEMENT SUR PLAQUE

EINIGE ERWÄGUNGEN ÜBER DIE AUSFÜHRUNGSMETHODEN UND AUSLEGUNGSKRITERIEN DER BELASTUNGSVERSUCHE AUF PLATTEN

G. MANFREDINI Research Assistant, Institute of Mining, University of Rome, Rome, Italy

S. MARTINETTI Italian State Electricity Board, Enel, Geotechnical Service, Rome

P.P. ROSSI Experimental Institute of Models and Structures, Bergamo

A. SAMPAOLO Italian State Electricity Board, Enel, Hydraulic and Structural Research Center, Milano, Italy

SUMMARY - Plate bearing tests are still a rapid and cheap means to assess rock mass deformability. Interpretation of the results, however, is complicated by the presence of loose zone having a much greater deformability than that of the undisturbed rock mass. The problem was tackled by means of an axissymmetrical finite-element model, and it was possible among other things, to establish the great influence exerted by even a thin loose zone of rock on the evaluation of the rock mass deformability. Based on this study, a method for interpretation of the test results was developed, whereby it is possible to obtain the deformability of both the loose zone and of the undisturbed rock through surface measurements of displacement of points located at different distances from the loading plate, and on the walls of a borehole drilled at the center of the loading area, if desirable. For this purpose, use it also made of seismic refraction measurements and seismic logging. The paper describes the equipment developed for the tests and provides a few results of a first measurements campaign.

RÉSUMÉ - L'interprétation des résultats des essais de chargement sur plaque est compliqué par la présence, en surface, d'une bande relâchée de matériel, ayant une déformabilité beaucoup plus grande que celle de l'amas rocheux intact. Le problème a été attaqué du point de vue théorique moyennant un modèle axe-symétrique composé d'éléments finis; l'étude a permis de faire ressortir l'influence élevée qui est exerxée par la presence d'une bande, même ayant une épaisseur mince, de matériel relâché. En se fondant sur cette étude l'on a mis au point un schéma d'effectuation des mesures qui prévoit le relèvement des déplacements en surface dans des points situés à différentes distance de la plaque de chargement (et, éventuellement, dans des points, aussi, situés sur la paroi d'un trou de forage au dessous du centre de la plaque elle même); en utilisant aussi les mesures de réfraction sismique en surface et de carotage sonique en trou il est possible ainsi d'obtenir soit les caractéristiques de déformabilité de la region relâchée soit les caractéristiques de l'amas rocheux intact.

ZUSAMMENFASSUNG - Die Plattenbelastungsversuche sind noch heute eine schnelle und ökonomische Methode für die Bewertung der Verformbarkeit der Gesteinsmassen. Die Ergebnisauswertung dieser Versuche wird jedoch durch das Erscheinen einer lockeren Materialschicht von unterschiedlicher Stärke an der Oberfläche erschwert die eine viel grössere Verformbarkeit im Vergleich zu der dahinter liegenden Gesteinsmasse hat. Das Problem wurde vom theoretischen Gesichtspunkt aus behandelt, und zwar mittels eines axisymmetrischen Modells mit der Methode der Finiten Elemente. Das studium hat under anderem ermöglicht, den grossen Einfluss hervorzuheben, der sich durch das Auftreten auch einer beschränkt starken Schicht lockeren Materials ergibt. Anhand dieses Studiums ist ein Schema der Messungsausführungen festgesetzt worden, welches die Aufnahme der Verschiebungen an der Oberfläche an Punkten verschiender Abstände von der Belastungsplatte (und eventuell auch an Punkten an der Bohrlochwand unterhalb der Mitte der Platte) vorsieht. Wenn man auch die Refraktion-Seismikmessungen an der Oberfläche und die Schallkernbohrungsmessungen anwendet, so ist es möglich, einerseits die Verformbarkeitseigenschaften der lockeren Zone und andererseits die der dahinter liegenden Gesteinsaufspeicherungen festzustellen.

1. FOREWORD

A "loose" zone of rock, that is, rock having distinctly inferior mechanical characteristics to those of "undisturbed" rock, forms from any underground or open-pit excavation in rock masses. This "loose" zone affects the results of the in-situ test that are carried out for the determination of the deformability of rock masses. However, the question of assessing the magnitude of this effect and its pratical significance has not been solved satisfactively yet. ENEL has always been interested in developing the knowledge of rock mechanics, and a few years ago it launched a vast research program, aimed partly at general matters and partly at applications to construction of new power-projects. The lines along which the program is proceeding were described in a recent paper (Dolcetta, 1972), to which the reader is referred also for the bibliography. Within the framework of this program, a study was also started on rock deformability measurements, which included a special investigation on the influence of a "loose" zone such as mentioned above. This paper summarizes the results obtained to date with reference only to plate bearing tests. The determination of the elasticity modulus of rock by means of this method requires relativity simple, sturdy equipment, which is generally easily handled. In addition, the test can be performed rather quickly and at a relatively low cost. Notwithstanding these advantages, the plate bearing test equipment and procedure have not yet been standardized, though the test is quite commonly adopted (Stagg. 1968). From the standpoint of the validity of the results, the factors that appear to be determinant are the bearing plane preparation, the loading method, and the sensitity and precision of the settlement recorders. As concerns the interpretation of the results, the method normally used is Boussinesq's theory for loads concentrated or spread over an elastic half-space, but this interpretation gives rise to a number of uncertainties, just as in some of the other tests. In tackling the matter of taking into account the presence of a superficial "loose" zone (unhomogeneous medium) in rock masses, we have therefore also performed a critical survey of some of the test procedures and equipment, in order to prevent any improvements in the theory from being obscured by faulty techniques (Benson, et al, 1966)

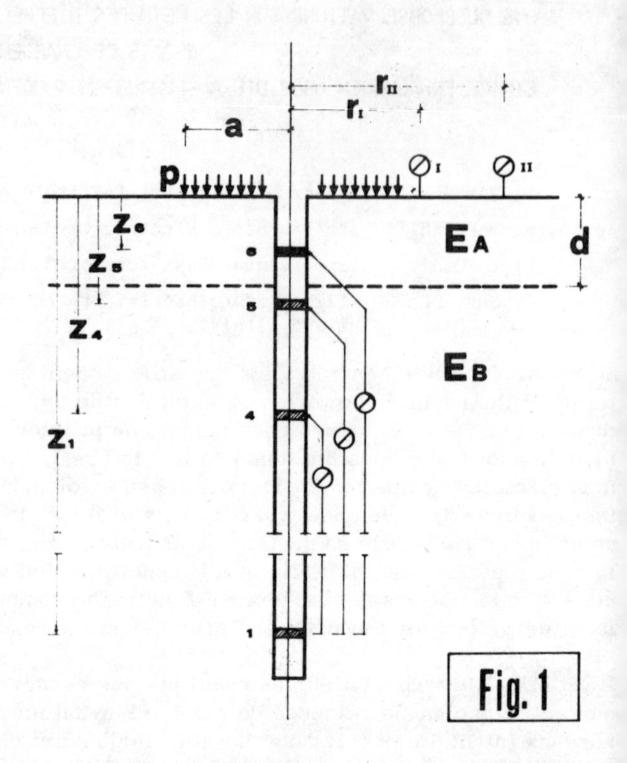

2. THEORETICAL STUDY OF STRATIFIED ROCK BEHAVIOR

The problem of determining the state of deformation of stratified rock was analyzed by means of photoelastic models and was solved analyti cally only for a few simple cases (Maury, 1970). In our study we have used the finite-element calculation method, which is known to be very flexible, and allows the use of less rigid and simplified theoretical schemes. At this stage, we considered the rock to be inhomogeneous but still isotropic and linearly elastic. However, the study can be extended as soon as sufficiently detailed information is available on the anisotropy and non-linearity of rock masses (Oberti et al, 1970; Martino e Ribacchi, 1972). The calculation in this study were performed by the Geotechnical Service of the National Studies and Design Center of ENEL, by means of a finite element computer code, AXSY, which is capable of solving linear-elasticity problems in axial symmetry conditions. A mesh of 790 linear-triangule elements and 435 nodis was developed. We considered the rock to be made up of only two constant-modulus layers (Fig. 1) even though it is to be expected that modulus will continually increase within the "loose" zone starting from very low values. However, the study could be easily extended to more realistic schemes.

A preliminary investigation was conducted for the purpose of checking the validity of some hy potesis and assumptions. The mesh validity check gave quite satisfactory results with known situation. The preliminary study also confirmed that the results obtained with a plate bearing test are largely dependent on the plate-to-rock rigidity ratio and on the presence or less of a block of concrete or other material. To avoi[d] uncertainties in the interpretation of the test results it is necessary to adopt loading systems that will simulate the theoretical interpretation models available today as faitfully as possible; for obvious techno lical reasons, the choice fell on the perfectly flexible plate model that can be realized by means of flat jacks resting directly on the loading surface. This preliminary study afforded, among other things, a confermation that the presence of a relatively large hole (0. 15 times the plate dimension in diameter) doe[s] not substantially affect the state of deformation, expecially when the reduction in total load due to the hole is taken into account. Based on these results, a detailed study was performed on the influence on the displacement of the individual points of the half-space exerted by each of the three essential parameters characterizing the model, that is, the modulus E_A of the loose zone, its thickness d, and the modulus E_B of the undisturbed rock. As Poisson's coefficient affects settlement very slightly (Stagg, 1968), it was assumed constant (ν =0, 2). Fig. 2 shows an adimensional representation of the settlement W in the direction of the applied load, calculated for a point at the surface, as a function of the ratios between the two rock moduli and between the thickness of the loose zone and plate radius. The figure show among other things that a small loose zone thickness causes an appreciable increase in settlement even if it is not very deformable.

Similar charts can be built for any other significant point, and the analysis can be repeated for other situations on the same mesh at very little cost. In determing the elastic moduli of the indisturbed and

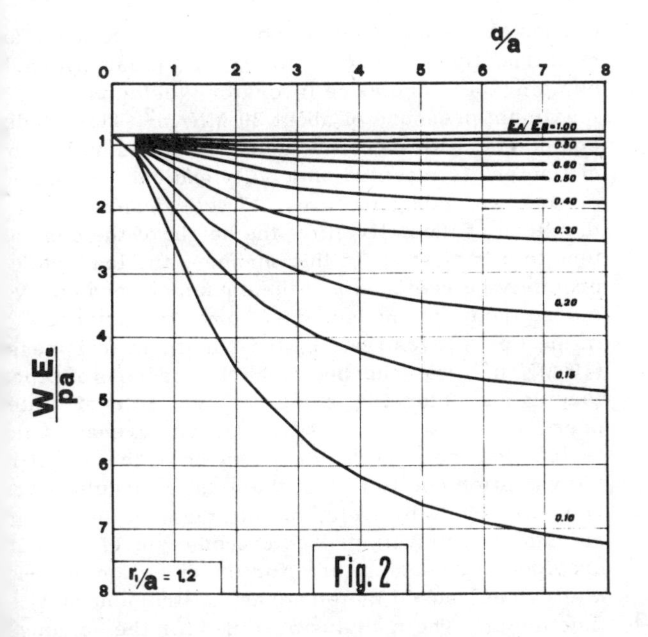

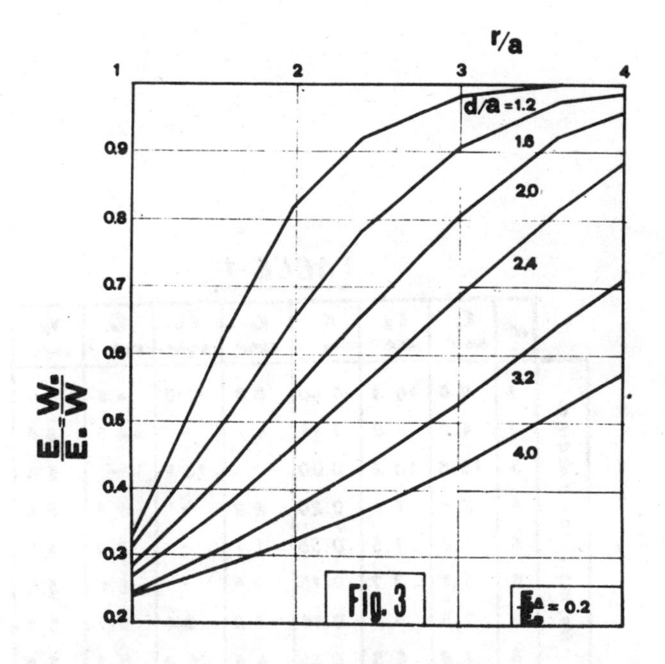

oose rock masses from the settlements measured in n-situ tests, consideration was given to the fact that ettlement of each point is affected differently by the resence of the loose zone. Fig.3 shows, as an example, how the settlement W at the surface varies in espect of the corrisponding settlement W_B of a omogeneous rock having an elasticity modulus E_B, as function of the distance from the plate center for ifferent thickness of the loose zone and for a constant E_A/E_B ratio. In the figure, E represents the "apparent" nodulus of the soil, for the point where settlement W as measured, computed, on the basis of Boussinesq's heory.

. FIRST APPROXIMATION CRITERION FOR INTERPRETATION OF THE PLATE BEARING TESTS IN A TWO-LAYER MEDIUM

n developing a first approximation criterion we have ried to avoid complicating the test. We assumed that nly superficial settlements were measured, that the tresses were of the usual order of magnitude (10-15 MN/m ^{2}) and that the settlements, measured with the sual dial gages or transducers, were never very reat. Theoretically, it would suffice to measure ettlement at three distinct points of the half- space nder the plate to derive the unknowns of the problem, amely, the moduli E_A and E_B, and the thickness d. ue to the inevitable random scattering of the readings nd to the difficulty of measuring small settlements, e different influence of the two-layer rock deformaility, as compared with homogeneous rock, on the ettlement of two adjacent points is hardly appreciable. n practice, it is hard to get meaningful readings at ore than two points at the surface. A rough estimaon of the thickness of the loose zone can be obtained ough the micro-seismic refraction curves (geophones cated 0.5-2m apart) taken along a line passing rough the center of the loaded area. It is known that the velocity of longitudinal elastic wave propagation in a rock mass is related to the deformability of the rock, and that by using appropiate instrument for the refraction tests it is possible to establish the thicknesses of the layers in stratified rock when the propagation velocity increases with depth. Today, by using closely special geophones it is also possible to measure thicknesses of a few tens of centimeters having a propagation velocity of 1-2Km/s. over a background having a velocity of a few Km/s. Based on ENEL's (Bertacchi and Sampaolo, 1970) and ISMES's wide experience with seismic methods for characterization of rock masses, it was seemed justified to try to evalute the thickness of the loose zone by seismic refraction measurements with standard instruments and techniques that had been appropiately adapted (Istituto Sperimentale Modelli e Strutture, 1973). In such a case, the problem is solved by the diagrams in Figs. 4 and 5. Indeed, settlements W_I and W_{II} allow "apparent" moduli E_I and E_{II} to be calculated through Boussinesq's theory. Once the d/a and E_I/E_{II} ratios are known, from the diagram in Fig. 4 we can determine E_A/E_B. When the latter ratio is known, we can obtain the value of E_I/E_B from the diagram in Fig. 5 for the same d/a ratio. And since E_I is known, we can first calculate E_B and then E_A.

4. EXPERIMENTAL VERIFICATION CAMPAIGN AND FUTURE DEVELOPMENTS.

The validity of the method described in the prceding Section was checked for the interpretation of the plate bearing tests performed within the framework of the investigation carried out for the excavation of the Pelos underground power station in the eastern Alps. The rock which is to be excavated is made of alternations of statified limestones and marly limestones. The drift (about 2,5 m in diameter) was bored by

TABLE 1

	N°	E_I GN/m²	E_{II} GN/m²	d m	E_A GN/m²	E_B GN/m²	V_A Km/s	V_B Km/s
Normal to bedding	1	9.8	10.3	0.60	8.3	12.0	4.5	5.6
	2	4.2	4.0	1.15	4.1	-	4.5	5.6
	3	13.6	13.2	0.00	-	13.3	-	5.6
	4	2.4	1.9	0.20	2.2	-	3.2	5.6
	5	1.8	1.5	0.55	1.7	-	3.2	5.6
	6	3.1	3.7	0.15	3.4	-	5.1	5.6
	7	7.9	8.1	0.45	7.2	8.4	5.1	5.6
	8	7.8	8.5	0.35	6.5	9.2	5.1	5.6
	9	7.3	8.1	0.10	3.3	8.1	3.7	5.6
	10	2.0	1.9	0.20	2.0	-	3.7	5.6
Parallel to bedding	11	14.3	12.8	0.00	-	13.6	-	5.2
	12	11.5	12.7	0.50	9.8	14.5	4.3	5.2
	13	5.2	5.1	0.65	5.2	-	4.3	5.2
	14	7.6	9.2	0.10	1.9	9.3	4.3	5.2
	15	5.7	8.3	1.20	7.0	-	4.3	5.2
	16	8.3	5.8	0.45	7.0	-	4.3	5.3
	17	16.9	17.9	0.50	15.5	19.3	4.3	5.3
	18	8.6	8.6	0.45	8.6	-	4.3	5.3
	19	6.5	8.5	0.40	4.3	10.5	4.3	5.3
	20	5.1	6.2	0.75	4.1	9.7	4.3	5.3

controlled blasting. Micro-seismic refraction profiles were taken in the drift, and twenty plate bearing tests were performed, with the load applied both perpendicularly and parallel to the stratification. All these were performed by ISMES. The loading areas were flattened by means of a little pneumatic hammer and smoothed with a thin layer of mortar. The equipment used in the test was developed by ISMES with the cooperation of the Hydraulic and Structural Research Center of ENEL's Studies and Research Direction and consisted of a central tube lodged between the walls of drift and connected, by large adjustment screws, to two plates under which the flat jacks in welded plate are located. The jacks have a diameter of 500 mm and are provided with rounded and enlarged rims. Shaped wooden shims are glued to both faces. The jacks a concurrently set in operation from a small hydraul pumping unit, and were laboratory tested up to a maximum pressure of about 20 MN/m². This loadi equipment which can be used in tunnels up to 4 m diameter, is mounted on a dolly and can be rotatec around two orthogonal axes. Two hydraulic jacks the sides of the dolly allow the height of the central tube to be adjusted. In this manner, the load can promptly be centered and the equipment can easily moved from one measurement point to another.

In the Pelos investigation, the maximum test press (10 MN/m²) was reached through a process of repe loading and unloading cycles at two intermediate pressure steps (4 and 7 MN/m²). The average valu (calculated from the harmonic mean of the moduli) a the variation coefficient of the elastic modulus we computed cycle by cycle, for each measurement point painstaking analysis proved extremely useful as it provided unbiased criteria for the detection of abnc mal values caused by temporary instrument malfunctioning. The modulus obtained for the various loading and unloading cycles were averaged separa for the values read on gages located near the plate those read on gages farther away, not taking to account the first - loading curve("vergin" deforma curve). Table I shows the values of the "apparent" moduli thus obtained, of the thickness of the loose assessed by seismic refraction means, of the moc E_A and E_B derived from the diagrams in figs. 4 anc with the procedures described in the preceding secti and of the average seismic velocities of the loose z and substratum. Fig. 6 correlates all the elastic moduli with the corresponding squared velocities, v reference only to the loading tests perpendicular the statification.

In studying the results, the first thing to be borne i mind is that, since the medium is stratified, the seismic velocities obtained have a different significance depending on whether the geophones were located at the sides of the drift. The velocities indicated in the lower half of Table I appear, at a fir glance, to be less meaningful than those in the upp half. On the other hand, when the velocities in the loose zone and substratum do not differ much (indicating nearly the same degree of fracturing), a the precision of the evaluation of the loose zone thic ness decreases. This may explain some of the gre differences in the results given in Table I, the mos evident being those relates to tests Nos. 6, 13, 17. At a rate, the first approximation method developed for interpretation of the plate bearing tests is capable providing a satisfactory indication of the average elasticity modulus of an undisturbed rock mass. Fig also illustrates further possible areas opened by su an interpretation of the plate bearing tests; indeed, possibility of better correlating deformability measu statically with the propagation velocities of longituc nal waves is extremely important for the complex problem of rock mass characterization (Kujundzic a Grujic, 1966)

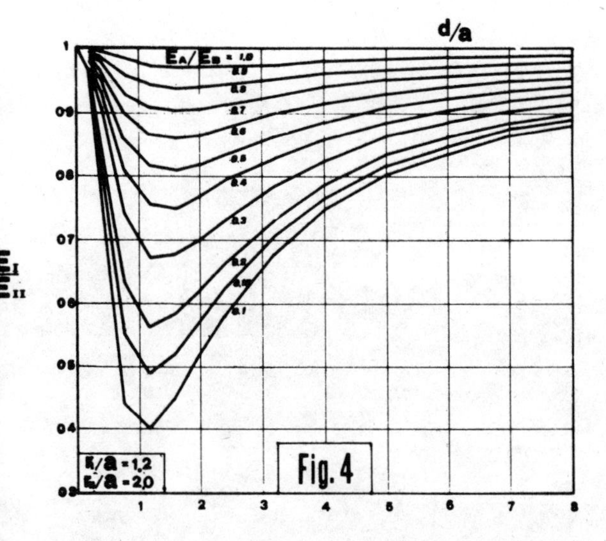

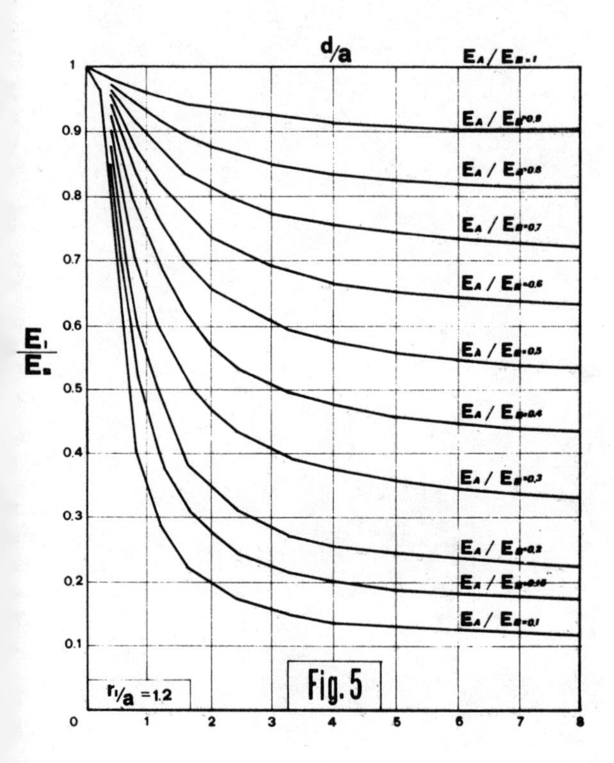

The moduli of a two-layer medium could indoubtely be assessed more easily if we could also find out the relative displacements of the points on the walls of a borehole drilled at the center of, and perpendicular to the loading area. On the basis of diagrams and procedures similar to those in Figs. 4 and 5 it would be possible not only to obtain independent estimates of E_A and E_B, but also to verify the validity of the estimate of the loose zone thickness obtained through seismic refraction methods. More specifically, it would be possible to produce, with the data already available, different diagrams that would allow the parameters E_A, E_B and d to be calculated directly from the "apparent" moduli derived from measured displacements. Drilling of a borehole at the center of the loading area and the installation of instruments are indoubtely complications in the performance of the plate bearing test. However, in the course of geomechanical investigations, boreholes are normally drilled for several purposes (sampling, for instance); some of them could easily be located in the loading test areas without unduty increasing costs. A borehole at the center of the loading area also allow the local state of fracturing to be determined in detail, especially through sonic logging. The aggregate information obtainable with the boreholes could be useful also to establish more justified relations between the quality indexes used for rock mass classification and the deformability of rock masses. Therefore, it was deemed convenient to develope a test method and test equipment to do this. The new equipment (Fig. 7), developed by ISMES with the cooperation of the Hydraulic and Structural Research Center of ENEL's Studies and Research Direction, includes devices that can be fixed at different depths in the borehole by means of six expansion anchors, and are connected by means of metal rods to displacement transducers mounted on a support that is rigidly atthached to the borehole mounth. A flat anular jack transmits the load to the rock and allows passage of the instruments. The anchors (Fig. 8) consist of two brass disks connected by a central screw and three wedges. By turning the screw, the three wedges are forced to adhere to the wall of the borehole at the desidered depth. The anchors are positioned by means of a locking key, which also allows their recovery after the test. The equipment is designed for boreholes 75mm in diameter and 6 m deep.
The displacement of each anchor relative to the deepest one taken as fixed, is measured by mean of weatherproof displacement transducers of the variable-inductance type, with a range of 10 mm and a sensitivity of 1 μ, connected to an automatic data recorder. The above described equipment was successfully used recently in an in-situ investigation campaign.
Processing of the results is still under way because in order to interpret them corretly it has been necessary to trim up statistical methods.
A first conclusion that can be drawn from our work so far is that the modifications we introduced in the plate bearing test technique and interpretation

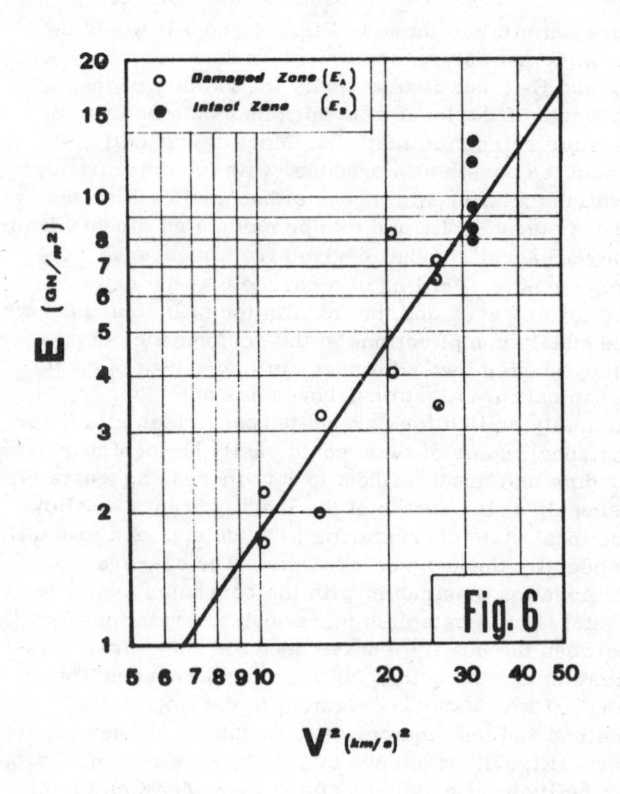

Fig. 6

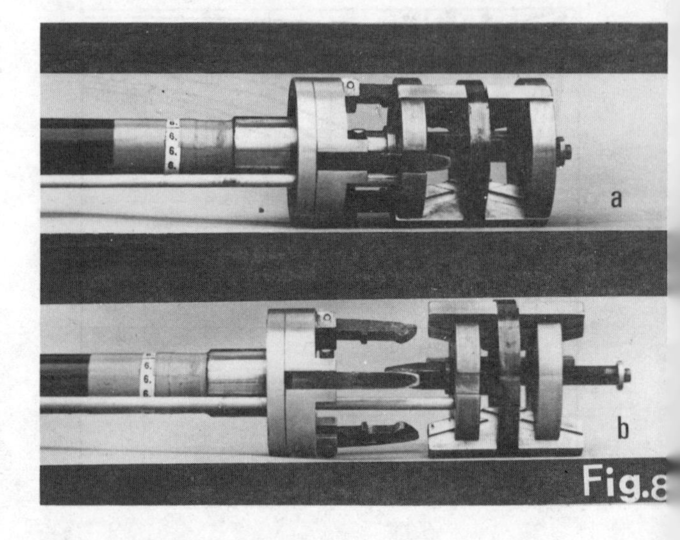

Fig. 8

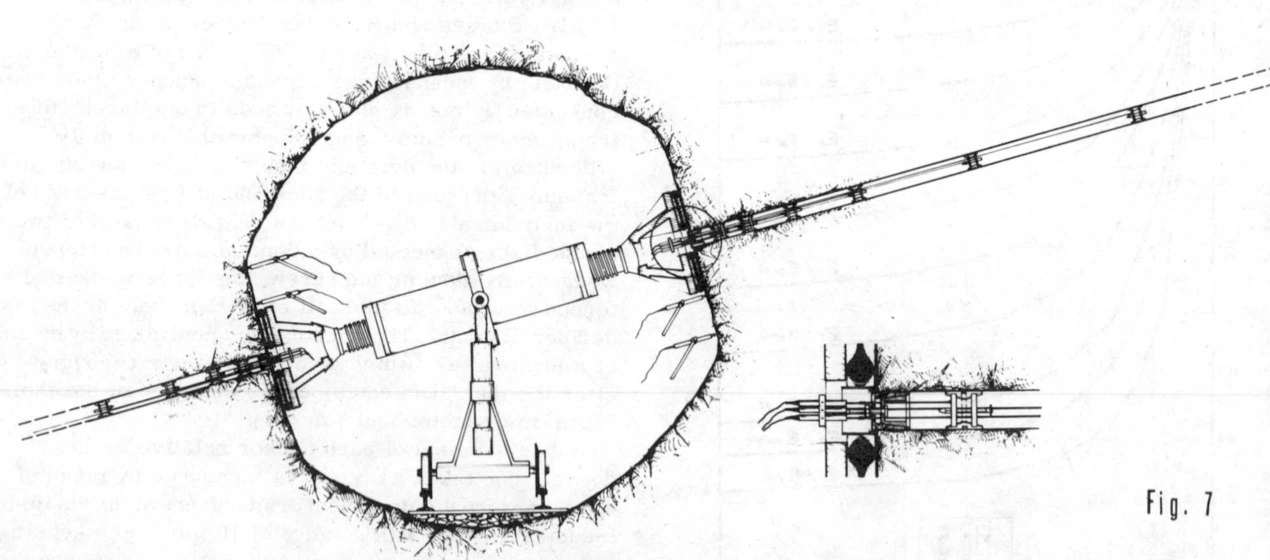

Fig. 7

criteria are satisfactory: without undue complications it has been found possible to take into account the effect of the superficial loose layer.

REFERENCES

Benson, R.P., Murphy, D.K., McCreath, D.R., Modulus Testing of Rock at the Churchill Falls Underground Powerhouse, Labrador. ASTM special Technical Publication 477, 1969.

Bertacchi, P., Sampaolo, A.,: Investigation on the Characteristics of Rock Masses by Geophysical Methods. Proc. 2nd Cong. Int. Soc. of Rock Mech., Beograd 1970, vol. 3, paper 8-13

Dolcetta, M.: Rock load on the support structures of two large underground hydroeletric powerstation Proc. Int. Symp. on underground Openings, Lucerne, 1972 pp. 405-446.

Istituto Sperimentale Modelli e Strutture: L'ISMES. Rassegna Tecnica di Problemi della Energia Elettrica. Vol. XXI, 1973.

Kuyundzic, B., Grujic, N.: Correlation between static and dynamic investigation of rock mass "in situ". Proc. I° Congr. Int. Soc. Rock Mech. Lisboa, 1966. Vol. I pp. 565-570.

Martino, D., Ribacchi, R.: Osservazioni su alcuni metodi di misura delle caratteristiche di rocce o ammassi rocciosi, con particolare riferimento al problema della anisotropia. L'Industria Mineraria, 5, 1972, pp. 193-203.

Maury, B.: Mécanique des milieux stratifiés. Dunod Paris, 1970

Oberti, G., Rebaudi, A., Goffi, L.: Comportement statique des massifs rocheux (calcaires) dans la realisation de grands ouvrages souterrains. II Cong Int. Soc. Rock Mech, Belgrade, 1970. Vol. II, pp. 705-13.

Stagg, K.G.: In situ tests on the Rock Mass in: Rock Mechanics in Engineering practice, edited by Stagg and Zienkiewicz; J. Wiley and Sons, London, 1968.

RESULT OF STATE-OF-STRESS MEASUREMENTS IN DIFFERENT TYPES OF ROCK MASSES

RÉSULTATS DES MESURES DE L'ÉTAT ORIGINEL DE CONTRAINTE DANS DES AMAS ROCHEUX DE TYPES DIFFÉRENTS

MESSUNGSERGEBNISSE DES URSPRÜNGLICHEN SPANNUNGSZUSTANDES VON GESTEINSAUFSPEICHERUNGEN VERSCHIEDENER ARTEN

S. MARTINETTI — Italian State Elecricity Board, Enel, Geotchnical Service, Collaborator with the CNR Research Center for Technical Geology

R. RIBACCHI — Professor of Rock Mechanics, Inst. of Mining, Faculty of Engineering, University of Rome

Rome, Italy

SUMMARY - The results of "in situ" measurements effected on six locations with the purpose of determining the natural state of stress through the utilisation of the CSIR "doorstopper" method are exposed. The paper also describes the criteria, based upon statistical models, which are applied in the interpretation of the results, the difficulties met in the practical execution of measurements, as well as the proposed improvements.

RESUME - On décrit les résultats de mesures "in situ" effectuées sur six lieux différents dans le but d'établir l'état de tension naturelle par l'emploi de la méthode CSIR "doorstopper". On décrit également les critères employés dans l'interprétation des résultats et qui sont basés sur des modèles de statistique, ainsi que les difficultés encourues dans l'exécution pratique des mesures et les améliorations proposées.

ZUSAMMENFASSUNG - Die Ergebnisse der in sechs verschiedenen Orten durchgefuehrten "in situ" Messungen werden hier wiedergegeben. Ziel dieser Messungen ist es, den natuerlichen Spannungszustand durch die CSIR "doorstopper" Methode festzulegen. Auch werden die auf statistischen Modellen basierten, in der Darlegung der Ergebnisse angewandten Kriterien beschrieben, die in der praktischen Durchfuehrung der Messungen getroffenen Schwierigkeiten sowie die vorgeschlagenen Verbesserungen.

FOREWORD

Starting from 1967 we have effected a good amount of "in situ" measurements in order to establish the states of stress, existing in rock masses involved in mining and civil engineering works (CAPOZZA et al., 1969; MARTINETTI and RIBACCHI 1970a, 1972) using mainly the CSIR "doorstopper" method (LEEMAN, 1970). In the present paper, we have tried to achieve a synthesis of the experience with reference to the problem of the determination of the primary state of stress.

C.S.I.R. "DOORSTOPPER" METHOD

We believe that CSIR "doorstopper" method, or any other method basing upon the same basic principles, is the most convenient from the standpoint of its utilisation "in situ". One of its most important advantages consists in the fact that it does not require the presence of instruments within the borehole (as well as the presence of the corresponding connecting cables which pass through the "body" of the drill) during the critical overcoring stage. Such advantage is particularly appreciated when effecting measurements on very fractured rocks (average spacing lower than 20 cm), when, in other words, many of the other methods fail. The main drawback connected with the method consists, on the contrary, in the fact that it is impossible to effect valid measurements when notable amounts of water are flowing within the hole; such a situation generally applies to the case of a rock which is fractured enough, and this is the case in which other methods too fail, even if for different reasons.

Until a few years ago, some perplexity reigned about the usability of the CSIR "doorstopper" method becaus of the uncertainty on the stress concentration factor at the center of the flattened bottom of the borehole Today, it can be safely said that the problem has bee satisfactorily resolved, at least as far as the isotropic rocks are concerned. One of the authors (RIBACCHI, 1971) has effected a study by means of the finit element method and he has compared the results with those provided in the literature. Except few cases, the recent published values agree reasonably; particu larly close each to other are the values provided by HITSCHER (1969), DE LA CRUZ (1969), RIBACCHI(1971), which are utilised by us.

From the standpoint of practical execution of the measurements, the experience which has been gained up to date shows that it is in general convenient to adopt the following provisions.

a) Careful checking of the flattening and smoothing bits. In quartz bearing rocks (but also in less abrasive rocks) after four or five measurements such bits start to wear out in remarkable way; this does not happen uniformly but particularly in the central area of the bit. The smoothing action on the bottom of the borehole is, therefore, impaired just in the region where the strain gauges are glued. In order to avoid a frequent replacemen of the bit, we have set out successfully a flattening bit in which the central region can be rotated by hand eccentrically in respect of the outward portion of the bit; this allows, after a few measurements have been done, to bring at the center of the tool a less damaged portion of the front surface extending practically the useful life of the tool by six times. Successively, it will suffice to substitute only the central portion of the bits. A more complex apparatus has been proposed and utilised by HILTSCHER (1969) and at present is being employed by us. It allows to achieve a high finiture for the bottom of the borehole, but is prone to mechanical failures, which we hope to eliminate soon.

b) Visual checks of the conditions at the bottom of the hole. Such checking operation must be effected immediately after the flattenning operation. It is particularily useful when dealing with highly fractured rocks, since it permits to avoid the loss of many cells. We are using a mechanical instrument which provides an image having an excellent resolution power.

It is to be recalled, finally, that we found convenient to effect measurements within boreholes having a slightly larger diameter than that originally indicated by the CSIR. Adopting 51 mm diameter cores (the external diameter of the borehole being of 65mm), a substantial reduction has been observed in the number of damaged "doorstoppers" during the overcoring operation.

INTERPRETATION CRITERIA IN THE ANALYSIS OF THE EXPERIMENTAL RESULTS

In order to determine the state-of-stress "in situ", 6 indipendent deformation measurements are, at least, needed; if the CSIR "doorstopper" method is utilised, the measurements must be obtained in at least three boreholes having different orientations. In the practice, however, it is impossible to get reliable values for the stress tensor from a number of measurements equal or only slightly exeeding the 6 measurements which theoretically are needed. In effects, the state of stress prevailing in a given portion of rock (having an amount of the order of some thousands of cubic meters) may be considered as the sum of a "regional" state of stress and of a component having only a "local" interest, with irregular variations (sometimes remarkably strong) and with an average nul value. In order to evaluate the deformations and the state of stress induced by large size engineering works only the knowledge of the first component is practically important. It is necessary, therefore, to effect a large number of measurements and to work on them by statistical methods; we believe that the same need prevails also when using those instruments (as for instance the triaxial CSIR) in which it would be theoretically possible to establish the state of stress through a single operation.

Using the symbols which have been indicated in figure 1, the relation existing between the deforma-

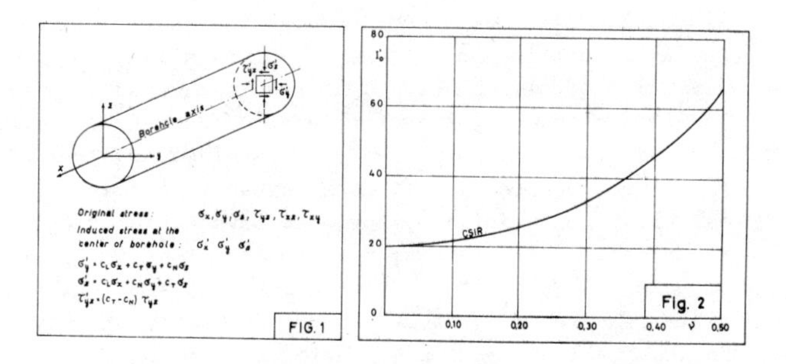

tion, measured through an extensometer on the bottom of the borehole, and the state of stress referred to a general system XYZ of axes, may be written as follows:

$$\varepsilon(\vartheta)=\frac{1}{E}\left[\cos^2\vartheta, \sin^2\vartheta, \sin\vartheta\cos\vartheta\right]\times\begin{bmatrix}0 & -\nu & 0\\ -\nu & 1 & 0\\ 0 & 0 & 2(1+\nu)\end{bmatrix}\times\begin{bmatrix}C_L & C_T & C_N & 0 & 0 & 0\\ C_L & C_N & C_T & 0 & 0 & 0\\ 0 & 0 & 0 & C_T-C_N & 0 & 0\end{bmatrix}\times G(H^{(f)})\times\begin{Bmatrix}\sigma_x\\ \sigma_y\\ \sigma_z\\ \tau_{yz}\\ \tau_{xz}\\ \tau_{xy}\end{Bmatrix}$$

wherein $G(H^{(f)})$ is the transformation matrix of the tensors (JAEGER & COOK, 1969), which is defined starting from the direction-cosine $H^{(f)}$ matrix for each of the reference system which is connected with the single borehole in respect of the general XYZ system. The deformation on the bottom of the hole in a given direction is, therefore, tied linearly with the six components of the primary stress through six coefficients, whose values depend on the hole orientation in respect of the reference system and on the position of the extensometers within the hole.

Assuming that the measured deformation is the sum of such theoretical deformation and of a random error, it is possible to derive the components of the tensor by means of the least square method, that is, substantially, through the application of a standard regression analysis (MARTINETTI & RIBACCHI, 1970b). The statistical method permits not only to evaluate the tensor components but also to derive their variances and their confidence limits. It is, therefore, possible to estimate the values of the principal stresses, of their direction and of their confidence limits. Even if some of the assumptions made in order to allow the application of the statistical method could be considered as not completely satisfactory, the application of this model has proved in practice very useful. The analysis method which has been set out would require long and tedius computations with consequent possible errors; therefore a computer program has been prepared (MARTINETTI et al., 1970). With such a program it is possible to analyse quickly all the data, and it is also possible to evaluate alternative assumptions; for instance, the influence of some doubtful measurement upon the final result can be assessed.

The importance must be finally pointed out of a careful study of the orientation of the measurement holes, which has a critical influence upon the precision with which the tensor components can be evaluated In fact, when the holes present only a slight angular deviation from each other, the resolving system is ill conditionated, and, therefore small measurement errors are able to completely modify the evaluated values of the tensor components. It does not suffice however to establish, once for all, the most favourable orientation for the holes since, in practice it is necessary to take into account the limitations imposed by the field requirements. It is, therefore, useful to have an index able to give a synthetic indication of the efficiency of a given arrangement of the measurement cells, in such a way to be able to compare different arrangements which are technically feasible. An inadequate arrangement of the strain cells obliges to effect many measurements before a reasonable precision may be obtained; the problem is very important, when considering the high cost of each measurement.

In order to evaluate a given arrangement of measurements, one may utilise, for instance, the sum Σ of the variances of the components of the stress tensor. Basing upon the regression analysis principles (which have been used to obtain such components), it can be demonstrated that such sum is:

(i) directly proportional to the error's variance $V(e)$ which is tied to the random errors introduced by the measurement method, and to the inhomogeneity of the rock mass. If the measurements are correctly effected, this factor is not modifiable by the experimenter;

(ii) inversely proportional, for a given configuration of the extensometers, to their number N (with a better approximation, to N-6, but the difference can be in practice neglected).

In order to take into account not only the influence of these two factors but also the fact that Σ depends on the orientation of the reference system in which the stress components are expressed, it has been deemed suitable to compute the mean value $\bar{\Sigma}$ in respect of all the possible orientations of the reference system, and to define the inefficiency index as:

$$I_o = \frac{N\bar{\Sigma}}{E^2 V(e)} \qquad (2)$$

I_o depends only on the mutual arrangement of the extensometers (that is on the hole orientation and on the strain cells orientation within the holes) and on the rock Poisson's coefficient.

Studying the behaviour of the inefficiency index for various measurement configurations (MARTINETTI & RIBACCHI, 1970c) the following main conclusions can be derived

(i) The extensometers within each hole should present a balanced configuration: this can be obtained for instance with "doorstoppers" having 3 extensometers placed at 120°: using the extensometers which are found at present on the market (vertical, horizontal and 45° extensometers) the inefficiency index is 1.33 times larger than with a balanced configuration. In the field we obtain, however, a balanced configuration using the pre sent equipment through the artifice of rotating by 90° the position of the doorstoppers when passing from a measurement to the next one. The adoption of doorstoppers with 4 extensometers placed at 45° would be, however, profitable, sin it would allow a direct evaluation of the valid ty of the measurements provided by each cell. This would, indeed, permit to discard the measu rements which are obviously erroneous (for instance because of the presence of a fracture on the bottom of the hole).

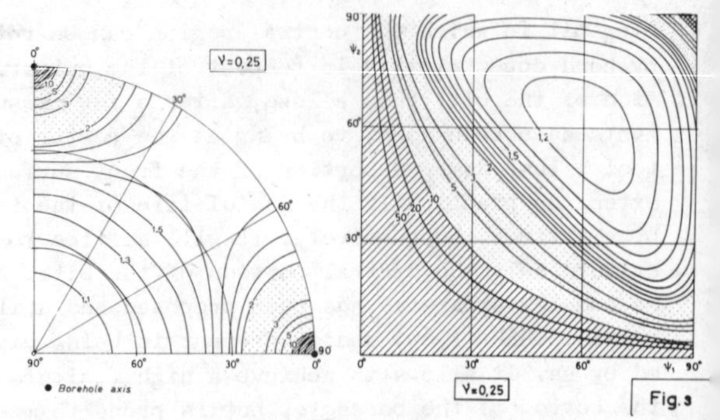

Fig.3

(ii) If the previous condition is satisfied and if i all the holes the same amount of measurements is effected (as generally is suitable), the hole arrangement providing the best results is that having 3 holes which are orthogonal to each oth Its inefficiency index I'_o depends only on the Poisson's coefficient of the rock (Fig. 2). The latter arrangement appears to be often inconvenient in the field; the validity of each other arrangement, caracterised by its own inefficier index I_o, can be, however, evaluated immediate on the basis of its relative inefficiency index I_R which is defined as the ratio I_o/I'_o. In Figu 3 (using the polar projection) the isograms of the index I_R are shown on the left side for al the arrangements having two orthogonal holes ar the third hole placed in a generic position. These curves are not much influenced by the val of the Poisson's coefficient of the rocks. On t right side of the same figure the corresponding curves are shown, referring to the case, very c mon in the practice, that the three holes lie c the same plane (which is usually the horizonta plane) and form each to other the angles ψ_1 and

An example will show the way in which the diagran can be used: let us assume that we effect measuremer on a rock mass having a Young modulus of 40 GN/m^2 a $\nu = 0.25$. Let be $s(e) = 100\mu\varepsilon$ the evaluate standar deviation of the error and let suppose that we want obtain for the tensor components a standard deviatic of 1.5 MN/m^2. If a configuration having 3 coplanar holes placed at 45° from each other is adopted, we g from the Figure 3:

$$I_R = 1.65 \qquad \text{and} \qquad I'_o = 28$$

and from the relation (2) we derive:

$$N = \frac{(100 \cdot 10^{-6})^2 \times 1.65 \times 28 \times (40 \cdot 10^3)^2}{1.5^2 \times 6} = 54$$

which means 6 doorstoppers for each hole. If, instead, a 30° arrangement for the holes had been adopted, the relative inefficiency index would have risen to 8.5 and, therefore, the amount of required measurement would have been 280.

It is to be observed, finally, that from the standpoint of the precision of the results, no advantage is gained by utilising more than three differently oriented holes; in some campaign, however, measurements within 4 boreholes have been effected in order to check the validity of interpretation method. The results which have been obtained utilising the measurements effected only within three holes (chosen at will) or within all the 4 holes, do not differ appreciably from each other (Table 1)

Tab. 1 - Magnitude and direction of principal stresses obtained at S. Fiorano from different triplets of boreholes

Boreholes	σ_1 MN/m²	φ_1 (°)	ψ_1 (°)	σ_2 MN/m²	φ_2 (°)	ψ_2 (°)	σ_3 MN/m²	φ_3 (°)	ψ_3 (°)	$s(e)$ $\mu\varepsilon$	I_0
1,2,3	7.6	352	29	3.4	244	29	0.8	118	47	442	1.8
1,2,4	8.1	344	27	5.4	241	25	0.7	115	52	416	1.3
1,3,4	8.0	347	20	4.5	250	18	1.6	122	62	365	1.3
2,3,4	8.8	345	38	3.8	249	8	0.0	149	51	390	1.1
1,2,3,4	8.1	346	29	4.3	244	19	1.0	126	54	404	1.0

In this table ψ and φ are the azimuth and the inclination on the horizontal plane of each principal stress.

PROGRAMMING OF AN IN SITU TEST

For a campaign intended to provide the knowledge of the natural state of stress in a rock mass, it is to be foreseen the execution of 3 or 4 boreholes, perforated starting from an exploration drift, at distances from the wall larger than twice the diameter of the drift. The number of measurements to be effected within each borehole depends on the error variance V(e), which can be evaluated basing upon the results which have been obtained for the first hole.

The standard team effecting the measurements is composed of 1 technician, 1 driller and 1 yardman; if two instruments are available, a team as above is able to place 1.5 - 2 "doorstoppers" pro day within each hole. Taking into account lost time and lost measurements, a campaign can be completed in average within about 1 month (20 working days).

Loss of measurements are due to many causes, some of which cannot be eliminated even employing a very experienced team and improving the apparatus. Our experience on this subject is illustrated in Table 2, from which it can be derived that among the various causes of the losses (altogether 30% approximately of all the measurements) the foremost one is represented by the fracturing of the rock.

Tab 2

Plant	Boreholes n°	Measurements n°	Lost measurements n°	Lost measurements %	Cause of the loss: Fracture of the core n°	%	Instruments fault n°	%	Not glued cells n°	%	Uncorrect flattening n°	%	Measures used in the computation n°	%
Lago Delio	3	48	12	25	6	13	2	4	2	4	2	4	36	75
Gesso A	6	138	36	26	21	15	-	-	6	4	9	7	102	74
Gesso C	4	57	18	32	3	5	9	17	3	5	3	5	39	68
S. Fiorano	3	141	24	17	9	6	-	-	9	6	6	5	117	83
P. di Ruschio	4	177	69	40	54	31	-	-	12	7	3	2	108	60
Salafossa	3	48	15	31	3	7	6	12	5	10	1	2	33	69
Pelos	4	156	38	24	8	5	6	4	18	11	6	4	118	76

The various items which compose the total cost of a typical campaign are

- drilling of 30 m of boreholes and labour assistance for the tests	$ 4,000
- 1 technician for the tests (20 days of work)	$ 1,500
- dispensable material (30 "doorstoppers" included)	$ 1,600
- interpretation and presentation of results (computer and personnel costs)	$ 200
Total	$ 7,300

Therefore, the average cost-per-doorstopper (considering only the "useful" measurements) is in the order of $ 350; this cost does not include the general costs, nor company profits nor the laboratory tests which are needed in order to characterise the rock material.

EXPERIMENTAL RESULTS

The tests have been effected in six different places; in five out of six, big underground stations were in a building or designing phase by part of ENEL, whereas the last was situated near a lead and zinc mine. The concerned rock formations have been the following:

Lago Delio: fine grained orthoquartzite, inserted in a gneiss formation, on the east side of Lago Maggiore (Western-Central Alps);

A-Gesso & C-Gesso: Biotitic Anatessites of the Argentera Massif, having a weakly oriented texture (Western Alps);

S. Fiorano: Phillitic micaschist from the higher section of Oglio River (Central Alps);

Piani di Ruschio: fine grained limestones thinly stratified, containing chert nodules (Central Apennines);

Salafossa: fine grained dolomite and limestones (Eastern Alps);

Pelos: Thin bedded limestones and marly limestones (Eastern Alps).

In order to characterise the rock types, reference

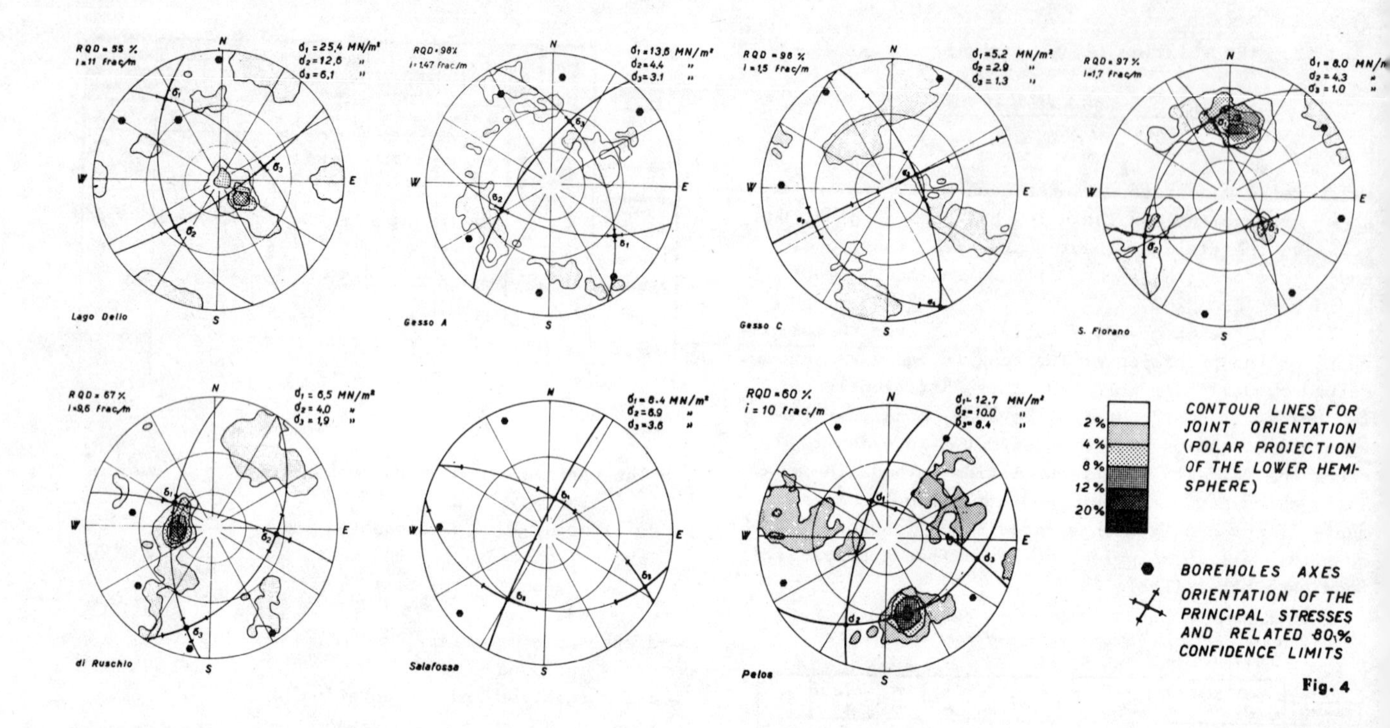

Fig. 4

can be made to Table 3 which lists the values of the strength and deformability (mean values $\bar{x}$, variation coefficients $\mathcal{V}(x)$ and standard deviations $s(x)$) obtained through laboratory tests on intact material. The rock mass is characterised in Figure 4 both by the R.Q.D. values and by the average fracture number per meter, i, both values being derived from the cores obtained through boreholes. In the abovesaid figure we find also the isofrequency contour lines of the orientations of the discontinuity existing in the rock mass. In the case of "Lago Delio" the fracturing appears to be overestimated because of the use of simple core barrels.

Tab 3

	Compressive strength		Tensile strength		Strength indexes (from irregular lump tests)				Mohr envelope parameters		Elastic parameters			
	$\bar{\sigma}_c$ MN/m²	" %	$\bar{\sigma}_t$ MN/m²	" %	I_s MN/m²	" %	I_c MN/m²	" %	c MN/m²	φ (°)	E GN/m²	" %	ν	$s(\bar{\nu})$
Lago Delio	66	75	6	34	-	-	-	-	+16	52	24,5	14	0,05	0,004
Gesso A-C	119	30	9	27	10	46	9	38	+20	48	36,8	28	0,07	0,003
S. Fiorano	80	26	14	28	13	54	9	52	-	-	11,8	104	0,00	0.010
P. di Ruschio	57	30	4	33	5	45	5	42	+13	40	38,0	54	0,26	0,051
Salafossa	92	50	6	54	-	-	-	-	+29	48	26,0	79	0,16	0.030
Pelos	60	48	3	43	-	-	-	-	×8	50	52,0	37	0,23	0.017

+ From triaxial test × From direct shear test

Table 4 gives the evaluated mean values for the stress tensor components, referred to a XYZ reference system having the X axis horizontal and directed northward, the Y axis horizontal and directed eastward, the Z axis vertical and directed downward. The standard error deviation is about 100 - 200$\mu\varepsilon$, in agreement with the results of other researchers (GRAY & BARRON, 1969). From the same table it is apparent that, after the first campaign at Lago Delio, a suitable choice o the hole direction has allowed to keep very low the inefficiency index I_o.

Tab. 4 - Stress tensor components and related standard deviations.

	$s(\varepsilon)$ $\mu\varepsilon$	I_o	σ_x (s.) MN/m²	σ_y (s.) MN/m²	σ_z (s.) MN/m²	τ_{xy} (s.) MN/m²	τ_{yz} (s.) MN/m²	τ_{xz} (s.) MN/m²
Lago Delio	182	17.2	20.5	13.9	9.7	-6.5	-4.9	1.6
			(9.7)	(6.1)	(4.2)	(5.0)	(1.6)	(1.8)
Gesso A	116	1.4	6.5	9.1	5.6	-3.9	2.5	-2.7
			(1.6)	(0.9)	(0.7)	(0.6)	(0.5)	(0.7)
Gesso C	85	1.0	4.6	2.2	1.4	-2.6	0.6	0.2
			(1.1)	(1.2)	(0.7)	(0.7)	(0.7)	(0.7)
S. Fiorano	404	1.0	6.6	3.7	3.0	-0.1	-1.7	2.5
			(1.0)	(1.1)	(0.6)	(0.6)	(0.7)	(0.6)
P. di Ruschio	85	1.2	2.3	4.5	5.5	-0.9	-0.9	1.0
			(1.1)	(0.9)	(0.8)	(0.4)	(0.3)	(0.4)
Salafossa	187	1.3	67	4.3	8.0	1.3	2.0	0.9
			(2.0)	(2.6)	(1.8)	(1.3)	(1.4)	(1.2)
Pelos	227	1.2	11.8	6.6	10.4	0.1	0.4	0.7
			(3.3)	(3.5)	(3.2)	(1.1)	(1.3)	(1.2)

From Table 5, it can be derived that the error variance, evaluated on the whole of the available measu rement values is not significantly different from the error variance evaluated within the holes. The latter is influenced only by the instrument errors and by th local irregularities in the state of stress, whereas the global variance is also tied both to a possible

Tab 5

	Extimated variance of the error in the boreholes $(\mu\varepsilon)^2$						
	1	2	3	4	5	6	All
Lago Delio	30'681	32'935	1'962	-	-	-	33'022
Gesso A	6'536	13'544	9'284	8'244	5'504	5'210	13'548
Gesso C	10'037	3'337	4'694	-	-	-	7'260
S. Fiorano	166'528	264'132	133'288	79'726	-	-	163'179
P.di Ruschio	8'344	15'348	4'140	1'863	-	-	7'168
Salafossa	35'622	41'468	19'998	-	-	-	34'999
Pelos	16'591	102'860	47'250	1'050	-	-	51'655

anisotropy of the rock and to an incorrect evaluation of stress concentration factors. The data given in Table 5 seems to show that, on the whole, these factors do not exert a remarkable influence. For a different measurement method (survey of the diametral deformations of boreholes) similar conclusions have been reached by GRAY & TOEWS (1973).

Finally, Figure 4 gives the average values of the principal stresses and their orientations; for the latter also the confidence limits have been indicated at a 80% level. It is to be noted that the width of the confidence limits (which are sometimes indeterminate) cannot be assumed as an index of the measurement precision, since this width depends also substantially on the difference between the values of the principal stresses. It has been observed that, generally, the stress which is parallel to the contour lines of the slope is higher than the others. Sometimes, furthermore, the vertical stress is higher than that corresponding to the overburden; however, there is no reason to think that this represents an anomalous result, because all the measurements were effected within slopes having a rugged topography.

Doubts about the validity of some results can arise owing to the fact that the interpretation has been effected always under the assumption of an isotropic behaviour of the rocks, even when this assumption (for instance in the case of S.Fiorano) was a coarse approximation. Therefore interpretation criteria are being now adjusted (RIBACCHI, 1973), to allow also for anisotropy of the rock. Anyway, the stress values measured at Lago Delio and S.Fiorano have been utilised to compute displacements around the workings and loads acting upon some braces; the comparison of the results with the measured data appears to be, altogether, satisfactory (DOLCETTA, 1972).

ACKNOWLEDGEMENTS

This work was partly supported by CNR (Contracts No. 70.01953.05 and 71.01244.05).

REFERENCES

CAPOZZA F., MARTINETTI S., RIBACCHI R. - Results of state of stress measurements in rock masses by means of borehole devices. Proc. Int. Symp. on the Determ. of Stresses in Rock Masses, Lisbon, 1969 pp. 540-559

DE LA CRUZ R.V. - Contribution to discussion. Proc. Int. Symp. on the Determination of Stresses in Rock Masses, Lisbon, 1969, pp. 86 - 89.

DOLCETTA M. - Rock load on the support structures of two large underground hydroelectric powerstations. Int. Symp. Underground Openings, Lucerne, 1972, pp. 405 - 446.

GRAY W., BARRON K. - Stress determination from strain relief measurements on the ends of borehole; planning, data evaluation and error assessment. Proc. Int. Symp. on the Determination of Stresses in Rock Masses, Lisbon, 1969, pp. 183 - 199.

GRAY W., TOEWS N. A. - Analysis of variance applied to data obtained by means of six-element borehole deformation gauge for stress determination. Min. Res. Centre, Dept. Energy Mines and Resources, Int. Rep. 73/103, Ottawa, 1973.

HILTSCHER R.- Beitrag zur Gebirgsspannungsmessung nach dem Bohrlochboden - Entspannungsverfahren. Proc. Int. Symp. on the Determination of Stresses in Rock Masses, Lisbon, 1969, pp. 245 - 264.

JAEGER J. C., COOK N.G.W. - Fundamentals of rock mechanics. Methuen, London, 1969.

LEEMAN E.R. - Experience throughout world with the CSIR "doorstopper" rock stress measuring equipment. Proc. II Congr. Int.Soc. for Rock Mech., Vol. 2, Beograd, 1970, pp. 419 - 425.

MARTINETTI S., RIBACCHI R. - Lesson drawn from field experience in rock stress measurements. Proc. II Congr. Int. Soc. for Rock Mech., Vol. 4, Beograd 1970a, pp. 390 - 394.

MARTINETTI S., RIBACCHI R. - Un criterio statistico per l'interpretazione dei risultati di misure dello stato di sollecitazione negli ammassi rocciosi. Rivista Italiana di Geotecnica, Vol. 4, 1970b, pp. 21 - 32.

MARTINETTI S., RIBACCHI R. - Determinazione sperimentale dello stato di sollecitazione negli ammassi rocciosi. Influenza della posizione delle basi di misura sulla precisione dei risultati. X Convegno di Geotecnica, Memoria T II - 10, Bari, 1970.

MARTINETTI S., MONTANI G., RIBACCHI R. - Interpretazione statistica dei risultati di misure per la determinazione dello stato di sollecitazione negli ammassi rocciosi. Programma di calcolo per elaboratore eletronico. X Convegno di Geotecnica, Memoria T II - 3, Bari, 1970.

RIBACCHI R. - Interpretazione dei risultati di misure dello stato di sollecitazione in situ in rocce anisotrope con il metodo CSIR "doorstopper". L'Industria Mineraria, Vol. 24, 1973.

A NEW DEVELOPMENT OF THE LNEC STRESS TENSOR GAUGE

NOUVELLE FORME DE LA CELLULE LNEC POUR DÉTERMINER L'ÉTAT DE CONTRAINTE

EIN WEITERENTWICKELTES MODELL DES VOM LNEC ENTWORFENEN SPANNUNGSTENSORMESSERS

Manuel ROCHA Director, Laboratori Nacional de Engenharia Civil, Lisbon
Professor of Rock Mechanics, Lisbon Technical University

Arnaldo SILVERIO Research Officer, Head of Underground Construction Div., LNEC

J. Oliveira PEDRO Research Officer, Head of Special Studies Division, LNEC

J. Sintra DELGADO Trainee Research Officer, LNEC

Lisbon, Portugal

SYNOPSIS A new development is presented of the LNEC stress tensor gauge, in the form of a hollow cylinder 2 mm thick (I.D. 31 mm, O.D. 35 mm), with electrical resistance strain gauges embedded midway from the inside to the outside surface.

The recent plastic gauge, to be installed like its solid forerunner in a standard EX borehole, is claimed to substantially reduce the incidence of practical situations where the gauge to rock bond fails on stress-relief overcoring.

Analitical expressions are deduced and checked, which enable the complete state of stress in the studied rock mass to be determined from the nine strains measured with the gauge.

RÉSUMÉ Comme forme nouvelle de la cellule LNEC pour déterminer les contraintes dans les massifs rocheux, on propose un cylindre creux de 2 mm d'épaisseur (D.I. 31 mm, D.E. 35 mm), avec des jauges de déformation électriques encastrées à mi-épaisseur de la paroi.

La récente cellule en plastique, à installer comme son précurseur plein dans un trou de forage EX standard, réduit substantiellement l'incidence des situations pratiques en lesquelles la liaison de la cellule au rocher se romp lors du surcarottage de libération des contraintes.

On déduit et vérifie des expressions analytiques que permettent d'établir l'état de contrainte dans le massif rocheux étudié, à partir des neuf déformations mesurées avec la cellule.

ZUSAMMENFASSUNG Ein weiterentwickeltes Modell des vom LNEC entworfenen Spannungstensormessers wird vorgestellt. Es hat die Form eines hohlen Zylinders (I.D. 31 mm, Ä.D. 35 mm mit einer 2 mm dicken Wand, in welcher elektrische Widerstandsdehnungsmesstreifen in gleichem Abstand von der inneren und der äusseren Oberfläche eingebettet sind.

Das neue Messer aus Kunststoff, das wie sein voller Vorgeher in ein Standard EX-Bohrloch eingeführt wird, verringert wesentlich die Zahl der in der Praxis vorkommenden Fälle, bei denen sich die Verbindung zwischen dem Messer und dem Gestein bei dem zur Entspannung nötigen Überkernen löst.

Es werden auch analytische Formeln abgeleitet und geprüft, die es erlauben, den vollständigen Spannungszustand in dem betrachteten Felsen anhand der neuen mit dem Messer erhaltenen Verformungen zu bestimmen.

INTRODUCTION

For some eight years now the Laboratório Nacional de Engenharia Civil (LNEC) has been carrying out stress measurements using a borehole strain gauge device of its own make which is commonly referred to as Stress Tensor Gauge (STG). This cell, a sort of tridimensional "doorstopper" including at least nine active electrical resistance strain gauges, is a solid plastic cylinder 35 mm in diameter and about 40 cm long, devised to be installed in an EX borehole (Rocha and Silvério, 1969).

When the initial state of stress is to be determined the positioned gauge must be overcored. The stress relief technique that has been used consists of the following steps: (i) drilling a borehole not less than 7.5 cm in diameter (NX borehole) to the neigbourhood of the point where a knowledge is required of the state of stress; (ii) drilling a coaxial hole with the diameter 3.7 cm (EX borehole) and the approximate length 90 cm, starting at the bottom of the previous hole; (iii) cementing the plastic cylinder on the wall of the narrower hole by means of a suitable adhesive; (iv) taking an initial reading on every embedded strain gauge which a common electrical cable connects to a strain indicator at the surface of the ground; (v) stress-relief overcoring to the larger diameter while keeping the cable connections; and (vi) taking final readings so as to determine the strains caused by stress relief, then the state of stress that existed at the test point.

Since the bond achieved in step (iii) above should hold good in steps (iv) through (vi), a considerable effort was spent in selecting the adhesive and working out the best conditions for its use. On one hand, the selected two-component cement has the rather long pot life that is required to allow the gauge to be inserted and oriented in the borehole, sets to a solid the deformability of which matches that of the plastic cylinder, and even under wet conditions provides a gauge to rock bond strong enough to withstand the stresses brought about by overcoring. On the other hand, the cement is carried to the bottom of the installation hole in a collapsible dispenser attached to the gauge, squeezed out when the positioning rods press the dispenser into the hole, and extruded through the narrow gap between gauge and borehole wall, thus pushing ahead water and drill waste eventually remaining in the hole, and leaving behind clean surfaces for the fresh cement to adhere to.

Despite all the care, failure of the bond due to overcoring has proved rather frequent. This is because compressive states of stress, as are predominant in rock masses, set up tensile stresses in the bond, when relieved by overcoring. Now, even the selected cement provides gauge to rock bonds that cannot withstand more than some 50 kgf/cm^2 (5 MN/m^2), as was shown in a number of tests for bond strength, carried out by pulling rock-cement prisms. Therefore, the bond fails whenever it becomes the seat of induced stresses exceeding the magnitude stated. It might be pointed out that under the most unfavourable conditions, which occur when hydrostatic compressive stresses are relieved in a rock mass of low modulus of deformation, the radial tensile stresses set up in the bond amount to more than 90 per cent of the magnitude of the relieved stresses.

DESCRIPTION OF THE NEW GAUGE

Although it was realized that high stresses are seldom present in a rock mass of high deformability, the mentioned failures prompted the LNEC to try to change the geometry of the gauge with a view to reduce the tensile stresses set up in the bond. This purpose was accomplished with no major alteration in the operation layout by substituting for the solid cylinder a hollow one and embedding the electrical resistance strain gauges midway from the inside to the outside surface. For the dimensions adopted, namely a 2 mm thickness defined by diameters I.D. 31 mm and O.D. 35 mm, calculations have shown that radial tensile stresses in the bond are kept bellow 10 per cent of the magnitude of the relieved stresses, even under the most unfavourable conditions referred to above.

Figure 1 is a schematic representation of the three strain gauge rosettes that have been used, set along the equator of the hollow cylinder at azimuthal angles 0, $\pi/2$, and $5\pi/4$. To sharpen the definition of these angles, three small-base independent strain gauges, centred on the same generatrix, are often substituted for each of the rosettes. The nine active gauges are

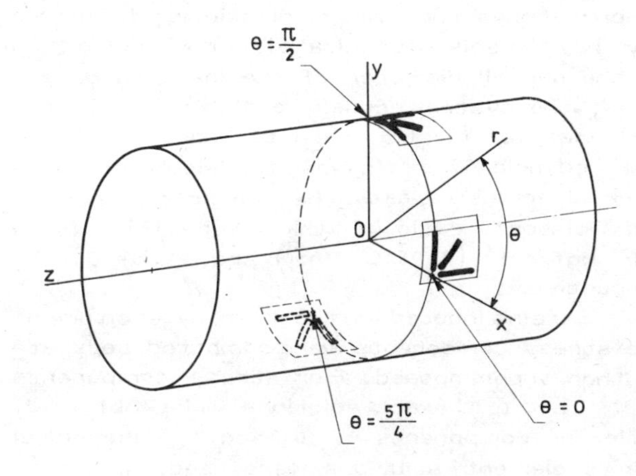

Fig. 1 Gauge geometry: configuration of the rosettes and definition of reference co-ordinates.

connected to an electrical cable which is partially embedded in the cylinder plastic to ensure perfect water-tightness. The cable is also connected to an extra strain gauge, trapped in a plastic layer 2 mm thick adherent to a rock prism some 5 cm x 1 cm x 1 cm in dimensions. This dummy prism hangs loose inside the plastic tube where it compensates the facing strain gauges for temperature changes during testing.

CALCULATION OF THE STRESSES IN THE ROCK MASS

Preliminary tests carried out in the laboratory showed that the tubular gauge rosettes do not behave as though they were cemented directly on the borehole rock wall. This means that one cannot use for the device under discussion the same general formulae as were used by Leeman and Hayes (1966) to interpret the stress measurement results yielded by their multicomponent cell. Therefore, expressions were derived for the strains in the cylindrical plastic layer due to a system of stresses in the surrounding rock.

The assumption underlying the analytical work was the identity of displacements in a rock mass brought about by overcoring (i) just the drilled installation hole, and (ii) the installation hole with the tubular gauge included. This means that for a given state of stress acting on the rock mass, $(\sigma_x, \sigma_y, \sigma_z, \tau_{xy}, \tau_{yz}, \tau_{zx})$, the strains in the included gauge were computed as strains in a plastic liner on the outer surface of which had been imposed such displacements as would occur at the wall of the empty installation hole. Furthermore, both rock and gauge plastic were treated as homogeneous, isotropic, and linearly elastic.

To make the envisaged task easier, the study was from the start restricted to the particular gauge under development. On the other hand, it was borne in mind that the chosen cement, which matches the cylinder plastic in deformability, has the sole mechanical effect of adding 2 mm to the overall diameter of the installed gauge. Thus, the system actually dealth with was a rock mass of elastic characteristics E, ν with a drilled hole 37 mm in diameter lined with a 3mm thick layer of a plastic the Young's modulus and Poisson's ratio of which were $E' = 29.5 \times 10^3$ kgf/cm^2 (2.95 GN/m^2) and $\nu' = 0.409$, respectively.

Strains induced in the liner by each one of the stress components were computed separately, then superimposed. For stress components σ_z, τ_{yz} and τ_{zx} exact solutions were obtained, while for components σ_x, σ_y and τ_{xy} numerical (finite element) solutions were used. In both cases, functions defining the variation of the strains across the thickness of the liner were approximated by polynomials of third degree. In the case of numerical solutions these functions were obtained by the least squares method.

Referring to the co-ordinate axes tied to the cylinder in Figure 1, let $(\sigma_x, \sigma_y, \sigma_z, \tau_{xy}, \tau_{yz}, \tau_{zx})$ denote the free-field state of stress acting on the rock mass, (r, θ, z) a point in the plastic layer, and

$$\rho = r - 15.5 \text{ (mm)}$$

the radial distance from the inner (free) surface of the layer to point (r, θ, z). The strains at point (r, θ, z), due to the state of stress $(\sigma_x, \sigma_y, \sigma_z, \tau_{xy}, \tau_{yz}, \tau_{zx})$ have been calculated as

$$\varepsilon'_r = M_1(\sigma_x + \sigma_y) + N_1(\sigma_x - \sigma_y)\cos 2\theta - M_2\sigma_z + 2N_1\tau_{xy}\sin 2\theta$$

$$\varepsilon'_\theta = M'_1(\sigma_x + \sigma_y) + N_2(\sigma_x - \sigma_y)\cos 2\theta - M'_2\sigma_z + 2N_2\tau_{xy}\sin 2\theta$$

$$\varepsilon'_z = M'_3(\sigma_x + \sigma_y) + M_3\sigma_z$$

$$\gamma'_{r\theta} = N_3(\sigma_x - \sigma_y)\sin 2\theta - 2N_3\tau_{xy}\cos 2\theta$$

$$\gamma'_{\theta z} = N_4(\tau_{yz}\cos\theta - \tau_{zx}\sin\theta)$$

$$\gamma'_{zr} = N'_4(\tau_{yz}\sin\theta + \tau_{zx}\cos\theta)$$

where

$$M_1 = [(0.20589 - 1.13124S) + \nu(0.32479 + 0.46268S)]/E$$

$$M'_1 = [(0.20589 + 1.13124S) + \nu(0.32479 - 0.46268S)]/E$$

$$M_2 = [(0.20589 - 1.13124S)\nu + (0.32479 + 0.46268S)]/E$$

$$M'_2 = [(0.20589 + 1.13134S)\nu + (0.32479 - 0.46268S)]/E$$

$$M_3 = 1/E$$

$$M'_3 = -\nu/E$$

$$N_1 = (1 - \nu^2)R/E$$

$$N_2 = (1 - \nu^2)T/E$$

$$N_3 = (1 - \nu^2)G/E$$

$$N_4 = 2.35021\ (1+\nu)\ (1-S)/E$$

$$N'_4 = 2.35021\ (1+\nu)\ (1+S)/E$$

$$S = 1 - 0.12903\rho + 0.01249\rho^2 - 0.00107\rho^3$$

$$R = 1.99153 - 0.45924\rho + 0.09937\rho^2 - 0.00987\rho^3$$

$$T = -2.87410 + 0.52370\rho - 0.10184\rho^2 + 0.00822\rho^3$$

$$G = -1.24033\rho + 0.18849\rho^2 - 0.01559\rho^3$$

To first check these expressions, Hooke's law may be applied to the strain components at $\rho = 0$ (inner surface of the plastic layer) to show that, disregarding numerical approximations, computed stresses σ'_r, $\tau'_{r\theta}$, and τ'_{zr} do vanish on the free surface of the plastic. On the other hand, computed strain components $\varepsilon'_\theta, \varepsilon'_z$, and $\gamma'_{\theta z}$ at $\rho = 3$ mm (plastic to rock boundary) may be seen to closely approximate the strains that are known to develop on the wall of the installation hole when this is drilled through the stressed rock mass (e.g. Leeman and Hayes, loc.cit.).

The above expressions are used with $\rho = 1$mm to compute the strains at the three gauge measurement points as linear functions of the relieved stresses $\sigma_x, \sigma_y, \sigma_z, \tau_{xy}, \tau_{yz}$, and τ_{zx}. Once a set of nine experimental values are then substituted for the strains, a linear system of nine equations with six unknowns is obtained. This system is solved by the least squares method, yielding the best values of stress components σ_x through τ_{zx}. Principal stresses in the rock mass, σ_1, σ_2, and σ_3, are finally calculated in magnitude and direction as the eigenvalues and eigenvectors of the matrix defined by the stress components.

A computer program has been devised to assist in performing all the steps indicated.

ASSESSMENT OF THE METHOD

To assess the validity of the derived expressions as well as the efficiency of the modified gauge, laboratory tests were carried out on cylinders of rock 90 cm in length and 12 cm in diameter, each of which housed a tubular gauge in a previously drilled 37 mm axial hole.

Marble, diorite, gneiss, and basalt specimens were wrapped in a plastic sleeve, laterally confined within a pressure jacket and axially loaded in a compression testing equipment. The loading schedules started with a uniaxial compression, a lateral compression, or else a hydrostatic all-around compression whereby almost as high initial stresses were applied to the specimens as were allowed by the strength of the rocks. The first rise to full load preceded the setting of the cement, and the gauge to rock bond was made to develop under full load. The specimens were then unloaded by steps at a rate intended to simulate the progress of stress relief on overcoring in situ, and subjected to a few loading-unloading cycles to further check the bond.

The strain components in the plastic layer were measured by the embedded strain gauges, while deformations of the host rock had been previously measured by strain gauge rosettes cemented on both the inside and outside surfaces of the rock specimens. Figure 2 is an exemple of the results that were obtained when diorite cylinders were used. In this figure the ranges of the measured strains are plotted together with the lines which represent the imposed strains, as yielded by the expressions derived.

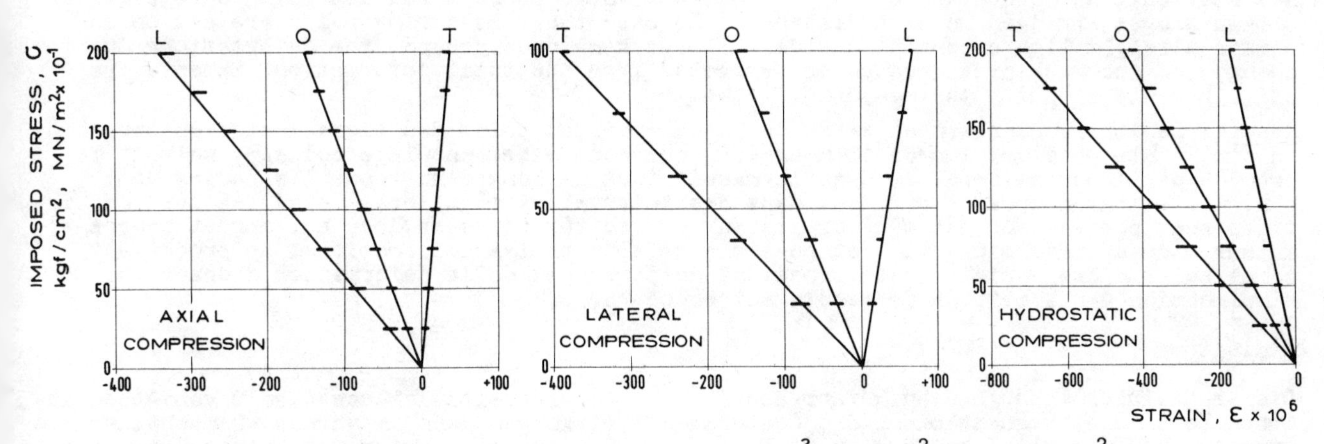

Fig. 2 Compression tests on diorite cylinders ($E = 652 \times 10^3$ kgf/cm^2 = 65.2 GN/m^2, $\nu = 0.20$): computed strains (straight lines) and ranges of measured strains (bars) versus imposed stresses, plotted for longitudinal (L), transverse (T), and at 45° (oblique, O) strain gauges.

In another set of laboratory tests, now in progress, tubular gauges are inserted in prisms of rock 84 cm high, with square ends 30x30 cm^2 in area, and tested as described in a previous paper (Rocha and Silvério, loc. cit.). The installation hole is either longitudinal (from centre to centre, top to bottom), transverse (through the centres of opposite side faces) or oblique (on the plane defined by the aforementioned directions and at a 45° angle to each of them). A fairly good agreement is being obtained between the imposed and measured states of stress.

Application of the method to practical problems is also under way both at home and abroad.

CONCLUSIONS

Insofar as it is much less rigid than its solid forerunner, the recent hollow cylinder substantially reduces the incidence of practical situations where the gauge to rock bond is unable to withstand the tensile stresses caused by overcoring. On the other hand, no installation difficulties arise from the tubular gauge that have not been solved on establishing the previous technique. It appears, therefore, that the latter development improves upon the former and that the new gauge should be preferred whenever stress-relief overcoring is required.

At present, recommendation of the solid gauge is restricted to long-time observations on compressive states of stress of increasing magnitude.

REFERENCES

Leeman, E.R. and D.J. Hayes, A technique for determining the complete state of stress in rock using a single borehole, Proc., 1st Cong.Int.Soc. Rock Mech., Lisbon, Vol.2, 1966, pp. 17-24.

Rocha, M. and A. Silvério, A new method for the complete determination of the state of stress in rock masses, Géotechnique, Vol.19, No. 1, 1969, pp. 116-132.

DEFORMATIONSMESSUNGEN MIT LANGMESSANKERN IM STEINKOHLENBERGBAU

DEFORMATION MEASUREMENTS WITH LONG MEASURING BOLTS IN THE COAL MINING INDUSTRY

MESURES DE DÉFORMATION PAR DES TIGES DE MESURE DANS L'INDUSTRIE HOUILLÈRE

F. SCHUERMANN
Dr.- Ing.

Abt. Bergtechnik, Steinkohlenbergbauverein
Essen, West-Germany

Zusammenfassung: Der Steinkohlenbergbauverein, Essen, hat mehrteilige, bis zu 18 m lange, mit Dehnungsmeßstreifen bestückte, Meßgeber aus Aluminium entwickelt, die nach dem Klebanker-Verfahren im Gebirge in Bohrlöchern auf ihrer ganzen Länge eingeklebt werden. Die Dehnungsmeßstreifen sind in gleichmäßigen Abständen paarweise angeordnet. Werden die Langmeßanker auf einer gemeinsamen Geraden in gegenüberliegenden Seiten eines Grubenraumes, z.B. Firste und Sohle, eingebaut, so können die durch Gebirgsdruckänderungen entstehenden Deformationen von der Gesamtdeformation abgetrennt werden. An der Vereinfachung des Meßverfahrens wird noch gearbeitet.

Summary: The Steinkohlenbergbauverein in Essen developed multisectional measuring bolts of aluminium up to 18 m long which are set on their whole length, according to the resin-set roof bolting method, in boreholes in the strata. These measuring bolts have pairs of strain gauges arranged in even distances. In case these measuring bolts are set on a common straight line on opposite sides of a working underground, the deformations due to changes of the rock pressure can be separated from the total deformation. Experts are still busy to simplify the measuring method.

Résumé: Le Steinkohlenbergbauverein de Essen a mis au point des tiges munies de jauges de contrainte en aluminium de 18 m de long qui sont mises en place collage, suivant le procédé de l'ancrage réparti, dans le massif tout le long d'un trou. Les jauges de contrainte sont disposées par deux dans des intervalles réguliers. Quand les longues tiges sont placées sur une même droite aux extrémités opposées, par ex. mur et couronne, autour d'un ouvrage minier il est possible de séparer les déformations, se produisant comme suite à des variations de pressions de terrains, de la déformation d'ensemble. La simplication de la méthode de mesure est en cours.

Einleitung

Die im Steinkohlenbergbau aufgefahrenen Grubenbaue -die Abbaustrecken, die Gesteinsstrecken und die Blindschächte- werden im allgemeinen durch Messung der Konvergenz und der eingetretenen Querschnittsverluste grob überwacht. Dadurch wird gewissermaßen das Ergebnis der unbekannt bleibenden Wechselwirkung von Gebirgsdruck, Gebirge und Ausbau ermittelt.

Beim ingenieurmäßigen Tunnelbau wird die Wechselwirkung von Gebirge und Ausbau durch Verwendung von Mehrfach-Extensometern gemessen. Die Meßergebnisse geben dem Ingenieur die Möglichkeit, den Ausbau den gegebenen Bedingungen anzupassen.

Von der Aufgabenstellung her ist der Steinkohlenbergbau im Vergleich zum Tunnelbau nur an einer begrenzten, der jeweils erforderlichen, Lebensdauer interessiert und außerdem nicht in der Lage, kostspielige Ausbauarten einzusetzen. Er muß außerdem den Einfluß von Abbaueinwirkungen berücksichtigen. Diese können sogar den Haupteinfluß auf die Standdauer der Grubenbaue ausüben.

Andererseits ist das Ausmaß von Abbaueinwirkungen kaum im voraus abzuschätzen. Der Bergingenieur wird fast immer überrascht. Manche Strecke übersteht Abbaueinwirkungen überraschend gut, manche überraschend schlecht. Die Ursachen für das gute oder schlechte Verhalten, z.B. einer Strecke, sind für den Bergbau jedoch sehr viel schwieriger zu erkennen als für den Tunnelbau. Während der Tunnelbau nur die Wechselwirkung Gebirge-Ausbau kennt, kommt beim Bergbau noch der sich häufig ändernde Gebirgsdruck als dritter und wichtigster Einfluß hinzu. Weil die Wechselwirkung der 3 Einflüsse Gebirge-Ausbau-Gebirgsdruckänderung nicht abzuschätzen ist, muß sie gemessen werden.

Beschreibung des Meßverfahrens (Abb. 1)

Die Bohrlöcher zur Aufnahme der Langmeßanker müssen mindestens so lang wie die Streckenbreite sein. Sie werden mit 42 mm Durchmesser mit einer P 2-2 der TURMAG, Sprockhövel, auf Lafette als Kernbohrung hergestellt. Das ergibt die notwendigen Informationen über den Gebirgsaufbau und die Festigkeitswerte des Gesteins.

Zur Mindestausstattung eines Meßhorizontes ist eine Bohrung in die Firste und eine in die Sohle notwendig. Die Bohrlöcher sollen

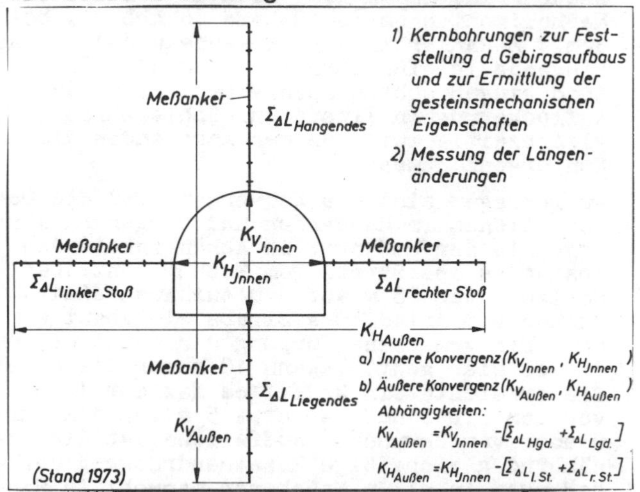

Meßanker-Anordnung für Abbau-, Gesteinsstrecken und Blindschächte **Abb. 1**

in ihrer Längsrichtung fluchtend hergestellt werden. In den Gesteinsstrecken und Blindschächten ist jeweils ein weiteres Paar Bohrlöcher in gleicher Weise in die Stöße hineingerichtet gebohrt worden. Das ist jedoch nicht unbedingt notwendig.

In die Bohrlöcher werden die als Langmeßanker bezeichneten Meßgeber mit Hilfe des Klebanker-Patronen-Verfahrens auf ihrer ganzen Länge eingeklebt und wegen ihrer leichten Verformbarkeit gewissermaßen ein Bestandteil des Gebirges.

Die Langmeßanker werden von der Bergbau-Forschung GmbH, 43 Essen-Kray, hergestellt und bestehen aus miteinander verschraubten dünnwandigen Rohren aus Reinaluminium. Sie besitzen in jeweils 50 cm Abstand angeordnete Paare von Dehnungsmeßstreifen (DMS). Ein 4,5 m langer Meßanker hat somit 9 Paare DMS, insgesamt also 18 Stück. Bei einem 6 m langen Meßanker sind 12 Paare, insgesamt somit 24 DMS eingebaut. Jeder DMS meldet die an seiner Stelle auftretende Deformation.

Die Verwendung von DMS-Paaren hat gewisse meßtechnische Vorteile. Man erhält gleichzeitig 2 Meßwerte aus einer Meßebene. Nimmt man das arithmetische Mittel der Meßwerte, so erhält man die Deformation in der nautralen Faser des Ankers, nämlich Längung oder Kürzung. Nimmt man die Differenz der Meßwerte, so bekommt man eine Information über die Größe der auftretenden Biegung des Ankers an dieser Stelle und bei Beachtung der Lage der DMS zueinander auch die Mitteilung in welcher Richtung eine solche Biegung stattfindet.

Aufzeichnung und Auswertung der Meßwerte

Das Ablesen der Meßwerte der Meßanker erfolgt am Einbauort unter Anschluß eines Meßstellenumschalters zur Anwahl der einzelnen DMS und eines manuellen Kompensators zum elektrischen Abgleich mit Halbbrückenschaltung. Die Meßeinrichtung arbeitet eigensicher. Die Meßgeräte werden von der Firma HOTTINGER-BALDWIN-MESSTECHNIK, Düsseldorf, geliefert und von der Bergbau-Forschung GmbH geringfügig umgebaut, damit sie den bergbehördlichen Vorschriften genügen.

Bei der Auswertung eines Meßanker-Ergebnisses wird wie folgt vorgegangen:

Die Spitze des Meßankers, die von dem Grubenraum den größten Abstand hat, wird als Meß-Nullwert angenommen. In gleicher Weise wird bei den im Tunnelbau üblichen Extensometern verfahren. Jede Verformungsänderung jeder Meßebene wird als Mittelwert der Meßwerte der ein Paar bildenden DMS errechnet. Die DMS, für die der Hersteller eine Gleichmaßdehnung von über 10 % garantiert, sind so geeicht, daß sie die eingetretene Längenänderung direkt in Mikrodehnung (μD) angeben. Eine μD ist eine Längenänderung der Größe 1 μm/m oder anders ausgedrückt 1 Tausendstel mm/m. Jede Verformungsänderung jeder Meßebene wird mit dem Abstand der Meßebenen (0,5 m) multipliziert.

Die auf diese Weise errechneten Deformationen in den einzelnen Meßabschnitten eines Meßankers werden von der Spitze des Meßankers beginnend nacheinander addiert, so daß sich als Abschluß die Gesamt-Deformation des Meßgebers ergibt. In gleicher Weise werden die Meßwerte grafisch aufgetragen.

Erste Meßergebnisse und ihre Deutung

Durch die grafische Auftragung erhält man einen Einblick in das Verhalten des Streckenmantels. Man erkennt dies z.B. an dem Ergebnis des ersten von uns gebauten und auf der Zeche Zollverein Ende 1970 in einer Anker-Türstockstrecke eingebrachten 3,5 m langen Aluminium-Meßankers (Abb. 2).

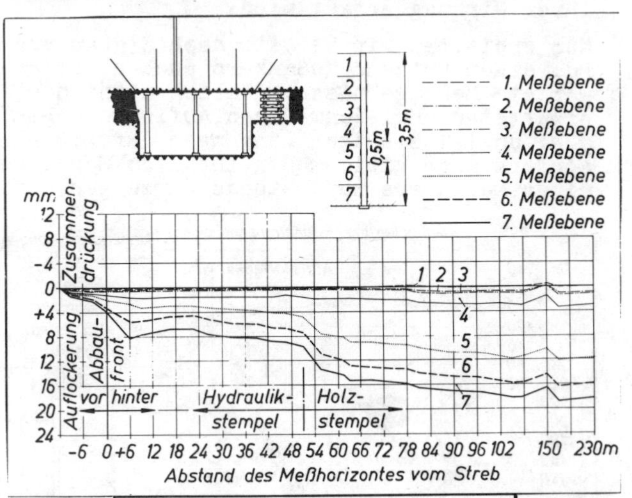

Anzeige Alu-Meßanker 1 **Abb. 2**

Die Auflockerung des geankerten Hangenden ist in Abhängigkeit des Abstandes des Meßankers von der Strebfront aufgetragen. Der erste Alu-Meßanker besaß 7 Meßebenen. Er wurde vor Ort der etwa 15 m weit dem Streb vorgesetzten Kohlenabfuhrstrecke eingebracht.

Das Meßergebnis entsprach weitgehend den Erwartungen. Die gesamte Auflockerung beträgt bis zum Durchgang des Strebs 4 mm und erreicht 6 m hinter dem Streb ein erstes Maximum von 8 mm. Nach einem vorübergehenden geringen Rückgang erhöht sich die Auflockerung 50 m hinter dem Streb auf 10 mm und nimmt erst durch eine Schwächung des Ausbauwiderstandes, nämlich durch Wegnehmen von Hydraulikstempeln und ihren Ersatz durch ungenügend vorgespannte Holzstempel, wieder zu. Die Gesamtauflockerung bleibt selbst 230 m hinter dem Streb unter 20 mm. Die Strecke stand in diesem Bereich auch gut. Betrachten wir nun das Meßergebnis der einzelnen Meßebenen. Die tiefsten Meßebenen 1, 2 und 3 lockern sich praktisch überhaupt nicht auf, auch nur unwesentlich hinter dem Streb. Die Meßebene 4, genau in der Mitte des 3,5 m langen Meßankers angeordnet, meldet bereits eine Deformation, die größer ist, als die der Ebenen 1 - 3 gemeinsam. Diese Meßebene liegt im Bereich der Ankerenden der 1,8 m langen Vollklebanker. Sie erfassen mit ihrer Wirkung die Meßebenen 5, 6 und 7 ganz, die Ebene 4 dagegen nur zur Hälfte. Der Ausbauwiderstand der zusätzlichen Hydraulikstempel allein betrug rd. 20 Mp/m^2 (200 kN/m^2). Dennoch lockert sich das Hangende vor allem im Bereich der Meßebene 5 bis zu 9 mm auf. Hier befand sich ein Lösen, auf das die Hälfte der insgesamt eingetretenen Auflockerung zurückzuführen war. Die nahe an der Firste der Strecke befindlichen Meßebenen 6 und 7 lockern sich besonders im Bereich des Strebdurchganges auf. Die grafische Auftragung der Meßwerte gibt also die Informationen, wo eine Auflockerung der Firste einsetzt, wie schnell sie zunimmt und welche Tiefe von ihrer Wirkung erfaßt wird.

Nun erhielten wir bereits nach Einbau von rd. einem Dutzend Meßankern auch nicht erwartete Meßergebnisse, nämlich nicht die erwarteten ungleichmäßigen Auflockerungen, d.h. ungleichmäßigen Längungen der Meßanker, sondern auch gleichmäßig in allen Meßebenen eines Meßgebers auftretende Kürzungen.

Abb. 3 zeigt ein solches Beispiel aus einer Rückbaustrecke in Flöz Röttgersbank auf der Zeche Erin. Es handelt sich um den ersten Meßhorizont nach dem Schema in Abb. 1, bei dem 1 Meßanker in das Hangende und 1 in das Liegende in einer Linie miteinander fluchtend eingebracht worden waren. Neben der Auflockerung in Firste und Sohle wurde gleichzeitig zwischen den Ankerenden die Konvergenz gemessen.

Aufgetragen sind die Konvergenz und die Deformationen im Hangenden und Liegenden als Ergebnis der Meßanker in Abhängigkeit des Abstandes des Strebs vom Meßhorizont. Der Horizont war 28 m vor dem Aufhauen einige Wochen vor Anlauf des Strebs eingebaut worden. Die gemessene Kürzung der Meßanker, um die es hier geht, begann 18 m vor dem Streb. Sie erreichte ein kräftiges Maximum 14 m vor dem Streb und war etwa 5 m vor dem Streb wieder verschwunden. Auffallend ist die annähernd gleichmäßige Zusammendrückung der Meßanker in allen Meßebenen, sowohl im Hangenden als auch im Liegenden. Die gemessene Zusammendrückung hat auch Einfluß auf die Konvergenz. Die Konvergenz nimmt zu, während die Meßanker verkürzt werden und sie nimmt wieder ab, sobald die Anker sich gewissermaßen wieder auf ihre alte Länge ausdehnen.

Dagegen trat die erwartete Auflockerung des Hangenden -das und nur das sollten die Meßanker feststellen- erst 3 m hinter dem Streb beginnend auf. Rd. 5 - 10 m hinter dem Streb wurde der Streckenausbau geraubt und der Anker im Hangenden meldete etwas über 80 mm Auflockerung, bevor das nicht mehr unterstützte Hangende hereinbrach.

Der Meßanker hat neben der erwarteten vom Gebirgs- und Ausbauverhalten abhängigen ungleichmäßigen Auflockerung, durch die er ungleichmäßig gelängt wurde, unerwartet auch gleichmäßige Kürzungen erfahren, die gleichmäßig wieder verschwanden. Die Frage ist daher zu stellen: Gibt es auch gleichmäßige Längungen? Die Antwort ist ja!

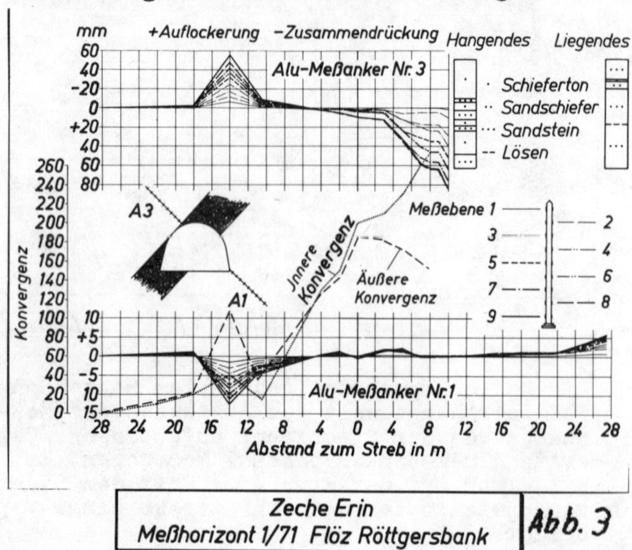

Zeche Erin
Meßhorizont 1/71 Flöz Röttgersbank **Abb. 3**

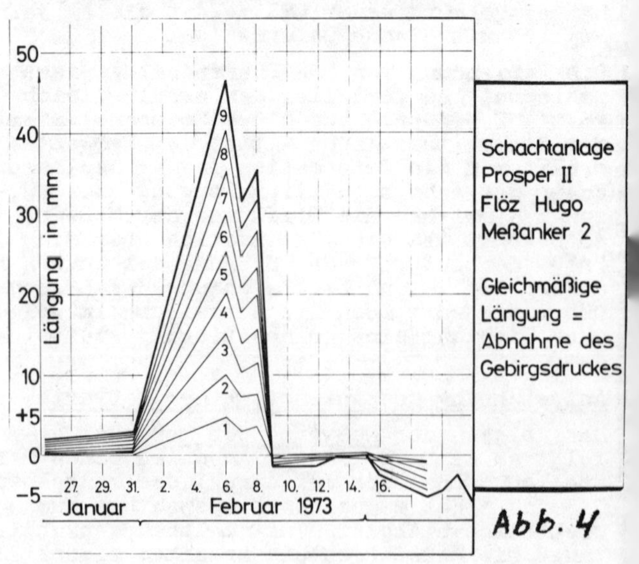

Abb. 4

In Abb. 4 ist die gleichmäßige Längung eines Ankers vergrößert als Ausschnitt (aus Abb. 7) dargestellt. Es handelt sich in diesem Beispiel um eine 10 Monate alte Basisstrecke, auf die ein Streb zulief. Bei einem Abstand des Strebs von der Basisstrecke von nur 42 m ergab sich diese gleichmäßige Längung des Meßankers 2, der im Liegenden eingebracht worden war. Der Anker im Hangenden zeigte übrigens die gleiche Längung, die hier fast 50 mm (siehe auch Abb. 7), betrug. Bezogen auf die Länge des Meßankers beträgt die Längung also über 1 %. Es handelt sich hierbei um eine überwiegend elastisch ablaufende Bewegung des Streckenmantels.

Die vorübergehende gleichmäßige Längung des Meßankers kehrt sich in eine gleichmäßige Kürzung um. Der Meßanker war bei Abwerfen der Basisstrecke und Stundung des Strebs nur 16 m von dieser entfernt um rd. 6 mm kürzer, als er 12 Monate vorher eingebaut worden war.

Wir haben bisher 3 verschiedene Deformationsmeldungen der Meßanker kennengelernt:

1. Die ungleichmäßige Längung. Sie gibt die Wechselwirkung von Gebirge und Ausbau an und ist ein Maß für den Ausbauerfolg und die erzielte Gebirgsbeherrschung.
2. Die gleichmäßige Längung. Sie bedeutet eine Verringerung des Gebirgsdruckes und damit eine Entspannung des Streckenmantels.
3. Die gleichmäßige Kürzung. Sie bedeutet eine Erhöhung des Gebirgsdruckes und damit eine Zunahme der Spannungen im Streckenmantel.

Verzichten wir vorerst auf eine Begründung dieser Erkenntnisse und wenden wir uns zunächst dem Begriff der Konvergenz zu, der dem Bergingenieur das Ergebnis der vielfältigen Wechselwirkung von Gebirgsverhalten, Ausbauverhalten und Gebirgsdruckänderung als Folge von Abbaueinwirkungen mitteilt. Wir messen diesen Wert mit der Genauigkeit von 0,1 mm zwischen den Enden der gegenüberliegenden Meßanker.

Weil die Konvergenz im Inneren des Grubenbaues gemessen wird, bezeichne ich sie im Folgenden als "INNERE KONVERGENZ", zum Unterschied von dem von mir unter Mitwirkung von Herrn Dr. Lütgendorf (1) eingeführten neuen Begriff "ÄUSSERE KONVERGENZ", den ich nun erläutern muß.

Die Abb. 1 zeigte das Meßverfahren. Die Meßanker stellen die in dem Streckenmantel eintretenden Deformationen fest. Zwischen ihren Enden an der Streckenwandung wird die "INNERE KONVERGENZ" als Differenz der sich ändernden Streckenhöhe oder Streckenbreite gemessen. Der Meßanker in der Firste, die Streckenhöhe und der Meßanker im Liegenden bilden gemeinsam eine so lange Meßbasis, wie sie bisher im Steinkohlenbergbau nicht bekannt war. Bei der Auswertung der Meßanker wurde die Spitze des Meßankers als Nullpunkt angenommen. Dieser Punkt ist aber im Bergbau, im Gegensatz zu den meisten Betrieben des Tunnelbaus, nicht als fix zu betrachten. Die Enden der Meßanker können sich nämlich sowohl aufeinander zu bewegen, wie z.B. bei einem Modell unter einer Presse, sie können sich aber auch voneinander weg bewegen; das tritt ein, wenn der Druck der Presse vermindert wird. Das Modell dehnt sich dann wieder um den elastischen Anteil der erlittenen Verformung aus.

Der Vergleich mit dem Modell unter einer Presse macht deutlich, daß eine Entfernung der äußeren Enden der Meßanker voneinander eine Verringerung des Gebirgsdruckes bedeuten muß.

Eine Annäherung der Enden der Meßanker aufeinander zu bedeutet eine Zunahme des Gebirgsdruckes, wenn gleichzeitig die Meßanker eine gleichmäßige Kürzung anzeigen. Zeigen dagegen die Meßanker eine ungleichmäßige Längung an, so handelt es sich um das Einsetzen von Bruchverformungen, wie dies vor allem in Abbaustrecken hinter der Strebfront immer auftritt.

Dieser Zusammenhang ist in Abb. 5 nochmals zusammengestellt.

MESSWERTE	BEDEUTUNG
Meßanker: Ungleichmäßige Längung Äußere Konvergenz: gleichbleibend	Normalverhalten des Mantels Stadium 1 nach Lütgendorf
Meßanker: Ungleichmäßige Längung Äußere Konvergenz: zunehmend Innere Konvergenz: nimmt zu	Bruchverhalten des Mantels Stadium 2 nach Lütgendorf a) $\Delta L < 100$ mm = ohne Einfaltung b) $\Delta L > 100$ mm = mit Einfaltung
Meßanker: Gleichmäßige Kürzung Äußere Konvergenz: zunehmend	Zunahme des Gebirgsdruckes
Meßanker: Gleichmäßige Längung Äußere Konvergenz: abnehmend	Abnahme des Gebirgsdruckes

BEDEUTUNG DER MESSANKERWERTE Abb. 5

Weitere Beispiele aus der Praxis

a) Abbaustrecken

Das Meßergebnis eines Meßhorizontes aus einer Rückbaustrecke enthält Abb. 6. Die Rechteckstrecke wurde von einem Continous Miner aufgefahren. Sie zeigt überwiegend Normalverhalten. Hangendes und Liegendes lockern sich wenig -aber ungleichmäßig- auf. Die innere und die äußere Konvergenz nehmen unter dem Einfluß eines beginnenden Anlaufbruches aus einem Nachbarstreb geringfügig zu. Die angeschnittenen Schichten -hier die Kohle- erleiden geringe Bruchverformung. Erst mit Anlauf des Rückbaustrebs Anfang Januar nimmt der Zusatzdruck etwas zu, wobei die zunehmende Bruchverformung in den Stößen den Druckanstieg reduziert. Äußere und innere Konvergenz laufen weitgehend parallel. Hangendes und Liegendes bleiben gut zusammen. Alle Bruchverformung findet in den Stößen statt. Dieses Gebirgsverhalten ist ideal für Rückbau und für Türstockausbau.

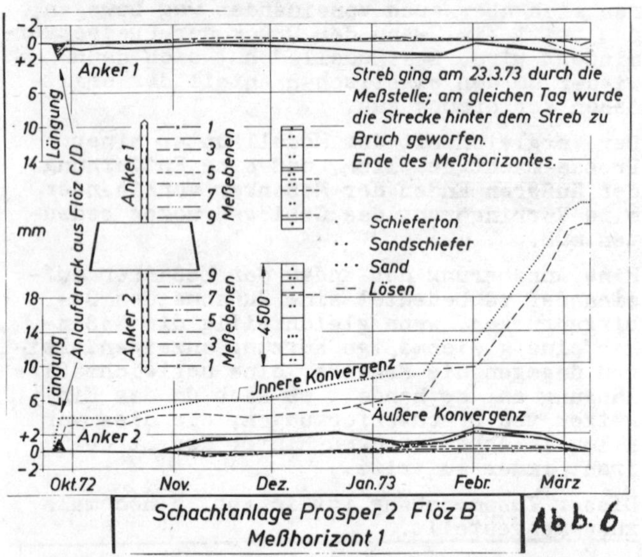

Schachtanlage Prosper 2 Flöz B Meßhorizont 1 — Abb. 6

Abb. 7 enthält das Meßergebnis aus einer Basisstrecke in Flöz Hugo. Der Meßhorizont wurde in der Mitte der Basisstrecke

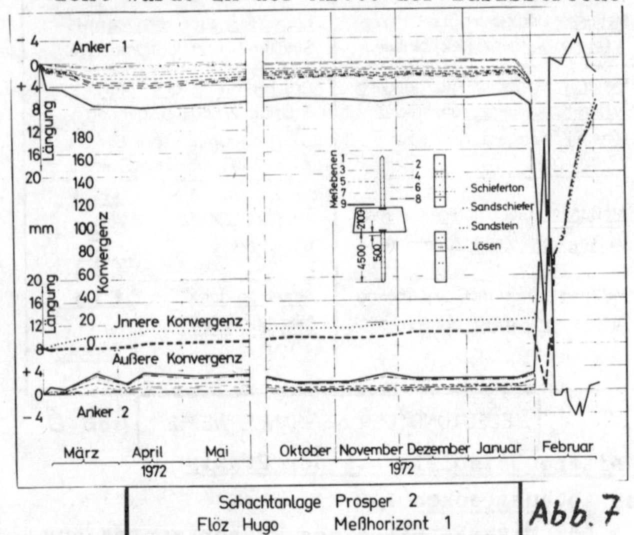

Schachtanlage Prosper 2 Flöz Hugo Meßhorizont 1 — Abb. 7

unmittelbar hinter dem zur Auffahrung verwendeten Continuos Miner am 26. März 1972 eingebaut und bis zum Abwerfen der Strekke beobachtet. Das Hangende bestand aus Schiefer mit 2 sichtbaren Löseflächen, das Liegende als Sandschiefer ohne erkennbare Lösen. Das Gebirgsverhalten ist normal. Die Längung der Meßanker ist ungleichmäßig. Die äußere Konvergenz ist minimal. Der Zeche wurde daher 10 Tage nach Einrichten der Meßstelle mitgeteilt, daß mit einem guten Verhalten der Strecke ohne Unterhaltungsarbeiten bis zum Herannahen der Strebfront gerechnet werden kann. Zur Begründung gehe ich hier etwas mehr auf die Einzelheiten des Verhaltens von Hangendem, Liegendem und Kohlenstoß ein, da sie aus dem Meßergebnis gut zu entnehmen sind.

Das Hangende weist in seinem Verhalten 2 Schwachstellen auf. Das Lösen in der Meßebene 9 und das Lösen in der Meßebene 3 wirken sich aus, dabei das Lösen in Ebene 9 besonders kräftig. Daraufhin konnte der Zeche empfohlen werden, die bis dahin verwendeten zusätzlichen Anker fortfallen zu lassen und statt dessen das Hangende bis zum Lösen nachzuschneiden. Da der Continuous Miner dies konnte und dadurch auch die Strecke die notwendige Höhe bekam, wurde so verfahren. Das Liegende verhielt sich entsprechend seinem gleichmäßigen und ungeschichteten Aufbau gleichmäßig. Die Kohle schließlich, die die angeschnittene Schicht bildet, gibt etwas nach, wirkt also spannungsausgleichend.

Der CM umfuhr zunächst die ganze Bauhöhe, bis im August der Streb anlief. In der ganzen Zeit hat sich die Strecke überhaupt nicht verändert. Erst, als der Streb auf etwa 200 m (November) an die Basisstrecke herangekommen war, nahmen die äußere und etwas langsamer auch die innere Konvergenz geringfügig zu, als Zeichen, daß sich der Gebirgsdruck erhöht. Zu diesem Zeitpunkt ist mit der Zeche abgesprochen, daß versucht werden soll, von dem in der Planung vorgesehenen -zum Schutz der Basisstrecke stehenbleibenden 50 m breiten Kohlenbein noch einen Teil abzubauen, aber nur soviel, daß die Basisstrecke noch zum Abtransport des Strebausbaus und der Fördermittel passierbar bleibt.

Am 31. Januar 1973 ist der Streb auf 51 m Abstand an die Basisstrecke herangekommen, als die Meßanker im Hangenden und Liegenden eine unerwartete Längung erfahren, die am 6. Februar bei 41 m Abstand zwischen Meßhorizont und Streb ein Maximum erfährt und sich dann umkehrt. Testbohrungen zeigten, daß keine Gebirgsschlaggefahr bestand. Das meldeten auch die Meßanker. Ihre Längung erfolgt gleichmäßig, die äußere Konvergenz geht zurück, also entspannt sich das Gebirge und, wie die Meßwerte zeigen, sogar sehr kräftig. Unmittelbar danach nimmt der Gebirgsdruck wieder zu, und zwar sogar über den alten Wert hinaus. Dabei verliert jedoch die Basisstrecke ihr Normalverhalten und geht in das Stadium der Bruchverformung über. Diese findet aber nur in den angeschnittenen Schichten statt. Hangendes und Liegendes bleiben gut zusammen, die Stöße, besonders der strebseitige Stoß, werden mit zunehmender Konvergenz sehr druckhaft. Bei 16 m Abstand von der Basisstrecke wird der Streb gestundet.

b) Gesteinsstrecken

Ein Meßhorizont wurde am 21. September 1971 unmittelbar hinter der Vollschnittmaschine vom Typ Robbins eingebracht. Abb. 8 gibt in der oberen Hälfte das Ergebnis der vertikal eingebrachten Meßanker 1 und 2 wieder. Das Nebengestein bestand überwiegend aus Sandstein. Löseflächen wurden im Hangenden 2, im Liegenden

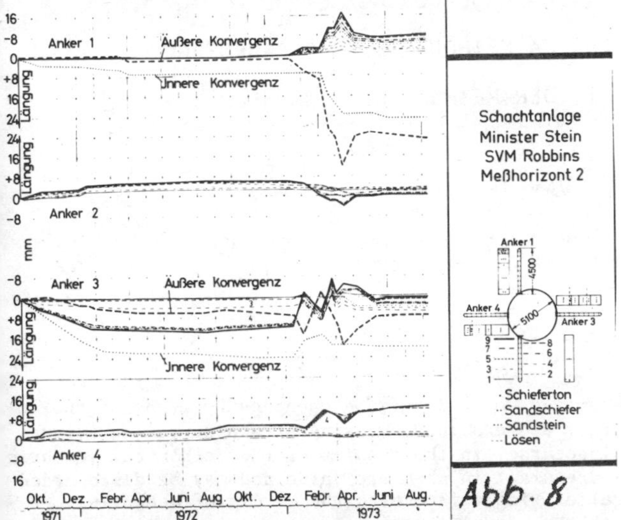

Abb. 8

nur eine festgestellt. Der Meßhorizont zeigt Normalverhalten. Die Meßanker melden ungleichmäßige Längung; die äußere Konvergenz ist unbedeutend. Die Firste bleibt gut zusammen, während sich die Sohle, wahrscheinlich als Einfluß von Wasser, vor allem im Bereich der Meßebenen 1 und 3 um etwa 4 mm auflockert. Das Lösen in über 4 m Tiefe hat also Einfluß. Mitte Januar 1973 kommt Abbaueinfluß auf die Strecke. Der Zusatzdruck erhöht sich kräftig bis zu einem Maximum Mitte April und läßt dann etwas nach. Dies wird angezeigt durch die Zunahme der äußeren Konvergenz und die gleichmäßige Kürzung der Meßanker, am Anker 1 besonders gut zu sehen.

Das Ergebnis der beiden horizontal eingebrachten Meßanker des gleichen Horizontes gibt der untere Teil der Abbildung wieder. Auch in den Stößen herrscht das Normalverhalten vor. Es ist jedoch nicht zu übersehen, daß in den angeschnittenen Schichten Bruchverformungen eintreten. Die Längungen sind ungleichmäßig und etwa viermal größer als die der vertikalen Meßanker. Die Verformungen reichen rd. 2,5 m tief in die Stöße hinein. Die angeschnittenen Schichten verhalten sich also anders, als die tragenden Schichten in der Firste und Sohle. Die ab Januar 1973 einsetzende Abbaueinwirkung ist erkennbar als Zunahme der äußeren Konvergenz und gleichmäßiger Zusammendrückung der Meßanker. Dieser Belastung sind die angeschnittenen Schichten jedoch nicht gewachsen, sie erleiden eine weitere Bruchverformung, die zunächst spannungsmindernd wirkt. Das Spiel wiederholt sich in gleicher Weise nochmals. Die Stöße verlieren dadurch etwas an Zusammenhalt.

Das Ergebnis eines weiteren Meßhorizontes ist in Abb. 9 beigefügt. Der Meßhorizont wurde am 15. April 1972 hinter dem 2. Bohrkopf, dem Nachschnitteil einer Streckenvortriebsmaschine vom Typ WIRTH eingebracht. Das Ergebnis der bankrechten Meßanker ent-

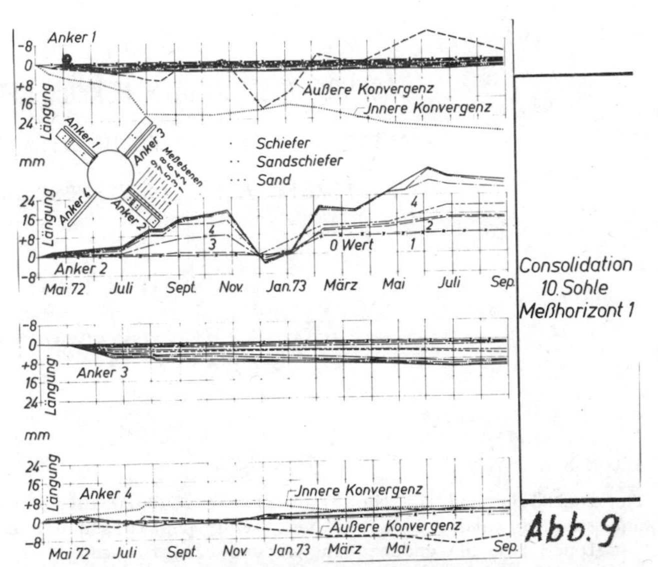

Abb. 9

hält der obere Teil der Abbildung. Rund 3 Monate lang zeigt sich das typische Normalverhalten, gekennzeichnet durch allmähliche ungleichmäßige Längung der Meßanker bei gleichbleibender "äußerer Konvergenz". Mitte Juli beginnen in der Sohle im Bereich der Meßebenen 3 und 4 kleinere Bruchverformungen, wodurch sich das Gebirge etwas entspannt. Anfang November erhöht sich der Gebirgsdruck. Dies ist an der Zunahme der äußeren Konvergenz und der gleichmäßigen Zusammendrückung des Meßankers 2 zu erkennen. Mitte Dezember nimmt der Gebirgsdruck wieder ab; das Gebirge im Bereich des Meßankers 2 längt sich wieder gleichmäßig. Nun zeigt sich aber, daß die vorübergehende Gebirgsdruckänderung Bruchverformungen hinterlassen hat. Auch die Meßebenen 1 und 2 an der Spitze des Meßankers in 4 - 4,5 m Tiefe sind jetzt von der Bruchverformung erfaßt. Anfang April 1973 geht die Entspannung des Gebirges nochmals weiter, wobei allerdings auch ein beachtlicher Teil der eingetretenen Entspannung auf die weitergehenden Bruchverformungen in der Sohle zurückzuführen ist. Maximal hat sich der Sohlenanker um 33 mm gelängt. An diesem Betrag ist allerdings ein Anteil elastischer Längung beteiligt. Das ist nicht zu übersehen, da auch die "äußere Konvergenz" um 12 mm abgenommen hat.

Die Ergebnisse der bankparallelen Meßanker 3 und 4 sind im unteren Teil der Abbildung dargestellt.

Weiteres Vorgehen

Bisher sind über 200 Langmeßanker für die verschiedensten Zwecke eingebaut worden. An einer Vereinfachung des Meßverfahrens wird gearbeitet.

Referenzen:

(1) LÜTGENDORF, H.O., 1971, Quantitative Gebirgsmechanik der Untertagebauten im geklüfteten Gebirge, Verlag Glückauf GmbH, Essen.

ACCURACY OF STRAIN MEASUREMENTS BY THE UNDERCORING METHOD

L'EXACTITUDE DES MESURES DE DILATION PAR LA MÉTHODE DE SOUS-CARROTAGE

GENAUIGKEIT VON DEHNUNGSMESSUNGEN MIT DER METHODE DES INNENKERNS

Y. TSUR-LAVIE F. VAN HAM

Mineral Engineering Department
Technion - Israel Institute of Technology
Haifa, Israel

S U M M A R Y

The technique and the theory of strain measurements on rock surfaces of underground openings by means of the undercoring method is described. Four possible sources of error are examined by using strain-stress equations developed for the undercoring stress-relief method: 1) the inaccuracy in the reading of the mechanical measuring gauge with which the displacements are measured; the errors are small in absolute value and may be disregarded when stresses are high; 2) the eccentricity of the stress-relief ring relative to the circle of measuring points; this error is negligeably small; 3) the deviation of the actual location of a measuring point from its true location on the circle of measuring points; the error caused by tangential dislocation of one point of a pair of measuring points and the error caused by radial dislocation of one point of a pair of measuring points is small; 4) a slight ellipticity of the stress-relief ring. The case of slight ellipticity of a borehole has been examined by Ramkrishna Agarwal, 1967, who concluded that its effect is relatively unimportant.

R E S U M E

La technique et la théorie des mesures de dilation sur des surfaces de roche dans des ouvertures sousterraines par la méthode de sous-carrotage sont décrit. Quatre sources d'erreur possibles sont examinées par l'utilization des équations de dilation-contrainte developées pour la méthode de detente des contraintes resultantes de la sous-carrotage: 1) l'inexactitude de lecture de la jauge méchanique avec laquelle on mesure les déformations Ces erreurs ont des valeurs absolues petites que l'on peut négliger dans le cas des contraintes élevées; 2) l'excentricité de l'anneau de détente des contraintes relative au cercle des points de mesure; cette erreur est negligeable; 3) la deviation de la location actuelle d'un point de mesure par rapport à sa location réelle sur le cercle des points de mesure; l'erreur due à la dislocation tangentielle d'un point d'une pair des points de mesure, et l'erreur due à la dislocation radiale d'un point d'une pair de points de mesure est petits; 4) l'anneau de détente des contraintes est en réalité faiblement elliptique. Ce cas a été examiné par Ramkrishna Agarwal, 1967, qui a conclu que l'effet d'un ellipticite faible d'un trou de forage est relativement insignifiant.

Z U S A M M E N F A S S U N G

Die Technik und die Theorie von Dehnungsmessungen an Felsflächen untererdischer Öffnungen mit der Methode des Innenkerns werden beschrieben. Vier mögliche Fehlergründe sind erforscht worden durch Benutzung der Dehnung-Spannung Beziehungen die entwickelt worden sind für die Felsentspannung verursacht durch Innenkern-Bohrung: 1) die Ungenauigkeit der Ablesung des mechanischen Messungsapparates womit die Deformationen gemessen werden; dieser Fehler ist klein in absolutem Wert und ist unbeachtlich wann die Spannungen gross sind; 2) die Exzentrizität des Entspannungsringes in Bezug auf den Kreis der Messungspunkte; dieser Fehler ist vernachlässig klein; 3) die Abweichung des wirklichen Platzes von einem Messungspunkt von seinem genauen Platz auf den Messungspunktenkreis; der Fehler verursacht durch tangentiale Fehlstellung eines Punktes von einem Punktenpaar, und der Fehler verursacht durch radiale Fehlstellung eines Punktes von einem Punktenpaar is klein; 4) die Elliptizität des Entspannungsringes. Dieser Fall ist bereits untersucht worden von Ramkrishna Agarwal, 1967, der bestimmt hat dass der Einfluss von einer leichten Elliptizität eines Bohrloches verhältnismässig unwichtig ist.

I N T R O D U C T I O N

Knowledge of the state of stress around any underground opening is essential for the design of underground structures in rock and the evaluation of their stability. No instrument has as yet been devised which measures stress directly: all stress determinations are calculated from strain measurements. The results are correct and exact only if the rock behaves like a linearly elastic material: the error caused by the slight deviation from truly linear elastic behaviour of many rocks is small in a practical sense. The state of stress in a point of a linearly elastic, homogeneous and isotropic material is defined by six independent stress components which can be calculated from six measured strain components.

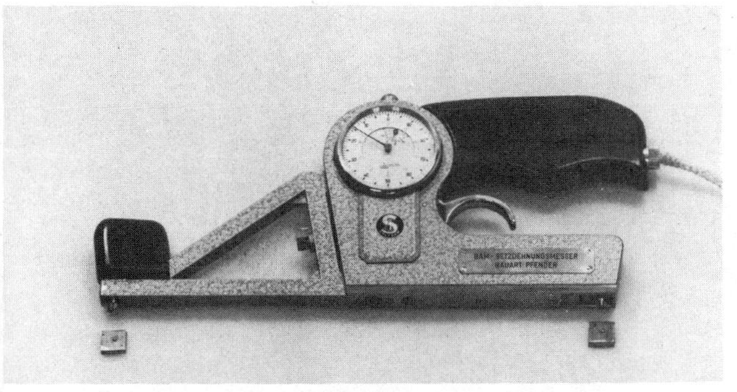

BAM-SETZDEHNUNGSMESSER

BAUART PFENDER

The subject of the present paper is exclusively that of the case of an exposed rock surface of an underground excavation. The principal stresses acting on this rock surface are calculated from only three strain measurements.

STRESS RELIEF METHODS FOR ROCK-STRAIN MEASUREMENTS

A. Strain Rosette Technique and Overcoring.

The strain rosette technique requires the measurement of three strain components in three different, known directions on the rock surface. Three measuring points are located at the apexes of an equiangular triangle on the rock surface; from the measurements of strain between the three pairs of these measuring points the directions and the magnitudes of the principal strains are calculated. If the part of the rock surface on which the measurements are actually made is "liberated" from the whole of the area for which the stress condition is sought, then the stress in this "liberated" part becomes zero, i.e. the stress in this part is relieved. From the difference in lengths of the distance between one pair of points, measured before and after the stress relief, one of the three strain components is calculated. R.S. Lieurance (1933) "liberated" a part of the rock mass with a series of drillholes located on the periphery of a circle: the length of each drillhole was at least equal to the diameter of the "liberated" part. O.J.Olsen (1957) used a large-diameter core drill to relieve the stresses around a strain rosette. E.M. Sipprelle & Teichmann (1950) used a diamond saw to stress-relieve a wedge of rock onto which an electric resistance straingauge rosette had been glued.

B. Undercoring Method.

For the undercoring method of stress relief the measuring points are fixed on the outside of the stress-relieved part of the rock, in contrast to the overcoring method of stess relief, whereby the measuring points are placed within the stress-relieved area of the rock.

a) The technique of the undercoring method. (Figure 1)

In order to obtain the three displacement components the following work-stages must be executed:-

1. Grind fairly flat and smooth an area of approx. 12 cm x 12 cm (5 inch x 5 inch) of the rocksurface on which the measurements are to be made. Do not polish.
2. Drill a 3mm (1/8 inch) diameter hole, 6mm(1/4 inch) deep at the approximate center of the smoothed area. This hole is designated "the center hole".

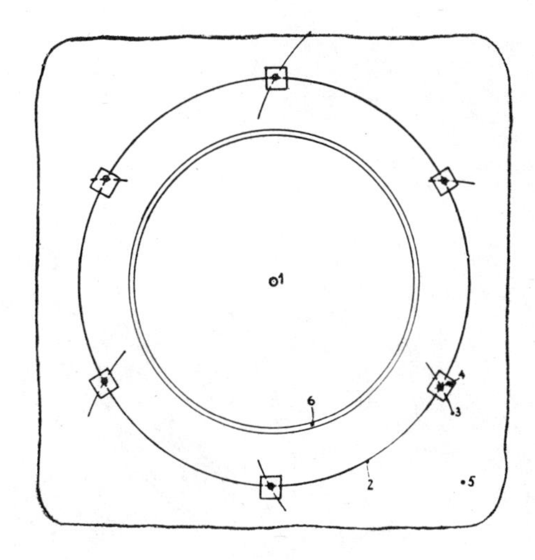

Figure 1: Undercoring method of stress relief. 1. center hole; 2. inscribed circle; 3. engraved division mark; 4. measuring point base and sphere; 5. smoothed area; 6. stress-relief ring.

3. Inscribe with a compass on the smooth rocksurface a circle of 100mm (4 inch) radius. The center of this circle coincides with the center hole.
4. Divide the circumference of the inscribed circle into six equal parts with six engravings made with the compass.
5. Smear epoxy-cement glue on two diametrically opposed engravings.
6. Smear epoxy-cement glue on the bases of two measuring points.
7. Place the bases of the two measuring points onto the two diametrically opposed engravings so that the actual measuring points will be as accurately as possible on the intersections of the engravings and the inscribed circle.
8. With the aid of the special placement tool adjust the measuring points with their bases to their correct positions.
9. Repeat operations 5 to 8 for the second pair of diametrically opposite engravings.
10. Repeat operations 5 to 8 for the third (and last) pair of diametrically opposite engravings.
11. Allow the epoxy-cement glue to set firmly.
12. Measure the lengths of the three distances between pairs of diametrically opposite measuring points with the special micrometer with dial gauge of reading accuracy of 0.001 mm.
13. Drill the undercore stress-relief ring with the 150 mm (6 inch) diameter thin-wall diamond core barrel to a depth of 25mm (1 inch). This core barrel is constructed with a central contractile guidance pin which fits into the center hole.
14. as (12).

Note. The measuring point consists of a tiny steel ball of 1.5mm (1/16 inch) diameter, which is embedded by the use of a special punch into the center of the brass measuring point base. This brass base is 10mm square and 3mm thick (3/8 x 3/8 x 1/8 inch).

b) The theory of the undercoring method. (figure 2)

Let σ_1 and σ_2 be the principal stresses acting in the plane of the exposed rock surface. The principal stress σ_3, perpendicular to the exposed rock surface, is zero (0). The equation for the radial displacement u of a point at distance r from the center of a

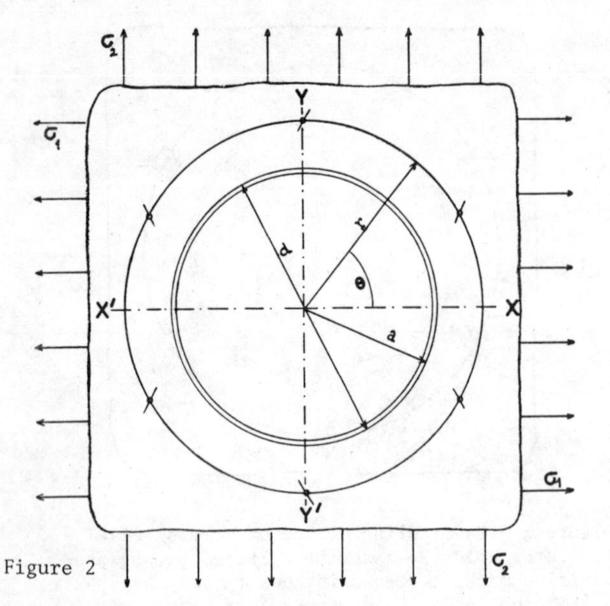

Figure 2

cylindrical hole with radius a, drilled perpendicular to the rock surface is: (see Appendix for its derivation).

$$u = \frac{1}{E}\{\frac{1}{2}(\sigma_1+\sigma_2)[(1-\nu)r + (1+\nu)\frac{a^2}{r}] + \frac{1}{2}(\sigma_1-\sigma_2)$$
$$[(1+\nu)r - (1+\nu)\frac{a^4}{r^3} + 4(1-\nu^2)\frac{a^2}{r}]\cos 2\theta\} \quad (1)$$

in which: u is the radial displacement. a is the radius of the cylindrical hole. r is the radius of the measuring points ($r > a$). θ is the angle between the direction of σ_1 and the radius vector r, in degrees.
For the case that the cylindrical hole has not yet been drilled the radius a is zero and the displacements would be:

$$u_o = \frac{1}{E}\{\frac{1}{2}(\sigma_1+\sigma_2)(1-\nu)r + \frac{1}{2}(\sigma_1-\sigma_2)(1+\nu)r\cos 2\theta\} \quad (2)$$

The difference between the displacements u and u_o is

$$\Delta u = u-u_o = \frac{a}{E}\{\frac{\sigma_1+\sigma_2}{2}(1+\nu)\frac{a}{r} + \frac{\sigma_1-\sigma_2}{2}$$
$$[4(1-\nu^2)\frac{a}{r} - (1+\nu)\frac{a^3}{r^3}]\cos 2\theta\} \quad (3)$$

After having drilled the stress-relief ring with diameter d=2a the diametrical displacement $\Delta\bar{u}$ between one pair of measuring points is $\Delta\bar{u} = 2(\Delta u)$. (3a)

Putting: $k = \frac{a}{r} < 1$; $M = \frac{(1+\nu)k}{2}$; $N = \frac{4(1-\nu^2)k-(1+\nu)k^3}{2}$;

$\bar{u}_i = \Delta\bar{u}$, one gets: $\bar{u}_i = \frac{d}{E}[(\sigma_1+\sigma_2)M+(\sigma_1-\sigma_2)N\cos 2\theta_i]$ (4)

Three measurements of $\bar{u}_i$ at angles θ_i of $(-\theta°+120°)$, $(-\theta°+60°)$ and $(-\theta°)$ give the necessary data for solving σ_1, σ_2 and θ. Because θ has been defined as the angle from σ_1 and we are interested to relate this angle from the direction of $\bar{u}_i$, the angle $(-\theta°)$ is used.
Entering the values for θ_i into equation (4), one gets:

$$\bar{u}_1 = \frac{d}{E}[(\sigma_1+\sigma_2)M+(\sigma_1-\sigma_2)N\cos 2\theta_1] \quad (5)$$

$$\bar{u}_2 = \frac{d}{E}[(\sigma_1+\sigma_2)M - (\frac{\sigma_1-\sigma_2}{2})N\cos 2\theta_1 -$$
$$- \frac{\sqrt{3}}{2}(\sigma_1-\sigma_2)N\sin 2\theta_1] \quad (6)$$

$$\bar{u}_3 = \frac{d}{E}[(\sigma_1+\sigma_2)M - (\frac{\sigma_1-\sigma_2}{2})N\cos 2\theta_1 +$$
$$+ \frac{\sqrt{3}}{2}(\sigma_1-\sigma_2)N\sin 2\theta_1] \quad (7)$$

Solving the equations (5),(6),(7) for the principal stresses gives (8), (9), (10), as follows:

$$\sigma_1 = \frac{E}{6d}[\frac{\bar{u}_1+\bar{u}_2+\bar{u}_3}{M} + \frac{\sqrt{2}}{N}\sqrt{(u_1-\bar{u}_2)^2+(\bar{u}_2-\bar{u}_3)^2+(\bar{u}_3-\bar{u}_1)^2}]$$

$$\sigma_2 = \frac{E}{6d}[\frac{\bar{u}_1+\bar{u}_2+\bar{u}_3}{M} - \frac{\sqrt{2}}{N}\sqrt{(\bar{u}_1-\bar{u}_2)^2+(\bar{u}_2-\bar{u}_3)^2+(\bar{u}_3-\bar{u}_1)^2}]$$

$$\theta_1 = \frac{1}{2}\tan^{-1}\frac{\sqrt{3}(\bar{u}_2-\bar{u}_3)}{2\bar{u}_1-\bar{u}_2-\bar{u}_3}$$

3) Accuracy of the undercoring stress-relief technique.

The possible sources of errors in this technique are:
a. the inaccuracy in the readings of the measuring gauge of the displacements $\bar{u}_i$.
b. the eccentricity of the stress-relief ring with respect to the circle of measurement points.
c. the deviation of the location of a measurement point from its true location on the circle of measurement points.
d. the stress relief ring is slightly elliptical.

a) The inaccuracy in the readings of the measuring gauge of the displacements $\bar{u}_i$.
The diametrical distances between the measurement points are measured with a mechanical dial gauge with direct reading of each 0.001 mm. The magnitude of the principal stresses and their directions can be calculated for each case separately by using equations (8) (9),(10) and the theory of calculation of errors. The possible error in the stress σ_1, caused by the limit of reading accuracy of 0.001mm of the dial gauge, can be calculated. If the stress field is defined by $\sigma_1 \neq 0$, $\sigma_2 = f(\sigma_1)$ (11)

equation (3) becomes

$$\Delta\bar{u} = \frac{a^2}{r}\frac{\sigma_1}{E}(1+\nu)\{(1+f)+(1-f)[4(1-\nu)-\frac{a^2}{r^2}]\cos 2\theta\} \quad (12)$$

Equation (12) is used to calculate the errors in the stress σ_1, caused by a reading error of 0.001mm on the dial gauge. The calculated values are shown on Table I, assuming the following values:

Modulus of elasticity of the rock : $E=70000$ kp/cm^2= 6.86×10^9 N/m^2
Diameter of circle of measuring points : 2r=2032mm(8.0inch)
Diameter of stress relief ring : 2a=1524mm(6.0inch)
Angle between direction of measurement and direction of principal stress σ_1. : $\theta = 0°, 30°, 45°$

b) The eccentricity of the stress-relief ring with respect to the circle of measuring points.
In evaluating the magnitude of the error caused by the stress-relief ring not being concentric with the circle of measuring points, the two following cases will be examined:
1) the center of the stress-relief ring is displaced in the direction perpendicular to the direction of diametrical measurement;
2) the center of the stress-relief ring is displaced in the direction of diametrical measurement.

angle θ	stress field $\sigma_1 \neq 0 : \sigma_2 = f(\sigma_1)$	Error in stress σ_1			
		ν = 0.25		ν = 0.333	
	f	Kp/cm²	KN/m²	Kp/cm²	KN/m²
0°	0.0	0.29	284	0.30	294
	0.5	0.36	353	0.36	353
	1.0	0.49	480	0.46	451
30°	0.0	0.44	431	0.45	441
	0.5	0.46	451	0.45	441
	1.0	0.49	480	0.46	451
45°	0.0	0.98	960	0.92	902
	0.5	0.65	637	0.61	598
	1.0	0.49	480	0.46	451

TABLE I. Error in the stress σ_1 caused by reading error of 0.001 mm on the dial gauge.

1) The center of the stress-relief ring is displaced in a direction perpendicular to the direction of diametrical measurement. (fig.3).
Let A and B be the measuring points located on their circle of radius z with center at 0'. The center of the stress-relief ring of radius a is at 0. The perpendicular distance 0 - 0' be b.
The direction of principal stress σ_1, indicated by the line X-X' makes an angle θ with the line A-B.
The radial displacement obtained after the "undercoring" makes an angle β with the line A-B.
The error in the measurement of the displacement derives from the measurement reading being the measurement component in the A-B direction only and not the radial displacements, i.e. OA and OB, which should be measured. Using equation (3) with reference to points A and B respectively, one gets:

$$\Delta u_{A,B} = \frac{a}{E}\{\frac{\sigma_1+\sigma_2}{2}(1+\nu)\frac{a}{r} + \frac{\sigma_1-\sigma_2}{2}[4(1-\nu^2)\frac{a}{r} - (1+\nu)\frac{a^3}{r^3}]\cos 2(\theta \pm \beta)\} \quad (13)$$

The displacement component *as measured* will be:

$$\Delta\bar{u}' = (\Delta u_A + \Delta u_B)\cos\beta \quad (14)$$

Substitution of (13) into equation (14) gives:

$$\bar{u}' = \frac{2a}{E}\{\frac{\sigma_1+\sigma_2}{2}(1+\nu)\frac{a}{r} + \frac{\sigma_1-\sigma_2}{2}[4(1-\nu^2)\frac{a}{r} - (1+\nu)\frac{a^3}{r^3}]\cos 2\theta \cos 2\beta\}\cos\beta \quad (15)$$

The radius r in the equations (13) and (15) is OA or OB (fig.3); thus $r = \frac{z}{\cos\beta}$; substituting this in equation (15) one obtains:

$$\bar{u}' = \frac{2a}{E}\{\frac{\sigma_1+\sigma_2}{2}(1+\nu)\frac{a}{z}\cos^2\beta + \frac{\sigma_1-\sigma_2}{2}[4(1-\nu^2)\frac{a}{z}\cos^2\beta - (1+\nu)\frac{a^3}{z^3}\cos^4\beta]\cos 2\theta\cos 2\beta\} \quad (16)$$

The error is $\Delta\bar{u} - \Delta\bar{u}'$ in which: (17)

$\bar{u}$ is the displacement which would have been measured if the stress relief ring was concentric with the circle of the measuring points, and $\Delta\bar{u}'$ is the displacement as actually measured.
Substitution of eq.(12) and eq.(16), into eq.(17) and applying eq.(11) gives:

$$\Delta\bar{u} - \Delta\bar{u}' = \frac{a^2}{z}\cdot\frac{\sigma_1}{E}(1+\nu)\sin^2\beta\{(1+f)+(1-f)\cos 2\theta [8(1-\nu) - \frac{a^2}{z^2}(3-2\sin^2\beta)]\} \quad (18)$$

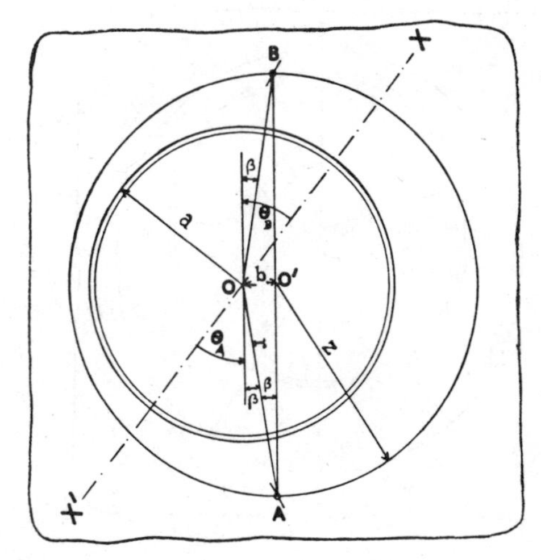

Figure 3. Perpendicular eccentricity of stress relief ring.

Eq.(18) is the expression for the absolute error in mm caused by perpendicular eccentricity of the stress relief ring and the circle of measuring points.
If the relative error e_p is defined as

$$e_p = \frac{\Delta\bar{u} - \Delta\bar{u}'}{\Delta\bar{u}} \cdot 100 \text{ percent}, \quad (19)$$ then (equation (20)):

$$e_p = \frac{\sin^2\beta\{1+f+(1-f)\cos 2\theta [8(1-\nu) - \frac{a^2}{z^2}(3-2\sin^2\beta)]\}}{1+f+(1-f)\cos 2\theta [4(1-\nu) - \frac{a^2}{r^2}]} \cdot 100\%$$

Table II shows the relative error percentages due to perpendicular eccentricity for three stress fields, two Poisson ratios and two angles θ. The percentages have been calculated for: a=76.2mm (3 inch); r=z=101.6 mm (4 inch); b=8.5mm (1/3 inch). Note that for θ = 45°, and also for f=1.0 the relative error is constant; $e_p = \sin^2\beta = 0.69\%$.

angle θ	Stress field $\sigma_1 \neq 0; \sigma_2 = f(\sigma_1)$	Poisson ratio	
	f	ν=0.25	ν=0.333
0°	0.0	1.07%	1.03%
	0.5	0.93%	0.90%
	1.0	0.69%	0.69%
30°	0.0	0.98%	0.95%
	0.5	0.85%	0.82%
	1.0	0.69%	0.69%

Table II, showing relative error e_p percentages due to perpendicular eccentricity.

Table II shows that the errors due to perpendicular eccentricity relative to the errors due to limitation of dial gauge accuracy are negligeably small.

2) The center of the stress relief ring is displaced in the same direction of the diametrical measurement. (Figure 4).
Refering to fig.4, let A and B be the measuring points located on the circle of radius z having its center at 0'. The center of the stress relief ring of radius a is located at 0. The co-directional eccentricity 0-0' is b.

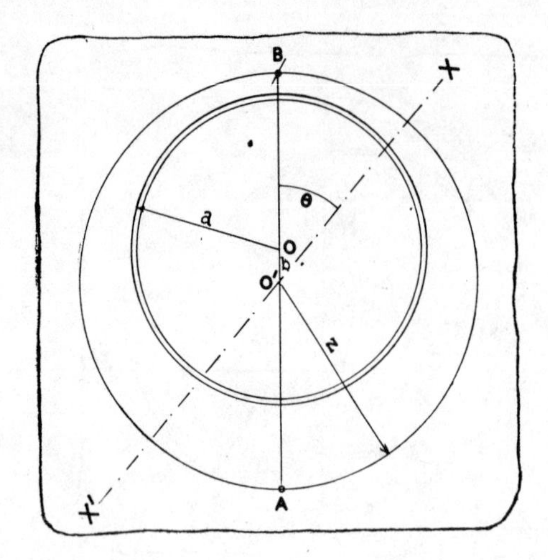

Figure 4. Co-directional eccentricity of stress relief ring.

Eq.(3) and eq.(11) and simplifying gives:

$$\Delta u = \frac{a^2}{r}\frac{\sigma_1}{2E}(1+\nu)\{(1+f)+(1-f)[4(1-\nu) - \frac{a^2}{r^2}]\cos 2\theta\} \quad (12)$$

Therefore: (21)

$$\Delta u_{A,B} = \frac{a^2}{(z\pm b)}\cdot\frac{\sigma_1}{2E}(1+\nu)\{(1+f)+[4(1-\nu) - \frac{a^2}{(z\mp b)^2}]\cos 2\theta\}$$

The displacement component as measured will be

$$\bar{\Delta u}' = \Delta u_A + \Delta u_B \quad (22)$$

Substitution of (21) into eq.(22) gives:

$$\bar{\Delta u}' = a^2 \cdot \frac{\sigma_1}{2E}(1+\nu)\{(1+f)(\frac{1}{z-b}+\frac{1}{z+b}) + (1-f)\cos 2\theta \left[\frac{4(1-\nu) - \frac{a^2}{(z-b)^2}}{z-b} + \frac{4(1-\nu) - \frac{a^2}{(z+b)^2}}{z+b}\right]\} \quad (23)$$

If, similar to eq.(19) we define the relative error e_c as

$$e_c = \frac{\bar{\Delta u} - \bar{\Delta u}'}{\bar{\Delta u}} \cdot 100 \text{ percent then:} \quad (24)$$

$$e_c = \frac{\frac{1+f}{z(1-\frac{z^2}{b^2})} + (1-f)\cos 2\theta\{\frac{4(1-\nu)}{z(1-\frac{z^2}{b^2})} - a^2(\frac{1}{z^3} - \frac{z^3+3z^2b}{(z^2-b^2)^3})\}}{\frac{1}{r}(1+f) + (1-f)\cos 2\theta\{4(1-\nu) - \frac{a^2}{r^2}\}}$$

Table III shows the relative error percentages due to co-directional eccentricity for three stress fields, two Poisson ratios and two angles θ. The percentages have been calculated for: Diameter of stress relief ring (2a) 152.4mm (6.0 inch) Diameter of circle of measuring Points (2z) 203.2mm (8.0 inch), co-directional eccentricity (b) 8.5 mm (1/3 inch). Note that for angle θ=45°, and also for f=1.0, the relative error is constant and is:

$$e_c = \frac{b^2}{b^2-z^2} = -0.70\%$$

Table III shows that the errors due to co-directional eccentricity relative to the errors due to limitation of dial gauge accuracy are negligeably small.

angle θ	Stress field $\sigma_1 \neq 0$; $\sigma_2 = f(\sigma_1)$	Poisson ratio ν	
	f	0.25	0.333
0°	0.0	3.74%	4.20%
	0.5	2.11%	2.29%
	1.0	-0.70%	-0.70%
30°	0.0	2.74%	2.83%
	0.5	1.11%	0.98%
	1.0	-0.70%	-0.70%

Table III, showing relative error e_c percentages due to co-directional eccentricity.

c. The deviation of the location of a measuring point from its true location on the circle of measuring points.

Two cases must be examined:

1) A diametrical pair of measuring points is located on the circle of measuring points, but one of the pair of points does not lie exactly on the diameter of the circle.

2) A diametrical pair of measuring points is located on the diameter, but one point of the pair does not lie exactly on the circumference of the circle.

First case: tangential deviation of one of a pair of measuring points. Refering to fig.5, let A and B be the measuring points of which B does not lie exactly on the diameter of the circle. The radius vector to B makes an angle 2α° with the true diameter A B'. The direction X-X' of the principal stress σ_1 makes an angle θ_A with the diameter AB'; the direction of the principal stress σ_1 with the radius vector OB is therefore $\theta_B = \theta_A + 2\alpha$, and with the radius vector OA is $\theta_A = \theta$

The displacement of point A is (eq.(3))

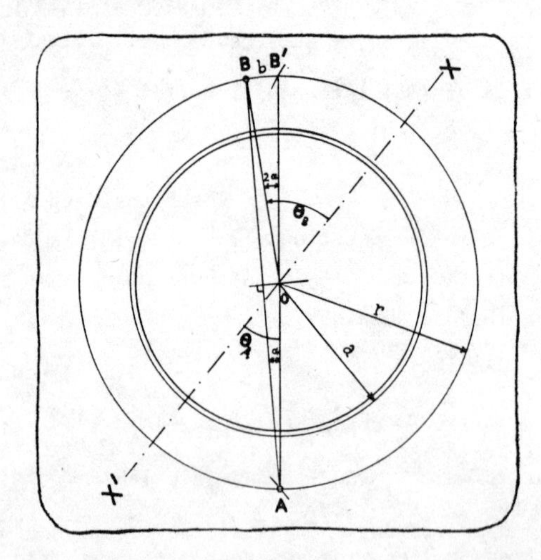

Figure 5: Tangential dislocation of one measuring point.

$$\Delta u_A=\frac{a}{E}\{\frac{\sigma_1+\sigma_2}{2}(1+\nu)\frac{a}{r}+\frac{\sigma_1-\sigma_2}{2}[4(1-\nu^2)\frac{a}{r}-(1+\nu)\frac{a^3}{r^3}]\cos 2\theta\} \quad (3')$$

The displacement of point B is (eq.(3))

$$\Delta u_B=\frac{a}{E}\{\frac{\sigma_1+\sigma_2}{2}(1+\nu)\frac{a}{r}+\frac{\sigma_1-\sigma_2}{2}[4(1-\nu^2)\frac{a}{3}-(1+\nu)\frac{a^3}{r^3}]\cos 2(\theta+2\alpha)\} \quad (3'')$$

The measurement of the displacement A B is

$$\Delta\bar{u}' = (\Delta u_A + \Delta u_B)\cos\alpha \quad (25)$$

The true diametrical displacement of A B' should be

$$\Delta\bar{u}=\frac{2a}{E}\{\frac{\sigma_1+\sigma_2}{2}(1+\nu)\frac{a}{r}+\frac{\sigma_1-\sigma_2}{2}[4(1-\nu^2)\frac{a}{r}-(1+\nu)\frac{a^3}{r^3}]\cos 2\theta\} \quad (3''')$$

The relative error is (compare eq.19)

$$e_{d_t} = \frac{\Delta\bar{u}-\Delta\bar{u}'}{\Delta\bar{u}}\cdot 100\% = (1-\frac{\Delta\bar{u}'}{\Delta\bar{u}})\ 100\%. \quad (26)$$

Substituting Eq.(3') and eq.(3'') into eq.(25), and eq.(25) and eq.(3''') into eq.(26) and simplifying, and using the stress field definition eq.(11) one obtains (27)

$$e_{d_t}=1-\frac{\{2(1+f)+(1-f)[4(1-\nu)-\frac{a^2}{r^2}][\cos 2\theta+\cos 2(\theta+2\alpha)]\}\frac{\cos\alpha}{2}}{1+f+(1-f)\ [4(1-\nu)-\frac{a^2}{r^2}]\ \cos 2\theta}$$

e_{d_t} is evaluated in table IV using: Diameter of stress relief ring (2a) 152.4mm (6.0 inch); Diameter of circle of measuring points (2r) 203.2mm (8.0 inch) Tangential deviation from diametrical location (b) 8.5mm (1/3 inch).

Angle θ	Stress field $\sigma_1\neq 0$; $\sigma_2=f(\sigma_1)$	e_{d_t} Poisson ratio	
	f	ν = 0.25	ν = 0.333
0°	0.0	0.6%	0.7%
	0.5	0.2%	0.4%
	1.0	0.1%	0.1%
30°	0.0	8.2%	7.7%
	0.5	4.6%	4.1%
	1.0	0.1%	0.1%
45°	0.0	0.1%	0.1%
	0.5	0.1%	0.1%
	1.0	0.1%	0.1%

Table IV, showing relative error to tangential error due to tangential deviation e_{d_t} of one of a pair of measuring points.

Second case: radial deviation of one of a pair of measuring points.
Refering to fig.6, the displacement of point A is (eq.(3)).

$$\Delta u_A=\frac{a}{E}\{\frac{\sigma_1+\sigma_2}{2}(1+\nu)\frac{a}{r}+\frac{\sigma_1-\sigma_2}{2}[4(1-\nu^2)\frac{a}{r}-(1+\nu)\frac{a^3}{r^3}]\cos 2\theta\} \quad (3')$$

The displacement of point B is (3'')

$$\Delta u_B=\frac{a}{E}\{\frac{\sigma_1+\sigma_2}{2}(1+\nu)\frac{a}{r+b}+\frac{\sigma_1-\sigma_2}{2}[4(1-\nu^2)\frac{a}{r+b}-(1+\nu)\frac{a^3}{(r+b)^3}]\cos 2\theta\}$$

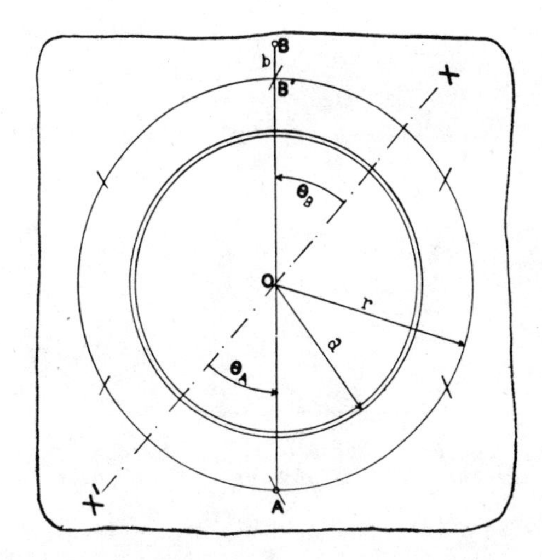

Figure 6: Radial dislocation of one measuring point.

The measurement of the displacement A B is:
$\Delta\bar{u}' = \Delta u_A + \Delta u_B$, which, after substitution of eq.(3') and eq. (3'') and using the stress field definition of eq.(11), and simplifying, becomes

$$\Delta\bar{u}' = \frac{a^2}{2}\frac{\sigma_1}{E}(1+\nu)\ \{\frac{1+f}{r}+\frac{1-f}{r}\ [4(1-\nu)-\frac{a^2}{r^2}]\ \cos 2\theta + \frac{1+f}{r+n}+\frac{1-f}{r+b}\ [4(1-\nu)-\frac{a^2}{(r+b)^2}]\cos 2\theta\ \} \quad (28)$$

The measurement of the correct displacement A B' should be,

$$\Delta\bar{u} = \frac{a^2\ \sigma_1}{rE}(1+\nu)\{1+f+(1-f)[4(1-\nu)-\frac{a^2}{r^2}]\cos 2\theta\} \quad (12)$$

The relative error percentage is

$$e_{d_r} = (1-\frac{\Delta\bar{u}'}{\Delta\bar{u}})\ .\ 100\% \quad (26)$$

After simplification one obtains:

$$e_{d_r} = 100\{1-\frac{\frac{r}{2}[(1+f)(\frac{1}{r}+\frac{1}{r+b})+4(1-f)(1-\nu)\cos 2\theta(\frac{1}{r}+\frac{1}{r+b})-(1-f)a^2\cos 2\theta(\frac{1}{r^3}-\frac{1}{(r+b)^3})]}{[1+f+4(1-f)(1-\nu)\cos 2\theta-(1-f)\frac{a^2}{r^2}\cos 2\theta]}\} \quad (29)$$

Table V shows the relative error percentages due to radial displacement from the circumferential position of one of a pair of measuring points. Table V has been calculated from the following data:
Diameter of stress relief ring (2a) 152.4mm(6.0 inch) Diameter of circle of measuring points (2r) 203.2mm (8.0 inch); Radial displacement of one of the pair of points (b) 2.5mm (0.1 inch); for angles θ=0°, 30° and 45° and stress fields and Poisson ratios as shown.

Under certain circumstances the relative error due to radial dislocation of one of a pair of measuring points can be quite large, and care should be exercised to locate the measuring points precisely on the circumference of the circle of measuring points.

angle θ	Stress field $\sigma_1 \neq 0$; $\sigma_2 = f(\sigma_1)$ f	e_{d_r}	
		$\nu = 0.25$	$\nu = 0.333$
0°	0.0	+0.8%	+0.7%
	0.5	+1.0%	+0.3%
	1.0	+1.3%	+1.3%
30°	0.0	+0.9%	+0.6%
	0.5	+3.4%	+0.4%
	1.0	+1.3%	+1.3%
45°	0.0	+1.3%	+1.3%
	0.5	+1.3%	+1.3%
	1.0	+1.3%	+1.3%

Table V, showing relative error e_{d_r} percentages due to radial deviation of one of a pair of measuring points.

d) The stress relief ring is not truly circular but slightly elliptic. This case has been examined by Ramkrishna Agarwal (1967) who concludes that the effect of a small ellipticity of the borehole is relatively unimportant (page 83).

C O N C L U S I O N

The undercoring method for the determination of the principal stresses on exposed rock surfaces of underground excavations from measurements of displacements is accurate. The reading of the micrometer dial gauge, accurate to 0.001 mm, is the main source of error, although these errors are small in absolute value and may be disregarded if the stresses are high. Slight eccentricity of the stress relief ring relative to the circle of measuring points, tangential dislocation of one of a pair of measuring points, radial dislocation of one of a pair of measuring points (which can be avoided by exercising care in the correct placement of the measuring points) and the effect of a slight ellipticity of the stress relief, all lead to negligeable errors.

ACKNOWLEDGEMENT

The authors wish to express their thanks to Professor Wilbur I. Duvall, former Research Director of the Rock Mechanics Laboratory, U.S.Bureau of Mines, Denver, Colorado, now retired, who suggested the subject of this paper.

R E F E R E N C E S

Lieurance, R.S. 1933 Stresses in foundations at Boulder Dam. U.S. Bureau of Reclamation, Techn.Memo. 346.

Sipprelle, E.M. & H.L.Teichmann, 1950 Roof studies and mine structure stress analysis. Bureau of Mines oil-shale mine, Rifle, Colo.. Transact. A.I.M.E., v.187.

Olsen, D.J. 1957 Measurement of residual stress by the strain relief method. 2nd Ann. Symp. Rock Mech.,Quart. Colo. Sch.Mines, v 52, no.3, 183-204.

Leeman, E.R. & D.J.Hayes, 1966 A technique for determining the complete state of stress in rock using a single borehole. Proc. 1st Congr.Int.Soc.Rock Mech., Lisbon, vII, theme 4, no.3, 17-24.

Obert, L. & W.I.Duvall, 1967 Rock Mechanics and the Design of Structures in Rock. Wiley, chapt.3.

Ramkrishna Agarwal, 1967 Sensitivity analysis of borehole deformation measurements of in-situ stress determination when affected by borehole eccentricity. "Status of practical rock mechanics" 9th Symp. rock mechanics, Golden, Colo., 79-83.

APPENDIX

Hooke's law defines the stress-strain relations of a elastic material in a cylindrical coordinate system:

$$\varepsilon_r=\frac{1}{E}[\sigma_r-\nu(\sigma_\theta+\sigma_z)];\varepsilon_\theta=\frac{1}{E}[\sigma_\theta-\nu(\sigma_r+\sigma_z)];\varepsilon_z=\frac{1}{E}[\sigma_z-\nu(\sigma_r+\sigma_\theta)$$

$$\gamma_{r\theta} = \frac{2(1+\nu)}{E}\tau_{r\theta} \qquad (1)$$

The strain-displacement equations in a cylindrical coordinate system are (Obert & Duvall, 1967):

$$\varepsilon_r=\frac{\partial u}{\partial r} \; ; \; \varepsilon_\theta=\frac{u}{r}+\frac{1}{r}\cdot\frac{\partial u}{\partial \theta} \; ; \; \varepsilon_z=\frac{\partial w}{\partial z} \; ; \; \gamma_{r\theta}=\frac{1}{r}\cdot\frac{\partial u}{\partial \theta}+\frac{\partial v}{\partial r}-\frac{v}{r} \qquad (2)$$

The stresses in a point (r,θ) in an infinite mass of elastic rock acted upon by the stresses S_x,S_y,S_z in the X,Y,Z direction resp. of a rectangular coordinat system (XYZ) and having a cylindrical opening (with dius a) in the Z-direction are (Leeman & Hayes 1966)

$$\sigma_\theta=\frac{S_x+S_y}{2}(1+\frac{a^2}{r^2})+(1+3\frac{a^2}{r^2})[\frac{S_x-S_y}{2}\cos 2\theta+T_{xy}\sin 2\theta]$$

$$\sigma_r=\frac{S_x+S_y}{2}(1-\frac{a^2}{r^2})+(1+3\frac{a^4}{r^4}-4\frac{a^2}{r^2})[\frac{S_x-S_y}{2}\cos 2\theta+T_{xy}\sin 2\theta]$$

$$\sigma_z = S_z - 4\nu\frac{a^2}{r^2}[\frac{S_x-S_y}{2}\cos 2\theta + T_{xy}\sin 2\theta]$$ and therefore

$$\sigma_\theta+\sigma_z=\frac{S_x+S_y}{2}(1+\frac{a^2}{r^2})-(1+3\frac{a^4}{r^4}+4\nu\frac{a^2}{r^2})[\frac{S_x-S_y}{2}\cos 2\theta+T_{xy}\sin 2\theta]+S_z$$

Substitution of the equation for σ_r and $\sigma_\theta+\sigma_z$ into equations (1) and (2) gives the radial strain:

$$\frac{\partial u}{\partial r}=\varepsilon_r=\frac{1}{E}\{\frac{S_x+S_y}{2}(1-\frac{a^2}{r^2})+(1+3\frac{a^4}{r^4}-4\frac{a^2}{r^2})[\frac{S_x-S_y}{2}\cos 2\theta+T_{xy}\sin 2\theta]$$

$$-\nu\{\frac{S_x+S_y}{2}(1+\frac{a^2}{r^2})-(1+3\frac{a^4}{r^4}+4\nu\frac{a^2}{r^2})[\frac{S_x-S_y}{2}\cos 2\theta+T_{xy}\sin 2\theta]+S_z\}$$

Integration of $\frac{\partial u}{\partial r}$ gives the radial displacement u.

$$u = \frac{r}{E}\{\frac{S_x+S_y}{2}[1-\nu+(1+\nu)\frac{a^2}{r^2}] +$$

$$\frac{S_x-S_y}{2}[1+\nu-(1+\nu)\frac{a^4}{r^4}+4(1-\nu^2)\frac{a^2}{r^2}]\cos 2\theta - \nu S_z +$$

$$T_{xy}[1+\nu-(1+\nu)\frac{a^4}{r^4}+4(1-\nu^2)\frac{a^2}{r^2}]\sin 2\theta\}$$

In the particular case of stress relief by undercori the stress S_z on the free surface of the underground opening is zero; and because the directions of the X and Y axes are chosen to coincide with the directions of the principal stresses, $S_x=\sigma_1;S_y=\sigma_2;T_{xy}=0$. The radial displacement is then

$$u = \frac{1}{E}\{\frac{\sigma_1+\sigma_2}{2}[(1-\nu)r+(1+\nu)\frac{a^2}{r}] +$$

$$\frac{\sigma_1-\sigma_2}{2}[(1+\nu)r-(1+\nu)\frac{a^4}{r^3}+4(1-\nu^2)\frac{a^2}{r}]\cos 2\theta$$

THE USE OF THE FLATJACK INSTALLED IN A SAWCUT SLOT IN THE MEASUREMENT OF IN SITU STRESS

L'EMPLOI DU VÉRIN PLAT INSTALLE DANS UNE FENTE MENAGÉE À LA SCIE POUR MESURER LES CONTRAINTES IN SITU

EINSATZ EINER IN EINE SÄGESCHNITTSCHLITZE EINGEFÜGTE TELLERPRESSE, UM IN SITU SPANNUNGEN ZU MESSEN

B.F. WAREHAM   B.O. SKIPP

Rock Mechanics, Ltd., Bracknell, U.K.

SUMMARY

A convenient method of measuring stress insitu using hydraulic flatjacks has been described by many authors. This paper discusses the techniques by which a sawcut slot may be used to release stress and the flatjack fitted directly onto the slot is shown to be the most suitable from the testing and economic viewpoints. The design of flatjacks is closely studied along with alternative methods of the manufacture of the jack.

Laboratory tests have been carried out in which stress applied to a large block of Darley Dale Sandstone was measured using flatjacks. Calibration techniques are suggested following consideration of frictional properties and the strain fields, to ensure that flatjack measurements are a more reliable evaluation of insitu stress. Guidelines for test procedures, strain measuring methods and analysis are presented along with a discussion of the likely sources of error.

RESUME

Bien des auteurs ont décrit une méthode pratique de mesurer les contraintes in situ par l'emploi de vérins plats hydrauliques. Ce mémoire-ci débat la technique de ménager une fente à la scie pour libérer les contraintes: un vérin plat, appliqué directement dans la fente, serait le moyen le plus pratique du point de vue essayage et économique. On a étroitement examiné l'etude des vérins plats actuels ainsi que d'autres methodes éventuelles de leur fabrication.

On a complété des tests de laboratoire au cours desquels on s'est servi de vérins plats pour mesurer les contraintes appliquées à un grand bloc de grès Darley Dale. A la suite d'une discussion des caractéristiques de frottement et des champs de déformation, on suggère des techniques d'étalonnage pour rendre plus exacte l'évaluation, par l'emploi de vérins plats, des contraintes in situ. On presente en outre un résumé de conseils concernant les procédés d'essayage et les méthodes de mesurer et d'analyser les déformations, ainsi qu'une discussion des sources éventuelles d'erreurs.

ZUSAMMENFASSUNG

Zahlreiche Autoren haben eine praktische Methode, um in Situ Spannungen mittels hydraulischer Tellerpressen zu messen, beschrieben. Die vorliegende Abhandlung bespricht die Technik, wonach eine Sägeschnittschlitze zur Entspannung verwendet wird; eine Tellerpresse, die direkt in die Schlitze eingefugt ist, hat sich in Hinsicht auf ein wirksames Versuchsverfahren wie auch aus ökonomischen Gründen am besten erwiesen. Der gegenwärtige Entwurf, sowie andere mögliche Fertigungsverfahren, der Tellerpresse ist eingehend untersucht worden.

Man hat Laborversuche ausgeführt, in denen die an einem groben Block Darley-Dale-Sandstein angebrachte Spannung mittels Tellerpressen gemessen wurde. Nachdem Reibungskennzeichen und Spannungsflächen behandelt worden sind, wird vorgeschlagen, der Einsatz von Tellerpressen wurde mit der Verwendung von Eichtechniken verlablichere Abwertungen der in Situ Spannungen gewahren. Richtlinien für Testverfahren, wie auch für Spannungsmebmethoden und - analyse werden angegeben, und eventuelle Irrtumsquellen werden besprochen.

INTRODUCTION

Insitu stress sometimes termed Residual Stress, occurs naturally in the ground as a result, in the first instance, of rock formation processes with the major mechanism in the change of these stress levels being the influence of the tectonic forces which result in folding, faulting, jointing etc. of rocks. It is not possible to predict the levels of insitu stress at a particular location although workers such as Hast (1962) have shown that general trends occur. Particular localities in which the rock engineer is concerned, such as deep mines or underground powerhouses, require accurate

estimate of insitu stress and so general trends are not sufficient. Changes in overburden conditions such as valley erosion or large scale opencast mining operations will produce a localised change in stress which may be predicted to a certain extent by finite element calculations or by photo-elastic modelling but not with sufficient accuracy.

Consequently measurements of the actual levels of insitu stress are required if full use is to be made of the sophisticated design techniques which are now available. These measurements may be made in several ways although the methods fall into four general categories.

1. Strain replacement methods
2. Strain change methods
3. Stiff inclusion stress meters
4. Hydro-fracturing

The flatjack method in which a hydraulic jack is installed into a slot in the surface of the rock and pressurised in order to replace the strain change due to cutting of the slot falls into the first of these categories.

2. THE FLATJACK METHOD

2.1 Choice of technique

It is considered that, unless unusual conditions dictate otherwise, the flatjack method is likely to provide an adequate estimate of insitu stress and may well be the most economic technique. Various techniques of carrying out the test and of interpreting the results have been reported. A study of the advantages and disadvantages of the various techniques reported into the literature has been considered by Wareham (1972), so only a brief summary will be given here.

2.2 History of the Flatjack Method

The estimation of insitu stress by stress relief was first reported by Lieurance (1933) in his records of investigations at the site of the Boulder Dam, U.S.A. but this work relied on the use of laboratory measured elastic parameters to convert strain change to stress. Although oil filled jacks had been used on the Civil Engineering field very much earlier their first reported use to estimate insitu stress was by Habib et al, (1952) who also carried out a simple laboratory evaluation of the technique. Following their early work three basic techniques have evolved and are reported by Alexander (1960), Panek and Stock (1964) and Rocha et al (1966). The method adopted in the series of tests reported here is similar to that reported by Rocha et al and is considered to have several advantages over any other.

2.3 Slot Cutting

Two methods are in common use. These at the overlapping hole slot in which a drill bit of a small diameter is used to form a series of holes along the line of the slot into which a rectangular flatjack is grouted and, the sawcut slot into which a flatjack made to the saw blade dimensions may be placed without grouting. The major advantage of using the sawcut slot is the ease and speed with which the test may be carried out. The contact between the flatjack and the rock must be intimate but no errors are introduced due to the stiffness of the grout compared with that of the rock. Certain difficulties may be experienced in the overlapping hole method which include the problem of fixing the position of adjacent holes, solved to some extent by using templates as described by Hughes (1969). There may be air voids in the grout which could cause failure of the jacks during loading. On the other hand installing a flatjack in a sawcut slot overcomes both these problems, and if failure of the flatjack due to faulty manufacture does occur then the flatjack may be replaced without cutting a new slot.

2.4 Type and size of Jack

The dimensions of the flatjack may vary according to the type of slot cut, but those designed to fit into a sawcut slot are manufactured to the dimensions of the sawblade. In general the most suitable size of blade available is 600mm diameter by approximately 5mm thick with a maximum penetration of 250mm. Fig. 1 shows a diagrammatic layout of the saw used in the laboratory tests described later and the flatjack most suitable for use with this saw and blade which is typical of those used for this test.

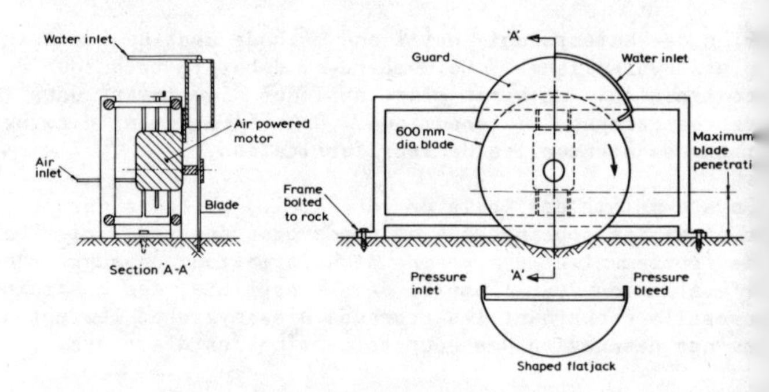

FIG. 1 SAW USED IN SLOT CUTTING

The edge welds of the flatjack require skilled design and execution as failures are not uncommon. The weld type and position should be chosen having regard to flatjack material type and its likely maximum pressure and displacement. The weld chosen for the flatjacks used in the experimental work was an argon arc weld with the edge design as shown in Fig. 2. No problems occurred in this case although a similar weld on a larger flatjack used for deformability testing failed at several positions due to the inadequate thickness.

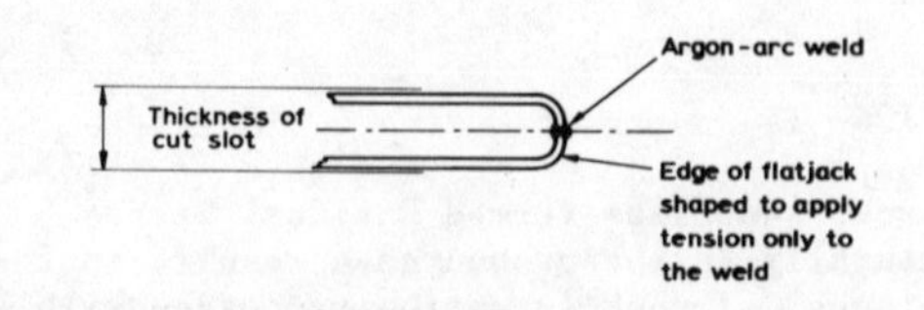

FIG. 2. EDGE DETAIL OF FLATJACK

2.5 Measurement techniques

Measurement of pressure on the flatjack provides no serious problems as hydraulic pressure is measured by gauges which are robust, easy to calibrate and require no sophisticated instrumentation to read. Hydraulic fluid used is generally oil although glycerine has been used.

Most of the conventional strain measuring devices have been employed during flatjack tests to estimate strain. The mechanical strain gauge by which distance is measured between two targets cemented onto the rock face, with an accuracy of 10 microstrain, meets the specification, is easy to use and transport and requires no further instrumentation to take readings. Calibration should be carried out on a standard bar although in general, in gauges made of invar, the calibration may be seen to be constant for an average temperature range.

Sufficient accuracy may be obtained by taking a single displacement measurement using the mechanical strain gauge although a second measurement after invertion provides a check against error and improves the basic accuracy. It is suggested that four sets of measuring points are used and for these the complete strain measuring operation may be carried out in a short period of time.

3. LABORATORY STUDY

3.1 Introduction

A programme of laboratory testing has been carried out in order to evaluate the technique and as a check on accuracy of measurement. Known uniaxial stresses were applied to a block of Darley Dale Sandstone and the flatjack method used to estimate these. All the equipment used was similar to that which would be used in the field. Previous studies by Rocha et al (1966) and Hoskins (1960) have shown accuracies of 6%- 20% although not all errors and corrections have been accounted for.

3.2 Test Method

A test rig was constructed in which a rock sample of end dimensions 610mm by 460mm and length 920mm could be subjected to uniform uniaxial stress of up to 10 MN/m^2. Load was applied by placing two flatjacks between the ends of the test rig and the rock sample and was controlled by hand pumping. During the early stages of the testing a considerable number of strain measurements were obtained which indicated that this method of loading produced a uniform stress within the rock.

The material chosen for the testing was Darley Dale Sandstone, a massive fine grained sandstone within the Millstone Grit series of Carboniferous age which outcrops and is quarried mainly in Derbyshire in the north of England. The choice was made because of easy quarrying and production of large blocks, the homogenety and isotropy of the material and its high reproducibility of test results.

Strain measurement was to be carried out using mechanical strain gauges of 203mm (8") and 305mm (12") gauge length, measuring between measuring points cemented onto the surface of the rock.

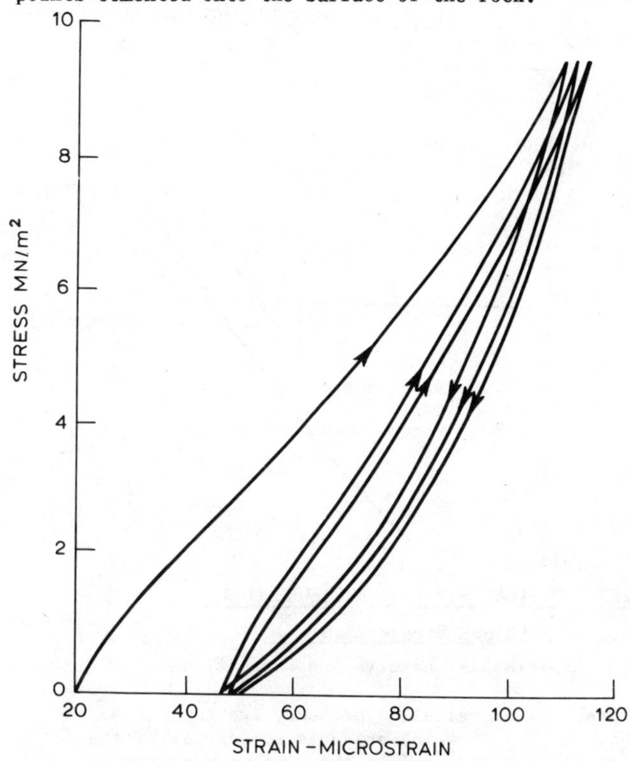

FIG. 3 STRESS-STRAIN CURVE FOR DARLEY DALE SANDSTONE

After being placed in the testing rig load-unload cycles were carried out, with strain measurement up to a maximum stress of 10 MN/m^2, determined by thr design of the loading frame, and stress-strain curves plotted. A typical curve is shown in Fig. 3. It may be seen that the curves follow the shape as would be expected for a fine grained sandstone containing no visible fractures. Variation of moduli calculated for each of the gauge lengths was a maximum of 10% for the first and second cycle of loading and 5% for the third. The fourth cycle was seen to follow the third almost exactly and so this was assumed to be reproducible and predictible for the later stages of testing. It is considered that the behaviour, in the main, was elastic as maximum applied stress was approximately 15% of the uniaxial compressive strength although for the third and successive cycles no residual strain remained on reduction of stress to zero, the shape of the loading curve may be seen to vary considerably from that of the unloading curve. This phenomena along with the general shape of the curve, even for perfectly elastic material, has been discussed by Walsh and Brace (1968) and the resultant curves here may be shown to follow their suggestions.

Following this initial study, which was to consider the behaviour of Darley Dale Sandstone in a large sample under uniaxial loading and to obtain a reading of strain in the block under various stresses, a slot was cut using a saw as shown in Fig. 1. A shaped flatjack was installed and used to obtain cancellation at various levels of stress applied within the block. A typical curve of strain against flatjack pressure for a pair of measuring points is shown in Fig. 4.

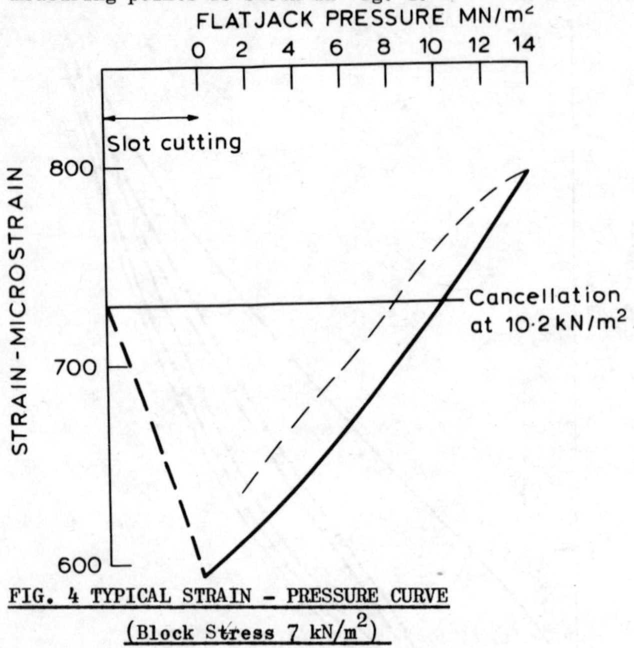

FIG. 4 TYPICAL STRAIN - PRESSURE CURVE
(Block Stress 7 kN/m²)

3.3 Experimental Results and Corrections

A graph of cancellation pressure against stress is shown in Fig. 5 which presents an average of the central measuring points only with two separate curves showing results from 203mm (8") and 305mm (12") gauge lengths. Also on this figure are shown the measured stress following application of the two corrections which are discussed below and the final errors in measurement which show large inaccuracies at stresses below $3\frac{1}{2}$ KN/m² and similar approximately constant errors above this level. It was considered that the total error due to the measuring systems would be no greater than 5%.

The early work using flatjacks to measure insitu stresses assumed that pressure applied in the flatjack was equal to the stress at right angles to the jack. By taking into account theoretical considerations it is obvious that two errors occur in this assumption, that is:-

1. Strain due to releasing insitu stress by forming a slot will consist of two parts - firstly due to the stress at right angles to the slot and secondly due to stress parallel to the slot. Strain replaced by the flatjack is purely as a result of applying stress at right angles to the slot.

2. In most cases, especially if the overlapping drillhole slot is used, the flatjack does not fully fill the slot and so the replaced stress field is different to that which was released.

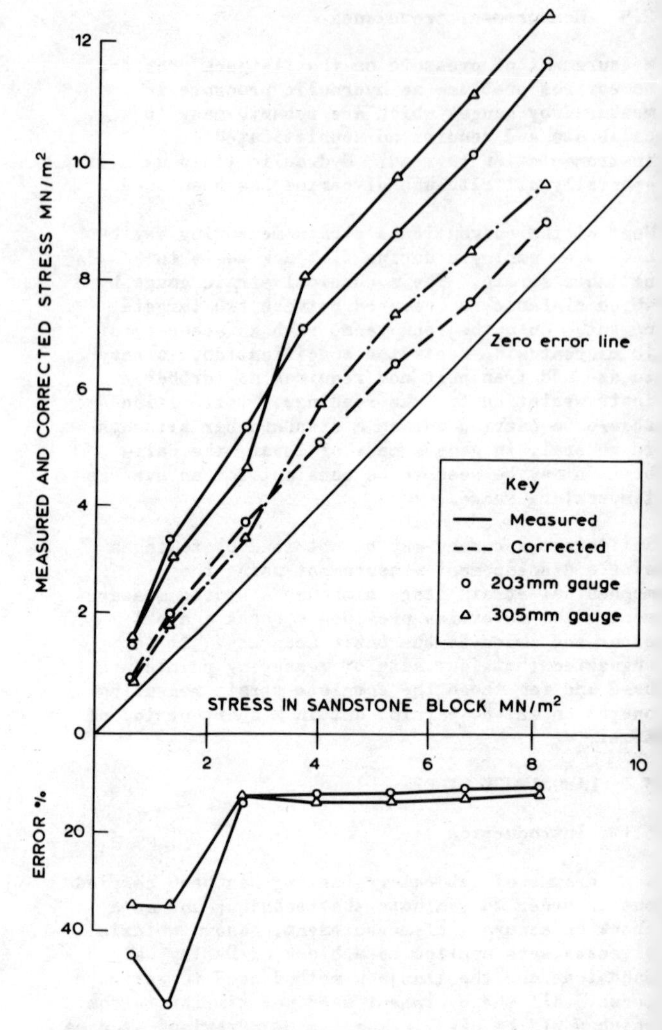

FIG. 5 LABORATORY TEST RESULTS

Alexander (1960) and Jaeger and Cook (1969) studied this problem and theoretically derived the following expression. The slot is considerd to be an elliptical hole in a biaxial stress field on an elastic half space and surface strain only is considered.

$S = A.P + B.Q$ where S = Rock stress normal to flatjack

Q = Rock stress parallel to flatjack

P = Jack pressure

Where A and B are constants depending on the geometry of the slot and Poissons Ratio of the rock. In the case of the flatjack and slots used in the experimental work it was found that the following expressions applied ($\nu = 0.27$).

$S = 0.96P + 0.02Q$ for the 203mm gauge
and $S = 0.95P + 0.02Q$ for the 305mm gauge

This theoretically applies only at the axis of the slot but may be applied to the mean cancellation pressure on those gauge lengths close to the axis.

In the case of the flatjacks used in the laboratory the constant A is close to 1.0 as the jack is designed to fit the slot but a typical value in the other type of test, that is with overlapping drillholes forming the slot, would be in the region of 0.85. These expressions assume linear elasticity in that the modulus connecting stress and strain is constant and the same both in loading and unloading.

Jaeger (1960) also suggests that as the flatjack is made usually by welding together two plates and area a near the edge (of the order of 3mm wide say) is inoperative and for the flatjacks used, the expression may be shown to be:-

$$S = 0.96P$$

This would be additional to that allowance made by equations for the flatjack being of different size to the slot. However, the type of adjustment above is more accurately predicted by calibration of the flatjack in a loading machine as other factors such as weld and material type and displacement have been shown to have an affect.

Calibration of the flatjacks in this case was carried out by placing the flatjacks on prepared steel plates between the plattens of a conventional compression testing machine so that the average stress applied by the flatjack could be measured and compared with its pressure (see Fig. 6). Two calibrations were carried out:-

1. with zero displacement of the jack

2. By allowing a measured displacement similar to that expected in the tests, which in fact was approximately that which took place against the stiffness of the load cell in the testing machine.

This calibration may be expressed in terms of an efficiency which is defined as:-

$$\text{Efficiency} = \frac{\text{Average Pressure Applied by Flatjack}}{\text{Hydraulic pressure in the flatjack}}$$

and it may be seen from Fig. 6 that the level of efficiency is displacement controlled. It has been shown by Pratt et al (1972) that this efficiency may also be seen to be controlled by the size of flatjack and it may be assumed that edge design is a major contributing factor. Consequently it is recommended that a calibration be carried out for all flatjacks prior to their use in the field.

After application of these two corrections the results of the experimental work show an error of approximately 10-14% overestimation of applied stress at stress levels above about $3\frac{1}{2}$ MN/m^2 (see Fig. 4).

When one considers the basis of the flatjack test, interpretation between measured stress and residual ground stress prior to excavation of the testing gallery must be made. Assuming that elastic redistribution of stress applies the basic concentration factors noted in the literature may be used if one assumes that the gallery shape approximates to a standard such as a circle or ellipse or improvements on this way be gained by accurately photographing the gallery cross section and obtaining stress concentration factors photoelastically or by finite element calculations.

4. CORRECTIONS AND ERRORS

Two corrections, one based on the geometry of the slot and flatjack and the other the construction of the flatjack, have been described above and were applied to the experimental results. The former of these, particularly for flatjacks fitted to the exact dimensions of the slot, applies only a small adjustment to the cancellation pressure and is considered to have an accuracy which is well within that achieved as a total of all the measuring devices. The latter correction which, it is suggested, may only be applied following a calibration of the flatjack which is used in the test is of fairly large magnitude (in this case a reduction of cancellation pressure by about 20% was required.)

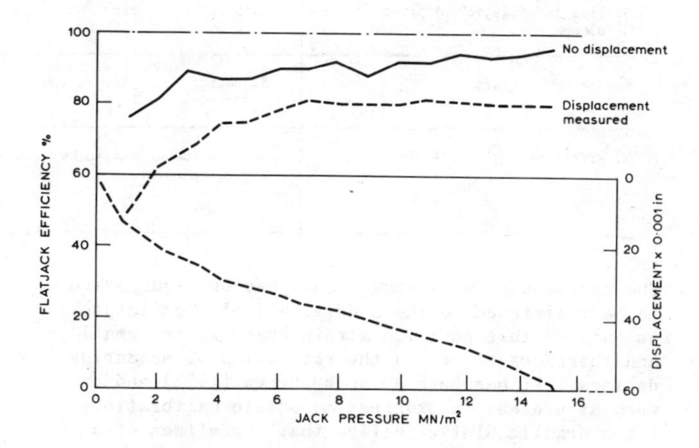

FIG. 6 FLATJACK CALIBRATION

In Fig. 6 it may be seen that the correction to be applied varies considerably with increasing resistance to displacement of the flatjack and a difference in correction of about 15% occurs between the completely rigid condition that allowing jack displacement against the load cell stiffness. The amount of displacement permitted therefore in the calibration of the flatjack should be, if possible, related to the expected stiffness of the rock insitu and if necessary a series of calibrations carried out varying controlled displacements, to represent varying stiffnesses.

As the flatjack is placed in the slot without grouting variation in its behaviour will occur depending on the clearance between the flatjack and the slot which may be of the order of 0.5mm on both sides. In the calibrations it is advisable to model the slot dimensions by placing spacers between the plattens of the testing machine and measuring the zero displacement with these in place. These spacers may be varied according to the expected dimensions of the slot. Further experimental work is required in order to establish the magnitude of such effects especially at lower stress levels.

TABLE 1 ERRORS AND UNCERTAINTIES IN THE MEASUREMENT OF INSITU STRESS USING SAWCUT SLOTS AND FITTED FLATJACKS

Cause of error or uncertainty	Adjustment, Calibration or Allowance	Likely magnitude of error and correction
1. Disturbed ground at test site	Careful excavation and testing of slot positions	Could invalidate the results completely
2. Fit in slot, change in contact area during loading of flatjacks	Calibrations carefully carried out in a modelled slot and with displacement measured and controlled to rock stiffness	Correction 10-15% at high stresses. Higher at low stresses.
3. Non-repeatable stress strain behaviour.	Cycling of flatjack loading in order to determine its extent. (Making allowances for any change in jack characteristics if original jack dimensions not recovered). Further experimental work needed on this aspect.	Depends on rock type and insitu stress level, could produce considerable errors at low insitu stresses.
4. Biaxial Stress Field	Mathematical correction based on linear elasticity.	Depends on slot geometry but probably between 0-5%.
5. Slot and flatjack different dimensions	Mathematical correction based on linear elasticity.	0-5% as flatjack is fitted to slot in this case.
6. Measuring system	Standard errors for equipment.	5% with equipment noted in this paper.
7. Effect of Rigid Inclusion.	Some Influence charts available but a mathematical study for the equipment used is best.	0-10% depending on flatjack geometry and relative stiffnesses.

The position of measuring points has been suggested to be restricted to the middle half of the flatjack as outside this position strain changes were small and therefore closer to the resolution of measuring devices. It has been shown by Brown (1973) and by work at present in progress to obtain calibrations for hydraulic Glotzel cells, that the effect of a rigid inclusion in a rock mass causes a change in the stress field and the stress distribution on its face follows that shown to occur beneath rigid foundations. That is with marked stress concentrations close to the periphery of the inclusion. By installation of the measuring points within the middle half of the flatjack this con entration may be avoided. Although the peak stress concentration is avoided by positioning of the measuring points the presence of the flatjack is likely to cause a general disturbance to the stress field which has been discussed by Brown (1973) who relates the action factor to aspect ratio (Cell thickness/Cell diameter) as well as the relative stiffnesses. His influence charts indicate an action factor, in the case of the laboratory tests here, of approximately 1.10. Finite element studies carried out in relation to the constant dimension Glotzel cell indicates an action factor of between 1.05 and 1.13 with the lower bound of these probably representing the flatjack situation closest. If an average value of 1.08 is applied then the measurements of applied stress in the sandstone block may be seen to be about the 5% accuracy of the measuring equipment, at stresses above about $3\frac{1}{2}$ MN/m^2.

5. INSITU TESTING

The preparation of the test surface is of major importance in testing work insitu as in conversion of measured stresses to the complete state of insitu stress assumptions must be made as to the redistribution effect of the test gallery or adit. It is possible that, unless careful excavation takes place, fractured rock may extend to some distance from the rock face and so make the results of the flatjack tests meaningless. Excavation and particularly blasting should be carried out very carefully in the area required for testing and all loose material should be removed before cutting of the slot. A useful test has been described by Alexander (1960) in which the rock was struck with a 1-2m long steel rod (drill rod) which gives a difference in tone between sound and fractured zones. Lighter bars and hammers were found not to be able to detect this difference.

The advantage of using a sawcut slot into which the flatjack may be installed and immediately pressurised may be seen here as the minimum time is required to carry out the test and therefore elastic assumptions on redistribution of stresses due to the excavation are more likely to be correct.

The basic procedure of testing has been discussed by several authors and in any case very little variation is possible. As a result of the work carried out in connection with this study the following points should be considered.

1. It is suggested that four sets of measuring points be installed across the slot and within its middle half.

2. Calibration of the flatjacks should be carried out prior to use in the field and by measuring displacement the approximate stiffness expected in the rock may be represented.

3. After correction of the cancellation pressure assumptions should be made concerning the effect of the flatjack as a rigid inclusion in a uniform stress field.

4. A complete set of flatjack tests may then be converted to principal stresses.

In order to estimate the complete state of stress at the point of interest a minimum of six flatjack tests in independant directions are required although it is usual to carry out up to nine in order to improve the estimation of stresses. Under certain circumstances, particularly when geological or other factors have determined the orientation of the proposed underground structure, assumptions may be made and a smaller number of independant tests carried out.

6. COMMENTS

The errors under laboratory conditions have been discussed above but no satisfactory comparison has been made in the field with other methods of measuring insitu stress. Seddon (1973) compares results from using the sawcut slot flatjack method with the C.S.I.R Leeman cell and suggests that similar levels of insitu stress are indicated although it is considered that insufficient suitable test results were available to make a proper comparison. Bonnechere and Fairhurst (1969) compare several methods of measuring insitu stress under controlled conditions and obtained variable results but did not include flatjacks in their work.

The effect of several factors on the assessment of insitu stress from flatjack tests has been discussed and a summary is presented in Table 1. It is considered that providing the excavation of the test chamber is carried out carefully as suggested, and the other calibrations and corrections applied, using the technique discussed above, a measure of insitu stress could be obtained with an accuracy of about 10%.

7. ACKNOWLEDGEMENTS

The authors are indebted to the Directors of Rock Mechanics Limited for permission to publish the information given in this paper, and for advice and help of Professor Hoek and the Rock Mechanics Group, Imperial College, London University where the research work was carried out.

REFERENCES

ALEXANDER, L.G. (1960) Field and Laboratory tests in Rock Mechanics. Proc. 3rd. Austr. N.Z. Conf. on Soil Mechanics. 161-8.

BONNECHERE, F. and C. FAIRHURST (1969) Results on Insitu comparison of different techniques for rock stress determination: Int. Symp. on Determination of Stresses, Lisbon, May 1969.

BROWN, S.F. (1973) The Measurement of Insitu Stress and Strain in Soils. Proc. of Conf on Field Instrumentation in Geotechnical Engineering British Geotechnical Society, Part 1, Butterworth.

HABIB, P., A. MAYER, and R. MARCHLAND, (1952) Underground Rock Pressure Testing. Proc. Int. Conf. on Rock Pressure and Support in Workings, Liege 1951.

HAST, N. (1962), The State of Stress in the Upper Part of the Earth's Crust. Engineering Geology Vol. 2 (1) p. 5-17. Elsevir Pub. Co.

HOSKINS, E.R. (1966), An Investigation into the Flatjack Method of Measuring Rock Stress. Int. Jnl. Rock Mech. and Min. Sci. Vol. 2 p 249-264.

HUGHES, M.D. (1969), Diamond Drilling for Rock Mechanics Investigations. Rock Mech. Symp. Stephen Roberts Theatre. University of Sydney, p 135-139.

JAEGER, J.C. (1960) Discussions on Technical Session No. 9, 3rd Austr. N.Z. Conf. on Soil Mech. and Found. Engineering. p. 248.

JAEGER, J.C, and N.G.W. COOK, (1969) Fundamentals of Rock Mechanics p 287-297 Meuthen 1969.

LIEURANCE, R.S. (1933) Stresses in Foundations at the Boulder Dam Tech. Memo No. 346. Bur. of Reclamation, Denver, Col.

PRATT, H.R, A.D. BLACK, W.S. BROWN, and W.F. BRACE, (1972) The Effect of Specimen Size on the Mechanical Properties of Unjointed Quartz Diorite. Int. Jnl. Rock Mech. and Min. Sci. Vol. 9 pp 513-529.

ROCHA, M. et al (1966) A new Technique for Applying the Method of the Flatjack in the Determination of Stresses Inside Rock Masses. Int. Congr. Rock Mechs. 1st Lisbon 4.10

SEDDON, B. (1973) Rock Investigations for Camlough Underground Power Station. Proc. of Conf on Field Instrumentation in Geotechnical Engineering. British Geotechnical Society. Part 1. Butterworth.

WAREHAM, B. (1972) The use of the Flatjack in Rock Mechanics with particular reference to insitu stress measurement and Deformability testing. M. Sc. Thesis University of London.

WALSH. J.B. and W.F. BRACE (1966) Elasticity of Rocks: A Review of Some Recent Theoretical Studies. Rock Mechanics and Engineering Geology Vol. 4 No. 4.

THEME 2 THÈME 2 THEMA 2

TECTONOPHYSICS TECTONOPHYSIQUE TEKTONISCHE PHYSIK

THEME 2

THÈME 2

THEMA 2

A

Laboratory Tests and Rock Properties

A

Essais en laboratoire et propriétés des roches

A

Laboratoriumsversuche und Felseigenschaften

ÉTUDE DE QUATRE ROCHES SOUS TRÈS HAUTES PRESSIONS

STUDY OF FOUR ROCKS UNDER VERY HIGH PRESSURE

UNTERSUCHUNG VON VIER GESTEINSARTEN UNTER SEHR HOHEN DRUCKEN

J. BERGUES Laboratoire de Mécanique des Solides - École Polytechnique, Paris
S. DERLICH C.E.A.
P. HABIB Laboratoire de Mécanique des Solides - École Polytechnique, Paris
H. MASSAT L.I.M.H.P. du C.N.R.S.
B. VODAR L.I.M.H.P. du C.N.R.S.
Paris, France

RESUME

Les auteurs présentent le matériel et les résultats d'essais triaxiaux sous très fortes pressions, jusqu'à 2 GPa (20 kbar) sur quatre roches de natures différentes.

SUMMARY

The authors present the material and the results of triaxial tests under very strong pressures, up to 2 GPa (20 kbar) on four rocks of different natures.

ZUSAMMENFASSUNG

Die Autoren stellen die Geräte und die Ergebnisse von Prüfungen in drei Archsrichtungen unter sehr hohen Druck, bis 2 GPa (20 kbar)vor, die an vier Gesteinsarten verschiedenen Ursprungs unternommen wurden.

INTRODUCTION

Des essais triaxiaux classiques ($\sigma_1 \geqslant \sigma_2 = \sigma_3 = P$) ont été effectués sur quatre roches soumises à des pressions de confinement très élevées pouvant atteindre jusqu'à 2 CPa (20 kbar), dans le but de déterminer les courbes intrinsèques. Ces essais ont été demandés par le C.E.A. et effectués par le Laboratoire de Mécanique des Solides en collaboration avec le Laboratoire des Hautes Pressions du C.N.R.S. Les roches étudiées sont de nature très différentes :

1) Un granite : c'est le granite constitutif du site des tirs nucléaires souterrains français au Hoggar. Il est composé de grains de quartz, de feldspath et de biotite d'une taille moyenne de 2 à 4 mm [1] .

2) Un grès d'origine sédimentaire : les échantillons proviennent des carottes du sondage de Wagon Wheel numéro 1 situé dans le Wyoming [2] . C'est un grès grawacke constitué de quartz, de silice amorphe, de feldspath de calcite et d'argile [3] . La taille moyenne des grains est de 0,1 à 0,2 mm.

3) Un calcaire portlandien [4] : c'est un calcaire lithographique à cassure conchoïdale contenant parfois de rares veines de calcite et des débris d'organismes calcifiés.

4) Un basalte d'origine volcanique : il provient de la carrière de St Jean de Centenier [5] . Il a une structure microlitique. Il est composé de cristaux d'alumine et surtout de baguettes de plagioclases et d'augite formant la pâte de cette roche noire et compacte.

I - MATERIEL D'ESSAI ET TECHNIQUE EXPERIMENTALE

La compression des roches soumises à un champ de contraintes hydrostatiques nécessite l'utilisation d'un appareillage spécialement conçu à cet effet afin d'éliminer toutes sources d'erreurs dûes à une instabilité de la haute pression de confinement pendant la phase de déformation de l'échantillon sous l'action du déviateur axial. Ceci est d'autant plus important que les déformations axiales de certaines roches sont très importantes et peuvent atteindre 50% pour une pression de confinement de 20 kbar et un déviateur de l'ordre de 30 à 40 kbar.(3 à 4 GPa).

De ce fait, l'appareillage a nécessité la mise au point d'un système de régulation particulièrement précis afin de maintenir la pression latérale constante au cours des essais. Dans les conditions actuelles de fonctionnement, les caractéristiques maximales de l'installation sont les suivantes :

- Haute pression de confinement P = 2 GPa
- Déviateur sur échantillon $[\sigma_1 - P]$ = 5 GPa
- Précision de la régulation de P :

de 0 à 1 GPa : ± 1/100
de 1 à 2 GPa : ± 2/100 .

Le principe de fonctionnement de la régulation est le suivant [6] .

Figure 1
Presse principale et Containeur
Main press and container
Hauptpresse und Container

La presse I fournit l'énergie nécessaire au multiplicateur de pression PM_1 calculé pour obtenir des hautes pressions HPI de 0 à 2 GPa mesurées par l'intermédiaire d'une jauge manganine JM_1 qui délivre un signal électrique proportionnel à la haute pression HPI (fig.2) :

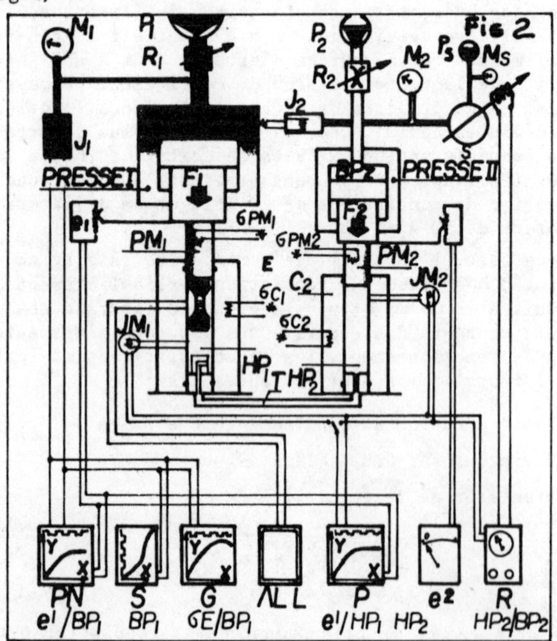

Schéma de principe du fonctionnement de l'appareillage
Diagram of the fundamentals of the working of the equipment.
Schema der Wirkungsweise der Apparatur.

La presse II (fig.3) comporte les mêmes éléments principaux ; l'intercommunication des deux presses est assurée par une tuyauterie haute pression T .

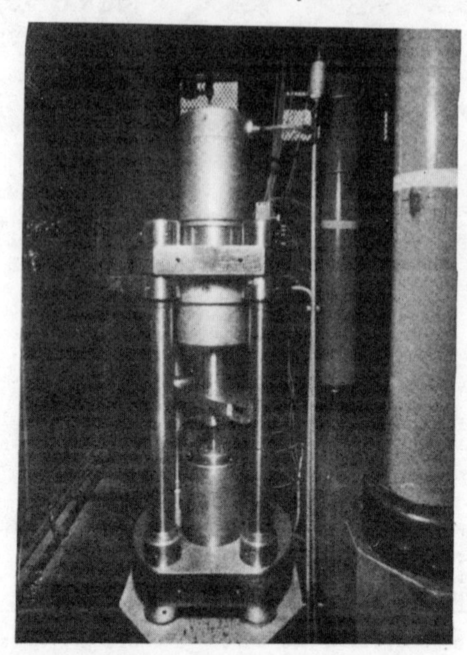

Figure 3
Presse auxiliaire
Auxilliary press.
Hilfspresse.

La basse pression BPII est régulée par l'intermédiaire d'une servovalve S pilotée et asservie à la haute pression (HPI ou HPII par exemple), au moyen d'un ensemble électronique R qui délivre un signal électrique tension-courant proportionnel à la haute pression. L'ensemble du système fluide haute pression fonctionne donc comme un vase communiquant, reversible et sensiblement indépendant des frottements et de la viscosité des ingrédients utilisés, pourvu que ceux-ci puissent circuler sans perte de charge excessive dans les tuyauteries. Pour une haute pression déterminée et stabilisée, le volume de fluide reste constant, ce qui permet d'obtenir une haute pression stable pendan toute la durée d'une expérience, et ceci qu elle que soit la force appliquée sur la presse I, pourvu qu'elle soit supérieure à la force nécessaire pour produire la haute pression HPI choisie.
Les échantillons de roche sont des cylindres de 10 mm de diamètre et 22 mm de hauteur équipés de jauges électriques disposées dans la direction de la charge maximale ; ces éprouvettes sont montées sur le piston principal de la grosse presse et sont protégées par une gaine en silastène imperméable pour empêcher toute pénétration de fluide dans l'échantillon au cours de l'essai.
La conduite d'un essai jusqu'à rupture s'effectue en deux temps :

1) mise en confinement hydrostatique jusqu'à la pression latérale désirée : $\sigma_1 = \sigma_2 = \sigma_3 = P$
Au cours de cette phase on enregistre les déformations du matériau.
2) mise en charge axiale $\sigma_1 > P$ jusqu'à la rupture en maintenant le confinement constant grâce à la régulation. Au cours de cette phase on enregistre d'une part les déformations de l'éprouvette données par les

jauges électriques, et d'autre part l'enfoncement du piston à l'aide d'un potentiomètre 10 tours.

II - RESULTATS EXPERIMENTAUX

Les résultats d'essai sont résumés dans le tableau ci-dessous pour les caractéristiques élastiques :

E = module élastique
ν = coefficient de Poisson
P_E = limite élastique du matériau sous chargement sphérique

	Granite	Grès	Calcaire	Basalte
E_{MPa}	74000	42000	79000	73000
ν	0,34	0,16	0,31	0,23
$P_{E\,MPa}$	1300	1400 environ	1110	1150

et par les figures 4, 7 , 10 et 12 représentant les courbes intrinsèques relatives à la limite élastique et à la rupture.

III - ANALYSE DES RESULTATS

L'analyse détaillée des caractéristiques mécaniques de chaque roche, définies à partir des courbes efforts-déformations, montre que les coefficients élastiques du tableau précédent sont sensiblement constants quelle que soit la pression de confinement si elle est inférieure à P_E : dans le domaine élastique le comportement du matériau est donc indépendant de l'état de contrainte et est indépendant du trajet de chargement, ce qui n'est plus le cas une fois le seuil élastique franchi.

1) Granite - (fig.4)

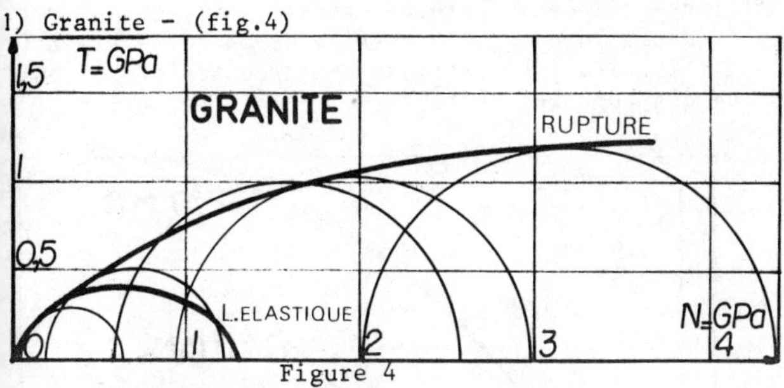

Figure 4
Courbes intrinsèques du Granite
Intrinsic graphs of granite.
Kurvung von Granit.

C'est un matériau très homogène et isotrope qui, à l'état naturel, ne présente aucune fissuration notable En effet, la figure 5 donnant la courbe de compressibilité du granite pour 2020 MPa de confinement ne montre aucune porosité de fissures. D'une manière générale le comportement mécanique de cette roche présente un caractère fragile même sous très forte pression de confinement. On a superposé sur la figure 6 quelques courbes efforts-déformations pour différentes pressions de confinement, on peut remarquer que les déformations plastiques longitudinales non linéaires jusqu'à la rupture s'éloignent très peu des déformations élastiques théoriques : c'est une caractéristique des ruptures fragiles.
L'observation au microscope d'échantillons rompus montre que la rupture provient essentiellement des joints de grains ; les cristaux eux-mêmes étant très peu affectés.

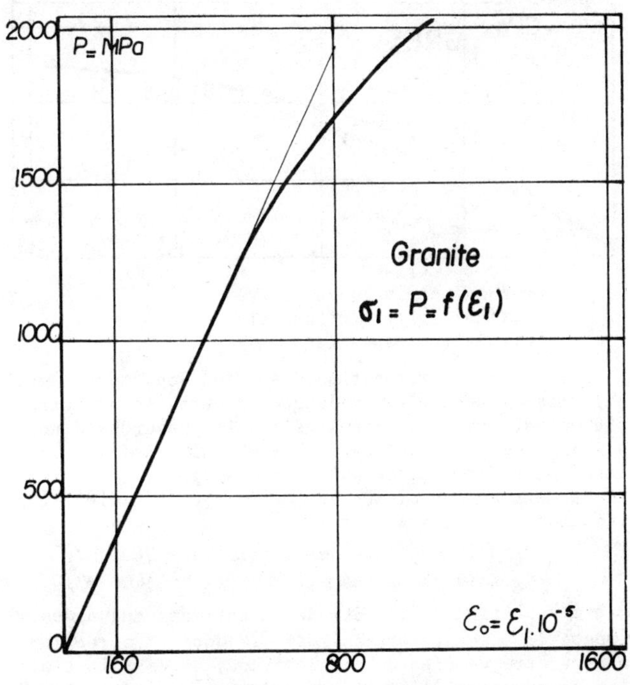

Figure 5
Compressibilité du Granite
Compressibility of granite
Druckfestigkeit von Granit

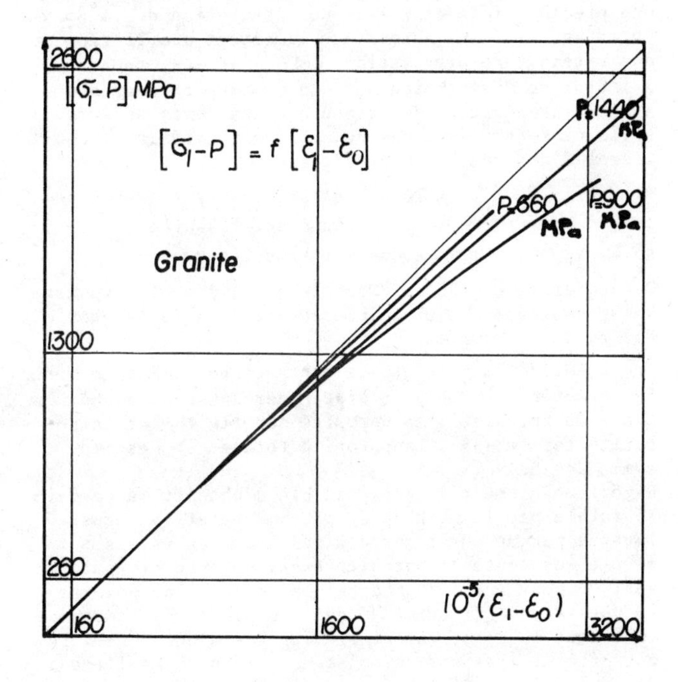

Figure 6
Courbe $\sigma_1 - P = f(\varepsilon_1 - \varepsilon_0)$ granite
Graph $\sigma_1 - P = f(\varepsilon_1 - \varepsilon_0)$ granite
Kurvung $\sigma_1 - P = f(\varepsilon_1 - \varepsilon_0)$ von Granit

2) Grès - (fig.7)

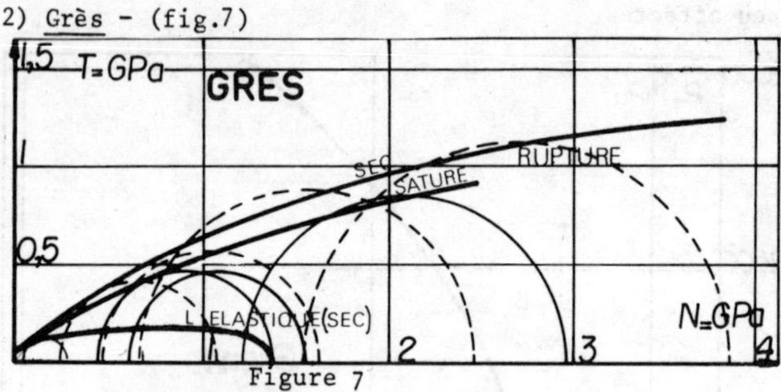

Figure 7
Courbes intrinsèques du Grès
Intrinsic graphs of sandstone
Kurvung von Sandstein

La mesure de la propagation des ondes longitudinales a permis de mettre en évidence une certaine anisotropie du matériau. Les vitesses ont été mesurées d'une part sur des éprouvettes prélevées suivant l'axe de la carotte, et d'autre part sur des éprouvettes prélevées suivant un diamètre. Les mesures ont donné les résultats suivants :

V_L suivant l'axe de la carotte = 3600 m/s
V_L suivant un diamètre = 3400 m/s .

Cette variation de l'ordre de 6% est sans aucun doute imputable à une légère anisotropie dont la direction n'a pu être repérée avec exactitude; de ce fait toutes les éprouvettes d'essais ont été prélevées dans la même direction. La vitesse de propagation des ondes transversales a été mesurée sur une éprouvette taillée suivant l'axe de la carotte; cette valeur V_T = 2400m/s associée à la vitesse des ondes longitudinales donne une première idée de l'état de fissuration de la roche. En effet, certains auteurs [7] admettent que le rapport des vitesses de propagation V_T/V_L est directement lié à l'état de fissuration, et que ce rapport augmente avec la propagation des fissures. Ces mêmes auteurs, après étude systématique de plusieurs matériaux, concluent d'une manière générale que :

si $V_T/V_L < 0,6$: la roche est peu ou pas fissurée
si $0,6 < V_T/V_L < 0,7$: la roche est fissurée
si $V_T/V_L \geqslant 0,7$: la roche est très fissurée .

De ce fait, le grès de "Wagon Wheel", dont le rapport V_T/V_L est égal à 0,67 se classerait dans la catégorie des roches fissurées.

Une étude de la porosité de cette roche permet de mieux la caractériser. On peut distinguer dans une roche deux types de porosité : la porosité ouverte n_o et la porosité fermée n_F . La porosité totale n_T est la somme des deux .

Expérimentalement il est possible d'obtenir la porosité totale par la méthode du picnomètre et la porosité ouverte par un porosimètre à mercure. Les essais ont révélé que toute la porosité était ouverte et égale à 11%. On peut aussi distinguer la porosité de pore et la porosité de fissures [8] qui jouent un rôle important dans le comportement rhéologique d'une roche. La porosité de fissures est mise en évidence par l'essai de compressibilité. La figure 8 donne la courbe efforts-déformations jusqu'à 1740 MPa de confinement ; on peut noter un serrage initial de la fissuration existante jusqu'à 50 MPa, et en déduire une valeur de la porosité de fissures : η_o = 270.10^{-5}. La porosité de pore est donc grande. Ceci est confirmé par la différence de comportement sous haute pression des grès secs et saturés montrant le rôle particulièrement important de la pression interstitielle.

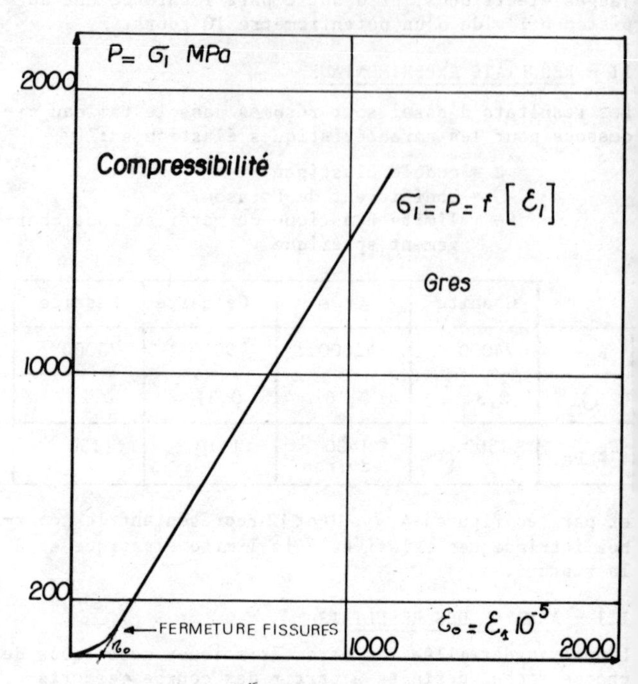

Figure 8
Compressibilité du grès
Compressibility of sandstone
Druckfestigkeit von Sandstein

Ce grès se présente donc comme un matériau anisotrope très poreux, dont la porosité de fissures est moyenne mais joue un rôle important lorsque la contrainte moyenne est faible. Les déformations plastiques peuvent atteindre 30% dans certains cas (fig. 9), ce qui met en évidence le caractère ductile de la roche à partir de P = 250 MPa : à partir de cette contrainte on observe des ruptures en tonneau.

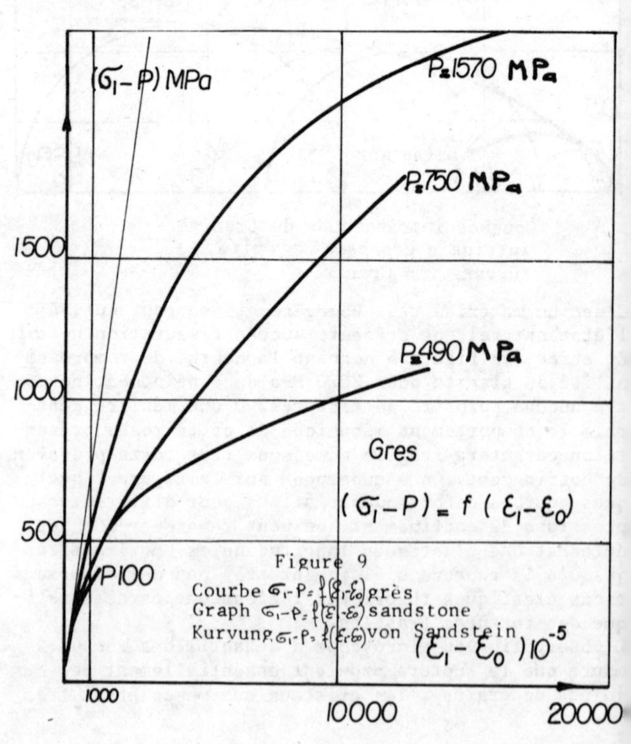

Figure 9
Courbe $\sigma_1 - P = f(\varepsilon_1 - \varepsilon_0)$ grès
Graph $\sigma_1 - P = f(\varepsilon_1 - \varepsilon_0)$ sandstone
Kurvung $\sigma_1 - P = f(\varepsilon_1 - \varepsilon_0)$ von Sandstein

3) Calcaire - (fig. 10)

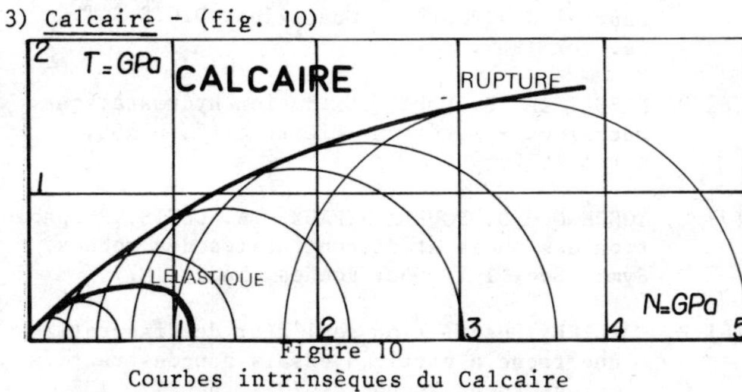

Figure 10
Courbes intrinsèques du Calcaire
Intrinsic graphs of limestone
Kurvung von Kalkstein

Des essais préliminaires sur ce calcaire compact à grains fins ont mis en évidence une très nette anisotropie de fissures. Ces fissures sont à lèvres jointives ; en effet l'essai de compressibilité ne révèle aucun serrage. En raison de cette anisotropie tous les échantillons ont été taillés suivant la même direction Jusqu'à 250 MPa de pression latérale, le comportement est fragile et la rupture se produit généralement en colonnettes avec deux limites élastiques bien distinctes sur les courbes efforts-déformations. Au-delà de P = 250 MPa, le comportement de cette roche est un peu comparable à celui d'un monocristal. Ceci est visible sur la figure 11 qui donne quelques courbes efforts-déformations pour des confinements différents. On distingue très nettement 4 phases, correspondant chacune à un mécanisme de déformation :

1) phase élastique
2) phase transitoire avec palier (glissement)
3) phase intermédiaire
4) phase de rupture (2ème glissement).

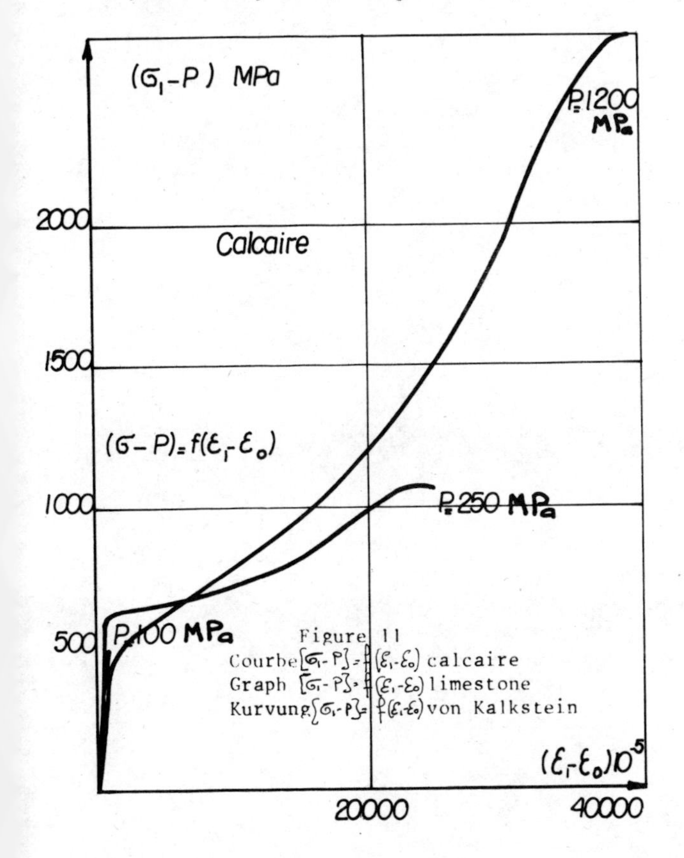

Figure 11
Courbe $[\sigma_1 - P] = f(\varepsilon_1 - \varepsilon_0)$ calcaire
Graph $[\sigma_1 - P] = f(\varepsilon_1 - \varepsilon_0)$ limestone
Kurvung $[\sigma_1 - P] = f(\varepsilon_1 - \varepsilon_0)$ von Kalkstein

Les éprouvettes ainsi rompues présentent 2 plans de rupture qui sont probablement en relation avec les deux systèmes de glissement.

4) Basalte - (fig.12)

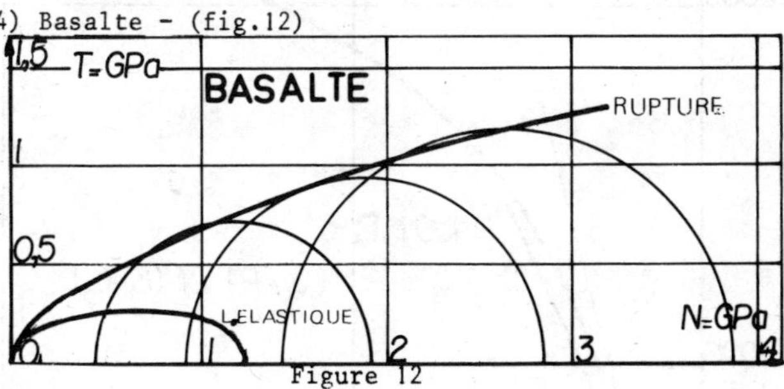

Figure 12
Courbes intrinsèque du Basalte
Intrinsic graphs of basalt
Kurvung von Basalt

Le rapport des vitesses de propagation des ondes transversales et longitudinales $V_T/V_L = 0,6$:

$$V_T = 3380 \text{ m/s}$$
$$V_L = 5360 \text{ m/s}$$

montre que le matériau est fissuré. Ce résultat se retrouve sur la courbe de compressibilité (fig.13), où l'on constate que toutes les fissures sont fermées pour une pression de 300 MPa. On en déduit de cet essai la valeur de la porosité de fissures $\eta_o = 210 \cdot 10^{-5}$.

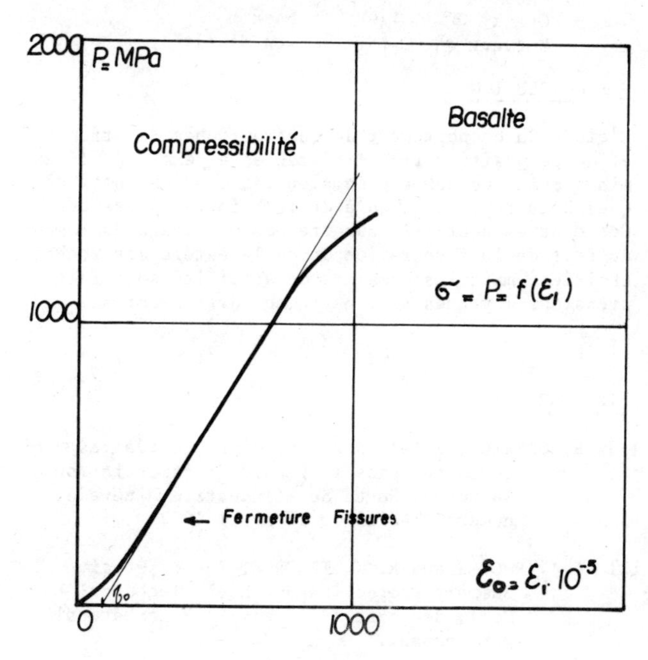

Figure 13
Compressibilité du Basalte
Compressibility of basalt
Druckfestigkeit von Basalt

Le passage du comportement fragile au comportement ductile se fait au-delà de P = 500 MPa. La figure 14 représente les courbes efforts-déformations pour trois confinements différents et met ce phénomène en évidence.

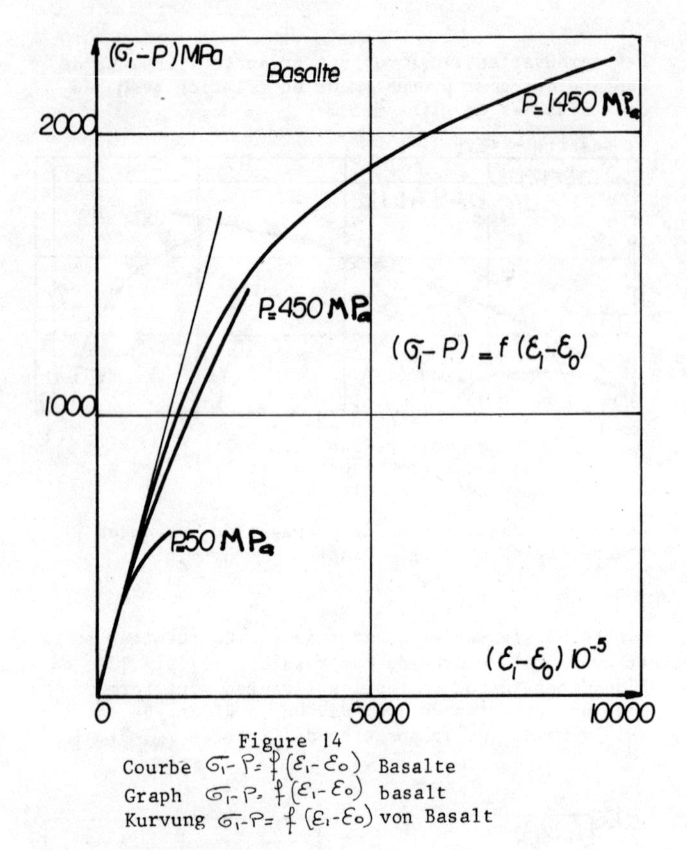

Figure 14
Courbe $\sigma_1 - P = f(\varepsilon_1 - \varepsilon_0)$ Basalte
Graph $\sigma_1 - P = f(\varepsilon_1 - \varepsilon_0)$ basalt
Kurvung $\sigma_1 - P = f(\varepsilon_1 - \varepsilon_0)$ von Basalt

V - CONCLUSION

L'étude du comportement de quatre roches de structure et de composition très différentes a permis de déterminer avec une bonne précision les courbes intrinsèques à la rupture jusqu'à de très fortes pressions. Ces courbes sont très ouvertes au voisinage du sommet du fait de la fissuration ou de la nature des roches choisies, mais les domaines de stabilité sous fortes pressions moyennes sont nettement différenciés.

OoO

BIBLIOGRAPHIE

[1] S. DERLICH, Effets des explosions nucléaires souterraines dans le granite : fracturation de la roche. Revue de l'Industrie Minérale, numéro spécial du 15 avril 1972.

[2] L.A. ROCERS and R. W. TERHUNE, Interpretative Summary Project Wagon Wheel. Technical Re-Port, december 1971, ed. El Pasa Natural gas Company.

[3] I.Y. BORG, Microscopic Examination of Underformed and Laboratory Deformed Wagon Wheel Rocks.

[4] P. GAVIGLIO and J. POLVECHE, Thermoluminescence naturelle d'une formation calcaire déformée C.R.Ac.Sc. Paris, t. 276, Série D 453, du 22 janvier 1973.

[5] Catalogue des caractéristiques géologiques et mécaniques de quelques roches françaises. Action concertée de Mécanique des Roches, Laboratoire Central des Ponts et Chaussées, D.G.R.S.T., février 1969.

[6] H. MASSAT and B. VODAR, Extrusion hydrostatique. Mécanique - Matériaux Electricité, n°268, avril 1972.

[7] C. TOURENQ - D. FOURMAINTRAUX - A. DENIS, Propagation des ondes et discontinuités des roches. Symp. Soc. Int. Mec. Roches, Nancy 1971.

[8] P. MORLIER, Description de l'état de fissuration d'une roche à partir d'essais non-destructifs simples. Rocks Mechanics,1971, pp. 125-138.

COEFFICIENTS OF FRICTION FOR SANDSTONE SLIDING ON QUARTZ GOUGE

COËFFIÇIENTS DE FROTTEMENT POUR GLISSEMENT DE SANDSTONE SUR FRAGMENTS DE QUARTZ

REIBUNGSKOEFFIZIENTEN FÜR SANDSTEIN AUF EINEM UNZEMENTIERTEN AGGREGAT AUS QUARTZ

Dr. James T. ENGELDER
Research Assistant, Center for Tectonophysics
Texas A + M University
College Station, Texas

SUMMARY-In triaxial sliding friction tests, precut cylinders of Tennessee Sandstone were slid on an uncemented aggregate of quartz fragments with a median diameter equivalent to that of fragments in natural quartz fault gouge (about 25μm). Below a confining pressure of 0.7 kb stick-slip was an observed mode for sliding whereas above 0.7 kb only stable sliding occurred. Coefficients of friction (μ') calculated as the ratio τ verses σ_n for each test were found to decrease with increasing confining pressure along different trends for the two modes of sliding. The coefficient of friction (μ), calculated as the slope of a curve from data of tests at a variety of normal stresses each plotted as τ verses σ_n, is also used to represent frictional characteristics of sandstone on gouge. Each mode of sliding has a unique coefficient of friction: μ = .72 for stick-slip and μ = .68 for stable sliding. Although the value of μ is not indicative of a particular mechanism of frictional sliding, it is sensitive to changes in the sliding mode.

ZUSAMMENFASSUNG-In Versuchen zur Gleitreibung unter drei-achsiger Belastung wurden vorgeschnittene zylindrige Proben aus Tennessee Sandstein zum Gleiten gebracht, und zwar auf einem unzementierten Aggregat aus Quartzbestandteilen mit einem mittleren Durchmesser, der dem von natürlichem Verwerfungsmaterial (gouge) aus Quartz gleicht (etwa 25μm). Unterhalb eines hydrostatischen Druckes von 0.7 kb war 'stick-slip' der beobachtete Modus des Gleitens; hingegen wurde oberhalb 0.7 kb ausschliesslich stabiles Gleiten beobachtet Reibungskoeffizienten (μ'), definiert für jeden Versuch als das Verhältnis τ zu σ_n, nahmen systematisch ab mit zunehmendem hydrostatischen Druck; jedoch geschah dies in verschiedener Weise für die zwei verschiedenen Modi des Gleitens. Wenn man den Koeffizienten μ benutzt (Berechnet als die Steigung der Kurve durch Datapunkte τ gegen σ_n von Versuchen mit verschiedenen Normalspannungen) um das Reibungsverhalten von Sandstein zu beschreiben, so ergeben sich unterschiedliche jedoch charakteristische Reibungskoeffizienten: μ=.60 für 'stick-slip', und μ=.70 für stabiles Gleiten. Obwohl der Betrag von μ keinen Hinweis auf einen speziellen Mechanismus des Gleitens bietet, so ist er dennoch deutlich abhängig von Modus des Gleitens.

RESUME-Pour les experiences triaxiales de glissement, les cylindres de 'Tennessee Sandstone', coupés en avance, ont été glissés sur une agregation noncementée de fragments de quartz; les derniers ayant un diametre median equivalent a cel des fragments de quartz dans une zone faillée (a pen prés 25μm). Pour des pression hydrostatique moindre de 0.7 kb, 'stick-slip' a été observé, tandis que au-desus de 0.7 kb seul glissement stable (stable sliding) a été observé. Pour tous les deux mode de glissement, on e trouvé que, le coefficient de frottment (μ') decroit guand la pression augmente. Le coefficient de frottement (μ) egale a la paute d'un graphique de τ en fonction de σ_n á été aussi utilisé pour characterise les proprietés de frottment de sandstone en presence des fragments de quartz. Les graphiques obtenus á partir des donnes aquerir pour nombrenx valeurs de pression normale montre que chaque regime de glissement a un μ characteristique: μ=0.72 pour stick slip et μ=0.68 pour glissement stable. Bien que μ ne soit pas indicative d'un mecanoisme particulier de glissement il (μ) est sensible aux chagements de regime de glissement.

INTRODUCTION

Geologists and engineers usually characterize frictional properties of the rock by equating the force (f_n) normal to a fracture and the shear force (f_s) parallel to that fracture necessary to initiate or maintain sliding. The simplest relationship between f_s and f_n, Amonton's Law, is that they are linearly related by a constant known as the coefficient of friction (μ) (Bowden and Tabor, 1950). Because experiments show that μ is independent of the area of contact, μ is also the ratio of shear stress (τ) across the surface to normal stress (σ_n) along the surface (Jaeger and Cook, 1969). This simple frictional law is useful because it gives a rapid means of characterising and comparing the frictional properties of various rock surfaces.

The purpose of this paper is to present data from triaxial sliding friction tests which suggest that Jaeger's (1959) interpretation of Amonton's linear frictional law is applicable when gouge is present on a sliding surface. The data, which assess the effects of quartz gouge on the frictional properties of quartzose sandstone, also demonstrate that changes in μ reflect changes in physical processes involved in frictional sliding.

A study of the effect of fault gouge on the sliding properties of rock is important because faults and shear fractures in rocks rarely consist of a single clean cut fracture; a fault breccia or gouge is often, if not always, found between the walls of a fault (Reid and others, 1913). Any attempt to characterize or model the faulting process, which may involve creep (aseismic faulting) or unstable slip (seismic faulting) must consider the influence of fault gouge.

BACKGROUND

There is some confusion in the geological literature concerning the meaning of the coefficient of friction. This is due in part to the complicated nature of sliding friction and in part to the lack of a standardized method for reducing experimental data to obtain the coefficient of friction.

The physical process of frictional sliding is influenced by many interrelated properties of the rock. Rock surfaces are not smooth; movement occurs when brittle asperities either climb over each other, plough through others, or shear off (Jaeger and Cook, 1969). The asperity may also deform without shearing off, if the yield stress of the asperity is exceeded (Logan and others, 1973). Because these frictional phenomena are so interrelated any simple law of friction does not model the physical processes of frictional sliding. Thus, it is not clear that the coefficient of friction is a sensitive measure of the frictional properties of a rock surface.

In the literature there is more than one method for evaluating the frictional properties of rock by calculating a coefficient of friction. In some cases a coefficient of friction (μ') is determined for each experiment where μ' is the ratio τ/σ_n as calculated from the data at some point along the force-displacement record of that experiment. μ' is found to decrease with increasing normal stress for sandstones and dolomites (Handin, 1969; Mauer, 1965). Logan and others (1973) find that μ' for limestones is not a function of normal stress. When μ' is used to represent the frictional properties of rocks, Amonton's Law is valid only if the value of μ' is independent of normal stress. However, another method of reducing frictional data gives a coefficient of friction (μ) which is generally independent of normal stress. Jaeger (1959), Hoskins and others (1968), and Jaeger and Rosengren (1969) calculate a coefficient of friction (μ) for fracture surfaces by reducing data from several experiments among which the normal stress is varied. In this case τ is plotted against σ_n and μ is the constant slope of the curve which fits that data points. Often this relation between τ and σ_n contains a second constant which is the equivalent of the cohesion term in the Mohr-Coulomb fracture criterion (Jaeger and Cook, 1969). The cohesive shear term (τ_o) represents the τ-intercept of Jaeger and Cook's friction curve:

$$\tau = \tau_o + \mu\sigma_n$$

This is a modified form of Amonton's Law. In other instances the experimentally determined relation between τ and σ_n is nonlinear; Mauer (1965) and Murrell (1965) indicate that their data for sliding friction tests fits a power law between τ and σ_n:

$$\tau = \mu\sigma_n^X$$

where μ is a constant and independent of normal stress across the sliding surface. Dieterich (1971) presents some data which fits neither a power law or the linear law.

To date no information is available on the relation among experimental results from different testing apparatuses. Frictional testing apparatuses in use include: two-block direct shear apparatus (Coulson, 1970; Patton, 1966; Pratt and others, 1972), three-block direct shear apparatus (Dieterich, 1972; Hoskins and others, 1968; Jaeger and Rosengren, 1969; Mauer, 1965), triaxial apparatus (Brace and Byerlee, 1966, Byerlee, 1967; Handin, 1969; Logan and others, 1973; Murrell, 1965; Raleigh and Paterson, 1965) and biaxial shear apparatus (Scholz and others, 1972).

An exact meaning of the coefficient of friction is further complicated because geologists have not picked data at a consistent point in a specimen's displacement history. Thus there is often a failure to distinguish among a coefficient of friction at the initiation of sliding (μ_i or μ_i') (Handin, 1969; Logan and others, 1973), a maximum coefficient of friction (Byerlee, 1967), a residual or kinetic coefficient (μ_k or μ_k') (Hoskins and others, 1968; Mauer, 1965; Murrell, 1965; Raleigh and Paterson, 1965) and a static coefficient of friction calculated at the onset of each slip event during stick-slip (μ_s') (Dieterich, 1972; and Scholz and others, 1972). Although the coefficient calculated at the initiation of a sliding friction experiment is a static coefficient, it is calculated for a surface with little surface damage due to sliding whereas the static coefficient calculated at the initiation of slip during stick-slip represents the frictional properties of a surface in which a certain amount of gouge is generated. This difference is equivalent to either determining the coefficient for an extension fracture with no gouge or to determining the coefficient for a shear fracture which already exhibits gouge and has a history of sliding. A distinction is also necessary between the kinetic coefficient for an experiment in which sliding is stable and that during which sliding is unstable. For stick-slip the assumption is made that the seismic efficiency is zero and μ_k is calculated at half the height of the force drop during unstable slip. μ_k for stable sliding is calculated from a smooth force curve during uninterrupted slip.

The τ/σ_n ratio may vary in one of several ways during a friction test. Jaeger and Rosengren (1969) show that the ratio continuously increases during the experiments with a three block direct shear apparatus. Byerlee (1967) shows that the ratio varies in two different ways in triaxial tests. From an initially low point the ratio increases to a maximum and then decreases. In other experiments Byerlee (1967) shows that the ratio continuously decreases from an initial maximum. Coulson (1970) has found four different variations of μ_k' with displacement during a two block direct shear test. The maximum coefficient of friction and μ_k' are the same only if μ_k' continues to increase with displacement through the duration of the experiment. However, the maximum resistance to sliding may occur very early in the experiment and therefore, is higher than the residual resistance. From these tests it is clear that μ_k' is a function of the position from where the data are picked during the displacement history. The point from where the ratio is picked should be determined by the nature of the experiment and the type of information required from the experiment.

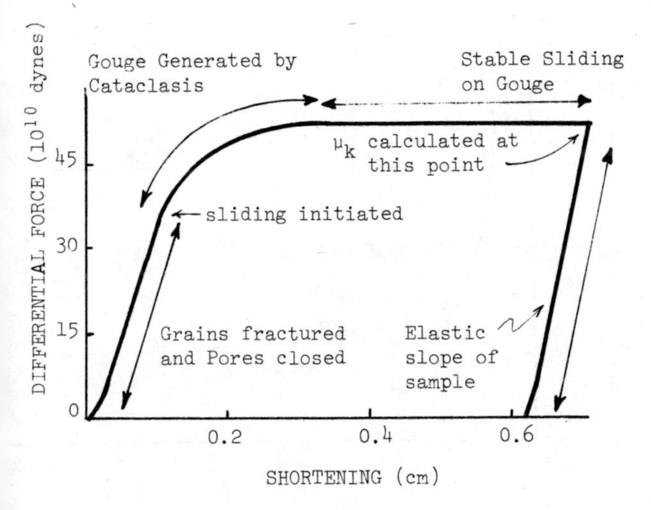

Figure 1. Differential force-shortening curve for precut Tennessee Sandstone sliding stably on a 0.12-cm thick layer of artificial, dry quartz gouge. Experimental conditions include a confining pressure of 1.0 kb, displacement rate of 10^{-3} cm/sec, and room temperature.

Thus the basic problems exist with the present non-uniform methods of reporting frictional data. It is necessary to distinguish μ and μ' as well as establish a consistent point in the displacement of the sample for calculating μ and μ'.

EXPERIMENTAL PROCEDURE

Precut cylinders of Tennessee Sandstone were used to obtain data on the effect of dry quartz gouge on the mode of sliding and the kinetic coefficients of friction at confining pressures to 2.7 kb and a displacement rate of 10^{-3} cm/sec. The cylindrical specimens, which are 5 cm in diameter and 10-cm long, were precut at approximately 35° to the cylinder axis and ground to ± 0.1° with an 80-grit wheel. The ends of the specimens were ground parallel to within 0.001 cm. Quartz grains between 100 and 250-μm in diameter were evenly distributed in a 0.20-cm layer along the precut. These quartz grains were cataclastically reduced during sliding to form an artificial quartz gouge with a uniform thickness. A 0.6-cm thick steel spacer powdered with MoS_2 on both sides was placed between the specimen and the upper piston in order to decrease friction between them and thus improve reproducibility. The 5 by 10-cm specimens were then jacketed by heat-shrink, polyolifin sleeves.

In addition, cylinders of intact, dry Coconino Sandstone were fractured and shortened different amounts by sliding along the induced fractures to simulate the natural development of fault gouge from host rock. These tests were done at confining pressures to 0.5 kb and a displacement rate of 10^{-3} cm/sec, and they gave data on the coefficient of friction for a fracture surface containing gouge.

A typical force-shortening curve is shown in Figure 1 for precut Tennessee Sandstone stable sliding on an 0.12-cm thick layer of dry gouge which is generated from a 0.2-cm thick layer of sand. A thin section study from tests at increasingly larger displacements shows the following correlation between the generation of quartz fault gouge and the force-shortening curve. Compaction and some cataclastic deformation of the sand occurs during the initial application of hydrostatic pressure on the specimen. These continue during the initial increase of differential stress. Because of this inelastic deformation, the slope of the initial part of the loading curve is nonlinear and not as steep as that of the linear unloading curve. The host rock behaves essentially as an elastic body throughout the experiment. At the "yield stress" sliding on the layer of sand begins and it is accompanied by still more intense cataclastic deformation. The grain size of the quartz sand between the precut samples decreases as displacement progresses. As cataclasis continues, the load necessary to maintain sliding increases until the ultimate strength is reached. Once the ultimate strength is reached, the resistance to sliding does not vary appreciably. At this point the size distribution of the experimental quartz aggregate approaches that of natural quartz gouge found in both faults and fractures in sandstone and also formed by cataclasis (Engelder, 1973). For this reason the experimental quartz aggregate is referred to as quartz gouge. The steady-state portion of the force-shortening curve is corrected for offset of the specimen halves and accompanying decrease of area of contact. Coefficients of friction are calculated from force data at 0.6-cm of sample shortening by making an appropriate adjustment for a changing sliding surface contact area.

EXPERIMENTAL RESULTS

The confining pressure effected the sliding mode of Tennessee Sandstone on quartz gouge (Figure 2). For all experiments stable sliding occurred during the initial cataclastic deformation of the original layer of sand. This was followed by stick-slip when the confining pressure is less than 0.7 kb. Stick-slip did not occur within the limits of the experimental displacements if the confining pressure was above 0.7 kb. The onset of stick-slip occurred earlier in the displacement history of the specimen as the confining pressure increased from 0.14 kb to 0.5 kb. One might expect stick-slip to occur with even less displacement at 0.7 kb confining pressure, but this was not what happened. At 0.7 kb the sliding was stable at displacements greater than those for which stick-slip occurred at 0.14 kb. Thus there was a stick-slip to stable-sliding transition as a function of confining pressure. Apparently a fundamental change in the sliding process occurs at this transition.

For all experiments at less than 0.7-kb confining pressure the gouge at the contact with Tennessee Sandstone was non-indurated (regular) and had a median grain size of 25μm. For experiments at confining pressures above 0.7 kb, gouge at the contact with the Tennessee Sandstone was indurated and had a median grain size of 0.5 μm (Engelder and McKee, 1973). The change in gouge formed at the contact corresponds with the change in mode of sliding. The nature of the gouge at the Tennessee Sandstone contact apparently influences the frictional properties of the Tennessee Sandstone but the reason for the change in sliding mode is not clear.

The change in sliding mode also correlates with a change in the coefficient of friction of Tennessee Sandstone sliding on quartz gouge. A kinetic

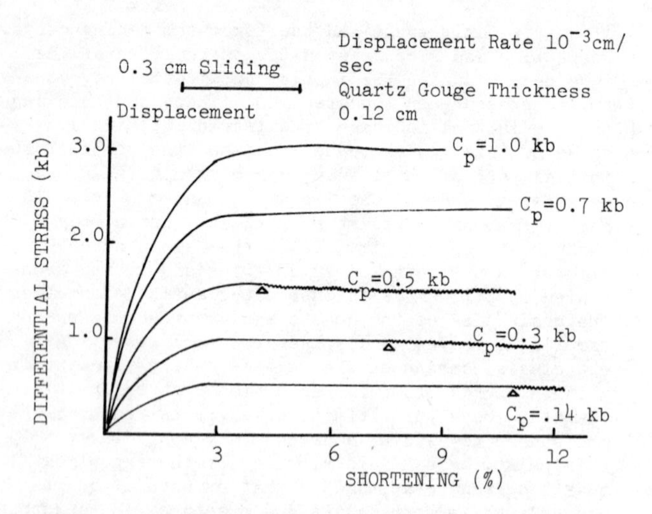

Figure 2. Differential stress-shortening curves showing the effect of confining pressure on frictional sliding of precut specimens of Tennessee Sandstone with a compacted 0.12-cm thick layer of dry quartz gouge. Smooth lines indicate stable sliding and jagged lines indicate stick-slip. Triangle marks the onset of stick-slip.

coefficient of friction (μ_k') is calculated for each experiment from force data at 0.8 cm of sliding

$$\mu_k' = \tau/\sigma_n.$$

For experiments which slid by stick-slip μ_k' was calculated from the mean value of the differential stress; that is at a point midway between the maximum and minimum stress of the stick-slip cycle. Changes in μ_k with respect to normal stress across the precut surfaces of Tennessee Sandstone sliding on quartz gouge are systematic and reflect the change in sliding mode (Figure 3). The value of μ_k' decreases from 0.88 as the normal stress increases for the stick-slip mode of sliding. At a normal stress of about 1.4 kb, the change in mode from stick-slip to stable sliding is accompanied by an increase in μ_k from 0.68 to 0.72. At the lower normal stress μ_k' decreases systematically whereas μ_k' approaches a constant value along a different trend at high normal stresses. Separate lines are drawn through μ_k' for stick-slip and for stable sliding to suggest that the data belong to different trends.

In order to determine the experimental reproducibility and thus the range of μ_k' among several experiments, up to five similar specimens are deformed. At 1.0 kb confining pressure μ_k' falls between 0.69 and 0.72 and has a standard deviation of 0.01. This standard deviation is assumed to apply to all other experiments because μ_k' calculated for two or more repeated tests never varies by more than 0.02 except at very low normal stresses.

In order to discover if Amonton's Law applies to Tennessee Sandstone sliding on quartz gouge, the data are plotted with shear stress as a function of normal stress (Figure 4). This plot shows two linear trends which differ in slope and τ-intercept. The lines represent a modification of Amonton's second law (Jaeger and Cook, 1969)

$$\tau = \tau_o + \mu_k\sigma_n$$

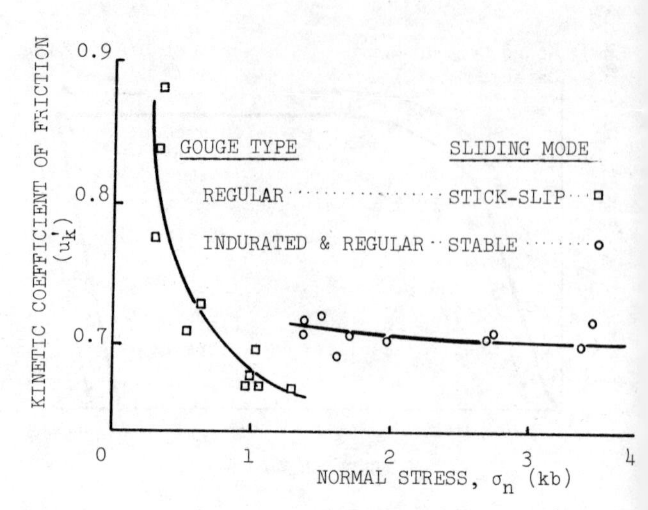

Figure 3. Kinetic coefficient of friction (u_k') versu normal stress for precut specimens of Tennessee Sandstone sliding on a compacted quartz gouge.

where the constant μ_k is the slope of the line and τ_o is the τ-intercept. According to Amonton's Law μ_k is the kinetic coefficient of friction of the sliding surface over a particular experimental range of σ_n. In this situation the two sliding modes are represented by a unique μ_k which is not a function of normal stress. At the lower normal stresses where stick-sli is observed, μ_k is 0.60 and τ_o is 80 bars; at higher normal stresses where stable sliding is observed, the μ_k is 0.70 and τ_o is 50 bars. The reduction of values for force from any point along the stick-slip loading cycle results in τ verses σ_n data points with a curve whose slope differs by 4° from the slope derived from the stable sliding data.

For precut Coconino Sandstone sliding on quartz gouge the μ_k and τ_o are the same as those for Tennessee Sandstone (Engelder, 1973). This similarity is important in light of the fact that the fracture strengt of the Coconino is 20 to 30% less than that of the Tennessee Sandstone. This suggests that the mechanical properties of the quartz fault gouge influence the frictional sliding of a fracture more than do the mechanical properties of the host sandstone within which the gouge forms.

Solid cylinders of Coconino Sandstone were fractured and then slid in order to obtain a μ_k and τ_o for a fractured surface separated by gouge. These experiments test the effect of an undulatory fracture surface on the μ_k and τ_o for a sandstone on gouge. At normal stresses to at least 1.0 kb a layer of gouge nearly 0.15-cm thick is generated. In this case both μ_k (0.72) and τ_o (120 bars) are higher than they are for Tennessee Sandstone with precut surfaces (Figure 4).

DISCUSSION

Jaeger and Cook (1969) point out that the plot of μ_k' verses σ_n is more complicated that a plot of μ_k verse σ_n. In the former case the coefficient of friction varies as a function of confining pressure whereas in the latter case the coefficient is independent of confining pressure for some range of σ_n. The primary advantages of the latter with respect to sliding on quartz fault gouge are that a change in sliding mode

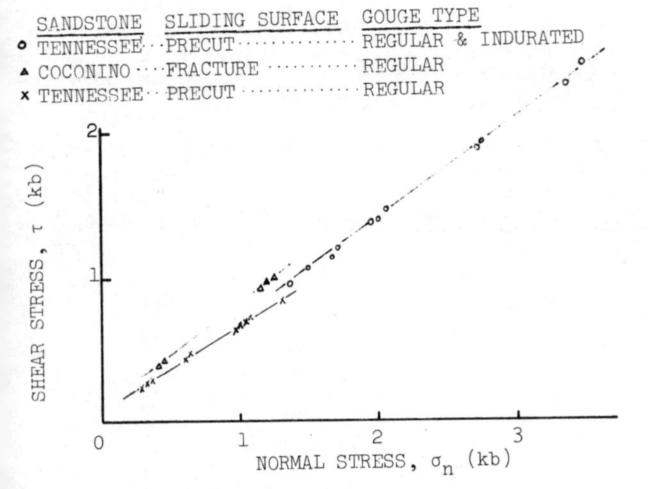

Figure 4. Shear stress versus normal stress data for sliding of precut Tennessee Sandstone on a 0.12-cm thick layer of dry quartz gouge and fractured Coconino Sandstone on a 0.10 to 0.15-cm thick layer of quartz gouge.

is characterized by a change in μ_k but for each mode μ_k is unique. Only two constants, τ_o and μ_k are necessary to represent the frictional resistance of the sliding surface. Both of these constants are sensitive to changes in frictional characteristics of the sliding surface without being effected by increasing normal stresses. In contrast there are trends in μ_k' for each sliding mode but there is no unique value for μ_k' and in some instances μ_k' has the same value for both modes of sliding (Figure 3).

The difference between μ_k' and μ_k is that in the latter case the term τ_o has been subtracted from the shear stress necessary to maintain sliding:

$$\mu_k = \frac{\tau - \tau_o}{\sigma_n}$$

τ_o is a constant which when added to the numerator gives the μ_k' increasingly larger values as τ and σ_n decrease. But if the rock surface does not have a characteristic τ_o, then $\mu_k = \mu_k'$.

The frictional data for sandstone on quartz gouge plotted in τ-σ_n space has a τ-intercept which Jaeger and Cook (1969) suggest is due to a fundamental cohesive shear strength of the surfaces. The quartz gouge experiments show that τ_o exists even when surfaces are sliding stably and all major asperities have been sheared from the sliding surface. Likewise, the curves in Figure 4 indicate that the sliding surface is represented by a unique τ_o for each sliding mode. It may be that the 'cohesive' strength between sliding surfaces represents the total strength of microscopic interlocked asperities.

If τ_o represents the fundamental shear strength of the sliding surface, a change in size or strength of asperities on the sliding surface should effect τ_o. For sliding on quartz gouge it was found that asperities (1 cm^2 in area with 0.1 cm of relief) due to the uneven fracture surface of Coconino Sandstone result in an increase of both τ_o and μ_k compared with those for precut Coconino Sandstone. Thus the term τ_o is sensitive to changes in shear strength of the sliding surface. The increase in μ_k due to asperities may be caused by increased frictional resistance of asperities with surfaces inclined to the sliding surface. This suggestion is based on Patton's (1966) observation that inclined teeth on the surface of plaster cause a change in slope of the maximum shearing strength curve in τ-σ_n space.

μ_k rather than μ_i and μ_s is used to represent the frictional properties of sandstone sliding on quartz fault gouge because the presence of gouge indicates a displacement history and μ_k represents the sliding resistance of gouge to sandstone in motion. Once an 0.12-cm thick layer of gouge has formed on the sliding surface the value of μ_i or μ_s and μ_k differs by less than 2% and μ_k is equal to μ_s when stable sliding occurs (Engelder, 1973). Although the use of μ_k and its similarity to μ_i is applicable to sandstone on quartz gouge, there is a greater difference between the values of μ_i, μ_k, and μ_s for stick-slip on clean surfaces of granite (Byerlee, 1967). In this latter situation μ_s may be more meaningful in characterizing the frictional properties of the rock involved in the experiments.

CONCLUSIONS

The purpose of this paper is to emphasize the need for a uniform system for measuring and reporting the frictional characteristics of rocks. Based on the examples presented in this paper, it seems that frictional data reduced to a plot in τ-σ_n space are most versatile. In this case Amonton's Law is satisfied and the frictional properties of the sliding surface may be represented by the constants μ_k and τ_o. However, when frictional data is reduced it should be made clear where from individual force-displacement curves τ and σ_n are picked.

Indurated gouge on the sliding surface causes a fundamental change in frictional properties of the sandstone; μ_k increases when the indurated gouge is present. Although μ_k does not indicate the mechanism of frictional sliding, it is a sensitive indicator of change in the sliding process.

ACKNOWLEDGEMENTS

This paper is based on a dissertation submitted in partial fulfillment of the requirements for a Ph.D. in Geology at Texas A&M University. The use of facilities at the Center for Tectonophysics, Texas A&M University, and the advice of Professor John Handin and his associates are greatly appreciated. The work was supported by the U.S. Geological Survey and the Advanced Research Projects Agency Order No. 1684.

REFERENCES

BOWDEN, F. P. and TABOR, D., 1950, The friction and lubrication of solids, Oxford, Clarendon Press, 337p.

BRACE, W. F. and BYERLEE, J. D., 1966, Stick-slip as a mechanism for earthquakes, Science, Vol. 153, pp. 990-992.

BYERLEE, J. D., 1967, Frictional characteristics of granite under high confining pressure, Journal of Geophysical Research, Vol. 72, pp. 3639-3648.

COULSON, J. H., 1970, The effects of surface roughness on the shear strength of joints in rock, Technical Report MRD-2-70, Missouri River Division, Corps of Engineers, Omaha, Neb. p. 283.

DIETERICH, J. H., 1972, Time-dependent friction in rocks, Journal of Geophysical Research, Vol. 77, pp. 3690-3697.

ENGELDER, J. T., 1973, Quartz fault-gouge: its generation and effect on the frictional properties of sandstone, (Ph.D. Dissertation), College Station, Texas A&M University, p. 154.

ENGELDER, J. T. and MC KEE, T. R., 1973, Electron microscopical study of indurated quartz gouge, Electron Microscopy Society of America 31st Annual Meeting, Proceedings, pp. 214-215.

HANDIN, J., 1969, On the Coulomb-Mohr failure criterion, Journal of Geophysical Research, Vol. 74, pp. 5343-5348.

HOSKINS, E. R., JAEGER, J. C., and ROSENGREN, K. J., 1968, A medium-scale direct friction experiment, International Journal of Rock Mechanics and Mining Sciences, Vol. 5, pp. 143-153.

JAEGER, J. C., 1959, The frictional properties of joints in rocks, Geofisica Pura y Aplicada, Vol. 43, pp. 148-158.

JAEGER, J. C. and COOK, N. G. W., 1969, Fundamentals of rock mechanics, London, Methuen, p. 513.

JAEGER, J. C. and ROSENGREN, K. J., 1969, Friction and sliding of joints, Australasian Institute of Mining and Metallurgy, Proceedings, no. 229, pp. 93-104.

LOGAN, J. M., IWASAKI, T., FRIEDMAN, M., and KLING, S. A., 1973, Experimental investigation of sliding friction in multilithologic specimens, in Pincus ed., Engineering Geology Case History Number 9, Geological Society of America, pp. 55-67.

MAUER, W. C., 1965, Shear failure of rock under compression, Journal of the Society of Petroleum Engineers, Vol. 5, pp. 167-176.

MURRELL, S. A. F., 1965, The effect of triaxial systems on the strength of rocks at atmospheric temperatures, Geophysical Journal, Vol. 10, pp. 231-281.

PATTON, F. D., 1966, Multiple modes of shear failure in rock, Proceedings of the First Congress of the International Society of Mechanics, Lisbon, Vol. 1, pp. 509-513.

PRATT, H. R., BLACK, A. D., and BONNEY, F. J., 1972, Frictional properties of Cedar City quartz diorite, Air Force Weapons Laboratory Technical Report Number AFWL-TR-71-56, p. 91.

RALEIGH, C. B. and PATERSON, M. S., 1965, Experimental deformation of serpentinite and its tectonic implications, Journal of Geophysical Research, Vol. 70, pp. 3965-3985.

REID, H. F., DAVIS, W. M., LAWSON, A. C., and RANSOME, F. L., 1913, Report of the committee on the nomenclature of faults, Geological Society of American Bulletin, Vol. 24, pp. 163-186.

SCHOLZ, C. H., MOLNAR, P., and JOHNSON, T., 1972, Detailed studies of frictional sliding of granite and implications for the earthquake mechanism, Journal of Geophysical Research, Vol. 77, pp. 6392-6406.

COMPORTEMENT MÉCANIQUE DES SOLS SOUS FORTS RECOUVREMENTS

MECHANICAL BEHAVIOR OF SOILS UNDER HIGH OVERBURDEN PRESSURES

MECHANISCHES VERHALTEN DER BODENSCHICHTEN UNTER GROSSEN ÜBERLAGERUNGSDRUCKEN

P. HABIB, Ing. EP

M.P. LUONG, Ing. ENPC

Laboratoire de Mécanique des Solides - Ecole Polytechnique

Paris, France

RESUME

Cette communication présente une étude systématique du comportement mécanique des sols sous forts recouvrements. Nous avons déterminé successivement la compressibilité, la résistance et la vitesse de propagation des ondes longitudinales dans une argile, un limon et un sable soumis à des fortes pressions de consolidation.

SUMMARY

This paper gives a systematic study of mechanical behavior of soils under high overburden pressures. Successively, we have determined the compressibility, the strength and the velocity of longitudinal waves through a clay, a loam and a sand consolidated under high pressures.

ZUSAMMENFASSUNG

Diese Arbeit stellt eine systematische Untersuchung des mechanischen Verhalten der Bodenschichten unten grossen Überlagerungsdrücken dar. Wir haben nacheinander die Zusammendrückbarkeit, die Festigkeit und die Fortpflanzungsgeschwindigkeit der Längswellen im Ton, im Lehm und im Sand, die starken Konsolidierungsdrücke ausgesetzt waren, bestimmt.

1-INTRODUCTION

Sous de forts recouvrements, les sols, argiles, limons ou sables, ont un comportement qui les apparente à des roches tendres. Leurs propriétés mécaniques sont alors assez mal connues. On rencontre de tels matériaux dans les cavités souterraines profondes, pour des tunnels de chemin de fer, pour des cavités de stockage ou pour des forages.

Le but de cette communication est de présenter une étude systématique de ces milieux lorsque la pression de consolidation est suffisamment forte pour que leur teneur en eau de saturation devienne plus petite que la limite de retrait, c'est-à-dire lorsqu'ils sont dans un état fragile et ont perdu leur plasticité au sens de la Mécanique des Sols.

2-PROPRIETES DES ARGILES SOUS FORTES PRESSIONS

2.1-Description de l'argile utilisée.

Il s'agit de l'argile plastique de la région parisienne. Elle fait partie du Sparnassien, étage de l'Eocène inférieur. Sa constitution minéralogique est voisine de l'Halloysite.

C'est une argile grise sale parsemée parfois de taches ou de veines plus foncées, noirâtres. Elle est très homogène, très fine et très grasse. Les limites d'Atterberg varient en fonction de la profondeur dans la couche du Sparnassien :

limite de liquidité	w_L	: de	105%	à	123%
limite de plasticité	w_p	: de	26%	à	33%
indice de plasticité	IP	: de	70	à	113
limite de retrait	LR	: de	17%	à	19%

Le poids volumique des particules solides est $\gamma_s = 2,69.10^4$ N/m^3. L'argile du Sparnassien est très étanche; en fonction de sa compacité, la perméabilité varie autour de 10^{-10} à 10^{-11} m/s.

La figure 1 représente la répartition granulométrique des particules, obtenue par densimétrie. 50% des grains ont une dimension inférieure à 2 μ.

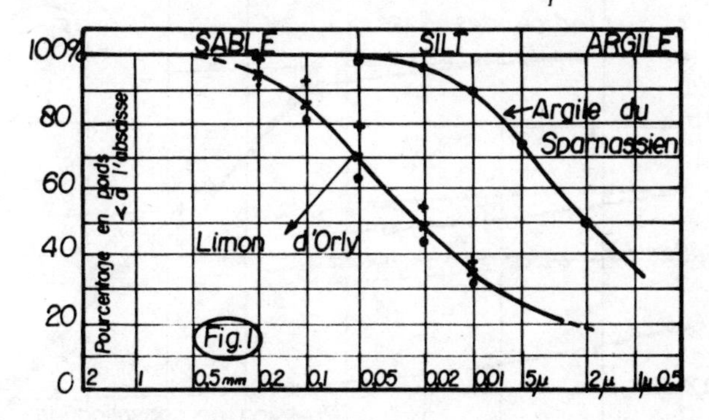

Fig.1 - Courbes granulométriques d'une argile du Sparnassien et d'un limon des plateaux de la région parisienne.

Grain size distribution curves of a Sparnassian clay and of a loam of Paris region.

Kornverteilungskurven eines Alttertiärtons und eines Lehms des Pariser Beckens

2.2-Préparation de l'argile consolidée.

La préparation de l'argile consiste à charger un échantillon sous une charge constante et à attendre la mise en équilibre par l'expulsion d'eau interstitielle. Pour les fortes pressions de consolidation, le char-

gement se fait par paliers successifs.
La figure 2 montre le dispositif qui permet de maintenir la charge normale de consolidation P_c sensiblement constante pendant la consolidation grâce à un ressort à plaques ondulées dont les déplacements compensent les tassements de l'échantillon.

Figure 2

Oedomètre pour fortes pressions de consolidation P_c.
Oedometer for high consolidation pressures P_c
Oedometer für starke Konsolidierungsdrücke P_c

On mesure le tassement sous charge, puis le gonflement lors de la décharge et on présente les résultats de l'essai dans les axes e, log P où l'indice des vides e est le rapport du volume des vides au volume des pleins et P la pression axiale. Les courbes de compressibilité de l'argile permettent de retrouver la pression de consolidation en prenant l'intersection des tangentes des deux branches de la courbe de compressibilité.
La figure 3 représente trois cycles de chargement croissant sur de l'argile plastique naturelle. Le premier cycle a été mené jusqu'à une pression de consolidation de 9,1 MPa (91. bar), le second jusqu'à 20. MPa, le troisième jusqu'à 40. MPa. On voit que le procédé simple proposé ci-dessus permet de retrouver à peu près la précédente pression de consolidation. On voit aussi que l'argile vierge présente la trace d'un chargement antérieur de l'ordre de 3. MPa, ce qui n'est pas en contradiction avec la géologie.

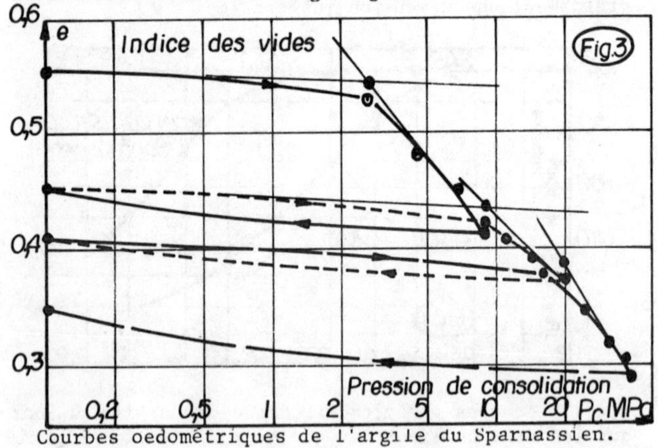

Courbes oedométriques de l'argile du Sparnassien.
Oedometric curves of Sparnassian clay
Druckporenzifferdiagramm des Alttertiärtons

2.3 - Propriétés mécaniques des argiles consolidées.

2.3.1. - Déformabilité.

Les éprouvettes prélevées dans les échantillons d'argiles consolidées ont été soumises à des essais de chargement à vitesse de déformation constante (de l'ordre de 10^{-3}/s à 10^{-4}/s), en charge comme en décharge. On en déduit les valeurs du module du premier chargement E_1 et du module de recharge E_2.

P_c (MPa)	3.	9,1	20.	40.
E_1 (MPa)	110	300	500	600
E_2 (MPa)	270	500	800	900

2.3.2. - Résistance.

Des essais de résistance à la traction (directe, par essais brésiliens, par extension d'une couronne), de résistance à la compression simple, des essais triaxiaux ont été effectués sur les différentes argiles consolidées. Les essais de traction sur l'argile consolidée sous 40. MPa ont donné une très grande dispersion entre 0. et 0,6 MPa probablement liée à la présence de slickenside . Les essais triaxiaux sont du type rapide non drainé. On obtient ainsi une courbe intrinsèque de résistance à court terme qui donne habituellement pour les sols à pression de consolidation modérée C_u et $\varphi_u = 0$. En utilisant les essais sous des pressions latérales égales aux pressions de consolidation, il est possible d'interpréter les essais dans la forme consolidé-rapide donnant C_{cu} et φ_{cu}

L'évaluation du volume des vides remplis d'air montre que les argiles étudiées sont assez loin de la saturation parfaite. La teneur en air observée est due en partie à une teneur en air initiale de l'argile naturelle, en partie au dégazage de l'eau interstitielle lié à la détente lorsqu'on ramène l'argile consolidée à la pression atmosphérique.
On constate expérimentalement que le déviateur à la rupture augmente avec la pression de confinement. Cet accroissement s'atténue au fur et à mesure que l'air dans les vides se comprime et passe en solution, et cesse lorsque les contraintes deviennent suffisantes pour créer la saturation, ce qui semble se produire lorsque la pression latérale s'approche, puis dépasse la pression de consolidation.

2.3.3. - Résultats expérimentaux.

2.3.3.1. - Argile naturelle.

La courbe intrinsèque de cette argile a une allure parabolique jusqu'à 6. MPa, puis devient parallèle à l'axe des abscisses ($\varphi_u = 0$), le déviateur à la rupture ne dépendant plus de la contrainte moyenne.

2.3.3.2. - Argile consolidée sous fortes pressions. (9,1 MPa, 20 MPa, 40 MPa)

Les résultats expérimentaux obtenus montrent que la consolidation de l'argile naturelle fissurée diminue la dispersion des caractéristiques mécaniques. Pour les pressions moyennes inférieures à la pression P_c de consolidation, les courbes intrinsèques présentent une allure parabolique jusqu'à P_c qu'on peut approximer par $\varphi_u = 20°$. Puis le déviateur à la rupture devient constant. On a alors un matériau parfaitement plastique obéissant au critère de Tresca $\varphi_u = 0$. La résistance mécanique est nettement plus faible que ce que l'on pouvait espérer en extrapolant les résultats connus de l'argile du Sparnassien consolidée sous de faibles compressions.

2.3.3.3. - Argiles naturelles consolidées sous 40 MPa, puis stabilisées sous 20 MPa et sous 10 MPa.

Le mode de préparation par consolidation sous forte charge, puis gonflement sous une charge inférieure permet de préparer des argiles très fortement surconsolidées. Les courbes intrinsèques en essais rapides non consolidées ont une allure parabolique et ne deviennent parallèles à l'axe des abscisses que pour des pressions latérales supérieures à 40.MPa. La résistance au cisaillement paraît surtout fonction de l'indice des vides ; en particulier, la courbe intrinsèque de l'argile consolidée sous 20.MPa est située à l'intérieur de celle de l'argile préalablement surconsolidée. On peut faire la même remarque en comparant l'argile consolidée sous 9,1 MPa et l'argile surconsolidée sous 40 MPa, puis consolidée sous 10.MPa. Les résultats obtenus sont présentés sur les figures suivantes (4,5,6) :

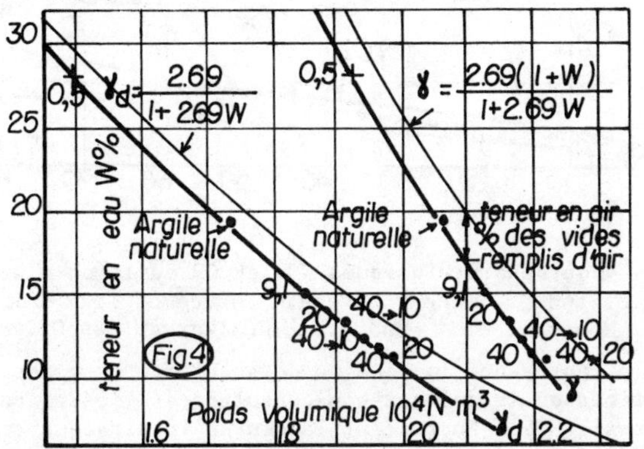

Relation entre la teneur en eau et les densités humide et sèche.
Relation between water content and wet and dry densities.
Beziehung zwischen dem Wassergehalt und den feuchten und trockenen Dichten

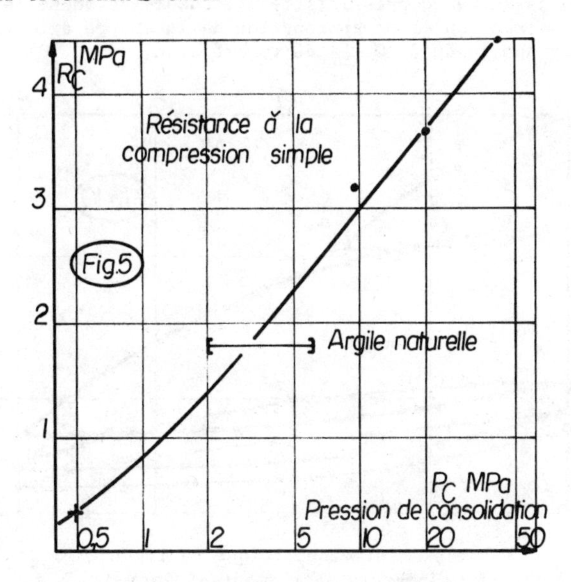

Résistance à la compression simple en fonction de P_c
Unconfined compression strength versus P_c.
Einachsige Druckfestigkeit gegenüber P_c.

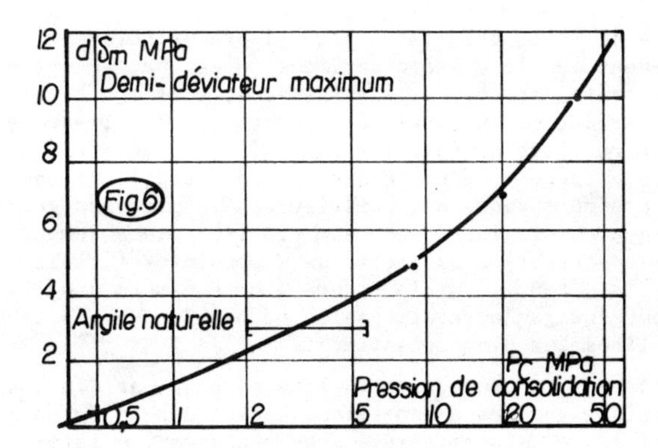

Variation du demi-déviateur maximum avec P_c.
Variation of maximum half stress deviator versus P_c
Variation des maximalen Halbspannungs-deviator mit P_c

La figure 7 résume les différentes courbes intrinsèques obtenues pour les différentes argiles en essais non consolidés rapides et explicite la courbe intrinsèque de l'argile en essais consolidés rapides.

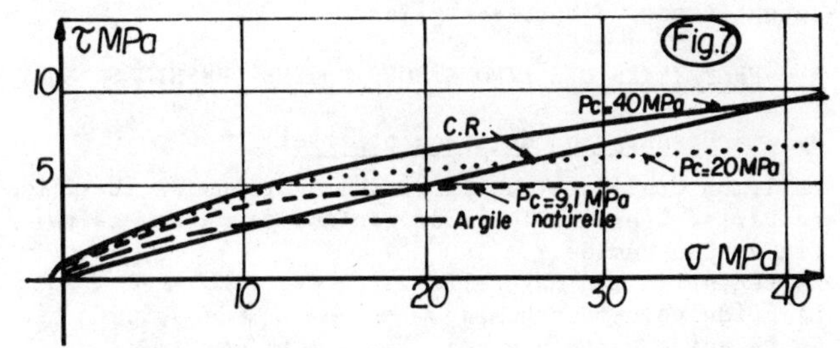

Courbes intrinsèques NCR et CR de l'argile du Sparnassien.
U.U and C.U shear strength curves of Sparnassian clay.
Mohrsche U.U. -und K.U.- Hüllkurven des Alttertiärtons

La figure 8 donne la vitesse de propagation des ondes longitudinales horizontales ou verticales dans l'argile sous contraintes en fonction de la pression oedométrique σ_1 . On peut noter la faible anisotropie de l'argile naturelle.

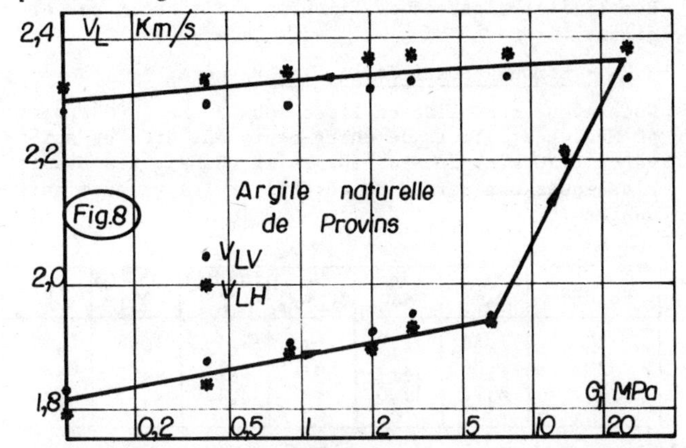

Célérité des ondes longitudinales en fonction de σ_1 .
Velocity of longitudinal waves versus σ_1 .
Geschwin digkeit der Längswellen gegenüber σ_1 .

2.4. - Conclusions.

2.4.1. - Les résultats de la figure 7 indiquent clairement que le critère de Tresca n'est pas acceptable. La pente des courbes intrinsèques, vers les faibles pressions moyennes est de l'ordre de 20°. Il ne serait pas réaliste de calculer avec $\varphi = 0$ une structure souterraine très profonde dans de l'argile lorsque la pression moyenne est inférieure à la pression géostatique. L'origine de ce fait provient probablement de la vaporisation partielle de l'eau interstitielle lors de la détente. Sur la figure 4 on constate que le pourcentage de saturation tombe à 80% pour les échantillons les plus consolidés.

2.4.2. - La courbe intrinsèque obtenue par des essais rapides sur des échantillons consolidés (c'est-à-dire ici les essais effectués avec une pression latérale égale à P_c) n'est pas une droite mais une courbe à concavité dirigée vers le bas. La pente de cette courbe passe progressivement de 20° à 8° lorsque la contrainte normale croît. Ce phénomène n'avait pas été signalé jusqu'à présent pour les argiles.

2.4.3. - La continuité des résultats obtenus (exemple fig.4) qui s'étendent sur plus de deux décades pour les contraintes, montre que les résultats obtenus touchent à des lois générales et doivent pouvoir être acceptés pour d'autres argiles.

3 - PROPRIETES DES LIMONS SOUS FORTES PRESSIONS

3.1. - Description du limon utilisé.

Le limon étudié est un limon des plateaux de la région de Paris. C'est un loess de couleur jaunâtre, calcaire fin et peu humide.
La teneur en eau naturelle varie peu : $22\% < w < 25\%$.
Le poids volumique humide moyen est : $\gamma = 1{,}9.10^4$ N/m^3 et le poids volumique sec $\gamma_d = 1{,}6.10^4$ N/m^3.
Le poids volumique absolu des grains γ_s varie de $2{,}58.10^4$ N/m^3 à $2{,}66.10^4$ N/m^3.
La teneur en $CaCO_3$ varie avec la profondeur de prélèvement de 10 à 30%.
Les analyses granulométriques effectuées montrent que le diamètre maximum des grains est de 0,5 mm et que pour 90 à 95% en poids du matériau on a $d < 0{,}2$ mm et pour 12 à 16% $d < 0{,}002$ mm (fig. 1).
Les limites d'Atterberg sont :

$32\% < w_L < 36\%$ $20\% < w_p < 24\%$ $12 < I_p < 14$

Ces limites classent ce limon parmi les sols peu argileux.

3.2. - Limons consolidés au laboratoire.

Nous avons consolidé ce limon sous 20.MPa, 30.MPa et 40.MPa. Les paliers de chargements ont été les suivants : 10.MPa, 20.MPa, 30.MPa et 40.MPa. Les essais classiques ont permis de déterminer les valeurs suivantes :

P_c MPa	% w	% w_s	% $S = w/w_s$	10^4 N/m^3 γ	10^4 N/m^3 γ_d	e
20	7,46	12,2	61.	2,13	1,98	0,32
30	7,06	11,5	61.	2,15	2,01	0,30
40	6,92	11,0	63.	2,17	2,03	0,29

3.3. - Propriétés mécaniques du limon.

3.3.1. - Courbe intrinsèque des limons consolidés.

Pour déterminer les caractéristiques mécanique des différents limons, nous avons effectué plusieurs séries d'essais triaxiaux dans des conditions rapides non drainés. Les courbes intrinsèques sont dessinées à partir des cercles de Mohr définis par les essais triaxiaux pour des pressions latérales de confinement variant jusqu'à 80 MPa (fig. 9).

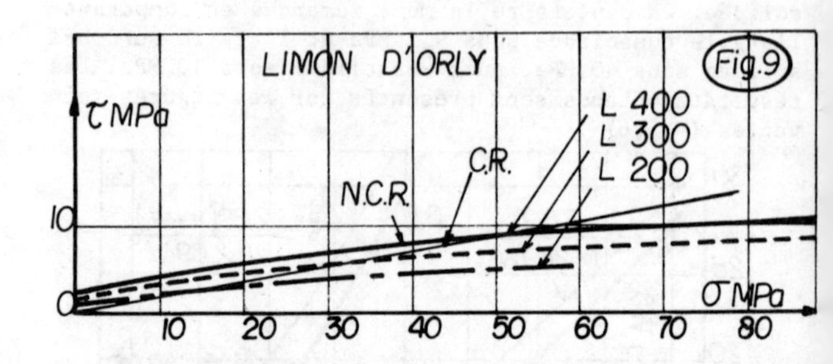

Courbes intrinsèques NCR et CR du limon d'Orly
U.U. and C.U. shear strength curves of loam from Orly
Mohrsche U.U. -und K.U.- Hüllkurven des Orly Lehms

Elle représente le domaine de stabilité dans des conditions où le sol est non consolidé et l'essai rapide (essais NCR). En traçant la courbe intrinsèque correspondant à une étreinte latérale $\sigma_2 = \sigma_3$ égale à la pression de consolidation à l'oedomètre, on obtient le domaine de stabilité en condition où le sol est consolidé et l'essai rapide (Essai CR).

3.3.2. - Compressibilité.

Un essai de compressibilité à l'oedomètre donne le tassement du limon en fonction de la charge axiale variant jusqu'à 80.MPa de compression, (fig. 10).

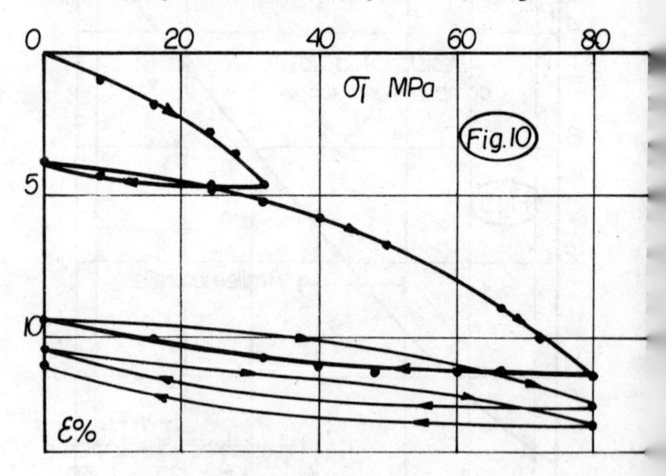

Tassement oedométrique du limon
Oedometric settlement of loam
Oedometrische Setzung des Lehms

L'indice des vides e a varié de 0,650 à l'état naturel jusqu'à 0,200 environ lorsque le limon est consolidé sous 80.MPa de compression.

3.3.3. - Célérité des ondes longitudinales.

Nous avons mesuré la vitesse de propagation des ondes longitudinales dans le limon sous divers états de compression axiale à l'oedomètre. La figure 11 donne la variation de V_L en fonction de σ_1.

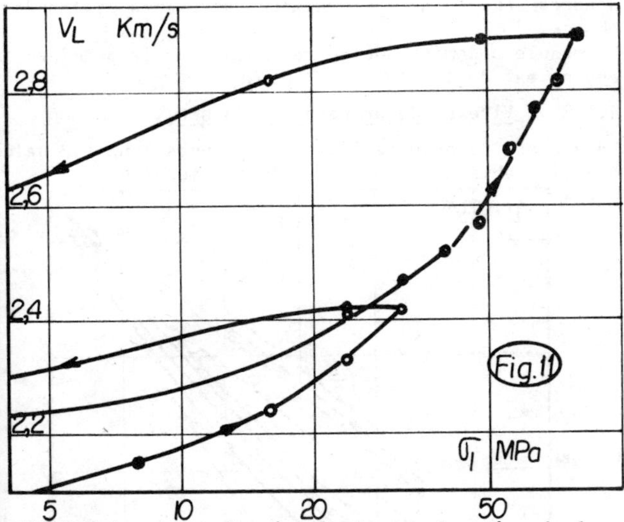

Célérité des ondes longitudinales en fonction de la compression oedométrique.
Velocity of longitudinal waves versus oedometric compression
Geschwin-digkeit der Längswellen als Funktion des oedometrischen Drucks

4 - PROPRIETES DES SABLES SOUS FORTES COMPRESSIONS

4.1. - Description du sable utilisé.

Il s'agit du sable du Stampien prélevé à Fontainebleau C'est un sable à grains siliceux très résistant, anguleux, fins et bien gradués. La figure 12 montre la courbe granulométrique A du sable naturel. Le coefficient de Hazen $d_{60}/d_{10} = \chi_A = 1,5$. La dimension moyenne des grains est de l'ordre de 0,25 mm.

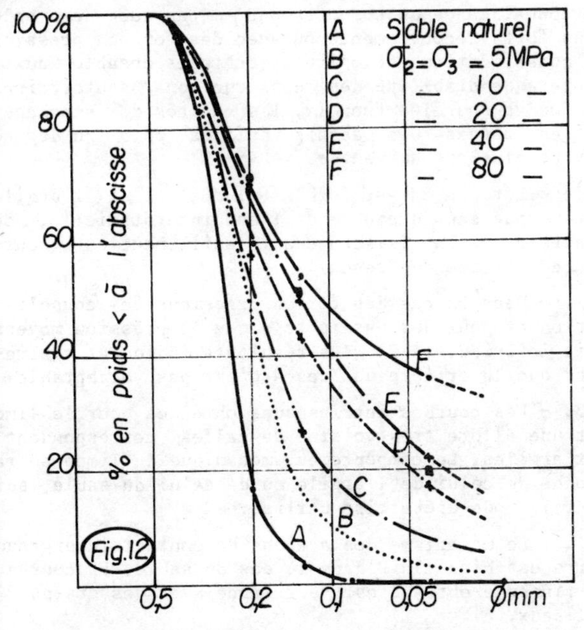

Courbes granulométriques du sable de Fontainebleau
Grain size distribution curves of Fontainebleau sand
Kornverteilungskurven des Sands von Fontainebleau

Les courbes B, C, D, E, F donnent la granulométrie du même sable après avoir été soumis à un essai triaxial dont la pression de confinement a été successivement de 5.MPa, 10.MPa, 20.MPa, 40.MPa, 80.MPa. Leur coefficient de Hazen vaut respectivement $\chi_B = 2,2$, $\chi_C = 3,8$; χ_D, χ_E, $\chi_F > 8$. On peut ainsi constater que des grains se cassent lorsque le sable est soumis à des cisaillements importants. La granulométrie devient continue pour donner une meilleure compacité. Suivant le mode de mise en place, le sable a un poids volumique sec variant de $1,45.10^4$ N/m^3 à $1,72.10^4$ N/m^3. Pour la commodité des essais, on a cherché le poids volumique stationnaire dans un essai de cisaillement appelé poids volumique critique γ_{cr} en le déterminant de la façon suivante : un échantillon d'environ un litre de sable est enveloppé dans une mince gaine de caoutchouc et soumis au vide à l'intérieur. L'échantillon est alors pétri dans tous les sens : puis on mesure le poids volumique.
Les essais ont montré que γ devient stationnaire et égale à γ_{cr}. Le tableau suivant montre les valeurs de γ_{cr} en fonction de la pression du vide.

P KPa	10	30	40	50
γ_{cr} 10^4 N/m^3	1,62	1,63	1,66	1,66

Les essais triaxiaux ont été effectués à poids volumique initial $\gamma_d^\circ = 1,65.10^4$ N/m^3. Dans l'oedomètre, avec un poids volumique initial $\gamma_d^\circ = 1,72.10^4$ N/m^3, on atteint un poids volumique $\gamma_d = 1,9.10^4$ N/m^3 pour une contrainte axiale $\sigma_1 = 80.$MPa.

4.2. - Caractéristiques mécaniques.

4.2.1. - Frottement interne.

L'angle de frottement interne a été mesuré à l'appareil triaxial. En appliquant le diagramme de Mohr, on peut obtenir l'angle φ par la relation suivante :

$$\sin \varphi = (\sigma_1 - \sigma_2)/(\sigma_1 + \sigma_2)$$

$\sigma_1 - \sigma_2$, étant le déviateur limite des contraintes. Les résultats obtenus pour φ sont étroitement associés au poids volumique γ. On obtient généralement pour chaque poids volumique initial γ_d° deux valeurs φ_{min} et φ_{max} pour l'angle de frottement interne. Il est à noter que pour de très grandes déformations φ et γ tendent vers des valeurs constantes indépendamment des conditions initiales. Quelques essais triaxiaux sous une pression de 0,1 MPa ont été effectués pour évaluer la variation de φ avec γ_d.

γ_d 10^4 N/m^3	1,57	1,63	1,65	1,72
φ_{max}	34°	37°	38°	42°
φ_{min}	30°	32°	34°	35°
e	0,720	0,656	0,636	0,570
e tg φ_{max}	0,485	0,494	0,497	0,513

Sous de très fortes pressions de confinement, on a obtenu, pour un même poids volumique initial $\gamma_d^\circ = 1,65$ 10^4 N/m^3, les courbes donnant le déviateur des contraintes $\sigma_1 - \sigma_2$ en fonction de la déformation axiale ε_1. Avec les valeurs limites estimées des déviateurs $(\sigma_1 - \sigma_2)_{min}$ et $(\sigma_1 - \sigma_2)_{max}$, on obtient le tableau des valeurs de φ_{min} et φ_{max} :

$\sigma_2 = \sigma_3$ MPa	5	10	40	60	80
$(\sigma_1 - \sigma_2)_{min}$ MPa	12	24	100	150	200
φ_{min}	33°1	33°1	33°7	33°7	33°7
$(\sigma_1 - \sigma_2)_{max}$ MPa	16	33	130	185	240
φ_{max}	38°0	38°5	38°2	37°3	36°9

La figure 13 présente la courbe intrinsèque de ce sable : elle est pratiquement rectiligne.

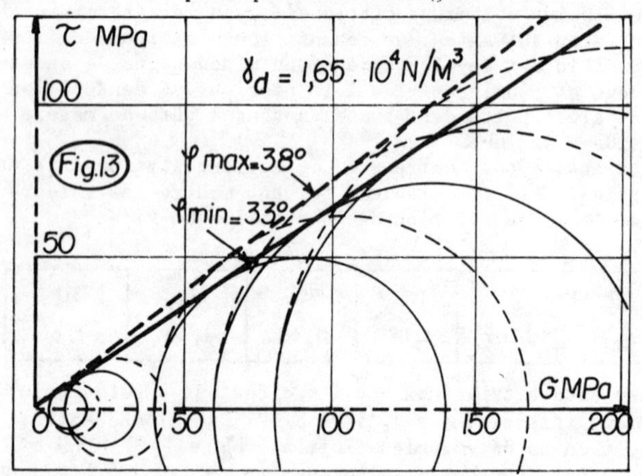

Courbes intrinsèques du sable de Fontainebleau
Shear strength curves of Fontainebleau sand
Mohrsche Hüllkurve des Sands von Fontainebleau

4.2.2. - Déformabilité.

Les résultats précédents montrent que l'évaluation de l'angle de frottement interne φ est relativement précise. Par contre, le module de déformabilité obtenu au cours des essais triaxiaux présente une certaine dispersion comme le montre le tableau suivant :

$\sigma_2 = \sigma_3$ MPa	5	10	40	60	80
E MPa	808	1333	527	830	1195

Les résultats semblent plus fidèles à l'oedomètre. La figure 14 montre la compressibilité du sable avec un poids volumique initial $\gamma_d^\circ = 1,72.10^4$ N/m3 en coordonnées semi-logarithmiques pour plusieurs cycles de charge.

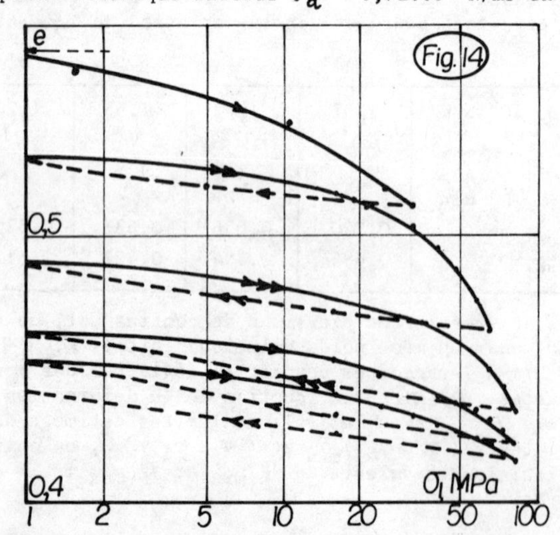

Compressibilité oedomètrique du sable
Oedometric compressibility of sand
Druckporenzifferdiagramm des Sands

Le module oedométrique correspondant à la première charge est de l'ordre de 1.200 MPa.

4.2.3. - Vitesse de propagation du son.

La vitesse de propagation V_L des ondes longitudinales dans le sable sous contrainte a été mesurée.

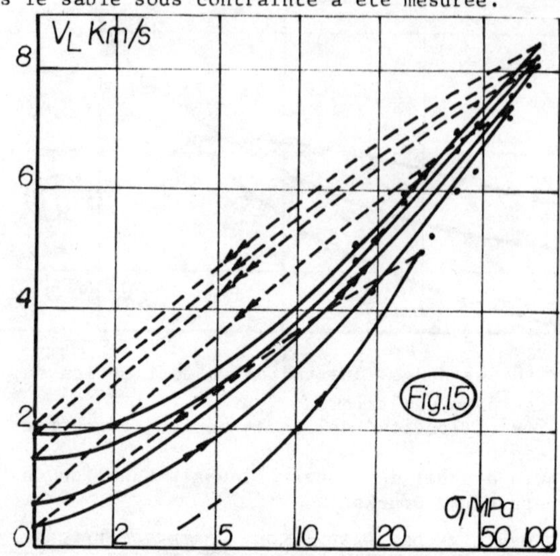

Célérité des ondes longitudinales en fonction de la compression oedométrique
Velocity of longitudinal waves versus oedometric compression
Geschwin-digkeit der Längswellen als Funktion der oedometrischen Drucks

5. - CONCLUSION GENERALE

La connaissance du comportement mécanique des sols sous forts recouvrements ou avec des fortes pressions de consolidation géologiques est indispensable aux projets de stabilité des constructions souterraines profondes pour les tunnels, les cavités de stockage ou les forages. Des essais réalisés, on a pu dégager les conclusions suivantes.

5.1. - Lorsque P_c est faible (<1 MPa) et si l'argile est rompue sans drainage de l'eau interstitielle, on constate que la résistance au cisaillement est constante (critère de Tresca).

5.2. - Dans le cas des fortes pressions de consolidation et pour des essais tels que la pression moyenne soit inférieure à P_c les résultats indiquent clairement que le critère de Tresca n'est pas acceptable.

5.3. - Les courbes intrinsèques obtenues pour le limon ont une allure très voisine de celles correspondant aux argiles. Le comportement mécanique du limon se rapproche de celui de l'argile ou de celui du sable, suivant le mode opératoire utilisé.

5.4. - Le mécanisme des actions de contact intergranulaire est bien clair dans le cas du sable. La courbe intrinsèque obtenue est rectiligne avec des grains siliceux.

5.5. - Les essais acoustiques ont montré que la vitesse de propagation des ondes longitudinales dépend bien de l'indice des vides du sol.

OoO

EFFECT OF POROSITY ON THE STRENGTH OF THE CLASTIC SEDIMENTARY ROCKS

ÉTUDE D'EFFET DE LA POROSITÉ SUR LA RÉSISTANCE DES ROCHES DES SEDIMENTS CLASTIQUES

DIE WIRKUNG DER POROSITÄT AUF DIE FESTIGKEIT DER SEDIMENTAREN TRÜMMERGESTEINE

Kazuo HOSHINO
Geological Survey of Japan
Tokyo, Japan

ABSTRACT The breaking strength of the porous clastic sedimentary rocks are closely related to the porosity, according to the high pressure experimentation under compression. The tests were done on dry samples, 20 and 12 mm in diameter, up to 40 % in porosity. There is a tendency that the strength is proportional to the logarithm of porosity.

$$n = A e^{-b \sigma_s}$$

where n is porosity, σ_s is strength, and A and b are constants.

The diminution of the porosity in sedimentary rocks is mostly a result of compaction process, which differs naturally from place to place according to the sedimentation and tectonic environments. If we take the results of the samples derived from geolgically, and petrologically same unit, in terms of texture, grain size, or mineral composition, the relation is quite clear to be expressed by the above equation. It is probable that the strengthening of the texture of the rocks by the consolidation in compaction process is most responsible for this strength-porosity relation. The increase of pore spaces by possible dilatancy effect could be another cause for this relation.

ZUSAMMENFASSUNG Die Festigkeit der porösen sedimentären Trümmergesteine bezieht sich auf die Porosität; es ist nach einer Experimentation mit Hochdruck erkläert. Das Experiment wurde von trocken Proben von 20 und 12 mm Durchmesser und zu 40 % Porosität ausgeführt. Es gibt die Tendenz, dass die Druckfestigkeit ist im Verhältnis zum Logarithm der Porosität.

$$n = A e^{-b \sigma_s}$$

Hier, n ist die Porosität, σ_s die Festigkeit, und A und b die Konstante.

Die Verminderung der Porosität in sedimentären Gesteinen stammt aus dem Kompaktionprozess, der naturlich verschieden von einem Platz zu anderem Platz nach der Sedimentation und tektonischer Umgebung ist. Wenn wir bemerken von Probenmaterialien, die wurde in dieselben Positionen vom Stundpunkt der Geologie und Petrologie, das heisst, Textur, Grösse des Korpuskels, oder mineralische Komposition gesammelt, das Verhältnis ist genau klar und wird mit der oben beschriebenen Gleichung gegeben. Es ist wahrscheinlich dass das Verhärten im Kompaktionprozess ist die wichtigste Ursache des Druckfestigkeit-Porositat Verhältnisses. Die Zunahme des Poreraums durch mögliche Wirkung der Erweiterung ist andere wichtige Ursache dieses Verhältnisses.

RÉSUMÉ Effet par examen de haute préssion, on peut dire que résistance à la compression de la roche des sédiments clastiques de porosité a des rapports intimes à la porosité. J'ai examiné des échantillons sec jusqu'à 40 % de porosité et de 20, 12 mm en diametre. Il y a tendance que la résistance est propotionnel au logarithme de porosité.

$$n = A e^{-b \sigma_s}$$

Ici, n la porosité, σ_s la résistance, et A,b les constantes.

La diminuation de la porosité en roches sédimentaires sont principalement le résultat du processus de la compacité qui different naturellement en chaques places dépent de sédimentations et l'environnements tectoniques. Cette relation exprimerait clairement par forme en haut, si prendrait les échantillons qui dérivent de même unité de géologique et pétrographique, en matrice, la granularité et la composition de minérals. C'est pourquoi, on peut savoir la raison principale, la relation de la résistance- la porosité que matrices des roches deviennent fort par la consolidation en processus de la compacité. De l'autre raison pour cette relation, on peut donc considerer l'augmentation de l'espace du poré par éffet de la dilatabilité.

INTRODUCTION

It has been shown as the results of many high pressure experimentations that the rocks exhibit surprising conformity in mechanical properties under high pressure and temperature, except clastic rocks, which diverge in wide range in mechanical properties such as strength or deformational behavior (e.g., Handin,1966). In order to do better application for analytical structural geology or civil engineering, it is important to know what factors are essential in determination of these properties.

Hoshino et al (1972) reported in an experimental work of one hundred kinds of samples from Tertiary sedimentary basins in Japan that in clastic rocks porosity is most important factor for the mechanical properties. They had described the relation to be semi-logarithm. Recently, Dunn et al (1973) published that in the sandstones, the relation is written in exponential curve.

The purpose of this study is to follow this problem focusing on the numerical relation between porosity and strength. The author would like to show that even for these sandstones the relation is well described in semi-logarithm curve. Also he makes discussion that the mechanism of the porosity dependence of the strength is well explained on a basis of semi-logarithm equation.

METHOD OF STUDY

The apparatus was reported in detail in Hoshino et al (1972). All specimens were tested on the dry samples of cylindrical shape, 19.5 mm in diameter and 39.0 mm long under compression. Some additional from Swiss Alps were tested at a later time and they are 12.0 mm in diameter and 24.0 mm long. Strain rate is approximately 10^{-4}/sec. All samples are cut 90 degree to the stratification. The samples were selected to be homogeneous as well as possible, avoiding the presence of planner anisotropy or any impurity such as thin inclusions, tuffaceous contents, or clay minerals.

Porosity was calculated from the following measurements for most samples:

- Wwa: weight of the sample in the air, which is saturated with water by putting into water for more than 4 days.
- Www: weight of the above sample in water.
- Wd: weight of the sample in the air, which is dried by being kept in a drier for more than 4 days at temperature of 110 degree c.

Then porosity n is given by

$$n = \frac{Wwa - Wd}{Wwa - Www}$$

In this method, if the porosity of the samples is more than 1 % or so, the accuracy is around a few % or less, good for the discussion. When the sample contains the materials that are soluble or swelling in water, it was cut in an exact cylindrical shape in accuracy of 1/500, then the volume was calculated from the diameter and length. In this method, the accuracy of density is much better.

The rocks fail in different manner as pressure increases. In low pressure, the rocks fail with visible fracture, accompanied by sudden drop of the stress-strain curve (brittle behavior). In high pressure, failure does not make any visible fracture, but the rocks flow (ductile behavior). In this report, the result of brittle behavior only was taken into consideration.

Then, from Hoshino et al (1972) data of 9 argillaceous rocks was taken and 2 additional argillaceous rocks from the flysch in Swiss Alps were studied. Porosity of these rocks ranges 0.6 % in minimum to 36.3 % in maximum. As arenaceous rocks, 17 kinds were selected from Hoshino et al (1972) and 6 kinds from the molasse and flysch sediments in Swiss. Of the 17 kinds, 5 kinds are rather soft and become ductile from comparatively low pressure, then excluded in cases of 500 bars or more in figures 3 and 4. Porosity of the arenaceous rocks studied is between 0.6 and 28.5 %. The distinction between argillaceous and arenaceous rocks is simply based on the particle size; that is, less than 0.0625 mm is argillaceous rocks and more than 0.0625 mm is arenaceous rocks. The smallest grain of the rocks here studied is probably 1 micron or somewhat less, while the biggest is of the rocks is not greater than 2 mm.

Most argillaceous rocks studied here are common type of the fine grained clastic sediments, which is characterized with a predominance of detrital components, containing little pyroclastic or carbonate materials. Sometime we have exceptionally hard shale, which contains a lots of tuffaceous or carbonate materials of clay size (1 or 3 micron). This type of rocks were excluded from the study. In case of 1 bar in figure 1, the values of such rocks are shown with * mark as an example.

RESULT

The results are summarized in figures 1 to 4. The vertical axis is for strength in normal scale, while the horizontal axis for porosity in percent in logarithmic scale. We see the points come in almost linear relation as already reported (Hoshino et al, 1972). The linear relation may be quite clear in argillaceous rocks in spite of the fact that the samples are collected from different sedimentary basins in different environments over Japan and Swiss.

For arenaceous rocks, linear relation is rather obscure for the first look. It would be probable that the difference of geological environments might have more effective influence on mechanical properties under high pressure in arenaceous rocks than in argillaceous rocks. If we take the results of the similar arenaceous rocks collected from the same area, we see the linear relation becomes clear. In figures 3 and 4, the data of Sasebo area is distinguished with solid marks. Then it is clear that these points representing Sasebo area come along a linear line. In figure 5, the points are plotted with different marks according to the areas for 1000 bars of confining pressure. Series K consists of 6 samples from Sasebo, northern Kyushu. Series O are 4 samples from Oshimo area, northwestern Kyushu. Series S is made up from 6 kinds of arenaceous rocks from the molasse and flysch

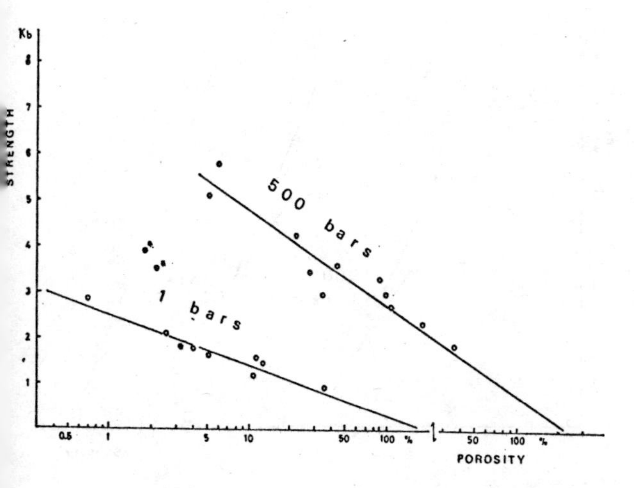

'ig. 1 Strength versus porosity for argillaceous rocks in semi-log scale. Confining pressure, 1 bar, and 500 bars.

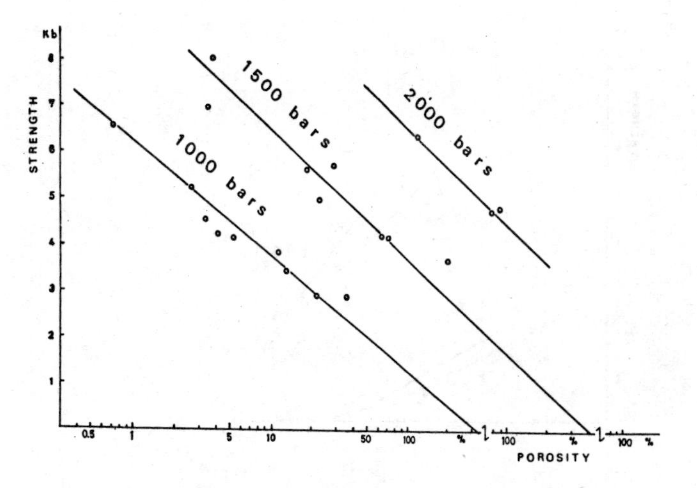

Fig. 2 Strength versus porosity for argillacous rocks in semi-log scale. Confining pressure, 1000, 1500, and 2000 bars.

›ediments in Swiss. Both K and S series make good inear relation respectively. Interesting thing is hat 4 samples of O series lay in almost horizontal irection, in other words, they are little affected ›y porosity. In fact, these 4 samples belong to ,eologically same formation, the same geological ge, whereas in K and S series, the samples came rom defferent geological horizons. We can see nother good example for the USA data reported by unn et al (1973). We see in figure 5 that series makes well linear relation in semi-log diagram.

n this way, we see there is a tendency expressed y the following equation

$$n = A\, e^{-b\sigma_s} \quad - - - - - \quad (1)$$

is porosity, σ_s is strength, and A and b are onstants. Table 1 gives the value of A and b for arious kinds of rocks at each confining pressure nd area as determined by the least squares method.

s indicated by this equation constant A is the orosity value at the strength zero. Value (1-A) s to indicate a critical amount of particles ecessary for producing minimum binding force ithin the rocks. Therefore, constant A is a kind f coefficient to indicate the consolidation of the ock texture by confining pressure. For arenaceous ocks, coefficient A is around 0.3 to 0.4 (30 % to 0 %). Carefully studied with each series, the oefficient is approximately 0.3 at low pressure, hen showing a tendency to increase at high ressure. This is probably due that at high confin- ng pressure an effect to increase the binding orce among the grains is getting stronger. The renaceous rocks of S series has comparatively high alue of A, which indicates that in Swiss Alps area here were characteristic geological process, ither tectonic or sedimentary, which helped unusual trengthening of the rock texture.

n argillaceous rocks coefficient A exceeds 1, and ttains approximately 6. They have numerical value f strength even at a state of porosity 1.0 (100 %), he state that the rocks are void. In table 1, he strength at porosity 1.0 is shown for each onfining pressure. The value is 320 bars even at atmospheric pressure, being increased up to 2120 bars at 2000 bars of confining pressure. This strength increases just proportional to the confining pressure. High value of coefficient A in argillaceous rocks would be derived from compaction process of the argillaceous rocks.

Argillaceous rocks

Pressure (kb)	A	b (/kb)	σ_s^{**} (kb)	σ_s^{*} (kb)
0.001	1.98	2.14	1.400	0.320
0.500	2.38	1.11	2.850	0.780
1.000	3.19	0.93	3.730	1.250
1.500	4.22	0.85	4.420	1.700
2.000	5.53	0.81	4.970	2.120

Arenaceous rocks (all)

Pressure (kb)	A	b (/kb)
0.001	0.20	1.49
0.500	0.38	0.74
1.000	0.38	0.52
1.500	0.54	0.50
2.000	0.34	0.32

Arenaceous rocks (K Series)

Pressure (kb)	A	b (/kb)	σ_s^{**} (kb)
0.001	0.27	1.40	0.720
0.500	0.27	0.53	1.900
1.000	0.28	0.35	2.950
1.500	0.36	0.34	3.730

Arenaceous rocks (depending on areas)
1000 bars confining pressure

Series (area)	A	b (/kb)	σ_s^{**} (kb)
K (Sasebo)	0.28	0.35	2.950
S (Swiss)	0.58	0.65	2.700
U (USA)	0.31	0.22	5.120

Tab. 1 Constants of the equation (1), A and b, and σ_s^{*} and σ_s^{**} (the strength at porosity 100 and 10 %) at each confining pressure.

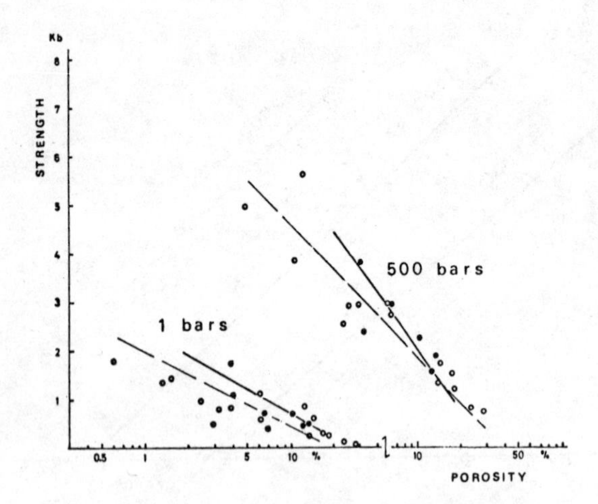

Fig. 3 Strength versus porosity for arenaceous rocks in semi-log scale. Solid circles are K series. Confining pressure, 1 bar, and 500 bars.

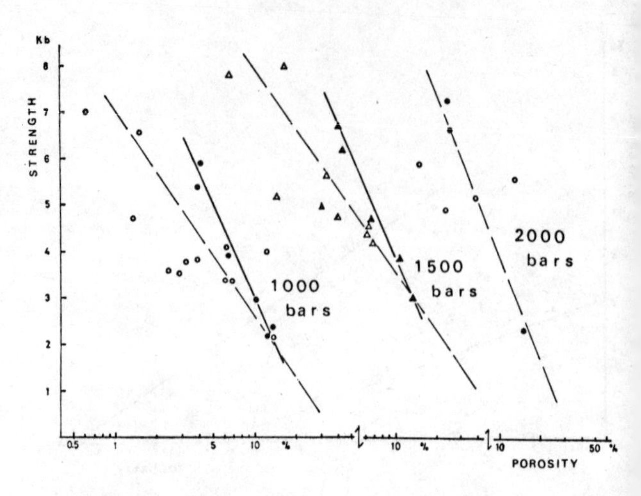

Fig. 4 Strength versus porosity for arenaceous rocks in semi-log scale. Solid circles and triangles are K series. Confining pressure, 1000, 1500 (triangles), and 2000 bars.

Constant b is related the degree of diminution of porosity for an increase of strength (unit, kilobars), or expresses the degree of strength-increase for a definite change of porosity. The value b in argillaceous rocks is almost two times of that in arenaceous rocks at each confining pressure. This indicates that the strength of argillaceous rocks are less affected by porosity than arenaceous rocks.

DISCUSSION

Equation (1) is quite similar to the next equation that describes the porosity-depth relation in compaction process of the sedimentary rocks (Athy, 1930).

$$n = n_o e^{-ch} \quad \text{- - - - - - -} \quad (2)$$

This relation is also approved for Japanese rocks studied here (e.g., Hoshino et al, 1972; Nagumo, 1965). Here we obtain values of constants like that: n_o is 0.7 and c is 0.54/km for argillaceous rocks, and n_o is 0.4 and c is 0.20/km for arenaceous rocks.

Since $p=\bar{\rho}gh$, where p is hydrostatic pressure at depth h and $\bar{\rho}$ is mean density between the surface and depth h, and g is acceleration of gravity, then equation (2) is written as follows

$$n = n_o e^{-c'p} \quad \text{- - - - - - - -} \quad (3)$$

where $c'=c/\bar{\rho}g$.

If we take 2.2 and 2.4 as the mean density of argillaceous and arenaceous rocks respectively here, we have 2.45/kb and 0.83/kb as c′ for argillaceous and arenaceous rocks respectively. These values are not so diverse as compared with value of b in table 1. In argillaceous rocks, b value at atmospheric pressure is 2.14, while c′ estimated above is 2.45. In arenaceous rocks, b value of K series is 1.40 and 0.53 at 1 and 500 bars respectively, whereas c′ forarenaceous rocks estimated is 0.83. Although the matters are different in equations (1) and (3); one concerning the failure by fracturing of the texture, the other concerning the rearrangement of grains within the rocks, the above accordance may indicate similar mechanism in pressure-porosity relation.

Compaction of the argillaceous rocks develops in the following succession (Hedberg,1936, Weller, 1959).

1. mechanical rearrangement stage
2. dewatering stage
3. mechanical deformation stage
4. recrystallization stage

The original porosity at the surface is 0.8 to 0.7. In stage 2, porosity ranges 0.45 to 0.35, in which each particle is considered to be just touched each other. In stage 3, which begins around 0.35 of porosity, however, the particles are pushed strongly then crushed or deformed partly. Cementing takes place among the particles. At around 0.1 of porosity it comes into stage 4, in which the grains are recrystallized and binding force by cementation becomes more strong. According to this succession, most argillaceous rocks studied are grouped in stage 4. Mark σ_s^{**} in table 1 gives the strength at porosity 0.1. The differential stress necessary to fail the material at the point just coming to the recrystallization stage is 1400 bar at atmospheric pressure, and then e.g. 2850 and 3730 bars at 500 and 1000 bars respectively.
In stage 1 and 2, less than 0.35 in porosity, the rock material has yet little cementation among the particles, therefore the rocks are not characterized by brittle fracturing but by ductile deformation.

In arenaceous rocks, compaction stages are not clear as compared with argillaceous rocks. If it is well sorted medium grained, the original porosity may be around 0.45 and at about 0.37 it advanced to stage 3 (Weller, 1959). Possibly the arenaceous rocks come into the mechanical deformation stage in later or at more porosity than argillaceous rocks, whereas the cementation develop quickly than argillaceous rocks as indicated by value of constant b. For comparision, strength at porosity 0.1 is given in table 1 for arenaceous

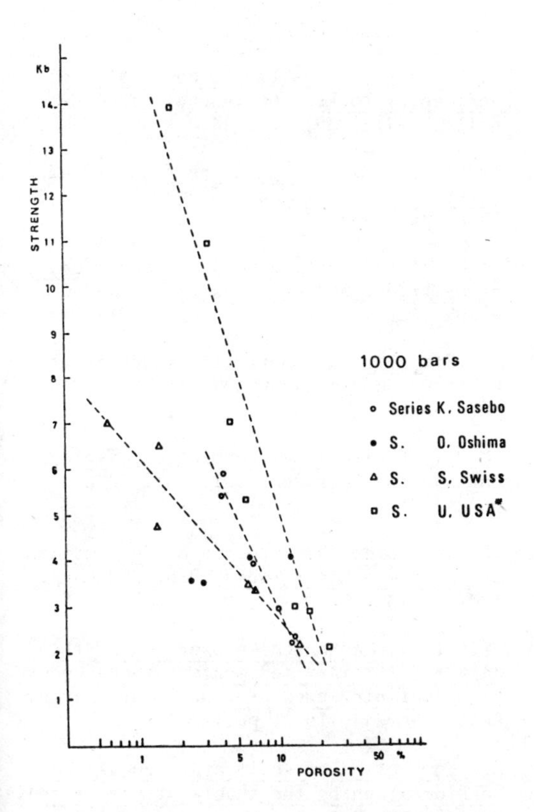

Fig. 5 Strength-porosity relation for different areas at 1000 bars confining pressure. *, data from Dunn et al, 1973

rocks. The strength of arenaceous rocks in Japan and Swiss are always lower than that of argillaceous rocks, about half at 1 bar and 70 or 80 % at 500 to 1500 bars.

Now, let's discuss the meaning of constant b. Equation (1) is written as

$$\frac{dn}{d\sigma_s} = -bn \quad ------ \quad (4)$$

On the other hand, provided that as porosity of a rock changed from n to n', the strength changed from σ_s to σ_s', then

$$\Delta n = n'-n = \frac{v'}{V'} - \frac{v}{V} \fallingdotseq n(r-1)\frac{\Delta V}{V} \quad --- \quad (5)$$

Here,

$$r = \frac{\Delta v}{v} \Big/ \frac{\Delta V}{V} \quad ---- \quad (6)$$

and V,v,V', and v' are the volume of the body and the pores before and after the change respectively; ΔV and Δv are the difference of volume before and after the change.

Here, if we assume the next relation, then place it into equation (5),

$$\frac{\Delta V}{V} = -\frac{\Delta\sigma_s}{k}$$

k is a constant.
Then we get

$$\frac{\Delta n}{\Delta\sigma_s} = -\frac{(r-1)}{k}n \quad ---- \quad (7)$$

Comparing equations (4) and (7),(r-1)/k should equal to b. Therefore if the above assumtion is permitted, (r-1) and k should change in the same increase-decrease direction and proportion as determined by constant b.

Constant k is seemingly comparable with bulk modulus by replacing the strength difference σ_s by pressure difference. Since this constant means strength difference per unit change of the volume, it indicates something like degree of resistance of the internal texture against failure. It is quite natural, accordingly, that constant k will increase as the rocks are getting less porous.

Next, let's check the value of (r-1). In the rocks at stages 1 and 2 of the above succession of the compaction process, most of the volume change of the body is done by that of the pore space, i.e., $\Delta V \fallingdotseq \Delta v$. In this case, by placing this relation into equation (6), we get r=1/n. Therefore, r increases as porosity decreases. Now porosity is 0.5 or 0.4 in stages 1 and 2, we have here 2.0 or 2.5 as value of r. The value reaches to 2.8 at porosity 0.35, approximately critical point from stage 2 to 3. If the things go on same in stages 3 and 4, constant r is further increasing up, e.g., 10.0 at porosity 0.1 and attains 100 at porosity 0.01. However, there should be the contact effect in stages 3 and 4, which means that in these stages the decrease of the change of the body volume is not entirely related to the pore, but partly attributed to the crushing and the deformation of the grains. Therefore it works as to decrease r. This effect becomes stronger as the porosity decreases.

If we take another extreme case that most of the total volume change is done by the contact effect, that is, $\Delta v=0$, we get r=0. Here, however, r can not be less than 1.0, because in equation (7), porosity and strength changes always in opposite direction and the right side of the equation should be always negative. Anyway, as a matter of calculation, r may decrease down by 1.0 in stages 3 and 4.

In fact, most rocks tested here belong to stages 3 and 4 from viewpoint of porosity. Therefore, constant r should increase in these stages, to satisfy the relation between equations (4) and (7). Because constant k will increase as mentioned above. We shall consider the value of r in stages 3 and 4 again. Taking a general form $\Delta v/\Delta V=m$, here m is an arbitrary coefficient, and by placing it into equation (5), we get r=m/n, instead of r=1/n. Now, in order that r increases further in stages 3 and 4, r should be more than 2.8, the value at porosity 0.35. So, by placing the figure of porosity n into the above formula, we know that m should be greater than 0.28 at porosity 0.1 and greater than 0.03 at porosity 0.01. Asuming that (1-m) may be an indication of the contact effect, it means that roughly estimating if the volume decrease by the contact effect is less than about 0.7 at porosity 0.1 and less than 0.97 at porosity 0.01, the value of r may always increase. It is considered resonable that in the initial and the midst of the recrystalline stage (stage 4) the ratio of the contact effect to the role of the pore spaces in the volume change would be not greater than 0.7 and 0.97 respectively. Therefore, these figures would be more than enough to conclude that (r-1) tends to increase up porosity decreases.

When the rocks fail with fractures, main fractures are preceded by the activity of microfractruing (Scholtz, 1970; Hoshino and Koide, 1970). This activity may open a number of minuite spaces in the rocks, and help to increase up constant r. Brace et al (1966) reported the dilatancy in the crystalline rocks of small porosity, which ranges in magnitude from 0.2 to 2.0 times the elastic volume changes. As a matter of fact, the increase of constant r in the rocks of small and medium porosity is possibly in a close relation to dilatancy.

Considering that constant b ranges from 2.14 to 0.81/kb in argillaceous rocks and from 1.40 to 0.36/kb in arenaceous rocks, and pressuming that (r-1) may be in order of 3.0 to 10.0 at small and medium porosity, constant k may be estimated roughly to be 3 to 10/kb in argillaceous rocks, and 3 to 30/kb in arenaceous rocks. This figures are about one-tenth of bulk modulus in argillaceous rocks and one-third to one-fifth in arenaceous rocks.

CONCLUSION

For porous clastic sedimentary rocks, porosity and strength have an empirical relation expressed by equation (1). This equation is well applicable for argillaceous rocks regardless the places of collection. For arenaceous rocks, the relation is proved according to each area, and the constants of equation (1) differs in areas. Probably the reason is that medimun grained rocks are influenced by tectonic history or sedimentary environments more than fine grianed rocks. The author is now conducting further experimentation on other various sedimentary basins, and would like to make another report on this problem.

Mechanism of the semi-logarithm relation is tentatively interpreted to be related to the equal-paced increase of both the consolidation of the texture by compaction process and the ratio of the pore spaces within the rocks. As a cause of the increase of the pore spaces dilatancy may play an important role.

ACKNOWLEDGMENTS

The author would like to express thanks to Prof. Hsu and the faculty of the Geological Institute of Swiss Federal Institute of Technology in Zurich, where he made an experimentation of the Swiss samples.

REFERENCES

Athy, L.F., Density, porosity and compaction of sedimentry rocks, Amer.Assoc.Petrol.Geol. Bull., 1-4, 1930, pp.1-24.

Brace, W.F. et al, Dilatancy in the fracture of crystalline rocks, Jour.Geophy.Res.,71-16, 1966, pp.3939-3953.

Dunn, D.E. et al, Porosity dependence and mechanism of brittle fracture in sandstones, Jour. Geophy.Res., 78-14, 1973, pp.2403-2417.

Handin, J., Strength and ductility, Handbook of Physical Constants, GSA Memoir 97, 1966, pp.223-290.

Hedberg, H.D., Gravitational compaction of clays and shales, Amer.Jour.Sci., 31, 1936, pp.241-287.

Hoshino, K. and Koide, H., Process of deformation of the sedimentary rocks, Proc.2nd Cong. ISRM, 2-13., 1970.

Hoshino, K. et al, Mechanical properties of the Japanese Tertiary sedimentary rocks under high confining pressure, Geol.Surv.Japan Report No.244, 1972, pp.1-200.

Nagumo, S., Compaction of sedimentary rocks - a consideration by the theory of porous media, Bull.Earthq.Res.Inst., 43, 1965, pp.339-348.

Scholz, C., The role of microfracturing in rock deformation, Proc.2nd Cong. ISRM, 2-8, 1970.

Weller, J.M., Compaction of sediments, Amer.Assoc. Petrol.Geol.Bull., 43-2, 1959, pp.273-310.

CHANGES IN THE P-WAVE VELOCITY WITH INCREASING INELASTIC DEFORMATION IN ROCK SPECIMENS UNDER COMPRESSION

CHANGEMENTS DE VITESSE DES ONDES-P EN FONCTION DE LA DÉFORMATION NON-ÉLASTIQUE PROGRESSIVE DANS DES ÉCHANTILLONS DES ROCHES SOUS COMPRESSION

SCHALLGESCHWINDIGKEITSÄNDERUNGEN ALS FUNKTION FORTSCHREITENDER DEFORMATION IN DRUCKVERSUCHEN AN GESTEINSPROBEN

F. RUMMEL
Institut für Geophysik
Ruhr-Universität Bochum
Bochum, West-Germany

Summary

Velocity changes of P-waves in specimens of Tennesse marble, Ruhr-sandstone and a Greek-marble were measured as a function of increasing axial compression throughout the complete stress-strain characteristic. The confining pressures ranged up to 1 kbar. Special attention has been paid to the relationship between the decrease of P-wave velocity and the dilatation in the pre-peak and post-failure range of the material. The test results indicate a significant decrease of P-wave velocities prior to the maximum load bearing capacity of the rock associated with the onset of microscopic failure. This effect is enhanced in the post-failure region, where the load bearing capacity decreases with increasing axial deformation. An analysis of the laboratory tests suggests that a quantitative relationship between the degree of rock disintegration and the velocity of elastic waves exists which may be used in determinating the load bearing capacity of broken rock insitusuch as the "plastic" zones around underground openings or to determine changes of the mechanical properties of rocks prior to rock burst and earthquakes by seismic measurements.

Zusammenfassung

Gesteinsproben von Tennessee Kalkstein, Ruhrsandstein und einem griechischen Marmor wurden in axialer Richtung bei Druckversuchen bis 1 kbar Manteldruck durchschallt. Die Geschwindigkeitsänderungen der P-Wellen wurden über den "vollständigen" Spannungs-Verformungs-Bereich als Funktion zunehmender axialer Verformung bestimmt. Besonderes Interesse galt dem Zusammenhang zwischen der Abnahme der P-Wellengeschwindigkeit und der Volumenzunahme (Dilatanz) der Proben im Bereich des einsetzenden Bruchs und im "Post-Failure" Bereich.
Die Meßergebnisse zeigen, daß die Geschwindigkeit elastischer Wellen vor Erreichen der maximalen Druckspannung bereits infolge des Auftretens von Mikrorissen nach einer Zunahme während der rein elastischen Deformation abnimmt. Dieser Effekt wird in verstärktem Maße im Post-Failure Bereich beobachtet, in dem die kritische Bruchspannung mit zunehmender axialer Deformation stark abnimmt. Eine Analyse der Labormessungen bestätigt das Bestehen eines quantitativen Zusammenhangs zwischen dem Grad der Strukturauflockerung durch den progressiven Bruch und der Geschwindigkeit elastischer Wellen. Diese Beziehung kann in der Zukunft in der Praxis verwendet werden, um durch Geschwindigkeitsmessungen Aussagen über den Grad der Auflockerung des Gesteins um unterirdische Hohlräume und über die Restfestigkeit von gebrochenem Gestein, wie es in Auflockerungszonen vorliegt, abzugeben. Von Bedeutung ist ebenfalls die seismische Bestimmung von Veränderungen in den mechanischen Eigenschaften des Gesteins vor Gebirgsschlägen und Erdbeben.

Résumé

On à measuré les changements de vitesse sonique des ondes-p dans des spécimens des roches suivantes: marbre du Tennessee, grès de la Ruhr, marbre grec en exercant une compression axiale allant jusqu'a 1 kbar de compression environnante. Un intérêt spécial a été parté à la relation existant entre le ralentissement des ondes-p et la dilatation des échantillons au début de leur désintégration et après leur rupture. Les résultats de cet experiment montrent que - après une certaine accélération au moment de la déformation purement élastique - la vitesse des ondes élastiques diminue déjà même avant que la tension maximale de compression soit atteinte. Ceci est dû à l'apparition des micro-fissures. Cet effet a été surtout constaté après la rupture, où la tension de rupture diminue considérablement une déformation axiale accroissante. L'analyse de ces mesures au laboratoire confirme qu'il existe une relation quantitative entre le degré de désintégration progressive des roches et la vitesse des ondes élastiques. Cette relation pourra dèsormais etre utile pour défenir le degré de désintégration rocheuse aux zones plastiques se trouvant autour des cavités suterraines et pour défenir aussi la consistance restante des roches fissurées aux zones meublies. De même on pourra déterminer par mesures simiques les changements des qualités méchaniques dans les roches avant les chutes de pierres en montage et les trémblement de terre.

1. INTRODUCTION

It is commonly known that rock specimens under dry conditions in laboratory compression tests show an increase in velocity of elastic waves with the load applied. This is partly due to the closure of pre-existing cracks in the rock within the elastic range of the stress-strain characteristic. For most rocks the increase in velocity is within a few per cent depending on the rock material, its original pore or crack volume and the confining pressure. The effect has been used in practice in attempting to determinate changes of the tectonic stress field around fault zones (EISLER 1969) or changes of the environmental stress field around underground structures due to blasting and excavating operations (DE FAZIO 1970) by seismic velocity measurements.

Zones of broken or partly disintegrated rock such as the material in fault zones or in "plastic" zones surrounding underground openings are often characterized by extremely low seismic velocities when compared with the undisturbed and unfractured rock mass. This indicates a decrease in velocity of elastic waves when the rock is stressed beyond its maximum load bearing capacity where continuous deformation is associated with progressive fracturing of the rock matrix.

Similarly a significant decrease in the ratio t_s/t_p of the travel times of shear waves to compressional waves and also an increase in t_p prior to earthquakes was reported for various earthquake regions (SAVARENSKY 1968, GEMENOV 1969, WHITHCOMB et al. 1973, AGGARWAL et al. 1973, SCHOLZ et al. 1973). The travel times are related to the reference basis of seismic stations within these regions. This observation suggests that the mechanical properties of the rock in the zones affected by the change in the stress field prior to an earthquake may vary with time. Assuming that t_s/t_p is proportional to v_p/v_s, where v_p and v_s are the spacial average velocities of the compressional and shear waves within these areas, and considering laboratory measurements of dilatancy of rocks during progressive failure it may be concluded that the decrease of v_p/v_s and also the decrease of v_p in situ are caused by localized progressive failure prior to the earthquake, associated also by a significant dilation of the rock material.

Only recently it was possible by the development of "stiff" and servo-controlled testing machines to observe changes in physical properties of rock specimens in laboratory tests during the complete stress-strain characteristic of a rock.

Here changes of the velocity of compressional waves in Tennessee marble, Ruhr-sandstone and Greek marble specimens during progressive deformation in laboratory compression tests will be reported. Confining pressure up to 1 Kb were used. Measurement of the volume changes associated with progressive failure of the Ruhr-sandstone and the Greek marble specimens have been performed throughout the complete stress-strain range and are more extensively reported by RUMMEL (1973).

2. DESCRIPTION OF ROCK SPECIMENS

2.1. Tennessee marble

The cylindrical specimens of the Tennessee marble were 2 inches in diameter and 4 inches long. They were drilled from large blocks of the coarse pink type Class I (WAWERSIK 1968) Tennessee marble which is quarried from the Holston phase of Chickamanga limestone near Knoxville, Tennessee, USA. The rock can be described as a low porosity (0.2 per cent), coarse-grained, recrystallized, fossiliferous limestone of 95 per cent calcite content in the form of crinoid fragments, ooids and clear calcite crystals. A petrographical description was presented by FRIEDMAN (1970) and HUDSON et al. (1972). Complete stress-strain curves of this rock were reported by WAWERSIK (1968) and RUMMEL and FAIRHURST (1970). The uni-axial compressive strength was about 16000 psi (1,1 Kb). The P-wave velocity of the unstressed rock specimens determined by the ultrasonic method was about 5,8 km/sec (all P-wave velocities reported in the following are related to ultrasonic measurements).

2.2. Ruhr-sandstone

Specimens of Ruhr-sandstone used were 6 cm long and 3 cm in diameter and were drilled perpendicular to the bedding plane. The rock is quarried at Witten-Annen/Ruhr-district, Germany. The rock material can be described as medium to fine grained, extremely homogeneous, and isotropic with respect to its mechanical properties. The porosity was determined varying within 2 to 3 percent, the permeability was about 5 milli-darcy. The uni-axial compressive strength σ_{1max} is about 1,5 Kb and increase approximately linearly with the confining pressure σ_3 (Fig. 1). Stress-strain curves both for the direction parallel and perpendicular to the applied axial stress σ_1 are presented as a function of the confining pressure σ_3 in Fig. 2. The P-wave velocity of the unstressed rock specimens was 4.0 km/sec.

2.3. Greek marble

The marble originates from NE Greece. The material is a coarse-grained, almost pure calcite marble with a medium grain size around 3 mm. The microscopic analysis reveals extensive inter- and intra-crystallive microfractures which are predominantly parallel to a significant s-structure. Specimens of 6 cm length and 3 cm diameter were drilled perpendicular to the s-planes. Uniaxial compressive strength of the specimens was approximately 550 bars. The variation of the maximum load bearing capacity with respect to the confining pressure σ_3 is given in Fig. 3. Complete stress-strain curves again for both the directions parallel and perpendicular to the applied axial stress σ_1 are shown in Fig. 4. The average P-wave velocity of the unstressed specimens was determined as 5.8 km/sec.

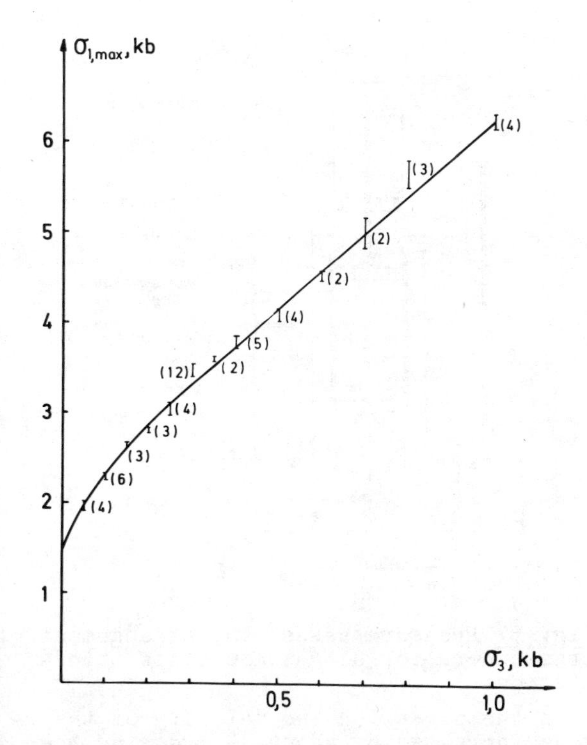

Fig. 1. Compressive strength $\sigma_{1,max}$ as a function of the confining pressure σ_3 for Ruhr-sandstone (I standard deviation, ( ) number of specimens tested).

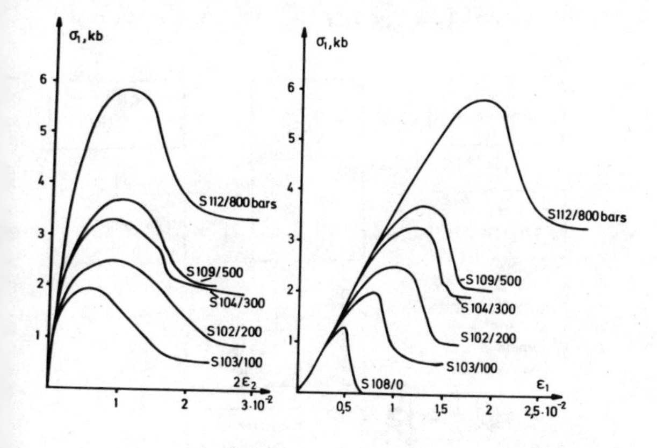

Fig. 2. Complete stress-strain curves for both the axial (ε_1) and lateral (ε_2) direction at various constant confining pressures σ_3 for Ruhr-sandstone (S 112/800 bars: Specimen number and confining pressure σ_3)

3. APPARATUS

3.1. Loading apparatus

The uni-axial compression tests for the velocity measurements on Tennessee marble specimens were carried out using the stiff loading system of the University of Minnesota with a 8,8 · 10^6 pounds per inch (ca. 1,6 · 10^6 kp · cm $^{-1}$) natural unloading stiffness (WAWERSIK 1968). The axial load in the compression test on Ruhr-sandstone and the Greek marble was generated by a 100-tons servo-controlled electro-hydraulic loading system at the Ruhr-University described by RUMMEL (1971, 1973). The axial displacement of the specimen which was measured by a double-cantilever, strain gauge and inductive gauge type system was chosen to generate the electric feedback signal.

The pressure vessel used for the compression test under constant confining pressure is designed for a maximum pressure of 4 Kb. By keeping constant the confining pressure by a second servo-system to within 0,2 per cent of the applied pressure it was also possible to monitor directly the increase in the cross-sectional area of the specimen perpendicular to the specimen axis. This increase of the cross-sectional area is due to elastic lateral expansion as well as to the progressive disintegration of the rock matrix during increasing axial compression. A detailed description of the pressure vessel and the lateral displacement monitoring system is presented by RUMMEL (1973). The specimens were jacketed with a 1.5-inch diameter polyolefin heat shrinkable tubing (Thermofit RNF-100, Raychem Company).

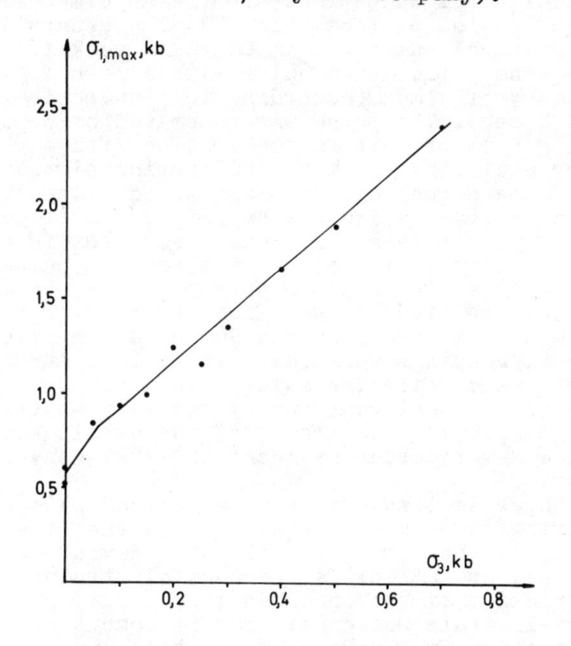

Fig. 3. Compressive strength $\sigma_{1,max}$ of Greek marble as a function of the confining pressure σ_3.

3.2. Velocity measurement instrumentation and procedure

The velocities of P-waves parallel to the specimen axis are measured by the high frequency ultrasonic pulse transmission technique using separate transducers for generating and receiving pulses. The system measures the transit time required for a elastic disturbance initiated at one end plane of the specimen to transverse the specimen to a pulse detector at the opposing end. Piezoelectric barium-titanate disc typ transducers are used as transmitter and receiver, acting in their axial and radial direction. They are located in the upper

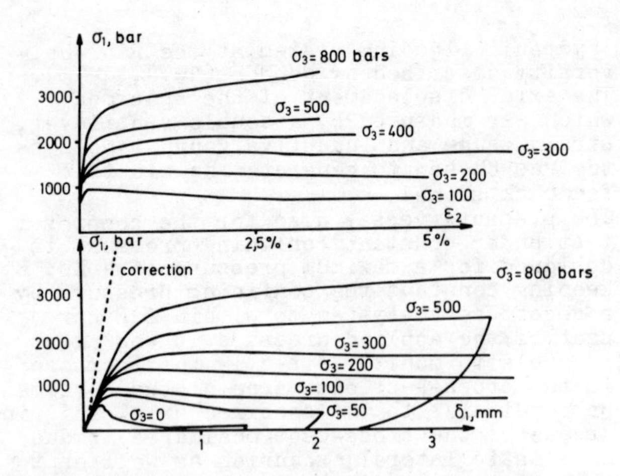

Fig. 4. Complete stress-strain curves for both the axial (ε_1) and lateral (ε_2) direction at various constant confining pressures σ_3 for Greek marble ($\varepsilon_1 \approx \delta_1/60$ mm).

and lower piston and springloaded to ensure a safe contact against 5 mm thick, hardened steel discs which separate the specimen from the loading pistons (Fig. 5). The generating electrical pulse was a 300 Volts peak to peak amplitude sine pulse with a main frequency of 1 MHz (according to a pulse length of 1 sec). The pulse was generated by a pulse generator unit in combination with a power amplifier. Both the generating signal and the signal of the transmitted pulse from the receiver which was amplified and filtered were displayed on a dual beam oscilloscope. Amplification of the transmitted pulse was varied in such a manner that the peak-to -peak amplitude of the first arrival of the signal remained constant during a complete test. Readings were taken at certain strain intervals while the axial strain of the specimen was kept constant by the servo-system, by displaying the traces of the oscilloscope on a x-y-recorder by means of a CRT-converter.

Changes in travel time were defined by measuring the time interval between the first peak of the first arrivals at a given strain and at initial zero-axial strain. Variation of the specimen length during axial strain was considered in computing the variation in P-wave velocities.

Both the pressure vessel arrangement and a block diagram of the ultrasonic pulse measurement system are presented in Fig. 5 and Fig. 6.

4. RESULTS

4.1. Tennessee Marble

Preliminary results have been obtained during uni-axial compression tests on cylindrical specimens of Tennessee Marble. Both the P-velocities parallel and perpendicular to the load axis were measured during increasing compressive axial deformation (For the velocity measurements perpendicular to the specimen axis the same apparatus was used with the only modification, that the transducers were clamped to the specimen cylinder surface at opposite locations). In

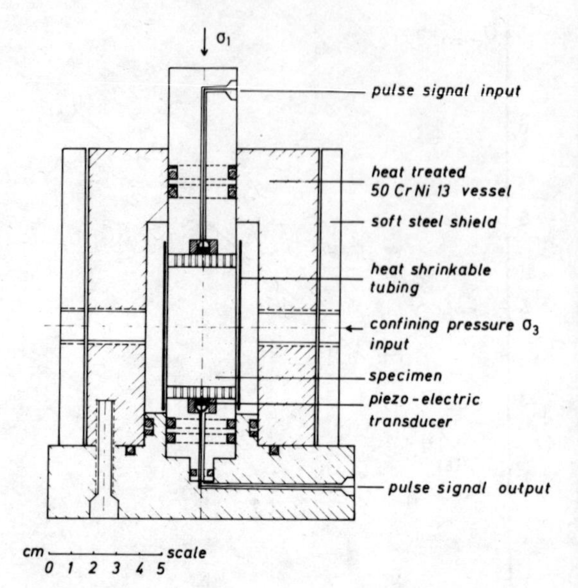

Fig. 5. Pressure vessel and arrangement of transducers for ultrasonic pulse transmission.

both the direction the velocity of the P-wave increased by about 10 % during the elastic stress-strain range due to the closure of pre-existing cracks. The onset of inelastic deformation is characterized by a following decrease in velocity with further deformation (Fig. 7). The decrease

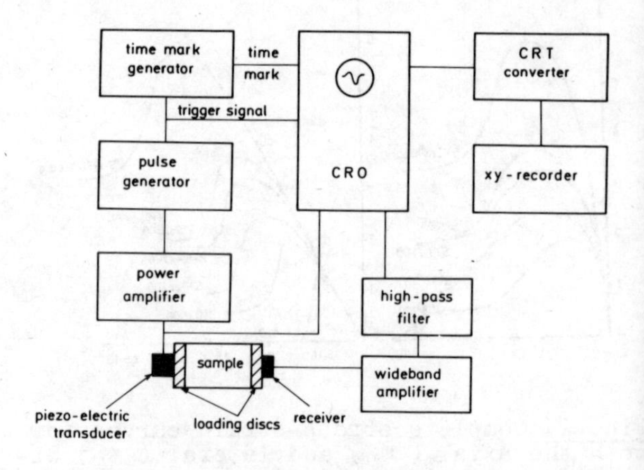

Fig. 6. Block diagram of the ultrasonic pulse transmission measurement system.

in velocity is significant in the lateral direction and is irreversible when unloading the specimen. The variation in velocity during the complete stress-strain range from initial load application to complete disintegration of the specimen occurs continuously. In particular, the maximum load bearing capacity (strength) is not characterized by any significant change in velocity. This is in agreement with the microscopic observations of loaded specimens

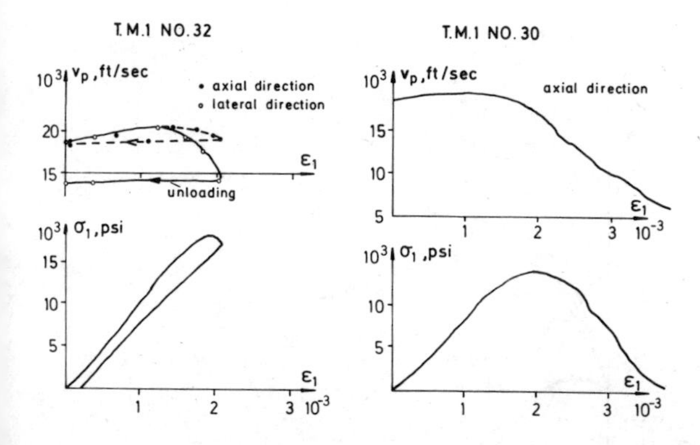

Fig. 7. Stress-strain (σ_1 - ε_1) curve for Tennessee marble and the change in P-wave velocity v_p as a function of axial deformation ε_1. (Pulse transmission parallel (a) and perpendicular (b) to the specimen axis).

reported by WAWERSIK (1968) and RUMMEL and FAIRHURST (1970), which show that the complete stress strain behaviour may be described as a continuous progressive structural break-down process. The marked decrease in velocity in the lateral direction leads to the assumption that under uni-axial compressive load conditions the structural change in the rock is caused by the formation of micro-cracks oriented predominantly parallel to the direction of the applied load.

4.2. Ruhr-sandstone

Velocity measurements in the Ruhr-sandstone specimens were only performed in the axial direction. Although the porosity of the extremely homogeneous sandstone was low (porosity about 3 %) the velocity was very much dependent on the confining pressures applied. The relative velocity increase as a function of the quasi-hydrostatic pressure ($\sigma_1 = \sigma_3$) is plotted in Fig. 8 up to a

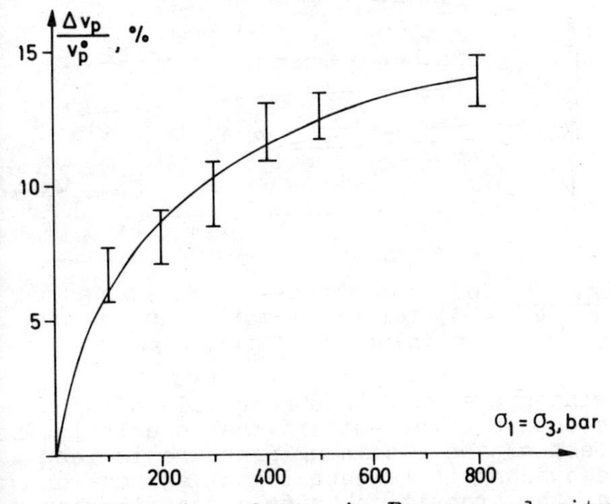

Fig. 8. Relative change in P-wave velocity, $\Delta v_p/v_p^o$, with hydrostatic pressure ($\sigma_1 = \sigma_3$) for Ruhr-sandstone. v_p^o is the P-wave velocity of the unstressed specimen (Istandard deviations).

pressure of 800 bars. The values of the velocity increase, Δv_p for different pressures are related to the velocity, v_p^o, measured at zero pressure. The curve indicates a rapid increase in velocity of about 10 per cent for pressures up to 300 bars. The increase is less significant for the higher pressures considered. In Fig. 9 the change in P-wave velocity with increasing axial deformation ε_1 under constant confining pressures σ_3 up to 800 bars is shown. The

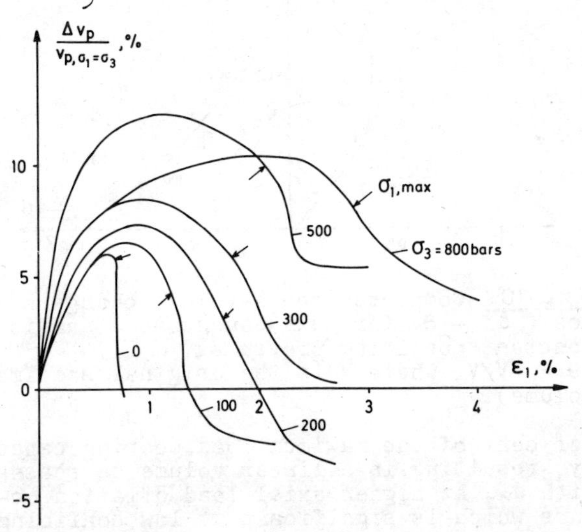

Fig. 9. Relative change in P-wave velocity, $\Delta v_p/(v_p)\ \sigma_1 = \sigma_3$ with increasing axial deformation, ε_1, at various constant confining pressures, σ_3 for Ruhr-sandstone. v_p, $\sigma_1 = \sigma_3$ is the P-wave velocity at the hydrostatic stress condition for various confining pressures, σ_3.

changes in velocity are related to the velocity observed for the hydrostatic stress condition before the test program (constant axial strain rate) was started. The curves indicate that the drop in P-wave velocity begins after a considerable initial increase at deformations well before the maximum load bearing capability (arrows in Fig. 9) of the rock is reached. The drop in velocity is extremely large for specimens subjected to zero or low confining pressures. When the residual strength is reached after microscopic failure along one or two conjugate shear planes had occured in tests at moderate or high confining pressure the velocity is approximately constant with further deformation.

For the interpretation of this effect it is interesting to compare the results of dilation measurements, which were conducted simultaneously on the specimens. The values of the relative change in volume ($\Theta = \Delta V/V$, where ΔV is the volume increase and V is the volume of the original specimen), were calculated from the stress-strain curves for axial and lateral deformation. The(σ_1, Θ)-curves (Fig. 10) show that Ruhr-sandstone behaves elastically for stresses below 70

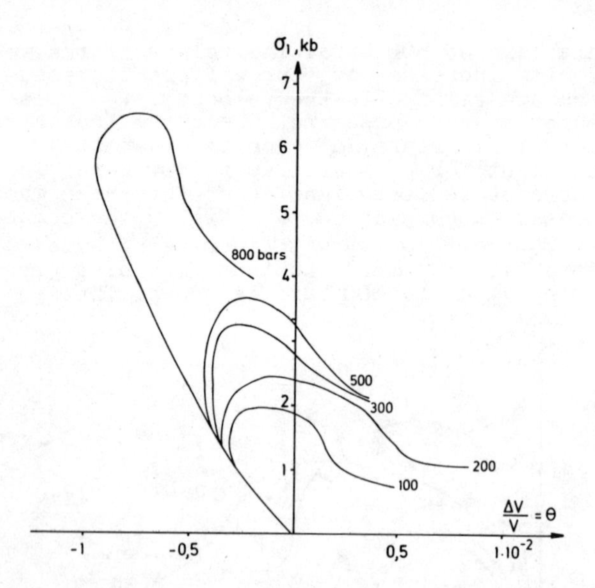

Fig. 10. Complete stress-volume change curves ($\sigma_1 - \Theta$) for Ruhr-sandstone at various constant confining pressures, σ_3.
($\Theta = \Delta V/V$, where V is the original specimen volume).

per cent of the maximum load bearing capacity, resulting in a linear volume decrease with σ_1. At higher axial load dilation occurs which is significant at low confining pressures and leading to an effective volume increase in the post-failure region. Dilation is much less at a confining pressure of 800 bars and is only dominant in the prepeak region. After shear failure along a single shear plane has been initiated the volume increases linearly with the decrease of the load bearing capacity at continuous axial displacement.

4.3. Greek marble

Stress strain curves for the axial direction and changes in P-wave velocity as a function of the axial deformation obtained for specimens of Greek marble subjected to different confining pressures are shown in Fig. 11. The results show that the increase in velocity within the "elastic" stress-strain range is small compared to the following velocity decrease during further axial deformation. Under uni-axial condition the velocity decreases by 30 percent during the descending portion of the stress-strain curve indicating a complete disintegration of the rock matrix. At high confining pressures the velocity decrease is still significant although the stress-strain curves indicate a typical ductile behaviour.
In all cases the decrease in velocity occurs extremely continuous with increasing axial deformation. The test results are also remarkably reproducible in respect to their deformation-velocity features.
The different behaviour of the Greek marble is indicated by the results of dilation measurements (Fig. 12). The curves show that the specimen volume increases almost from the begin of load application, demonstrating

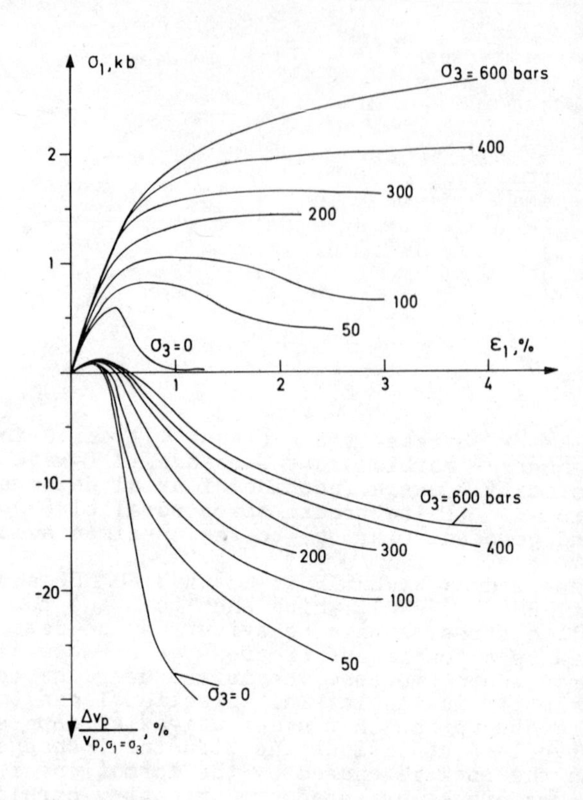

Fig. 11. Relative change in P-wave velocity with increasing axial deformation, ε_1, at various constant confining pressures, σ_3 and the associated axial stress-strain curves for Greek marble.

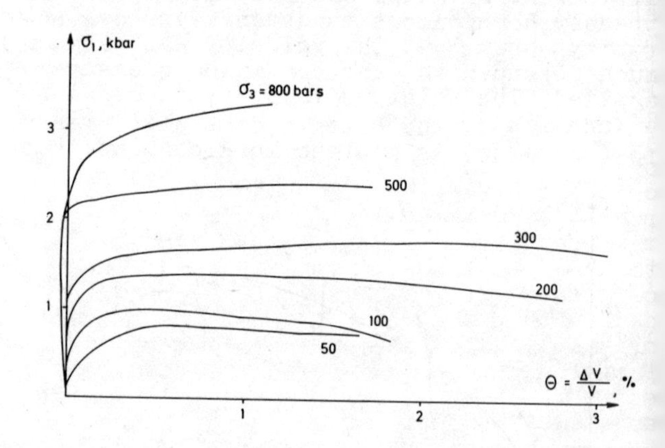

Fig. 12. Complete stress-volume change curves ($\sigma_1 - \Theta$) for Greek marble at various constant confining pressures, σ_3.

disintegration of this material throughout the entire stress-strain characteristic. The effect of the confining pressure is less predominant in respect to the assumption that the transition brittle-ductile should be characterized by a marked decrease in dilation. Therefore it must be concluded that intra-crystalline shear deformationsin marbl become dominant at much higher confining pressures (EDMUND and PATERSON, 1972). The results of the velocity measurement confirm the assumption of a kataclastic deformation at confining pressures in the range of σ_3 = 800 bars.

5. CONCLUSIONS

The velocity measurements on the three different rocks show that the P-wave velocity is extremely sensitive to structural changes in the material. The velocity increase within the elastic stress-strain region due to the elastic compression is, except for the porous Ruhr-sandstone, only within few per cents. The velocity decreases markedly well before the maximum load bearing capacity of the rock is reached. The onset of this velocity decrease characterizes the onset of localized crack initiation which is also indicated by the onset of dilation. The continuous decrease in velocity with increasing deformation throughout the complete stress-strain curve suggests the possibility to characterize the state of deformation or the state of disintegration, in particular in the post-failure region, in terms of velocity data.

Rock masses within fault zones or around underground openings can be thought of as being in a analoguous situation, i. e. its load bearing capacity has been exceeded. Therefore in-situ measurement of velocities by seismic methods can give an idea of the state of deformation or fracture as well as of the residual existing load bearing capacity of the material at any particular point in the rock mass, if laboratory measurements on this material are taken into consideration. In this respect the prediction of the state of in-situ rock obtained by seismic measurements could be a most economic aid in mining and tunnelling.

If the results of the laboratory investigations concerning the decrease in velocity as well as dilation due to failure in rock specimens are transferred to in-situ rock conditions, as we find them in earthquake regions, the observed changes in travel times in these areas prior to earthquakes lead to the conclusion, that due to the action of tectonic stresses cracks are being opened in the material. This will reduce the original fluid pressure existing in the material and thus increase the normal stresses and the shear strength of the material, an effect commonly known as "dilatancy hardening". The further process leading to the final stage in the development of the earthquake is described by WHITCOMB et al. (1973). Here only the initial stage in this development, the stage of dilatancy hardening is considered, where extensive fracturing leads to a decrease in velocity. Since, as WHITCOMB et al. mention, the velocity of S-waves is only little influenced by this process, in situ measurement of a change in the P-wave velocities may allow to define this initial stage in the development of an earthquake in certain regions and also, considering the laboratory measurements, could give a rough approximation of the state of deformation in these focal areas.

****

LITERATURE

Aggarwal, Y.P., L.R. Sykes, J. Armbruster and M.L. Sbar, 1973, Premonitory changes in seismic velocities and prediction of earthquakes, Nature, 241, 101-104.

De Fazio, T.L.,1970, High precision in-situ measurements of seismic phase velocity at 500 cps. PhD-Thesis, MIT.

Edmund, J.M. and M.S. Paterson,1972, Volume changes during compression of rocks at high pressure. Int. J. Rock Mech. Min. Sci., 9, 161-182.

Eisler, J.D., 1969, Investigation of a method for determining stress accumulation at depth, Bull. Seism. Soc. Amer., 59 (1), 43-58.

Friedmann, M.,Pers. comm., 1970.

Hudson, J.A., F.T. Brown and F. Rummel, 1972, The controlled failure of rock discs and rings loaded in diametral compression, Int. J. Rock Mech. Min.Sci., 9, 241-248.

Rummel, F.and C. Fairhurst, 1970, Determination of the post-failure behaviour of brittle rock using a servo-controlled testing machine, Rock Mech. 2, 189-204.

Rummel, F., 1971, Uni-axial compression tests on right angular rock specimens with central holes, Symp. Int. Soc.Rock Mech., Nancy, Oct. 1971; in press.

Rummel, F., 1973, Dilatation von Ruhrsandstein- und Marmorproben bei konstantem Manteldrücken bis 1 kb, SFB 77, Jahresbericht 1972, 74-94 , Karlsruhe.

Savarensky, F.F., 1968, On the prediction of earthquakes, Tectonophysics, 6(1), 17-27.

Scholz, C.H., L.R. Sykes, Y.P. Aggerwal, 1973, The physical basis for earthquake prediction. Lamont Geol. Obs. Contr. No. 1939.

Semenov, A.M., 1969, Variations in the travel time of transverse and longitudinal waves before violent earthquakes, Izv., Bull. Acad. Sci., USSR, Physics of Solid Earth, 3, 245-248.

Wawersik, W.R., 1968, Detailed analysis of rock fracture in laboratory compression tests. PhD-thesis, Univ. of Minn.

Whitcomb, J.H., J.D. Garmany and D.L. Anderson, 1973, Earthquake prediction: Variation of seismic velocities before the Son Andreas Earthquake, Sci., 180 (4086), 632-635.

SOME PERMANENT STRUCTURAL CHANGES IN ROCKS DUE TO PRESSURE AND TEMPERATURE

EFFETS PERMANENTS DE LA TEMPERATURE ET DE LA PRESSION SUR LA STRUCTURE DES ROCHES

EINIGE BESTÄNDIGE STRUKTURELLE VERÄNDERUNGEN IN FELSEN DURCH DRUCK UND TEMPERATUR

E. SPRUNT W.F. BRACE

Department of Earth and Planetary Sciences

Massachusetts Institute of Technology

Cambridge, Mass.

U.S.A.

Summary

Temperature to 400°C and confining pressure to 10 kbar produced permanent changes in the pore structure of rocks, as observed with the scanning electron microscope for ion-thinned sections. Confining pressure by itself produced changes starting at a pressure which depended on porosity; for Katahdin granite, about 0.5 kbar was required, for Westerly granite 1 kbar. For diabase, no changes were detected to 5 kbar. For granite, pressure collapsed tiny bridges between nearby low aspect ratio cavities, and enlarged some pores. These effects suggest that certain crack-dependent properties of rocks may depend slightly on pressure history; some experience with electrical conductivity bears this out. Temperature by itself caused fairly extensive cracking, particularly along grain boundaries. 5 kbar pressure suppressed the cracking in granite that would normally occur at 400°, 1 bar pressure

Résumé

L'étude de certaines roches en surfaces amincies par bombardement ionique a permis d'observer la structure des microcavités internes, et d'en étudier les modifications permanentes sous l'effet de la température (jusqu'à 400°C) et de la pression (jusqu'à 10 kbars). Les effets de la pression de confinement (seule) débutent à une pression qui varie avec la porosité; pour le granit de Katahdin, cette pression est d'environ 0.5 kbars, pour le granit de Westerly, 1 kbar. Pour une diabase, 5 kb n'ont pas d'effet décelable. Pour le granit, la pression détruit les minuscules "ponts" qu'on observe entre cavités de petit rapport dimensionnel, et élargit quelques pores. Ces effets suggèrent que les propriétés des roches dépendant de la fissuration peuvent varier avec l'histoire de la pression, point de vue que confirment certaines experiences de conductivité électrique. La temperature (seule), engendre une fissuration assez importante, surtout aux frontières des grains. Mais pour le granit, une pression de 5 kbars supprime la fissuration que produiraient normalement 400°C.

Zusammenfassung

Eine Temperatur bis zu 400°C und ein Druck bis 10 kbar verursachten bestaendige Veraenderungen in der Porenstruktur von Felsen wie mit dem Elektronen-Mikroskop fuer ionengesetzte Schichten beobachtet wurden. Ein Druck allein verursachte Veraenderungen, die bei einem Druck, der von Porositaet abhaengt, anfingen; fuer Katadhin Granit, zirka 0.5 kbar wurde benoetigt, fuer Westerly Granit, 1 kbar. Fuer Diabas wurden bis zu 5 kbar keine Veraenderungen beobachtet. Bei Granit, zerstoerte der Druck winzige Bruecken zwischen naheliegenden Hohlraeumen und vergroesserte einige Poren. Diese Effekte weisen darauf hin, dass einige rissabhaengige Eigenheiten von Felsen etwas von deren Druckgeschichte abhaengen; Einige Versuche mit elektrischer Konduktivitaet fuehren darauf hin. Die Temperatur allein verursachte weitgehende Risse, besonders laenglich der Kornbegrenzungen. Ein 5 kbar Druck unterdrueckte Risse in Granit, die normalerweise bei 400°C (1 kbar Druck) erscheinen wuerden.

INTRODUCTION

Uniform pressure and temperature changes do not cause structural changes in homogeneous crystals unless the field of thermodynamic stability is exceeded. In contrast, rocks, which are polycrystalline aggregates, often become altered as pressure and particularly temperature are cycled. Rayleigh [1934] noted the loosening of the grain structure of a marble following temperature cycling. Cycling to 1000°C drastically lowered sound velocity in granite, norite, gabbro and diabase [Ide, 1937; Barbish and Gardner, 1969]; the effect was believed due to open cracks caused by thermal stress. Pressure of several kilobars applied during thermal cycling apparently suppressed cracking [Birch and Bancroft, 1940; Birch, 1943; Brace, 1965a]. Structural changes due to pressure alone have not been observed directly, at least for rocks with porosity less than a percent Slight hysteresis [Birch and Bancroft, 1940

Birch, 1943] suggested to Birch and Bancroft that flow or fracture occurred near grain contacts with application of pressure.

With the scanning electron microscope we have directly observed the structural damage caused by a pressure or temperature cycle in rocks like granite. In this note, we show the size and location of new cracks induced by thermal stress, the more subtle changes caused by an application of pressure, and we test directly the widespread assumption [Ide, 1937; Birch, 1943; Brace, 1965a; Goetze, 1971] that pressure suppresses thermal cracking.

EXPERIMENTAL PROCEDURE

Cores about 1 cm in diameter were taken from small quarried blocks. One end of a sample about 1 cm long was machine-ground, then hand-ground, and, finally, ion-thinned, following the procedure in Brace et al [1972] and Sprunt and Brace [in press]. Ion-thinning exposes microcavities and other structural features in rocks as they exist in the interior of a specimen, uninfluenced by the damage usually caused by thin or polished sectioning.

Fields in samples of Westerly granite, Chelmsford granite, Katahdin II granite, and Maryland diabase [Sprunt and Brace, in press] were selected under the scanning electron microscope (SEM); the fields showed typical grain boundaries and microcavities in these rocks and were photographed before and after a pressure or temperature cycle. We chose this procedure although it had one disadvantage, namely that some damage could result from the exposure of our fields of study during cycling. The alternate method, namely preparation of a new ion-thinned section after each cycle, appeared to have an even greater drawback, in that delicate structural features could not be followed through successive cycles.

During a temperature cycle, to about 400°C, the specimen was heated and cooled in air at a rate of about 50°/hour. The gold-palladium coating on the surface [Brace et al, 1972] often became slightly spotted or locally detached during such a cycle.

For a room temperature cycle to high pressure a second identical sample was placed end-to-end against the study sample, separated by 0.05 mm thick lead foil. The foil eliminated any grain-to-grain crushing at points of contact. The sample assembly was then placed in a soft rubber jacket, the cylindrical ends of which were sealed by tight-fitting steel plugs. By placing the study specimen in contact with another identical sample, contact effects against the steel were avoided. Confining pressure was raised or lowered in the petroleum ether pressure medium at about 1 kb/min. The gold-palladium coating was somewhat torn, although still usable after a pressure cycle.

For a high pressure-high temperature cycle, the sample assembly was the same, except that annealed copper replaced the lead foil, and copper replaced the rubber jacket. Pressure was first raised at about 0.1 kb/min to 4 kbar, and then temperature to 300° at 20°/min. Pressure was then raised to 5 kbar and temperature to 400° at the same rates. After a wait of 5 minutes, temperature was first dropped at the same rate, and finally pressure.

This was intended to be an exploratory application of our recently developed ion-thinning-SEM techniques [Brace et al, 1972; Sprunt and Brace, in press], and only a few pressure and temperature cycles were made. Chelmsford granite was cycled to 0-400 (where the first number is pressure in kilobars, with room pressure zero, and the second number is temperature in °C, with room temperature zero). Westerly granite was cycled successively to .25-0, 1-0, 5-0, 5-400, and 0-400. The sequence of cycles was based on the desire to minimize structural damage during early cycles. Katahdin granite was cycled to .5-0, 1-0, 10-0, and 0-400. Diabase was cycled to .5-0, 1-0, and 5-0. The same fields were located in the SEM and photographed after each cycle.

OBSERVATIONS

We previously showed some effects of thermal cycling [Sprunt and Brace, in press], including the widening and lengthening of low aspect ratio cavities. For example, one feature in Chelmsford granite which was 0.6 to 1 μm wide enlarged to 1.5 μm after cycling to 0-400. Lengthening occurred by rupture of bridges between adjacent slots, or by extension of a single slot into intact material. New cracks were sharp-ended and nonbridged and were most commonly at grain boundaries; length was 10 to 30 μm.

Pressure by itself produced permanent effects starting at a pressure which depended on rock type. A .5-0 cycle broke bridges between individual cavities and caused tiny grains to separate in the medium-grained Katahdin granite (Figures 1, 2). Bridge collapse did not become pronounced in the fine-grained Westerly until a 1-0 cycle (Figure 3), and even up to 5-0 many low aspect ratio cavities remained unchanged (Figures 4, 5). A sequence of .5-0, 1-0, and 5-0 cycles produced no detectable changes in diabase.

The scale of the damage induced by a pressure cycle was small. Thus, in Figures 1, 2 and 3, crushing of bridges extended 2 to 3 μm, and flaking to perhaps 5 μm; the most conspicuous effect was the detachment of the 10 μm grain seen in Figure 2. Further minor effects of a pressure cycle included slight closure of low aspect ratio cavities

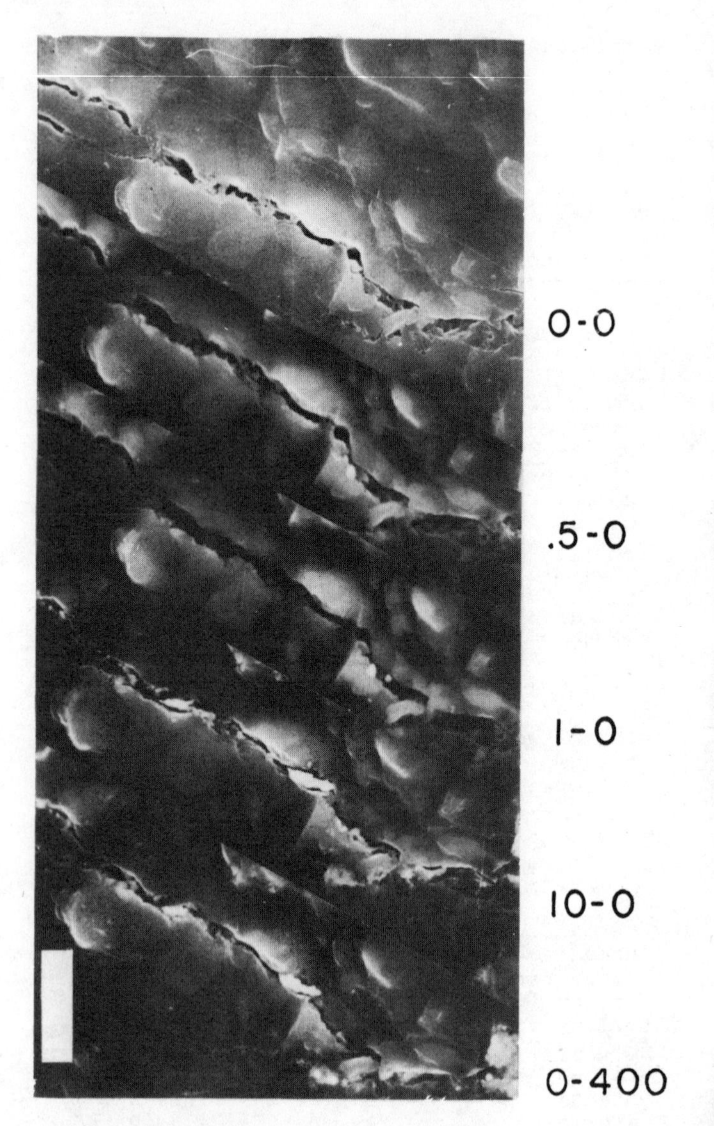

Fig. 1 Successive changes in cavities in Katahdin granite following pressure or temperature cycle (kbar-°C with room pressure and temperature called zero). Bar is 10 μm.

particularly at 5 to 10 kbar, for the Katahdin granite (Fig. 1). Some 10 μm or less high aspect ratio cavities, or pores, have slightly enlarged after exposure to 5 or 10 kbar.

The effects of combined pressure and temperature, 5-400 cycle, were only observed for Westerly granite. The structural changes included formation of a few 2 to 4 μm closed cracks emanating from old cavities (Figure 4) and slight widening of existing low aspect ratio cavities. These changes cannot be seen on the scale of Figure 5.

The final 0-400 temperature cycle for Westerly granite produced changes very

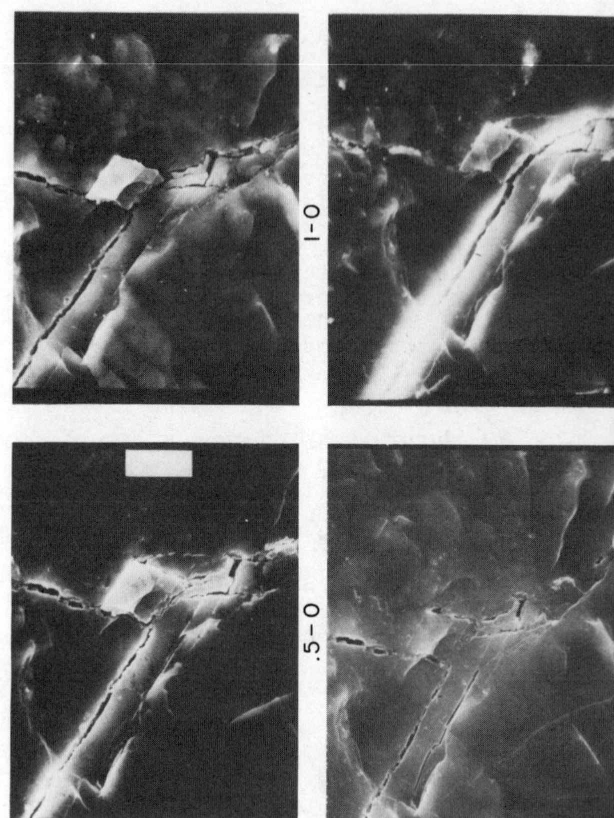

Fig. 2 Successive changes in cavities in Katahdin granite following pressure or temperature cycle (kbar-°C). Bar is 10 μm. Note detachment of rhomboid grain in center. Different shading among the photographs has no structural significance.

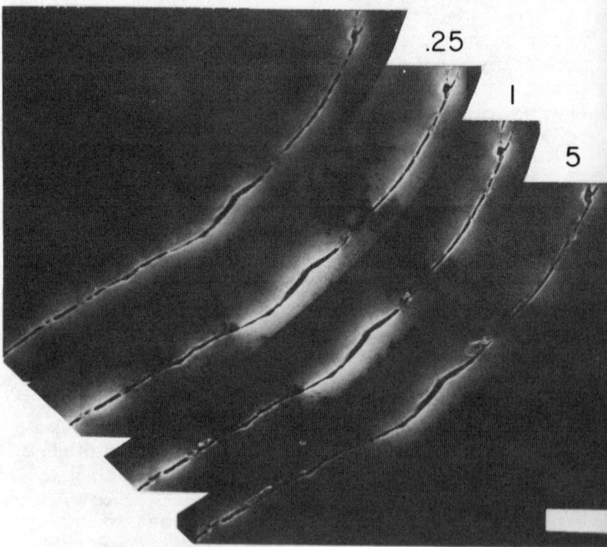

Fig. 3 Successive changes in cavities in Westerly granite following pressure cycle (kbar). Temperature was 0. Bar is 20 μm. The mottling in the lower three exposures has no structural significance.

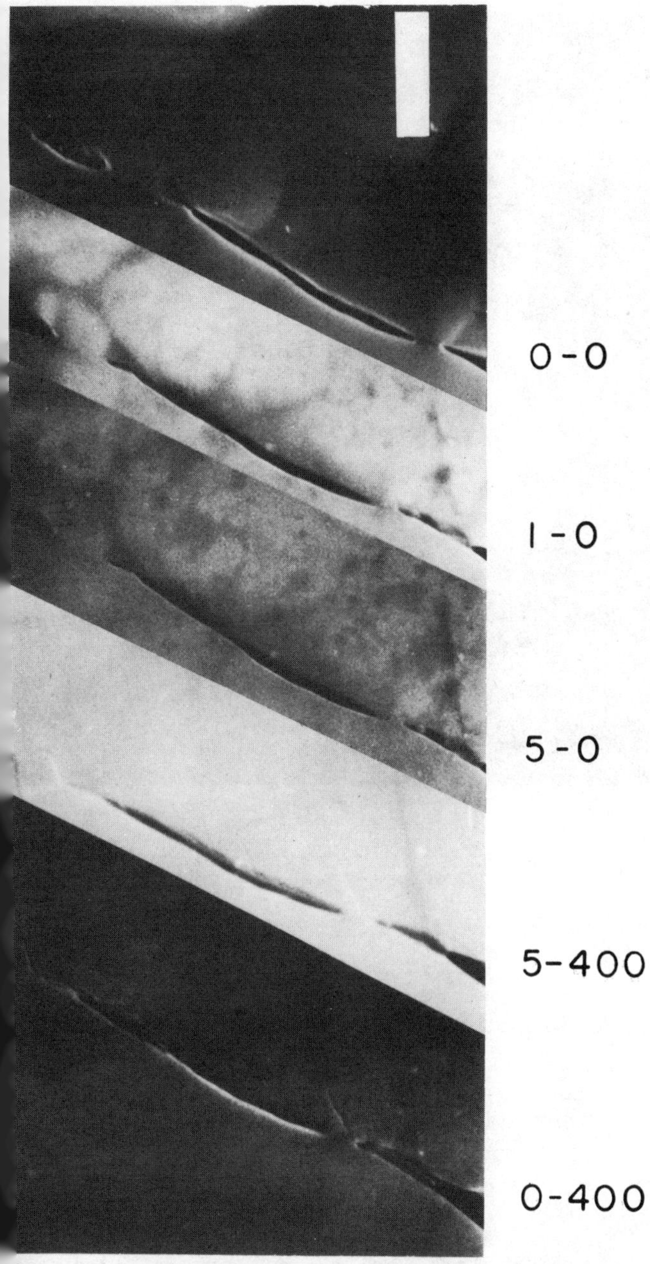

Fig. 4 Successive changes in cavities in Westerly granite following pressure or temperature cycle (kbar-°C). Bar is 5 μm.

similar to those noted above for Chelmsford granite. Fine existing cracks opened somewhat (Figure 4) and a number of new open cracks 10 to 40 μm long appeared along grain boundaries (Figure 5). A 0-400 cycle produced no detectable changes in Katahdin granite (Figures 1 and 2); apparently the previous pressure cycles had already joined the numerous grain boundary cavities into single long cracklike features.

DISCUSSION

Actually the bridge collapse, cracking, pore-widening and other structural changes we observed probably represent the maximum damage that could have occurred during these cycles. Some of this damage could have been caused by the metal foil which was pressed under high pressure against the surface we viewed. Perhaps the damage produced in the interior of a sample was less. In any event, the changes we observed in a pressure cycle seem relatively insignificant and quite local. Apparently the bridge collapse and flaking on the scale of a few μm represents the "flow or fracture" suggested by Birch and Bancroft [1940] on the basis of velocity measurements. Cracks due to a pressure cycle are very rare and quite small; we could have overlooked even smaller, closed cracks a μm or less in length.

The abundant new cracklike cavities due to a 0-400 cycle show strong preference for grain boundaries. These plus the widening of existing cavities in the grain boundaries are evidently responsible for the "grain loosening" first noted by Rayleigh [1934]. Comparison of fields such as in Figure 5 show that, roughly, structural changes in granite for temperature greatly exceed those for pressure, at least for the cycles chosen here; both are much less significant than the results we observed [Sprunt and Brace, in press] for mechanically stressed samples.

Also, for the particular cycle we chose, pressure tended to suppress the cracking that would normally accompany a temperature cycle. At the scale of Figure 5, the field after a 5-400 cycle was indistinguishable from that of the 5-0 cycle shown, but of course very different from that of the 0-400 cycle. The relation of pressure to temperature is more complex at the scale of an existing cavity such as in Figures 1 and 4. There, both tend to join shorter features into a single longer feature, pressure by crushing bridges, and temperature by pulling bridges apart. By contrast, pressure tends to narrow a slot-like cavity, whereas temperature tends to widen it.

All of these effects certainly depend on the magnitude of the pressure or temperature change as well as on mineralogy, and much careful work is needed to determine, for example, the minimum pressure needed to counter the effects of a particular temperature change. The calcite rocks would be a particularly interesting group to study, owing to the extreme thermal anisotropy of that mineral. Some empirical results are available [Ide, 1937; Brace, 1965b] which should be verified.

The structural changes we note here due to a pressure cycle of a kilobar or less could influence various rock properties. If bridges are crushed during a pressure cycle, then perhaps the effective aspect ratio and

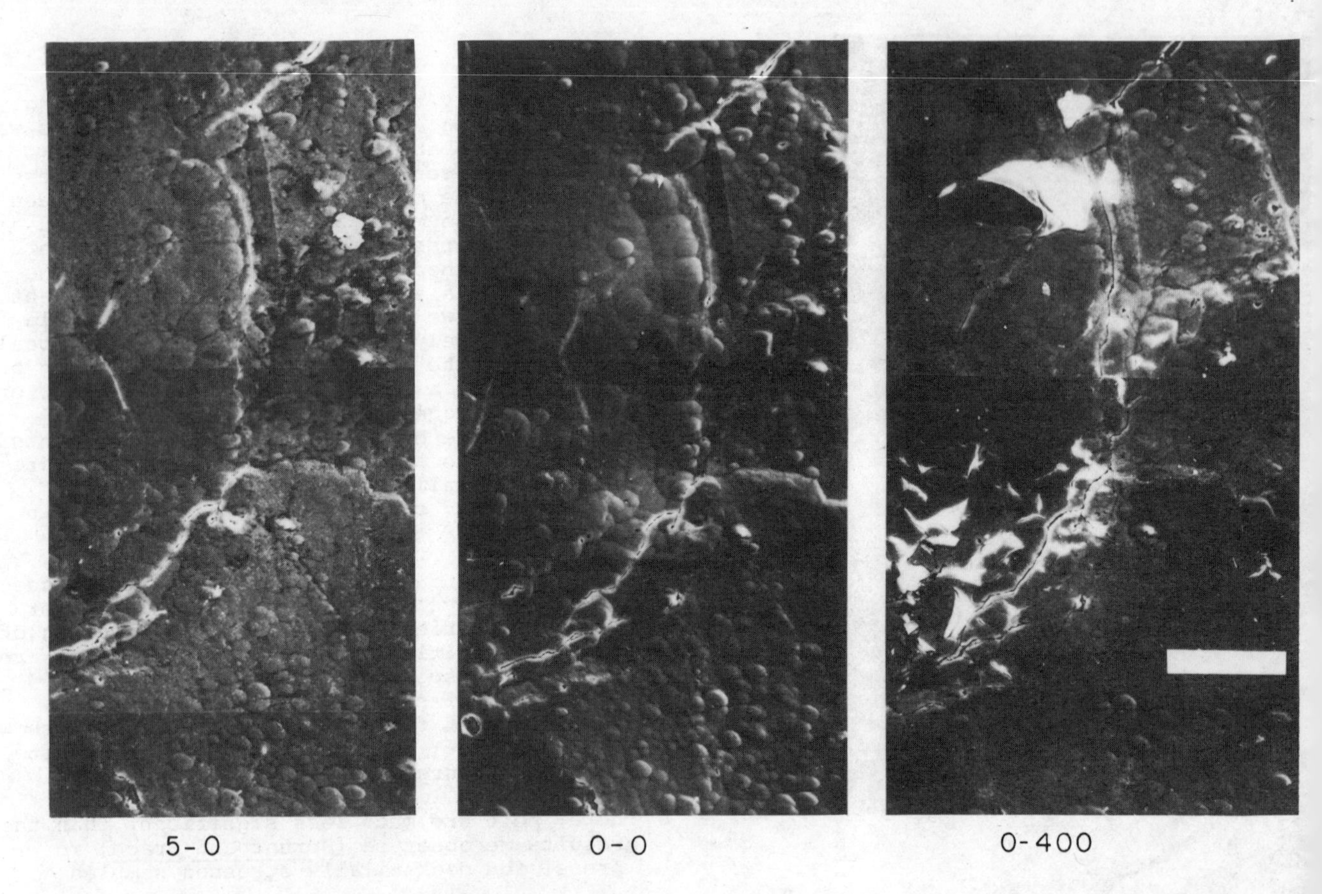

Fig. 5 Successive changes in cavities in Westerly granite following pressure or temperature cycle (kbar-°C). Bar is 100 μm. The bright white patches in the 0-400 exposure are tears in the gold-palladium foil and are unrelated to structural features in the underlying rock.

length of "cracks" in a rock become changed. Modulus or velocity might differ during successive pressure cycle [Sprunt and Brace, in press]. The usual pressure seasoning required for strain gauges may rule out their use to test this possibility.

The crushing of bridges and other local damage caused by pressure might tend to lower electrical resistivity of water-saturated rocks [Brace and Orange, 1968] because of the resulting increase in connectivity of pore space. Some measurements are available to test this possibility. In Figure 6 we give the changes which have been observed in the course of various studies [Brace and Orange, 1968; Stesky and Brace, 1973; Mitchell and Brace, 1973] as confining pressure was cycled. Granite was slightly more resistive on the second cycle, whereas gabbro, basalt and diabase were more conductive. The initial curvature for gabbro and basalt suggest that crack porosity had increased slightly as a result of a pressure cycle of about 6 kbar; this would be the effect predicted by our SEM observations. The changes shown for the granite and diabase in Figure 6 appear to be independent of pressure and are, thus, unlikely to be due to new cracking or an effective lengthening of old cracks. The reason for the changes is unknown; for the granite they are within the reproducibility typical of crystalline rocks of low porosity [Brace and Orange, 1968].

ACKNOWLEDGMENTS

This work was in part supported by the U.S. Army Research Office, Durham, under Contract DAHCO4-73-C-0017. Discussion with C. Goetze was particularly helpful.

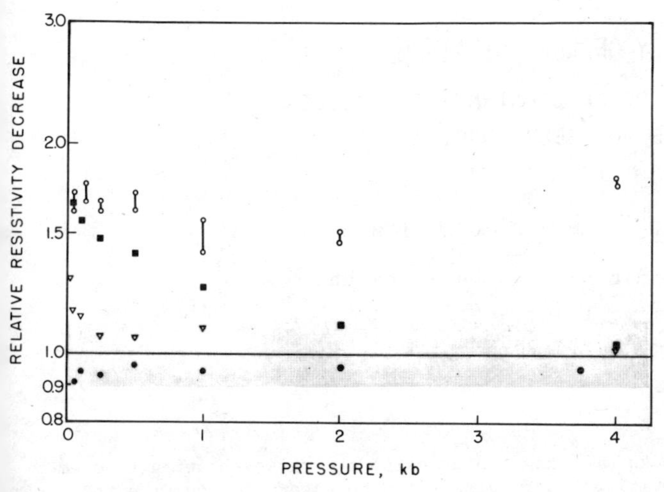

Fig. 6 Relative decrease in electrical resistivity after a 6 kbar pressure cycle, as a function of confining pressure. Closed circles refer to Westerly granite [Brace and Orange, 1968], triangles to an oceanic basalt [Stesky and Brace, 1973], squares to San Marcos gabbro [Brace and Orange, 1968], and open circles to diabase [Mitchell and Brace, 1973]. The upper set of open circles shows the further changes that accompanied a second 6 kbar cycle. The stippled region gives the typical reproducibility in a measurement of resistivity.

REFERENCES

RAYLEIGH, Lord, 1934, The bending of marble, Proceedings, Royal Society of London, Vol. 144, p. 266.

IDE, J.M., 1937, The velocity of sound in rocks and glasses as a function of temperature, Journal of Geology, Vol. 45, p. 689.

BARBISH, A.B., and G.H.F. GARDNER, 1969, The effect of heat on some mechanical properties of igneous rocks, Journal of the Society of Petroleum Engineers, December volume, p. 395.

BIRCH, F., and D. BANCROFT, 1940, New measurements of the rigidity of rocks at high pressure, Journal of Geology, Vol. XLVIII, p. 752.

BIRCH, F., 1943, Elasticity of igneous rocks at high temperatures and pressures, Bulletin of the Geological Society of America, Vol. 54, p. 263.

BRACE, W.F., 1965b, Relation of physical properties of rock to fabric, Journal of Geophysical Research, Vol. 70, p. 5657.

BRACE, W.F., 1965a, Some new measurements of linear compressibility of rocks, Journal of Geophysical Research, Vol. 70, p. 391.

GOETZE, C., 1971, High temperature rheology of Westerly granite, Journal of Geo-Physical Research, Vol. 76, p. 1223.

BRACE, W.F., E. SILVER, K. HADLEY, and C. GOETZE, 1972, Cracks and pores: A closer look, Science, Vol. 178, p. 162.

SPRUNT, E., and A.F. Brace, in press, Direct observation of microcavities in crystalline rocks, International Journal of Rock Mechanics and Mining Sciences.

BRACE, W.F., and A.S. ORANGE, 1968, Further studies of the effect of pressure on electrical resistivity of rocks, Journal of Geophysical Research, Vol. 73, p. 5407.

STESKY, R.M., and W.F. BRACE,1973, Electrical conductivity of serpentinized rocks to 6 kb, Journal of Geophysical Research, Vol. 78, p. 7614.

MITCHELL, T., and W.F. BRACE, 1973, Electrical resistivity of partially saturated rocks, Transactions of the American Geophysical Union, Vol. 54, p. 1209.

CONTINUUM THEORY OF ROCK DILATANCY

LA THÉORIE CONTINUÉ DE LA DILATANCE DES ROCHES

KONTINUUMSTHEORIE VON GESTEINSDILATANZ

William D. STUART James D. DIETRICH

National Center for Earthquake Research

U.S. Geological Survey

Menlo Park, California

U.S.A.

SUMMARY

Dilatancy and nonlinear material response of brittle rocks are examined by using the representation theorem of continuum mechanics. In the second order theory six empirical coefficients are necessary to describe the gener constitutive law. Two of the coefficients are contained in the generalized Hooke's law. Only three of the remaining constants can be evaluated by a series of uniaxial compression tests at different confining pressures a shear or general triaxial test is required for the fourth. Dilatancy is shown to be a linear function of the pressure squared, and of the second stress-deviation invariant. Direction-dependent properties induced by stress, such as acoustic wave velocity, and nonlinear tectonic boundary-value problems can be solved if the Hooke's law solution is known.

ZUSAMMENFASSUNG

Dilatanz und nichtlineares Verhalten von spröden Gesteinen werden untersucht mittels des Representationstheorem der Kontinuummechanik. In der Theorie zweiter Ordnung sind sechs empirische Koeffizienten notwendig, um das allgemeine konstitutive Gesetz zu beschreiben. Zwei der Koeffizienten sind in dem verallgemeinerten Hookeschen Gesetz enthalten. Nur drei der übrigen Konstanten können mittels einer Reihe einachsiger Kompressionsversuche zu verschiedenen Manteldrucken berechnet werden, während ein Scher- oder allgemeiner dreiachsiger Versuch für d vierte erforderlich ist. Dilatanz wird als eine lineare Funktion des quadrierten Druckes und der zweiten Spannungsdeviation-Invariante nachgewiesen. Durch Spannung hervorgebrachte, richtungsabhängige Eigenschaften, z. B. die Geschwindigkeit der akustischen Wellen, sowie nichtlineare tektonische Grenzwertprobleme können gelös werden, wenn die Hookesches-Gesetzlösung bekannt ist.

RÉSUMÉ

La dilatance ainsi que le comportement non-linéaire des roches brisantes sont étudiés en utilisant le théorème représentatif de la méchanique des milieux continus. Dans la théorie du second ordre, six coefficients sont nécessaires à la description de la loi constitutive générals. Deux des coefficients sont déja inclus dans la loi généralisée de Hooke. Uniquement trois coefficients parmi les constantes restantes peuvent être évalués au moyen d'une série de tests de compression uniaxiale, effectués pour differentes pressions latérales de confinement. Un essai de cisaillement ou un essai triaxial est nécessaire afin de pouvoir déterminer le quatrieme coefficient. On a démontré que la dilatance est une fonction linéaire de la pression élevée au carré et du second invariant de la déviation de la contrainte. Les properiétés anisotropiques induites par la contrainte, celles que la vitesse de propagation des ondes, ainsi que les problemes tectoniques non-linéaires aux limites peuvent être resolus si la solution de la loi de Hooke est connue.

INTRODUCTION

Early experimental investigations of the mechanical properties of rocks clearly established that rocks obeyed nonlinear constitutive laws (von Karman, 1911; Adams and Williamson, 1923), although stresses and strains were in most cases proportional over large ranges. Recent experiments (e.g. Brace et al., 1966) also indicate that nonlinear behavior is accompanied by volume increases relative to the volume changes expected from the generalized linear Hooke's law of classical elasticity. This volumetric effect due to distortion was first noted by Reynolds (1885) who termed it "dilatancy" but said nothing definitive of its nonlinear character.

Moreover, observations of deformed rock in the nonlinear range show that physical properties such as acoustic wave velocity vary with direction in the sample (Shimozuru, 1955; Tocher, 1957; Nur and Simmons, 1969). This directional dependence has led to the confusing and erroneous inference that the stress-strain transformation for rocks, even if initially isotropic, becomes anisotropic during distortion. The error arises because of the analogy with anisotropic crystals which maintain certain symmetries due to internal structure, regardless of the stress state. On the other hand, polygranular rocks which have no average structural symmetry in some hydrostatic reference state, but attain a symmetry due to and identical with external stresses are still properly called isotropic in the terminology of tensor-valued tensor functions. Thus in this paper anisotropy refers to direction-dependent physical properties caused solely by stresses, for example wave velocity, but not to the stress-strain transformation itself.

Fortunately many rocks under pressure, temperature, and strain rate conditions of the upper crust do in fact satisfy as a first approximation Hooke's law for infinitesimal strain. This observation is the basis for assuming Hooke's law in analytical and numerical solutions for many tectonic boundary value problems, such as dislocation analysis of crustal faults. For certain other applications, however, Hooke's law is inadequate.

The current interest in predicitng earthquakes by means of various premonitory geophysical phenomena has led to the hypothesis that many of the apparent precursory anomalies are due to the influence of small flat cracks opening in response to increasing shear stress in the focal region before the earthquake (Nur, 1972; Scholz et al., 1973). The crack mechanism is appealing because it provides a single explanation for several phenomena that are observed both in the laboratory and near crustal faults. Laboratory experiments and theoretical work indicate that crack dynamics account for much of the observed nonlinearity and velocity anisotropy and also that the planes of open cracks show a preferred orientation to the principal stress directions (Walsh, 1965; Nur, 1971). Even a very small volume percentage of cracks causes significant nonlinearity and therefore a proper calculation of the crustal stress and strain states, for some earthquake-related problems at least, must abandon Hooke's law in favor of a more general constitutive law.

In this paper, we attempt to deduce the constitutive laws of rocks which show nonlinearity and its special case, dilatancy. Rather than attaching additional terms to equations of classical elasticity, assuming phenomenological models of classical rheology, or postulating a microscopic physical mechanism, we start with the most general assumptions of modern continuum mechanics. Further assumptions, justified by laboratory observations of brittle rocks, yield a constitutive law of surprisingly simple form. Laboratory data are still inadequate to define fully the constitutive law for any rock, but several qualitative effects relevant to earthquake mechanics are examined. Finally, the procedure for computing the stress state using the nonlinear constitutive laws and existing mathematical solutions based on Hooke's law is outlined.

CONSTITUTIVE EQUATIONS

We make use of the well known representation theorem (1) of rational mechanics, first given by Reiner (1945, 1948) and later discussed in more detail by Truesdell (1952) and Truesdell and Noll (1965).

$$\underline{\varepsilon}=\phi_o\underline{1}+\phi_1\underline{\sigma}+\phi_2\underline{\sigma}^2$$

$$\phi_k=\phi_k\ (I_1,\ I_2,\ I_3) \qquad k=0,1,2 \tag{1}$$

The theorem embodies the definition of an isotropic tensor-valued tensor function relating two symmetric second-order tensors $\underline{\sigma}$ and $\underline{\varepsilon}$. In this paper $\underline{1}$ is the unit tensor, $\underline{\sigma}$ is the stress tensor, $\underline{\varepsilon}$ is the infinitesimal strain tensor whose components are

$$\varepsilon_{ij}=1/2\left(\frac{\partial u_i}{\partial x_j}+\frac{\partial u_j}{\partial x_i}\right) \qquad i,j=1,2,3$$

where u are displacement components, and x are coordinates. Scalar coefficients ϕ_o, ϕ_1 ϕ_2 can be expanded as infinite series in the principal invariants of $\underline{\sigma}$, I_1, I_2, and I_3, which are defined below in terms of principal values of $\underline{\sigma}$.

$$I_1=\sigma_{ii}$$

$$I_2=1/2\sigma_{ii}\sigma_{jj} \qquad i\neq j$$

$$I_3=\Pi\sigma_{ii}$$

$i,j=1,2,3$, summation implied by repeated indices

If a material is completely described by (1), then it is necessarily elastic: the stress state depends only on the local deformation gradients, and path- and time-dependent behavior is ruled out. It is assumed that if (1) applies, it applies at every material point in a body.

Equation (1), as will be noted below, includes Hooke's law as a special case (called Cauchy's law in the continuum mechanics literature). Magnitudes of coefficients in ϕ are to be evaluated experimentally for an individual rock, although one might expect rocks of similar composition and origin to have similar ϕ's. An important point is that relation (1) must be satisfied by any constitutive law derived from more fundamental physical theory based on additional assumptions, for example the presence of cracks or pores. Equation (1) also implies that principal stress and strain directions coincide.

Scalar functions ϕ are in reality infinite series, but we restrict ourselves to consideration of the lowest order deviations from linearity by expanding (1) through powers of σ^2 only; experimental errors and variations between and within samples probably dominate the higher order terms. The result given in both tensor and cartesian component form is

$$\underline{\varepsilon}=(\alpha+AI_1+BI_1^2+CI_2)\underline{1}+(G+HI_1)\underline{\sigma}+M\underline{\sigma}^2$$

$$\varepsilon_{ij}=(\alpha+AI_1+BI_1^2+CI_2)\delta_{ij}+(G+HI_1)\sigma_{ij}+M\sigma_{ik}\sigma_{kj} \tag{2}$$

$$i,j,k=1,2,3$$

α,A,B,...are scalar constants, and δ_{ij} is the Kronecker delta. I_3, the third stress invariant, appears only if σ^3 and higher terms are retained.

If all constants vanish except A and G, (2) reduces to Hooke's law $\varepsilon'_{ij}=AI_1\delta_{ij}+G\sigma_{ij}$. A is identified with $-\nu/E$ and G with $(1+\nu)/E$ where ν is Poisson's ratio and E is Young's modulus. An important and useful feature of (2) is that nonlinear material response enters through constants other than A and G and therefore can be considered as a perturbation to Hooke's law. Rewriting (2) as (3) clarifies the partition of $\underline{\varepsilon}$ into two strains, $\underline{\varepsilon}'$ and the remainder $\underline{\varepsilon}''$. The strain tensor $\underline{\varepsilon}''$ contains only the deviations from Hooke's law (nonlinearities), including dilatancy.

$$\underline{\varepsilon}=\underline{\varepsilon}'+\underline{\varepsilon}''$$

$$\underline{\varepsilon}'=AI_1\underline{1}+G\underline{\sigma}$$

$$\underline{\varepsilon}''=(\alpha+BI_1^2+CI_2)\underline{1}+HI_1\underline{\sigma}+M\underline{\sigma}^2 \tag{3}$$

Dilatant volume increase is simply $V''=\varepsilon_{ii}''=\varepsilon_{11}''+\varepsilon_{22}''+\varepsilon_{33}''$ and vanishes when α=o if either $\underline{\sigma}=\underline{0}$ or $(BI_1^2+CI_2)\underline{1}+HI_1\underline{\sigma}+M\underline{\sigma}^2=\underline{0}$.

$\underline{\sigma}$ and $\underline{\varepsilon}$ are measured from a reference state, not necessarily zero absolute stress, in which the rock shows no mechanical anisotropy of any kind. Birch (1961) noted that the acoustic anisotropy of some rocks vanishes at confining pressures of several kilobars, so in these cases the reference state should be a pressure at least this great. An extremely high confining pressure, though, is probably not a good choice for a reference state because of the increasing importance of time- and path-dependent processes which violate the assumptions of equation (1). In the following discussions $\alpha=0$ because $\underline{\sigma}=\underline{\varepsilon}=\underline{0}$ at the reference state.

Consider the case of uniaxial compression with $\sigma_{22}=\sigma_{33}=0$. In this instance $I_1=\sigma_{11}$, $I_1^2=\sigma_{11}^2$, $I_2=I_3=0$, and

$$\underline{\varepsilon}'=A\sigma_{11}\underline{1}+G\underline{\sigma}$$

$$\underline{\varepsilon}''=B\sigma_{11}^2\,\underline{1}+H_{11}\underline{\sigma}. \quad (4)$$

The term $M\underline{\sigma}^2$ vanishes when two principal stresses are equal (Truesdell and Noll, 1965). Components of (4) are

$$\varepsilon'_{11}=(A+G)\sigma_{11} \qquad \varepsilon'_{22}=\varepsilon'_{33}=A\sigma_{11}$$

$$\varepsilon''_{11}=(B+H)\sigma_{11}^2 \qquad \varepsilon''_{22}=\varepsilon''_{33}=B\sigma_{11}^2 \quad (5)$$

and the dilatant volume V'' becomes (6).

$$V''=(3B+H)\sigma_{11}^2=(3B+H)I_1^2$$

$$=-3(3B+H)J_2 \quad (6)$$

where $J_2=-1/3\ I_1^2+I_2=-1/3\ I_1^2$.

Only four independent coefficients A, B, G, and H appear in (5) and (6). They may be evaluated from an experiment by taking partial derivatives of (5) with the definition of $\underline{\varepsilon}=\underline{\varepsilon}'+\underline{\varepsilon}''$ or by solving sets of simultaneous equations obtained by direct substitution.

$$\frac{\partial\varepsilon_{11}}{\partial\sigma_{11}} = (A+G)+2(B+H)\sigma_{11}$$

$$\frac{\partial^2\varepsilon_{11}}{\partial\sigma_{11}^2} = 2(B+H)$$

$$\frac{\partial\varepsilon_{22}}{\partial\sigma_{11}} = A+2B\sigma_{11} \quad (7)$$

$$\frac{\partial^2\varepsilon_{22}}{\partial\sigma_{11}^2} = 2B$$

Geometrically, the coefficients A and G of Hooke's law may be interpreted as the slopes of the stress-strain curves at $\underline{\sigma}=0$; coefficients 2(B+H) and 2B are the slopes of $\partial\varepsilon_{11}/\partial\sigma_{11}$ and $\partial\varepsilon_{22}/\partial\sigma_{11}$ vs. σ_{11} curves. Note that a single uniaxial test at the confining pressure of the reference state permits only the constants A, B, G, and H to be determined without ambiguity. No information whatsoever about C or M is available from this test.

Consider now the case of uniaxial compression as above, but at a different confining pressure $\sigma_{22}=\sigma_{33}\neq0$. Stress invariants become

$$I_1=\sigma_{11}+2\sigma_{22} \qquad I_1^2=\sigma_{11}^2+4\sigma_{11}\sigma_{22}+4\sigma_{22}^2$$

$$I_2=(\sigma_{22}^2+2\sigma_{11}\sigma_{22})$$

The component forms for $\underline{\varepsilon}$ are given as equations (8) and contain the additional constant C.

$$\varepsilon_{11}=(A+G)\sigma_{11}+2A\sigma_{22}+(B+H)\sigma_{11}^2+(4B+C)\sigma_{22}^2+(4B+2C+2H)\sigma_{11}\sigma_{22}$$

$$\varepsilon_{22}=\varepsilon_{33}=A\sigma+(A+G)\sigma_2+B\sigma_{11}^2+(4B+C+2H)\sigma_{22}^2+(4B+2C+H)\sigma_{11}\sigma_{22} \quad (8)$$

Dilatant volumetric strain, analogous to (6) becomes

$$V''=(3B+H)I_1^2+3CI_2$$

which also can be written as a function of I_1^2 and J_2 namely

$$V''=(3B+C+H)I_1^2+3CJ_2.$$

Hence, dilatancy clearly depends not only on the second stress deviator invariant J_2, a measure of distortion only, but also on the square of the mean normal stress $S=1/3I_1$.

As in (7), the coefficients are determined from experimental stress-strain functions by partial differentiation or by substitution.

By repeating the same steps as outlined above for uniaxial compression, the component expressions of $\underline{\varepsilon}$ for the general triaxial compression test with $\sigma_{11}\neq\sigma_{22}\neq\sigma_{33}\neq0$ are obtained.

$$\varepsilon_{11}=(A+G)\sigma_{11}+A(\sigma_{22}+\sigma_{33})+(B+H+M)\sigma_{11}^2+B(\sigma_{22}^2+\sigma_{33}^2)+$$
$$+(2B+C)\sigma_{22}\sigma_{33}+(2B+C+H)(\sigma_{11}\sigma_{22}+\sigma_{11}\sigma_{33})$$

ε_{22}, ε_{33} by symmetry.

The dilatant volume is

$$V''=(3B+H+M)I_1^2+(3C-2M)I_2$$

$$V''=(3B+C+H+\frac{M}{3})\ I_1^2+(3C-2M)J_2$$

The preceding analysis shows that when terms of the representation theorem (2) are expanded through order of σ^2, the two terms of $O(\sigma)$, $AI_1\underline{1}$ and $G\underline{\sigma}$, describe classical linear elasticity. In the most general triaxial case, four new terms of $O(\sigma^2)$ describe the nonlinear response. The are $BI_1^2\underline{1}$, $CI_2\underline{1}$, $HI_1\underline{\sigma}$, and $M\underline{\sigma}^2$. Only A, B, G, and H can be evaluated from a single uniaxial test at the reference confining pressure. Additional tests at different confining pressures permit C to be evaluated, but only if σ_{11}, σ_{22}, and σ_{33} are varied independently can M be determined by compression or extension tests.

It is easily shown that a simple shear stress experiment with confining pressure serves to determine G, C, and M, but not A, B, or H. A purely hydrostatic compression test will also determine C if A, B, G, and H are already known. Thus a test program including both uniaxial tests at several different confining pressures and simple shear stress tests will be sufficient to calculate the coefficients of (2) and provide a test of its applicability to the specimen.

In all cases the volume changes due to dilatancy are linear functions of I_1^2 and J_2. Coefficients needed for V'' in the triaxial case include all of B, C, H, and M. B, C, H are sufficient to determine V'' if $\sigma_{22}=\sigma_{33}\neq 0$, and only B and C are required if $\sigma_{22}=\sigma_{33}=0$.

Equation (2) is an hypothesis whose validity must be tested by a series of experiments on a rock. Figure 1 shows an attempt to apply (2) to results reported by Brace et al. (1966, figs. 1b and 1c) of uniaxial compression tests on Westerly granite at confining pressures of 1.0 and 4.1 kbars. The reference state is chosen as 4.1 kbar pressure and coefficients are A=-0.23 Mbar^{-1}, B=.028 Mbar^{-1}, C=-0.05 Mbar^{-1}, G=1.57 Mbar^{-2}, and H=-0.052 Mbar^{-2}. Heavy solid curves in the figure are observations, light solid curves are computed with (2) and the preceding coefficient values, and straight dashed lines indicate the response predicted by Hooke's law. At 4.1 kbars agreement between calculated and observed curves is good, but at 1 kbar a less satisfactory fit is obtained. More data at different confining pressures are needed to verify the adequacy of equation (2) for Westerly granite. The cause of the discrepancies is not known, but may be due to sample differences, nonhomogeneous deformation, nonrandom grain orientations, time-dependent effects, deformation history, or neglect of higher order terms.

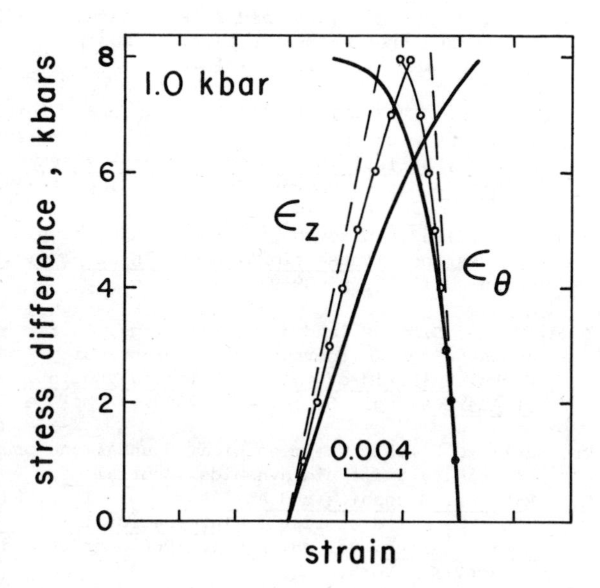

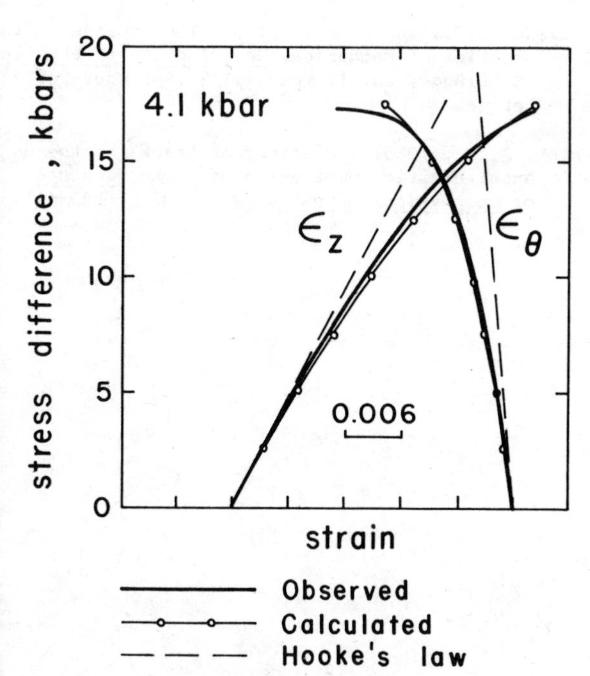

Figure 1. Observed and calculated stress-strain curves for Westerly granite at 1.0 and 4.1 kbar confining pressure. Experimental data from Brace et al. (1966). ϵ_z is longitudnal strain; ϵ_θ is circumferential strain.

APPLICATIONS TO TECTONICS

We outline here possible applications of the preceding theory to earthquake tectonics; a detailed discussion will be given elsewhere. Relation (2) allows the static solution of a boundary value problem for a portion of the Earth's crust if the following conditions are met: a) rock constitutive properties are described satisfactorily by (2), b) coefficients ϕ, problem geometry, and boundary stresses are known, and c) the reference state in which the rocks show perfect symmetry is known. None of these requirements are presently satisfied, although geometry and boundary conditions can be approximated. Only the constants A and G of Hooke's law are known with confidence, and no information regarding B, C, H, and M has been published, although the requisite experiments have been performed on a few rocks.

A tectonic problem, for example the determination of the stress and strain staces near a fault prior to an earthquake, is solved by first obtaining the solution for $\underline{\sigma}$ and $\underline{\epsilon}'$ at every point using classical infinitesimal elasticity theory (3). The nonlinear solution for $\underline{\epsilon}=\underline{\epsilon}'+\underline{\epsilon}''$ follows immediately from (2) because I_1, I_2, and the principal strain directions are derivable from $\underline{\sigma}$. In fact, some qualitative knowledge of dilatancy is available merely by contouring $V''(I_1^2,J_2)$ fields from the linear solution. The relevance of V'' to earthquake mechanics is that the size of the dilatant zone prior to an earthquake, a central issue to the premonitory dilatancy hypothesis, can be computed from a postulated dislocation distribution.

When the crust is distorted, seismic wave velocity will generally become direction-dependent, and a method of determining theoretically the dependence would be useful. Because strains associated with seismic waves are orders of magnitude smaller than the strain at failure, stress- and direction-dependent elastic moduli can be computed from classical definitions. A Young's modulus, for example, can be determined from the definition $\partial\sigma_n/\partial\epsilon_n$, where σ_n and ϵ_n are the normal stress and strain in the same direction, by performing a rotation of (2) with respect to a coordinate frame coincident with principal stress directions. Similar operations are possible for Poisson's ratio and other parameters. For wave propagation studies, such as those discussed by Todd et al. (1974), it seems preferable to calculate directly from (2) the elements of the fourth-order, elastic constant tensor. Thus, a means is available for computing the directional dependence of seismic wave velocities when the scalar functions ϕ and the stress rate are independently known.

CONCLUSIONS

Application of the representation theorem appears to provide a nonlinear constitutive law of brittle rocks that expresses infinitesimal strain as a tensor function of stress. When terms of order stress squared are retained, only four constants are needed to describe nonlinearity, including dilatancy, plus two more constants that are related to moduli of classical linear elasticity. The specification of all six constants requires a series of triaxial compression tests in which all three principal stresses are independently varied, or a series of uniaxial tests at different confining pressures and simple shear stress tests under confining pressure.

The nonlinear volume changes attributed to dilatancy are shown to be linear functions of the square of the pressure and the second stress-deviation invariant. The constitutive law allows direction-dependent constants of classical elasticity to be calculated readily, as well as the solution of nonlinear boundary value problems related to fault mechanics.

ACKNOWLEDGEMENT

We are grateful to J. C. Savage for helpful comments.

REFERENCES

Adams, L. H., and E. D. Williamson, 1923, On the compressibility of minerals and rocks at high pressures, Journal of the Franklin Institute, vol. 195, p. 475-529.

Birch, F., 1961, The velocity of compressional waves in rocks to 10 kilobars, Part 2, Journal of Geophysical Research, vol. 66, p. 2199-2224.

Brace, W. F., B. W. Paulding, Jr., and C. H. Scholz, 1966, Dilatancy in the fracture of crystalline rocks, Journal of Geophysical Research, vol. 71, p. 3939-3953.

Karman, Th. von, 1911, Festigkeitsversuche unter allseitgem Druck, Zeitschr. Ver. deutsch Ingenieure, vol. 55, p. 1749-1575.

Nur, A., 1971, Effects of velocity anisotropy in rocks with cracks, Journal of Geophysical Research, vol. 76, p. 2022-2034.

Nur, A., 1972, Dilatancy, pore fluids, and premonitory variations of t_s/t_p travel times, Bulletin of the Seismological Society of America, vol. 62, p. 1217-1222.

Nur, A., and G. Simmons, 1969, Stress-induced velocity anisotropy in rock: An experimental study, Journal of Geophysical Research, vol. 74, p. 6667-6674.

Reiner, M., 1945, A mathematical theory of dilatancy, American Journal of Mathematics, vol. 67, p. 350-362.

_________, 1948, Elasticity beyond the elastic limit, American Journal of Mathematics, vol. 70, p. 433-446.

Reynolds, O., 1885, On the dilatancy of media compose of rigid particles in contact, Philosophical Magazine, vol. 20, p. 469-481.

Scholz, C. H., L. R. Sykes, and Y. P. Aggarwal, 1973, Earthquake prediction: A physical basis: Science, vol. 181, p. 803-810.

Shimozuru, D., 1955, Elasticity of rocks under initia stresses, with special reference to the fracture problem, Bulletin of the Earthquake Research Institute, Tokyo University, vol. 33, p. 437-450

Tocher, D., 1957, Anisotropy in rocks under simple compression, Transactions, American Geophysical Union, vol. 38, p. 89-94.

Todd, T., G. Simmons, and W. S. Baldridge, 1973, Acoustic double refraction in low-porosity rocks, Bulletin of the Seismological Society of America, vol. 63, p. 2007-2020.

Truesdell, C., 1952, The mechanical foundations of elasticity and fluid dynamics, Journal of Rational Mechanics and Analysis, vol. 1, p. 125-300, corrected reprint in International Science Review Series, vol. 8, pt. 1, 1966, Gordon and Breach, New York.

Truesdell, C., and W. Noll, 1965, The nonlinear fiel theories of mechanics, Encyclopedia of Physics, (S. Flügge, ed.,), vol. III/3, Springer-Verlag, Berlin.

Walsh, J. M., 1965, The effect of cracks on the uniaxial elastic compression of rocks, Journal of Geophysical Research, vol. 70, p. 399-411.

THEME 2

THÈME 2

THEMA 2

B

State of Stress

B

État de contrainte

B

Spannungszustand

THE EFFECT OF APPLIED STRESS UPON THE PERMEABILITY OF SOME PERMIAN AND TRIASSIC SANDSTONES OF NORTHERN ENGLAND

EFFET DES CONTRAINTES APPLIQUÉES SUR LA PERMÉABILITÉ DES CERTAINES ROCHES PSAMMITIQUES PERMIENNES ET TRIASIQUES DU NORD DE L'ANGLETERRE

DIE WIRKUNG ANGEWANDTER SPANNUNGEN AUF DIE PERMEABILITÄT EINIGER IN NORD-ENGLAND VORKOMMENDER PERM- UND TRIASSANDSTEINE

G.P. DAW Cementation Research Ltd., Rickmansworth, Herts., England

F.T. HOWELL Senior Lecturer, Department of Civil and Structural Engineering, UMIST, Manchester, England

F.A. WOODHEAD formerly SRC Research Student, Department of Civil and Structural Eng., UMIST, Manchester, England

SUMMARY.

The Permian and Triassic sandstones of Northern England exhibit a range of intergranular and field permabilities. Laboratory permeation tests indicate that the intergranular permeation is not significantly reduced by high applied stresses, but that permeation through fissures in the rock is greatly reduced. Measurements of pore sizes, calculations of fissure dimensions, and scanning electron microscope photography have been used to determine the dimensions of the passages in the sandstones. The findings contribute towards the understanding of regional and depth dependent variations in the magnitude and mechanism of permeation in these sandstones, and in the selection of appropriate ground treatment processes to reduce the inflow of groundwater into major civil engineering and mining excavations.

RESUME

Les roches psammitiques du Permien et du Trias du nord de l'Angleterre presentent toute une gamme de perméabilités intergranulaires et de terrain. Des essais de perméabilité effectués en laboratoire indiquent que la perméabilité intergranulaire n'est pas diminuée d'une manière significative par des contraintes appliquées importantes mais que la perméabilité dans les fissures des roches est fortement réduite. Des mesures de la dimension des pores, des calculs sur la dimension des fissures et des photographies au microscope par balayage d'électrons ont été utilisés pour déterminer la dimension des passages dans les roches psammitiques. Les résultats de ces travaux aident à mieux comprendre les variations régionales et dépendant de la profondeur dans l'importance et le mécanisme de la perméabilité dans ces roches psammitiques et dans le choix des traitements du terrain appropriés pour diminuer la pénétration des nappes d'eau souterraine dans les excavations importantes pour les travaux de mines et de construction de génie civil.

KURZFASSUNG

Die Perm- und Triassandsteine Nordenglands besitzen einen Permeabilitätsbereich zwischen den Körnern und im Felde. Durchlässigkeitsversuche im Laboratorium zeigen, dass der Durchfluss zwischen den Körnern durch hohe angewandte Spannungen nicht bedeutend verringert wird, dass aber der Durchfluss durch Felsgesteinrisse erheblich verringert ist. Messungen der Porengrösse, Berechnung der Abmessungen der Risse und Photographie mit dem Elektronenrastermikroskop wurden zur Bestimmung der Durchgangsabmessungen der Sandsteine benutzt. Die gefundenen Ergebnisse liefern einen Beitrag zum Verständnis der örtlichen und tiefeabhängigen Unterschiede in Grösse und Mechanismus des Durchflusses in diesen Sandsteinen und sind zur Auswahl geeigneter Bodenbehandlungsverfahren zur Verringerung des Grundwassereindringens in wichtige Baugruben und bergbauliche Ausschachtungen nützlich.

Introduction

Deposits of Permian and Triassic sandstones, which locally attain thicknesses in the order of 3000 feet (1000m), are preserved in a number of deep and extensive sedimentary basins in Northern England (Fig.1). In some areas these sandstones overlie valuable deposits of evaporite minerals or coal. The sandstones, by virtue of their great thickness and the nature of their permeation properties can, on occasion, pose very serious groundwater problems when they are encountered in major excavations, tunnels, and shafts.

In the planning and construction of such projects it is essential not only to be able to predict the probable magnitude and consequences of any ingress of groundwater, but also to be able to formulate appropriate ground treatment programmes to alleviate such problems.

Since the total field permeability and storage of these rocks may be the result of both intergranular and fissure flow components, it is desirable to assess the relative magnitudes of these components in the presence of increasing overburden pressures at increasing depths.

The authors' association with such projects has stimulated research into the permeation characteristics of the Permian and Triassic sandstones of parts of Northern England. Many assessments were made of the field permeability of these rocks from insitu tests in deep waterbores, excavations, and geotechnical boreholes. Attempts to evaluate the intergranular flow component at some of these sites have been made on unfissured rock core samples in the laboratory.

This research indicated that the Permian and Triassic sandstones of northern England were porous and permeable, and that there were marked regional differences not only in the magnitude of these properties but also in the relative importance of the intergranular and fissure flow components in the field (Crook & Howell, 1970; Crook et al, 1971; Crook et al, 1973).

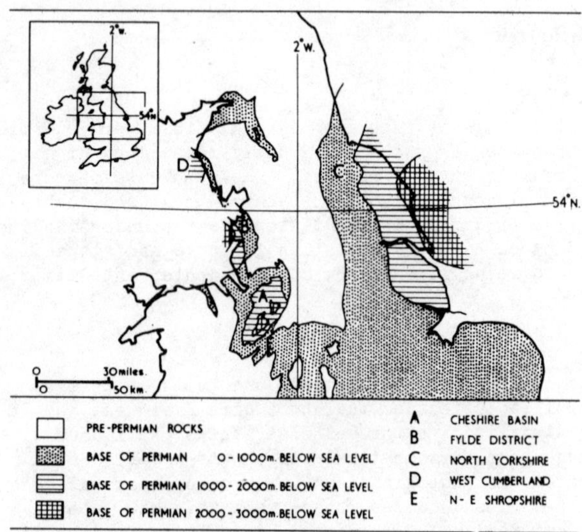

Fig. 1 SKETCH MAP (AFTER TECTONIC MAP OF GT. BRITAIN) SHOWING BASINS CONTAINING PERMIAN AND TRIASSIC ROCKS IN NORTHERN ENGLAND.

In arriving at these conclusions it had been assumed that the intergranular permeabilities, which were measured at low applied stresses in the laboratory, were applicable to the rock at depth.

In these studies, in each of the regions, fissures were occasionally observed in rock exposures at the surface, and in excavations and borings. Since such exposed surfaces are likely to be in zones of stress relief, it is probable that the nature and permeation properties of these fissures may differ from similar fissures concealed below surface, in zones subject to overburden pressure.

Other workers report that in many rocks, including sandstones, intergranular permeation (Fatt & Davis, 1952; Gray et al, 1963; Wilhelmi & Somerton, 1967) and fissure permeation (Bernaix, 1969; Le Tirant & Baron, 1972) respond differently to the application of stress.

However, as far as can be established, no such studies have been made on the important Permian and Triassic sandstones of northern England.

The purpose of this paper is to describe the response, in the laboratory, of both intergranular and fissure permeation to applied stress in typical members of this suite of Permian and Triassic sandstones and to discuss some of the geotechnical applications of the findings.

Examination of the Rock Fabric

In order to establish the nature of the fabrics of the Permian and Triassic sandstones and their influence on intergranular permeation and consequent ground treatment techniques, these rocks have been examined by the use of the polarising microscope and the scanning electron microscope.

The studies indicate that these sandstones have a range of fabrics. In general, the properties of the end members of this range are distinctive; namely, those which are poorly-cemented, weak, coarse-grained, and of high intergranular permeability, and those which are well-cemented, strong, fine-grained, and of very low intergranular permeability (Plate 1). In some instances coarse-grained, well-cemented sandstones with correspondingly low intergranular permeabilities are noted.

The variations within the range appear to have some regional distribution. For example, sandstones from the Cheshire Basin have, in general, affinities with the poorly-cemented types, while the sandstones from west Cumberland have affinities with the well-cemented types.

The dimensions of the intergranular pores of a large number of sandstone specimens have been determined by the mercury injection method (Ritter & Drake, 1945). Typical distribution curves for a range of samples including the two end members are shown in Fig. 2.

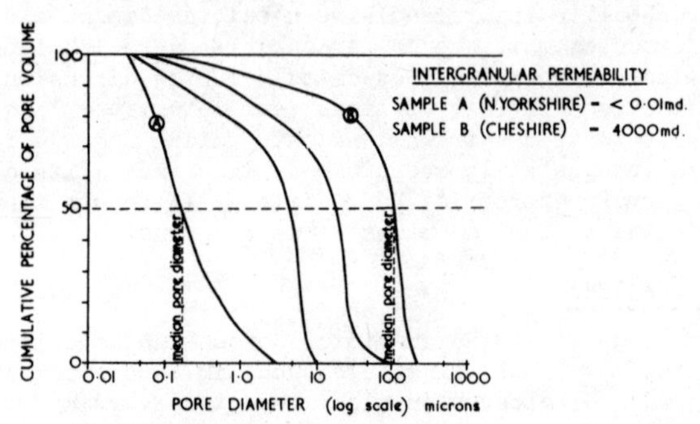

Fig. 2 PORE SIZE DISTRIBUTION CURVES OF TYPICAL SAMPLES OF PERMIAN AND TRIASSIC SANDSTONES FROM PARTS OF NORTHERN ENGLAND.

A useful correlation has been established between the median pore diameter of a specimen and its intergranular permeability as illustrated in Fig. 3. (The median pore diameter of a sample is defined as the 50% value on the cumulative distribution curve i.e. 50% of the pores, by volume have larger diameters, and 50% have smaller diameters.)

It will be noted that a sandstone with an intergranular permeability as high as 5000md is likely to have a median pore diameter of only some 100 microns and a maximum pore size probably not exceeding 300 microns. (1 millidarcy [md] $\simeq 1.0 \times 10^{-6}$ cm/sec.)

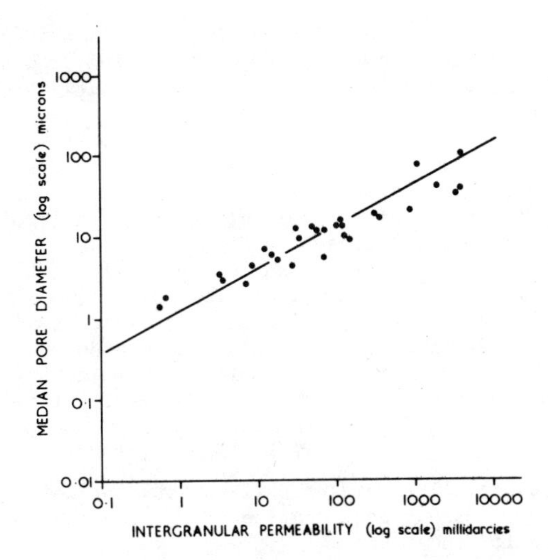

Fig. 3 RELATIONSHIP BETWEEN MEASURED MEDIAN PORE DIAMETER AND INTERGRANULAR PERMEABILITY OF SOME PERMIAN AND TRIASSIC SANDSTONES OF NORTHERN ENGLAND

Laboratory Assessment of the response of permeation properties to applied stress

Since the in-situ formation stresses are rarely known accurately, it is extremely difficult to simulate true field conditions in the laboratory. Nevertheless, various attempts have been made to simulate formation conditions. Fatt and Davis (1952) and Wilhelmi and Somerton (1967) applied a hydrostatic pressure to the sample surfaces, while Gray et al (1963) extended this approach by independently varying the vertical and horizontal stress components. Wyble (1958) used the simpler approach of applying purely a radial stress to cylindrical cores.

In spite of the use of differing techniques the results of all these investigations, frequently conducted on samples from the same formations, are in good agreement. It does seem, therefore, that in the absence of measurements of the true formation stresses the simple approach of Wyble is quite acceptable, and for this reason it has been adopted in this instance.

The permeability tests under applied stress were carried out in a Hoek/Franklin triaxial cell modified for the measurement of permeability (Daw, 1971) (Fig. 4). With this arrangement the applied stress is identified with the sleeve sealing pressure. Either de-aired water or air was used as the permeating fluid. In each test the following procedure was adopted; a sandstone core was cut with an axial orientation parallel to the natural stratification of the rock and mounted in the Hoek/Franklin cell. The application of sleeve pressure to cores cut in this way simulates overburden pressure and one component of horizontal stress.

The response of the intergranular permeability to increments of increasing applied stress up to 5000 lb/in^2 (350 kg/cm^2) was first noted.

Subsequently, the core was artificially fissured along an axial plane, i.e. parallel to the natural stratification, thereby simulating a natural open bedding plane within the rock mass. The response of the overall fissured permeability to increments of increasing applied stress up to 5000 lb/in^2 (350 kg/cm^2) was observed in the permeability cell.

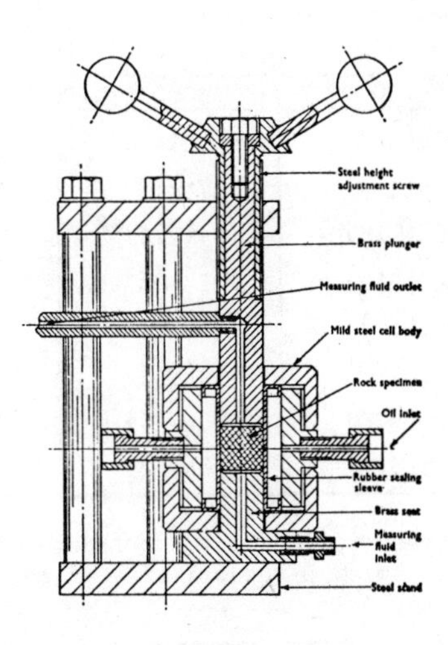

Fig. 4.

MODIFIED HOEK - FRANKLIN CELL (AFTER DAW, 1971)

The behaviour of typical samples of unfissured and fissured Permian and Triassic sandstones is summarised in Tables I and II, and Fig. 5.

TABLE I

The effect of Applied Stress on the Intergranular Permeabilities of Typical Permian and Triassic Sandstones

	Intergranular permeability in millidarcies at sleeve pressure (in lb/in^2) of		
Region	100	1000	5000
A	1230	1130(92)	1070(87)
D	114	110(96)	103(90)
C	7.8	7.4(95)	7.0(90)
A	212	196(92)	188(89)
D	30	27(90)	25(83)
A	110	99(90)	93(86)
E	990	935(93)	920(92)
D	8.7	8.2(94)	7.9(90)

Figures in brackets denote the percentage of the intergranular permeability at 100 lb/in^2.

TABLE II

The effect of Applied Stress on the Fissured Permeabilities of Typical Permian and Triassic Sandstones

	Overall fissured permeability in millidarcies at sleeve pressure (in lb/in^2) of		
Region	100	1000	5000
A	9100(1230)	2600(1130)	1200(1070)
D	945(114)	147(110)	109(103)
C	175(7.8)	14(7.4)	7.3(7.0)
A	540(212)	242(196)	211(188)
D	960(30)	196(27)	31(25)
A	875(110)	150(99)	98(93)
E	7700(990)	1900(935)	1000(920)
D	185(8.7)	16(8.2)	8.3(7.9)

Figures in brackets denote the corresponding unfissured intergranular permeabilities at the same sleeve pressures.

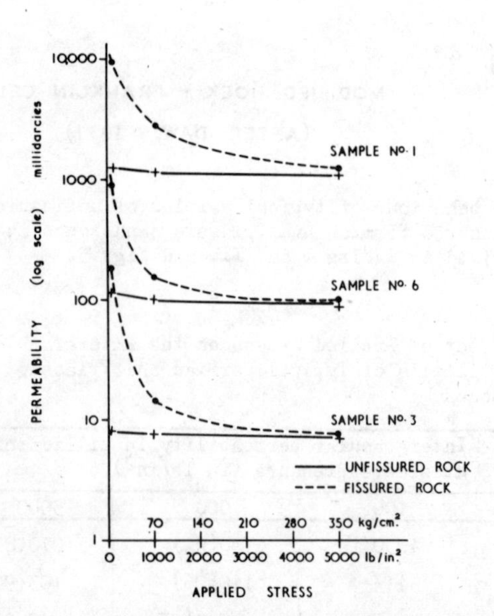

Fig. 5. TYPICAL CURVES ILLUSTRATING THE RESPONSE OF INTERGRANULAR AND FISSURE CONTROLLED PERMEATION TO APPLIED STRESS IN PERMIAN AND TRIASSIC SANDSTONES OF NORTHERN ENGLAND.

The overall impression from these experiments is that in the unfissured state the intergranular permeability of these sandstones is not significantly reduced by the application of high stress. The average reductions in intergranular permeability at 1000 lb/in^2 (70 kg/cm^2) and 5000 lb/in^2 (350 kg/cm^2) from that at 100 lb/in^2 applied pressure were 7% and 12% respectively.

In the case of fissured samples quite different results are noted. When only low stress is applied the artificial fissure contributes greatly to the overall permeability of the samples as compared with the unfissured intergranular permeability at that same stress. However, the contribution from the fissures diminishes rapidly as the applied stress is increased. At an applied stress of some 5000 lb/in^2 (350 kg/cm^2) the overall permeability of fissured samples is very similar to the unfissured intergranular permeability at that same stress and the fissure is effectively closed. Calculated estimates of the effective fissure widths at three applied stresses are shown in Table III and illustrated in Fig. 6. They indicate that at 5000 lb/in^2 (350 kg/cm^2) the effective fissure width is of the same order of size as the measured median pore diameter of the unfissured sample, confirming that at this pressure the fissure is effectively closed.

TABLE III

Calculated Fissure Widths at various Applied Stresses for Typical Samples of Permian and Triassic Sandstones

	Calculated effective fissure width (microns) at sleeve pressure (in lb/in^2) of			Measured median pore diameter
Region	100	1000	5000	(microns)
D	58	21	11	14
A	43	22	18	11
D	38	6.9	2.3	1.4

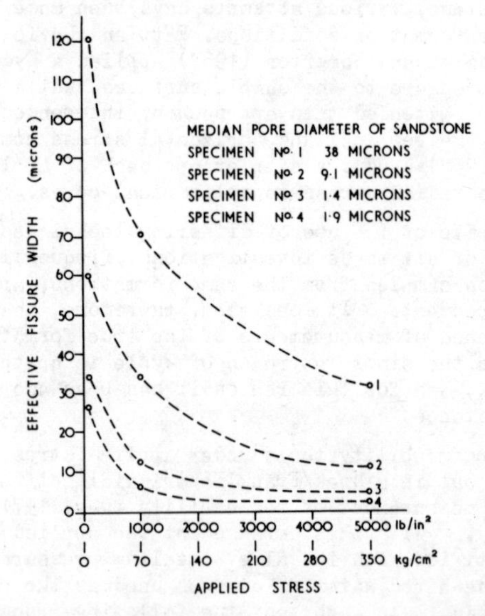

Fig. 6. RESPONSES OF THE EFFECTIVE FISSURE WIDTH TO APPLIED STRESS IN A TYPICAL RANGE OF PERMIAN AND TRIASSIC SANDSTONES OF NORTHERN ENGLAND

Application of the findings to geotechnical practice

It is considered that the intergranular permeability of the Permian and Triassic sandstones will not be significantly reduced by overburden pressures. Thus, in deep mining projects, large intergranular flows of groundwater may, on occasion, be encountered. As an illustration of this problem it can be shown that a deep shaft, some 20 feet (6m) in diameter encountering 100 feet (30m) of continuous sandstones under a pressure head of some 2500 feet

(800m) of water, would be subject to an inflow in excess of 100 gallons of water per minute, even if the sandstones had an average permeability as low as 10md (1.0×10^{-5} cm/sec).

At the site investigation stage of major projects, such as shafts and tunnels, it is necessary to evaluate the groundwater conditions likely to be met during construction. For this purpose it is general practice to sink exploratory cored boreholes at, or near, the proposed site. These boreholes not only allow a visual examination of the strata but also allow the assessment of the groundwater conditions in the borehole or specific zones of the borehole by inflow or injection tests.

A comparison of the in-situ field permeability, calculated from the borehole tests, and the intergranular permeabilities of core samples from the borehole, in conjunction with a visual examination of the cores, provides a good indication not only of the magnitude of groundwater flow but also of the mechanism by which groundwater will flow into the proposed excavation, i.e. whether by intergranular flow, by fissure flow, or by some combination of these two mechanisms. This information is of great importance in the selection of the most suitable process or processes by which groundwater inflow may be minimised during the construction work.

A number of processes are available, namely groundwater lowering, freezing, and grouting. In the planning of each individual project the processes must be assessed for their suitability. With the exception of relatively shallow excavations, where groundwater lowering may be feasible, grouting is probably the most widely used process in these sandstone formations.

If a grout is to be effective in reducing groundwater flow it must enter those passages in the rock which have the greatest potential to transmit groundwater.

Thus, before a grout is selected, it is necessary to determine the dimensions of the appropriate passages in the rock and to know the limiting size of passages into which the particular grouts can be injected.

In the context of intergranular grouting the mercury injection technique is particularly appropriate for obtaining the dimensions of the pores, for the method is itself based on an injection principle and establishes a "pore entry" dimension. Reference to Figures 2 and 3 shows that the maximum pore size requiring grouting in these sandstones is unlikely to exceed 300 microns and in some instances it may be necessary to grout sandstones with pores less than 50 microns in diameter.

It is variously reported that the use of cement grouts is limited to passages greater than 200-300 microns in size (Morfeldt, 1972). Thus cement grouts cannot be injected into the pores of these sandstones and especially fluid and penetrating chemical grouts are required. To grout sandstones with pores of less than about 50 microns, highly refined chemical grouts with negligible particulate content and a viscosity very similar to that of water are necessary. An example of their successful use in these sandstones has been reported (Moller, 1972).

In some instances where favourably arranged systems of open fissures occur at or near the surface or where stress relief has allowed the fissures to open, fissure flow is important and will greatly enhance the total permeability of the rock. However, it is considered that the permeation derived from fissures will be greatly diminished at depth, and that fissure contribution to field permeability will, for the most part, have been eliminated at depths where the effective stress exceeds some 5000 lb/in^2 (350 kg/cm^2). These conclusions, in general, are in accordance with experience in these sandstones.

If the exploratory boreholes indicate significant fissure flow then it will be necessary to grout these fissures. A careful examination of the cores will give some indication of fissure spacings and references to idealised calculations, such as illustrated in Fig. 7, indicates the order of size of the fissure openings.

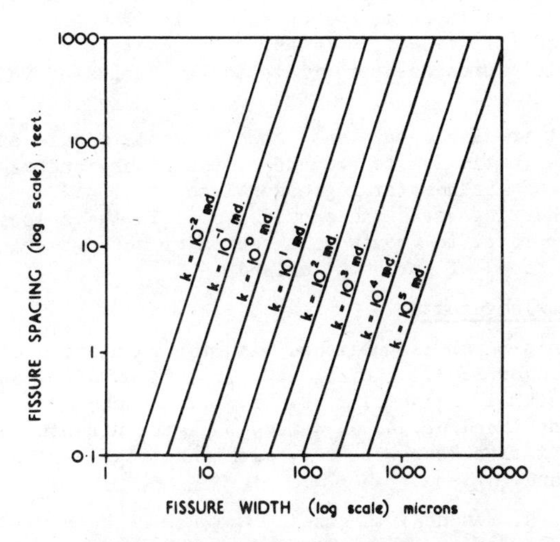

Fig. 7 HORIZONTAL PERMEABILITY OF ROCK CONTAINING IDEALIZED SYSTEMS OF HORIZONTAL FISSURES.

In near-surface projects and in zones of stress relief it may be possible to inject cement-based grouts into the fissures. However, reference to Table III and Fig. 6 suggests that, in most cases at depth, fissure openings will, in the absence of high grout injection pressures, be too small to accept cement-based grouts. Since there is a risk that high injection pressures may fracture the bedrock producing an increase in the field permeability and reducing control of the grouting process (Little et al, 1963), chemical grouts will be necessary to treat such fissures most effectively. In these cases, the chemical grout when set must be very stable and possess sufficient mechanical strength to resist extrusion from these fine fissures.

Conclusions

The intergranular permeability of the Permian and Triassic sandstones of northern England ranges from less than 0.01md to 10,000md and is considered to be only slightly reduced by overburden pressures even at the depths associated with deep mining.

Conversely, the fissure flow component of permeation is virtually eliminated by high applied stress and it is considered that fissure flow is, for the most part, a near surface phenomenon.

Thus the field permeability at any site in these sandstones results from a combination of intergranular flow, which tends to be a regional property, and fissure flow which tends to be a depth-dependent property.

Consequently the sandstones with high intergranular permeability will be very permeable at whatever depth they occur, and sandstones with negligible intergranular permeability will only be significantly permeable where favourable open fissure systems exist, in general, near ground surface.

The size of the pores and fissures is considered to restrict the use of cement grouts to the reduction of fissure permeation in near-surface situations, and in the majority of situations very fluid chemical grouts are required.

The findings show that the measurement of intergranular permeability at low applied stress in these sandstones is quite adequate, but that assessments of the contribution from fissure flow must be made at applied stresses appropriate to the depths of interest.

It is considered that these comments should enable better estimates to be made of the nature and magnitude of groundwater ingresses into civil and mining engineering works and should assist in the selection of appropriate grouts in these major water-bearing formations of northern England.

Acknowledgements

This paper is published with the permission of Professor A. N. Schofield, Department of Civil and Structural Engineering, U.M.I.S.T., Manchester, England, and Dr. A. N. James, Managing Director of Cementation Research Ltd., Rickmansworth, Herts., England.

F. A. Woodhead thanks the Science Research Council for the award of a maintenance grant.

The authors wish to acknowledge the initial contribution to this research made by Dr. J. M. Crook, formerly an S.R.C. Research Student in the Department of Civil and Structural Engineering, U.M.I.S.T., Manchester, England, and Dr. F. R. Morgan and Mr. D. C. Skinner, formerly with Cementation Research Ltd., Rickmansworth, Herts., England.

References

Bernaix, J. (1969). New laboratory methods of studying the mechanical properties of rocks. Int. J. Rock Mech. and Min. Sci., Vol.6, p.43.

Crook, J. M., and Howell, F.T. (1970). The Characteristics and Structure of the PermoTriassic Sandstone Aquifer of the Liverpool and Manchester Industrial Region of N. W. England. Int. Symp. on Groundwater, Palermo, Sicily, pp. 217-223.

Crook, J. M., Daw, G. P., Howell, F. T. and Morgan, F. R. (1971). The Permeation Properties of Unfissured Bunter Sandstones of Lancashire and Yorkshire. Geotechnique, 21, No.3, pp. 256-259.

Crook, J. M., Howell, F. T., Woodhead, F. A., Worthington, P. F. (1973). Permeation Properties of Bunter Sandstones from the Cheshire and Fylde Basins. Geotechnique, 23, No.2, pp. 262-265.

Daw, G. P. (1971). A Modified Hoek/Franklin Triaxial Cell for Rock Permeability Measurements. Geotechnique, 21, No.2, pp. 89-91.

Fatt, I. and Davis, D. H. (1952). Reduction in Permeability with Overburden Pressure. Technical Note 147, Petroleum Transactions, A.I.M.E., 195, p.329.

Gray, D. H., Fatt, I., and Bergamini, G. (1963). The Effect of Stress on Permeability of Sandstone Cores. Soc. Pet. Engnrs.J., 3, p.95.

Le Tirant, P. and Baron, C. (1972). Écoulement dans les roches fissurees et contraintes effectives application à la production d'hydrocarbures et à la fracturation hydraulique des reservoirs. Symp. Int. Soc. Rock Mech. and Int. Assoc. Engnr. Geol., Stuttgart, Sept. 1972.

Little, A. L., Stewart, J. C. and Fookes, P. J. (1963). Bedrock Grouting Tests at Mangla Dam, West Pakistan. Grouts and Drilling Muds in Engineering Practice. Butterworth, London, pp. 67-74.

Moller, K. (1972). Grouting now. The Consulting Engineer, Vol. 36, No. 8, Aug. 1972.

Morfeldt, C. O. (1972). Drainage problems in connection with tunnel construction in pre-Cambrian granitic bedrock in Sweden. Symp. Int. Soc. Rock Mech. and Int. Assoc. Engnr. Geol., Stuttgart, Sept. 1972.

Ritter, H. L. and Drake, L. C. (1945). Pore-size distribution in porous materials. Ind. and Engnr. Chem. Analytical Ed. Vol. 17, p.782.

Wilhelmi, B. and Somerton, W. H. (1967). Simultaneous Measurement of Pore and Elastic Properties of Rocks under Triaxial Stress Conditions. Soc. Pet. Engnrs. J., 7, p.283.

Wyble, D. O. (1958). Effect of Applied Pressure on the Conductivity, Porosity, and Permeability of Sandstones. Tech. Note 2022, Pet. Trans., A.I.M.E., 213, p.430.

1. M.M.

A

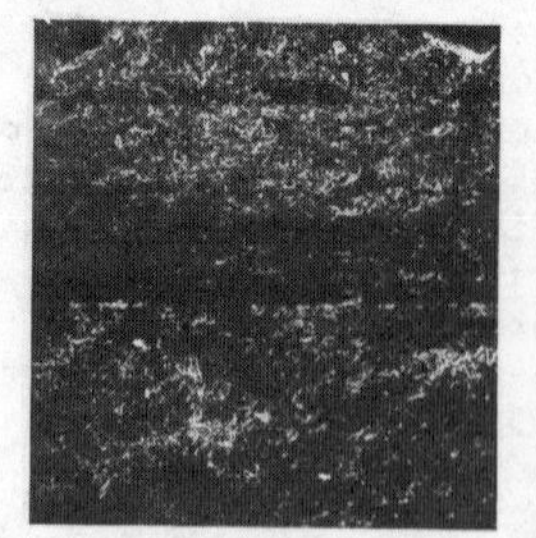

. 1. M.M.

B

Plate 1

A Coarse-grained, poorly-cemented sandstone.

B Fine-grained, well-cemented sandstone.

A STUDY OF THE STRESS STATE OF VIRGIN ROCK MASSES

D'ÉTUDE DE L'ÉTAT DE TENSION DES MASSIFS ROCHEUSES VIERGES

STUDIUM ÜBER DEN SPANNUNGSZUSTAND UNBERÜHRTER FELSMASSIVE

N.A. FILATOV
Cand. of Sciences

G.A. KRUPENNIKOV
Professor

VNIMI, Leningrad, U SSR

Summary

Our knowledge and concepts of stress states in virgin rocks depending on their genesis, basic characteristics and subsequent sustained influences play an important role in the studies of rock mechanics. Accurate data on initial stress in virgin rocks provide reliable and rational means of rock pressure control and underground timbering to be employed in commercial workings.

The report deals with integrated field, laboratory and analytical methods for research on this problem. Experimental determination both under field conditions and on models made of equivalent and optically - sensitive materials is exemplified; calculations of stresses in tectonically-disturbed, e.g. fractured, folded, areas as well as calculations to solve other yet inadequately - studied problems, such as stress in rocks under mountainous surface are reported.

A sequence of stress measurements requiring few basic data on the parameters of the whole rock mass and its individual components and on the mass geometry is suggested on the basis of the literature analysis and the authors' own experimental and theoretical studies.

Resume

Dans les études intéressant la mécanique des roches, les renseignements et les notions sur l'état de contrainte des massifs vierges en fonction de leur genèse, leurs propriétés initiales et des actions ultérieures jouent un rôle important. Le fait de connaître les tensions initiales dans de tels massifs permet de trouver, dans la mise en exploitation ultérieures de mines, des solutions plus sûres et plus économiques des preblèmes intéressant le contrôle de la pression régnant dans le roc et le soutenèment des ouvrages souterrains.

Dans ce rapport, on rend compte des procédés méthodiques complexes utilisés dans l'étude de ce problème, sur la base de l'emploi des méthodes extérieures, analytiques et de laboratoire. On donne des exemples de la détermination expérimentale des contraintes en conditions naturelles, ainsi que sur des modèles réalisés en matières équivalentes et optiquement sensibles; on présente plusieurs calculs des contraintes (tensions) pour les terrains à formes tectoniques (rompus, plissés) et pour quelques autres problèmes peu connus, y compris pour une région montagneuse.

L'analyse de l'état du problème, ainsi que les recherches expérimentales et théoriques exécutées par les auteurs, leur ont permis de proposer un schéma de succession de la détermination des valeurs des tensions, lequel exige une gamme limitée des données de départ sur les propriétés de l'ensemble d'un massif et de ses divers constituants, ainsi que des données sur la géométrie du massif.

Zusammenfassung

Eine wichtige Rolle spielen bei den Untersuchungen der Mechanik der Felsengesteine die Angaben bzw. Vorstellungen über den Spannungszustand ungestörter Gebirgsfelsenmassive je nach deren Genesis, Ausgangseigenschaften und nachfolgenden Einwirkungen. Die Kenntnis der Ausgangsspannungen in solchen Massiven ermöglicht eine sicherere und ökonomischere Lösung der Steuerungsaufgaben über den Gebirgsdruck und der Befestigung der unterirdischen Grubenbaue bei nachfolgenden Bergbaubetrieben.

Im Vortrag sind complexe Verfahrenswege bei Untersuchungen der angegebenen Problematik auf Grundlage naturgemässer, analytischer bzw. Labormethoden erörtert. Es wurden Beispiele experimenteller Feststellung von Spannungen unter den Naturverhältnissen sowie an Modellen aus äquivalenten und optisch empfindlichen Materialien angeführt. Es wurden einige Spannungsberechnungen für tektonisch gestörte Abschnitte (Bruchstörungen, Faltenzonen) sowie wenig untersuchte Aufgaben darunter auch für Gebirgsland angegeben.

Die Analyse der Problematik sowie die von den Autoren durchgeführten speziellen experimentellen bzw. theoretischen Untersuchungen ermöglichten ihnen die Vorlage eines Schemas der Reihenfolge bei der Feststellung der Spannungsgrössen, das geringe Ausgangsdaten über die Eigenschaften des gesamten Gebirgsmassives und dessen einzelne Komponenten sowie über die Geometrie des Massives erfordert.

The problem of state of stress in virgin rocks has constantly attracted the attention of many researchers. At present, there are over 150 original papers dealing with hypotheses, descriptions of research techniques, findings of various analytical and experimental investigations of this problem.

An analysis of earlier studies (G.A.Krupennikov) shows stresses in the earth crust interior to be variable in space and with time and dependent on many factors, such as gravitation, inertia forces due to the Earth rotation and forces generated by geoidal re-distribution of temperatures, to name the most important ones. Gravitation effect is characterized by both permanent and periodic, diurnal and annual components. Interior forces originate from the tectonic activity, e.g. continental drift, earthquakes, fractures and interaction of the crust portions.

A peculiar feature of the multistage re-distribution of interior stresses is that the development of this process is almost smooth within the stages and is extremely irregular in the intervals between adjacent stages. This is due to the stages being separated by limiting mechanical states of rocks. For instance, the compression stress in a heated part of the crust continuously grows, until the rock's ultimate strength value is reached. Once a rock failure occurs in this part, stress values show a sharp fall and, subsequently, tend to change gradually, until another limiting state has developed. When the limiting state is reached in brittle rocks, the stress development undergoes sudden abrupt changes of the type of second - order discontinuities. When it occurs in non-brittle rocks, these changes are characterized by considerable gradients of stress. To obviate this, rocks are sometimes frozen, sometimes - melted, drained or moistened; measures may be taken to reduce the head of underground waters and to regulate their flows. The extraction of water, oil and gases relieves the counter-pressure bearing on the overlying rock cover; likewise, the preliminary stoping of one of coal layers of the suite results in a stress re-distribution and ensures safety of mineral working (I.M.Petukhov).

Considering the existence of such a wide spectrum of possible combinations of actual mechanical systems, states, influences and interactions in the crust interior, it is difficult to formulate a single concept of the genesis and specific features of the stress state development in rocks and to evolve optimal methods of calculation of these stresses. However, owing to the great endeavour and ingenuity of many investigators and particularly, such as M.V.Gzovsky, Zh.S.Erzhanov, G.N.Kuznetsov, N.N.Maslov, I.A.Turchaninov, L.Müller, E.Leeman, L.Obert, G.Everling and others, some of the difficulties are being surmounted, and our knowledge of the initial mechanical states of rock masses is steadily extending and becoming more precise, although not so quickly, as the mining science and practice would require (L.Müller).

During nearly a century, the studies of this problem in different countries were carried on, chiefly, by analytical methods, and it was only recently that the results of experimental (both laboratory and field) as well as integrated investigations have been reported.

Conclusions on stress states in virgin rocks are generally sought for two purposes: (a) to get description of a region and (b) to solve some specific practical problems of rock mechanics. In the first case, detailed specific values of stresses and comprehensive characteristics of rock states are not required. It is sufficient to use the available data on the problem, which are arranged to meet the requirements of the task. The characteristics of the initial stresses in rocks were exemplified and discussed at the 1st and 2nd Congresses on Rock Mechanics (1966, 1970). The more correct the geometry of rock masses and the less forces they are subjected to, the less complicated and more specific is their state of stress. Under certain conditions, it is necessary to take into account the irregularity of the earth surface relief. Similarly, it would be wrong to disregard the multi-stage nature of the stress field formation, when doing research for seismic areas. The authors participated in doing analytical studies at the VNIMI for such areas; the results are given in [illegible] 1. Also, solutions for such problems by means the method of finite elements.

The determination of parameters of stress states in some specific rock masses requires, as a rule, to carry out field and laboratory studies and, sometimes, - individual analytical calculations. The combination of methods used of the VNIMI for solving such problems is shown in Table 1; the sequence of procedures for stress determination in such cases - in Table 2 (General instructions on use of methods).

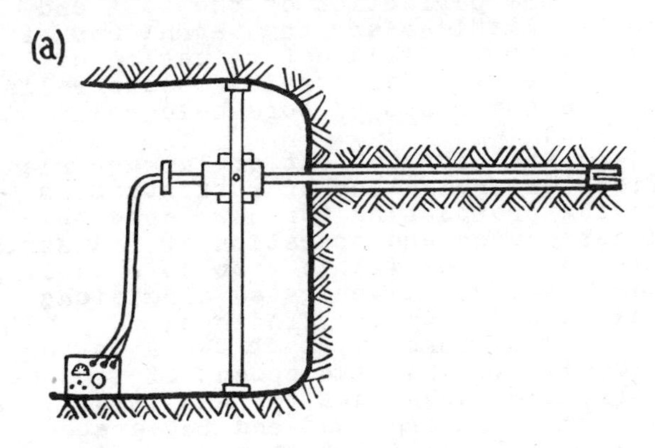

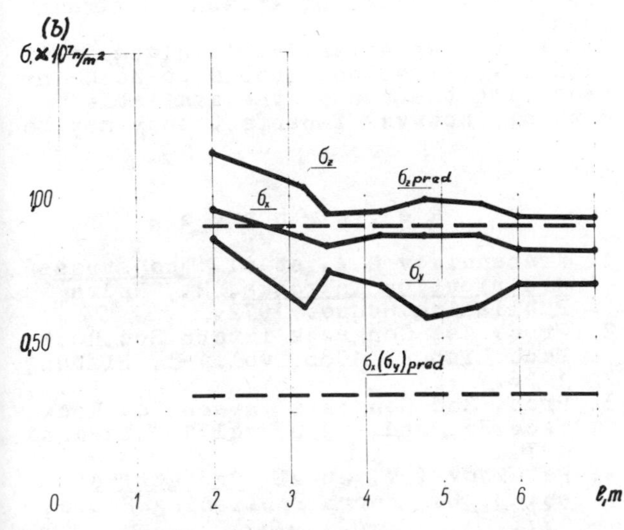

Fig.1. Stress measurements by complete relief of rock mass elements: (a) experimental scheme (b) measurement results.

Fig.1 shows the results of an underground measurement of stresses in virgin rocks obtained by means of the method of complete stress relieving (developed at the VNIMI) on an experimental site. It was confirmed for a number of specific rock masses that the mean vertical stress σ_z is, as a rule, a function of the thickness of the overlying rock cover. The elastic lateral pressure $\sigma_x (\sigma_y)$ is directly proportional to σ_z For different areas, $\sigma_x (\sigma_y) = \lambda \sigma_z = (0.5 - 0.9) \sigma_z$, although in some cases involving tectonic activity, and abnormal stress ($\lambda > 1$) was observed.

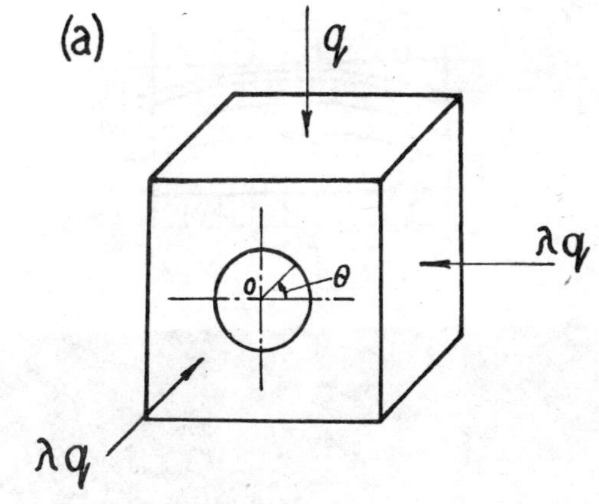

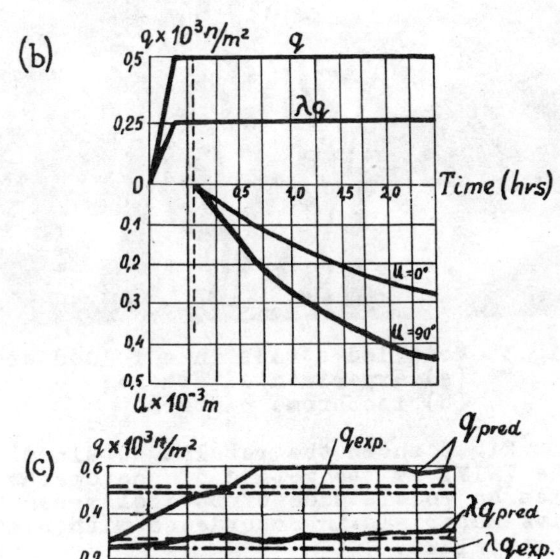

Fig.2. Improvement of methods for stress measurements by radial displacement of bore hole walls. (a) experimental scheme; (b) displacement measurement; (c) comparison of predictions and experimental data.

Fig.2 shows experimental results obtained from models made of equivalent materials. The experiments were carried on with a view to improve the method for measuring of bore hole wall displacement employed in underground determinations of stresses in rocks. These studies were carried out on an a VNIMI Special three-dimensional test bench (G.N.Kuznetsov).

(a)

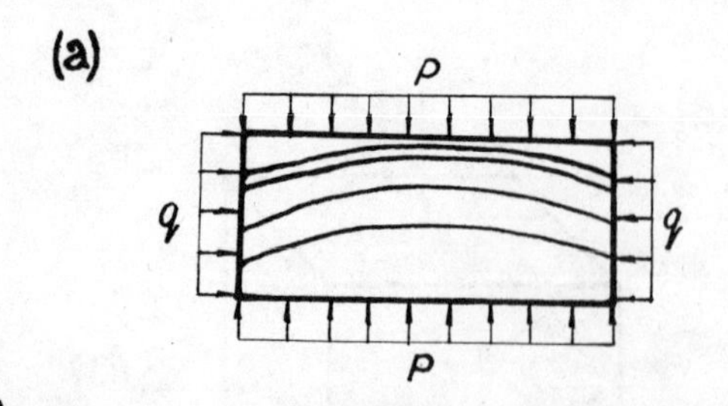

(b)

Fig.3. Modelled stress in a folded area:
(a) experimental scheme;
(b) isochrome pattern.

Fig.3 shows the results obtained at the VNIMI by the method of photomechanics on models made of optically-sensitive materials in accordance with similarity laws.

Recent years have seen the intensification of contacts between experts on this problem, the rapprochement of viewpoints; our knowledge of stresses in virgin rocks has improved (I.A.Turchaninov). Cooperation between scientists from the USSA, CSSR and other countries has been started. Special consideration in these studies has been given to the problems of accuracy and reliability of data measurements. It has been established that the deviation of stress values due to the inaccuracy of basic data is as high as 20-30% of the mean value of the desired parameter for gravitation-induced stress fields and about 40-50% - for mixed gravitational-tectonic stress fields, respectively.

Further development and improvement of techniques of forecasting states of stress in virgin rocks are generally regarded as most important and urgent ones. Priority will be given to the following aspects in future studies:

- the perfection of the best and most reliable means and techniques of experimental field determination of stresses, such as strain rosette-relief and measurements of bore hole wall strain;
- the carrying out of large-scale field determination of rock stresses during prospecting for new deposits, construction and operation of industrial enterprizes with a view to extending the range of investigated conditions and to refining the findings;
- the improvement of the existing methods and the development of fundamentally new techniques for analytical, laboratory, underground and integrated studies of states of stress in virgin rocks.

A further extensive development of such investigations should go hand-in-hand with the use of the available methods, however imperfect they may be.

The VNIMI was represented by V.M.Barkovsky, Cand.of Sci. (Tech.).

References

1. Krupennikov G.A. et al. The stress distribution in rocks, M., Nedra Publishing House, 1972.
2. Proc. 1st Congress Intern.Soc.Rock Mech.Lisbon, 1966, vol.1-3, Lisbon, 1966.
3. Proc. 2nd Congress Intern.Soc.Rock Mech.Beograd, 1970, vol.1-3,Beograd, 1970.
4. Petukhov I.M. et al. Protective seams. L., Nedra Publishing House, 1972.
5. Müller L. Rock mechanics. Translated from German. M., Mir Publishing House, 1971.
6. General instructions on use of methods for integrated studies of geomechanical problems. Transactions of the VNIMI, vol.81, L., publ-d by the VNIMI, 1970.
7. Turchaninov I.A. et al. The laws of present-day stress state of the earth crust established by means of direct observations. Theses Report Gen. Assem.Intern.Geodes. and Geophys.Un. M., publ-d by the All-Union Institute of Research and Technological Information, 1970.
8. Kuznetsov G.N. et al. Models of rock pressure manifestations. L., Nedra Publ. H., 1968.

Table 1

The system of methods for integrated studies

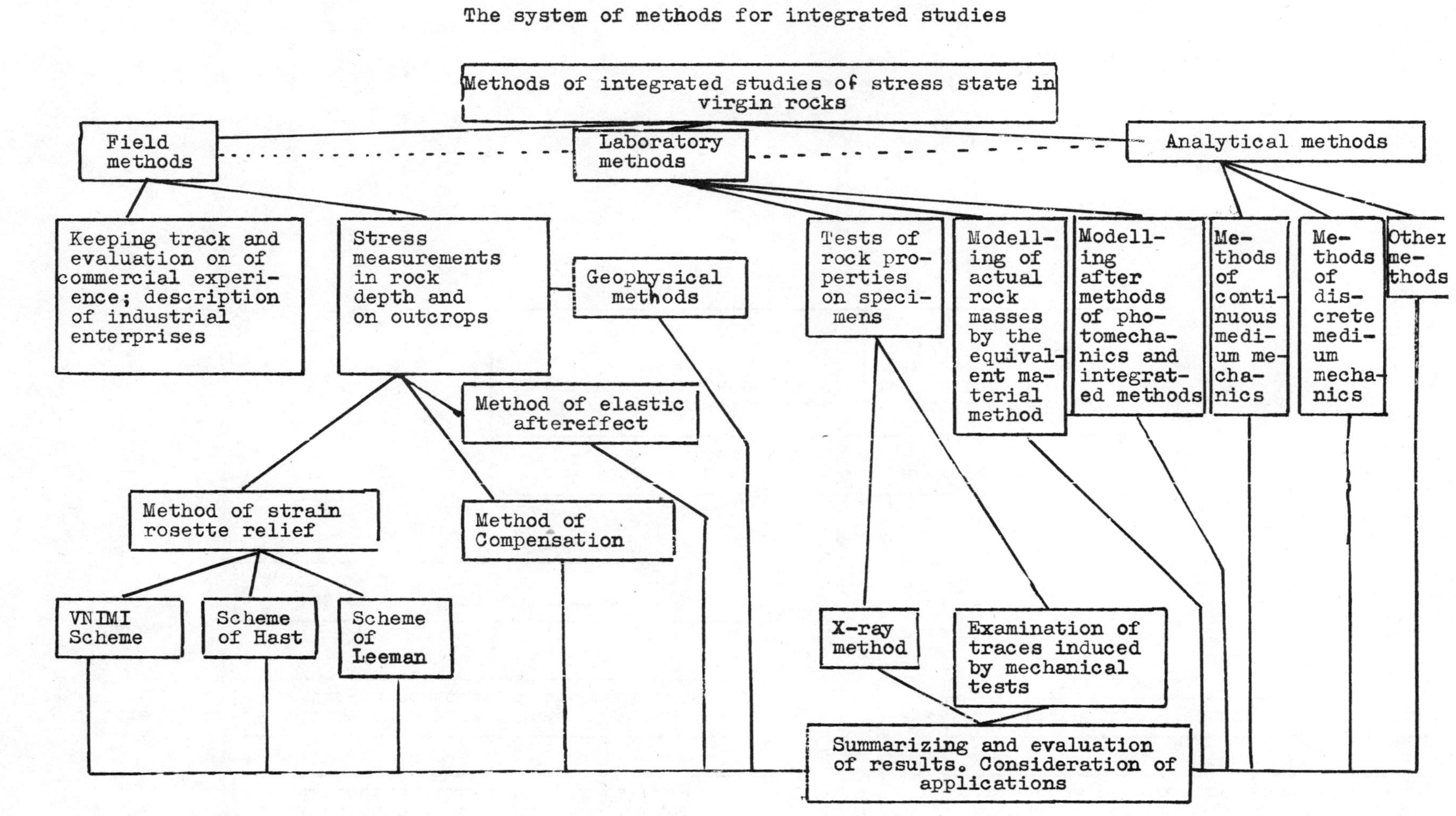

Table 2

The sequence of procedures for stress determination in virgin rocks

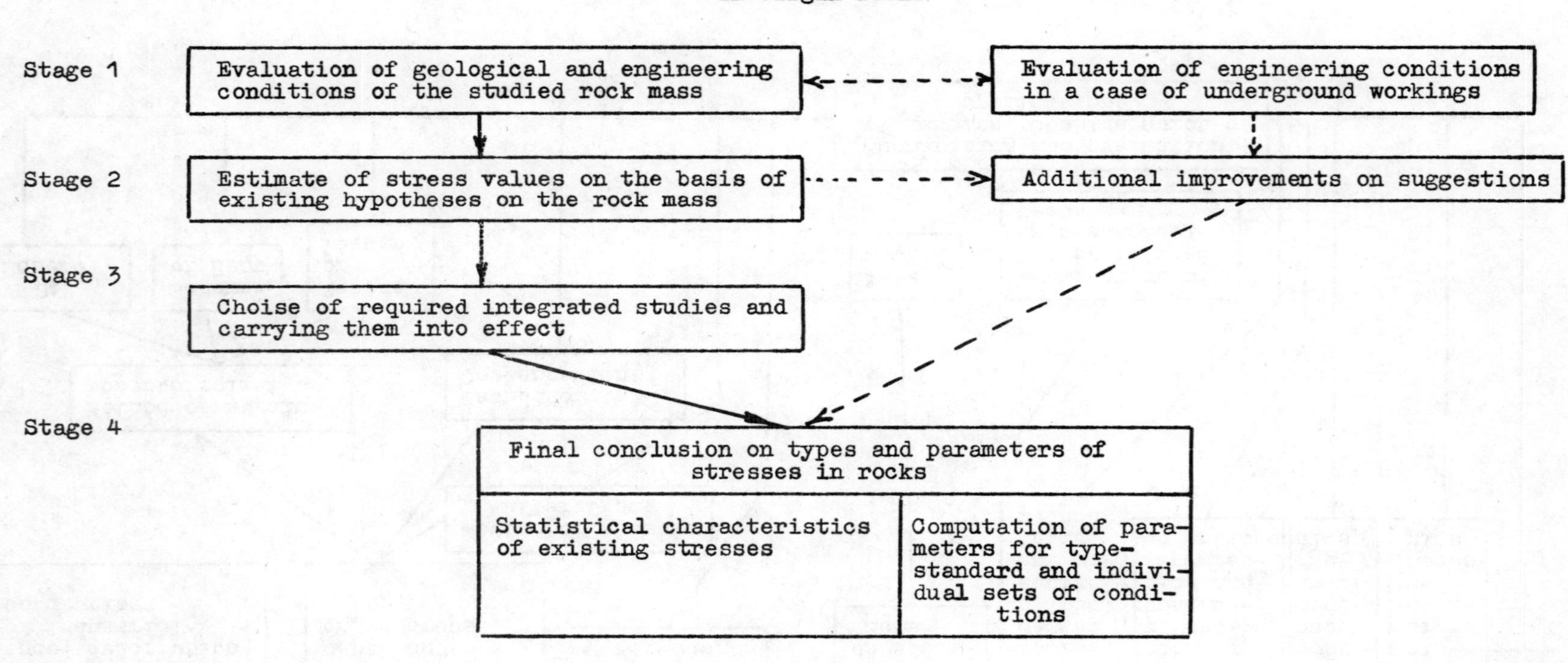

INTERNAL STRESSES IN ROCK AS A RESULT OF GRANULAR STRUCTURE AND AXIAL CATACLASIS; ACOUSTIC MEASUREMENTS

LES CONTRAINTES INTERNES, COMME RÉSULTAT DE LA STRUCTURE GRANULAIRE ET DE LA CATACLASE AXIALE; DES MESURES ACOUSTIQUES

INTERNE SPANNUNGEN IM GESTEIN ALS FOLGE DER KÖRNIGEN STRUKTUR UND DER ACHSIALEN KATAKLASE; AKUSTISCHE MESSUNGEN

J. GRAMBERG

Mining Engineer

Laboratory of Mining Technology

Delft University of Technology

Delft, The Netherlands

SUMMARY

The elastic and cataclastic-plasto-elastic equilibrium in rock is considered depending upon three kinds of stress :

a) Loading macro stresses;

b) vagabond micro stresses between grains and crystals and

c) induced minute-micro stresses at the boundaries of inhomogeneities.

The equilibrium of stresses in the rock material is discussed; measuring vagabond micro stresses by means of acoustic travel time (velocity) measurements and numerical results are treated.

ZUSAMMENFASSUNG

Das elastische und kataklastisch-plasto-elastische Gleichgewicht in Gestein scheint abhängig zu sein von drei verschiedenen Spannungsarten :

a) von der Belastung : Makrospannung,

b) von den vagabondierenden Mikrospannungen zwischen den Gefügeteilen wie Mineralkörner,

c) von den induzierten sehr kleinen Mikrospannungen (minute-micro stress) an den spitzen Grenzen von Inhomogenitäten z.B. von Rissen und Mikro-Rissen.

Das Spannungsgleichgewicht im Gestein wird diskutiert, die Ergebnisse der Messungen der vagabondierenden Mikrospannungen und die numerischen Resultate werden betrachtet.

RÉSUMÉ

L'équilibre cataclastique-plasto-élastique interne des roches est considéré dépendant de trois types de contraintes :

a) La pression causée par la charge, la contrainte macro (macro stress),

b) Les contraintes micro-vagabondes entre les grains des minéraux,

c) Les contraintes minuscule-micros, aux confins pointus des inhomogénités.

L'équilibre des contraintes dans les roches est discuté; les résultats des mesures acoustiques des contraintes micro-vagabonds par les ondes ultrasoniques et des résultats numériques sont traités.

INTRODUCTION

Rock fracturing is caused by stresses.
As a result of fracture analysis we come to the conclusion that generally three kinds of stress are involved.
Fracturing in the sense of fracture initiation and propagation is the result of internal minute micro stresses, which refer to very small volumes of atomic dimensions. These minute micro stresses are controled by the very local and vagabond micro stresses in the grains and granules.
The value of the average of these micro stresses represents the loading macro stresses, usually known as "the stresses" which should match the stresses calculated on the basis of the theory of elasticity. One of the topics of interest of rockmechanicists and geomechanicists is the knowledge of the relationship between these calculated macro stresses and the fracture phenomena as a result of minute micro stresses.
The vagabond micro stresses, however, seem to escape from the attention, whereas in fact they control the minute micro stresses and the cataclastic equilibrium as well (Ref. 6).
In this paper the author will try to explain the relationship between the three kinds of stress in the case of a most simple and systematic fracture phenomenon : the axial cleavage fracture (by some authors also denoted as extension fracture).

I. THEORY OF THE AXIAL CLEAVAGE FRACTURE

1. The ellipse-with-notch model.

The axial cleavage fracture is a non-complex fracture type. It is caused by induced tensile stress, which has developed perpendicular to the compression, where no shear stress is involved, fig. 1-b, c, d. The occurence of the axial cleavage fracture can be explained with the ellipse-with-notch model (Ref. 1, 5a, 5b).
The line of thought is depicted in Fig. 2. The model has been inspired by the Theory of Griffith, see fig. 2-a, (Ref. 7, 9). To explain the axial cleavage fracturing, however, a new model of a more composite nature has been proposed, see fig. 2-b, c, a model ellipse and a notch on top of

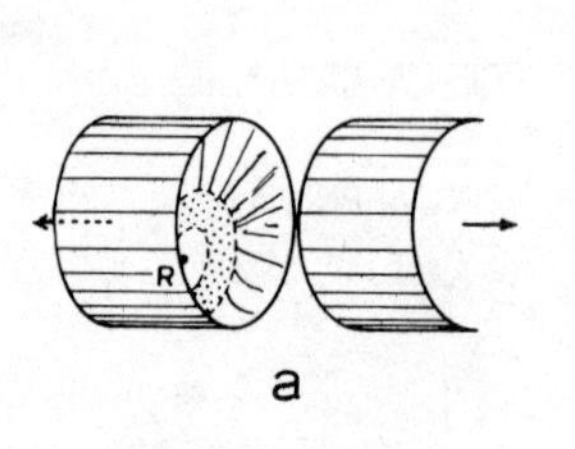

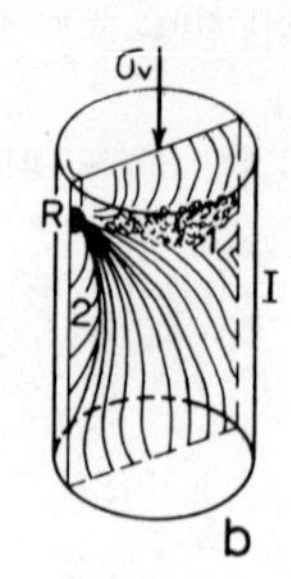

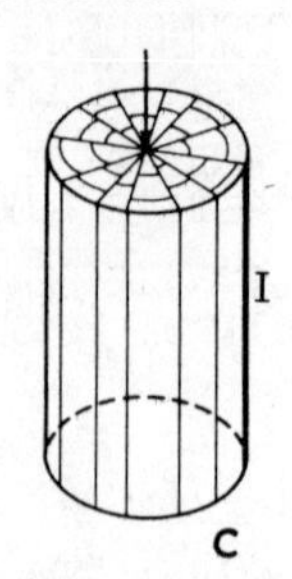

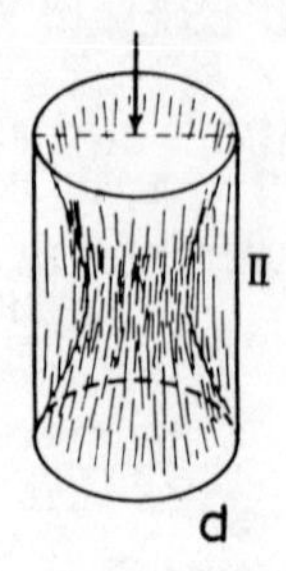

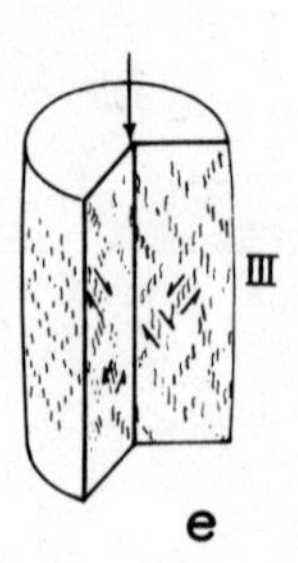

Fig. 1 Primary fracture phenomena : a. Lineations on direct tensile fracture plane. b. The same kind of lineations are found on the axial cleavage fracture plane, caused by indirect, induced, tension : monofracture. c. axial cleavage fracture repeated : multifracture. d. axial cleavage cataclasis. e. primary multishear cataclasis exists as well.

it. The main axis of the model ellipse extends in the direction of the main pressure. This ellipse represents the crack or part of it. The dimensions of the model-ellipse are relatively large and its shape may vary from very long and flat to short and roundish.
The short axis might have the dimension of some 3,000 atom diameters or about 1μ. Material and model ellipse are considered to match the rules of the theory of elasticity. According to this theory, an opening with elliptical section situated in the above mentioned position in a uniaxial stress field, shows tensile stresses at the top of the ellipse. These tensile stresses σ_{ti} are perpendicular to the compression, i.e. the tension has been induced by the compression. In this way the mechanism of induction is explained, fig. 2-b. However, the value of the induced tension σ_{ti} is relatively small. In order to cause fracture begin or propagate stress concentration is required. This occurs at the very sharp notch in the ellipse top, representing the very fracture tip, the site where the atomic cohesive forces are severed. Both the fracture tip and the induced stress field have very, very small dimensions called minute micro dimensions. Therefore this stressfield is called the induced minute micro tensile stressfield. In this way the situation in minute micro dimensions compares directly with the Griffith-cracktip in a tensile loading condition, see fig. 2-a. Thus a stress concentration with a concentration factor n proportional to $1/\rho$, develops very locally ρ being the radius in the top of the notch, the very fracture tip, represented again by a minute ellipse in the sense of Griffith, fig. 2-c.
The fracture tip in this figure is in fact a section through the edge of the fracture. This edge forms a line which cuts through the material. At any moment the progressing edge meets with a complex of different grains, crystals, and inhomogeneities. In this way we come to the hypothesis, that his state of affairs leads to an average factor n which is constant for a particular material and that it is incorporated in the value of the experimental tensile strength σ_t, determined by a relevant method, such as the Brazilian or Disk test.
Based on this hypothesis we may consider that we are only dealing with the relatively large model ellipse.
As a conclusion this model-ellipse shows the section of a cavity and it has an axial ratio of V = a/b. It is thought situated within a continuous elastic medium, which is subject to the stresses P and Q or σ_1 and σ_3.
The induced stress at the top of the ellipse has the value σ in the equation :

$$\sigma = P\ (k - 1 + 2\ kV) \qquad (1a)$$

$$k = Q_p \text{ or } \sigma_3/\ \sigma_1;\ V = a/b$$

or

$$= -P + Q\ (1 + 2a/b) \qquad (1b)$$

Negative values of σ, referred to as σ_{ti}, denote that a tensile stress is induced and that only then axial fracturing is possible.
σ_{ti} occurs wher $0 \leq Q < 1/3$ P.
or when $0 \leq k < 0{,}333$.
In the case of axial fracturing $_{ti}$ must have reached the value of σ_t, i.e. the average tensile strength.
With the help of these models a number of fracture phenomena can be explained, such as were observed in the laboratory as well as in underground mines, caused by mining operations (Ref. 3, 2) and also phenomena observed in exposures at the surface due to natural tectonics (Ref. 4a, 4c).

2. Two observations contributing to the acceptance of the internal pressure Q_i.

a) In uniaxial laboratory tests on cylindrical specimen of rock several kinds of axial cracking may occur. In the case of hypidiomorphic granular structure (e.g. granite, quartzite) an axial cleavage cataclasis develops, fig. 1-d. The axial cracks are the result of induced minute micro stresses σ_{ti}, but the development of these stresses must have been hampered by an internal transverse pressure Q or Q_i or σ_{3i} (Ref. 6.1, fig. 24 and P.62). It develops within the material as a result of both axial loading and the structure of the material. The latter is concluded from the observation that the fracture propagation in fine grained brittle material is not at all or only slightly hindered. As a result axial mono- and multi-fractures form, fig. 1-b, 1-c.
The induced transverse pressure Q_i reduces the induced stress σ_{ti} according to the term Q_i (1 + 2 a/b) in equation 1-b.
Q_i or σ_{3i} is an internal supporting pressure by which the supporting capacity of the material i

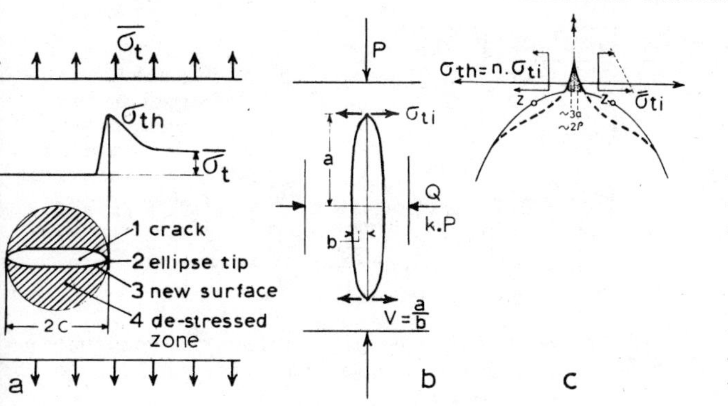

Fig.2a Fracture initiation after Griffith (Griffith crack). b, c. Ellipse-with-notch model. P : loading macro stress. Q : vagabond micro stress. σ_{ti} : minute microstress

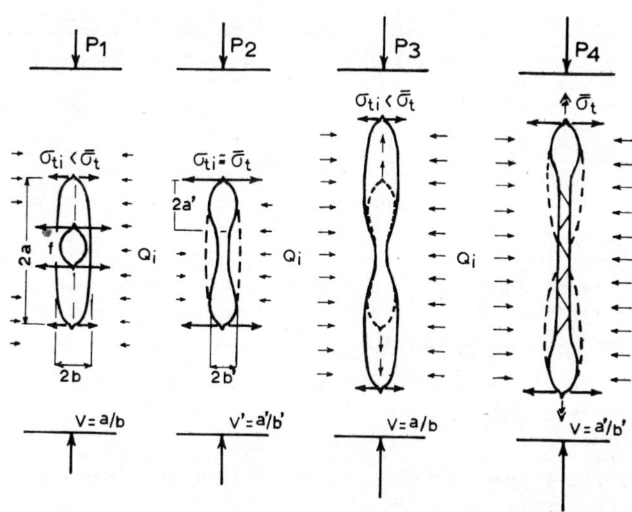

Fig. 3 Intermittent development of the axial crack a. crack initiation in flaw R, i.e. $\sigma_{ti} = \bar{\sigma}_t$; in the meantime Q_i develops locally and it reduces σ_{ti} to a value $< \bar{\sigma}_t$. Crack development stops. b. Constriction of the central part as a result of Q_i (time effect) makes the "boundary ellipses" short and roundish; consequently σ_{ti} increases again to $\bar{\sigma}_t$ and fracture develops further on : c, d.

controlled and improved.

b) In the case of the development of axial cataclasis the crack development can be followed by detecting and counting the micro seismic crack pulse activity. From these observations it is obvious that the cracks develop intermittently, see fig. 3.
In this system P is the loading macro stress; Q_i or σ_{3i} represents the vagabond micro stress and σ_{ti} is the induced minute micro stress.

II THE APPLICATION OF MICROSEISMIC AND ACOUSTIC METHODS TO ESTIMATE Q_i OR σ_{3i}

1. The meaning of acoustic travel time

It was shown above that axial cataclasis is related to an internal transverse pressure Q_i in the material.
From the theory of elasticity, in which theory the material of a test cylinder is considered to be continuous and without containing discontinuities such as grainboundaries and micro-cracks, it follows - on the contrary - that transverse tensile stress will develop in the inside up to about 0,01 P.
In that case the axial fracture is not hampered and it will propagate continuously as mono- and multifracture. This occurs indeed in the case of fine grained material, fig. 1-b, c.
In the case of axial cleavage cataclasis, however, fig. 1-d) the occurrence of the transverse pressure Q_i is very obvious, and it is supposed to be the result of hypidiomorphic granular structure.
In order to investigate this point, measurements of the acoustic travel time (velocity) of the elastic wave were carried out.
The obtained travel time of the acoustic wave in rock is the result of two structural elements, mainly :
a. The massive structure of the intact and unfractured parts of the rock, such as grains, crystals and fragments of these; the travel time through these parts is almost insensitive to pressure differences.
b. The discontinuities such as cracks and micro cracks in grains and crystals and the grain- and crystal boundaries, i.e. pores of a planar shape; they increase the travel time considerably.
This increase is very sensitive to pressure.

Volarovich (Ref. 10) states : "The increase in velocity is connected with the increase in number and area of contacts between the grains of minerals. This is due to the closing of micro-fractures under pressure and the partial closing of volume pores ....".
The traveltime reaches its maximum when the contacts between the walls of the flat pores and cracks have become perfect.
According to Volarovich this is the case for granites at pressures between 1,500 and 2,000 kgf/cm^2.
In our experiments travel time decrease (velocity increase) is called "compaction", compaction is the result of better contact and therefore it is interpreted as a pressure increase in the direction of the wave propagation.
Travel time increase (velocity decrease) is the result of looser structure. It is called "decompaction" and it is interpreted as a pressure decrease. If at some moment the travel time reaches a value above that at zero load, whereas no fracturing has occurred, it denotes that at that moment the structure was looser than the original one. This condition indicates the presence of an internal tensile stress within the solid.

2. Travel time measurements in different materials

In order to check the above interpretation, travel time measurements were carried out with a number of very different materials in uniaxial compression. Steel 37, steel 64, nodular cast iron (perlendite), optical glass BK 7, lithographic limestone of the bluish-gray quality, a pyroxenite with granular structure but with high density and a granite - see Table I.

Table I
Lateral compaction (positive) and decompaction (negative) in % of zero-load traveltime and per 1,000 kgf/cm² load increase.

Steel 37	-0.027%	decomp.)	transverse
Steel 64	-0.039%	decomp.)	tension
Cast iron	+0.516%	comp.)	
glass BK7	+0.09 %	comp.)	
lith.limest	+0.10 %	comp.)	transverse
Pyroxenite		)	compression
Cycle I	+0.50%	comp.)	
Cycle II	+1,36%	comp.)	
Granite		)	
Cycle I	+7 to +17%	comp.)	see also
Cycle II	+7 to +17%	comp.)	fig. 7b.

Steel 37 and 64 show small, but significant transversal decompactions between - 0.027 and -0.039% per 1,000 kgf/cm². This indicates that there is a looser structure in that direction, in this case, however, it is not caused by the opening of micro cracks or by cracking.
We will associate this effect with internal transverse tensile stresses, which is in accordance with the theoretical calculations. All other materials, however, show a lateral compaction, which is associated with a transversal pressure Q_i.
When comparing the different materials we arrive at the conclusion that the percentage of the transversal compactions seems to be higher in the case where the original structure was looser, i.e. in the case where the material originally contains more micro cracks and crystal boundaries. The conclusion is that the lateral compaction and the internal lateral pressure Q_i are indeed the result of the presence of planar discontinuities and granular structure as was already deduced from the occurrence of axial cataclasis

3. Vagabond micro stresses

In order to explain the role of the granular structure we imagine a section in the axial direction through a test cylinder - fig. 4.
The horizontal components of the vagabond micro stresses in the mineral grains form an equilibrium in the micro-sense, i.e. between grains and parts of grains.
The horizontal compressive components are considered responsible for the locally better contacts and also for the travel time decrease (compaction), which has been interpreted as $+Q_i$.
It follows from the equilibrium that there must exist micro tensions $-Q_i$ as well, carried by the massive parts of the grains and the crystals themselves.

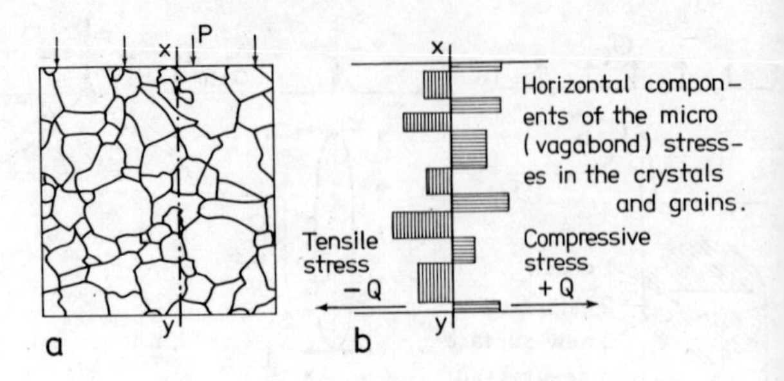

Fig. 4 Equilibrium of the horizontal components of the micro-vagabond-stresses in the section x-y.

III AN ATTEMPT TO MEASURE THE DEVELOPMENT OF THE INTERNAL PRESSURE Q_i DURING THE COMPRESSION TEST

1. The four load trajects

It is known that rocks, with a hypidiomorphic granular structure such as granite and quartzite, show the first signs of destruction by cracking at about 50% of the maximum failure load.
The total load traject can be divided into 4 part

A : 0 - 50% the intact traject,
B : 50 - 75% the cataclastic-stable traject,
C : 75 - 98% the cataclastic-unstable traject,
D : 98 - 100% the process of failure, which can be investigated with the "stiff compression machines".

We confine ourselves, however, to the trajects A, B and C.

2. A simple model for the cataclastic equilibrium in granite

In order to demonstrate our ideas on the possible mechanisms and effects of compaction, decompactio

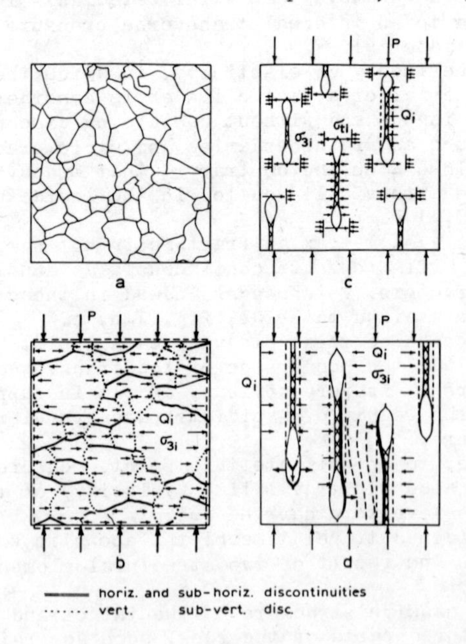

Fig. 5 The cataclastic model

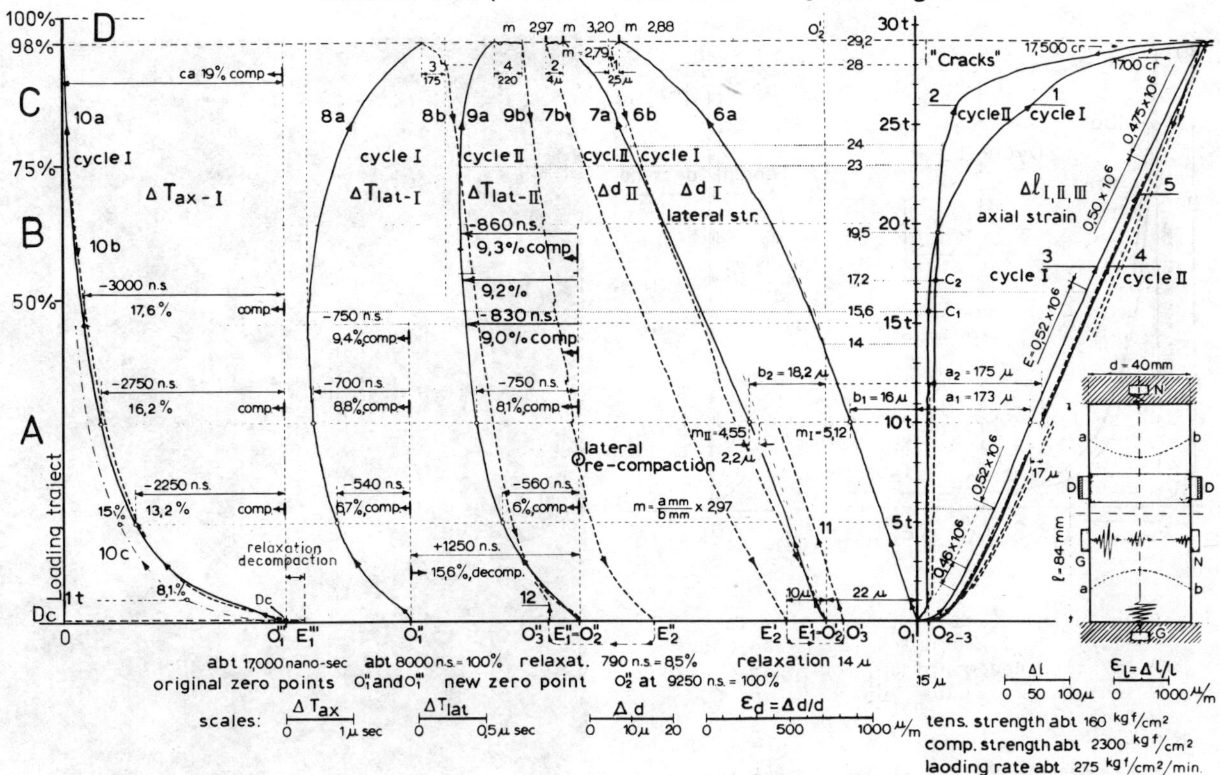

Fig. 6.

Uniaxial compressive test on hard granite; the specimen, diameter 40 mm, length 84 mm, has been loaded three times : 0 - 29,2 ton in Cycle I and II; the third time it collapsed at 28 ton.

Line 1-2	: crack pulse counting.
Line 3-5	: stress-strain curves for the axial direction.
Line 6-7	: stress-strain curves for the lateral direction.
Lines 8-9	: travel time differences showing compaction; the data in % are based on the 100% travel time of resp. 8,000 n.s. for intact and 9,250 n.s. for cataclastic structure.
Line 10c	: travel time difference in the axial direction for the same specimen, registrated during the first intact traject only.
Line 10 a-b:	travel time difference of a different specimen of the same rock

and lateral expansion before and after axial cracking a very simple cataclastic model is constructed, fig. 5.
The hypidiomorphic granular structure is characterised by the presence of planar pores in the shape of crystal boundaries and granular cracks, evenly spread in all directions. Fig.5-a. These planar pores are schematically divided in a horizontal and sub-horizontal and a vertical and sub-vertical group, respectively, fig. 5-b.
In the cataclastic model these planar pores, including cracks, are being regarded - idealized - as planar interfaces, more or less systematically arranged in the horizontal and vertical direction. Such planar pores and newly formed axial cracks prove to have a similar effect on the travel time of the elastic wave. Therefore the axial or vertical system is very schematically represented by the picture of model-cracks, fig. 5-c.
The material between these model-cracks and later on also between the virtual axial cracks, is considered solid and thus forms laminae, fig. 5-d.

3. Uniaxial compressive test with granite

With the aid of this model a number of phenomena can be explained, occurring in granite under uniaxial compression, fig. 6.
This figure shows the record of a two-cycle axial compressive test, cycle I and II. Within the load traject A the properties of the original structure are revealed. During the load trajects B and C, however, the structure is changed by axial cataclasis, with its additional effects. The following elements are considered with respect to the structural behaviour, before and after axial cataclasis.

a) Axial compaction (i.e. in the vertical direction) is caused by the closure of horizontal planar cracks as a result of uniaxial pressure. The compaction approaches its maximum value at a pressure between 1,500 and 2,500 kgf/cm^2, in full accordance with Volarovich's statement - line 10-a, fig. 6. It is not or almost not affected by axial cracking in the load trajects

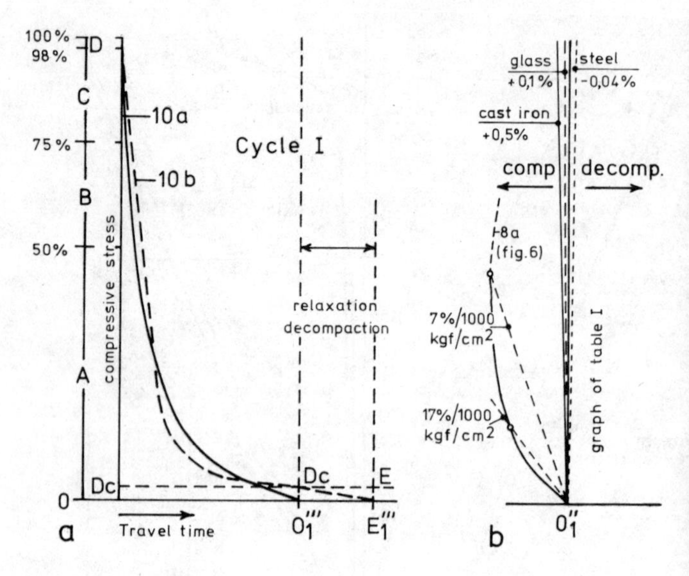

Fig. 7a Longitudinal (axial) travel time in loading (10a) and unloading (10b). Dc-E = relaxation decompaction, associated with a tensile stress OD_c, up to 30 and 60 kgf/cm^2

b Graphical representation of table I. Steel shows transverse decompaction, which is principally different from glass, cast iron and rock, all of them showing lateral compaction.

B and C.

b) Axial strain is only to a minor extent affected by axial cataclasis occurring in the trajects B and C, see line 3. In the second cycle it differs only 15 to 17 μ from the first cycle - line 4.

c) Lateral compaction, associated with the lateral pressure Q_i, is caused by the closure of the vertical model-cracks, see fig. 5-c. In this model it is considered mainly a result of bending of the laminae, fig. 5-d. and of Poisson--expansion of the laminae. Probably other mechanisms play a role as well, but they can not be demonstrated by this simple model. The lateral compaction is considerable. In the first loading, cycle I, the maximum is 750 n.s., (see line 8-a), whereas the second loading, cycle II, shows a larger lateral compaction of 860 n.s. The difference is due to new cracks formed in the traject B and C during the first cycle. This is registrated as 1,700 crackpulses, fig. 6, line 1.

d) Lateral expansion, the large lateral strain - line 6a and 7a in fig. 6, is mainly due to the forming of new cracks and the further extension of existing ones - see line 1 and 2, resp. 1,700 and 17,500 crackpulses being registered.
The effect after unloading is a semi-permanent strain of resp. 22μ and (22+10) = 32μ, showing 14μ relaxation within 2 days (E'_2 - O'_3).

e) Relaxation decompaction is observed during unloading both in the axial direction and in the transverse or lateral direction. It is followed

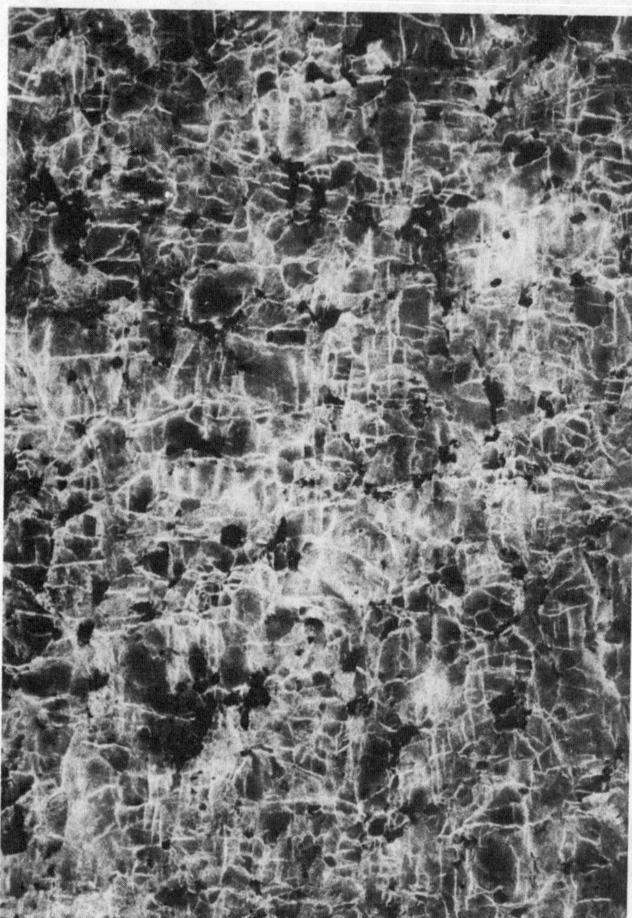

Fig 8 Central part of a section through a cylindrical specimen of granite, after triaxial loading. Confining pressure 150 kgf/cm^2, maximum load 4,700 kgf/cm^2. Cracks are made visible in infra-red light after treatment with zyglo Super Pentrex ZL-22. Note that the vertical cracks, due to axial cleavage cracking are more straight than the horizontal ones, due to relaxation (Ref. 6, p. 94; 8, fig. 10).

by recompaction, a time effect.
Small lateral recompactions are shown on line 9-b (circle) and large lateral recompaction is shown on the base of the figure between the points E_2" and O_3" denoted by "relaxation 790 n.s. = 8,5%". This process has taken 2 days.
Relaxation decompaction in the axial direction is denoted by the distance D_c - E" in fig. 6, line 10-b and fig. 7.
Under extreme circumstances relaxation decompaction can result in relaxation cracking - fig. 8. The phenomena of compaction, decompaction and relaxation are related to the vagabond micro stresses, Q_i or σ_{3i}.

4. Numerical estimation of Q_i

According to the simple cataclastic model it is supposed that axial and lateral compaction are

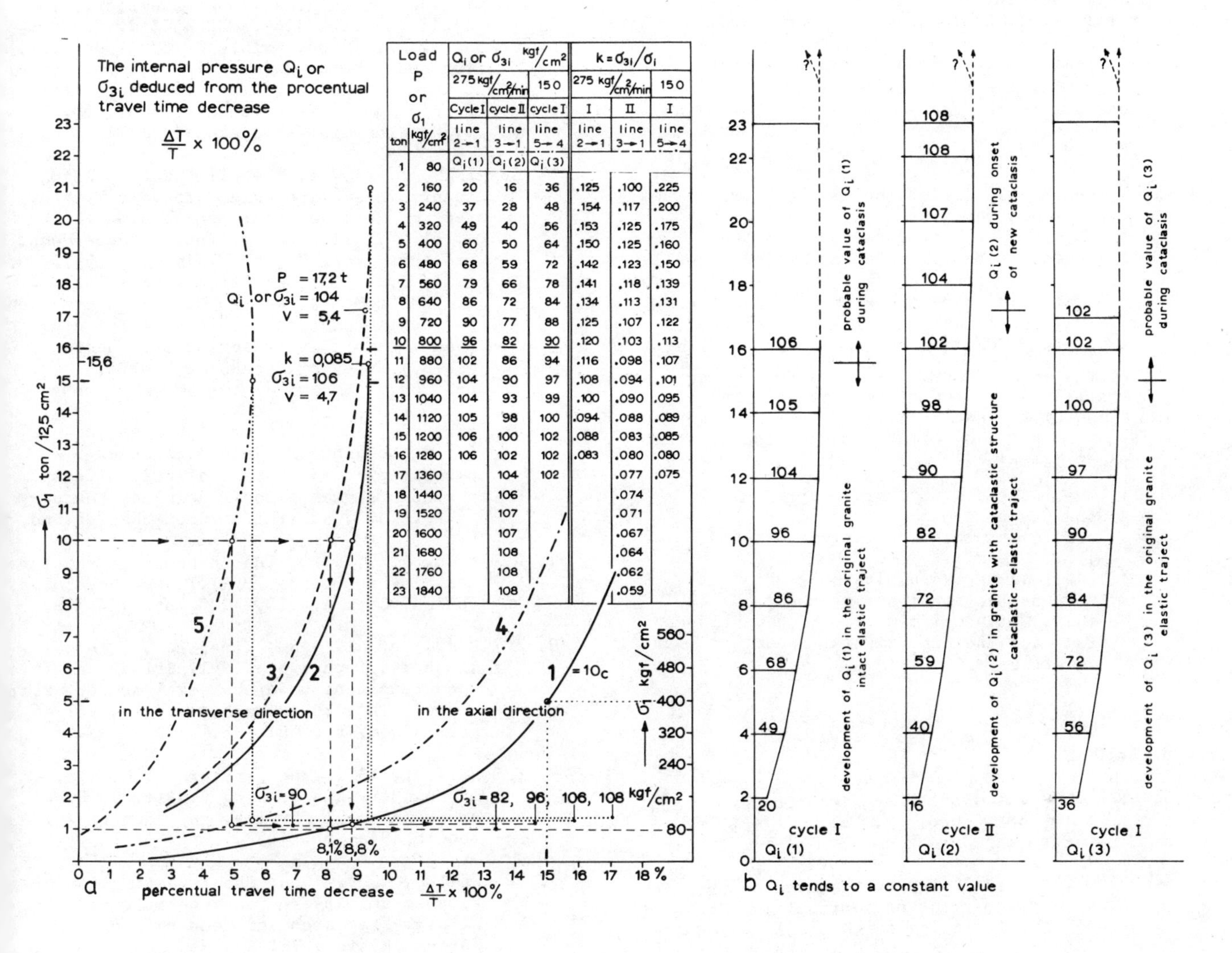

Load P or σ_1 (ton)	Load P or σ_1 (kgf/cm²)	Q_i or σ_{3i} kgf/cm², 275 kgf/cm²/min, Cycle I, line 2→1, Q_i(1)	Q_i or σ_{3i}, 275 kgf/cm²/min, cycle II, line 3→1, Q_i(2)	Q_i or σ_{3i}, 150, cycle I, line 5→4, Q_i(3)	$k = \sigma_{3i}/\sigma_i$, 275 kgf/cm²/min, I, line 2→1	k, 275 kgf/cm²/min, II, line 3→1	k, 150, I, line 5→4
1	80						
2	160	20	16	36	.125	.100	.225
3	240	37	28	48	.154	.117	.200
4	320	49	40	56	.153	.125	.175
5	400	60	50	64	.150	.125	.160
6	480	68	59	72	.142	.123	.150
7	560	79	66	78	.141	.118	.139
8	640	86	72	84	.134	.113	.131
9	720	90	77	88	.125	.107	.122
10	800	96	82	90	.120	.103	.113
11	880	102	86	94	.116	.098	.107
12	960	104	90	97	.108	.094	.101
13	1040	104	93	99	.100	.090	.095
14	1120	105	98	100	.094	.088	.089
15	1200	106	100	102	.088	.083	.085
16	1280	106	102	102	.083	.080	.080
17	1360		104	102		.077	.075
18	1440		106			.074	
19	1520		107			.071	
20	1600		107			.067	
21	1680		108			.064	
22	1760		108			.062	
23	1840		108			.059	

Fig. 9.

Estimation of the internal pressure Q_i

Lines 1 and 4 : percentual travel time decrease in the axial direction versus axial load for two different specimens of the same granite

Lines 2 and 3 : percentual travel time decrease in the transverse direction for Cycle I and II of the same specimen;

Line 5 : the same for the other specimen,

Cycle I. According to the cataclastic model for the hypidiomorphic granular structure and the axial cataclasis the paths of the arrows show the procedure to attain the values for Q_i or σ_{3i}

Note that Q_i seems to attain a constant value.

generated in the same way.
This hypothesis holds only in the case that there is no principal difference between the horizontal and the vertical or axial structural systems.
In the case of the hypidiomorphic granular structure of granite, where the discontinuities are mainly of the planar type, the above mentioned may be considered valid also with respect to cycle II, i.e. after the occurrence of axial fracturing during traject B and C in cycle I.
For a first approach it therefore seems acceptable to use the relationship between pressure and compaction in the axial (vertical) direction in order to calibrate the observed transversal compactions. This has been carried out in fig. 9-a.
It is supposed that a similar percentual compaction means a similar pressure along the planar interfaces.
For a first approach the travel time 100 % has been associated with the zero-load. This was 17,000 n.s. for the axial direction in both cycle I and II. In the lateral direction for Cycle I and II these 100% travel times have been taken 8,000 and 9,250 n.s. resp. It is, however, also possible to consider the 100% with respect to the moment that all planar pores and interfaces are closed,

which is not applied in this case.
For this first approach we have followed the first mentioned way. The result is shown in fig. 9-b. It seems that Q_i tends to a constant value of about 100 kgf/cm^2. The possible meaning of this, however, is not within the scope of this paper.

IV CONCLUSION

a. A fundamental difference exists between the microstress patterns of steel and rock.
The micro stress in rock controls the fracture initiation and propagation as well as the structural changes in the rock and therefore also the variations in the Young's modulus and and Poissons' ratios during the destruction trajects B, C and D in the different directions

b. In the case of axial cleavage fracturing the equilibrium at the tip of the axial crack is given by the equation :
$\sigma_{ti} = - P + Q_i\ (1+2V)$, containing 4 different elements :

1. the induced minute micro stress σ_{ti}
2. the vagabond micro stress Q_i or σ_{3i}, controling the minute micro stress σ_{ti}.
3. the loading macro stress P, which is responsible for the system (Q_i, σ_{ti}).
4. the adaptive element V, which enables us to adapt the experimental results to the equation.

REFERENCES :

1. GRAMBERG, J., 1965, The axial cleavage Fracture, Engg. Geology, Vol. 1, 1965, pp. 31-72.

2. GRAMBERG, J., 1966, Theory on the occurrence of various types of vertical and subvertical joints in the earth crust. Proceedings 1st Congress Int. Soc. Rock Mech. Lisbon, 1966.

3. GRAMBERG, J., 1967a, Bruch und Bruchsysteme in sprödem Gestein, Bericht über das 9. Ländertreffen des Internationalen Büro's für Gebirgsmechanik, Nov. 1967, pp. 13-27, Akademie-Verlag - Berlin 1968.

GRAMBERG, J., 1967b, English Translation (not published) entitled : Fracture and Fracture system in Brittle Rock. (Available on request).

4. GRAMBERG, J., 1969a, Bruchbildung, Bewegungen und Spannungen um eine Abbaustrecke bei Einseitigem Abbau. Gebirgsdruck und Grubenausbau, Informationstagung, Luxemburg, 13-14 Nov. 1969, EUR 4533 d, f.
GRAMBERG, J., 1969b, Analyse des Cassures, Mouvements et Contraintes aux Alentours d'une Voie de Chantier. Pressions des Terrains et Soutenement dans les Mines, Journées d'Information à Luxembourg, le 13-14 Novembre 1969, EUR 4533 d, f.
GRAMBERG, J., 1969c, Axiale Sprödbildung zweiter und höherer Ordnung infolge scherender Bewegung. Ländertreffen des Internationalen Büro's für Gebirgsmechanik, 1969, pp. 109-128, Akademie Verlag Berlin 1971.

5. GRAMBERG, J., 1970a, The Ellipse-with-Notch theory to explain Axial Cleavage Fracturing of Rock, a Natural Extension to the First Griffith Theory. Int. J. Rock Mech. Min.Sci., Vol. 7, No. 5, 1970, pp.537-559.
GRAMBERG, J., 1970b, Klastische en Kataklastische Processen en hun Betekenis voor de Gesteentemechanica - Inleiding tot een Breukmechanica voor Gesteente. Thesis (Ph.D.) Univ. of Technology Delft, 1970, pp. 264.

6. GRAMBERG, J., 1973, Internal Stress in Rock during Loading and Unloading under Laboratory conditions. National Symposium on Rock Fragmentation, Adelaide, February 26-28, 1973, Australian Geomechanics Soc.

7. GRIFFITH, A.A., 1920, The Phenomena of Rupture and Flow in Solids. Phil.Trans. Royal Soc. London, Ser. A. 221, 1920. pp. 163-198.

8. KOTTE J.J. et al, 1968, Stress - Strain Relations and Breakage of Cylindrical Granitic Rock Specimens under Uniaxial and Triaxial Loads., Int.J.Rock.Mech.Min.Sci., Vol. 6, Febr. 1968, pp. 581-595.

9. PETCH, N.Y., 1934, The Fracture of Metals, B. Chalmers and R. King (Editors), Progress in Metal Physics, Pergamon Press. London 1934, pp. 1-52.

10. VOLAROVICH, M.P., 1965, The Investigation of Elastic and Absorption Properties of Rock at High Pressures and Temperatures. Tectonophysics, Vol. 2, No. 2/3, 1965, pp. 211-217.

Delft, August 1973

DEEP STRESS MEASUREMENTS IN TUFF AT THE NEVADA TEST SITE

MESURE DES CONTRAINTES EN PROFONDEUR DANS LE TUF DE LA RÉGION D'EXPÉRIMENTATION NUCLÉAIRES DU NEVADA

TIEFE STRESS-MESSUNGEN IN TUFFSTEIN IN DER NEVADA TEST-SITE

B.C. HAIMSON Department of Metallurgical and Mineral Engineering, University of Wisconsin-Madison, Madison

J. LACOMB Defense Nuclear Agency, Mercury, Nevada

A.H. JONES Terra Tek, Inc., Salt Lake City, Utah

S.J. GREEN Terra Tek, Inc., Salt Lake City, Utah

SUMMARY The hydrofracturing technique was used to determine the stresses in tuff near the eastern edge of the Rainier Mesa, Nevada Test Site, Nevada, U. S. at elevations of 1830 to 2000m. Twelve measurements were performed; five measurements in five different 25m horizontal and vertical test holes drilled from an underground tunnel, and seven at different elevations of a long vertical hole drilled from the surface to the tunnel level. The horizontal principal stresses at tunnel level were 35 bars at N 55° W, and 88 bars at N 35° E. The vertical stress at a depth of 380m calculated from the measured density of the rock was 70 bars. The magnitudes and directions of these stresses are comparable to those measured in the same tunnel with a borehole deformation gage. The results also reinforce a suggestion based on a seismic investigation of the Benham nuclear explosion after shocks that the principal stress directions at the Nevada Test Site (NW-SE, NE-SW) are a regional characteristic. In general, the results verify the reliability of the method both in underground and surface holes at long distances from the operator, and in a rock like tuff (porous, impermeable, soft, ductile) which is unlike the hard, brittle, homogeneous rocks previously tested.

RÉSUMÉ La technique d' hydrofracturation a été utilisée pour determiner les contraintes dans le tuf aux environs de la bordure est due plateau Rainier Mesa, Nevada Test Site, Nevada, U.S.A., à des altitudes de 1830 a 2000m. Douze mesures ont été effectuées: cinq ont été faites dans des trous de 25m, horizontaux ou verticaux, percés á partir d'un tunnel: les sept autres ont été faites à different niveaux dans un trou reliant la surface au tunnel. Les contraintes moyennes horizontales mesurées au nivau du tunnel sont = 35 bars ā N55 W et 88 bars á N35 E. La contrainte verticale ā 380 m de profondeur calculee ā partir de la densité du rocher est de 70 bars. L'intensité et la direction des contraintes sont comparables aux mesures. Les résultats semblent confirmer le fait suggére par des mesures sismiques effectuées apres une explosion nucléaire que les directions des contraintes principales (NO - SE, NE - SO) sont typiques de la région. La methode qui a été utilisée avec succès dans des roches dures et fragiles est donc aussi applicable aux tufs moux et poreux.

ZUSAMMENFASSUNG Die Hydrobruch-Methode wurde benutzt für die Bestimmung der Stresse in Tuffstein am östlichen Rand der Rainier Mesa, Nevada Test Site, Nevada, U.S.A., in Höhen von 1830-2000 m. 12 Messungen wurden gemacht; 5 Messungen in 5 verschiedenen 25m horizontalen and senkrechten Testlöchern von einem unterirdischen Tunnel aus gebohrt und 7 in verschiedenen Höhen in einem langen senkrechten Loch, das von der Oberfläche bis zum Tunnel gebohrt wurde. Die durchschnittlichen horizontalen Hauptstresse in der Tunnelhöhe betrugen: 35 bar bei N35°W, und 88 bar bei N35°O. Der senkrechte Stress bei einer Tiefe von 380m war 70 bar, berechnet von der gemessenen Dichte des Steins. Die Grössen und Richtungen dieser Stresse entsprechen Messungen im selben Tunnel mit einem Bohrloch-Deformationsmass. Die Resultate ferner stimmen überein mit dem Vorschlag, basiert auf seismischen Untersuchungen der Erschütterungen nach der Benham Atomexplosion, da die Hauptstressrichtungen in der Nevada Test Site (NS-SO, NO-SW) ein lokale Eigenschaft sind. Die Resultate bestätigen weithin die Zuverlässigkeit der Methode sowohl in underirdischen Löchern als in Löchern an der Oberfläche, weit entfernt von der Leitung, in einen porösen, weichen, plastischen, undurchdringlichen Stein wie Tuff, der sehr verschieden ist von den bisher undersuchten harten, bruchigen, homogenen Steinen.

INTRODUCTION

The field of tectonophysics as well as underground mining and tunneling, subsurface storage and disposal, oil, gas and geothermal steam extraction would benefit substantially if reliable deep in situ stress determination methods were available. The stress-relief techniques developed in the last two decades (1) require overcoring, (2) are restricted to a few meters from the point of access and (3) require the material properties to deduce stresses from measured displacements. A method which is potentially unlimited in depth and does not require sophisticated instrumentation or overcoring is "hydrofracturing". This method has recently been theoretically developed and experimentally verified both in the laboratory and in the field (Haimson, 1969, 1974). The first major test of this method was the investigation at Rangely, Colorado, where the stress at 1920m below the surface were determined by hydrofracturing at the bottom of a newly drilled oil well. The stresses measured at Rangely were in accord with the type and direction of slip of the neighboring main fault. Furthermore, other experiments showed that the measured stresses could be used to predict the critical pore-pressure necessary to induce slip along the fault (Haimson,

1973; Raleigh, et al., 1972). The success of this stress measurement prompted scientists to consider the hydrofracturing method of determining in situ stresses among the more important tools for future earthquake prediction and modification research.

A second major test of hydrofracturing as a method of determining deep stresses took place recently at the Nevada Test Site, Nye County, Nevada, (Edwin, 1968) where the in situ stresses in the tuff of Rainier Mesa (Ege, et al., 1971) were measured.

The location chosen was in the vicinity of tunnel complex "U12n", near the eastern edge of the mesa (Ege, et al., 1971). Previous measurements in this same tunnel were carried out by the U. S. Bureau of Mines using a borehole deformation gage (Hooker, et al., 1971). Determining stresses from the borehole deformations is difficult for a material which exhibits such strong non-linear stress-strain response as does tuff. Additionally, these overcoring tests were run in close proximity to the tunnel wall (tunnel diameter was 5m, the maximum distance from tunnel wall was 5.5m), and hence some uncertainties existed because of the closeness to the tunnel opening. The reported in situ stress measurements were to be determined away from any excavation by hydrofracturing both long holes drilled from the tunnel and a deep vertical hole drilled from the surface down to the tunnel level.

A total of 12 hydrofracturing tests were conducted; five in two horizontal and three vertical holes drilled 22 to 28m from the tunnel and seven at different elevations in the vertical hole. The vertical hole was drilled to a depth of 250m to reach the tunnel level; however, the horizontal distance from the hole to the tunnel was about 300m. Figure 1 details the position of the test holes; the testing procedure and results are discussed in the following sections.

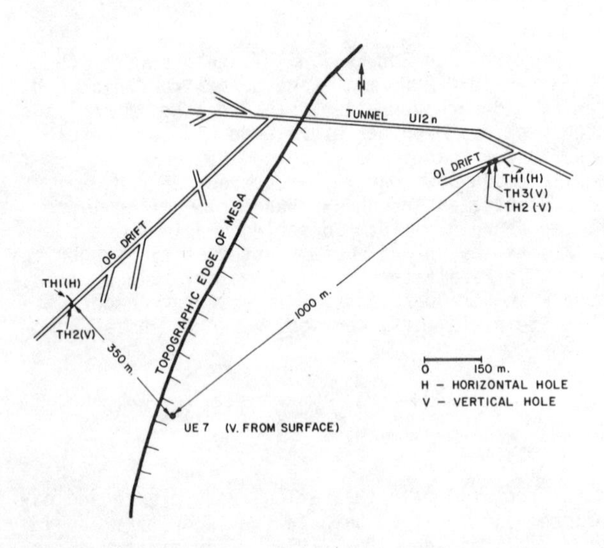

Fig. 1 Tunnel Complex U12n and Stress Measurement Locations

IN SITU STRESS MEASUREMENT BY HYDRAULIC FRACTURING

The hydraulic fracturing technique for in situ stress determination consists of sealing off a section of the borehole with packers and pressurizing this section by injecting a "fracturing fluid" (water, oil, sand-water mixture or grouts). The pressure is continuously raised until the rock surrounding the hole fractures (this is the breakdown pressure). For a constant pumping rate the pressure drops momentarily at fracture; as pumping is accelerated the flow rate and the pressure reach approximately constant levels (this is the fracture extension pressure) while the fracture opens and propagates. During the entire operation, including the time after pumping stops, the pressure is recorded. The pressure required to rupture the formation, the pressure needed to keep the fracture open at pump shut-off (this is the shut-in pressure), and the [hydraulic fracture] tensile strength are used to determine the magnitudes of the principal in situ stresses. The inclination and azimuth of the hydraulic fracture can be detected by the use of impression packers, and this orientation determines the directions of the in plane stresses. Inherent in the determination of stresses, however, is the assumption that the borehole be parallel to one of the principal stresses. Complete details regarding the different fracture possibilities and the respective stress calculations are given elsewhere (Haimson, 1974

FIELD TESTING PROCEDURE

At the Nevada Test Site each test commenced with the placement of a straddle packer in the predetermined position inside a 12cm diameter hole especially drilled for hydrofracturing. Each packer was approximately 3m long and the straddled segment was 2.5m. The packers were connected by a string of drill pipes to a pump at the collar of the hole. A 20 liter/min air actuated pump was used in pressurizing the packers and in hydrofracturing.

The packers were inflated with water to a pressure high enough to prevent leakage from the straddled interval, but low enough to prevent blowouts or rock fracturing (55 to 100 bars). The packers were then "set" by pulling on the drill pipe with a force of approximately 20,000 N, and then turning the pipe five complete turns. This procedure locked the pressure in the packers and opened the hydraulic line to the straddled interval. The interval was then pressurized and the pressure at the hole collar, as determined by a pressure transducer, was continuously recorded on a dual-channel strip-chart plotter. (Pressures at the fracture zone were corrected for the hydrostatic head where appropriate. All pressures in Table 1 are pressures in the fracture zone.) The water flow was also recorded continuously (in most tests) on the second channel of the same strip-chart plotter. Pumping at a constant rate of 20 liters/minute was continued for two to four minutes. In each case after pumping was stopped for several minutes, the test was repeated to verify the uniqueness of the shut-in pressure. The packers were finally extracted from the hole and a 3m impression packer was inserted to the straddled interval. A pressure of 70 bars of water was applied and maintained for about 15 minutes to ensure intimate contact with the surface of the hole. The impression packer was then deflated, extracted from the hole and examined.

Orientation of the impression packer was achieved by scribing a line on the ends of the drill pipes used. In tightening one pipe segment into the other, careful matching of the scribed lines was maintained so that one straight line was formed between the pipe ends at the collar of the hole and the impression packer. This allowed determination of the orientation of fracture traces found on the impression packer after deflation and extraction from the hole.

The underground measurements (from the tunnels) were conducted close to the bottom of the drilled holes. The seven tests in the vertical hole drilled from the surface were conducted at different depths between 102 and 249m (Table 1).

IN SITU STRESS DETERMINATION

The magnitudes of two in situ principal stresses may be calculated from the hydraulic fracturing pressures if it is assumed that the third principal stress acts in a direction parallel with the test hole. If the test hole is vertical, the third principal stress (σ_V) is taken as the weight of the overlying strata

$$\sigma_V = \gamma \cdot d \tag{1}$$

where γ is the weight gradient of the rock (.183 bars/m depth at the reported site, Butters, et al., 1973) and d is the depth beneath the surface.

The horizontal principal stresses (σ_{Hmin}, σ_{Hmax}) are determined from two relationships (Haimson, 1968)

$$P_c = 3\,\sigma_{Hmin} - \sigma_{Hmax} + T \tag{2}$$

$$P_{isi} = \sigma_{Hmin} \tag{3}$$

where P_c is the breakdown pressure necessary to bring about fracturing, P_{isi} is the instantaneous shut-in pressure, T is the [hydraulic fracturing] tensile strength of the rock (compressive stresses are considered positive).

Equations (2) and (3) are adequate for the particular case where the initial pore pressure in the rock is zero, the permeability of the formation is negligible, and the breakdown pressure is relatively low. All three conditions were satisfied in the described tests. The formation pore pressure was assumed to be zero based on observations that water does not fill drill holes at the test location, even when these drill holes were left open for months (LaComb, 1972). The permeability of the tuff was determined to range between 1 and 50 microdarcies (LaComb, 1972), and hence flow through the rock for the short duration of a hydrofracturing test can be considered negligible. The breakdown pressures in the described tests were limited to below 70 bars. Even though some experimental results have shown that rocks become permeable around the hydrofracturing hole as the pressure is raised, at pressure levels encountered in the tests here, Eq. (2) is believed to remain valid (Haimson, 1968; Haimson and Edl, 1972).

The tensile strength of rock used for the calculations here should be determined under conditions as similar to those encountered in hydraulic fracturing as is possible. Measurements of the tensile strength were conducted in the laboratory and are described in the Appendix; the average value was 30 bars (see Table 2). The repeatability of the fracture extension pressure (P_f) and the shut-in pressure in the second pressurizations attest the reliability of the monitored pressures (Table 1). The average shut-in pressure from the two pressurizations was used to calculate the minimum in situ stresses.

The directions of the horizontal principal stresses were determined from the fracture orientation. It is assumed that the direction of the fracture is perpendicular to the smallest principal stress (Haimson, 1968).

RESULTS AND DISCUSSION

In Situ Stress Magnitudes

Table 1 summarizes the pressures recorded and the calculated in situ stresses in each of the 12 tests. In the two horizontal holes from the tunnel as well as in two of the tests for the surface hole no breakdown pressure was recorded. Rather, in each of these four cases the pressure rose gradually to the final pressure, believed to be the fracture extension pressure. Such behavior usually indicates that instead of fracturing the formation, the pressurized fluid merely opens an existing discontinuity in the rock, either a crack, joint, parting, or fault. The shut-in pressure in these four cases agrees well with the measured shut-in pressure for tests at about the same depth, suggesting that the discontinuities ran in a direction perpendicular to the minimum horizontal stress.

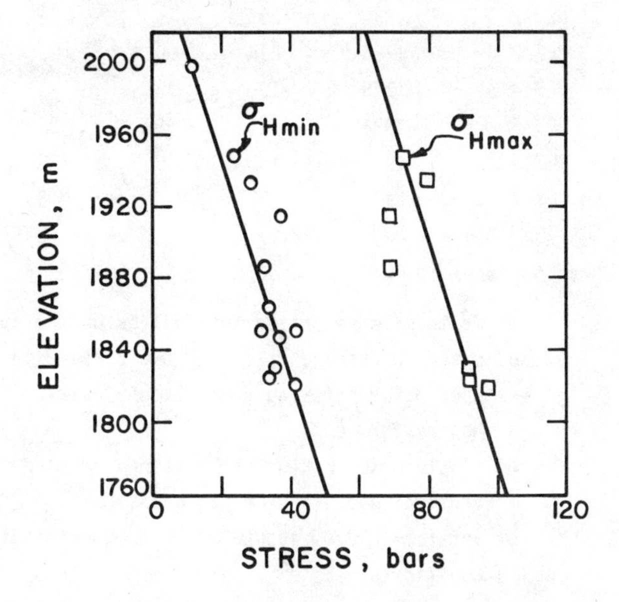

Fig. 2 Maximum and Minimum Principal Stresses Determined at Rainier Mesa (Tunnel Complex U12n), Nevada Test Site, Mercury, Nevada.

The calculated maximum and minimum horizontal stresses show a general decrease in magnitude with an increase in elevation, as shown in Figure 2. This is reasonable considering that the magnitude of the stresses are in part proportional to the weight of the overlying strata, and in part due to some tectonic loading on the local area. The sensitivity of hydrofracturing to subtle changes in stress over a range of under 200m was a surprising and very encouraging characteristic. Minor inconsistencies with the trend shown in Fig. 2 are to be expected especially in the σ_{Hmax} values since this stress is a function of P_c, P_{isi} and T; the latter, in particular, can vary to account for much of the variability.

Table 1. Hydrofracturing Data and Calculated Stresses

Hole Test	Elevation (m)	Depth[α] (m)	First Pressurization P_c (bars)	P_f (bars)	P_{isi} (bars)	Second Pressurization P_f (bars)	P_{isi} (bars)	Calculated Stresses $\sigma_{H\,max}$ (bars)	$\sigma_{H\,min}$[β] (bars)	σ_v (bars)
Horizontal Tunnel Holes										
01 TH1	1846	244	--[γ]	66	34[ε]	60	37	---	36	45
06 TH1	1850	380	--[γ]	36	31[ε]	--[δ]	--[δ]	---	31	70
Vertical Tunnel Holes										
01 TH2	1819	268	47	47	41[ε]	45	40	107	41	49
01 TH3	1824	263	46	50	37[φ]	46	30	92	33	48
06 TH2	1830	400	42	40	35[ε]	36	33	91	34	73
Vertical Surface Hole										
UE7-1	1850	249	(119)	42	41[ε]	42	41	(34)	41	41
UE7-2	1864	235	--[γ]	32	32[ε]	32	32	---	33	43
UE7-3	1885	214	56	35	32[ε]	33	32	69	32	39
UE7-4	1915	183	73	40	37[ε]	36	34	68	36	33
UE7-5	1934	165	38	34	30[ψ]	30	27	80	28	30
UE7-6	1946	153	26	26	23[ψ]	25	23	73	23	28
UE7-7	1996	102	--[γ]	13	11[ε]	10	10	---	11	19
Mean Stresses at Tunnel Elevation, 1850m (depth of 380m), (see Fig. 2):								88	35	70

α Depth of pressurized interval below the surface

β Based on average P_{isi} from two pressurizations

γ Opening of existing rock discontinuity

δ Not performed

ε Fracture impression not obtained

φ Vertical hydrofracture at N 35° E

ψ Vertical hydrofracture of unknown orientation

( ) Questionable Data

The vertical stress based on overburden weight is given by Eq. (1).

Direction of the Principal Stresses

The directions of the principal horizontal stresses were inferred from the pressure measurements and the impression packer results. Only three impressions were obtained because of technical problems, including the use of excessively hard rubber sleeves (excellent however for the high temperatures encountered in deeper holes), insufficient pressurization time for packers in position and the inexperienced use in tuffs. The three good impressions obtained were all in vertical holes (see Table 1) and indicated near vertical fractures. The orientation of the vertical fracture in hole 01 TH3 was reliabily determined at N 35° E, suggesting that the minimum horizontal principal stress direction is N 55° W.

Stresses at Tunnel Level

Based on the calculated stresses (Table 1), the resulting Fig. 2, and fracture orientation results, the following mean stresses were determined to represent average principal stresses in the vicinity of tunnel U12n, at elevation of 1850m (depth of 380m).

σ_v = 70 bars (vertical)

σ_{Hmin} = 35 bars (horizontal at N 55° W),

σ_{Hmax} = 88 bars (horizontal at N 35° E).

The U. S. Bureau of Mines results (Hooker, et al., 1971) at approximately the same elevation, obtained by using a borehole deformation gage at a distance barely exceeding one diameter from the tunnel wall, were:

$\sigma_V = 60$ bars (vertical)

$\sigma_{Hmin} = 24$ bars (horizontal at N 46° W)

$\sigma_{Hmax} = 80$ bars (horizontal at N 44° E).

These values are derived from principal stresses which were determined to be slightly off vertical and horizontal (see Figure 3 and Hooker, et al., 1971). The stresses as computed from the two methods are surprisingly comparable, with the directions being in very good agreement.

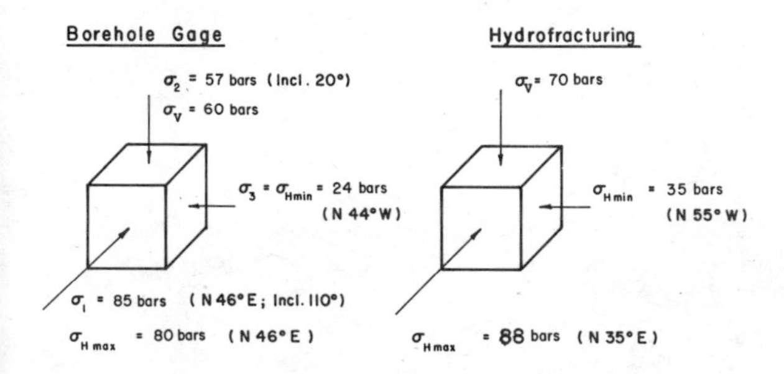

Fig. 3 Comparison Between the In Situ Stress in the Vicinity of Tunnel U12n, Nevada Test Site, as Measured by the Borehole Deformation Gage and the Hydrofracturing Method.

It is of interest to note that the general direction of the smallest horizontal principal stress is northwest-southeast which roughly corresponds with the topography of the area (Fig. 1). The edge of the mesa runs in a north to northeast direction indicating the likelihood that the general direction of the smallest horizontal principal stress is northwest-southeast.

Additional support for the direction of the principal stresses comes from a seismic investigation of aftershocks following the Benham nuclear explosion (Hamilton and Healy, 1969). The resulting fault plane solutions in the Pahute Mesa area indicate that the smallest horizontal stress direction is northwest-southeast. Our results reinforce Hamilton and Healy's suggestion that the principal stress directions at the Nevada Test Site are a regional characteristic.

CONCLUSIONS

A set of twelve in situ stress hydrofracturing measurements were conducted in the vicinity of tunnel U12n, Nevada Test Site, Nye County, Nevada. The consistent results obtained in different test holes, both from surface and underground tunnels, serve to verify the reliability of both the method and the measured stresses. It was shown that the hydrofracturing method of determining in situ stresses is effective even in variable, coarse grained, soft rock such as the tuff of the Rainier Mesa. Comparisons with overcoring stress measurements, the secondary effect of the mesa general topography, and fault plane solutions in the area attest the reliability of the obtained results.

ACKNOWLEDGEMENTS

This work was performed under the auspices of Field Command, Defense Nuclear Agency, under Contract No. DNA001-73-C-0212 with Terra Tek, Inc.

REFERENCES

Butters, S. W., R. J. Reid, R. Lingle, A. H. Jones and S. J. Green (1973), Materials Properties for Husky Ace Containment Evaluation, Terra Tek Report TR 73-41.

Eckel, E. B. (1968), Nevada Test Site, Memoir 110, The Geological Society of America, Inc.

Ege, J. R. and W. H. Lee, (1971), Geologic Atlas of Rainier Mesa, Nevada Test Site, Nye County, Nevada, USGS Technical Letter, Rainier Mesa 13.

Haimson, B. (1968), Hydraulic Fracturing in Porous and Nonporous Rock and Its Potential for Determining In Situ Stresses at Great Depth, Technical Report MRD-4-68, Missouri River Division, Corps of Engineers.

Haimson, B. C. and J. N. Edl (1972), Hydraulic Fracturing of Deep Wells, SPE 4061, presented at the 47th Annual Fall Meeting, American Institute of Mining and Metallurgical and Petroleum Engineers, Society of Petroleum Engineers.

Haimson, B. C. (1973) Earthquake Related Stresses at Rangely Colorado, in New Horizons in Rock Mechanics, Hardy, H. G. and Stefanko, R., editors; American Society of Civil Engineers, N. Y., pp. 689-708.

Haimson, B. C. (1974), A Simple Method for Estimating In Situ Stresses at Great Depths, in Field Testing and Instrumentation of Rock, STP 554, American Society of Testing and Materials.

Hamilton, R. M. and J. H. Healy (1959), Aftershocks of the Benham Nuclear Explosion, Bulletin of Seismological Society of America, 59, pp. 2271-2281.

Hooker, V. E., J. R. Aggson and D. C. Bickel (1971), In Situ Determination of Stresses in Rainier Mesa, Nevada Test Site, U. S. Bureau of Mines Report.

Hudson, J. (1971), A Critical Evaluation of Indirect Tensile Strength Tests for Brittle Rocks, Ph. D. Thesis, University of Minnesota.

Johnson, J. N., R. J. Clifton and E. R. Simonson (1973), Analysis of Fracture for Hollow Cylindrical and Spherical Rock Specimens Subject to Internal Pressure, Terra Tek, Inc. Report TR 73-50.

LaComb, J., Private Correspondence, 1972.

LaComb, J., Shipment of 6-Inch Nevada Test Site Cores, 1973.

Raleigh, C. B., J. H. Healy and J. D. Bredehoeft, (1972), Faulting and Crustal Stress at Rangely, Colorado, in Flow and Fracture of Rocks, Geophysical Monograph 16, American Geophysical Union, Washington, D. C., pp. 275-284.

APPENDIX

The Hydraulic Fracture Tensile Strength of Nevada Test Site Tuff

The relationship between the breakdown pressure in a hydrofracturing test and the in situ principal stresses is calculated to be a function of the tangential stress necessary to induce a fracture in the wall of the test hole when $\sigma_{Hmin} = \sigma_{Hmax} = 0$. This value, T, should correspond for a brittle material like rock to the tensile stress that it can bear, the rock tensile strength. Since the apparent tensile strength of rock can vary with the type of test it is necessary to evaluate this parameter under conditions as similar to those encountered when the value is used as possible (Haimson, 1968; Hudson, 1971; Johnson, et al., 1973).

To measure the [hydraulic fracture] tensile strength six cylindrical specimens, 15cm in diameter and 17 to 20cm long, with axial holes 2.5cm in diameter, were prepared from a horizontal drill hole in Area 12, Tunnel Bed 3A (LaComb, 1973) in the general proximity of the stress measurement location. These cores were taken 5 to 8m from the tunnel wall. Each cylinder was subjected to internal pressurization under openhole conditions until failure. The axial load applied for sealing the pressurized fluid was 38 bars (except in one case 52 bars was used); all induced fractures were vertical. The measured burst pressures (P_b) are listed in Table 2. Consistent results were obtained in specimens 1, 2, 4, 5. Specimen 3 which failed at a much lower value of P_b had a visible transverse crack prior to testing. In one test, unreported in Table 2, the specimen failed prior to pressurization.

To calculate the [hydraulic fracture] tensile strength, an elastic thick-walled cylinder analysis was performed

$$T = P_b \frac{b^2 + a^2}{b^2 - a^2}$$

where b and a are the outside and inside diameters respectively.

Table 2. Laboratory Hydrofracturing Tensile Strength

Specimen No.	Applied Vertical Stress (bars)	Applied Horizontal Stress (bars)	P_b (bars)	T (bars)
1	52	0	24	27
2	38	0	24	27
3	38	0	7	--
4	38	0	30	33
5	38	0	29	32
			Average T	30

FIELD MEASUREMENTS OF RESIDUAL STRAIN IN GRANITIC ROCK MASSES

MESURES SUR LE TERRAIN DE DÉFORMATION RÉSIDUELLE DANS DES MASSES GRANTIQUES

IN-SITU MESSUNGEN VON RESTVERFORMUNGEN IN GRANIT

Henri S. SWOLFS Senior Scientist, Applied Geosciences, Terra Tek,Inc., Salt Lake City, Utah

John HANDIN Director, Center for Tectonophysics, Texas A+M University, College Station, Texas

Howard R. PRATT Manager, Applied Geosciences, Terra Tek, Inc., Salt Lake City, Utah

SUMMARY Field measurements of strain relief have been made in large volumes of quartz diorite ranging up to $15 m^3$. These results indicate that the *in situ* state of strain is composed of at least two components: *i.e.*, an applied strain component associated with active tectonism and a residual strain component. The orientation of the applied strain (N 55° W) corresponds with a major regional fault system: the Hurricane Fault. The magnitude of maximum strain relief is about 500×10^{-6} and is independent of the size of rock relieved. The orientation of the residual strain (N - S) is more closely aligned with the local geology of the area. In contrast to the applied-strain relief, the magnitude and sign of the residual-strain relief is highly dependent on the size or volume of the rock freed from its surroundings. The maximum relief of residual strain varies from -700×10^{-6} (contraction) in large blocks to 1400×10^{-6} (expansion) in small, conventional overcores. Additional measurements both in the field and in the laboratory suggest that the residual strain component is dominant in this rock and to a large extent controls the fracture direction, bulk anisotropy in strength and sonic velocity, and morphology of the rock mass. An important aspect of this investigation is the indication that the residual strains or stresses are locked in the rock on a scale measured in cubic meters. This observation implies that excavations and other structural disturbances of the rock, either natural or induced by man, could cause the release of residual strain energy resulting in large strains and displacements not accounted for in conventional structural analyses.

RESUME Des mesures sur le terrain ont permis de déterminer les relâchements de déformation a l'intérieur d'importants volumes (pouvant atteindre $15 m^3$) de diorite quartzique. Les résultats indiquent que l'état de déformation *in situ* comprend au moine deux composantes: une composante appliquée associée au tectonisme actif et une composante de déformation résiduelle. L'orientation de la déformation appliquée (N 55° W) correspond à un important systéme de failles régional: La Faille Hurricane. L'amplitude maximale de son relâchement est d'environ 500×10^{-6} et ne dépend pas des dimensions de la roche affectée. L'orientation de la déformation résiduelle (N - S) correspond mieux à la géologie locale de cette région. Contrairement aux charactéristiques du relâchement de la déformation appliquée, l'amplitude et le signe du relâchement de la déformation résiduelle dépendent très fort des dimension de la roche dégagée. Le relâchement maximum de déformation résiduelle varie de -700×10^{-6} (contraction) dans de larges blocs à 1400×10^{-6} (expansion) dans de petits noyaux conventionels. D'autre mesures, à la fois sur le terrain et en laboratoire, suggèrent que dans cette roche la composante de déformation résiduelle domine et contrôle largement la direction de la fracture, l'anisotropie de la résistance a la rupture, l'anisotropie de la vitesse sonique, ainsi que la morphologie de la masse rocheuse. Cette étude indigue aussi un résultat très important, le fait que les déformations et tensions résiduelles sont retenues dans une roche dont les dimensions peuvent être mesurées en metres cubes. Cette observation implique que des excavations ou d'autre dérangements, soit naturel soit créé par l'homme, pourraient causer le relâchement d'energie residuelle provoquant ainsi d'importantes déformations et déplacements négligée dans l'analyse structurelle conventionnelle.

ZUSAMMENFASSUNG *In situ* Messungen von verformungsrueckspruengen sind an Granitbloecken bis zu $15 m^3$ Groesse durchgefuehrt worden. Die Ergebnisse deuten darauf hin, dass der *in situ* Verformungszustand aus zwei Komponenten besteht: einer aeusserlich durch aktive tektonische Vorgaenge hervorgerufenen Komponente und einer Restverformungskomponente. Die Orientierung der aeusserlich verursachten Verformung (N 55° W) stimmt mit der Richtung eines grossen regionalen Stoerungssystems (Hurricane Fault) ueberein. Der groesste beobachtete Verformungsruecksprung betraegt 500×10^{-6} und ist von der Groesse des Messblockes unabhaengig. Die Restverformung (N - S) liegt annaehernd parallel zu lokalen geologischen Erscheinungsformen des Aufnahmegebietes. Im Gegensatz zu dem aeusserlich verursachten Verformungsruecksprung sind Groesse und Vorzeichen der Restverformung stark von der Groesse des freigelegten Gesteinsblockes abhaengig. Die groessten gemessenen Restverformungen betragen zwischen -700×10^{-6} (Stauchung) in grossen Bloecken und 1400×10^{-6} (Streckung) in kleinen, herkoemmlichen Ueberbohrungen. Zusaetzliche Aufnahmen sowohl *in situ* als auch im Laboratorium lassen darauf schliessen, dass die Restverformungen im vorleigenden Unterschungsgebiet ueberwiegen und weitgehend die Bruchrichtung, Festigkeitsanisotropie, seismische Geschwindigkeitsanisotropie sowie die Morphologie des Gesteinskoerpers bestimmen. Die vorliegende Arbeit erbringt den wichtigen Hinweis, dass Restverformungen und Restspannungen in Bloecken der Groessenordnung von Metern erhalten bleiben. Diese Beobachtung zeigt, dass Ausschachtungen und andere sowohl natuerliche als auch kuenstliche Eingriffe im Gebirgskoerper zur Abgabe von betraechtlicher Restspannungsenergie fuehren kann. Als Folge koennen grosse Verformungen und Verschiebungen auftreten, die nicht in herkoemmlichen Berechnungsverfahren beruecksichtigt werden.

INTRODUCTION

The *in situ* state of stress arises from the superposition of gravitational and externally applied loads (natural or man-made) on a rock in which there exists a self-equilibrating system of residual stresses. The applied stresses, as defined here, are related to loads imposed by the present structural and topographic framework of the region, active tectonism and work of man. Residual stresses, as defined here, are related to physico-chemical and tectonic events that took place in the geologic past during and subsequent to the formation of the rock mass.

That rocks are subjected to stress when they are loaded externally is almost intuitively obvious, but one may less readily visualize that the same rock, free of external loads, can still sustain within itself residual stresses of high and significant magnitudes. These stresses are completely internal to the body of rock and they form balanced systems that can vary continuously over a large scale (Varnes and Lee, 1972). On a microscopic scale these stresses can vary from grain to grain because of differences in physical properties. The residual-stress domains or equilibrium volumes are of comparable size; they are composed of "locking" and "locked-in" stresses (Friedman, 1972). If the residual-stress domains are small compared with the size of the specimen, excavation, or other engineering structure and if they are distributed homogeneously throughout the rock body, the effects of residual stress average out so as to be negligible. In other words, these microstresses vary in complicated ways over small distances and they would not generate uniform stress fields throughout the volume of rock. In this case, the strain relief measured in the field can properly be related to applied, regional or tectonic stresses.

However, complex processes that involved crystallization, cementation, plastic or ductile flow, creep, phase transformations and attendant volume changes, non-uniform cooling and recrystallization of the rock mass generate complicated stress distributions in domains that are both microscopic and macroscopic in scale. That the residual stress domains can be large in a body of rock has been postulated by Varnes and Lee (1972) and confirmed experimentally by Swolfs, *et al.* (1973).

Stress-relieving mechanisms, for example, annealling recrystallization or the removal of overburden by uplift, erosion and weathering, are responsible for the dissipation of residual-strain energy through time. Upon unloading, residual-stress differences can become sufficiently large over time to initiate microfractures, which, in turn, can coalesce to form macrofractures and joints. Exfoliation or sheeting of granites and massive sandstones is a stress-relief mechanism, but individual sheets can retain their integrity and resist weathering for long periods of time because of large, internal compressive stresses in the plane of the sheets. Fractures, horizontal, vertical or inclined, generally have preferred directions in common so as to induce a bulk anisotropy in the rock mass. By mapping these geologic structures and anisotropy fields of seismic velocity, strength, and other bulk properties, one gains some insight into the scale and magnitude of the residual-stress field in massive bodies of rock.

Evidence of residual stress in rocks has been forthcoming in the geologic and engineering literatures for many years (Emery, 1964, 1968; Voight, 1966, 1967; Denkhaus, 1967; Friedman, 1967, 1972; Varnes, 1970; Varnes and Lee, 1972; among others). However, attempts to measure these stress in the field have been frustrated by their very nature and distribution and by the fact that they are difficult to distinguish from applied-stress systems. Because these self-equilibrating stress systems persist in the absense of externally applied loads, their distributions and dimensions cannot be uniquely determined *a priori*. As Varnes and Lee (1972) point out: "If the measurement sample is smaller than the equilibrium volume, the residual-stress component will be finite and will probably approach some maximum limiting value as the sample size becomes negligible compared with the equilibrium volume...," the inference being that *in situ* measurements can be seriously misinterpreted and erroneously related to tectonic events.

We will briefly summarize the results we have obtained by excavating large volumes of rock and then relate them to geological and geophysical measurements made by ourselves and others in the same area.

GEOLOGY AND GEOPHYSICS OF THE CEDAR CITY QUARTZ DIORITE

The selected area is located near Cedar City in the southwestern corner of Utah. The exposed intrusive rock, probably laccolithic, is a quartz diorite. This area lies 15 km west of the Hurricane Fault, one of the large, regional faults that mark the boundary between the Colorado Plateau and the Basin-and-Range province. The surface is characterized by isolated hills, knobs and bare rock-flats that are largely devoid of soil cover. The bare rock-flats reveal little surface weathering and appear sound and rigid under blows from a hammer. Occasionally, small blisters and arches can be found by gently tapping the surface. The rock is unusually porous in places, reaching a value as high as 9 percent.

A characteristic feature of the outcrop is a well developed and strongly oriented (N - S) fracture system (Figure 1). The fractures (or joints) are spaced up to several meters apart. They are nearly vertical, appear to be tight and can be traced by continuous coring to depths as great as 150 meters.

From a systematic seismic refraction survey of the area along as many as 10 traverses in different directions at a particular site, Kolb *et al.* (1970) have measured strong variations of velocity with direction (Figure 2). The direction of greatest velocity (3.4 km/sec) is parallel to the preferred fracture direction, suggesting that these fractures may be responsible for the pronounced anisotropy in the horizontal velocity field. Similar surveys were made at several different localities; all show an anisotropy coincident with the fracture system. It should be noted, however, that this anisotropy may also result from the unusually high crack-porosity of the rock. The directional attenuation of sound waves suggests that microcracks are also preferentially oriented (Walsh *et al.*, 1970) and that their contribution may outweigh the effect of large, widely spaced fractures.

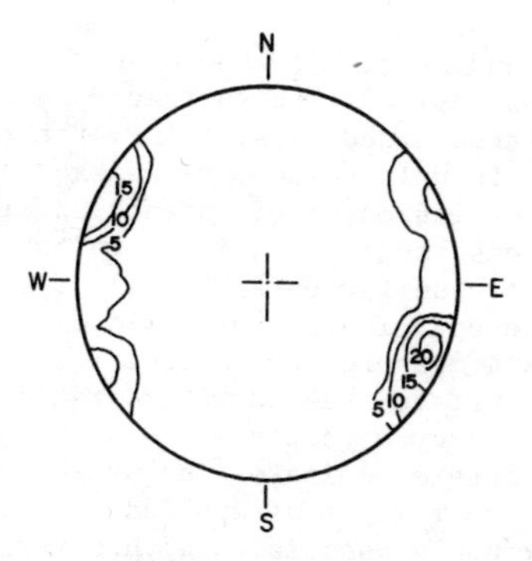

Fig. 1. Poles to macrofractures (joints) in quartz diorite. Data is plotted in lower hemisphere, equal-area projection.

To illustrate the pronounced effects of microcracks, the Twin Cities Laboratory of the U.S. Bureau of Mines (S. S. Peng, personal communication, 1973), at our request, measured the ultrasonic velocity and attenuation fields in an oriented sample of the quartz diorite (Figure 3). Their results correlate well with the *in situ* fracture and velocity-anisotropy orientations. They also agree with the measurements of residual-strain relief made in the same rock in the field (Swolfs *et al.*, 1973). Other relations between residual stress and rock fabric, and microfracture, ultrasonic-velocity, and breaking-strength anisotropies measured in rocks in the laboratory are shown by Friedman (1972), Friedman and Logan (1970), Willard and McWilliams (1969) and others. We present evidence that these same relations hold in the field as well.

STRESS-RELIEF EXPERIMENTS IN THE CEDAR CITY QUARTZ DIORITE

In situ overcoring measurements were made prior to the selection of a suitable location for the large

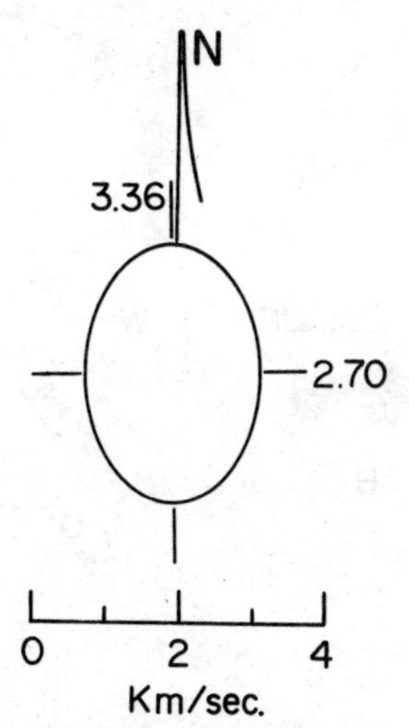

Fig. 2. Horizontal velocity field in quartz diorite obtained from seismic refraction measurements by Kolb *et al.* (1970).

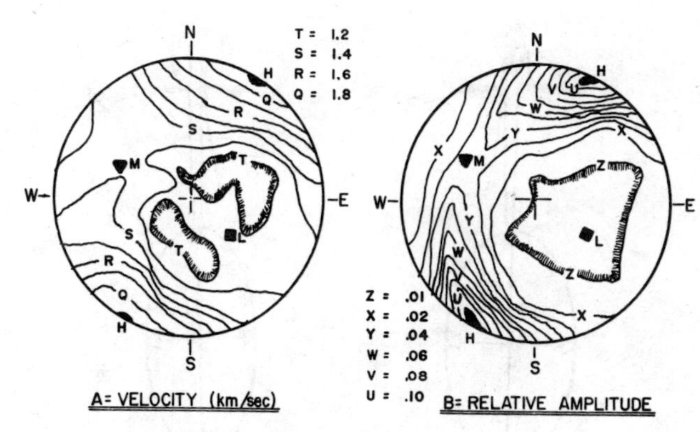

Fig. 3. Diagrams illustrating the ultrasonic velocity (A) and relative amplitude (B) fields in quartz diorite. Data is plotted in lower hemisphere, equal-area projection. H, M and L are axes of high, medium and low values, respectively. Attenuation symmetry in (B) is shown by H and L positions reversed.

strain-relief experiment. The technique involves drilling around a strain-gage rosette to a predetermined depth, usually twice the diameter of the diamond bit. The resulting core (15 x 30 cm) remains attached at its base. The recorded strain changes at each of the three gages are used to calculate the magnitude and orientation of the two horizontal principal components of strain relief, where expansions denote the relief of an initial compressive strain (or stress) in the rock, and contractions indicate tensions. Stresses are obtained as a first approximation by multiplying the principal strains by an appropriate modulus (for quartz diorite, 0.8×10^{11} dynes/cm^2). To correct the mechanical strain changes for thermal strains induced by climatic variations during the experiments, rock-surface temperatures are recorded simultaneously with a temperature-sensitive foil-resistance gage. (The details of the technique are discussed by Swolfs *et al.*, 1973).

The strain relief recorded by overcoring an intact rock in the field is properly called an *in situ* measurement. The relative contributions of the applied and the residual stresses to this *in situ* measurement can only be determined by overcoring an oriented specimen that is free of all external loads across its boundaries. The strain relief so recorded is completely residual. The result of the small, *in situ* tests along with a laboratory measurement of strain relief are shown in Figure 4. The principal orientations and magnitudes are nearly identical for both, a result that strongly implies that the residual-stress domain at the surface of the quartz diorite intrusive is larger than the size of the overcore. A similar correlation between field and laboratory tests on Barre granite from Vermont has been found by Nichols (1972).

The large field experiment was designed to answer two principal questions: (1) how does one differentiate between applied and residual stresses in the field, and (2) on what scale are residual stresses distributed in an unweathered rock? A suitable area (2.5 x 2.5 meters) was selected and instrumented with 35

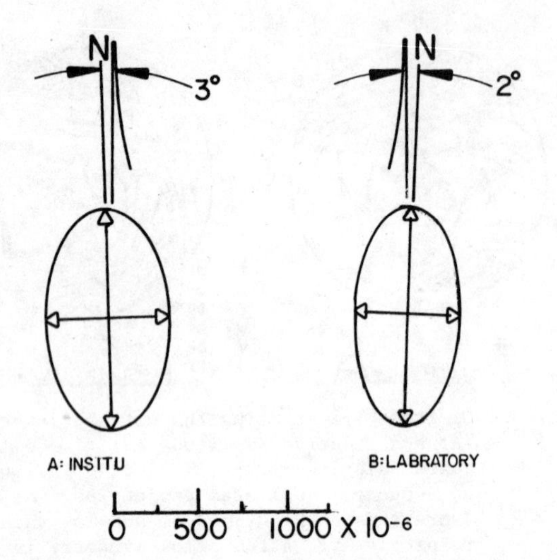

Fig. 4. *In situ* strain relief (A) and residual strain relief (B) in small samples of quartz diorite. Open arrowheads indicate expansion.

strain-gage rosettes. The excavation is oriented such that the east side is adjacent and parallel to a vertical, north-south trending fracture; that is, parallel to the principal directions of the residual-stress field. Four slots were drilled and broached to produce a cube of rock measuring 2.5 meters on a side and 2.5 meters deep. The first strain relief (Figure 5) in the block is a nearly uniform expansion of the surface with maximum elongations oriented N 55° W. This result is significantly different from that obtained by relieving the small core (Figure 4A), both in orientation and magnitude. Because the greatest relaxation of residual stress takes place adjacent to the new surfaces freed by slotting, the ratio of free surface-area to unit volume of the excavated mass may be a sensitive indicator of whether applied or residual stress is preferentially released. In the large block the surface-area to volume ratio is small (0.5) and the contribution of residual-strain relief to the *in situ* measurement is restricted to the periphery. The surface-area to volume ratio of the small core is greater by a factor of 16, and the relaxation of residual stress dominates the measurement. In the large block the release of applied stress predominates and it is probably associated with a regional, biaxial compression related to the nearby Hurricane Fault (N 35° E).

A smaller block was next relieved within the now isolated starting block (Figure 6). The relief of residual strain in this smaller block and the remaining wall of rock shows a distinctly different pattern: contractions perpendicular to the slots and expansions parallel to them. Furthermore, within the 1.9 meter block the strain relief decreases rapidly away from the new, vertical surfaces. Two additional, successively smaller cubes were cut with similar results. The incremental strain changes decreased continually as the blocks became smaller. Nichols (1972) describes an identical pattern (except for the magnitudes of the relieved strains) in a small (0.3 meter) cube of Barre Granite, and ascribes it to the release of an initial tensile residual-stress field. At the time of this writing, the proper interpretation of our results is not altogether clear, although we have suggested several possibilities (Swolfs *et al.*, 1973) Our data are severely limited because strain changes

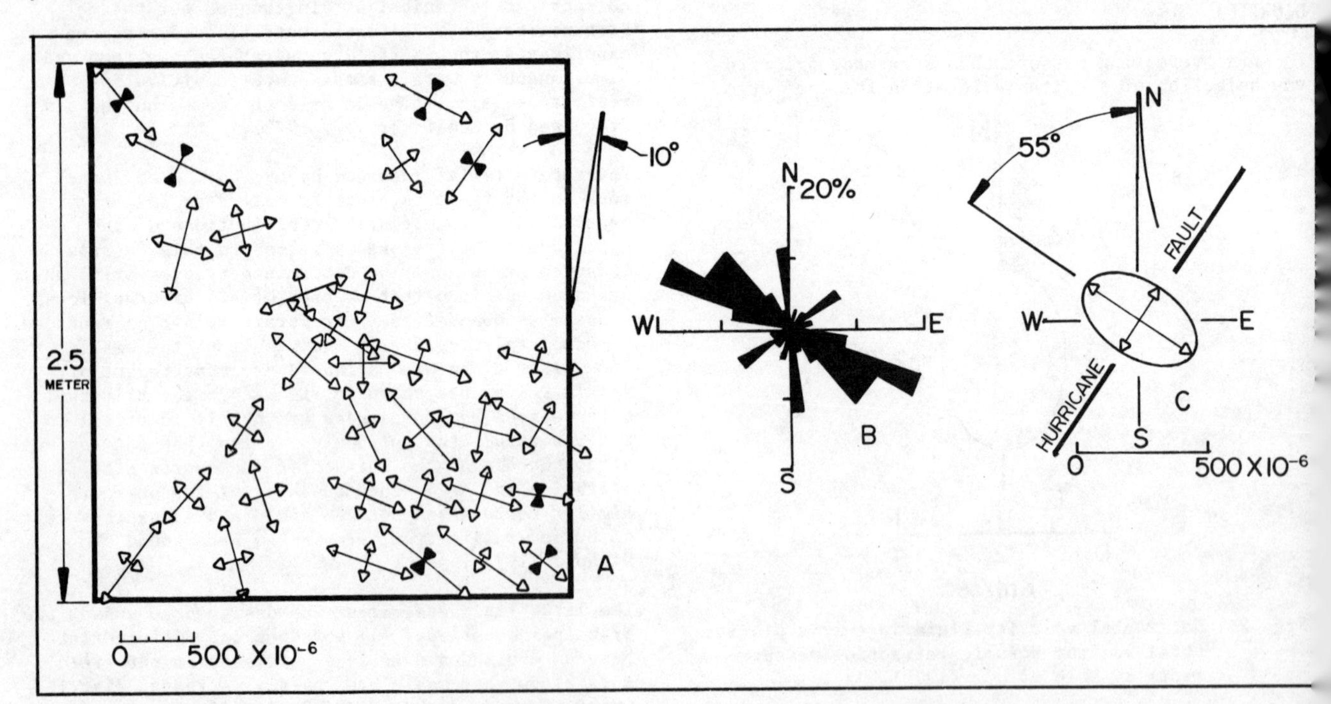

Fig. 5. *In situ* strain relief on large block of quartz diorite at the completion of slotting (A). Expansions are shown by open arrowheads; contractions by solid arrowheads. Histogram of the directions of greatest elongations (B). Average orientation and magnitude of the relief of applied strains associated with the Hurricane Fault (C).

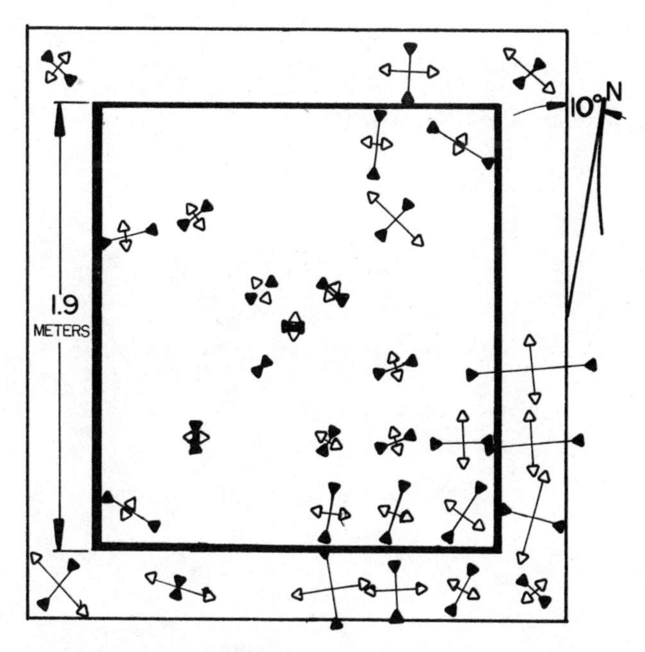

Fig. 6. Residual-strain relief in the 1.9 meter block and remaining wall of quartz diorite. Contractions are shown by solid arrowheads; expansions by open arrowheads.

are measured only at the surface and the act of slotting alters the initial state of residual stress in the rock. This fact was clearly demonstrated nine months later when we found that the rock, which had long resisted weathering before it was excavated, had disintegrated to a depth of 10 to 15 cm. Clearly we destroyed its original integrity by relieving the residual stresses and greatly increasing the rate of weathering. Adjacent outcrops of undisturbed bare rock are still intact.

CONCLUSIONS

Although our data are insufficient to fully reconstruct the initial residual stress state in the rock, the following conclusions seem clear:

1. Residual stresses are locked in domains that are large compared with the size of the relieved specimens.
2. Residual stresses are dominant in the surface of the quartz diorite and to a large extent govern the bulk mechanical behavior, anisotropy and morphology of the rock mass.
3. Residual stresses can be larger in magnitude by factors (about 3 in the quartz diorite) than the applied stresses. Their principal directions need not coincide.
4. The relaxation of residual stresses is dependent on the size and the surface-area to volume ratio of the excavation and in the quartz diorite varies from -700×10^{-6} (contraction) in large blocks to 1400×10^{-6} (expansion) in small cores.

In this paper we have tried to emphasize the fundamental nature of residual stresses in bodies of rock. These self-equilibrating, non-hydrostatic systems of stress are distributed in rock over a continuous range of scale, from the microscopic grain to grain variation of stress balanced over small volumes to the macroscopic domains exemplified by the massive sheets of exfoliated rocks. These stresses and their domains are an inherent property of rock and their effects can be enhanced by the inhomogeneous nature of rock at all scales. Excavations and other structural disturbances of rock, either natural or induced by man, can cause the redistribution of internal stresses and the release of residual-strain energy on a large scale resulting in strains and displacements not accounted for in conventional structural and tectonic analyses.

ACKNOWLEDGEMENTS

This work was supported by the U.S. Geological Survey under Contract No. 14-08-0001-13073.

REFERENCES

Denkhaus, H., 1967, Residual Stresses in Rock Masses, *General Reporter Theme IV, Proceedings, 1st Congress, International Society of Rock Mechanics*, Vol. 3, pp. 312-319.

Emery, C. L., 1964, Strain Energy in Rocks, in *State of Stress in the Earth's Crust*, W. R. Judd (Editor), American Elsevier, New York, N.Y., pp. 234-279.

Emery, C. L., 1968, Strain in Rocks, *Proceedings, 6th Annual Symposium, Engineering Geology and Soils Engineering*, Boise, Idaho, pp. 355-364.

Friedman, M., 1967, Measurements of the State of Residual Elastic Strain in Rocks by X-ray Diffractometry, *Norelco Reporter*, Vol. 14, pp. 7-9.

Friedman, M., 1972, Residual Elastic Strain in Rocks, *Tectonophysics*, Vol. 15, pp. 297-330.

Friedman, M. and J. M. Logan, 1970, The Influence of Residual Elastic Strain on the Orientation of Experimental Fractures in Three Quartzose Sandstones, *Journal of Geophysical Research*, Vol. 75, pp. 387-405.

Kolb, C. R., Farrell, W. J., Hunt, R. W. and J. R. Curro Jr., 1970, Geological Investigation of the Mine Shaft Sites, Cedar City, Utah, *U.S. Army Engineer Waterways Experiment Station Report MS-2170*, pp. 322.

Nichols, T. C. Jr., 1972, Deformations Associated with Relaxation of Residual Stresses in the Barre Granite of Vermont, *Thesis, Texas A&M University*, College Station, Texas, pp. 93.

Swolfs, H. S., Pratt, H. R. and J. Handin, 1973, Applied and Residual Strain Measurements in Quartz Diorite, Cedar City, Utah, *Transactions American Geophysical Union*, Vol. 54, p. 458.

Varnes, D. J., 1970, Model for Simulation of Residual Stress in Rock, in *Rock Mechanics - Theory and Practice, Proceedings, 11th Symposium on Rock Mechanics*, W. H. Somerton (Editor), New York, pp. 415-426.

Varnes, D. J. and F. T. Lee, 1972, Hypothesis of Mobilization of Residual Stress in Rock, *Geological Society of America Bulletin*, Vol. 83, pp. 2863-2866.

Voight, B., 1966, Restspannungen im Gestein, *Proceedings, 1st Congress, International Society of Rock Mechanics*, Vol. 2, pp. 45-50.

Walsh, J. B., Brace, W. F. and W. R. Wawersik, 1970, Attenuation of Stress Waves in Cedar City Quartz Diorite, *Air Force Weapons Laboratory Technical Report No. AFWL-TR-70-8*, pp. 76.

Willard, R. J. and J. R. McWilliams, 1969, Microstructural Techniques in the Study of Physical Properties of Rock, *International Journal of Rock Mechanics and Mining Sciences*, Vol. 6, pp. 1-12.

THE STRESSED STATE OF ROCK MASSES IN A FIELD OF BODY FORCES

ÉTAT DES CONTRAINTES DES MASSIFS ROCHEUX SOUMIS À UN CHAMP DES FORCES VOLUMIQUES

SPANNUNGSZUSTÄNDE DER ROCKMASSIVE UNTER EINWIRKUNG VOLUMENKRÄFTE

Z.G. TER-MARTIROSYAN Assistant-Professor, Moscow Civil Engineering Institute

D.M. AKHPATELOV Researcher, All-Union Research Institute of Hydrology and Engineering Geology

R.G. MANVELYAN Post-graduate, Moscow Civil Engineering Institute

Moscow, U.S.S.R.

SUMMARY Results of theoretical investigations of a stressed state of rock masses subject to dead load and seismic forces are set forth within the limits of the plane problem of the theory of elasticity. The rock mass under consideration occupies a semi-infinite region having a curvilinear boundary in the form of a quadratic parabola and other curves of more complicated shape, specified in parametric form.

The problems are solved in the closed form by means of the Kolosov-Muskhelishvili method of complex potentials, making use of conformal mapping and cauchy integral. This enables all the components to be computed for the stressed state of rock masses subject to gravity and seismic forces. In addition, a formula for determining the stability number is proposed for evaluating the state of a rock mass at a given point.

On the basis of the obtained solutions several examples of calculations for the stressed state of rock masses subject to gravity and seismic forces are given in the form of isolines of the maximum stresses and stability numbers for parabolic profiles, as well as for a complex profile in the form of a valley. Analysis revealed that in the case of symmetrical canyons, seismic action in the horizontal direction deteriorates the stability condition of one slope and, on the contrary, improves the stability condition of the opposite slope.

In the case of a parabolic profile, seismic action in the horizontal direction does not substantially affect the shape of the isolines of the maximum tangential stresses.

The theoretical solutions of the plane problem of the theory of elasticity developed in this paper enable an accurate quantitative evaluation to be made of the stressed state of rock masses with simple and complex profiles in a field of body forces of gravity and seismic action.

RESUME On présente dans ce rapport les résultats de recherches théoriques sur l'état de contraintes des massifs rocheux sous l'action de leur poids propre et de forces sismiques, recherches effectuées dans le cadre de la théorie de l'élasticité plane. Les massifs étudiés sont des demi-espaces limités par des paraboles ou des courbes plus complexes données sous forme paramétrique.

La solution de ces problèmes est obtenue sous forme implicite par la méthode des potentiels complexes de Kolossov et Mouskhélichvili, en utilisant une transformation conforme et des intégrales de Cauchy. Elle permet de calculer toutes les composantes du tenseur des contraintes des massifs rocheux soumis à la pesanteur et à des forces sismiques. De plus pour décrire l'état des massifs rocheux, on propose une formule donnant le coefficient de stabilité en chaque point.

Sur la base des solutions obtenues, on donne quelques exemples de calcul de l'état de contraintes de massifs rocheux soumis à la pesanteur et à des forces sismiques: les résultats sont présentés sous forme de courbes d'iso-contraintes tangentielles maximales et d'iso-coefficients de stabilité pour un profil parabolique et un profil plus complexe en forme de vallée. L'analyse a montré que, pour les vallées symétriques, les forces sismiques horizontales diminuent la stabilité sur l'une des pentes et l'améliorent sur l'autre.

Pour les profils paraboliques, l'action des forces sismiques horizontales n'a pas d'effet notable sur le caractère des courbes d'égales contraintes tangentielles maximales.

Les solutions théoriques présentées dans le rapport pour le problème de l'élasticité plane permettent de déterminer exactement l'intensité des contraintes à l'intérieur de massifs rocheux limités par des surfaces simples ou complexes et soumis à l'action de la force de pesanteur et de forces sismiques.

ZUSAMMENFASSUNG Im Beitrag sind Ergebnisse der theoretischen Untersuchungen des Spannungszustandes der Felsgesteinmassive unter Einwirkung des Eigengewichts und Kräfte der Seismik angeführt. Man betrachtet das im Rahmen der planen Aufgabe der Elastititätstheorie. Der betrachtende Bereich der Felsmassive nimmt ein halbendloses Gebiet mit einer krummlinigen Grenze in Gestalt der quadratischen Parabel und anderer mehr komplizierten Kurven der vorgegebenen parametrischen Form ein.

Aufgabelösungen sind in geschlossener Form erhalten durch Methode der Komplexpotentialen von Kolossow-Mushelischwili mit der Nutzung der Konformwidergabe und der Integrale von Koschi-Typ, sie geben eine Möglichkeit alle Komponenten des Spannungszustandes der Felsgesteinmassive unter Einwirkung der seismischen und Gravitationskräfte zu berechnen. Außerdem wird eine Formel des Standsicherheitsbeiwertes für die Einschätzung des Felsgesteinzustandes im betrachtenden Punkt vorgeschlagen.

Auf Grund der erhaltenen Lösungen sind im Beitrag einige Beispiele von Berechnungen des Spannungszustandes der Felsgesteinmassive angeführt unter Einwirkung der Gravitations- und Seismikkräfte in Form der Isolinien der maximalen Tangentialspannungen und der Standsicherheitsbeiwerte für ein Parabelprofil und durch für ein kompliziertes Profil in Form einer Vertiefung Analyse hat gezeigt, daß für symmetrische Talschluchten die Wirkung der Seismik in Horizontalrichtung die Standsicherheitsbedingung auf einem Hang stört und auf der anderen Seite die Standsicherheit verbessert.

Für Parabelprofil beeinflußt die Wirkung der seismischen Kräfte in Horizontalrichtung nicht stark den Charakter der Isolinien von maximalen Tangentialspannungen.

Die im Beitrag ausgearbeiteten theoretischen Lösungen der planen Aufgabe der Elastizitätstheorie erlauben eine genaue quantitative Einschätzung des Spannungszeitstandes von Felsgesteinmassive mit einfachen und komplizierten Profilen im Feld der Volumenkräfte der Gravitation und Seismik zu geben.

The stressed state of rock masses in a field of body forces (gravitational, seismic and others) determines to a considerable degree the short- and long-term stability of these masses, the provision of which is essential in solving many engineering problems of the construction of unique and large-scale structures on rock bases.

This paper, which was prepared in the Department of Soil Mechanics, Bases and Foundations of the Moscow Civil Engineering Institute, sets forth the solutions of a number of problems for calculating the stressed state and the stability number for a rock mass subject to gravity and seismic forces. The solutions are dealt with within the limits of the plane problem in the theory of elasticity and are exact.

Formulation of the problem. The rock mass is regarded as a continuous, homogeneous, linearly-deformable semi-infinite region having a curvilinear boundary whose asymptote is a straight line, inclined at a certain angle α to the horizon (Fig.1). To be found are all the components of the stressed state at any point of this rock mass subject to body forces of gravity and seismic action.

The solution of this problem, as is known, should comply with the differential equations of equilibrium

$$\begin{aligned}\frac{\partial \sigma_x}{\partial x}+\frac{\partial \tau_{xy}}{\partial y}&=\gamma(\sin\alpha+K_s\sin\beta)=\gamma K_{xy}\\ \frac{\partial \tau_{xy}}{\partial x}+\frac{\partial \sigma_y}{\partial y}&=\gamma(\cos\alpha-K_s\cos\beta)=\gamma K_y\end{aligned}\qquad(1)$$

the compatibility condition

$$\Delta(\sigma_x+\sigma_y)=0 \qquad (2)$$

and the boundary conditions

$$\begin{cases}P_{x\nu}=\sigma_x l+\tau_{xy}m\\ P_{y\nu}=\tau_{xy}l+\sigma_y m\end{cases}\qquad(3)$$

where σ_x, σ_y and τ_{xy} = stress components γ = unit weight of the rock

β=angle of deflection of the y-axis from the direction of the seismic force

$P_{x\nu}$ and $P_{y\nu}$ = stress components on the boundary of the region

l and m= direction cosines on the boundary curve

K_s= seismicity coefficient which is the ratio of the seismic acceleration to the acceleration of gravity. This coefficient varies in the limits from 0.025 to 0.1, respectively, as the earthquake force varies in magnitude from 7 to 9 (Tsytovich, et al, 1972).

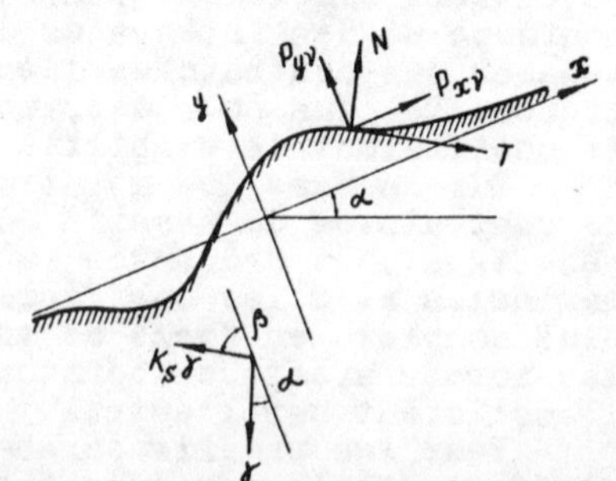

Fig.1. Diagram of the formulated problem.

It has been proved (Muskhelishvili, 1966) that there always exists a biharmonic function $\varphi(x, y)$, called the Airy stress function, which enables stresses to be determined as its partial differentials, that is

$$\begin{cases} \sigma_x = \dfrac{\partial^2 \varphi}{\partial y^2}; \quad \sigma_y = \dfrac{\partial^2 \varphi}{\partial x^2}; \\ \tau_{xy} = -\dfrac{\partial^2 \varphi}{\partial x \partial y} + \gamma (K_{xy} y + K_y X) \end{cases} \qquad (4)$$

The formulated problem can be solved in various ways, depending on the type of its boundary curve. In some cases, when the boundary lines of the semi-infinite region occupied by a mountain mass are of simple configurations, the solution can be readily obtained directly from a system of the basic equations, or by searching for the stress function in the form of polynomial of a certain power, or certain other elementary biharmonic functions. Thus, for instance, the solution of the problem of the stressed state of ponderable infinite slopes, taking the seismic forces into account, can be presented in the form

$$\begin{cases} \sigma_x = K\gamma(\cos\alpha - K_s \cdot \cos\beta) \cdot y = \gamma \cdot K \cdot K_y \\ \sigma_y = \gamma(\cos\alpha - K_s \cdot \cos\beta) \cdot y = \gamma K_y \\ \tau_{xy} = \gamma(\sin\alpha + K_s \cdot \sin\beta) \cdot y = \gamma K_{xy} \end{cases} \qquad (5)$$

where K is the coefficient of lateral pressure, related to Poisson's ratio ν by the equation $K = \nu : (1-\nu)$.

First let us consider the solution of the formulated problem for a parabolic boundary by selecting the Airy stress function in the form of a polynomial of a certain power. It should be noted that the solution of this problem for the case of a complex boundary curve involves serious mathematical difficulties. However, in cases when a mapping rational function is found for the region under consideration, the application of the Kolosov-Muskhelishvili method of complex potentials (Muskhelishvili, 1966) proves to be the most expedient.

Let us consider the solution of a problem for the parabolic boundary $y = -aX^2, (a > 0)$. We are searching for an Airy function of the type

$$\varphi(X,y) = \gamma(C_1 y^2 + C_2 X^2 y + C_3 X y^2 + C_4 X^3 y) \qquad (6)$$

Making use of (4) we obtain

$$\sigma_x = \gamma(2C_1 + 2C_3 X); \quad \sigma_y = \gamma(2C_2 y + 6C_4 X y);$$
$$\tau_{xy} = -\gamma(2C_2 X + 2C_3 y + 3C_4 X^2 - K_{xy} y - K_y X) \qquad (7)$$

The condition that there are no stresses on the boundary taking the values of the direction cosines into account, will be of the form

$$P_{x\nu} = (2aX\sigma_x + \tau_{xy}) : \sqrt{1 + 4a^2 x^2} = 0$$
$$P_{y\nu} = (2aX\tau_{xy} + \sigma_y) : \sqrt{1 + 4a^2 x^2} = 0 \qquad (8)$$

Substituting the stress values from (7) into (8), and taking into account that $y = -aX^2$ on the boundary, the following system is obtained:

$$\begin{cases} (4C_1 a - 2C_2 + K_y)x + (6C_3 a - K_{xy} a)x^2 = 0 \\ 2(K_y a - 6C_2 a)x^2 + (4C_3 a^2 - 2K_{xy} a^2 - 12C_4 a)X^3 = 0 \end{cases} \qquad (9)$$

from which it is simple to obtain expressions for coefficients C_1, C_2, C_3 and C_4, namely:

$$C_1 = \frac{K_y}{3}; \quad C_2 = -\frac{K_y}{2a}; \quad C_3 = \frac{K_{xy}}{6}; \quad C_4 = -\frac{2K_{xy} a}{15} \qquad (10)$$

Substituting (10) into (7), we will obtain, finally, for the stress components:

$$\begin{cases} \sigma_x = \dfrac{\gamma}{3a}(6a \cdot K_{xy} X - 5K_y) \\ \sigma_y = -\dfrac{2\gamma y}{15}(6K_{xy} a X - 5K_y) \\ \tau_{xy} = \dfrac{\gamma}{15}(5K_y X + 12K_{xy} y + 6a K_{xy} X^2) \end{cases} \qquad (11)$$

where
$$\begin{cases} K_{xy} = \sin\alpha + K_s \cdot \sin\beta; \\ K_y = \cos\alpha - K_s \cdot \cos\beta. \end{cases} \qquad (12)$$

It is evident that the obtained solution satisfies the equilibrium equation and the boundary conditions.

Now let us consider a solution of this problem for the case when the boundary curves can be described by parametric equations of the type

$$\begin{cases} X = c\left[t - \dfrac{(Bt - b)(t + a)}{(t + a)^2 + 1}\right] \\ y = -c\,\dfrac{Bt - b}{(t + a)^2 + 1} \end{cases} \qquad (13)$$

where c = proportionality factor
B, b and a = constants
t = real variable.

Equation (13) is obtained from the equation

$$z = \omega(\zeta) = c\left[\zeta - \frac{B\zeta - b}{\zeta + a - i}\right], \quad \begin{pmatrix} z = x + iy; \\ \zeta = \xi + i\eta; \ \eta < 0 \end{pmatrix} \qquad (14)$$

defining the conformal mapping of the lower half-plane on the region of the boundary described by equations (13) at $\eta = 0$ and $\xi = t$. These regions represent profiles of symmetric and asymmetric canyons, valleys, hills, mountains, etc., and have the x-axis as an asymptote.

The Muskhelishvili (1966) method of

complex variables is based on the fact that the stress function $\varphi(x,y)$ is presented in the form of combinations of two functions of the complex variable, $\Phi_1(z)$ and $\Psi_1(z)$, that are called complex potentials. Here the stress components are related to these functions by the following equations:

$$\begin{cases} \sigma_x + \sigma_y = 4 \operatorname{Re} \Phi_1(z) \\ \sigma_y - \sigma_x + 2i\tau_{xy} = 2\left[\bar{z}\Phi_1'(z) + \Psi_1(z)\right] \end{cases} \quad (15)$$

Here and in the following a line over a quantity denotes conjugacy.

The boundary conditions are written in the following form

$$\Phi(t) + \overline{\Phi(t)} + \frac{1}{\overline{\omega'(t)}}\left[\overline{\omega(t)}\,\Phi'(t) + \omega'(t)\cdot\Psi(t)\right] = N + iT \quad (16)$$

where t = point of the real axis on plane ξ

N and T = given functions, which are boundary values of the parallel and tangential stress components σ_η and $\tau_{\xi\eta}$.

Functions $\Phi(\xi)$ and $\Psi(\xi)$, holomorphic in the lower half-plane, are determined from two equations which result from the boundary condition (16) and its conjugate by multiplying by the Cauchy kernel $[2\pi i(t-\xi)]^{-1}$ and by integrating both expressions along the boundary of the half-plane.

However, this method of finding complex potentials assumes an absence of body forces, i.e. the equilibrium equations are homogeneous. To bring the equilibrium equation to the homogeneous form, it proves sufficient to find any particular solution of the nonhomogeneous equation (1) and to present the general solution as the sum of solutions

$$\sigma_x = \sigma_x^o + \sigma_x^p;\ \sigma_y = \sigma_y^o + \sigma_y^p;\ \tau_{xy} = \tau_{xy}^o + \tau_{xy}^p \quad (17)$$

where σ_x, σ_y and τ_{xy} = general solution

σ_x^p, σ_y^p and τ_{xy}^p = particular solution

σ_x^o, σ_y^o and τ_{xy}^o = additional solution.

It is evident that the additional stresses must satisfy the homogeneous system of equilibrium equations and specific conditions of the boundary, but with the absence of body forces. Then the formulated problem is reduced to the determination of the stress distribution in the considered region with a curvilinear boundary, with properly specified boundary conditions.

The conditions on the boundary are determined by rewriting the boundary conditions (4) in the form

$$N = \frac{\sigma_x+\sigma_y}{2} - \frac{\sigma_x-\sigma_y}{2}\cos\theta - \tau_{xy}\sin 2\theta$$
$$T = -\frac{\sigma_x-\sigma_y}{2}\sin 2\theta + \tau_{xy}\cos 2\theta \quad (18)$$

where θ is the angle between axis ξ and axis x.

Taking (17) into account we have

$$N = \frac{\sigma_x^o+\sigma_y^o}{2} - \frac{\sigma_x^o-\sigma_y^o}{2}\cos 2\theta - \tau_{xy}^o\sin 2\theta + \frac{\sigma_x^p-\sigma_y^p}{2} - \frac{\sigma_x^p-\sigma_y^p}{2}\cos 2\theta - \tau_{xy}^p\sin 2\theta;$$
$$T = -\frac{\sigma_x^o-\sigma_y^o}{2}\sin 2\theta + \tau_{xy}^o\cos 2\theta - \frac{\sigma_x^p-\sigma_y^p}{2}\sin 2\theta - \tau_{xy}^p\cdot\cos 2\theta. \quad (19)$$

The condition of the absence of stresses on the contour leads to N = T = 0, i.e

$$\frac{\sigma_x^o+\sigma_y^o}{2} - \frac{\sigma_x^o-\sigma_y^o}{2}\cos 2\theta - \tau_{xy}^o\sin 2\theta = -\frac{\sigma_x^p-\sigma_y^p}{2}\cos 2\theta + \tau_{xy}^p\sin 2\theta;$$
$$-\frac{\sigma_x^o-\sigma_y^o}{2}\sin 2\theta + \tau_{xy}^o\cos 2\theta = \frac{\sigma_x^p-\sigma_y^p}{2}\cdot\sin 2\theta - \tau_{xy}\cos 2\theta. \quad (20)$$

Equations (18) describe the equilibrium conditions on the boundary in a semi-infinite region. But, on the other hand, equations (18) specify the boundary conditions for the components of the additional stresses σ_x^o, σ_y^o and τ_{xy}^o, acting inside a region with the same boundary upon the absence of body forces. It can readily be seen that the conditions on the boundary in a region, without taking the body forces into account, can be written as

$$N^o = \frac{\sigma_x^o+\sigma_y^o}{2} - \frac{\sigma_x^o-\sigma_y^o}{2}\cos 2\theta - \tau_{xy}^o\sin 2\theta$$
$$T^o = -\frac{\sigma_x^o-\sigma_y^o}{2}\sin 2\theta + \tau_{xy}^o\cos 2\theta. \quad (21)$$

Comparing (19) and (20), we obtain boundary conditions for the components of the additional stresses, that can be used to find these components. Thus

$$N^o = -\frac{\sigma_x^p+\sigma_y^p}{2} + \frac{\sigma_x^p-\sigma_y^p}{2}\cos 2\theta + \tau_{xy}^p\cdot\sin 2\theta$$
$$T^o = \frac{\sigma_x^p-\sigma_y^p}{2}\cdot\sin 2\theta - \tau_{xy}^p\cdot\cos 2\theta \quad (22)$$

or, making use of the well-known Euler formula,

$$N^o + iT^o = -\frac{\sigma_x^p+\sigma_y^p}{2} + \frac{\sigma_x^p-\sigma_y^p}{2}\cdot e^{2i\theta} - \tau_{xy}^p\cdot e^{2i\theta} \quad (23)$$

The obtained boundary condition is expressed as a function of points on the real axis $\eta = 0$ of plane ξ and is denoted by t. Making use of expression $e^{2i\theta} = \omega'(\xi) : \omega'(\xi)$ we obtain

$$N^\circ+iT^\circ=-\frac{\sigma_x^p+\sigma_y^p}{2}+\left(\frac{\sigma_x^p-\sigma_y^p}{2}-\tau_{xy}^p\cdot i\right)\frac{\omega'(t)}{\overline{\omega'(t)}}; \qquad (24)$$

Thus, the plane problem involving body forces is reduced to a problem involving surface forces that are determined by equation (24).

Assuming that the stressed state of the rock mass with a curvilinear boundary originated from a stressed state of an infinite slope and additional stresses σ_x°, σ_y° and τ_{xy}°, which were developed as a result of the distortion of the boundary, equations (5) will be used as a particular solution.

Taking into account the fact that $y=[\omega(t)-\overline{\omega(t)}]:2i$ and employing equations (14) and (5), the following expression for the boundary stresses is obtained from equation (24):

$$N^\circ+iT^\circ=\frac{C(Bt-B)\gamma}{2}\left\{\frac{K_x+K_y}{(t+a+i)(t+a-i)}-\frac{(K_x-K_y-2K_{xy}\cdot i)\cdot}{(t+a-i)^3}\right. \qquad (25)$$
$$\left.\frac{\cdot(t+a+i)[(t+a-i)^2-Ba-B+Bi]}{[(t+a+i)^2-Ba-B-Bi]}\right\},$$

where $K_x=K\cdot K_y$.

Taking (14) into account, the boundary condition conjugate to (14) will take the form:

$$N^\circ+iT^\circ=\Phi(t)+\overline{\Phi(t)}+\frac{(t+a-i)^2[t(t+a-i)-Bt+B]\overline{\Phi'(t)}}{(t+a-i)[(t+a-i)^2-Ba-B-Bi]}+$$

$$+\frac{(t+a-i)^2[(t+a+i)^2-Ba-B+Bi}{(t+a+i)^2[(t+a-i)^2-Ba-B+Bi]}\overline{\Psi(t)} \qquad (26)$$

On the basis of this equation, integrating it from $-\infty$ to $+\infty$, the complex potentials $\Phi(\xi)$ and $\Psi(\xi)$ are obtained.

By separating the imaginary part from the real part, formulas are obtained for calculating the stress components σ_x°, σ_y° and τ_{xy}°. The final solution of the formulated problem is reached by adding the obtained solution to the particular solutions obtained on the basis of equation (17). However, the stress expressions are so cumbersome, that it is not expedient to give them here. The obtained solution is programmed on an electronic computer for calculating all the stress components, as well as the principal stresses, which are determined by the following equations:

$$\sigma_1=\frac{\sigma_x+\sigma_y}{2}+\tau_{max};$$
$$\sigma_2=\frac{\sigma_x+\sigma_y}{2}-\tau_{max}; \qquad (27)$$
$$\tau_{max}=\frac{1}{2}\sqrt{(\sigma_x+\sigma_y)^2+4\tau_{xy}^2}$$

Besides, stability numbers F_s, for analysing the strength condition at various points, were computed from the following expression

$$F_s=\frac{[2C\cdot\cot\varphi-(\sigma_x-\sigma_y)]}{2\tau_{max}\cdot\cos^2\varphi}\sin\varphi-\frac{\sin^2\varphi}{\cos^2\varphi}=\frac{\tau_\alpha^\kappa}{\tau_\alpha} \qquad (28)$$

where c and φ = Coulomb strength parameters

τ_{max} = maximum tangential stress

τ_α^κ = limiting tangential stress

τ_α = acting tangential stress.

The rock at this point is in a stable state when $F_s \geq 1$; when $F_s < 1$ the rock is in a state of plastic flow.

Several examples for various boundary curves were calculated by an electronic computer on the basis of the obtained solutions. The results of some of these calculations are shown in Figs. 2,3 and 4

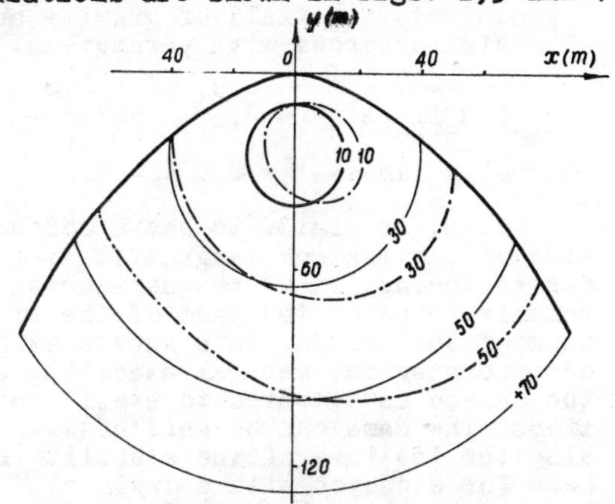

Fig.2. Isolines $\tau_{max}\cdot 10^3\cdot g/cm^2$, in a rock mass having a parabolic profile subject to a field of gravity and seismic forces with parameters: K_s =0.01, γ = 2 g/cm³
Solid line: K_s = 0, α = 0
Dot-dash line: K_s =0.1, β =90°, α = 0.

Isolines of the maximum tangential stresses due to the action of gravity alone (continuous lines) and due to simultaneous action of gravity and seismic forces (dot-dash lines) are shown in Fig.2. It is evident, that the action of a horizontal seismic load, with an intensity of about magnitude 9, does not lead to a substantial change in the distribution of the tangential stresses in a rock mass. However, at a greater intensity of the horizontal seismic load, substantial changes occur in the stressed state of a rock mass. This is clearly shown in Figs. 3 and 4, where isolines of the maximum tangential stresses and the stability numbers for curvilinear regions in the form of asymmetric canyons are given for the action of gravity alone and for the simultaneous action of gravity and seismic forces (on Fig.3, values τ_{max} are referred to $\gamma h 10^{-2}$)

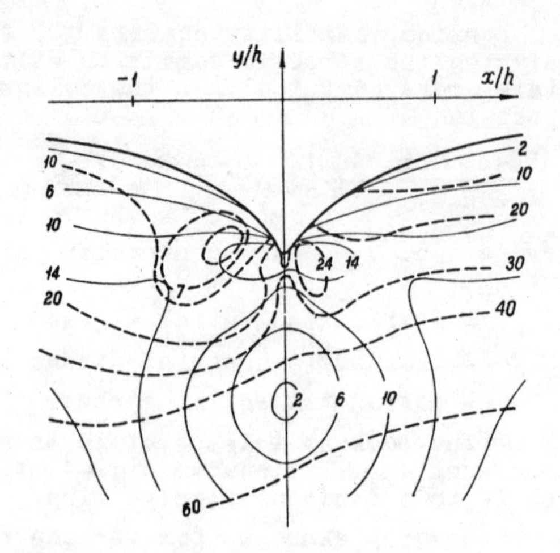

Fig.3. Isolines of the maximum tangential stresses in a symmetrical canyon subject to a field of gravity and seismic forces with parameters:
$B = a = 0$, $b = -0.9$, $K = 0.8$.
Dash lines: $\alpha = 0$, $\beta = 90^o$, $K_s = 0.27$.
Solid lines: $-\alpha = 0$, $K_s = 0$.

Thus, in Fig.3, we see a concentration of the maximum tangential stresses due to the action of the horizontal seismic force at the base of the right bank of the canyon. This substantally deteriorates the general stability of the canyon as compared to static conditions. The same can be said after analysing the isolines of the stability numbers for a canyon with a depth of h = 100 metres, shown in Fig.4.

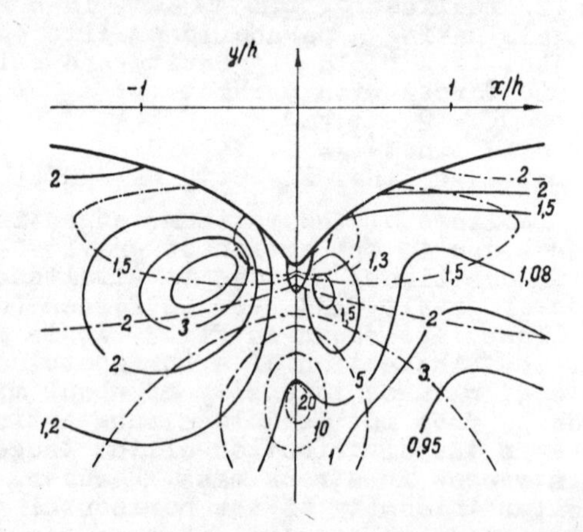

Fig.4. Isolines of the stability numbers in a symmetrical canyon subject to a field of gravity and seismic forces with parameters:
$B = a = 0$, $b = -0.9$, $K = 0.8$,
$h = 10^4$ cm, $\gamma = 1.9$ g/cm^3
$C = 2 \cdot 10^2$ g/cm^2, $\varphi = 15^o$.
Solid lines: $-K_s = 0$, $\alpha = 0$.

Dot-dash lines: $K_s = 0.27$, $\beta = 90^o$, $\alpha = 0$.

Consequently, the theoretical solutions of the plane problem of the theory of elasticity set forth in this paper enable an accurate quantitative evaluation to be made of the stability of rock masses having simple and complex profiles and subject to the action of gravity and seismic forces.

Acknowledgement. The authors wish to express their thanks to Professor N.A.Tsytovich, Corresponding Member of the USSR Academy of Sciences, for his unfailing interest and aid in carrying out this work

REFERENCES

AKHPATELOV, D.M., TER-MARTIROSYAN, Z.G.(1971) "The Stressed State of Ponderable Semi-Infinite Domains". Bulletin of the Armenian Academy of Sciences, Mechanics, XXIV No.3, Yerivan.
MUSKHELISHVILI, N.I.(1966) "Certain Basic Problems of the Mathematical Theory of Elasticity", Nauka Publ.House, Moscow.
TER-MARTIROSYAN, Z.G., AKHPATELOV, D.M. (1972), "The Stressed State of an Infinite Slope with a Curvilinear Boundary Subject to a Field of Gravity and Percolation" Journal "Problems in Geomechanics" No.5, Yerevan.
TER-STEPANYAN, G.I. (1967) "Natural and Artificial Slopes", Papers of the First International Conference on Rock Mechanics, Moscow.
TSYTOVICH, N.A., et al (1972) "Bases and Foundations", Visshaya Shkola Pub. House; Moscow.
TSYTOVICH, N.A. (1973) "Problems of Soil and Rock Mechanics in Geomechanics", Special Lecture, Proceedings of the VIII Inter. Conf. on Soil Mechanics and Foundation Engineering, vol.IV, Moscow.

COMPLEX ANALYSIS AND EXPERIMENTAL DETERMINATION OF COMPLETE STRESS TENSOR IN THE ROCK MASS

L'ANALYSE COMPLEXE ET LA DETERMINATION EXPÉRIMENTALE DU TENSEUR COMPLETE DES CONTRAINTES DANS UN MASSIF DES ROCHES

DIE KOMPLEXANALYSE UND DIE EXPERIMENTELLE BESTIMMUNG DES SPANNUNGSTENSORS IM FELSGEBIRGE

Igor Alexandrovich TURCHANINOV — Doctor of Sciences, Director of the Mining and Metallurgical Institute

Gennady Alexandrovich MARKOV
Victor Ivanovich PANIN
Vladimir Ivanovich IVANOV — Candidates of Science
Apatity, U.S.S.R.

Summary

To define the complete stress tensor application of complex analysis of stress distribution in rock mass is considered. The complex analysis is based on making use of methods giving in succession ever increasing information about the stress acting in the area under study:

(a) Evaluating the stresses to be expected on the basis of geological data;
(b) Preliminary determination of the stress field structure and the magnitudes of the stresses from observations on rock pressure in underground workings and boreholes;
(c) Determination of the directions and the magnitudes of the stresses by ultrasonic method;
(d) Determination of the magnitudes of the principal stresses and their actions in rock masses by stress relief method with orientation of measuring holes in the principal stress directions.

The application of the complex analysis in experimental determination of the stresses in the rock masses at the mines of the Kola Peninsula proved to be the most efficient way of determining the complete stress tensor with sufficiently high reliability.

Résumé.

La détermination du tenseur complet des contraintes se base sur l'emploi de l'analyse complexe de la répartition des contraintes dans un massif des roches. L'analyse complexe part de la condition de l'emploi d'une serie de methodes donnant de plus en plus grande information sur les contraintes dans une region étudieé:

a) l'évaluation des contraintes supposées sur la base des données géologiques;
b) la détermination préalable de la structure du champ et des valeurs des contraintes d'après les observations de la pression des terrains dans des excavations souterraines et dans des trous de sonde;
c) la détermination des directions et des valeurs des contraintes par la méthode ultrasonique;
d) la détermination des valeurs des contraintes principales normales et des directions de leur fonction dans des massifs des roches par la méthode de détente avec une orientation des trous dans la direction des contraintes principales.

L'emploi de l'analyse complexe dans les déterminations expérimentales des contraintes dans des massifs des roches des mines de la presqu'île de Kola a montre que c'est la voie la plus effective de la détermination du tenseur complet des contraintes avec une assez grandesûreté.

Zusammenfassung.

Es wird die Anwendung der Komplexanalyse der Spannungsverteilung im Felsgebirge zur Bestimmung des Spannungstensors beim Dreiaxialdruckzustand besprochen.

Bei der Komplexanalyse geht man von den Anwendungsbedingungen der Verfahren aus, die immer zunehmende Information über die im Untersuchungsgebiet wirkenden Spannungen fortlaufend geben. Es handelt sich dabei um die folgenden Verfahren:

a) Die Bewertung der zu erwartenden Spannungen auf Grund der geologischen Verhältnisse;
b) Die Vorbestimmung der Feldstruktur und der Spanunugswerte anhand von Gebirgsdruckäußerungen im Grubenbau und in Bohrungen;
c) Die Bestimmung der Spannungsrichtungen und der Spannungswerte durch das Ultraschallverfahren;
d) Die Bestimmung der Hauptnormalspannungswerte und Wirkungsrichtungen dieser Spannungen im Felsgebirge durch das Entspannungsverfahren mit der Anordnung der Meßbohrlöcher in der Richtung der Hauptspannungen.

Die Ausnutzung der Komplexanalyse bei mehreren experimentellen Spannungsbestimmungen im Felsgebirge in Gruben der Kola-Halbinsel hat gezeigt, daß dieses Verfahren auch zur

Bestimmung des Spannungstensors beim Dreiaxildruckzustand mit großer Zuverläßigkeit wirkungsvoll ist.

In studying the state of stress in rock mass the problems of the complex application of various methods for the purposes of obtaining the maximum information about acting stress field are of particular importance.

Taking into consideration distinguishing features typical of each method it is neccessary to choose a rational order of their application for obtaining more complete and reliable information on the principal stresses in rock mass and stress tensor components. In the general case the stress state in rock mass is given by the tensor of second order[5]. As is presently established, principal acting force factors in rock mass are gravitational and tectonic forces. The stress tensor components include, therefore, the gravitational and tectonic components. Under certain conditions the stress tensor can be expressed in terms of the principal stresses σ_1, σ_2 and σ_3. In this case $|\sigma_1| < |\sigma_2| < |\sigma_3|$. It is the principal stresses that one must know to solve the most of rock mechanics problems.

At the Mining and Metallurgical Institute of the Kola Branch of the USSR Academy of Sciences a complex of methods has been proposed. Application of the methods in a certain order enables to obtain more complete and reliable information on the action direction and the magnitude of the principal stresses.

The point of general technique lies in a preliminary estimate of the stress state in a rock mass based on analysing the geology, tectonics and seismicity of an area, visual inspections of mine workings and instrumental impulsive seismic (ultrasonic) measurements. As a result of the preliminary estimate the principal stress direction in the rock mass is determined. Then measurements made by the stress relief method in the boreholes oriented in the principal stress directions are considered. These measurements provide refined parameters of the stress field in the site under study.

I. Investigation of the stress state at the site should be started with the analysis of geological structure, tectonics and seismicity of the area. This permits to obtain the preliminary estimate of the stress field. The rock mass type should, firstly, be determined; whether these are crystalline basement rocks, platform folding regions expressed by contrast, weakly metamorphosed mantle rocks or sedimentary complexes not subjected to metamorphism at all. The effects of tectonic forces can, as a rule, be expected in the rock masses of the first two types. The horizontal compressive stresses here can exceed several times vertical ones. In the rock mass of the third type the tectonic stresses are generally missing or very small. The stress field of the rock masses of the fourth type is controlled by the gravitational force action, i.e. by the weight of the overburden of rock.

Data on analysing modern movements of the earth's crust can be important criteria for the preliminary estimate of the stress field. For example, there is evidence for the territiry of Fennoscandia indicating that the probable direction of the maximum stress is orthogonal to the isoline of the modern movements. Information on the principal stress direction obtained from analysing data on the movements at the considered site should be compared to data on spatial orientation of the earth's erust tectonic faults of various orders. In this case, by making use of the earth's crust movement inheritance principle [6] and of the observational data on the modern movements it is expedient to ascertain which faults have remained active so far and to correlate the principal stresses directions with their directions. A large body of information available is indicative of the stresses being orthogonal to the zones of modern seismie effects, i.e. to seismic belts.

II. The visual inspection of underground workings permits to obtain an idea of the stress field structure within the limits of deposit under study. It should be noted that the visual inspection gives the most informing results when acting stresses are sufficiently high [more than half rock compression strength ($\sigma_3 > 0.5\ \sigma_{comp}$)].

The visual inspections make it possible to bring out, in general, qualitative criteria typical of stress field structure. Nevertheless, by means of the visual inspection the following alternative problems can be solved:

(a) Whether the stress field is hydrostatic or non-hydrostatic;
(b) Whether the direction of maximum compressive stress σ_3, in case of non-hydrostatic stress field, is close to horizontal or vertical direction;
(c) Whether the maximum principal stress if horizontal is oriented in latitudinal, meridional or intermediate-diagonal direction;
(d) Whether the stress field at the site under study is homogeneous or non-homogeneous.

The above problems are solved on the basis of studying the mode and location of rock fracture on the contour of horizontal, vertical and inclined unsupported workings as well as boreholes located beyond the zone of stoping influence.

One can approximately determine the stress value in the rock mass from observations on the rock fracture around mine workings. Given brittle rock fracture marks in the workings with rock outburst effects the stress value can be calculated from the approximate equation

$$\sigma_z = \frac{\sigma_{comp}}{4} \qquad (1)$$

where σ_z is the stress in the rock mass,
σ_{comp} is the rock uniaxial compressive strength.

With core disking occuring in boreholes the stress value can be estimated from the equation (1) when a borehole face is close to the contour of a mine working or from the following equation

$$\sigma_z = \frac{\sigma_{comp}}{2} \qquad (2)$$

Equation (2) is applicable providing the face is at some distance from the contour of the mine working $\ell \geqslant \frac{d}{2}$ where d is the largest size or diameter of the working.

III. The results of the preliminary estimates for the acting stress field are taken into account in instrumental determining the stresses by the ultrasonic method [8]

Expressability is a distinguishing feature of the ultrasonic method based on dependence of elastic wave parameters in rocks on their stress state. Application of the ultrasonic method allows to get information on the state of the considered site sufficiently fast. The nature of the information depends on the acoustic properties of the rock making up the site. Informability of the ultrasonic method [9] is determined by the acoustic properties of rocks

$$J = 1.445 \ln \frac{\Delta C_p}{P_c} \qquad (3)$$

where ΔC_p is the increase in longitudinal elastic wave velocity in rock specimens when loaded up to rupture,
P_c is the statistically significant difference between the values of the velocity in the specimens and those in situ due to heterogeneity in the acoustic rock properties and errors in laboratory and in situ measurements,
J is the amount of information in bits.

The parameter P_c can approximately be calculated with the following equation

$$P_c = \frac{t k_c \sqrt{2}}{\sqrt{n}} \qquad (4)$$

where n is the number of measurements
k_c is the average variation coefficient determined as an average between the coefficient of measurement variation on the specimens and an error in situ point measurements,
t is the Student's coefficient defined by given probability and by the number of definitions [8].

When the informability of the method $J>1$ bit quantitative definitions are not improbable. In this case the principal stress directions are found from velocity indicatrixes in the rock mass determined from direct in situ measurements in the orthogonal planes (Fig.1).

Parameters of velocity vector corresponding to the maximum principal stress are calculated from equations*

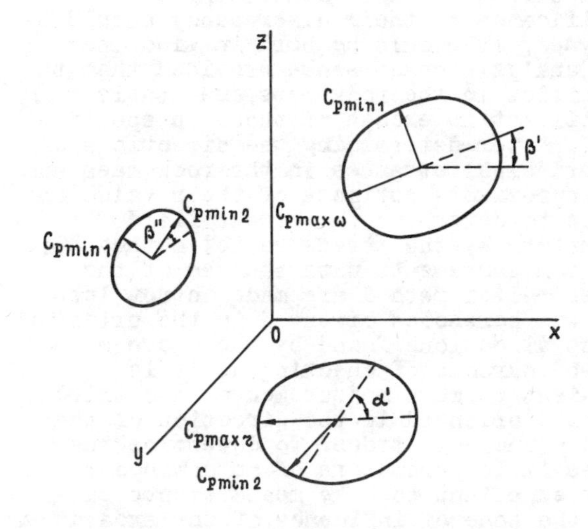

Fig.1 .Velocity indicatrixes from measurements in the roof and walls of the mine workings.

$$\alpha = \arccos \frac{c_{pmax\,w} \cdot \cos\beta'}{\sqrt{c^2_{pmax\,z} + c^2_{pmax\,w} \cdot \sin^2\beta'}} \qquad (5)$$

$$\beta = \arccos \frac{c_{pmax\,z} \cdot \sin\alpha'}{\sqrt{c^2_{pmax\,z} + c^2_{pmax\,w} \cdot \sin^2\beta'}} \qquad (6)$$

$$\gamma = \arccos \frac{c_{pmax\,w} \cdot \sin\beta'}{\sqrt{c^2_{pmax\,z} + c^2_{pmax\,w} \cdot \sin^2\beta'}} \qquad (7)$$

$$c_{pmax} = \sqrt{c^2_{pmax\,z} + c^2_{pmax\,w} \cdot \sin^2\beta'} \qquad (8)$$

where α, β and γ are the angles made by the maximum stress with coordinate axes
c_{pmax} is the velocity corresponding to the maximum stress
$c_{pmax\,w}$ is the projection of the maximum velocity from measurements in the wall
$c_{pmax\,z}$ is the projection of the maximum velocity from measurements in the roof
α' is $c_{pmax\,z}$ projection azimuth
β' is $c_{pmax\,w}$ projection inclination.

The stress values are calculated from the difference between the velocities measured on specimens and those in the rock mass with the use of adequate calibration plots or equations.

When the informability of the method $J<1$ bit the ultrasonic measurements can be used only for justification or denial of the information obtained due to the analysis of geology and tectonics of the area and the visual inspection of the mine workings. For this purpose the velocity distribution in

* Expressions for determining the parameters of the other two vectors can be found in a similar manner in terms of equations of analytic geometry in space.

given directions with evaluating a significance of their discrepancy should be analysed. It should be born in mind that such analysis makes sense provided that the velocities in the rock mass are statistically significant in excess of those in specimens.

IY. After determining the directions of the principal stresses in the rock mass and the approximate estimate of their value one starts to determine the stress field parameters by the stress relief method [7].

The measurements with the use of the stress relief method are made in not less than two boreholes oriented in the principal stress directions found by the above method. For the purpose of checking up it is expedient to make measurements in a third borehole oriented in the direction of the third principal stress. To determine the stress field parameters of an unmined rock it is expedient to take measurements outside the zone of influence of the excavation and stoping. Blind single horizontal workings are best suited to such measurements.

The values of the actual principal stresses in the rock mass (Fig.2) are calculated from the equations presented in Table 1.

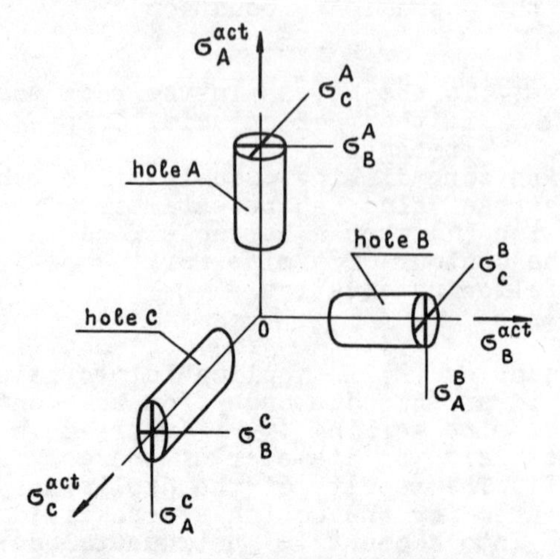

Fig.2. Diagram of mutual position of stresses and measuring holes. $\sigma_A^{act}, \sigma_B^{act}, \sigma_C^{act}$ the actual principal stresses acting in the rock mass $\sigma_B^A, \sigma_A^C, \sigma_B^C, \sigma_C^B, \sigma_C^A, \sigma_A^B$ are the mean values of measured stresses oriented parallel to the boreholes A, B and C

Table 1

Equations for calculating the actual principal stress values in the rock mass.

Notation of principal stresses	When measuring in two mutually orthogonal boreholes A and B	When measuring in three mutually orthogonal boreholes A,B and C
σ_A^{act}	$\frac{K_\ell}{K_\ell^2 - K_\alpha^2}\sigma_A^B - \frac{K_\alpha}{K_\ell^2 - K_\alpha^2}\sigma_B^A$	$\frac{K_\ell}{K_\ell^2 - K_\alpha^2}\sigma_A^C - \frac{K_\alpha}{K_\ell^2 - K_\alpha^2}\sigma_C^A$
σ_B^{act}	$\frac{K_\ell}{K_\ell^2 - K_\alpha^2}\sigma_B^A - \frac{K_\alpha}{K_\ell^2 - K_\alpha^2}\sigma_A^B$	$\frac{K_\ell}{K_\ell^2 - K_\alpha^2}\sigma_B^C - \frac{K_\alpha}{K_\ell^2 - K_\alpha^2}\sigma_C^B$
σ_C^{act}	$\frac{1}{K_\ell}\sigma_C^B + \frac{K_\alpha^2}{K_\ell(K_\ell^2 - K_\alpha^2)}\sigma_A^B - \frac{K_\alpha}{K_\ell^2 - K_\alpha^2}\sigma_B^A$	$\frac{K_\ell}{K_\ell^2 - K_\alpha^2}\sigma_C^A - \frac{K_\alpha}{K_\ell^2 - K_\alpha^2}\sigma_A^B$

Note: K_ℓ and K_α are the stress concentration coefficients determined from the plots in Fig.3

The equations (Table 1) include the mean values of stresses measured in separate boreholes. The stresses at each point of measurements in the boreholes are computed from the equations for the conditions of flat deformation [7].

When generalizing the results of the measurements carried out by the stress relief method the application of statistico-probabilistic estimate of the stress values and their directions is necessary.

The considered technique of experimental complete stress tensor determination proved successful under the conditions at the mines at the Kola Peninsula. The tectonic stress values exceeding many times the stresses resulted from the rock overburden

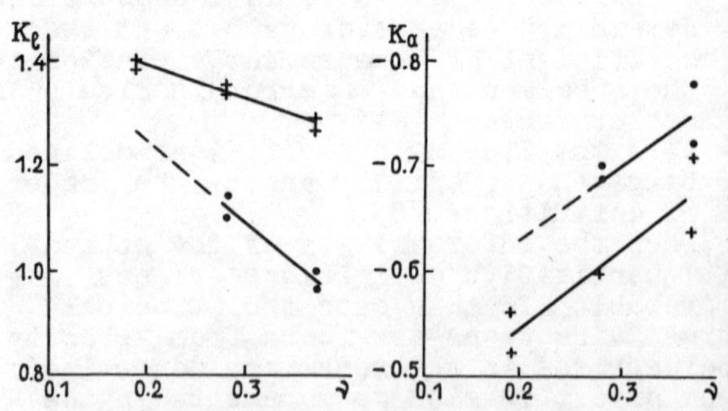

Fig.3. Dependence of the concentration coefficient K_ℓ and the influence coefficient K_α on the lateral deformation coefficient (Poisson's Ratio) 1-flat face, 2-truncated coneshaped face [7].

weight are estimated, the complete tensor and the principal stress directions in rock mass are determined.

For example, in the Khibiny massif measurements have been made from five levels in a depth interval from 100m to 600m [10]. The stress values in the unmined rock mass have been determined from the results based on 1,500 single measurements of elastic strain and 4,500 definitions for longitudinal wave velocities c_p . Horizontal compressive stress σ_3 acting in sublatitudinal direction proved to be the largest in absolute value. This stress value varies from 30 to 80 MN/m^2. The other horizontal principal stress σ_2 acting in submeridional direction is approximately 0.3 σ_3 . Vertical stress predominantly corresponds to the effect of the rock overburden weight, i.e. generally $\sigma_1 = \gamma H$. Variation gradient of the horizontal principal stress σ_3, as a depth increases, accounts for 0.04 MN/m^2 /1m.

The data obtained as well as the stress measurements reported by Hast [3,4] and Coates [1,2] point to the horizontal tectonic stresses large in magnitude acting within old crystalline shields such as the Canadian Shield and Scandinavian Shield resembling each other in geological structure.

In planning and carrying out mining operations as well as in hydrotechnical engineering these stresses must be taken into account.

References

1. Coates,D.F.,Grant F.Stress Measurements at Elliet Lake.Canad.Mining and Metallurg.Bull.,Vol.59,no.649,1966
2. Coates,D.F.,Ignatieff A.,Prediction and Measurement of Pillar Stresses. Canad.Mining J.,Vol.87,no.1,1966
3. Hast,N.,The State of Stresses in the Upper Part of the Earth's Crust. Engng.Geol.,Vol.2,no.1,1967
4. Hast,N.,The State of Stresses in the Upper Part of the Earth's Crust. Tectonophysics,Vol.8,no.3,1969
5. Jeffreys,H.,The Earth. Its Origin, History and Physical Constitution.Cambridge at the university press,1959
6. Nikolayev,N.I.,Problems of Tectonic Movement Nature.Vestnik MGU,ser.IY geol.,no.6,1965
7. Turchaninov I.A.,et al.,Instructions for In Situ Determination of Stress State in Rock by Stress Relief Method.Izd.Kolskogo filiala Akad. Nauk SSSR.Apatity,1970
8. Turchaninov I.A.and Panin V.I., Instructions for In Situ Determination of the Stress State in Rock by Ultrasonic Method. Izd. Kolskogo filiala Akad.Nayk SSSR. Apatity,1970
9. Turchaninov I.A.and Panin V.I., The Principle of Evaluation of Efficiency of New Methods Regarding the Stress State Investigation. In Zbornik Izmerenie napryazhenii v massive gornyh porod,Novosibirsk, 1972
10. Turchaninov I.A. et al., Tectonic Stress Field from Measurements in the Khibiny Massif. Kn. Napryazhennoe sostoyanie zemnoi kory, Published by 'Nauka' Moscow,1973

STRESS HISTORY AND ROCK STRESS

HISTOIRE DE LA CONTRAINTE ET LA CONTRAINTE DES ROCHES

SPANNUNGSGESCHICHTE UND FELSSPANNUNG

B. VOIGHT Department of Geosciences Pennsylvania State University, University Park, Pa.

Beauregard H.P. St. PIERRE Directeur Institut de Géomancy Côte d' Ivoire, visiting Lecturer of Natural History, Pennsylvania State University, University Park, Pa.

Summary: We present an approach by which the "stress history" effect of gravitational, thermal, and tectoni stress components on the state of stress of a rock mass can be assessed in detail. Implications with respect to geotechnics and tectonophysics are significant.

Résume: Nous présentons une méthode par laquelle on peut détailler l'effet de "l'histoire de la contrainte" de la gravitation, ainsi que d'origine thermale et tectonique, sur l'état de la contrainte des roches. Les implications par rapport à la géotechnique et la tectonophysique sont importantes.

Zusammenfassung: Wir opfern eine Annäherung womit man den Effekt der "Spannungsgeschichte" von schwerkräftigen, thermalen und tektonischen Spannungskomponenten auf den Spannungszustand einer Felsmass detailliert bewerten kann. Es ergeben sich Resultaten, die für die Geoteknik und Tektonophysik belangreich sind.

In many cases it appears necessary to consider the complete gravitational, thermal, and tectonic loading history in detail, in order to ascertain those aspects of geological history which have left an imprint on existing force fields within the rock mass. The purpose of this paper is to suggest a method by which the important effects of stress history on the in-situ stress state can be outlined.

An Example: Burial, Diagenesis, Denudation: We consider incremental stress-strain relations; for simplicity, elastic isotropy and homogeneity are assumed, i.e.

$$d\mathcal{E}_x = d\mathcal{E}_y = \frac{1}{E}\left[d\bar{\sigma}_x - v\,(d\bar{\sigma}_z + d\bar{\sigma}_y)\right] + \alpha T$$

where $d\bar{\sigma}_i$ are incremental effective stresses, E is Young's modulus, v is Poisson's ratio, α is linear coefficient of thermal expansion, and dT is the incremental temperature changes. Assumed: $d\mathcal{E}_x = d\mathcal{E}_y = 0$; thus $d\bar{\sigma}_x = \bar{\sigma}_y = (\frac{v}{1-v})\, d\bar{\sigma}_z - \frac{\alpha E dT}{1-v}$.

The loading and thermal history of a sedimentary rock is traced here from initial conditions of sedimentation and subsequent burial to a depth of 1 km, to, finally, unroofing by uplift and denudation. Total overburden pressure (σ_z) is about 250 bar/km; "effective" vertical pressure $\bar{\sigma}_z$ is given by $\sigma_z \cdot (1-\lambda)$, where λ is the ratio of pore fluid to overburden pressure. Lateral pressures are approximated by $\bar{\sigma}_x = \bar{\sigma}_y = \int_0^{\bar{\sigma}_z} (v/(1-v))\, d\bar{\sigma}_z + \int_{T_0}^{T_1} (\alpha E/(1-v))\, dT$. Parameters can be expected to vary as a function of geological history of the deposit; any analytical consideration treating total overburden rather than load increments must thus consider "weighted average" parameters. Hence for practical purposes

$$\bar{\sigma}_x = \bar{\sigma}_y = (\nu^*/(1-\nu^*))\bar{\sigma}_z + (\alpha^* E^* (T_1 - T_0)/(1-\nu^*)),$$

where T_0 and T_1 are initial and subsequent temperatures, and "asterisk" terms refer to "averaged" values of previously defined parameters.

Employing "stage I" parameters assumed suitable for sandstone (Table 1) at 1 km, for a

Table 1: Properties of Typical Sandstone

Material	E*(mb)	ν*	α*(10^{-6} °C^{-1})
Stage I (not lithified)	.01	.21	10.0
Stage II (lithified)	.45	.13	10.8

thermal gradient of 25°C/km,

$$\bar{\sigma}_z = 250\,(1-.4) = 150 \text{ bar}$$

$$\bar{\sigma}_x = \bar{\sigma}_y = (.21/(1-.21))\,150 + (10.0\times10^{-6}\times10^{4}\times25)/(1-.21) = 44 + 3 = 47 \text{ bar}.$$

The small thermoelastic effect on lateral stress reflects the small E* assumed for burial. Drastic changes occur in E* as a consequence of diagenesis; intergranular pressure can remain about the same throughout this process, while unstrained crystalline cement is deposited within a hydrostatically-pressured fluid environment. Next assume that uplift and denudation occurs; stress changes associated with the final condition are $\Delta\bar{\sigma}_z = -150$ bar, $\Delta\bar{\sigma}_x = \Delta\bar{\sigma}_y = -(.13/(1-.13))\,150 - (10.8 \times 10^{-6} \times .45 \times 10^{6} \times 25)/(1-.13) = -22 - 140 = -162$ bar, for each denuded kilometer. Surficial stresses are given by superposition, i.e., $\bar{\sigma}_z = 150 - 150 = 0$, $\bar{\sigma}_x = \bar{\sigma}_y = 47 - 162 = -115$ bar, which values could exist only if rock strength is not exceeded. Because the long-term tensile strength To* is about 24 bar, jointing is here predicted; the associated "strain" is estimated by $\mathcal{E}_x^e = (1/E^*)[\bar{\sigma}_x^e - \nu^* \cdot \bar{\sigma}_y^e]$ where $\bar{\sigma}_i^e$ are "excess" stresses given by, e.g., $\bar{\sigma}_x^e = \bar{\sigma}_x - \bar{\sigma}_f$, where $\bar{\sigma}_f$ is an appropriate fracture criterion; e.g., for $\bar{\sigma}_1 + 3\bar{\sigma}_3 < 0$, $\bar{\sigma}_3 = \bar{\sigma}_x$, $\bar{\sigma}_x^f = -$To*. Average joint spacing Ωx is given by $\Omega_x = W_x/\mathcal{E}_x^e$, where W_x is joint separation (gap). For the present case $\mathcal{E}_x^e = \mathcal{E}_y^e = (-115+24)(1-.13)/(.45 \times 10^6) = 1.8\times10^{-4}$. For $W_x = W_y = -.3$ mm, $\Omega_x = \Omega_y = .3\times10^{-3}/1.8\times10^{-4} = 1.7$ m.

'he effective lateral pressures become tensile. It s important to note that the primary effect of denuda- ion in this case is indirect, viz. cooling associated ith a geothermal gradient, rather than simply loss f overburden pressure. An important conclusion: enudation cannot account for large lateral com- ressive stress.

)istortion of the Sedimentary Basin: The assumption $\mathcal{E}_x = \mathcal{E}_y = O$ may be questioned, if, following)allmus, sediments are deposited on a progressively lattened earth. Assuming that a "surface" of sedi- nentation subsides to a chord; associated strains are hen a function of basin diameter. The resulting ompressive stress changes, if proportional to Stage I) E* are small. Subsequent unflexing from hord to arc following lithification results in exten- ion, non-negligible stress changes (tension) and rittle fracture; e.g., for a 3° basin, extension = 0^{-4}.

dditional Tectonic Considerations: Next examine he effect of a superposed uniform tectonic pressure $\sigma_x^T = 400$ bar; prior to denudation, for loads ap- lied slowly enough such that $\lambda = 0.4, \bar{\sigma}_z = 150$ bar, $\bar{\sigma}_x = 47 + 400 = 447$ bar, $\bar{\sigma}_y = 47 + 0.13\ (400) = 99$ ar. After denudation of 1 km, $\bar{\sigma}_z = 150-150 = 0$, $\bar{\sigma}_x = 447-162 = 285$ bar, $\bar{\sigma}_y = 99-162 = -63$ bar.

'hus jointing is predicted in planes $\perp$ y, and com- ression remains in x. For $\sigma_x^T > (115$ bar$/0.13)$ 885 bar, stresses in both x and y remain com- ressive, even after denudation: for $\sigma_x^T < 115$ bar, ensile stresses possibly exist in both x and y follow- ig denudation; tensile fracturing will occur most in- ensively $\perp$y, and fractures $\perp$y will be generally lder than fractures $\perp$x.

s an example of a more complicated tectonic case e consider a doubly-plunging anticline, with fold adius of curvature $R_{xz} < R_{yz}$. Assuming $(R_{xz}/t) = 250$, $(R_{yz}/t) = 2250$, and a central neutral fiber, fiber tress components associated with folding are, rough- , $\sigma_x^f = \pm E^* t/2R_{xz} = \pm .45 \times 10^6/2 \times 225 = \pm 1000$ bar, $\sigma_y^f = .45 \times 10^6/2 \times 2250 = \pm 100$ bar. Stresses at arious locations (Table 2) are given by super- osition, e.g., at the top of the anticline, $\bar{\sigma}_x = 447 - 000 = -553$ bar.

Table 2: Stresses at Hinge of Anticline

ocation	Stress	Denudation	
		Pre-	Post-
op of Layer	$\bar{\sigma}_z$	150	0
	$\bar{\sigma}_x$	-553	-715
	$\bar{\sigma}_y$	-1	-163
iddle	$\bar{\sigma}_z$	150	0
	$\bar{\sigma}_x$	447	285
	$\bar{\sigma}_y$	99	-63
ottom	$\bar{\sigma}_z$	150	0
	$\bar{\sigma}_x$	1447	1285
	$\bar{\sigma}_y$	199	37

Magnitudes given here do not reflect rock strength, e.g., such large stresses are impossible to achieve without inducing tensile and/or shear fracture. In order to maintain balance of bending moments, all stresses will be reduced, with changes in stress typically associated with a shift of the neutral surface.

For rapidly applied loading, $0.4 < \lambda < 1$; change in $\bar{\sigma}_x$ and $\bar{\sigma}_y$ are accompanied by a predictable decrease in $\bar{\sigma}_z$, leading to fracture at decreased "effective" confinement. These fractures may subsequently close when excess λ dissipates.

Stress Conditions on the Microscopic Scale: For the previous tectonic case, we note that $\bar{\sigma}_x$, $\bar{\sigma}_y$, $\bar{\sigma}_z = 447, 99, 150$ bar, respectively, calculated assuming a solid material. If pore space is randomly distributed and occupies 15% of total rock volume, the average intergranular stress is proportionately greater, e.g., ignoring stress concentration effects, $\bar{\sigma}_x = 447/.85 = 526$ bar, $\bar{\sigma}_y = 116$ bar, $\bar{\sigma}_z = 177$ bar. These stresses are largely "locked in" the grains by the cementation process. This cement is initially stress free, but as the applied macro-scale stress system is changed, the tendency for the intergranular stress to change is resisted by the cement. With complete release of macro-scale stress, forces and moments at rock boundaries vanish, and the integral of residual stresses within the cement and grains must vanish to provide static equilibrium. The distribution of balanced forces is complex on this scale, but approximately, $\sigma_i A_g + \Delta\sigma_g A_g + \Delta\sigma_c A_c = O$, where σ_i is the intergranular stress at the time of cementation, $\Delta\sigma_g$ and $\Delta\sigma_c$ are stress changes in "grains" and "cement" induced by relaxation of boundary stresses, and A_g and A_c are the proportion of area of grains and cement to total area of an "average" section. $\Delta\sigma_g \cong \Delta\sigma_c$ if grain and cement materials are the same, as assumed here, hence for the x direction, $\Delta\sigma_g = \Delta\sigma_c = -\sigma_i A_g / (A_g + A_c) = -526\ (.85) = -447$ bar, i.e. the negative of the macroscopic stress for a solid material. Thus the average residual intergranular stress is 526-447=79 bar, and the average residual cement stress is -442 bar. Intergranular and cement stresses at other states of total stress are given by direct superposition of these micro-scale residual stresses with macro-scale stresses (Fig. 1). Micro-scale intergranular stresses are typically opposite in sign to cement stresses, and of smaller magnitude because of volumetric proportions. Of significance is the fact that failure can be predicted first in specific portions of the micro-scale system. For example, in the post-denudation condition, cement stresses average -162 bars (tension), and tensile fracture within cement is thus predicted in the micro-scale statistically $\perp$ to both x and y. Because intergranular stresses in x are compressive, propogation of a macro-scale extension fracture in the yz plane is not likely. However, xz macro-fractures (and/or grain boundary detachments) are predicted, inasmuch as intergranular stresses in y are also tensile, although of smaller magnitude than cement tensile stress. Finally, upon full relaxation of boundary stresses, cement stresses increase in tension in x, and further development of yz microfractures within cement are predicted.

The development of microfractures is important because it marks significant local release of residual stress from the micro-scale to the "macroscopic" field. The "spring-yoke" analogy follows: once a tensile element releases, the "compressed springs" tend to expand. If no local resistance exists, the compressive forces vanish and displacements occur; an example of this is the outward displacements associated with microfractures parallel to a free surface. Wedge effects at the edges of microfracture clusters enhance, by stress reorientation and superposition, tensile stresses associated with adjacent residual stress systems, and thus promote the development of exfoliation-type macrofractures (Fig. 2). Microfractures oriented at a high-angle to a free surface tend to promote subsequent elastic strain release parallel to that surface. If abundant pre-existing, cross-cutting, open fractures exist, displacements associated with residual elastic strain release can cause partial closure of these fractures. If such open fractures do not exist (or are restricted in orientation), or if pre-existing fractures are mineralized, displacements are not permitted (or are restricted in orientation); hence elastic strain energy is not fully released. Compressive stresses are thus imposed upon the rock mass on macroscopic scale, as a consequence of residual strain energy "unlocking" in the microscopic scale. The statistical maximum of available compressive strain energy is oriented perpendicular to the statistical maxima of microfracture trends; thus, maximum compression induced from this mechanism can be predicted from observed microfracture fabric. However, it should be noted that anisotropy in the form of preferred orientation of macroscopic-scale fracture systems can strongly control imposed stress fields.

There is some justification of the above from available field evidence. In Appalachian granites, several workers have shown that measured orientations of maximum compression are approximately $\perp$ to predominant trends of microfractures in quartz. Residual stresses on the microscopic scale are created as a consequence of temperature-induced volumetric expansion imbalance between quartz (4.52%) and feldspar (1.18%). A crude approximation for the tensile stress in quartz is given by the thermoelastic equation for thermal stresses σ_r, σ_θ in a spherical inclusion within an infinite body, i.e., $\sigma_r = \sigma_\theta = -2E(\alpha_g - \alpha_f)(T_1 - T_0)/3(1-v) = -4.5$ kb. Consequently, quartz microfracture or grain boundary detachment releases "locking" strains complexly distributed in adjacent grains. Cooling of granite also leads to large macro-scale contraction; most openings appear to be filled with various dike and vein materials. Some late-stage fractures may be unfilled. Elastic strain energy on the microscopic scale, if largely detached at that scale at a late stage, can remain unreleased on the macroscopic scale if pre-existing macrofractures are predominantly filled.

Thus exposed granitic rocks, although fractured and veined as a consequence of tension in early cooling phases, could now be typically characterized by sheet fractures and lateral compressive stresses. The maximum amount of available compression is a function of mineral content, and varies from 10^2 bar for a few percent quartz to $1\text{-}2 \times 10^3$ bar for typical granites. This mechanism can be considered as a viable alternative to compressive stress mechanisms associated with contemporary or prior tectonic activity. Where this mechanism prevails, the observed (typical) linear increase of lateral stress with depth should not prevail below several km for granites, i.e., where $\sigma_x \cong 10^3$ bar.

FIGURE 1

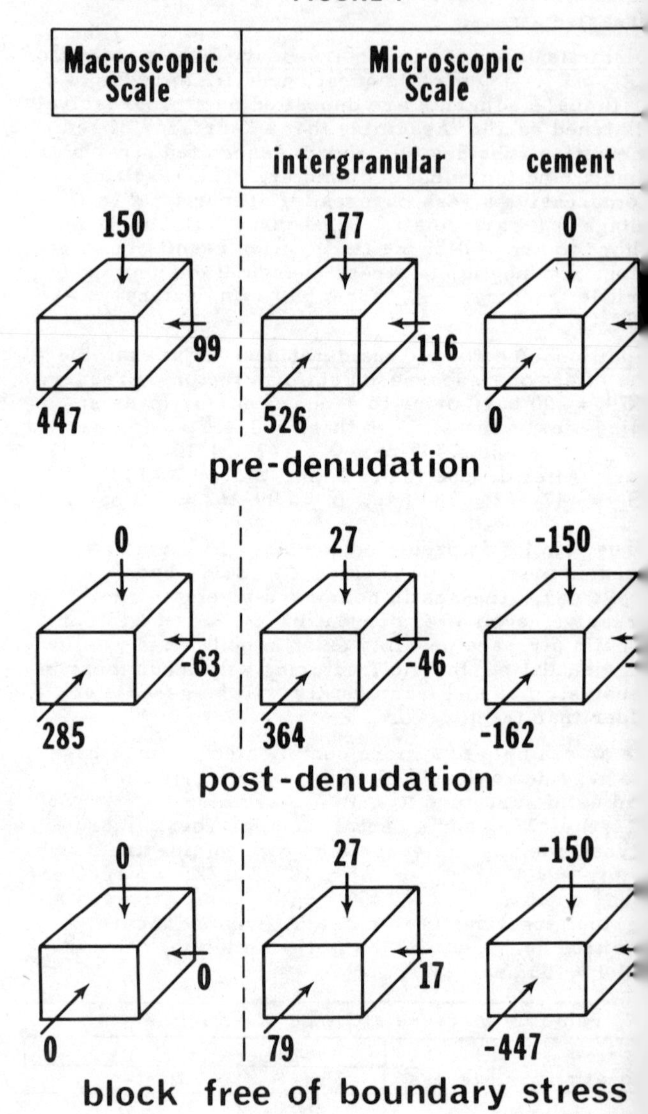

FIGURE 2

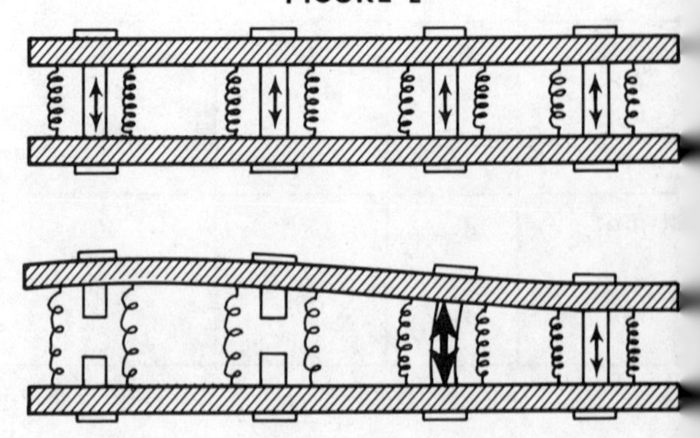

HEME 2

THÈME 2

THEMA 2

C

C

eologic Structures and ectonic Models

Structures géologiques et modèles tectoniques

Geologische Strukturen und tektonische Modelle

A PHOTOELASTIC STUDY OF THE EFFECTS OF SURFACE GEOMETRY ON FAULT MOVEMENTS

UN ÉTUDE PHOTOÉLASTIQUE DES EFFETS DE LA GÉOMETRIE DE SURFACE DES FAILLES SUR LEUR MOUVEMENTS

EINE SPANNUNGSOPTISCHE ERFORSCHUNG VON WIRKUNGEN VON VERWERFUNGSEBENEGEOMETRIE AUF VERWERFUNGSBEWEGUNGEN

David W. BARBER
George M. SOWERS
Center for Tectonophysics
Texas A+M University
College Station, Texas

SUMMARY The influence of fault-surface geometry on the plane deformation of photoelastic models of faults with abrupt, discontinuous changes in orientation("ramps") has been investigated. Irregular, fault-plane geometry causes variable fault displacements. Stress concentrations develop near the obstructions where little or no fault displacement occurs. These concentrations can be described by the action of cracks and contact loads. The unobstructed parts of the fault act as cracks. Contact loads develop by crack-face separation and slip on obstruction. Slip in models depends on local deformation of the ramp. Local deformation is affected by slip on the ramp, and the opening, as well as the orientation, of the cracks. It is concluded that geometric irregularities increase the stability of faults by locally increasing resistance to slip. However, local deformation affects strain-energy releases during intermittent slip events. Stress concentrations and fault surface separation occurring on both sides of an obstruction could create significant dilatant effects around pre-existing faults.

SOMMAIRE Cette étude porte sur l´examen de failles charactérisées par des changements d´orientation abruptes et discontinus (obstruction de "rampe"), marquant l´influence de la géométrie de surface des failles considérées sur la déformation plane de modèles photoélastiques. La géométrie irrégulière du plan de faille causent les déplacements variables le long des failles. Des concentrations de tension se développent dans les voisinages des obstructions, là où le déplacement de la faille est faible ou nul. Ces concentrations peuvent être décrites par l´action des fissures et charges de contact. Les parties de faille non obstruées agissent comme des fissures. Les charges de contact se devéloppent par la séparation des faces de la fissure, et le glissement général le long de la faille. Le glissement dans les modèles dépend de la déformation locale de la rampe. La déformation locale est affectée par le glissement sur la rampe ainsi que par l´ouverture des fissures et leurs orientations propres. On en conclut que des irrégularités géométriques augmentent la stabilité des failles, en augmentant localement leur résistance au glissement. Cependant, la déformation locale affecte les relâchements d´énergie de déformation lors de glissements intermittents. Aussi, les concentrations de tension et la séparation des surfaces de la faille qui apparaissent des deux côtés d´une obstruction, peuvent créer des effets dilatants significatifs aux alentours d´une faille préexistante.

ZUSAMMENFASSUNG Der Einfluss von Verwerfungsebenegeometrie auf die ebene Formänderung spannungsoptischer Modelle von Verwerfungen mit abgebrochenen, unzusammenhängenden Veränderungen der Richtung (Rampe") wurde untersucht. Unregelmassige Verwerfungsebenegeometrie verursacht unbeständige Verwerfungenverschiebungen Druckverstärkungen entstehen neben den Versperrungen mit wenig oder keinen Verwerfungenverschiebungen. Diese Verstärkungen können durch die Tätigkeit vom Spalten und Kontaktdruck dargestellt werden. Die Spalten stellen die freien Teile der Verwerfung dar. Kontaktdruck entsteht durch Oberflächenspaltenteilung und Gleitung auf der Versperrung. Die Gleitung bei den Modellen hängt von der lokalen Formänderung der Rampe ab. Lokale Formänderung ist durch Gleitung auf der Rampe, der Oeffnung sowohl der Richtung der Spalten beeinflust. Es folgt daraus, dass geometrische Unregelmässigkeiten das Gleichgewicht der Verwerfungen durch lokal zunehmenden Widerstand zum Gleiten steigert. Allerdings bewirkt lokale Formänderung die Freigabe von Spannungsenergie durch unterbrochene Gleitungen. Druckverstärkungen und Verwerfungsebeneteilung auf beiden Seiten einer Versperrung könnten bedeutende Erweiterungen bereits vorhandener Falten verursachen.

INTRODUCTION

Resistance to sliding along faults affects the mechanical behavior of a rock mass. This research investigates the influence of irregular fault-plane geometry on this resistance. Changes in fault-surface orientation should locally increase resistance to slip and hence produce geometric obstructions. In order to describe the increased resistance and associated local deformations, states of stress around faults in photoelastic models are observed during uniaxial compression tests.

We study relatively large obstructions instead of small-scale asperities. Therefore, the faults act as internal boundaries of the models, and their boundary conditions need evaluation. Because direct measurement is difficult, these boundary conditions are inferred from the deformations observed. Therefore, these models help reveal the critical physical aspects of the deformation but are not scale models of the exact deformations produced by geologic obstructions.

The basic obstruction studied is a ramp. Jaeger and Cook (1969) show the effect of a ramp inclined at an angle θ to the macroscopic sliding surface as

$$\mu_{app} = \frac{\mu + \tan\theta}{1 - \mu \tan\theta}$$

where μ is the "true" coefficient of friction and μ_{app} is the "apparent" coefficient. However, their treatment deals with a small-scale asperity and neglects its elastic deformation. In this study, the elastic deformation of the ramp is considered by photoelastic models.

Our results are relevant to the study of shallow-focus earthquakes. Resistance to slip along pre-existing faults affects accumulation and release of elastic strain energy around fault zones. Initial and final stress for stress-relaxation models of earthquake sources (Knopoff, 1958; Archambeau, 1968; Burridge, 1969) depend, in part, on this resistance. In addition, fault seismicity may be controlled, in part, by variations in this resistance (Burridge and Knopoff, 1967; Dieterich, 1971). Therefore, this research should help the further development of a plausible heuristic model of an earthquake source mechanism.

EXPERIMENTAL METHODS

Photoelastic models are suitable for studying both static and dynamic stress states. This study uses a low-modulus (E=70 bars), polyurethane rubber to gain an appropriate scaling factor at the expense of brittle behavior. Since describing the state of stress and boundary conditions along the fault is our goal, brittle behavior is not necessary.

The polyurethane models are cut from 0.635-cm thick sheets obtained commercially. A surface grinder is used to prepare the surfaces. A relatively smooth surface is obtained, but only plane surfaces are readily formed. A good fit between model segments is difficult to achieve. These models are durable; repeated tests on the same model can be made. Also, the high stress-optical sensitivity (0.7 bar/fringe/cm) is ideal for observing small changes in stress state.

Model shape and size are a compromise. Close machining and testing of large models is not possible with our equipment. The surface irregularity is placed in the center to isolate it from the edges; distance to edge is usually 4 to 5 times the size of local stress concentrations. The faults are continued to the edges to avoid large stress concentrations at their ends which would interfere with the measurements.

The strain frame (Figure 1) contains a mechanically driven, loading plate, suspended on two steel bars that travel through linear ball bearings. The low-friction bearings provide smooth plate travel and require negligible loads to initiate motion. One side of the model is clamped to the plate; the other is attached to a wheeled carriage, suspended by a pulley system and counter balance by which the vertical load is adjusted. The applied loads and displacements are measured by gages to an accuracy of about five percent.

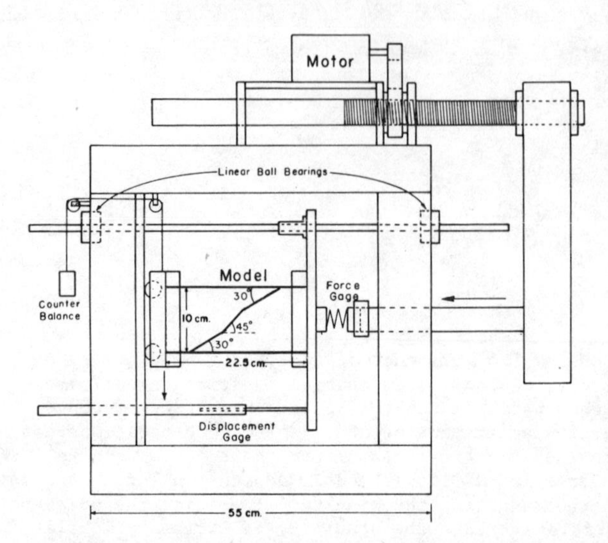

Figure 1. Schematic diagram of strain frame with single-ramp model in test configuration.

EXPERIMENTAL RESULTS

The results show that abrupt changes in fault-surface orientation produce variations in distribution and magnitude of normal and shear tractions on the fault. These variations cause non-uniform displacements along the fault, creating strain-energy concentrations where displacements are relatively small. Cumulative slip changes these spatial variations through time.

Single-Ramp Model

The simplest ramp model contains two en-echelon planes oriented at 30° to the applied load, connected by a 45° ramp (Figure 1). Three stages in loading history are recognized: (1) slip along the en-echelon planes and loading of the ramp; (2) slip along the ramp with increased local deformation in its vicinity; and (3) slip along the ramp with no increase in local deformation. These stages are studied in detail by stopping the test at representative times during each stage. First, however, consider the force-displacement record of a continuous test.

Force-displacement record. The applied force-displacement record (Figure 2) separates the three main stages. The steep force rise between points A and B represents Stage 1. Slip occurs only on the en-echelon segments while the ramp is pinned. At point B, slip along the ramp begins. Force continues to increase between points B and C, but with a lower slope. This represents Stage 2. At point C, which marks the beginning of Stage 3, force reaches a high value and remains constant for the rest of the test.

Stage 1. Here stresses are continuous across the fault (Figure 3). Stress concentrations occur at the top and bottom of the ramp. Shear stresses are higher on the en-echelon segments than on the ramp. External load and stored strain energy are increasing. Ramp loading is unequally distributed along its length; it begins in the center and spreads toward the stress concentrations at each end.

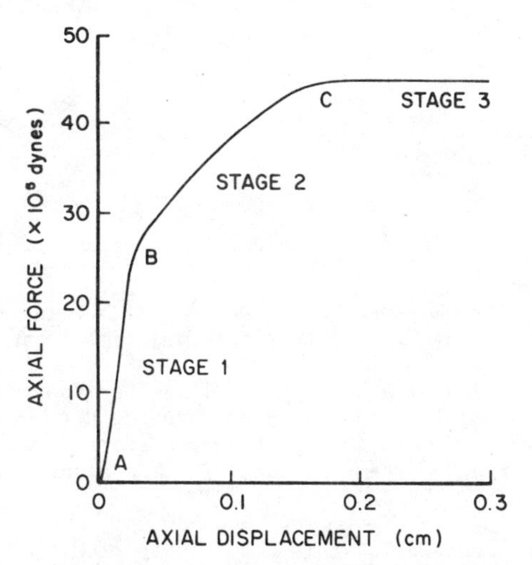

Figure 2. Idealized force-displacement record for single-ramp model.

Slip on the favorably oriented, en-echelon segments is intermittent. Slip events cause small, sharp increases in strain concentrations at the ends of the ramp, and magnitude of shear stresses on the en-echelon segments decreases sharply. Between events, total strain energy in the model increases slowly. These events recur regularly, closely resembling the type of slip commonly referred to as "stick-slip." However, no external force drops are seen. Whether this behavior is related to material properties or to geometry of the surface is unresolved. Whatever the cause, these events occur throughout the loading cycle.

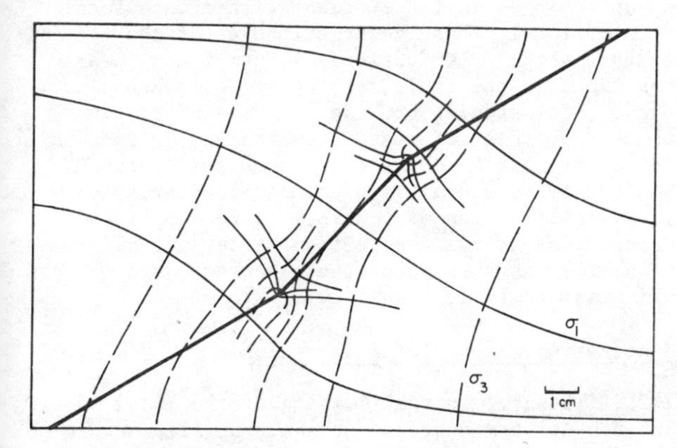

Figure 3. Principal-stress orientations for single-ramp model during Stage 1. The maximum compressive, principal stress is σ_1.

Stage 2. After about 0.1-cm displacement along the ramp, local deformation changes significantly (Figure 4). Stress singularities occur at the points marked U, and the segment of the ramp between them supports most of the load. The surface here is a plane of maximum shear stress. Between points U and T, shear stress on the ramp is smaller, and a discontinuous distribution of strain energy occurs across the fault. In area H, the maximum shear stress is relatively high, and in L it is relatively low. At T, the stress intensity has exceeded 2.2 bar. The strain-energy concentrations here have increased from Stage 1. They continue to increase as deformation proceeds. Between points T and S, no shear stress acts on the fault surface, and normal stresses are discontinuous across it. The side labeled C is in compression while the opposite side (E) is in extension. Thus, the fault has separated here because of slip on the ramp, forming a crack.

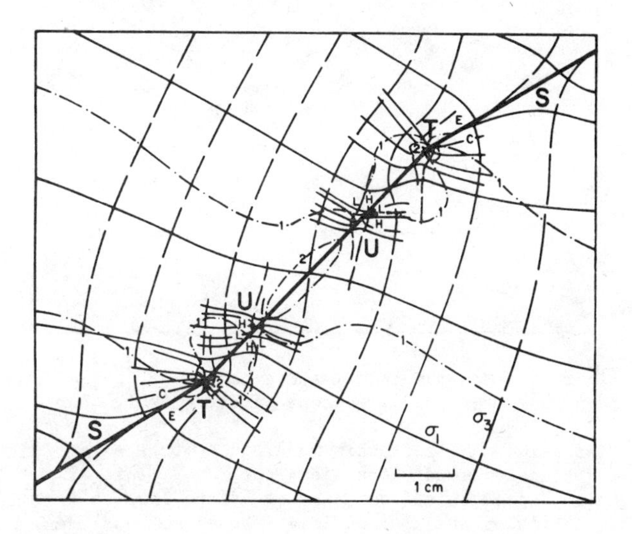

Figure 4. Principal-stress orientations and maximum-shear-stress contours, single-ramp model, Stage 2. Contour interval is 1.1 bar.

Stage 3. After about 0.3-cm displacement along the ramp, maximum loading is reached. The entire ramp is a plane of maximum shear stress (Figure 5). The stress concentrations at T dominate model behavior. The maximum shear-stress at T exceeds 5.5 bar (Figure 6). Each stress concentration has two opposing lobes with different values of maximum shear stress. The lobe with the higher stress intensity, (H), is the one adjacent to the side of the crack in compression. Slip events recur regularly and travel the entire ramp. The amount of strain energy released is about the same for each event and has reached a maximum value.

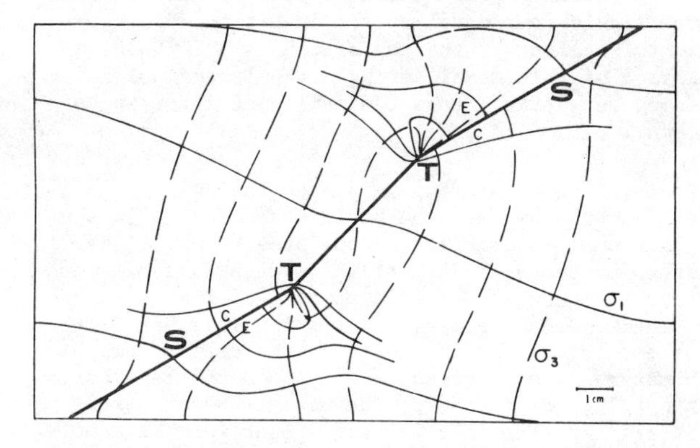

Figure 5. Principal-stress orientations, single-ramp model, Stage 3.

The overall behavior of the model is stable during Stages 1 and 2 since the external load and the stored strain energy continue to increase. The slip events allow sudden release of strain energy only from local stress concentrations. However, large-magnitude events, seen in the force-displacement record, also occur during this stage. Dynamic photoelastic techniques are needed to study the detailed character of these events.

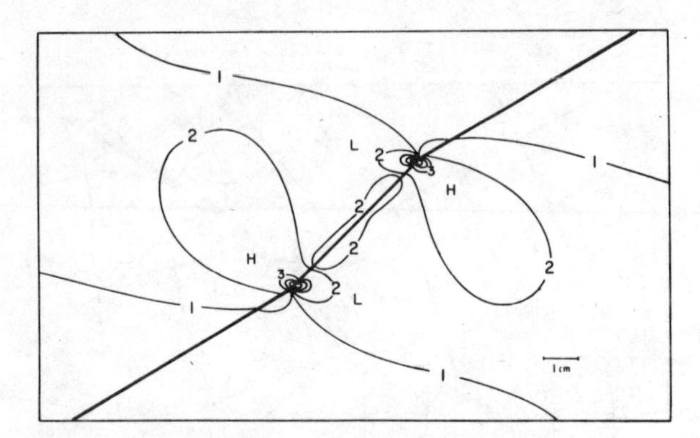

Figure 6. Maxumum-shear-stress contours, single-ramp model, Stage 3. Contour interval is 1.1 bar.

Discussion. Slip in this model is controlled by the boundary conditions along the ramp. Initially, these depend on the orientation of the ramp to the direction of the applied load. However, local deformation of the ramp during slip changes the boundary conditions and causes the time interval between events and the amount of strain energy released by an event to increase. A knowledge of the physical mechanisms for the local deformation is needed to understand these changes and their effects on the slip events.

The stress concentrations at the ends of the ramp produce most of the local deformation. These concentrations are associated with the advancing tips of the cracks which form on the en-echelon segments. An additional model is constructed to determine the influence of the orientation of these cracks.

Horizontal-Crack Model

The horizontal-crack model (Figure 7) differs from the single-ramp model by the insertion of a horizontal segment at the top of the ramp. The behavior of this model during Stage 1 remains the same, but during Stage 2 significant differences occur.

Again slip on the ramp separates the adjacent, fault surfaces. However, the horizontal crack allows additional deformation of the area below it, as shown by the asymmetry of the stress-intensity contours (Figure 7). The lower side of the crack has a maximum shear stress greater than 1.1 bar. The stress concentration at the bottom of the ramp has a maxumum shear stress greater than 3.3 bar, but, at the top of the ramp, the maximum shear stress is greater than only 2.2 bar. Therefore, the horizontal crack allows more area to deform, reducing the magnitude of the upper stress concentration.

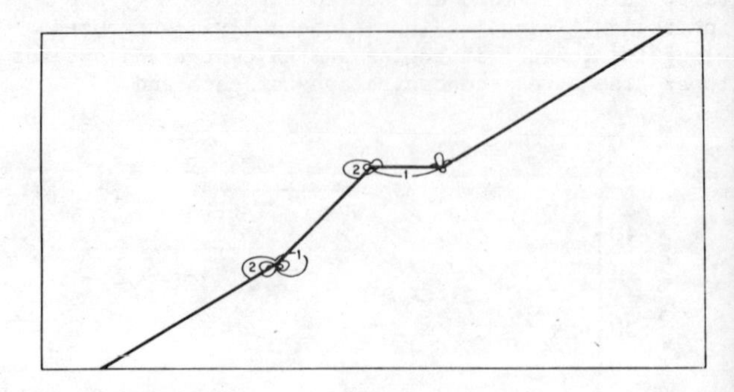

Figure 7. Maximum-shear-stress contours, horizontal-crack model, Stage 2. Contour interval is 1.1 bar.

This model sustains a lower total load than the single-ramp model, only 0.4 as compared to 0.7 bar. Apparently, the reduction of the upper stress concentration reduces the resistance to slip along the ramp.

The dynamic behavior of this model is similar to that of the single-ramp model, except that the strain energy released during a slip event is smaller.

Summary of Ramp Models

These models show that slip along a fault with a ramp depends on progressive deformation of the ramp. This deformation is a function of the total amount of relative slip, and the development and orientation of open cracks at the ends of the ramp. Furthermore, the ramp strongly affects the dynamic response of the models.

DISCUSSION

Abrupt changes in fault orientation create local deformations. These deformations alter the initial (before slip) distributions of normal and shear tractions on the fault, affecting fault behavior. These model studies provide general information about the local deformations which can be used to infer the possible physical mechanisms involved. The following scheme is used in this discussion: (1) identification of possible sources of local deformation from a generalized history of deformation; (2) description of these sources; and (3) application to fault stability.

Generalized History of Deformation

Initial Stage. Initial loading of the model produces a uniform state of strain. No slip occurs on the fault; the model behaves as if it were intact. Thus, the initial distribution of normal and shear tractions on the fault surface is a function only of the orientation of the fault with respect to the uniform "regional" stress field.

Initiation of Slip. When the minimum load needed for slip on the most favorably oriented fault-segments is reached, the state of strain becomes non-uniform. Only the favorably oriented segments slip, producing strain concentrations at the ends of these segments. These concentrations are superposed on the uniform strain field, effecting a non-homogeneous strain state which changes the initial distribution of normal and shear tractions on the fault. For the rest of the deformation, the state of stress remains non-homogeneous, and the distribution of surface tractions continues to change.

Development of Slip. After slip begins, two factors influence further motion on the fault: (1) orientations of non-slipped parts of the fault; and (2) changes in distribution of surface tractions. Separating these effects by model studies is difficult without a good understanding of the sources of the stress concentrations. One probable source is cracks formed by the favorably oriented segments. Another source is contact loads which develop when the cracks open, as shown by the increase of stress intensity along the center of the ramps during Stage 2. Also, their interplay may be important to the stability of faults.

Sources of Local Deformation

Cracks. The state of stress along the en-echelon segments near the ends of the ramp closely resembles the state which would be induced on a crack. The crack tip initially separates the slipped part of the fault (the crack) from the unslipped part (the ramp). When the ramp slips, the crack tip separates parts with different amounts of slip.

These cracks are physically different from cracks in an intact body. However, both produce discontinuities of displacement across a surface in the body, and their strain fields can be described using dislocation mechanics (Steketee, 1958). The major differences are: (1) slip on a fault can produce a crack tip at a point where slip is prohibited or retarded as well as at the end of the fault; and (2) areas on the fault where slip is retarded influence crack-tip extension by prohibiting the transmission of extensile strain around the crack tip.

The simplest type of dislocation, a Volterra dislocation, arises from a rigid-body displacement of each side (Bilby and Eshelby, 1968). Although non-uniform rather than rigid-body displacements occur in the models, the Volterra dislocation gives a convenient approximation. In particular, Chinnery (1966) uses it to describe the stress state at the end of a strike-slip fault inclined at 30° to the direction of a uniaxial compressive stress. Stress intensity contours for this case are comparable to the contours at the bottom of the ramp in the horizontal-crack model (Figure 8). Both stress concentrations have two lobes separated by regions of relatively low stress intensity. The lobes are cut by the faults asymmetrically with the larger part of the left-hand lobe above the fault and the larger part of the right-hand lobe below it. Differences are the relative clockwise rotation of the right-hand lobe in the ramp model and the lack of continuity of the contours across the 30° segment. Slip on the ramp possibly causes the rotation. Non-uniform displacement along the crack probably causes the lack of continuity. (Volterra dislocations require continuity of stress; more general dislocations allow discontinuity in stress).

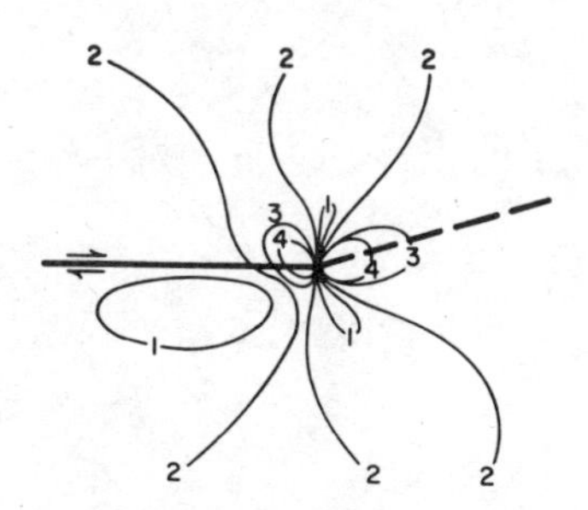

a. AFTER CHINNERY, 1966a FIGURE 4b. p.170.

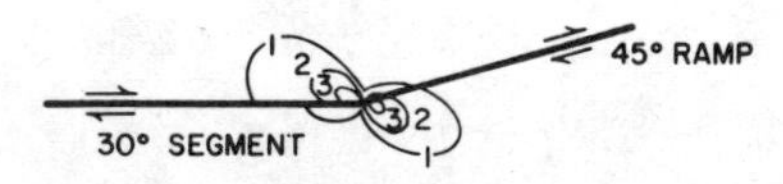

b. HORIZONTAL CRACK MODEL, 2nd STAGE DETAIL OF STRESS INTENSITY CONTOURS AT BASE OF RAMP.

Figure 8. Maximum-shear-stress contours for dislocation model of strike-slip fault (a) and for horizontal-crack model (b). To simplify comparison, dashed line in 8a indicates position of ramp in 8b.

Contact Loads. In general, two factors contribute to contact loads: (1) area of contact, and (2) degree of fit between shapes of contact surfaces. During Stage 2, crack-face separation decreases the area of contact along the fault and increases the contact load on the ramp. The crack-face separation is caused not only by slip on the ramp but also by local strains. The increase in stress intensity on the ramp between slip events shows the effects of the local strains on the contact load. A mismatch occurs either by initial imperfections or by slip along the obstruction. In ramp models, the initial fit is fairly good. After slip begins on the ramp, a mismatch develops at each corner. This mismatch possibly produces the observed rotation of the stress intensity contours at the bottom of the ramp in the horizontal-crack model (Figure 8).

Influence of Shape on Fault Stability

The changes in boundary conditions on a fault surface introduced by local deformation clearly modify the behavior of the fault. Thus the local deformation produced by geometric obstructions can affect the stability of faults. Surface irregularities increase the resistance to slip, enhancing fault stability. However, they also allow local deformations and strain-energy concentrations to develop. The strain energy can be relieved by a variety of instability mechanisms.

One mechanism is overcoming the obstruction by sliding over the top or by secondary faulting. The latter is more likely to occur in nature, except for shallow faults with small obstructions.

Unstable sliding is another mechanism. One phenomenon which produces unstable sliding is stick-slip, observed experimentally in the sliding of plane rock surfaces. The physical mechanisms which cause this behavior have not been sorted out. Stick-slip in the polyurethane models could result from mechanisms independent of the geometry. However, shape does influence the nature of the slip and needs to be considered in determining fault stability.

CONCLUSIONS

1. Irregular, fault-plane geometry produces large stress concentrations, which store strain energy, by obstructing movement on certain segments of the fault. The resulting local deformation has been observed in photoelastic models of faults with abrupt, discontinuous changes in orientation ("ramp" obstructions).

2. The stress concentrations near geometric obstructions can be described by the action of cracks and contact loads. The unobstructed parts of the fault act as cracks, which can be described mathematically by dislocation theory. Contact loads develop on the obstruction because: (1) separation of crack faces decreases area of contact; and (2) slip along the obstruction produces mismatch between shapes of contact surfaces.

3. Initial orientation of fault with respect to load direction determines: (1) fault segments where cracks form; and (2) loads necessary for slip.

4. Slip on ramp obstructions depends on local deformation around the ramp. As slip continues, local deformation is affected by the amount of slip, and the opening, as well as the orientation, of cracks at each end of the ramp.

5. Geometric irregularities increase fault stability by locally increasing resistance to slip. However, large stress concentrations result and these contribute significantly to faulting by controlling amount of strain energy released during intermittent slip events on the fault.

6. Deformations produced by geometric obstructions could cause significant dilatant effects. The recently proposed dilation model of earthquakes (Scholz, et al, 1973), which explains many precursory phenomena, requires such effects. The large stress concentrations could produce an increase of volume of the rock mass similar to that observed during triaxial compression tests just prior to failure (Brace, et al, 1966). Also, the fault-surface separation which occurs on both sides of an obstruction provides what in nature would appear as dilatancy. These mechanisms for creating dilatant effects around pre-existing faults support the concept of the dilation model for earthquake prediction.

ACKNOWLEDGEMENTS

We gratefully acknowledge the many helpful suggestions and thoughtful criticisms of this work by Dr. John W. Handin and the other members of the Center for Tectonophysics. We also thank J. C. Coyne for his assistance in model preparation.

This work was supported by the U.S. Geological Survey and the Advanced Research Projects Agency Order No. 1684 and completed during the first author's tenure as a National Science Foundation Trainee, 1972-1973.

REFERENCES

ARCHAMBEAU, C. B., 1968, General theory of elastodynamic source fields, Reviews of Geophysics, Vol.6, pp. 241-288.

BILBY, B. A. and J. D. ESHELBY, 1968, Dislocations and the theory of fracture, Fracture, Vol. 1, Liebowitz, H., Editor, New York, Academic Press, pp. 99-182.

BRACE, W. R., B. W. PAULDING, JR., and C. H. SCHOLTZ, 1966, Dilatancy in the fracture of crystalline rocks, Journal of Geophysical Research, Vol 71, pp. 3939-3953.

BURRIDGE, R., 1969, The numerical solution of certain integral equations with non-integrable kernels arising in the theory of crack propagation and elastic wave diffraction, Philosophical Transactions of the Royal Society, London, Vol. 265, pp. 353-381.

BURRIDGE, R. and L. KNOPOFF, 1967, Model and theoretical seismicity, Bulletin of the Seismological Society of America, Vol. 57, pp. 341-371.

CHINNERY, M. A., 1966, Secondary faulting. I. Theoretical aspects, Canadian Journal of Earth Science, Vol. 3, pp. 163-174.

DIETERICH, J. H., 1971, Computer modeling of earthquake triggering by fluid injection, Report of Progress 1970-1971, United States Geological Survey, 74 pp.

JAEGER, J. C. and N. G. W. COOK, 1969, Fundamentals of Rock Mechanics, London, Methuen, 513 pp.

KNOPOFF, L., 1958, Energy release in earthquakes, Geophysical Journal. Vol. 1, pp. 44-52.

SCHOLZ, C. H., L. R. SYKES, and Y. P. AGGARWAL, 1973, The physical basis for earthquake prediction, Lamont-Doherty Geological Observatory Contribution Number 1939, 34 pp.

STEKETEE, J. A., 1958, On Volterra's dislocations in a semi-infinite elastic medium, Canadian Journal of Physics, Vol. 36, pp. 192-205.

TECTONOPHYSICAL ASPECTS IN SOUTHEASTERN BRAZIL

ASPECTS TECTONOPHYSIQUES AU SUD-EST DU BRÉSIL

TEKTONISCH-PHYSIKALISCHE BETRACHTUNGEN BEZÜGLICH SÜD-OST BRASILIEN

A.J.S. BJORNBERG, Professor, University of Sao Paulo, and Chief, Engineering Geology Div., Promon Engenharia, S.A.
P. RIDEG, Senior Structural Geologist, Promon Engenharia, S.A.
M. A. KANJI , Assistant Professor, University of Sao Paulo, and Chief, Rock Mechanics Div., Promon Engenharia, S.A.

Sao Paulo, Brazil

SUMMARY - Results of research in fault tectonics in various areas of east-central and south-central Brazil are presented. The internal shear angles of rock masses located in three different tectonic settings were calculated through four different methods: statistical analysis of fault patterns; analysis of fold axis orientations; analysis of low-angle thrust fault orientations; and analysis of conjugate shear angle orientations. The results are tied to a regional tectonic scheme which considers the geologic age of the lithologies in the various subareas of the investigated regions. A preliminary attempt is made to explain the possible relationship between observed fault patterns and forces active during the separation of the continents of South America and Africa. It is the authors' belief that geotechnical foundation problems found in rock masses within the investigated areas can best be understood when analyzed within the global framework provided by the continental drift theory.

RÉSUMÉ - Les résultats des recherches à propos de la tectonique des failles dans plusiers régions du sud-est Brésilien sont présentés ci-dessous. Les angles de frottement internes des massifs rocheux situés dans trois systèmes tectoniques diffenrents on été calculés à partir de 4 methodes: analyse statistique des systèmes de failles; analyse de l'orientation des axes des plis; analyse de l'orientation des angles des failles inverses et analyse de l'orientation des angles conjugués de cisaillement. Les résultats sont liés au système tectonique régional correspondant à l'âge géologique des roches existantes. Une tentative préliminaire a été faite pour expliquer une relation possible entre des systèmes de faille observées et les efforts tectoniques actifs pendant la séparation des continents Sud Americains et Africains. Dans les massifs rocheux des fondations des régions étudiées, differents problèmes geotechniques ont été rencontrés; les auteurs jugent que ces mêmes problèmes pourront être mieux compris après leur analyse à travers d'un système global provenant de la théorie de la dérive des continents.

ZUSAMMENFASSUNG - Die Ergebnisse der Erforschung der Verwerfungtektonik in mehreren Gebieten des zentralen Ostens und des zentralen Südens von Brasilien werden dargestellt. Die inneren Scheerwinkel der Felsmassen in drei verschiedenen tektonischen Fassungen sind nach vier verschiedenen Methoden berechnet worden: die statistische Analyse der Verwerfungsgruppen; Analyse des Orientierung der Faltenachsen; Analyse der kleinwinkelingen Verwerfungstrichtungen; Analyse des konjugierten Scheerwinkel Richtungen. Die Ergebnisse sind mit dem Schema der regionalen Tektonik verbunden die das geologische Alter der Lithologien in den verschiedenen untersuchten Gebieten in Betracht zieht. Es wird versucht, die mögliche Beziehung zwischen den beobachteten Verwerfungsgruppen und den damals wirkenden Kräften die während der Trennung der Kontinente von Südamerika und Afrika gewirkt haben zu erklären. Der Verfasser glaubt, dass die geotechnischen Gruendungsprobleme die in Felsmassen in den zur Zeit erforschten Gebieten gefunden werden, besser verstanden werden können, wenn sie innerhalb des Gesamtrahmens der Trennung der Kontinente betrachtet werden .

INTRODUCTION

In the last decade geologic literature has emphasized research in global tectonics, particularly from the point of view of continental drift and sea-floor spreading. The coastal belts of South America and Africa, though not very thoroughly studied, are some of the most promising areas for this type of study.

The theory concerning the separation of the South American and African continents is well established and accepted. New data supporting the theory are constantly being disclosed as geologic and structural studies progress. The relationship between geologic effects resulting from processes active during continental rifting and the various related branches of geology becomes increasingly important in orienting various types of geologic investigations.

This paper presents the results of research in fault tectonics in various areas of east-central and south-central Brazil (Fig. 1).

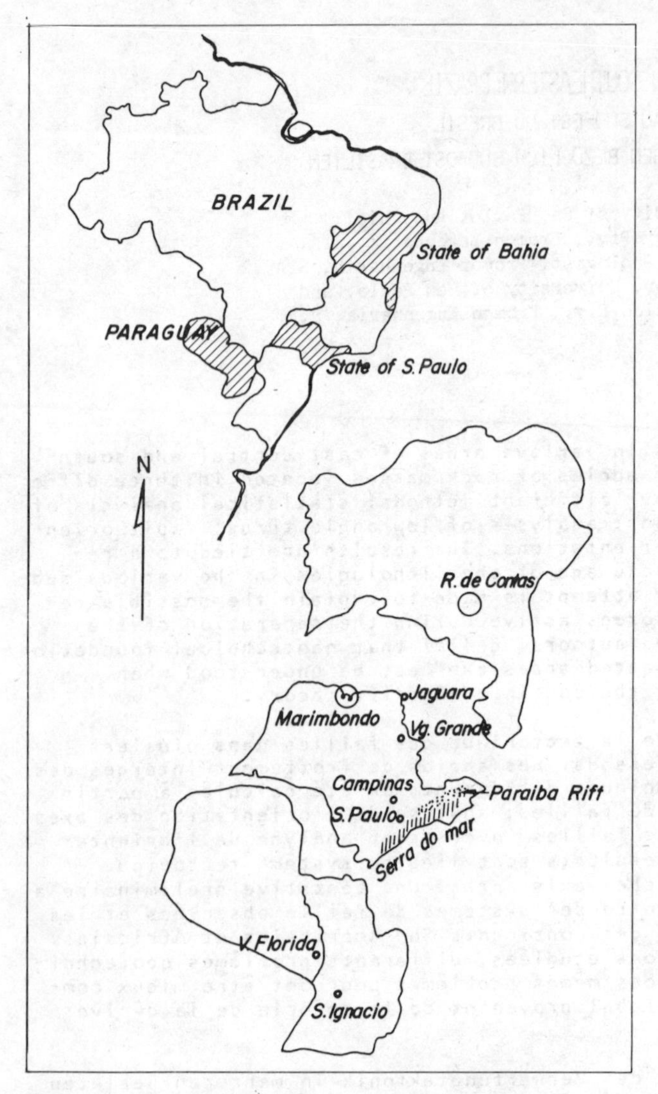

Figure 1. Location map of the principal investigated areas in southeastern Brazil and in Paraguay.

Figure 1. Plante de location des régions principales étudieés dans de sud-est du Brésil et au Paraguay.

Bild. 1. Gebiet der Hauptuntersuchungen in Suedost Brasilien und in Paraguay.

The internal shear angles of rock masses were calculated for the investigated areas and sub-areas, and the results are tied to a regional tectonic scheme.

The possible relationship between observed shear patterns that occur in lithologies of different geologic ages and forces active during the separation of South America and Africa are discussed. The stresses active during various periods of geologic time, as inferred through the analysis of fracture patterns in the investigated areas, seem to agree remarkably well with the forces active during various phases of continental rifting.

METHODS OF STUDY

Tectonic studies covered approximately 150,000 km^2 in south-central Brazil and about 20,000 km^2 in the east-central portion of the country. While many of the studies were carried out on a regional basis, most of them were localized detailed investigations at sites of large hydroelectric dam projects and other large scale engineering undertakings. Although most of the studies were carried out in the general regions cited above, a few localized investigations in other areas, such as in Paraguay, are also included

More than 3,000 fault planes and slickensides were measured during field mapping. Field work, supported by air-photo interpretation, also included investigations of geomorphologic character for the purpose of locating tilted tectonic blocks. Tilting of tectonic blocks was confirmed through statistical treatment of fault plane data and through the detection of anomalies in regional foliation trends.

Statistical analysis of structural data also permitted the determination of the position of the principal forces active during various phases of faulting. Other methods were also used, for purposes of comparison, to determine these principal stresses, including the conjugate shear angle method, analysis of the attitudes os small thrust planes, and analysis of other structural data, such as fold axis orientations.

SUMMARY OF TECTONIC EVENTS IN THE INVESTIGATED AREAS

The oldest rocks in the investigated areas occur along the coastal belt in the east-central region and along the SE portion of the south-central region. About 550 ± 100 m. y. ago the Brazilian tectonic-orogenic cycle (ALMEIDA, 1971) affected these rocks, producing the regional NE-SW structures that are seen today. Sediments in the eastern portions of the Paraná Basin (Fig. 1, east of Marimbondo area) were deposited on an inclined basement surface (LOCZY, 1968) indicating that crustal arching to the west also occurred during this tectonic cycle.

Since the end of the Jurassic the most intense diastrophism that affected eastern Brazil was the Lower Cretaceous reactivation (Wealdian Reactivation of ALMEIDA, 1969). The ancient NE-SW faults were reactivated and new faults were formed. Large vertical movements predominated. Crustal arching accompanied these events, tilting the faulted blocks westward (LOCZY, 1968). The volcanism in the Paraná Basin occurred during this cycle through fissures opened by arching. Radiometric dating methods (K-Ar) yield ages between 140 and 120 m.y. for these basalts (AMARAL et al, 1966). This diastrophian lasted throughout the Cretaceous and attenuated in the Tertiary (ALMEIDA, 1969).

RESULTS AND INTERPRETATION OF RESULTS

Table 1 summarizes the geologic and structur

(1) LOCATION (STATE)	(2) PREDOM. LITHOL.	(3) AGE	(4) PREDOM. TRENDS	(5) σ_1 (acc. to 4)	(6) PREDOM. FOLD AXES	(7) σ_1 (acc. to 6)	(8) σ_1 FROM CONJUGATE SHEARS	(9) σ_1 FROM THRUST FAULTS	(10) ANGLE 2θ IMFERRED
PARAIBA RIFT (S. PAULO)	sedim.	Tert.	~NS N70-80E N10-20W	N40E			NS N60E	N40E	65°-75°
S. PAULO BASIN (SP)	sedim.	Tert.						NS N50E	
MARIMBONDO (SP-MG)	basalt	J-K	NS N30-45E EW	N45E N20E N63E			N50W N20E	N0-20E N60W	50°-65°
CAMPINAS (S. PAULO)	diabase	J-K	N30-40W ~NS N70-80E	N20W N40E N70W			N20W N45E	N80W N20W	65°-75°
SAN IGNACIO (PARAGUAY)	sands.	Tr-J			N65W	N20E		N25E	
SERRA DO MAR (S. PAULO)	metam. gneiss gran.	Pre-Є	N55E N50W	EW	N40E N70E NS	N60W N20W EW		EW N0-20W N40E	60°
V. FLORIDA (PARAGUAY)	ign. intr.	Pre-Є	N55-65W N60-80E	N85W					25°-50°
V. GRANDE (S. PAULO)	gneiss	Pre-Є	~NS N30-40W N70-80E	N20W N40E N70W			N20W N50E	N45E	20°-40°
JAGUARA (SP-MG)	qtzite	Pre-Є	N30-40W N0-10W N20-30E N60-70E	N45E N35E N75E	N45W	N45E	N20W N45E	N45E	40°-60°
PIRAQUARA (PARANÁ)	metam. ign.	Pre-Є	N75-85E N65-75W N5-15E N35-45E	N45E N80E N60-70W					30°-50°
R. DE CONTAS (BAHIA)	metam. ign. intr.	Pre-Є	~EW N40-50E N20-30W	N10E N70E N60W	NS	EW	NS N70E		15°-20°

Table 1. Summary of tectonic orientations and stress orientations.

Table 1. Résumé des directions tectoniques et des tensions predominantes.

Tabelle 1. Zusammenfassung der tektonischen Richtungen und der predominanten Spannungen.

al characteristics of each of the investigated areas. For each area the following information is given: predominant lithologic types, ages of the rocks (based principally on radiometric age data by others), predominant fault trends, predominant fold axis trends, predominant stress orientations and conjugate shear angles of the rock massifs. The orientation of predominant stresses for each region were deduced using four different approaches: (1) direct analysis of predominant fault orientation; (2) analysis of predominant fold axial trends; (3) analysis of thrust fault trends and (4) analysis of conjugate shear angle planes. The internal shear angle, Ø, was inferred on the basis of the predominant stresses active during each tectonic episode.

For simplicity in presentation, Fig. 2 was prepared to illustrate the relationship between the orientation of principal stresses and the time of formation of faults in each of the various areas. In analysing this graph we must keep in mind that more recent tectonic movements will necessarily have affected older lithologies, so that while younger rocks will reflect simple fault patterns, older rocks will exhibit increasingly complex patterns.

Through inspection of Fig. 2 we can readily identify the principal stress directions active in three well defined geologic periods In Precambrian time the major principal stress, σ_1 , seems to have been oriented in approximately an E-W- direction. If other stress directions existed at this time they are obscured by subsequent tectonisms. In Jurassic-Cretaceous time three principal stress directions are observed, although at least one of these must be a reflection of other tectonisms. Stresses at this time seem to have been oriented ± N70°E, N20°W and N60°-70°W. This last trend may be linked to the Precambrian E-W stress direction. In Tertiary time, two well defined stress orientations are observed: N40°E and NS-N10°E.

Whenever available, stress orientations derived through analysis of thrust fault directions and fold axis trends agree very well with the trends inferred through analysis of fault planes. The stress orientations derived through analysis of conjugate shear angle planes, however, differ, sometimes markedly, from the trends obtained through the other methods. This is probably due to the fact that the two trends measured in the field were not always formed during the same tectonic event but reflect individual faults of different ages.

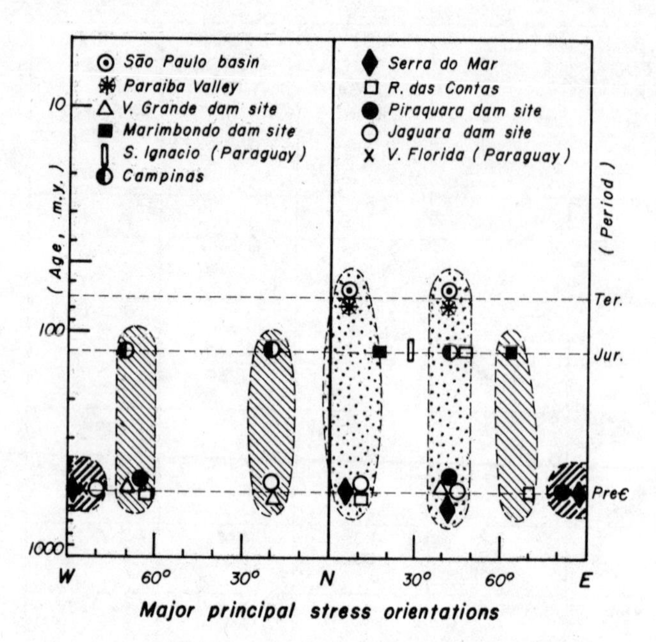

Figure 2. Principal stress orientations plotted against the geologic age of the corresponding lithology.

Figure 2. Directions de la tension principale, relatives à l'âge géologique des roches correspondantes.

Bild 2. Beziehung swischen den Hauptspannungsrichtungen und dem geologischen Alter der entsprechenden Lithologie.

More careful analysis of Fig. 2 shows that a certain scatter does occur in stress directions, particularly in those of Jurassic-Cretaceous time. Two possibilities exist : (1) continental arching accompanying both the Precambrian and the Mesozoic events obscure the data to a certain extent, or (2), and more likely, the data that was used for certain areas may reflect conditions of local character. Although most of the regions that were investigated for the study represent large territories mapped in detail, nevertheless some of them were restricted to areally small dam sites. In any event, it is stressed that the results presented in this study are of a preliminary nature, and, as such, they show remarkably good agreement in all respects.

The interpretation of tectonic events and stress field orientations has traditionally been carried out through the analysis of conjugate shear planes (BADGLEY, 1959; MOODY & HILL, 1956). In this method the acute angle 2 θ formed by the two shear planes is equal to 90°, so, the internal shear angle of the rock mass, can be easily obtained. A certain amount of care must be exercised in using this method, however, for the following reasons: (1) rocks exhibit greater ductility with increasing confirming pressures (MOGI, 1972), so Ø consequently becomes progressively smaller; (2) Ø decreases with increasing temperature (BAIDYUK, 1967); (3) Ø also depends on lithologic type. As a result, for today's engineering applications, the general belief that the Ø angles of a rock mass can be obtained from the measurement of conjugate shears is not valid unless the depth of tectonism is known, so that a correction can be applied to the Ø angle with respect to temperature and pressure. At present the major interest in determining the stress field orientation is for the purpose of obtaining some clue as to the orientation of residual stress within a rock mass for underground constructions.

An attempt was made to determine the Ø angles in the region of study through the statistical analysis of the distribution of fault or shear planes. The 2 θ angles of the Precambrian terrains were found to be somewhat lower than those of Mesozoic and Cenozoic terrains, that is, the Ø angles in older rocks were found to be greater than those in younger lithologies. Metamorphic grade achieved in Precambrian time, however, was much higher than the metamorphic grade achieved in more recent geologic time. Admitting also that in Precambrian time the earth's geothermal gradient was higher than it is today (WINKLER, 1967), the Ø angles corresponding to Precambrian terrains should be lower than those corresponding to younger rocks. The apparent discrepancy between the theory and the results obtained in the study can best be explained by the existence of superimposed phases of tectonism that created a pattern of predominant faults too complicated for simple direct analysis. Furthermore, it must also be kept in mind that the orientation of fault planes created during a second event will be affected by pre-existing fault planes originated during a prior event (according to experimental results by DONATH, 1961).

Investigations in this vein are being continued. An attempt is being made to first characterize the tectonic patterns of younger orogenies and their effects on older lithologies in order to identify the fault patterns originated in the more ancient disturbances.

GEOTECHNICAL INFERENCES

The relationships outlined above between the geologic age of rock masses and the principal stresses active during the various tectonic episodes are of fundamental importance in the analysis of geotechnical conditions that may eventually be found in the investigated areas. These stresses define the fracture patterns observed in the different regions, and are thus the basic factors that control the existence of various types of geotechnical problems. In Cenozoic terrains, then, it is expected that relatively simple fracture patterns will be encountered in rock masses, whereas more complicated patterns originated through two or more tectonic episodes will be found in older rocks. At a large hydroelectric dam site in the mid portions of the Rio Grande area (Fig. 1, Marimbondo), for exemple, stresses active in both the Mesozoic and the Cenozoic contributed to create a pattern consisting of faults and fractures oriented N-S, N30-45E, and E-W (Table 1). Continental arching during this time induced the formation of large sub-horizontal fractures. These structures created a set of geotechnical conditions concerning slope stability, underground water percolation through fissures, accelerated weathering of the rock mass, etc necessitating careful analysis for the development of the project. Furthermore, the knowledge of predominant patterns can help greatly to predict in what orientations one can expect the occurence of adverse geologic features; also, as mentioned before, the recognition of past orientation of the stress field can help interpreting results of measurements of residual stresses.

CONSIDERATIONS REGARDING POSSIBLE RELATIONSHIP BETWEEN STRESS PATTERNS AND FORCES ACTIVE DURING SEPARATION OF THE CONTINENTS

Based on the investigations by various authors concerning geologic processes active during continental rifting, the authors have elaborated certain preliminary ideas to explain the structural patterns observed in south-eastern Brazil.

It has been suggested (RIDEG, 1974) that the Brazilian tectonic-orogenic cycle which occurred at the end of the Precambrian (± 550 ± 100 m.y. ago) corresponds to an episode of continental collision which resulted in the suturing together of portions of the present South American and African continents. During this episode of collision the major regional NE-SW and subordinate NW-SE structural trends were formed. Large scale horizontal movements predominated, as evidenced by the existence of large transcurrent faults in the crystalline rocks of the coastal belt of Brazil. It is inferred that the greatest compressive stress, , acted approximately in an E-W direction during this episode, an inference which is supported by data given in Table 1 and Figure 2. Crustal arching accompanied these phenomena, tilting the faulted blocks to the west. High grade metamorphism also affected these rocks, attesting to high temperatures and pressures during this episode.

The tectonic movements that occurred during the Early Cretaceous reactivation possibly correspond to a rifting episode in the former supercontinent Pangaea, which resulted in the separation of Africa and South America (RIDEG, 1973). It has been suggested (LOWELL & GENIK, 1972) that regional arching of the lithosphere represents the first stage of rifting. Crustal arching is followed by crustal extension of the lithosphere (NELSON and TEMPLE, 1972) with the formation of horsts and grabens and tilting of tectonic blocks. Faulting during the Early Cretaceous reactivation consisted of great vertical movements (ALMEIDA, 1969) along ancient reactivated fault planes and also along new ones. In this manner, the large faults originated during the Brazilian tectonic cycle formed planes of weakness which controlled the geometry of rifting.

According to LE PICHON and HAYES (1971) and FRANCHETEAU and LE PICHON (1972), the separation of South America and Africa occurred in two distinct stages. The early stage of rifting, beginning about 130 m.y. ago, occurred at a pole of relative rotation of the continents situated at 21.5°N latitude and 14.0°W longitude. The tensional forces produced by this stage of rifting would roughly correspond to E-NE to EW trend in Brazil, in which case σ_1 of this tectonism would be oriented approximately NNW-NS. One of the stress directions observed in Mesozoic rocks, ± N20°W (Fig. 2) diverges only slightly from this trend.

The late stage of rifting, which began about 80 m.y. ago, entailed a shift in the pole of relative rotation between the two continents, so that it was situated at 63.2°N latitude and 36.7°W longitude. Preliminary inspection of the position of the principal stress, , active during this phase of rifting is inferred to correspond roughly to a NE-SW trend, compatible with the N40°E stresses indicated by analysis of fault patterns in Tertiary lighologies in Brazil. During this phase, the stress would necessarily be compressive due to the distance separating the continental margins from the mid-Atlantic Ridge, focus of the new oceanic crust being created and carried, or pushed, by convective currents towards the continental plates.

CONCLUSIONS

The principal orogenic episodes which occurred in south-eastern Brazil since late Precambrian time are reflected in the pattern of small fault orientations in lithologies of different geologic ages. Analysis of these fault patterns, coupled with the analysis of other structural features in the rocks (fold axis orientations, thrust fault orientations) indicate that the stress fields active during the tectonic events were oriented with: (1) σ_1, approximately E-W during the Brazilian orogenic cycle in the late Precambrian (compressive forces due to continental collision); (2) tension in an ENE-WNW to E-W direction during the Early Cretaceous reactivation (tensional forces associated with convective upwelling in oceanic crust during the early phase of the separation of the continents); and (3) σ_1, approximately NE-SW during Tertiary disturbances (compressive forces due to spreading of oceanic crust against continental crust associated with a shift in the pole of relative rotation of the separating continents). These preliminary results obtained in seeking the relationship between forces active during the separation of continents and stress fields observed in the analyses of fault planes in southeastern Brazil seem to be in very good agreement.

Inferences concerning the internal shear

angles of the rock masses during the orogenic episodes yield results contrary to those expected through theoretical considerations in that the internal shear angle, Ø, was calculated to have been larger in the Precambrian than in more recent events. This discrepancy is best explained by the fact that superimposed tectonisms mask the shear patterns of individual episodes. Studies are being continued in this trend in an attempt to separate the fracture patterns of the individual orogenies and to establish a listing of shear patterns which could be expected in lithologies of various ages. In this manner, knowing the geologic age of any specific area in southeastern Brazil, it would be possible to foresee the geotechnical conditions and the possible orientations of adverse geologic features of the area, as well as to estimate the orientations of residual stresses within the rock masses.

It is also concluded that the computation of Ø angles from conjugate shear angles for application in engineering projects should be avoided and should be done only with a great deal of care and judgement.

ACKNOWLEDGEMENTS

The authors gratefully acknowledge the firm Promon Engenharia S.A. for encouraging the elaboration of this paper, as well as for the final typing of the manuscript and preparation of the drawings.

BIBLIOGRAPHY

ALMEIDA, F.F.M., 1969, Structure and dynamics of the Brazilian coastal area, Pan American Symposium of the Upper Mantle, No. 22-B, Mexico.

ALMEIDA, F.F.M., 1971, Geochronological division of the Precambrian of South America, Rev. Bras. Geociencias, V.1, No.1, p. 13-21.

AMARAL, G., CORDANI, U.G., KAWASHITA, K., REYNOLDS, J., 1966, Potassium-argon dates of basaltic rocks from southern Brazil, Geochim. et Cosmochim. Acta, V. 39, p. 159-189.

BADGLEY, P.C., 1959, Structural problems for the exploration geologist, Harper and Brothers, N.Y., p. 206-209.

BAIDYUK, B.V., 1967, Mechanical properties of rocks at high temperatures and pressures, Inst.Geol.Devel.Min.Res.Moscow, Cons. Bureau, N.Y., 75 p.

DONATH, F.A., 1961, Experimental failure in anisotropic rock, Geol.Soc.Amer.Bull., V.72, p. 985-990.

FRANCHETEAU, J. and LE PICHON, X, 1972, Marginal fracture zones as structural framework of continental margins in South Atlantic Ocean, Amer.Assoc.Pet.Geol.Bull. V. 56, p. 991-1007.

LE PICHON, X. and HAYES, D.E., 1971, Marginal offsets, fracture zones, and the early opening of the South Atlantic, Journ. Geophys. Research, V.76, p.6283-6293.

LOCZY, L., 1968, Geotectonic evolution of the Amazon, Parnaiba and Paraná basins, Anais Acad.Brasileira de Ciências, V.40, supplement, p. 231-253.

LOWELL, J.D. and GENIK, G.J., 1972, Sea-floor spreading and structural evolution of the southern Red Sea, Amer.Assoc.Pet. Geol.Bull., V.56, p. 247-249.

MOGI, K., 1972, Fracture and flow of rocks, Tectonophysics (The Upper Mantle), V.13, No. 1-4, p. 541-568.

MOODY, J.D. and HILL, M.J., 1956, Wrench fault tectonics, Geol.Soc.Amer.Bull., V.67, p. 1207-1248.

NELSON, T.H. and TEMPLE, P.G., 1972, Mainstream mantle convection: a geologic analysis of plate motion, Amer.Assoc.Pet.Geol. Bull. V.56, No. 2, p. 226-246.

RIDEG, P., 1974, Petrology and structure of a portion of the Serra do Mar in eastern São Paulo, Brazil, State University of New York, Binghamton, N.Y., Ph.D.dissertation, 166 p.

WINKLER, H.G.S., 1967, Petrogenesis of metamorphic rocks, Springer Verlag, N.Y., 2nd edition, 237 pp.

THE MECHANICS OF DOME FOLDING IN THE EARTH CRUST

MÉCANIQUE DE LA FORMATION DES COUPOLES DANS LES COUCHES DE L'ÉCORCE TERRESTRE

DER KUPPELBILDUNGSMECHANISMUS IN DEN ERDRINDESCHICHTEN

Zhakan Suleymenovich ERZHANOV — Academician of the Kasakh Academy of Sciences, Doctor of technical sciences, Professor,

Igor Alexandrovich GARAGASH — Candidate of physico-mathematical sciences

Alma-Ata, U.S.S.R.

Summary

The report considers the mathematical modeling of the conditions of formation of dome structures in stratum competent and uncompetent layers under the influence longitudinal tectonic forces. The original structures are connected with non-homogenity stratum and irregular distribution of the forces. It is reduced to the solution of the problem of local instability for the stratum in boundary of some competent layer. Adjacent equilibrium forms for the layer is investigated and the convexity and concave parts determined by the form of the domain are found. The convexity parts are considered as embryo of domes.

The observed difference of forms, dimensions and deflections of the folds are explained. The reaction of the uncompetent layers is strated; it is shown, that viscosity does not influence the value of folding forces. The calculations show, that dome folding is originated by forces with an order of 10^5 newton/m^2. The following growth of it is considered as a finite deflection of the equivalent viscoelastic layer in the medium with mean viscosity. The solution of the obtained nonlinear equation as well as qualitative study on the phase show that closure velocity increases from the certain value for given physical and geometrical conditions after what it begins to slow down. The generation of the dome for thr geosyncline is explained with the help of the mechanism of imposition of linear folds with different age and without reorientation of the tectonic forces. The calculations have shown the reality of this imposition.

Résumé

Sont communiqués les resultats de la simulation mathématique des conditions de la formation des structures en forme de coupole, dans la masse des couches compétentes et incompétentes sous l'action des efforts tangentiaux tectoniques. La naissance des structures est liée à l'hétérogénéité de la masse et à l'inégalité de la répartition des efforts en fonction de la profondeur; elle est réduite à la résolution du problème sur la stabilité élastique locale de la masse dans les limites d'une couche compétente quelconque. Sont étudiées les formes contigües de l'equilibre de la couche, et sont déterminés les secteurs de la convexité et de la concavité, bornés par les curvilignes de coordonnées définies par la forme de la région où la formation des plis se fait. Les secteurs de convexité sont présentés en tant que germes des structures en forme de coupole. Sa croissance ultérieure est considérée comme le fléchissement d'amplitude aux extrémités de la couche viscoélastique équivalente dans le milieu à viscosité réduite. La résolution de l'équation non-linéaire obtenue de type Liénard ainsi que l'étude qualitative sur le plan de phase font remarquer que la vitesse de la formation de coupole augmente jusqu'à une valeur bien déterminée pour les conditions physiques et géométriques données. Cette valeur atteinte, elle commence à ralentir. La formation des coupoles sur les géosynclinales est expliquée à l'aide du mécanisme de la superposition des plis linéaires de divers âge et de divers étendue sans que, la direction d'action des forces tectoniques soit réorientée. Les calculs démontrent la validité et la praticabilité d'une telle superposition.

Zusammenfassung

Die Resultate einer mathematischen Modelierung der Bildungsverhältnissen für kuppelartige Strukturen in der Dicke von kompetenten und nichtkompetenten Schichten unter Wirkung von tangentialer tektonischer Kräfte werden berichtet. Die Entstehung dieser Strukturen ist mit der Heterogemtät der Dicke und der Ungleichmässigkeit der Kräfteverteilung je nach der Tiefe verbunden; sie ist zur Rechnung einer Aufgabe von der lokalen elastischen Stabilität der Dicke in den Grenzen einer ompetenten Schicht reduziert. Die angrenzende Formen des Schichtengleichgewichts werden untersucht und die Konvexitäts - und Konkavitätsbereiche, die von den krummlinigen Koordinatenlinien begrenzt sind, welche seinerseits durch die Form des Faltenbildungsbereichs bestimmt sind, wurden festgestellt. Die Konvexitätsbereiche sind als Keime der kuppelartigen Strukturen betrachtet. Ihre folgende Entwicklung wird als eine endlich-amplitüdische Durchbiegung einer äquivalenten viskos-elastischen Schicht in einem Medium mit reduzierter Viskosität betrachtet. Die Rechnung der gefundenen nichtlinearen Gleichung, sowie die qualitative Untersuchung auf einer Phasenfläche zeigen, dass die Geschwindigkeit der Kuppelbildung bis zu einer für die gegebene physikalische und geometrische Bedingung bestimmte Grösse anwächst, danach fängt sie aber an sich zu verlangsamen. Die Kuppelbildung auf Geosynklinen ist durch den Auferlegungsmechanismus von linearen Falten verschiedenen Alters und verschiedener Strecke ohne Umorientierung der Wirkungsrichtung der tektonischen Kräfte erklärt. Die Berechnungen zeigen die Realität solcher Auferlegung.

To the geological description of the stratum in the upper part of the Earth crust with complicated fold constitution are devoted many publications. Some types of folding - the dome folding developped on the platform, linear and cross folding, spreading in the geosyncline - are distinguished. The oil and gas fields connected with dome and cross fold structures determine the actuallity of mathematical models of their formation conditions allowing to define the known and to find the new regularities, which are essential for the prospecting works. So far the main results in this direction obtained by M.A.Biot (1957, 1965), G.Ramberg (1962, 1963) Zh.S.Erzhanov and A.K.Egorov (1968, 1970) were confined to the linear folds. The process of formation of dome and cross folding was not subjected to systematic quantitative analysis. In the given article the principal pecularities of the mechanism of formation of dome and cross structures in the stratification of Earth crust by the longitudinall tectonic forces are determined by mathematic and mechanic methods.

I. Dome folding. Let the stratum covered by the alluvium to consist of sufficiently great number horizontal competent layers of different thickness, passessing flexural rigidity and separated uncompetent layers. The behaviour of very competent layer (named later a simple layer) submits to the creep law in the form (Erzhanov, 1964) of

$$E\varepsilon(t)=\sigma(t)+\int_0^t \mathcal{L}(t,\tau)\sigma(\tau)d\tau, \qquad (I)$$

where $\varepsilon(t)$, $\sigma(t)$ are the deformation and the stress at the moment of observation; E is the modulus of elasticity; $\mathcal{L}(t,\tau)=\delta(t-\tau)^{-\alpha}$; α and δ are the parameters of the creep. Uncompetent layers are supposed to be a viscous uncompressible body with a viscosity coefficient η_m.

Let us by means of an arbitrary vertical cylindrical surface cut out the region of folding from the stratum, (fig. I).

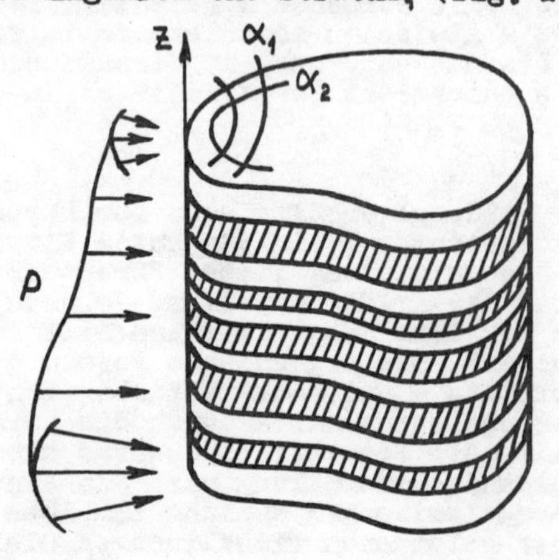

Fig. 1

Choose the curvelinear system of axes α_1, α_2, z so that its lateral surface coincides with co-ordinate surface. The region is under the action of its own weight, uncluding the weight of the alluvia and of lateral pressure P being in general the function of the co-ordinates α_2, z. It is admited that the forces appeared non-inertially in a moment of time $t=0$ and all the layers do not slip along the line contact.

Because of its relative short duration let us consider the original stage of folding (first stage) as stability loss of the forms of elastic equilibrium neglecting the physical dependence (I) by influence of time. It is important that for the non-homogenity stratum the instability primarily shows itself locally, for example, in the single layer. Let's use a general statical criterion of stability for definition of the stress in this layer. Passage from principal state before the loss the stability to adjacent is accomplished in consequence of the turning of volume of the body elements. Corresponding equations of the equilibrium and boundary conditions are shown by V.V.Novozhilov (1948); their general decision was recently obtained by A.N.Guz (1968). However later on we shall follow A.Yu.Ishlinski (1954) who solved the problem of stability with reference of the body elements only for boundary conditions. Having written out the equation of the equilibrium in displacements (Lame's equations for adjacent state,

$$\nabla^2\bar{u}' + \frac{1}{1-2\nu}\,\mathrm{grad}\,\mathrm{div}\,\bar{u}'=0, \qquad (2)$$

where $\nabla^2\bar{u}'=\mathrm{grad}\,\mathrm{div}\,\bar{u}'-\mathrm{rot}\,\mathrm{rot}\,\bar{u}'$; ν is Puasson's ratio; let's present his solution in B.G.Galerkin's form

$$2G\bar{u}'=2(1-\nu)\nabla^2\bar{\Psi}-\mathrm{grad}\,\mathrm{div}\,\bar{\Psi}+\bar{\Phi}. \qquad (3)$$

Here $\bar{\Psi}$ is the biharmonic vector; G is the modulus of elasticity in shear; $\bar{\Phi}$ is harmonic vector satisfying to condition $\mathrm{div}\,\bar{\Phi}=0$.

Boundary conditions of elastic stability of the layer are

$$q\bar{n}=-(\bar{\sigma}_1^{\,o}+\bar{\sigma}_1')H_1^{-1}\frac{\partial u_z'}{\partial\alpha_1}-(\bar{\sigma}_2^{\,o}+\bar{\sigma}_2')H_2^{-1}\frac{\partial u_z'}{\partial\alpha_2}-(\bar{\sigma}_z^{\,o}+\bar{\sigma}_z'), \qquad (4)$$

where q is the own weight of the abovelaying stratum; H_1, H_2 are Lame's parametres; $\bar{n}$ is normal to flexural surface of the layer. The competents of stress and displacement with index "o" refer to the principal state and components wirh the stroke refer to adjacent state. Satisfaction of boundary conditions on the layer's outline are supposed in an integral sense.

For the layer loaded on the boundary of the region of folding by uniform pressure the projection of the vector from the solution (3) are presented so:

$$\Psi_z=(C_1\,\mathrm{ch}\,kz+C_2\,z\,\mathrm{sh}\,kz)\,\Omega(\alpha_1,\alpha_2),$$
$$\Psi_1=\Psi_2=0,\quad \Phi_1=\Phi_2=0,\quad \Phi_z=C, \qquad (5)$$

where C, C_1, C_2 are arbitrary constants; $\Omega(\alpha_1,\alpha_2)$ is a function. If this function admits the separation of variables, then the solution fits the simple support of the infinite layer along a close curve composed from the parts of the co-ordinate lines α_1, α_2.

Compatibility condition of the equations (4) for the layer with the thickness $2b$ is leading to a critical relation in the form of

$$(p-q)_{cr} = 2G \frac{sh2\kappa b - 2\kappa b}{(1-2\nu)sh2\kappa b + 2\kappa b} \quad (6)$$

Appropriate relief of the flexural surface of the layer defined by the function Ω in the general case depends on the intensiveness and distribution of the load p as well as on the longitudinal dimensions and form of the region of folding. Just this explain the generally observed unequal distribution and different evolution of their dome structures in the Earth crust, the difference of their forms, dimensions and rise amplitudes.

In the Decart's co-ordinate sistem x, y, z for the case of rectangular region, the function

$$\Omega = \sin k_1 x \sin k_2 y \quad (7)$$

describes the layer shown in the figure 2 .

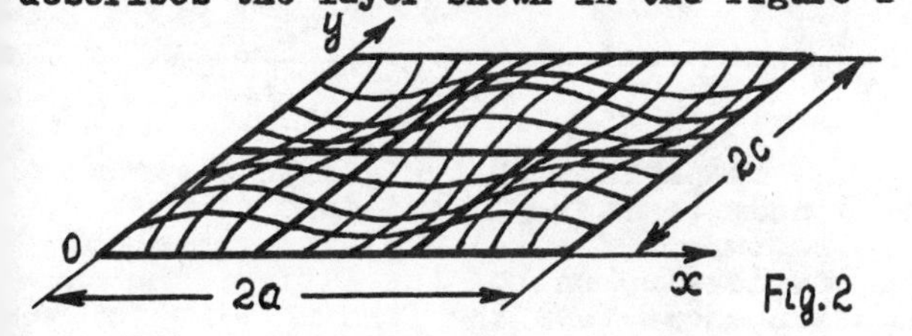

Fig.2

Here $k_1 = \frac{m\pi}{2a}$; $k_2 = \frac{n\pi}{2c}$; $k_1^2 + k_2^2 = \kappa^2$; $2a$ and $2c$ are dimension of the folding region; $m, n = 1, 2, \ldots$.

If one of the dimensions of the region is directed to infinity ($c \to \infty$; $k_2 \to 0$; $k_1 \to \kappa$) then the function Ω obtain the simple form

$$\Omega = \sin \kappa x \quad (8)$$

and the forming folding is nearly linear (fig. 3).

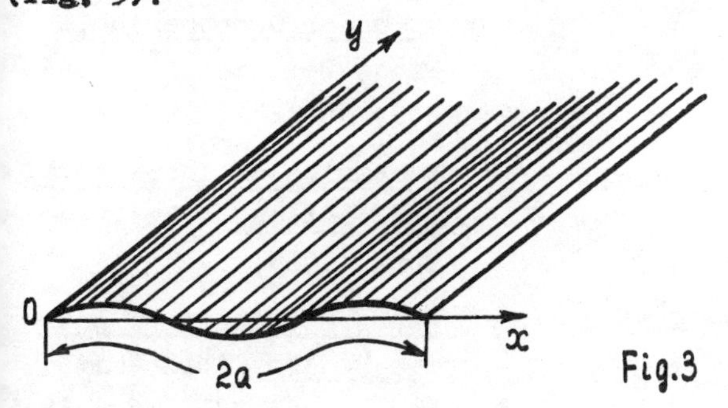

Fig.3

From the correlation (6-8) it followes that for some discrete magnitudes $(p-q)_{cr}$ the layer surfaces are bending in dome and linear structures. The number of the folds is defined by m and n so that the case $m=0$, $n=0$ corresponds to the initial state.

By the analysis of the layer instability we neglected the reaction of the viscose uncompetent layers having the form

$$q_n = -4\eta_m b \frac{d}{dt}(\varkappa_1 + \varkappa_2), \quad (9)$$

where $\varkappa_1$, $\varkappa_2$ are the curvature of the middle plane in the directions α_1, α_2. It is correct for when the outer forces are critical the deflection of the layer does not depend on time, i.e. $q_n = 0$.

Locally formed folds as a result of the following interaction of the layers shall spread on the whole regions of folding. For the linear folds such interaction was described in the monograph of Zh.S.Erzhanov and A.K.Egorov (1968).

The calculations according to formula (6) shows that intensity of tectonic forces forming dome structures is extremely insignificant. For the geometrical and physical parametres observed in folding complexes they do not exceed some 10^5 newton/m^2.

Different elements of folding structure are prevalent in the sediment cover. Appeareing on different depths, different in size and age they are often located on one and the same areas. Such a variety of the folds is a result of the smallness of forming forces, when even insignificant variation of the tectonic forces can causes the forming of the folding structure of different scale and age. It's necessary also to note that in coal pits worked out in sediment cover essential tectonic forces are not detected. This facts apparently prove the real smallness of the order $(p-q)_{cr}$. The high level of such forces as known is observed only in crystalline rocks not including the uncompetent layers (Erzhanov and Egorov, 1968).

2. Cross folding. Let us stady the possibility of formation of the dome structures with help of imposition of the linear folding complexes of different age and stretch. In the literature it is connected with the change of the direction of action of tectonic forces. But this contradicts the known principle of the inheritance and constancy of the direction of principal vector of tectonic forces in the geosyncline. Therefore we shall build the mechanism of the cross folding not connecting it with mentioned change of the forces.

Let the layer in which the folding generates have the form of a strip with a width $2c$ stretching arbitrary relatively the principal vector of the tectonic forces. The normal p and shear τ stresses applied to its boundary lead to the primary complex of oblique and elongated folds. We introduce the co-ordinate oblique angle system x^1, x^2, z with axe x^1 directed along the strip and composing the angle φ with axe x^2 parallel to axes of the original folds. We present the equation of the flexure middle plane of the strip (layer) in the case of simple support of the edges in form of

$$u_z' = F \sin k_1 x^1 \sin k_\varphi x^2 \quad (10)$$

and in the case of a fixed edge -

$$u_z' = F \sin k_1 x^1 (\sin k_\varphi x^2)^2. \quad (11)$$

Here F is the maximum deflection; $k_1 = \pi/2l$; $k_\varphi = n\pi \sin\varphi/2l$; $2l$ is the length of the halfwave (width of the fold).

Using the expressions (10) and (11) and with the help of the Bubnov-Galerkin's method we obtain the expressions for the critical (folding) forces. Analisis showed that when the width of the fold is considerably smaller than the width of the region then the critical shear forces are independent from the type of fixation of the strip's edges and do not exceed 10^6 newton/m^2, whereas $\varphi = 60^\circ$. In the process of the fold growth the strip boundaries get closer. If this is difficult to do then there appear normal extension forces on the contour which increase with the increasing of the deflection F. At $F/c = 0,05$ already such sorces exceed 10^7 newton/m^2 and along the strip sides fracture can begin. As a result, the region of folding become insensitive to shear stresses and capable to resist only to the normal component of the tectonic forces. In this case the growth of the primary folds stops and the increase of intensity of tension ρ can generate the second fold complex of folds desorientation with the first folds. Forces necessary for this are found by investigation of the anisotropic plane strip equivalent to the layer crimped by the primary folding in sense of flexural rigidity. Corresponding equilibrum equation in the oblique angle co-ordinate system is solved by Bubnov-Galerkin's method. The calculations showed that the appearance of second folding is possible at forces not exceeding the some 10^6 newton/m^2, which are decreasing with the increasing of the frequency of primary folds. The numeral data indicate the reality of the offered mechanism of fold imposition.

3. About the peculiarity of the growth of dome structures. The investigation of the growth regime of the formed structures requires the definition of great deflections of the layers in the stratum in dependence of time. This problem comes to analysis of the aftercritical viscoelastic bending of the equivalent single layer in the medium of the uncompetent layers with a reduced coefficient of viscosity. Applying the Karman's equations we obtain the nonlinear correlation with help of the Bubnov-Galerkin's method,

$$\frac{\eta_m}{\tau}\frac{df}{dt} = \frac{1}{2}\left[(\rho-q)f - (\rho-q)_{cr}\bar{E}f\right] - f\bar{E}f^2\frac{b^2A^2}{8}, \qquad (12)$$

where τ is the number of the layers; $f = \frac{F}{2b}$; $(\rho-q)_{cr} = \frac{4}{9}Eb^2K^2$; $A^2 = \frac{k_1^4 + k_2^4}{K^2}$. Analysing the equation (12), which replaces the temporal differential operator $\bar{E}$, we use the single viscoelasticity equation for Maxwell's body and standard linear body. In both cases this gives nonlinear equations, which have no exact solutions. The solution of some limit problems $\tau \to \infty$, absolute viscocity layer) and qualitative investigation on the phase plane of the full equations show that the growth velocity of the dome structure increases untill the deflection does not reach the value

$$f^* \simeq \frac{1}{Ab}\sqrt{\frac{\eta_m}{\tau\eta} - \frac{(\rho-q)-(\rho-q)_{cr}}{2E}}$$

(for Maxwell's body) and

$$f^* \simeq \frac{1}{Ab}\sqrt{\frac{\eta_m}{\tau\tau_\varepsilon E} - \frac{(\rho-q)-(\rho-q)_{cr}}{2E}}$$

(for standard linear body), after which the process begins slow down. Further on it decreases for increasing deflection (unlimited creep) or for deflection coming to value

$$f_{max} = \frac{1}{Ab}\sqrt{\frac{\tau_\sigma\left[(\rho-q)-(\rho-q)_{crd}\right]}{\tau_\varepsilon E}}.$$

Here τ_ε, τ_σ are the relaxation time and delay time; $(\rho-q)_{crd}$ is limit of long stability; η is the viscosity coefficient of the layer. For the linear folds the equation (12) does not contain the nonlinear item.

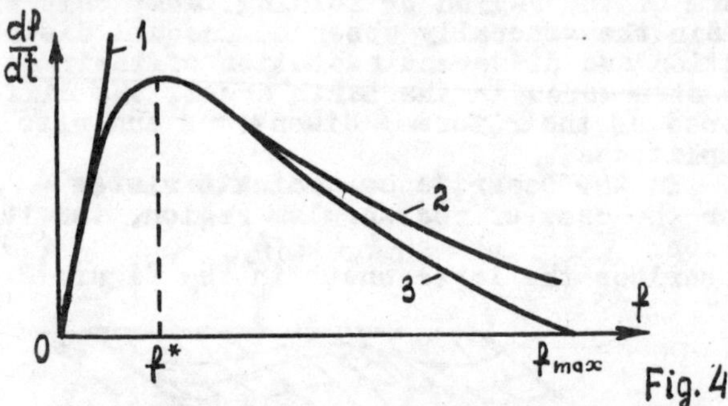

Fig. 4

The comparison of the growth regimes for linear (curve 1) and dome (curves 2, 3) structures (fig. 4) explains the observed low development of the latter. The calculation shows that the forming time for the linear fold is approximately by two orders less than for the formation of gently sloping dome.

References

Biot M.A. Folding Instability of a Layered Viscoelastic Medium under Compression. Proc. Roy. Soc., A, vol. 242, N° 1231, 1957.

Biot M.A. Mechanics of Incremental Deformation. Wiley, New York, 1965.

Guz A.N. About Stability of Elastic Bodies. Appl. Math. Mech., vol. 35, N° 5, 1968

Erzhanov Zh.S. Theory of Rock Creep with Supplements. Alma-Ata, 1964.

Erzhanov Zh.S., Egorov A.K. Theory of Folding in the Earth Crust. Alma-Ata, 1968.

Erzhanov Zh.S., Egorov A.K. — The Mathematical Theory of Formation of Folds in the Earth's Crust. Proc. 2nd Congr. ISRM, Beograd, 1970.

Ishlinski A.Y. — Consideration of Stability Elastic Bodies with Point of View Mathematic Theory of Elasticity. Ukr. Math. J., vol. 6, N° 2, 1954.

Novozhilov V.V. — Foundations of Nonlinear Theory of Elasticity. Moscow-Leningrad, Gostekizdat, 1948.

Ramberg H. — Contact Strain and Folding Instability of a Multilayered Body under Compression. Geol. Rundshau, vol. 51, N° 2, 1962.

Ramberg H. — Fluid Dynamics of Viscous Buckling Applicable to Folding of Layered Rocks. Bull. Amer. Assoc. Petrol. Geol., vol. 47, N° 3, 1963.

RECHERCHE DE LA FISSURATION NATURELLE D'UN RESERVOIR PÉTROLIER

RESEARCH ON NATURAL FRACTURING OF A PETROLEUM RESERVOIR

NACHFORSCHUNG DER NATÜRLICHEN RISSEBILDUNG EINES ERDÖLVORKOMMENS

P. HABIB, Ing. EP

J. QUIBLIER, Ing.

Laboratoire de Mécaniques de Solides - École Polytechnique

Paris, France

RESUME

On étudie la déformation faible d'un terrain stratifié sous l'effet du pointement d'un dôme de sel profond. La théorie de l'élasticité permet de donner l'allure générale de la distribution des contraintes dans les terrains déformés. L'introduction d'un critère de rupture "à long terme" permet alors de tirer des conclusions quant à la localisation des zones éventuellement fissurées.
Des applications concernant l'exploitation des hydrocarbures sont présentées.

SUMMARY

The case of sedimentary stratas slightly strained by the ascension of a still deeply burried salt dome is studied. The theory of elasticity is shown to be able to give the general outline of the stress distribution in the strained rock. The introduction of a long term failure criterium allows us to draw conclusions as to the localisation of possibly fractured zones.
Applications to oil recovery are presented.

ZUSAMMENFASSUNG

Es wird die schwache Verformung eines Schichtengeländes unter der Einwirkung der Ausbuchtung eines tiefen Salzdomes untersucht. Die Elastizitätstheorie gestattet die allgemeine Wiedergabe der Verteilung der Kräfte in den verformten Geländen. Die Einführung des "Langzeit" - Bruch - Kriteriums gestattet dann, Schlüsse hinsichtlich der Lokalisierung eventuell aufgerissener Zonen zu ziehen. Anwendungsmöglichkeiten bezüglich der Gewinnung von Kohlenwasserstoffen werden dargestellt.

INTRODUCTION

Le débit d'un puits de pétrole est fonction de la perméabilité. Celle-ci dépend pour une part des caractéristiques du niveau poreux matriciel, mais aussi à un degré important, de la présence d'un système de fissures. On sait que ces dernières se développent à l'occasion de la déformation des roches qui préside à la constitution des pièges structuraux où s'accumule le pétrole. Le rendement économique d'un puits est évidemment amélioré s'il est installé dans une zone particulièrement fissurée d'un tel piège. Le but de cette étude est de présenter une tentative de détermination de la fissuration naturelle d'un réservoir pétrolier à partir des informations géologiques et des lois de la Mécanique des Roches. Le problème étudié correspond au cas d'une structure dont la déformation a été simple. Mais le principe proposé peut, et a déjà été étendu à d'autres formations, pour autant que géologie et géophysique permettent d'en détailler le développement structural.

APERÇU GEOLOGIQUE DU SITE

Le dôme étudié est connu par les travaux réalisés par l'ERAP pour le compte de la NIOC dans l'Est du Golfe Persique. La constitution de la série géologique est bien reconnue par les forages. Sur une couche probablement puissante de sel infracambrien, 5.000 m de sédiments environ se sont progressivement déposés. Le sel, instable sous cette charge, s'est mis en mouvement à plusieurs reprises et notamment au Cénomanien, c'est-à-dire il y a environ 100 millions d'années, développant un pointement correspondant à la naissance en profondeur, d'un dôme de sel (fig.1).

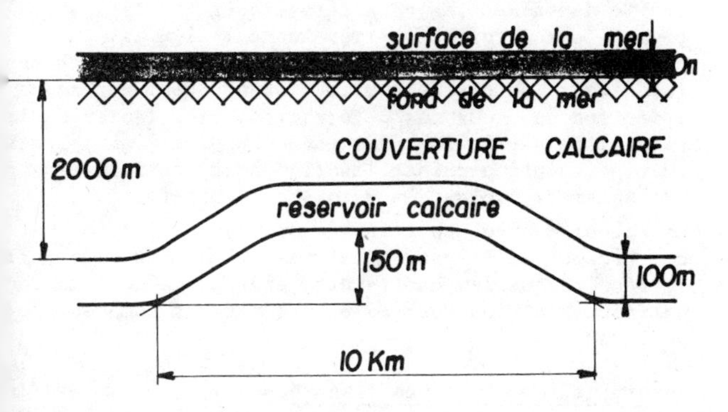

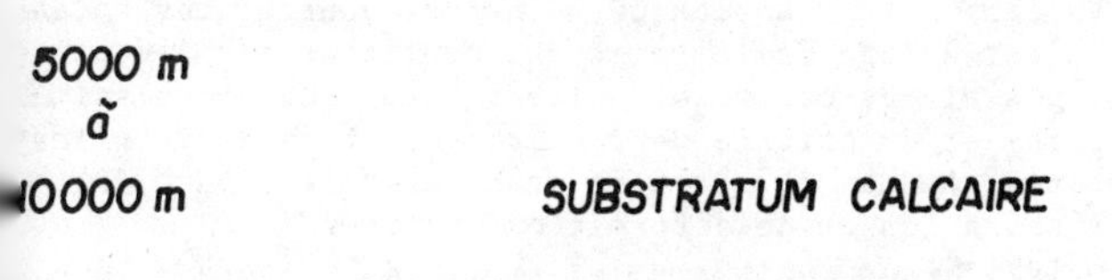

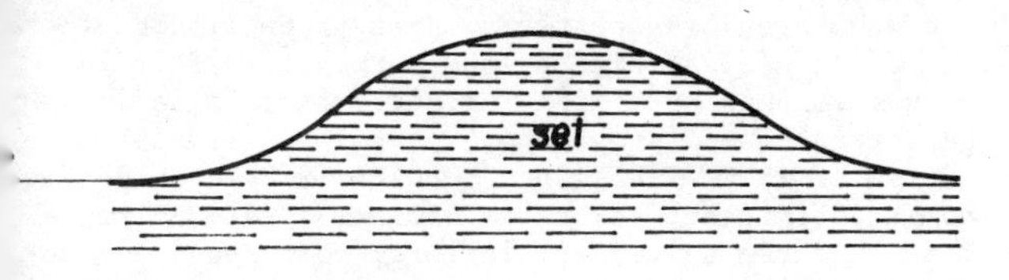

igure 1 : Coupe schématique du réservoir et de la situation géologique.

Schematic section of the oil deposit and of the geological site.

Schematischer Schnitt des Reservoirs und der geologischen Lage.

Un tel mouvement profond a déformé les couches susjacentes en voie de compaction et de consolidation, y faisant naître en particulier dans les assises calcaires une certaine fissuration. Ces fissures sont normalement cicatrisées par des dépôts de calcite, (fig.2), véhiculée par l'eau. Le processus de déformation s'est accéléré il y a 10 millions d'années environ et la vitesse de déformation a alors augmenté et s'est multipliée par 10. Une fissuration beaucoup plus importante s'est alors ouverte dans une couche calcaire située actuellement à 2.000 m de profondeur, ce qui permet d'en récupérer l'huile : c'est à partir de ce moment qu'on peut parler de la formation d'un gisement. A l'époque du début de cette phase de déformation accélérée, le fond de la mer était horizontal, situé à quelques dizaines de mètres de profondeur, il est maintenant enfoui à -500 m sous des dépôts plus récents et la forme structurale qu'il a prise permet d'évaluer la déformation différentielle qui sera considérée ici comme responsable de la fissuration ouverte, c'est-à-dire de la fracturation actuelle du réservoir.

Figure 2 : Photographie d'une cicatrice de Calcite.

Photograph of a Calcite scar.

Foto einer Kalzitnarbe.

En fait, tout n'est pas si simple : la position du plan de référence n'est connue qu'à une translation près et elle n'est plus parfaitement horizontale. Mais, surtout, le mouvement ascendant d'un point n'est pas obligatoirement vertical et la composante horizontale du déplacement n'est pas connues ; si la déformée du gisement donnée par la géophysique est une information géologique sûre, par contre la correspondance point par point reste incertaine. Cette mauvaise définition n'est pas un obstacle insurmontable : on peut en effet imaginer pour les conditions aux limites deux cas extrêmes entre lesquels la réalité doit se trouver : le glissement libre (qui se traduit analytiquement en écrivant que la contrainte de cisaillement est nulle à la base de la couche), et le glissement empêché (c'est-à-dire continuité des déplacements). Les calculs effectués ont montré que la différence entre les cas extrêmes pour la détermination des zones de rupture n'était pas très grande et que l'essentiel est de connaître le plus parfaitement possible la géométrie du site et la chronologie des mouvements. La montée du sel a provoqué des déformations ductiles en certaines zones du massif et des fissurations dans d'autres ; on peut tenter de localiser ces différents domaines par la Mécanique.

PRINCIPE DE LA RECHERCHE DES ZONES FISSUREES

a) Mode de calcul.

On suppose que le comportement de la matière est élastique et que le milieu est isotrope et homogène. L'hypothèse de l'élasticité exclut les cas de déformation des roches à comportement visqueux du type de ceux étudiés par BIOT (1965) ou par RAMBERG (1970-1971). Elle est acceptable pour des roches sédimentaires calcaires, à température modeste, et dans la mesure où les déplacements sont grands mais les déformations faibles. Celle de l'isotropie ne paraît pas fondamentale et les conclusions de cette étude seraient probablement peu modifiées par un écart modéré entre les propriétés mécaniques dans les différentes directions. Enfin, l'hypothèse de l'homogénéité (c'est-à-dire la possibilité de décrire l'ensemble de la formation par deux coefficients seulement) paraît ici tout à fait acceptable.

La déformation engendrée à la base du gisement par le pointement de sel se traduit au point de vue mécanique comme la donnée d'une déformation à la frontière du corps. Plusieurs méthodes peuvent être utilisées dont celle du tenseur d'influence, ou celle des éléments finis. On a cependant utilisé la méthode mise au point par H.D. BUI (1968) et les calculs programmés par J. QUIBLIER (1972), méthode qui est particulièrement adaptée à ce problème et qui, utilisant des intégrales littérales, est très économique en temps de calcul sur ordinateur.

Le principe est le suivant : en un certain nombre de points T du mur du réservoir initialement plan, on impose un déplacement $\tilde{u}$ de composantes $(\tilde{u}_1, \tilde{u}_2, \tilde{u}_3)$. Sous l'effet de cette déformation du plan de base, tout le milieu supérieur est déformé et un point M dont ρ est la distance au point T, subit un déplacement $u(u_1, u_2, u_3)$. La théorie de l'élasticité permet d'exprimer u en fonction de $\tilde{u}$:

$$u_i(M) = -\iint_P K_{ij}(M,T)\,\tilde{u}_j(T)\,dS_T$$

où : dS_T est l'élément d'aire du plan de base centré en T

: $K_{ij}(M,T)$ est la matrice de Bashelivshvili qui s'écrit :

$$K_{ij}(M,T) = \frac{\mu}{\pi(\lambda+3\mu)}\left[\delta_{ij} + \frac{3}{2}\frac{\lambda+\mu}{\mu}\frac{\partial\rho}{\partial t_i}\frac{\partial\rho}{\partial t_j}\right]\frac{x^3}{\rho^3}$$

où λ et μ sont les coefficients de Lamé du milieu élastique. La connaissance des déplacements permet par dérivation d'obtenir les déformations d'où les contraintes.

b) Evaluation des déplacements

La forme actuelle $\tilde{u}_T$ du mur du réservoir représente le déplacement total depuis le début de la montée du sel. On peut raisonnablement penser que le déplacement qui s'est produit depuis 10 millions d'années, est une partie proportionnelle de $\tilde{u}_T$, qu'on peut écrire $k\tilde{u}_T$ avec $0<k<1$. En imposant un déplacement $k\tilde{u}_T$ à la base du gisement et en calculant le déplacement des points M du plan actuellement à la cote 500 m on a trouvé que la correspondance entre la forme calculée et la forme mesurée par la prospection sismique était excellente pour k = 0,5 . Ce résultat n'était pas évident a priori, la forme calculée aurait pu être systématiquement plus plate ou plus pointue que la forme mesurée ; cela montre en particulier que les hypothèses faites (élasticité, homogénéité) ne sont pas grossièrement erronées.

c) Evaluation des contraintes

Les contraintes dans le massif sont obtenues par superposition des contraintes naturelles, y compris la pression interstitielle, et des contraintes induites par la déformation tectonique.

Pour les contraintes naturelles, par la présence sous-jacentes du sel, qui est un matériau particulièrement ductile, et par les informations données par la fracturation hydraulique, on peut penser qu'un état initial isotrope est acceptable. Il est cependant prudent pour le calcul de tester plusieurs cas au voisinage d'une répartition hydrostatique des contraintes dues au poids propre.

Pour les contraintes induites par la montée du sel, la connaissance des déformations permet de calculer les contraintes si l'on connaît les caractéristiques élastiques de la matière. Or il s'agit des caractéristiques à long terme et s'il est tout à fait acceptable d'admettre la proportionnalité des contraintes et des déformations, il est par contre beaucoup plus difficile d'évaluer les caractéristiques élastiques au cours d'une déformation très lente : il n'est pas prouvé en effet que les essais à long terme menés en laboratoire en quelques mois fassent appel aux mêmes processus que ceux des déformations très lentes de la nature. En particulier les phénomènes chimiques lents du type solution-cristallisation sous contraintes sont probablement exclus des essais de laboratoire.

Le calcul montre que l'influence d'une variation du coefficient de Poisson n'est pas très importante ; il en résulte que les contraintes liées à la déformation salifère sont connues, au mieux, par des nombres proportionnels.

d) Détermination des zones fissurées

La comparaison en chaque point des contraintes totales (c'est-à-dire de la somme des contraintes à l'état de repos et des contraintes liées à la tectonique salifère) et du critère de rupture permet de définir les zones rompues et aussi de préciser s'il s'agit de fissuration ou de déformations ductiles.

Mais il faut connaître le critère de rupture à long terme ; cette difficulté est de même nature que celle que nous avons rencontrée au paragraphe précédent pour le module d'élasticité à long terme et en fait les deux problèmes sont liés. La détermination de la courbe intrinsèque d'une roche à partir des limites de linéarité (BIENIAWSKI 1967, MORLIER 1972) considérées comme définissant la charge ultime, c'est-à-dire celle dont la durée de vie est infinie, correspond à une expérimentation en laboratoire comportant une comparaison avec les essais de fluage qui appellent les mêmes critiques que celles qui ont été faites plus haut pour le module d'élasticité différé ; tout au plus peut-on espérer que la stabilité à long terme soit à peu près définie par une homothétie dans le temps du critère de rupture et nous avons procédé de la façon suivante (figure 3) :

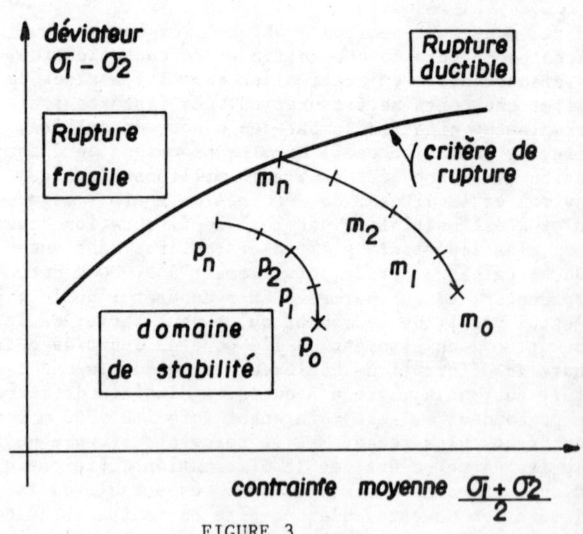

FIGURE 3

un critère de rupture à long terme vraisemblable déterminé à partir d'essais sur des échantillons intacts ayant été obtenu, on le représente dans les axes (contraintes moyenne, déviateur) et on choisit une valeur de module d'élasticité à long terme E suffisament faible pour que les déformations, puis les contraintes calculées en des points M et P , d'après les méthodes exposées en (b) et (c) ci-dessus et sommées avec les contraintes naturelles initiales constantes, correspondent à la stabilité, c'est-à-dire pour que les points représentatifs des contraintes m_o et p_o soient situés à l'intérieur du critère.

Si on augmente progressivement la valeur du module d'élasticité de $n.\Delta E$ les points représentatifs des contraintes m_n et p_n se déplacent progressivement et l'un deux, par exemple m_n , finit par rencontrer le critère : on en déduit que le danger de rupture est plus grand en M qu'en P . La comparaison des contraintes en tout point permet de déterminer le point de rupture commençante dans la couche géologique correspondant au réservoir pétrolier.

On voit ainsi que le rapprochement des deux incertitudes, module d'élasticité à long terme et critère de rupture à long terme, donne finalement un résultat qui est relativement précis. La nature des déformations de rupture est par contre plus difficile à affirmer. Il est vraisemblable que les déformations de rupture sont dutype ductile lorsque la contrainte moyenne est élevée, qu'il se produit des surfaces de glissements lorsque la contrainte moyenne est modérée et enfin, il est à peu près certain que des fissures s'ouvrent lorsqu'une au moins des contraintes de rupture est une traction.

CARTE DE LA FISSURATION DANS LE MASSIF ROCHEUX

La méthode utilisée ci-dessus permet de dire que la rupture est plus probable au point M qu'au point P de la figure 3. En définitive la valeur du module $(E + n.\Delta E)$ permet de définir un certain risque de rupture et tous les points M, M', M''... dont les images m_n, m'_n, m''_n... rencontrent le critère pour la même valeur du module, ne peuvent pas être distingués. Si l'on tient compte des restrictions apportées par la cote dans la formation, c'est-à-dire par exemple que l'on souhaite extraire de l'huile plutôt que de l'eau salée ou du gaz, on aboutit à une carte d'isorisque de fracturation de la formation dont la figure 4 donne un exemple. Les indications de cette carte peuvent être complétées par la nature de la rupture, traction ou compression, et par la localisation des zones de plasticité. La comparaison entre le système des fractures réellement observées et ce type de carte peut aussi se révéler intéressante.

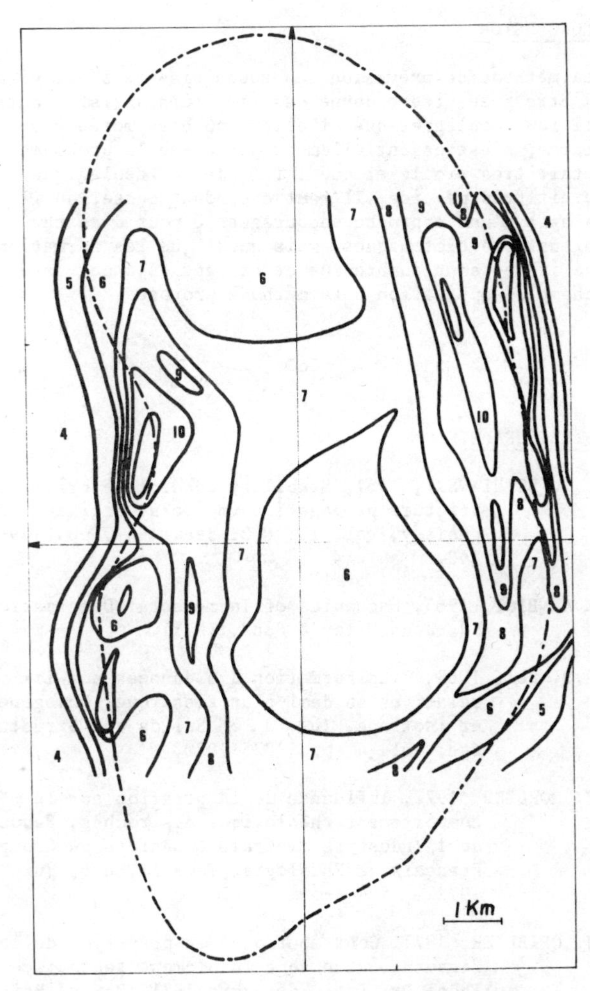

Figure 4 : Carte d'iso-risque de fracturation de la formation.

Chart of formation fracturing iso-risk.

Karte gleicher Bruchgefahrlinien der Schichtung.

La vérification expérimentale de la validité de la théorie qui vient d'être présentée n'a pas encore été faite ; elle consisterait à implanter un puits dans un gisement dans une zone de risque de fissuration maximal ce qui est évidemment une opération coûteuse. Tout ce qu'il est possible de dire pour l'instant c'est, d'une part que le débit des puits installés est classé dans le même ordre que le risque de fissuration calculée, et d'autre part que l'observation directe des carottes provenant des zones de traction a montré une combinaison de fractures subverticales ouvertes recoupant une stylolithisation horizontale : il s'agit là de deux indices non négligeables de la qualité de la prévision de la fissuration par la méthode de calcul proposée.

CONCLUSION

La méthode de prévision des zones fissurées qui vient d'être présentée a donné des résultats satisfaisants. Il faut souligner que si elle a pu être menée à son terme, c'est essentiellement parce que le problème était très simple et que l'information géologique était très précise. Il faut cependant penser qu'il s'agit d'une approche encourageante pour d'autres situations tectoniques, mais aussi que les formations salifères sont nombreuses et offrent déjà un vaste champ d'application à la méthode proposée.

OoO

BIBLIOGRAPHIE

Z.T. BIENIAWSKI, 1967, Stability concept of brittle fracture propagation in rocks. Engineering geology, vol. II, N°3, déc. 1967, pp. 149-162.

M.A. BIOT, 1965, Mechanics of Incremental Deformations Ed. John Wiley & Sons, (N.Y).

H.D. BUI, 1968, Transformation des données aux limites relatives au demi-plan élastique, homogène et isotrope. Int. J. of Solids and Structures, vol. 4, pp. 1025-1030.

P. MORLIER, 1972, Influence de la pression sur le comportement rhéologique des roches. Revue de l'Industrie Minérale : Cahiers du Groupe Français de Rhéologie, Tome II, n°6, juin 1972.

J. QUIBLIER, 1971, Contribution à la prévision de la fissuration en zone faiblement tectonisée. Thèse Dr. Ing., décembre 1971, Paris, Editions Technip.

H. RAMBERG, 1969, Experimental and Theoretical Study of Salt-Dome Evolution. Third Symposium on Salt, Tome I, pp. 261-270.

H. RAMBERG, 1970-1971, Folding of Laterally compressed Multilayers in the Field of Gravity. In: Physics of the Earth and Planetary Interiors, 2, pp. 203-232, juin 1970, et 4, pp. 83-120, février 1971.

GÉOMETRIE DES PLIS ET EFFORTS TECTONIQUES DANS LES MASSIFS ROCHEUX

FOLD GEOMETRY AND TECTONIC PRESSURE IN ROCK MASSES

GEOMETRIE DER FALTEN UND TECTONISCHEN BEANSPRUCHUNGEN IM FELSGEBIRGE

M. A. HACAR

Dr. Ing. C.C.P., Lic. C.E., C.F.

Mi. F. BOLLO

Ing. C. C. P.

Spain

ésumé: Le but de cette publication est le développement des applications géologiques de la éomorphometrie avec deux aspects principaux:
- Le traitement de grandes quantités de données topographiques du point de vue géologique.
- L'étude et dépouillement géologique structural des données des sondages.

es premières formules presentées sont destinées à obtenir la pente maximale PM pour chaque oint, ainsi que la pente moyenne Pm. dans la zone considerée. Par la suite on étudie le paraboloide osculateur à la surface en chaque point et le coefficient de gauchage Gs. 'histogramme de Gs. renseigne sur le degré de fracturation, et le tracé des points auxquels s=0 sur les directions des axes de plissement. La condition de thalweg T, peut etre aisement éfinie. Le tracé des points à T=0 permet de dessiner les lignes d'eau, soit superficielle, oit souterraine, lors du contact avec une couche imperméable. L'histogramme de log abs (1/T) ermet dévaluer la régularité de la surface. Ce factuer est intéressant lors de l'évaluation ur les directions des efforts tectoniques et l'importance relative de leurs differentes amilles.

ummary: The aim of this publication is the development of the geomorphometric geological pplication in two main ways:
- The geological treatment of big amounts of topographical data.
- The study and geological structural analysis of the sounding data.

he first formules are appointed to get the maximal slope PM for every point and also the verage slope in the same zone. Afterwards it is studied the equivalent paraboloid to the urface in every point and the warping coefficient Gs. he Gs hystogramme informs about the fracturation degree and the outlined points when Gs=0 n the directions of the fold axis. The thalweg condition is easily defined. The outlined oints when T=0 allow to draw the lines of shallow or deep water when in contact with an npervious layer. The log abs (1/T) hystogramme allows to evaluate the surface regularity. his point is interesting when doing the evaluation of the hydrological importance of an npervious layer. Finally the study of the curvatures informs about the directions of the ectonical efforts and the relation between the several families.

usammenfassung: Der Zweck dieser Veroeffentlichung ist die Entwicklung der geologischen nwendungen der Geomorphometrie mit zwei prinzipiellen Gesichtspunkten:
- Die Behandlung grosser Anzahl von topographischen Daten vom geologischen Gesichtspunkt aus.
- Die strukturell geologische Studie der Bohrungsdaten.

ie erstgenannten Formeln dienen zur Erlangung der groessten Abhaenge in jedem Punkt PM, owie die Durchschnittsabhaenge in der bedachten Zone Pm. Als naechstes studiert man den leichwertigen Parraboloid zu der Oberflaeche in jedem Punkt und den Verbiegungskoeffizient s. Das Hystogramm von Gs informiert uns ueber den Berechungsgrad und den Verlauf der Punkte s=0 ueber die Richtungen der Faltenachsen. Die Kondition Thalweg T definiert man leicht. ie Zeichnung der Punkte, in welchen T = 0, erlaubt die Wasserrinnen zu zeichnen, die sich n der Oberflaeche der unterirdisch ueber einer undurchdringlichen Schicht befinden. Das ystogramm von log abs (1/T) laesst die Regelmaessigkeit an der Oberflaeche messen. Dieser aktor ist fuer die Schaetzung der hidrologischen Bedeutung einer Quelle wichtig. Die Studie er Kruemmung informiert uns ueber die Richtungen der tektonischen Beanspruchung und entprechenden Bedeutung.

1 INTRODUCTION

La géomorphométrie s'occupe de l'étude mathématique-statistique du relief. Constitue une science annexe a la géomorphologie. La présente étude cherche a établir un rapport entre les résultats géomorphométriques et les caractéristiques géologiques.
D'autres applications de cette même science présentent un grand intérêt:
- L'étude des <u>pentes</u> et des <u>pentes moyennes</u> (coefficient de pente) qui a des applications en agriculture (classement des zones pour irrigation, culture locale ou terrains forestiers).
- Préparation d'histogrammes d'altitudes et pentes qui permettent des interprétations concernant les cycles d'érosion, définition des types de relief, etc.
- Collaboration dans les études d'écoulement dans les bassins (hydrologie).
  L'écoulement dépend du "coefficient de pente moyenne", P_m et des histogrammes d'altitudes et pentes.
- En Géologie Structurale l'étude des pendages et des mouvements des plis (glissements gravitatoires, charriages) peut etre utilement completée par des déterminations des caractéristiques concernant courbures et gauchage. Ces données facilitent les déductions concernant les efforts tectoniques qui ont conformé les couches géologiques.

La méthode analytique proposée peut etre réalisée directement a partir des valeurs des coordonées topographiques cartessiennes x,y,z si les valeurs peuvent etre introduits en bande magnetique par l'appareillage de restitution photogrammétrique. D'autres moyens d'entrée en ordinateur existent dans le cas ou une $z=f(x,y)$ est connue, ou bien, si les données peuvent etre passées par une prise digitale discrète.
Un <u>annexe</u> rappelle l'<u>essentiel des bases géométriques</u> indispensables pour la compréhension du texte. Il donne les formules mathématiques approximatives pour des calculs simplifiés rapides sans ordinateur.

2 BASES DE L'ETUDE

La géomorphométrie d'une zone doit etre analysée par éléments à limite ponctuelle (differentiels). La superficie à étudier se trouve définie assez souvent par une maille soit orthogonale (carrée) ou d'autre configuration.
Dans l'annexe on considère les deux cas et on arrive à définir les situations caractéristiques (par z vertical).
- Elément superficiel au-dessus du plan tangent: CONCAVITE
- Elément superficiel au-dessous du plan tangent: CONVEXITE
- Elément superficiel constituant un maximum SOMMET
- Elément superficiel constituant un minimum FOND DE DEPRESSION
- Elément superficiel tangent à un plan horizontal passant des deux côtés: COL

Le cas de <u>plan tangent suivant une droite</u> inclue dans la supface consideré, correspon à une surface développable. Elle peut être du type conique ou cylindrique (sommet a l'infini). Ce cas est intéressant dans la pratique car une couche plissée en surface développable n'a subi que des flexions.

Le cas général d'une <u>surface gauche</u> est au si intéressant car la déformation qui a c crée la courbure a donné lieu à une depens énergetique liée à cette courbure. L'étude des énergies mises en oeuvre par la tectonique peut apporter des données intéressantes pour la Géodynamique.

Comme cas caractéristiques en géomorphométrie on peut considérer (1) avec les symboles de la note:

- <u>Point elliptique:</u>
  Superfieie à un seul coté du plan tangen critère $r_0 t_0 - s_0^2 > 0$
  - CONCAVE si r_0 ou $t_0 > 0$;SOMMET si $p_0 = q$
  - CONVEXE si r_0 et $t_0 < 0$;FOND si $p_0 = q_0 =$

- <u>Point hyperbolique:</u>
  Superficie des deux cotés du plan tange critére $r_0 t_0 - s_0^2 < 0$
  COL pour plan tangent horizontal($p_0 = q_0$

- <u>Point parabolique:</u>
  Superficie <u>développable</u> critère $r_0 t_0 - s_0^2$ due a des mouvements ou seulement intervient la flexion.
  Pour des plissements géologiques il est intéressant de differentier plis coniqu et cylindriques.
  CYLINDRE:
  La direction des génératrices du cylind peuvent être définies théoriquement à p tir de deux points. Dans la pratique (v Annexe) on part d'un certain nombre de points et on ajuste les résultats deux par deux.
  CONE:
  La définition du sommet du cône (foyer [illegible]clinal) se fait par recherche du poin d'intersection de trois plans tangents. (voir Annexe)
  On peut définir comme COEFFICIENT DE GA CHAGE le valeur $r_0 t_0 - s_0^2$ qui s'annulle pour le point parabolique.

- <u>Thalweg</u>: La condition caractéristique d thalweg est la suivante: Points auxquel le plan osculateur de au moins une de s lignes de courbure est verticale.

---

(1) - Mathématiquement définis par $r_0 t_0 - s_0^2 \gtrless 0$ lorsque le paraboloide osculateur à la superfieie est:

$z = z_0 + p_0 x + q_0 y +$
$1/2 \quad (r_0 x^2 + 2 s_0 xy + t_0 y^2)$ et le plan tangent $z = z_0 + p_0 x + q_0 y$

Rappelons:

$$z = f(x,y) \qquad \partial z/\partial x = p \qquad \partial z/\partial y = q$$

$$\partial z/\partial x^2 = r \qquad \partial z/\partial y^2 = s \qquad \partial z/\partial x \partial y = t$$

Cela veut dire que la projection horizontale de la perpendiculaire au plan tangent se confond avec la tangente à une de ses lignes de courbure fondamentale, ce qui mathématiquement implie:

$$pq(1+p^2+q^2)r+(q^2(1+q^2)-p^2(1+p^2))s-pq(1+p^2+q^2)t + T = 0$$

C'est assez simple de programmer le dessin des points auxquels cette condition est satisfaite.

3 CONSIDERATIONS ET RESULTATS PRATIQUES

Dans les superficies topographiques réelles, définies par les points d'une maille ou réseau, on peut obtenir facilement des valeurs et diagrammes de caractère tridimensionnel des diverses caractéristiques:

a) Pentes maxima pour chaque point PM
b) Coefficient de pente moyenne PM
c) Coefficient de gauchage Gs
d) Foyers des plissements de type péri-clinal
e) Directions des plissements cylindriques
f) Détermination des thalweg

Ces caractéristiques permettront le traitement mathématique de nombreux problèmes pratiques tel qu'indiqué sur la partie 1.

Pour mieux fixer les idées nous considérons par la suite un exemple pratique (fig.1)

fig. 1 Représentation tridimensionelle des paramètres étudiés.

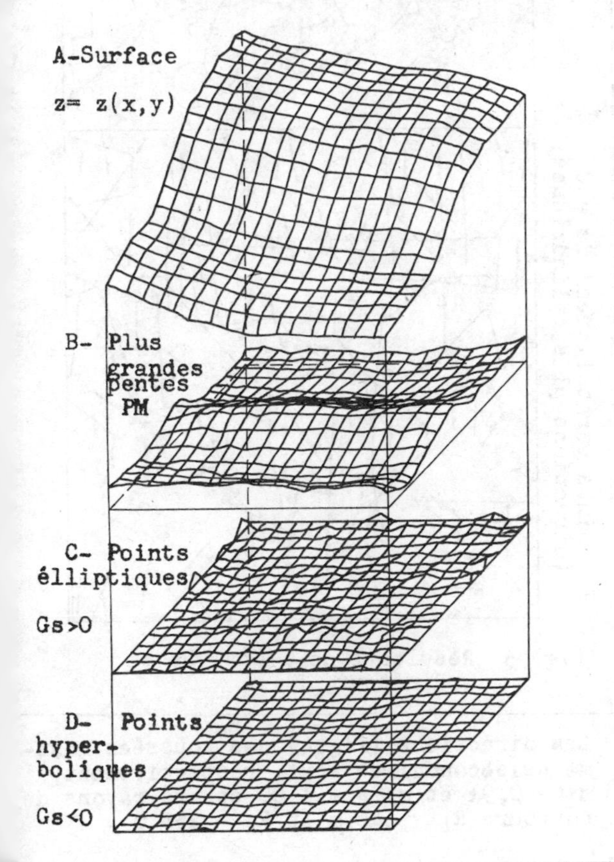

La représentation tridimensionelle supérieure (A) est le relief original, crée par des soulevements et des plissements en général non développables.
Le programme d'interprétation estime les derivées partielles de premier et second ordre dans chaque point et dessine sous la surface originelle:

(B) Les pentes maximales a chaque point
(C) Les valeurs du coefficient de gauchage pour les points elliptiques.
(D) Les valeurs du coefficient de gauchage pour les points hyperboliques.

On apprécie que la plupart des points sont elliptiques, ce qui veut dire que la surface n'est pas développable en général et correspond a un soulevement et un plissement complexe. A cause de ça, il n'y a pas d'intérêt à chercher des foyers.
Par contre, les directions des plissements cylindriques peuvent etre visualisées par les points de valeur 0 dans le coefficient de gauchage (fig. 5-E).
Nous n'allons pas insister ici sur l'interprétation des histogrammes de pentes ou altitudes, car ils sont déjà habituellement utilisés.
Les histogrammes du coefficient de gauchage et du coefficient de thalweg ou valeur de l'expression qui les define ont aussi d'intéressantes proprietés:

- Le premier nous define la proportion des points hyperboliques et elliptiques et leur structure. Cette proportion mesure le degré de cassement des couches, maximale lorsque les points sont tous hyperboliques. (Voir fig. 2 et 1C, 1D).

fig. 2 Histogramme du coefficient de gauchage G_s.

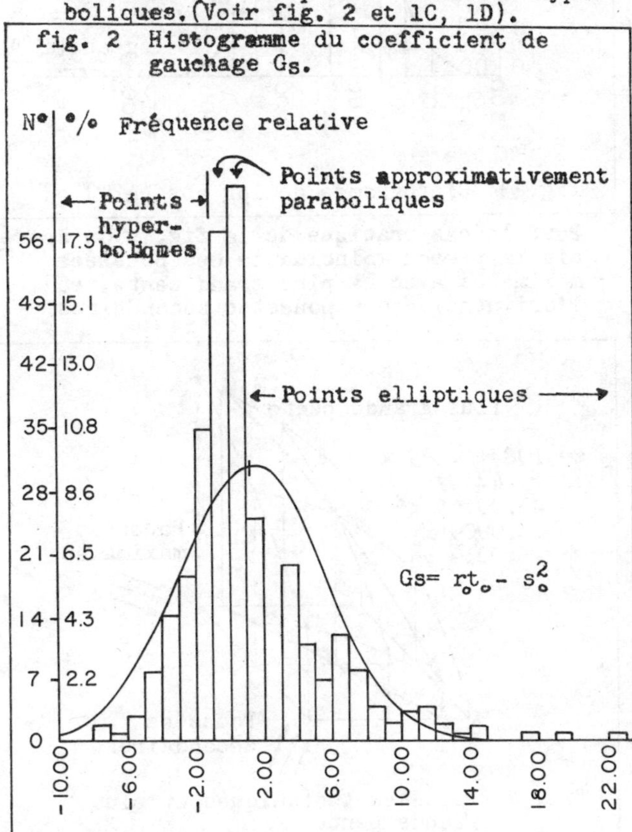

- Le deuxième nous renseigne sur la proportion des points thalweg par rapport au total. Si on applie l'operateur log abs 1/T ou T est l'expression de thalweg et on représente l'histogramme, on appreice qu'il y a assez de points eloignés du reste (voir flèche fig.3). Cela veut dire le relief est complexe; cette proportion constitue un coefficient de complexité structurale qui peut se relationer avec l'énergie dépensée lors des plissements, soulevements et cassements.
- Etude des courbures: Les formules de l'Annexe expriment le rayon de courbure d'une section normale en fonction de l'angle $m = tg\alpha = dy/dx$. Le maximum et minimum de cette courbure nous renseignent sur les directions des poussées tectoniques fondamentales et sécondaires.

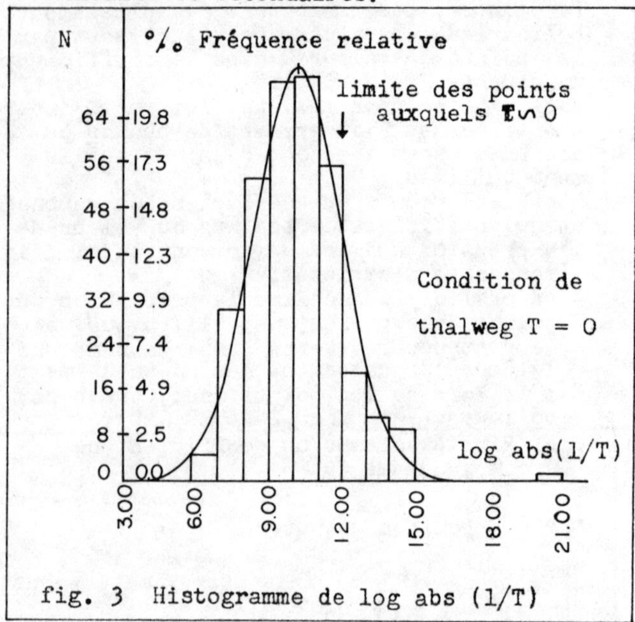

fig. 3 Histogramme de log abs (1/T)

Pour le cas pratique de la fig. 4 on apprécie la presque coïncidance des poussées maximales avec la plus grand pente, et l'orientation des poussées sécondaires.

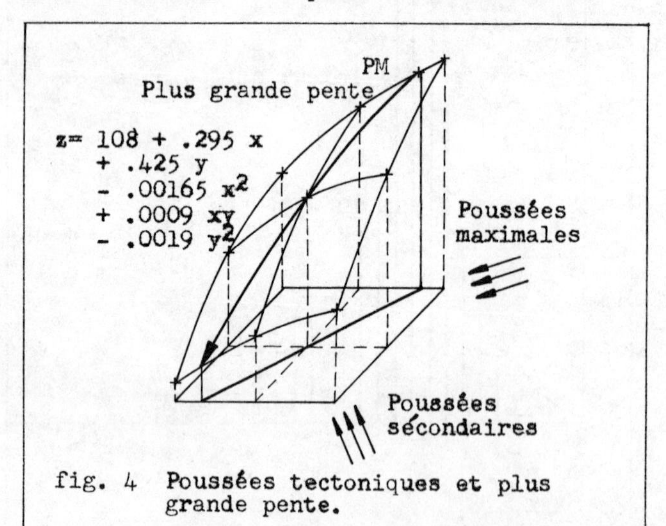

fig. 4 Poussées tectoniques et plus grande pente.

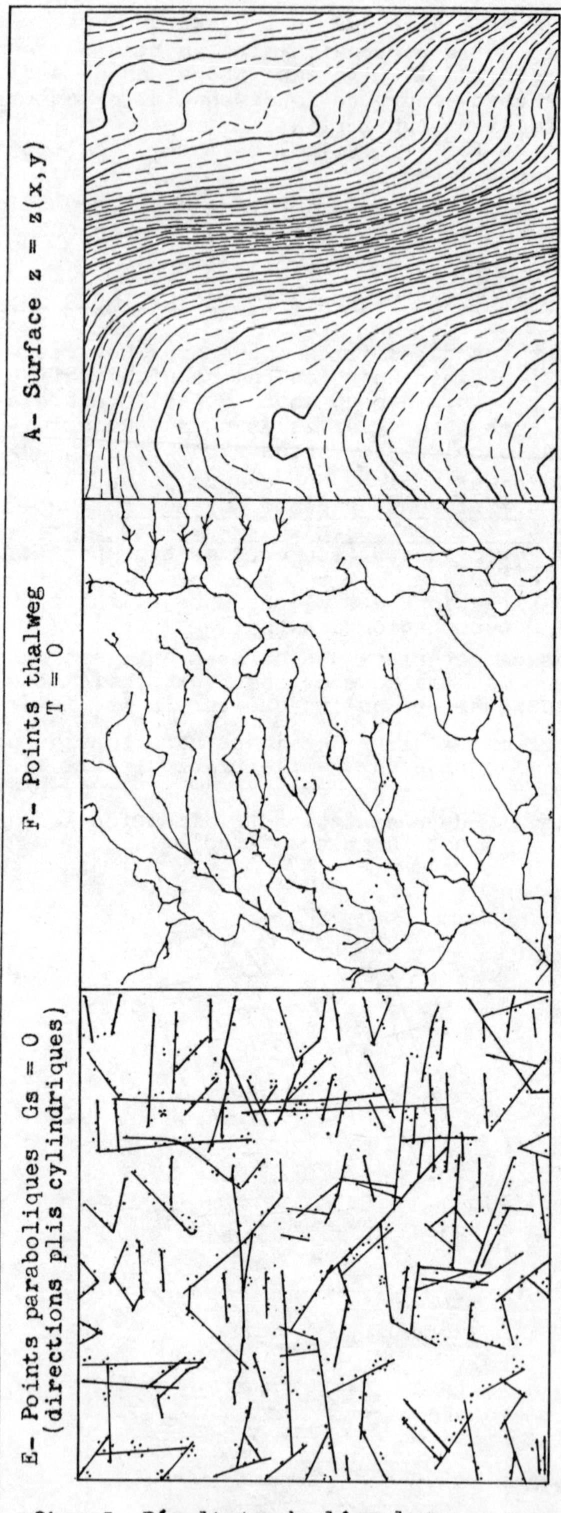

fig. 5 Résultats de l'analyse en ordinateur.

Les directions (fig.4) des poussées maximales, sécondaires sont, respectivement, $m_1 = 0{,}91$ et $m_2 = -1{,}00$ et les rayons de courbure $R_1 = 546$ m et $R_2 = 258$ m .

ANNEXE

Considérations géométriques basiques

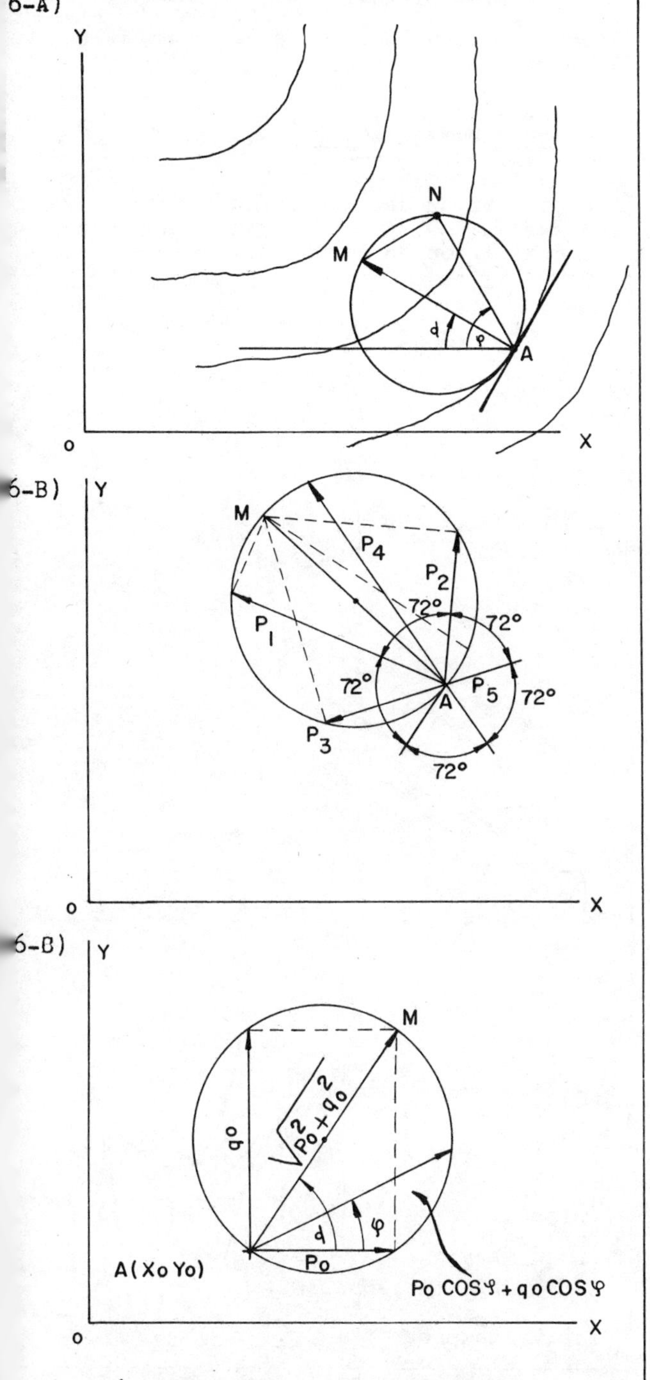

fig. 6 Plus grande pente PM dans un point

Si les pentes P_1 et P_2 en deux directions perpendiculaires sont connues dans un point de la superficie topographique et donc sur le plan tangent à la surface en ce point, la plus grande pente PM s'exprime: (fig.6A)

$$PM = \sqrt{P_1^2 + P_2^2}$$

Nous pouvons généraliser cette propieté: Soit n directions qui forment entre elles des angles égaux, la pente maximale est déterminée par

$$PM = \sqrt{2(P_1^2 + P_2^2 + \ldots\ldots + P_n^2)/n} \quad (1)$$

En effet, soit α l'angle que forme la normale a la courbe de niveau avec une direction n quelconque, la radical est égal à:(fig. 6B)

$$\frac{2}{n}\sum_1^n P_M^2 \cos^2\left(\alpha + \frac{360}{n}\right) =$$

$$= \frac{2PM^2}{n}\left(\cos^2\alpha \sum_1^n \cos^2\frac{360}{n} + \sin^2\alpha \cdot \sum_1^n \sin^2\frac{360}{n} - \frac{1}{2}\sin 2\alpha \sum_1^n \sin\frac{720}{n}\right)$$

mais pour $n > 2$ $\sum_1^n \cos^2\frac{360}{n} = \sum_1^n \sin^2\frac{360}{n} = \frac{n}{2}$

et $\sum_1^n \sin\frac{720}{n} = 0$ donc (1).

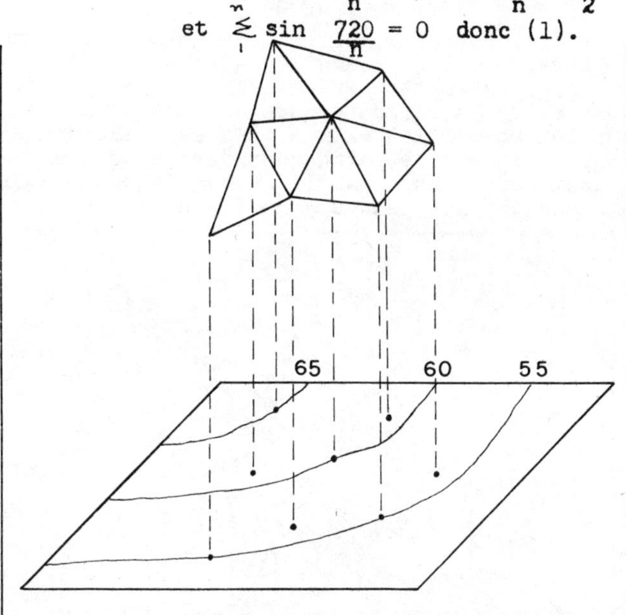

fig. 7 Surface topographique définie par une maille arbitraire

La plus grand pente(maximale)est, en direction et magnitude, le gradient de Z et sa projection sur le plan XOY forme un angle φ avec l'axe OX tel que $\operatorname{tg}\varphi = \frac{q_o}{p_o}$

La pente correspondante a une direction est determiné par

$$p = p_o \cos\varphi + q_o \operatorname{sen}\varphi \quad \text{(fig. 6C)}$$

Si la surface topographique est définie par une maille arbitraire, le coefficient d'inclination ou le coefficient de la pente moyenne P_m sera la moyenne pondérée des pentes moyennes dans les triangles élémentaires

$$P_m = \frac{P_1 S_1 + \ldots\ldots\ldots\ldots + P_n S_n}{S_1 + \ldots\ldots\ldots\ldots S_n} \quad \text{(fig.7)}$$

Dans le cas ou la surface est définie par des mailles rectangulaires de cotés a, les plus grandes pentes $\sqrt{(p_o^2 + q_o^2)}$ peuvent etre calculées

$$PM = \sqrt{((Z(i+1)-Z(i-1))^2+(Z(j+1)-Z(j-1))^2)}/2a$$

$$P_m = \frac{\sum_1^n PM\ (\ i(n)\ ,\ j(n)\ )}{n}$$

On peut aussi estimer le coefficient P_m a partir d'un plan topographique existant. Soit 1 la longeur des courbes de niveau sur l'aire considerée, S sa surface et h l'équidistance entre les courbes de niveau

$$P_m = \overline{PM} = h \textstyle\sum 1/s$$

Si la surface Z=Z(x,y) est analytique, le coefficient P_m sera:

$$P_m = \frac{\iint \sqrt{(p^2+q^2)}\ d_x\ d_y}{\iint d_x\ d_y}$$

En fin, pour une maille triangulaire irregulière, la plus grande pente pour chaque triangle, est obtenu graphiquement comme le diamètre de la circonférence qui passe par le point et par les extremitées des vecteurs qui joignent le point consideré avec les deux autres du triangle et magnitudes proportionelles aux pentes dans chaque direction.

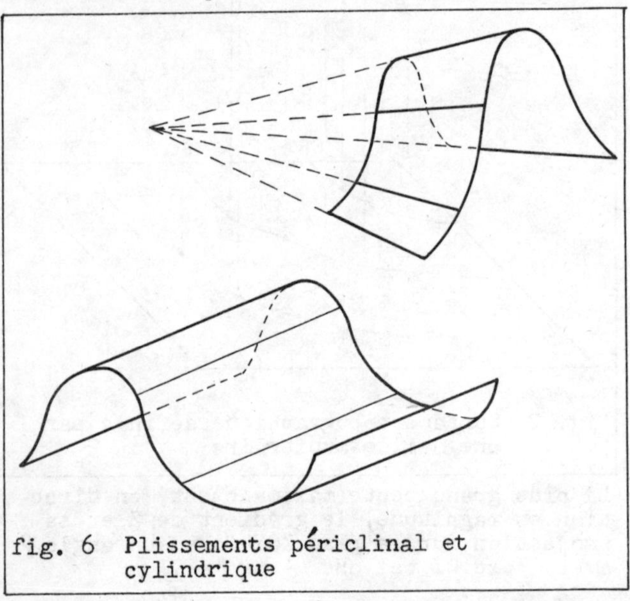

fig. 6 Plissements périclinal et cylindrique

Analytiquement, si l'équation du plan défini par les trois points est:

$$\frac{x}{a} + \frac{y}{b} + \frac{z}{c} = 1$$

on obtient $\quad p = c\sqrt{\frac{1}{a^2} + \frac{1}{b^2}}$

Directions d'un plissement cylindrique:

Soit $\quad Z = az \qquad Y = bz$

Si on impose que la normale au plan tangent soit normale a cette droite et en prenant des paires de points, on aura à resoudre:

$$ap_1 + bq_1 = 1$$

$$ap_2 + bq_2 = 1$$

Foyer d'un plissement conique

Le plan tangent contient le point. Si on prend les points, trois a trois

$$z_o - z_i = pi(x_o - x_i) + q_i\ (y_o - y_i)$$

Rayon de courbure d'une section normale en fonction de $m = \frac{dy}{dx} = tg\varphi$

$$R = \frac{1+p^2+2pqm+(1+q^2)\ m^2}{r + 2s\cdot m + tm^2}\sqrt{1 + p^2 + q^2}$$

Les directions des angles φ qui forment avec les axes OX, OY les projections des tangentes aux lignes de courbure, sont définie

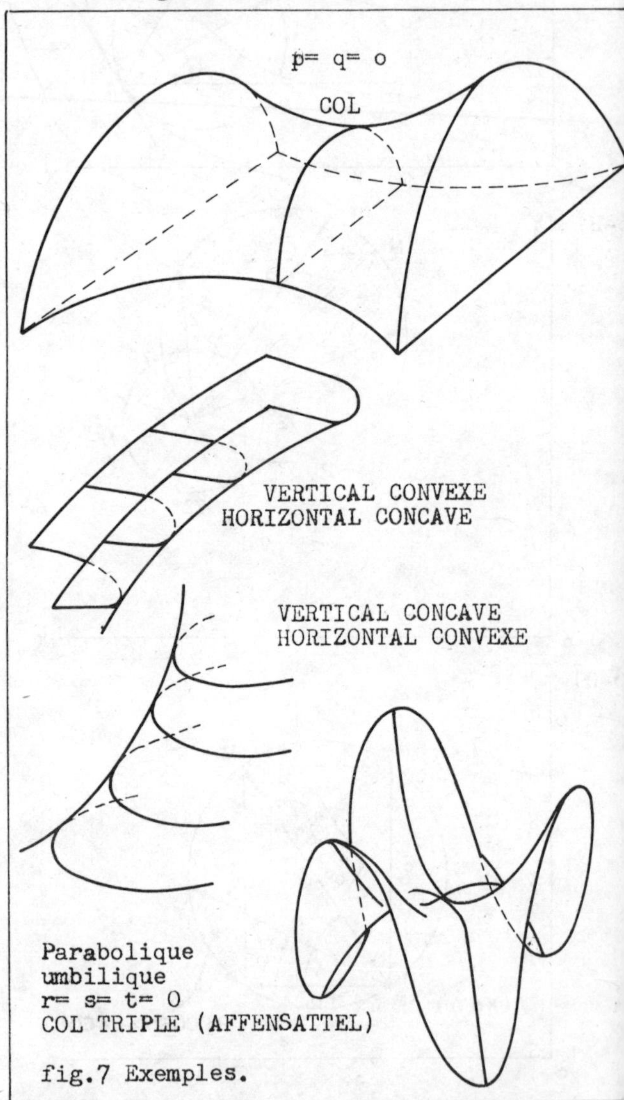

fig.7 Exemples.

par ses tangentes m_1, m_2 qui satisfaisent l'equation:

$$((1 + q^2)\ s - pqt)\ m^2 + (r(1 + q^2) - t(1+p^2)\ \cdot m + pqr - (1 + p^2)\ s = 0$$

TIEFLIEGENDE, OBERFLÄCHENPARALLELE KLÜFTE

DEEP-SEATED JOINTS PARALLEL TO THE SURFACE WALL OF A ROCK MASS

DIACLASES PARALLÈLES À LA SURFACE, SITUÉES À UNE PROFONDEUR RELATIVEMENT GRANDE

Georg HORNINGER
Professor

Wien, Austria

ZUSAMMENFASSUNG

In einem alten Luftschutz-Stollensystem im Konglomerat des Mönchsbergs in Salzburg wurden als einzige Klüfte zwei steile Zerrklüfte angetroffen. Die eine, 50 m hinter der Außenwand, konnte auf 42 m Länge verfolgt werden, die andere, 60 m hinter der Außenwand, auf 145 m . Beide streichen parallel zur ehemaligen Felswand. Obwohl tatsächlich oberflächenparallel, fügen sie sich doch nicht in das Konzept der "oberflächenparallelen Klüfte" im Sinne von exfoliation joints. Daher paßt die für letztere derzeit allgemein angenommene Erklärung ihrer Entstehung durch Entspannung zur freien Oberfläche nicht auf jene Klüfte im Stollensystem. Nach den örtlichen Verhältnissen versprechen einerseits ein Erklärungsversuch von R.WOLTERS, der auf der Auswirkung tiefreichenden Frostes im ehemaligen Periglazialbereich fußt, anderseits Vorstellungen von H.CRAMMER, zur Lösung des Problems zu führen. CRAMMER nahm an, daß Außenzonen des Konglomerats auf einer leicht verformbaren Unterlage bei deren Ausweichen mitgezerrt wurden.

RESUME

Dans un système de cavernes dans les conglomérats du Mönchsberg à Salzbourg, les seules diaclases que l'on ait trouvées sont deux diaclases de traction raides. L'une d'elles, située à 50 m derrière la paroi extérieure a pu être suivie sur 42 m, l'autre, qui se trouve à 60 m derrière la paroi extérieure, sur 145 m. Les deux ont une direction parallèle à la paroi rocheuse. Donc, quoique parallèles à la surface, elles n'entrent pas dans la conception des diaclases parallèles à la surface dans le sens des "exfoliation joints". Pour cette raison l'explication généralement adoptée à présent, qui considère leur formation comme conséquence d'une relaxation vers une surface libre,n'est pas valable pour les diaclases dans ce système de tunnels. Suivant les conditions locales, c'est d'une part l'explication tentée par R.WOLTERS, basée sur l'action profonde de la gelée dans les masses rocheuses d'une région periglaciale, et d'autre part les idées de H.CRAMMER qui promettent le plus d'aboutir à une solution du problème. CRAMMER suppose que les zones extérieures des conglomérats sont entraînées sur leur substratum assez déformable lors de son déplacement en cédant au poids du rocher sujacent.

SUMMARY

Two steeply dipping tension joints virtually are the sole joints in a system of galleries, built as air-raid shelters in the Mönchsberg conglomerate ("nagelfluh"),Salzburg. The one joint, at 50 metres' distance from the surface, is exposed over 42 m. length, and the other one at 60 m. distance from the surface wall, extends over 145 m. Both joints strike exactly parallel to the steep surface wall of the Mönchsberg. Notwithstanding this geometrical fact, they do not fit in the narrow meaning of the German technical term of "oberflächenparallele Klüfte" (sheeting, exfoliation). By that, the widely adopted concept of stress relief as a main cause of exfoliation does not explain those deep-seated cracks. To judge from local conditions,R.WOLTERS' assumption, and H.CRAMMER's ideas seem promising to solve this problem. The former tries to explain exfoliation by deep reaching frost under periglacial conditions. The latter scientist points to the drag on surficial parts of a rock mass exerted by lateral flow of an easily deformable underlying rock as a possible cause of cracking parallel to the surface wall.

EINLEITUNG

Unter den Luftschutzstollenanlagen, die in der Stadt Salzburg während des Zweiten Weltkriegs im Mönchsberg und im Kapuzinerberg angelegt wurden, verdienen die Kavernen im Südost-Bereich des Mönchsbergs wegen eines felsmechanischen Problems Interesse. Diese Kavernen liegen im Abschnitt zwischen dem Friedhof St.Peter und dem Alten Festspielhaus. Vgl.Abbildung 1.

Das Stollensystem bildet ein in einer Ebene angelegtes Netz rechtwinklig zueinander angeordneter Tunnel auf Straßenniveau. Bergeinwärts reicht die Anlage etwa 80 m weit gegen WSW. Die Felsüberlagerung über Firste beträgt zwischen 22 und 39 Meter. Diese

Stollen liegen zur Gänze in der "Salzburger Nagelfluh", einem sandig-mergelig gebundenen, weichen Konglomerat. Es entstand als eine nach WSW bis WNW einfallende Deltaschüttung in einen See des Mindel-Riß-Interglazials. Die Nagelfluh ist also geologisch sehr jung. Daher ist sie - zumindest in dem in Rede

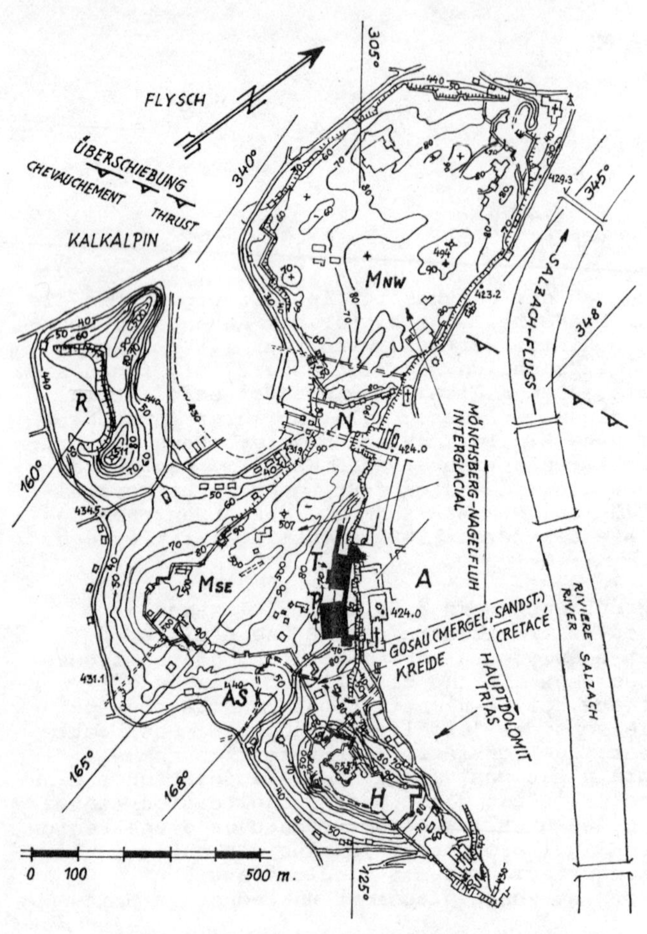

A — Altstadt von Salzburg – La cité de Salzbourg – Salzburg City.

AS — Südlicher Almkanal- Wasserstollen durch den Mönchsberg. Galérie du sud traversant le Mönchsberg. Part de l'"Almkanal", un ancien chenal pour l'adduction d'eau à la cité. "Almkanal" water supply system. Southern tunnel through the Mönchsberg.

N — Neutor, Straßentunnel – N., tunnel routier – N., road tunnel.

R — Rainberg. H — Hohensalzburg.

MSE — Mönchsberg-Südostteil—M., partie sudest—M., southeastern p.

MNW — Mönchsberg-Nordwestteil—M., partie nordouest—M., northwestern p.

345°/165° — Auffallende Achsrichtungen in der Morphologie d. Mö.-Plateaus (nach Stereo-Luftbildern). Directions morphologiques prononcées au plateau du Mönchsberg. (Stereo-photos aériennes). Conspicuous linear features of the Mönchsberg. (Air photos).

P — Stollen Tunnels St. Peter — T — Stollen Tunnels Toscaninihof

ABBILDUNG 1 · FIGURE 1 · FIGURE 1

ÜBERSICHT, GEOLOGISCHE GRUNDLAGEN. PLAN D'ENSEMBLE, SITUATION GEOLOGIQUE GENERALE. LAYOUT, ESSENTIAL GEOLOGICAL FEATURES.

stehenden Südabschnitt des Mönchsbergs - noch keinen tektonischen Beanspruchungen ausgesetzt gewesen (Kieslinger, 1972).

Die nächstgelegene tektonische Grenze ist die Linie, längs der das Kalkalpin nach N auf den Flysch aufgeschoben ist. Sie streicht etwa 600 m weiter nordwestlich, im Untergrund verborgen unter der Nordhälfte des Mönchsbergs durch. Selbst wenn sich an dieser tektonischen Grenze noch bis in die Gegenwart Nachbewegungen ereignet haben sollten, haben sie schon an der Nagelfluh im Neutor, einem großquerschnittigen, unausgekleideten Tunnel durch den Mönchsberg, auf halber Strecke zwischen jener Grenze und dem Stollensystem, keine Spuren mehr hinterlassen. Umso weniger ist der Stollenbereich davon beeinflußt worden.

In letzter Zeit haben Bohrergebnisse die ältere Annahme bestätigt, daß die Mönchsberg-Nagelfluh einer unruhig gestalteten, wohl periglazial überformten Landoberfläche seicht aufruht. Die Grenzfläche ist im grossen und ganzen nicht tiefer als wenige dutzend Meter unter dem Straßenniveau der Stadt zum Teil auch noch seichter anzusetzen.

Die Schichtung der Deltaschotter hat sich im ganzen Mönchsberg als ausgeprägtes Lagengefüge mit Schichtstärken zwischen 5 cm und etwa 1 1/2 m erhalten. Sie bewirkt eine ziemlich einheitlich orientierte Anisotropie der Felsmasse. Wegen des erwähnten Wegfalles tektonischer Beanspruchung der Nagelfluh blieb, abgesehen von einer Anzahl oberflächennaher, wandparalleler Klüfte in den äusseren 15 bis 20 m, die Bildung von Kluftschnitten im Fels des Mönchsbergs auf einige wenige Bereiche beschränkt. Die erwähnten oberflächennahen, zu den Wänden parallelen Klüfte sind am Mönchsberg kräftig entwickelt. Sie haben in der Altstadt von Salzburg in vergangenen Jahrhunderten zu folgenschweren Bergstürzen Anlaß gegeben. Gerade an den Wänden vor dem hier besprochenen Stollensystem fehlen aber solche Klüfte; sehr wahrscheinlich deshalb, weil hier im 17. Jahrhundert die natürliche, ursprüngliche Wand bis zu 20 m zurückverlegt wurde (Kieslinger, 1972).

Als wesentliche Ursache für das Zustandekommen "oberflächenparalleler Klüfte" klassischer Art, wie den eben erwähnten (exfoliation joints), werden heute von der Mehrzahl der Forscher Entspannungsvorgänge in der äußersten Zone des Gesteins angesehen (Bradley, 1963, Brunner-Scheidegger, 1973, Kieslinger, 1950, Müller, 1962). Dieser Art von Klüften werden allgemein folgende Eigenheiten als charakteristisch und entstehungsbedingt zugeschrieben:

- Sie zeigen die Merkmale von Zugrissen.
- Sie treten vorwiegend in sonst ausgesprochen kluftarmen Bereichen eines Felskörpers auf.
- Ihre Intensität, beurteilt nach der Spaltweite, nimmt von der Oberfläche gegen das

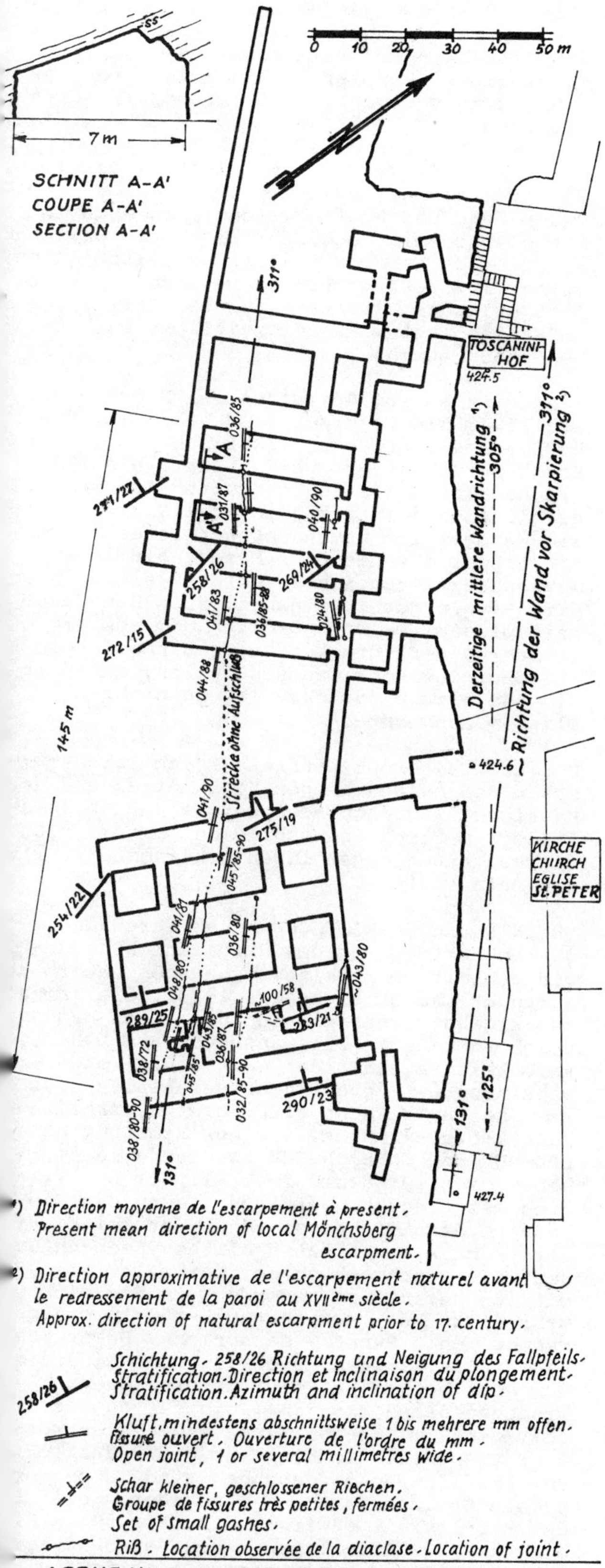

¹) Direction moyenne de l'escarpement à present.
Present mean direction of local Mönchsberg escarpment.

²) Direction approximative de l'escarpement naturel avant le redressement de la paroi au XVIIème siècle.
Approx. direction of natural escarpment prior to 17. century.

258/26 Schichtung. 258/26 Richtung und Neigung des Fallpfeils. Stratification. Direction et inclinaison du plongement. Stratification. Azimuth and inclination of dip.

Kluft, mindestens abschnittsweise 1 bis mehrere mm offen. Fissure ouvert. Ouverture de l'ordre du mm. Open joint, 1 or several millimetres wide.

Schar kleiner, geschlossener Rißchen. Groupe de fissures très petites, fermées. Set of small gashes.

Riß. Location observée de la diaclase. Location of joint.

ABBILDUNG 2 / FIGURE 2 / FIGURE 2
STOLLENANLAGE ST. PETER - DIE KLÜFTE
Les GALÉRIES et les diaclases / JOINTING in TUNNELS

Berginnere ab.

- Der Abstand von Kluft zu Kluft wächst mit zunehmender Entfernung ab Außenfläche.
- Die Aufspaltungen reichen etwa 20, höchstens aber 50 m unter die Felsoberfläche.

Man verbindet derzeit mit dem eng gefaßten deutschen Fachausdruck "oberflächenparallele Klüfte" häufig von vornherein die Vorstellung, daß die betreffenden Klüfte gleiche Entstehungsursache haben.

DIE ISOLIERT AUFTRETENDEN RISSE PARALLEL ZUR OBERFLÄCHE

In dem in Rede stehenden Stollensystem von St.Peter treten nun - von einigen unbedeutenden, kurzen Rißchen abgesehen - als einzige Klüfte einige wenige zueinander parallele, lange Steilklüfte auf. Sie laufen eindeutig in derselben Richtung wie die äussere Bergwand und sind Zerrklüfte. Darüber hinaus aber fehlen ihnen wesentliche Merkmale, die sie aufweisen sollten, um den Exfoliationsklüften zugezählt werden zu können. Die bedeutendste dieser Trennfugen, die über 145 m Gesamtlänge verfolgt werden kann, liegt 60 m weit im Berge drinnen. Stellenweise ist sie in 2 Paralleläste aufgespalten. Ein 42 m langer Parallelriß dazu verläuft in 50 m Abstand von der Oberfläche. In den äußeren 50 m findet man nur 3 kurze, fast oder ganz geschlossene Risse von je einigen wenigen Metern Länge, die man zu keinem geschlossenen Zug verbinden kann.

Die beiden langen Klüfte sind, aus 5 bis 10 m Entfernung gesehen, eben bis flachwellig mit horizontal liegenden Wellungsachsen. Auf Leseentfernung gesehen sind die aber rauh, mit Erhebungen und Vertiefungen an der Kluftfläche, die cm-Beträge erreichen können. Beide Klüfte klaffen über einen großen Teil ihrer aufgeschlossenen Länge 1 bis 6 mm weit. Dort wo sie klaffen, sind sie teilweise leer, teilweise aber mit "Kluftlehm" gefüllt, abschnittsweise auch durch Kalksinter verklebt. Die Bindung der meisten Sinterstellen und Tropfstellen an diese Klüfte, häufiger als an die so zahlreich vorhandenen Schichtgrenzen, läßt annehmen, daß sich diese Risse flächenhaft von den Tunnelaufschlüssen noch weit in den Berg hinein erstrecken. Bei Betrachtung aus der Nähe sieht man, daß die Ränder der Steilklüfte, abgesehen von örtlich begrenzten, unbedeutenden Ausnahmen ohne Anzeichen für vertikale oder horizontale Versetzungen an den Kluftr+ändern zusammenpassen. Gelegentlich gehen die Risse durch kleinere Gerölle der Nagelfluh durch. Meist laufen sie aber durch das ursprünglich sandig-lehmige, durch sekundäre Kalkeinwanderung gehärtete Bindemittel. Diese isolierten, langen Klüfte sind also nach ihrem Aussehen ausgesprochene Zugrisse.

ZUR ENTSTEHUNG DER ZERRKLÜFTE

Ein auf 145 m Länge aufgeschlossener Einzelriß, im wesentlichen nur von einem einzigen

Parallelriß begleitet, entsteht bestimmt nicht in einer rein zufälligen Richtung. Es lag daher nahe, nach morphologischen oder strukturellen Zügen am oder im Mönchsberg zu suchen, die mit den im Stollensystem angetroffenen Klüften in Kausalzusammenhang gebracht werden könnten.

Die Schräglage des Streichens der langen Zugrisse zum Grundriß des Stollensystems spricht dagegen, daß die Risse erst als Folge der Stollenbauten entstanden seien. Ebenso spricht die Feststellung dagegen, daß bevorzugt an und unmittelbar neben den beiden Kluftrissen faustgroße, karbonatische Geröllkörner in der Nagelfluh zu finden sind, die selektiv ungewöhnlich starke stoffliche Veränderungen erlitten haben. Man kann den Inhalt solcher (Dolomit-) Gerölle, die bisweilen noch eine mm-starke, hartgebliebene Kruste haben, mit dem Taschenmesser schneiden. In einzelnen Fällen ist der Inhalt solcher Gerölle weich wie Zahnpaste. Solche stoffliche Veränderungen hängen ersichtlich mit bevorzugtem Lösungstransport in den Kluftrissen zusammen. Sie können sich kaum erst in den letzten 30 Jahren entwickelt haben.

Im Überblick gesehen zeigen die Umrißformen des Komplexes aus Festungsberg, Mönchsberg und Rainberg (Abb.1) nichts, was als Ausdruck einer übergeordneten, großräumigen Entstehungsursache - Tektonik, Eisstromrichtung o.dgl. - zu deuten wäre . Ein Vorläufer der heutigen Salzach hat vielmehr über die ganze Strecke vom Festungsberg im SE bis zum Ende des Mönchsbergs im NW jenen weit nach SW ausgreifenden Prallhangbogen mit Steilwänden geschaffen, den nun die Altstadt von Salzburg einnimmt. Dagegen sind die Plateauflächen vor allem der südlichen Mönchsberghälfte und des Rainbergs nach einheitlich orientierten SE - NW - Achsen großzügig und zweifelsohne auf natürliche Weise modelliert (Abb.1 : 168° - 348°, 165° - 345° und 160° - 340°). Diese besonders an Stereo-Luftbildpaaren auffallenden SE-NW ausgerichteten Oberflächenformen verraten aber nur die Richtung ehemaliger Überarbeitung durch Eis, sekundär vielleicht auch durch Wasser. Sie lassen keinen Zusammenhang mit Gesteinsstrukturen erkennen. Es war kein kausaler Zusammenhang zwischen diesen Oberflächenformen und den beiden Zerrklüften im Stollen zu erwarten. Eine Winkeldivergenz von 35° zwischen den Längsachsen der Plateauformen und den Zerrklüften im Stollen hätte jede Annahme in dieser Richtung illusorisch gemacht.

Unverkennbar und überzeugend ist aber die Lagebeziehung zwischen den Zerrklüften in den Stollen und dem 200 m langen Wandabschnitt vom Friedhof St.Peter bis zum Alten Festspielhaus, also dem Wandbereich unmittelbar vor dem Stollensystem. In Abb.2 ist außer der heutigen Wandflucht die ungefähre Rekonstruktion des natürlichen Wandverlaufs aus der Zeit vor der schon erwähnten Felsskarpierung aus dem 17.Jahrhundert eingezeichnet. Diese künstliche Rückverlegung der Wand mußte an ihrem SE-Ende wegen der dort angebauten älteren Kirche - Abb.2, unten rechts, bei Punkt 427.4 - auf Null auslaufen. Damit kommt diese Skarpierung einer leichten Verschwenkung der Wandflucht aus der früheren Richtung 131° - 311° auf 125° - 305° gleich. Die rekonstruierte, ältere Felslinie paßt so gut zur Richtung der 145 m langen Zerrkluft, daß sich ein ursächlicher Zusammenhang zwischen Wand und Kluft, welcher Art auch immer dieser sein möge, förmlich aufdrängt.Da nun die Mönchsbergwand erst nacheiszeitlich durch Flußerosion ihre endgültige Grundrißform erlangte, ist auch für die Zerrklüfte im Stollensystem nacheiszeitliche Entstehung anzunehmen.

Wieso ist es zum Aufreißen der Nagelfluh erst 60 m hinter einer Wand gekommen, die übrigens selbst schon künstlich um ein Stück zurückverlegt worden war ? Die klassischen "hangparallelen Klüfte" im Sinne von exfoliation joints können, falls sie in diesem Wandbereich überhaupt entwickelt waren, nie tiefer als die paar Meter, die im 17. Jahrhundert weggenommen worden waren, in den Berg hinein gereicht haben. Nach dem Wandverlauf unmittelbar nördlich der aus dem 15.Jahrhundert stammenden Kreuzkapelle im Friedhof ist sehr wahrscheinlich, daß dort die künstliche Zurückverlegung nicht mehr als 5 m ausmachte.

Der breite, großkluftfreie Felsbereich zwischen den beiden langen Zerrklüften und der heutigen Tagfläche des Berges paßt keinesfalls zum Erscheinungsbild der Exfoliation, die von außen gegen innen abklingend zu finden sein müßte.

BRUNNER und SCHEIDEGGER haben ihre Überlegungen zur Deutung der Exfoliation sensu stricto mit Überschlagsrechnungen unterbaut (Brunner und Scheidegger, 1973). Sie kamen zum Ergebnis, daß die Annahme eines Bruchs durch induzierte Zugspannungen aus hoher vertikaler Auflast der weitverbreiteten Erscheinung der "oberflächenparallelen Klüfte am ehesten gerecht wird. Die physikalische Modellvorstellungen, die der Rechnung nach BRUNNER und SCHEIDEGGER zu Grunde lagen, haben sich für den Normalfall der Exfoliation als tragfähig erwiesen, denn die Diskussion der Ergebnisse führte zu keinem Widerspruch mit den tatsächlichen Beobachtungen. Die Beschreibung der Merkmale ist damit zur Definition geworden, in der nichts mehr Platz hat, was ihr auch nur in einem wesentlichen Punkt widerspricht. Damit müssen die isolierten, tiefliegenden Risse in den Stollen von St.Peter andere (Haupt-) Ursachen haben als jene, die für die Exfoliation im engeren Sinne angenommen werden; Ursachen, die nicht so grundsätzlich an Oberflächennähe gebunden sind. Hohe vertikale Auflast hätte am Mönchsberg gewiß in der Riß-Eiszeit gewirkt, als etwa 500 m Eis auf der Nagelfluh lagen. Auch der Würmgletscher war nicht viel weniger mächtig.(Del-Negro, 1966). Es darf aber nicht übersehen werden, daß die mit der Lage der Klüfte kausal zu koppelnde Richtung der Mönchsbergwand erst durch nacheiszeitliche fluviatile Erosion gestaltet wurde, also zu einer Zeit, als das Eis schon weg war.

Zwei Erklärungswege bieten sich nun an, um den Gegebenheiten von St.Peter gerecht zu werden:

R.WOLTERS hat Vorstellungen über die Bildung oberflächenparalleler Klüfte durch die Wirkung tiefreichender Frost- und Auftauvorgänge entwickelt (Wolters, 1969). Er weist u.a. darauf hin, daß in Periglazialräumen der Frost bis über 150 m tief eindringen kann und daß ein nachfolgender Auftauvorgang von zwei Fronten her, von innen und von außen, fortschreitet. WOLTERS hatte bei seinem Erklärungsversuch wohl nur die klassischen oberflächenparallelen Klüfte"in den Teufen von 20 bis 30 m unter Oberfläche" im Auge. Aber auch tiefer im Berg bedeuten Gefrieren und das Auftauen nach tiefgreifendem Durchfrieren Zustandsänderungen in der wasseraufnahmefähigen Nagelfluh, die selbst über eine Zwischenzone hinweg Spannungen im Gestein hervorrufen können. Hier zeichnet sich eine Möglichkeit ab, auch ohne gewagten Rückgriff auf eine strukturell oder vom Untergrund her vorgezeichnete "Soll-Bruchstelle" eine Haupt- oder zumindest eine Teilursache für die Klüfte von St.Peter zu sehen.

Eine leicht verformbare Unterlage, die unter dem Gewicht darüberliegender Massen zum freien Vorland hinausdrängt, kann gewiß das Zustandekommen oberflächenparalleler Klüfte in einer auflagernden Felsmasse begünstigen. H.CRAMMER versuchte schon vor 70 Jahren (Crammer, 1903), die von ihm im Steinbruch am benachbarten Rainberg beobachteten Exfoliationen in diesem Sinne zu erklären.Die leicht verformbaren Unterlagsgesteine der Nagelfluh, Grundmoräne und Gosaumergel, waren damals gut aufgeschlossen und an den Wänden des Steinbruchs konnte er 5 solche aufeinander folgende oberflächenparallele Aufspaltungen zählen. Er übertrug seinen durchaus einleuchtenden Erklärungsversuch auf alle Klüfte ähnlicher Art an den Nagelfluhwänden des Mönchsbergs. Wenn man auch heute die bekannten anderen Vorstellungen über die Hauptursache der Exfoliation hat, wird gewiß für manche Fälle am Mönchsberg der von CRAMMER angenommene Mechanismus wenigstens als Teilursache zutreffen. Nebenbei bemerkt gibt es aber an den Mönchsbergwänden Stellen mit sehr großen, wandparallelen Klüften, die nachweislich nicht bis zum Fuß des Berges, geschweige denn, zur Konglomeratunterfläche hinabreichen.

Es liegt nahe, CRAMMERs Erklärung auch für die Klüfte in der Stollenanlage von St.Peter heranzuziehen. Die Voraussetzungen - Nagelfluh über seicht liegender, leicht verformbarer Unterlage - sind gegeben. Nur wenig mehr als 100 m südlich vom SSE-Ende der Kavernen durchstößt z.B. der Almstollen (siehe Abb.1, "AS"), ein Wasserleitungsstollen auf Höhe des Straßenniveaus der Stadt, den Berg. Dieser Stollen wurde im 12.Jahrhundert angelegt (Zillner, 1864). Die alten Bergleute haben sich dabei an die schmale Zone weicher Gosaumergel zwischen dem Hauptdolomit des Festungsberges und der nordwestlich anschließenden Nagelfluh des Mönchsberges gehalten. Da Gosaumergel und Grundmoräne auch an anderen Stellen als seicht liegende Unterlage der Nagelfluh des Mönchsberges nachgewiesen sind, darf man diese Voraussetzung für die Anwendbarkeit der Vorstellungen CRAMMERs auf St.Peter als gegeben ansehen. Eine Schwierigkeit bleibt wieder, daß auch der Erklärungsversuch CRAMMERs für oberflächennahe Klüfte plausibler ist als für die isoliert, tief im Berge liegenden.

Sollte eine Nebenursache für das Aufreißen der Nagelfluh so tief im Berge bei einer Vorzeichnung im Untergrund der Nagelfluh, etwa einer harten SSE-NNW-Rippe, zu suchen sein ? Der Gedanke wäre nicht so abwegig, wie es zunächst scheint. Erst im Sommer 1973 erschlossen Untersuchungsarbeiten, die an eine merkwürdige Einzelkluft anknüpften, im NW-Teil des Mönchsbergs in der Basis der Nagelfluh eine Höhle von 25 x 25 m^2 Grundrißfläche. Wir führten diese Höhle auf ein altes Toteisloch zurück. **Auch sie war unvorhersehbar.**

SCHLUSSFOLGERUNGEN

Das Aufreißen der Klüfte in den Stollen von St.Peter kann aus der herkömmlichen Vorstellung über das Zustandekommen oberflächenparalleler Klüfte nicht befriedigend erklärt werden. Dagegen erscheinen die Vorstellungen nach WOLTERS und CRAMMER unter den gegebenen Verhältnissen am ehesten zielführend. Ob sie Teilursachen oder das ganze Phänomen erklären bleibt vorläufig offen.

\- - - - -

LITERATUR

Bradley, W.C., 1963, Large-Scale Exfoliation in Massive Sandstones of the Colorado Plateau. Bulletin of the Geological Society of America, 74, 1963, S.519-528.

Brunner, F.K. und Scheidegger, A.E., 1973, Exfoliation. Rock Mechanics 5, 1973, S.43-62.

Crammer, H., 1903, Das Alter, die Entstehung und Zerstörung der Salzburger Nagelfluh. Neues Jahrbuch für Mineralogie, Geologie und Paläontologie, XVI, Beil.-Bd., 1903, S.325-334.

Del-Negro, W., 1966, Das Pleistozän im Salzburger Becken und seinen Ausläufern. Veröffentlichungen der Gesellschaft für Bayerische Landeskunde, H.19-22, 1966, S.166-216.

Kieslinger, A., 1959, Restspannungen und Entspannung im Gestein. Geologie und Bauwesen 24, 1959, S.95-112.

Kieslinger, A., 1972, Felsgeologische Probleme beim Neuen Festspielhaus in Salzburg. Schweizerische Bauzeitung, 90,1972, S.814-818.

Müller, L., 1962, Über die Entstehung oberflächenparalleler Klüfte. Geologie und Bauwesen 27, 1962, S.146-152.

Pippan, Th., 1961, The Late Glacial Terraces and Remnants of Interglacial Sedimentation in the Salzburg Basin. Report 6th International Congress on Quaternary, Warzawa, Vol.III, 1961, S.265-272.

Wolters, R., 1969, Zur Ursache der Entstehung oberflächenparalleler Klüfte. Rock Mechanics, 1, 1969, S.53-70.

Zillner, 1864, Die Wasserleitung der Alm. Mitteilungen der Gesellschaft für Salzburger Landeskunde, 4, 1864.

RHEOLOGISCHE GRUNDLAGEN FELSMECHANISCHER MODELLVERSUCHE

RHEOLOGICAL PRINCIPLES OF ROCK MECHANICAL MODEL TESTS

LES PRINCIPES RHÉOLOGIQUES D'EXPÉRIENCES SUR MAQUETTE RÉALISÉES DANS LE DOMAINE DE LA MÉCANIQUE DES ROCHES

M. LANGER

West-Germany

Zusammenfassung

Auf der Grundlage der vom Verfasser entwickelten Strukturrheologie der Gesteine und Gebirgskörper (LANGER, M.: Rheologie der Gesteine, Z.dt.geol.Ges.119, S.313-425, 1969) wird die Bedeutung der Zeit für den Ansatz und die Aussagekraft von felsmechanischen Modellversuchen diskutiert. Die zugrunde zu legenden rheologischen Stoffgesetze des im Modell darzustellenden Bereiches beeinflussen die Wahl des Modellmaterials. Das allgemeine rheologische Verhalten von Gebirgskörpern läßt sich mit Hilfe eines erweiterten Schofield-Scott-Blair Körpers beschreiben. Modellmaterialien mit entsprechendem Stoffgesetz liegen vor, die dazugehörenden Stoffkennwerte werden mitgeteilt.

Modellversuche auf rheologischer Grundlage können für viele Fragen zwar keine eindeutigen Antworten geben, sind jedoch hilfreich beim Ansatz und Deutung von felsmechanischen in-situ Messungen und bei der Verifizierung bestimmter tektonischer Hypothesen.

Summary

Basing on the structural rheology of rock and rock bodies such as developed by the author (LANGER,M.: Rheologie der Gesteine, Z.dt.geol.Ges.119, p.313-425, 1969) the importance of time for the set-up and for the enunciative value of model tests is discussed. The discussion deals, in particular, with the problem in which way certain general rheological principles exert an influence on the choice of model material.

The general rheological behavior of rock is descripted by means of a special SCHOFIELD-SCOTT-BLAIR body. There exist model materials with corresponding constitutive equations, some numerical characteristics of the material are indicated.

As a conclusion it is said that model tests carried out on the basis of rheological principles are not able to give unquestionably clear answers to many questions but, on the other hand, that they supply a valuable help in checking up certain hypotheses (for instance tectonic theories) and confirming the interpretation of some rock mechanical in-situ measurements.

Résumé

Se fondant sur la rhéologie structurelle des roches et des masses rocheuses telle qu'il l'a développée lui-même (LANGER,M.: Rheologie der Gesteine, Z.dt.geol.Ges.119, p.313-425, 1969) l'auteur discute l'importance du temps lorsqu'on veut se référer aux expériences mecaniques et en montrer la force d'évocation.

L'auteur discute en particulier comment, certaines lois rhéologiques, relatives au domaine à figurer par un modèle, influencent le choix de la matière du modèle. Le comportement rhéologique général des massifs montagneux se laisse décrire à l'aide d'un corps de SCHOFIELD-SCOTT-BLAIR généralisé. Il existe pour de tels modèles des matériaux conformes à la corresondance voulue par la loi de la matière; les caractéristiques des matiéres y relatives sont indiquées.

Comme conclusion concernant l'exécution d'essais avec modèles, l'auteur souligne le fait que les expériences ne sont pas réellement en mesure de donner, sur une base rhéologique, des réponses claires sans équivoque pour beaucoup de questions, bien qu'elles apportent une assistance valable pour vérifier certaines hypothèses tectoniques et mecaniques des roches.

1. Einleitung

Die Rheologie hat die Untersuchung der mechanischen Verformbarkeit realer Stoffe in den Mittelpunkt gestellt. Hauptziel ist dabei das Aufstellen von Stoffgesetzen, also die Darlegung der Beziehung zwischen gegebenen Kräften und Deformationen in Abhängigkeit von Zeit und Temperatur. Auch die speziellen Gesetze und der Mechanismus der Verformung von Gebirgskörpern sind bereits ausführlich behandelt worden: In seiner Arbeit "Rheologie der Gesteine" hat der Verfasser die rheologische Grundlage für den Ansatz und die Auswertung felsmechanischer und tektonischer Versuche geschaffen (LANGER,1969a). Die dabei abgeleiteten strukturrheologischen Leitsätze und Arbeitshypothesen liegen auch den folgenden Ausführungen zugrunde, die sich vor allem mit der Bedeutung der Zeit für die Durchführung felsmechanischer Modellversuche beschäftigen. Die Größe "Zeit" wird dabei, wie in der Physik allgemein üblich, als eine unabhängige Variable und nicht als ein Faktor ("Zeitfaktor") angesehen. Es wird gezeigt, daß diese besondere rheologische Ausgangsbasis zu interessanten Schlußfolgerungen für den Ansatz, die Auswertung und Bewertung felsmechanischer Experimente führt. Ähnliches gilt auch für tektonische Modellversuche (LANGER,1972b).

2. Modellmechanische Grundsätze

Die besondere Bedeutung eines exakt konstruierten Modells liegt darin, daß das Modell im Verlauf der Beanspruchung eine Entwicklung durchmacht, die der Verformung im Original, also in der Natur entspricht.Die Wissenschaft, die sich mit der Frage beschäftigt, inwieweit Schlußfolgerungen aus Beobachtungen von physikalischen Erscheinungen in einem System (hier Natur) auf ein ähnliches System anderen Maßstabes (hier Modell) möglich sind, ist die Modellmechanik bzw. Ähnlichkeitsmechanik (HUBBERT,1937; HOSSDORF,1971, LANGHAAR,1962).

Exakte Übertragungsgesetze vom Modell auf Vorgänge in der Natur und umgekehrt lassen sich jedoch nur finden, wenn sämtliche ein komplexes Phänomen beeinflussende Größen erkannt sind und die mechanischen Gesetze, d.h. die das Phänomen beschreibenden Differentialgleichungen und Ausgangsbedingungen bekannt sind. Es sind dies

1. Differentialgleichung des Gleichgewichtes bzw. Bewegungsgleichungen.
2. Stoffgesetz (rheologische Gleichung).
3. Spannungsverteilung im Ausgangszustand.
4. Randbedingungen.

Je komplexer die Struktur, die simuliert werden soll, je größer die Anzahl der Größen, die für den Prozeß maßgebend sind, desto unwahrscheinlicher wird die exakte Konstruktion des Modells, desto weniger quantitativ die Versuchsergebnisse (Quasi-Modell).

Eine der wichtigsten dieser physikalischen Größen ist die Zeit. Die Zeit als unabhängige Variable beeinflußt den Modellversuch in dreifacher Weise:

a) als Zeitraffung (Zeitmaßstab des Modells);
b) durch die Bewegungsgleichung (Trägheitskräfte durch Erdbeschleunigung in der Natur);
c) im rheologischen Stoffgesetz (Zeitabhängigkeit der Deformation).

Alle physikalischen Größen, die für den zu simulierenden Bewegungsablauf relevant sind, müssen entsprechend ihrer Dimension maßstabsgerecht behandelt werden, z.B. dieGeschwindigkeit im Verhältnis $\Lambda . T^{-1}$ oder die Beschleunigung im Verhältnis $\Lambda . T^{-2}$. Da die Beschleunigung in die Bewegungsgleichung eingeht, darf also für den Fall, daß sowohl in der Natur als auch im Modell die Erdbeschleunigung wirkt (also z.B. keine Zentrifugalmodelle benutzt werden), der Zeitmaßstab T nicht unabhängig vom Längenmaßstab Λ gewählt werden; es sei denn, was allerdings für viele Prozesse mit guter Näherung angenommen werden kann, Trägheitskräfte keine entscheidende Rolle spielen, die Bewegungen also langsam genug ablaufen.

Entscheidend ist jedoch der Einfluß der Zeitraffung auf die Stoffparameter des zu wählenden Modellmaterials; denn auch diese Stoffgrößen müssen selbstverständlich aufgrund ihrer Dimensionsbehaftung maßstabsgerecht behandelt werden, also z.B. Elastizitätsmodul, Festigkeit, Fließgrenze, Viskosität. Insbesondere ergibt sich aus der Definition der kinematischen Ähnlichkeit, bei der das Modell zu jeder Zeit des Bewegungsablaufes geometrisch ähnlich bleiben soll, daß der Modellwerkstoff das gleiche rheologische Verhalten, also das gleiche rheologische Stoffgesetz zeigen muß, mit maßstabsgerecht veränderten Stoffkonstanten.

Eine der Hauptaufgaben bei der Durchführung felsmechanischer Modellversuche ist also

a) die rheologischen Eigenschaften des zu modellierenden Gebirgsbereiches so genau wie möglich zu erfassen, und
b) nach Festlegung des Längenmaßstabes Λ bzw. der Zeitraffung T die passenden rheologischen Modellstoffe auszuwählen.

Deswegen wird im folgenden näher auf das rheologische Verhalten von Gebirgskörpern und Modellstoffen eingegangen.

3. Strukturrheologische Grundsätze

Rheologie, d.h. die Erforschung der zeitabhängigen Deformation realer Körper, läßt sich auf drei verschiedene Weisen betreiben:

1. Die phänomenologische Behandlung. Der Körper wird als strukturloses Ganzes betrachtet; es wird Homogenität und Kontinuität vorausgesetzt. Die Verformbarkeit wird meßtechnisch in Abhängigkeit von Zeit und Temperatur erfaßt und daraus mathematisch das Stoffgesetz abgeleitet. Dabei ist es üblich, das komplizierte rheologische Verhalten von Stoffen dadurch mathematisch zu erfassen, daß man es mit idealen rheologischen Körpern vergleicht, die nach bekannten Forschern benannt sind. Die Stoffgesetze verbinden den Spannungstensor σ_{ij} mit dem Deformationstensor ε_{ij}. Es ist unerläßlich, dabei zwischen der volumetrischen Komponente (s_p bzw. e_p) und der Verzerrungskomponente (s_{ij} bzw. e_{ij}) zu unterscheiden, da beide Verformungsarten unterschiedliches rheologisches Verhalten zeigen können. Die Zeitabhängigkeit der Verformung (als Funktion der Spannung) läßt sich dann allgemein mit Hilfe linearer Differentialoperatoren (P, Q, R, S) darstellen:

$$P\, s_p = Q\, e_p \quad \text{(reine Volumenänderung)}$$

$$R\, s_{ij} = S\, e_{ij} \quad \text{(volumenänderungsfreie Verzerrung)}$$

also
$$p_1\, s_p + p_2 \frac{\delta s_p}{\delta t} + p_3 \frac{\delta^2 s_p}{\delta t^2} + \ldots$$
$$= q_1\, e_p + q_2 \frac{\delta e_p}{\delta t} + q_3 \frac{\delta^2 e_p}{\delta t^2} + \ldots$$
$$r_1\, s_{ij} + r_2 \frac{\delta s_{ij}}{\delta t} + r_3 \frac{\delta s_{ij}}{\delta t^2} + \ldots$$
$$= s_1\, e_{ij} + s_2 \frac{\delta e_{ij}}{\delta t} + s_3 \frac{\delta^2 e_{ij}}{\delta t^2} + \ldots$$

Die Darstellung von rheologischen Stoffgesetzen in Operatorenform ist besonders bei der Lösung von Grenzwertproblemen, wie es auch Modellversuche sind, von Vorteil. Mit Hilfe des sogenannten Korrespondenzprinzips lassen sich nämlich unter bestimmten Voraussetzungen einfache Modellversuche mit rheologischen Stoffen rechnerisch überprüfen. Das Korrespondenzprinzip sagt aus: Wenn ein spezielles quasi-statisches Problem für eine unabhängige Variable (hier im allgemeinen die Verformung) im elastischen Körper gelöst werden kann, dann genügt diese Variable in der rheologischen Lösung der gewöhnlichen Differentialgleichung, die sich daraus ergibt, daß die elastischen Konstanten (E-Modul, Schubmodul etc.) in der elastischen Lösung durch die entsprechenden rheologischen Operatoren ersetzt werden. Das Lösen von Grenzproblemen mit rheologischen Medien bedeutet also mathematisch gesehen die Prüfung, ob im speziellen Falle die Integration der so entstandenen Differentialgleichung durchführbar ist (z.B. mit Hilfe der Laplace-Transformation). Einige Beispiele aus der felsmechanischen Praxis hat z.B. LANGER (1969a) gegeben. Die hier interessierenden phänomenologischen Stoffgesetze für Gesteine, Gebirgskörper und Erdkruste/Erdmantel werden im Kapitel 4 näher besprochen.

2. Die strukturelle (strukturrheologische) Behandlung. Der Körper wird in seine ihn aufbauende Strukturelemente zerlegt betrachtet, die mechanischen Eigenschaften des Gesamtkörpers in Abhängigkeit von den Strukturelementen und deren Anordnung gedeutet. Dadurch ist ein Erfassen des Mechanismus der Verformung möglich. Homogenität und stetige Raumerfüllung ist Voraussetzung.

Als Strukturelemente werden diejenigen Elemente eines Körpers bezeichnet, durch die für eine bestimmte Größenordnung (Bereich) des Körpers dessen Struktur (Gefüge) gekennzeichnet werden kann, also z.B. Gitterebenen im Kristall, Mineralkörner im Gesteinsstück, Trennflächen im Fels, Faltungsachsen im geologischen Körper (Gebirge).

Man kann zeigen (LANGER,1969c; MURRELL,1967, und andere Autoren in Geophys.J.,Bd.14,1967),daß die gut erforschte Elastizität und Plastizität der Kristalle (vor allem Metalle) ihr strukturelles Analogon im Gestein und Gebirge haben, wobei die angesprochenen Strukturelemente entsprechend der Dimension des Bereiches vergrößert sind. So können das Wandern von "Versetzungen" und Strukturkrümmungen im Kristall analog zu den plastischen Verschiebungen von Kluftkörpern entlang Trennflächen und Rotationen der Kluftkörper im Fels bzw. analog zu translativen Gleitungen längs der Absonderungsflächen und Drehungen nicht kugelförmiger Minerale im Gestein gesehen werden. Dies führte den Verfasser zur Feststellung,daß der Bewegungsmechanismus von Strukturelementen bereichsunabhängigen Gesetzen folgt,wenn die jeweilige Wahl der Strukturelemente der Größe des Bereiches und der Ausdehnung der Beanspruchung angepaßt ist (2. Leitsatz der Rheologie der Gesteine, LANGER,1969a, S.327). Dieser Leitsatz findet seine Bestätigung in der Tatsache,daß die phänomenologischen Stoffgesetze von Kristallen - Fels - Gebirge - Erdkruste ähnlich aufgebaut sind, wenn auch mit unterschiedlichen Stoffkonstanten (vgl. Tab.1). Für die Auswertung von Modellversuchen ist dies von entscheidender Bedeutung, denn dadurch wird gewährleistet, daß durch Maßstabsverkleinerung im Modell keine anderen, grundsätzlich verschiedenen physikalischen Gesetze ins Spiel kommen. Ein instruktives Beispiel für die Anwendung solcher strukturrheologischer Grundlagen für den gebirgsmechanischen Modellversuch unter besonderer Berücksichtigung der Größe Zeit, hat kürzlich ALBRECHT (1972) vorgelegt.

3. Die diskontinuumsmechanische Behandlung. Hierbei werden einzelne wirksame Unstetigkeitsflächen betrachtet und deren mechanische Wirksamkeit untersucht. Im Felsbereich ist dafür die Entscheidung notwendig, ob die Trennflächen im betrachteten Bereich als "homogenisierende" Trennflächen vorliegen oder nicht (vgl.LANGER,1969a, S.33o/331). In der Diskontinuumsmechanik wird die Voraussetzung der Homogenität und Kontinuität fallengelassen. Die Kompatibilitätsbedingungen gelten nicht mehr. Die Grundlagen für eine solche Kiskontinuumsmechanik (Gebirgskörpermechanik) könnten deshalb z.B. in der auf rheologische Stoffgesetze erweiterten inkompatiblen Elastizitätstheorie gesehen werden (LANGER, 1966).

4. Rheologische Stoffgesetze und Kennziffern von Gebirgskörpern und Modellmaterialien

Das prinzipielle rheologische Verhalten von Gebirgskörpern ist bereits recht gut bekannt (vgl.LANGER,197o). Gebirgskörper zeigen mehr oder weniger ausgeprägt alle drei Grundarten rheologischer Verformung, nämlich die

elastische Verformung $\varepsilon_1 = e_{el}$ die bei Lastaufnahme sofort eintritt,
nachelastische Verformung $\varepsilon_2 = e_{nel}$, die bei Belastung unter Verzögerung eintritt,
plastische Verformung $\varepsilon_3 = e_{pl}$, die bei Entlastung nicht rückgewinnbar (irreversibel) ist.

Der dazugehörige ideale rheologische Körper ist der erweiterte SCHOFIELD-SCOTT BLAIR-Körper, dessen Stoffgleichung (s.Tab.1) aus einem Hooke-Glied (e_{el}).einer Kette von Kelvin-Gliedern (e_{nel}) und einem Bingham-Glied (e_{pl}) besteht.

Interessant ist nun, daß sich die in der Natur bekanntgewordenen rheologischen Modelle von Gestein, Fels, Gebirge, Erdkruste/Erdmantel, in Tab.1 mit zunehmender Größe des Bereiches geordnet, zwanglos in dieses allgemeine rheologische Modell einordnen lassen. So läßt sich das Kriechen von Gesteinen (Handstückbereich), z.B. nach LOMNITZ (1956) oder MURRELL (1967) mit Hilfe einer Kette von Kelvin-Gliedern (e_{nel}) oder bei höheren Temperaturen (größer als die Hälfte der Schmelztemperatur) mit Hilfe des Maxwell-Körpers (e_{visk}) in erster Näherung beschreiben. Das zeitabhängige Deformationsverhalten von Fels (Baubereich) ist von LANGER (1969a, 1969b, 1972a) ausführlich beschrieben worden. Für kurze Beanspruchungszeiten und bei niedrigen Temperaturen überwiegt der elastische und nachelastische Anteil der Deformation gegenüber der plastischen Deformation; der SCHOFIELD-SCOTT BLAIR-Körper vereinfacht sich daher zu einem erweiterten Nakamura-Körper ($e_{el}+e_{nel}$). Für Steinsalz hingegen ist eher mit dem Bingham-Körper (e_{pl}) zu arbeiten. GZOVSKY (1959) legt seinen tektonischen Experimenten ebenfalls ein rheologisches Verhalten von Gebirgen (tektonischer Großbereich) zugrunde, das dem Burgers-Körper ($e_{el}+e_{nel}+e_{pl}$) entspricht. Auch über das zeitabhängige Deformationsverhalten der Erdkruste und des Erdmantels als Ganzes liegen bereits einige Untersuchungen vor, z.B. SCHEIDEGGER (1963), der je nach Beanspruchungszeit (größer oder kleiner als 15 ooo Jahre) nachelastisches (Kelvin-Körper) oder plastisches Verhalten (Bingham-Körper) annimmt. Ein ähnliches Konzept (das sogenannte Rheid-Konzept) hat CAREY (1954) vorgeschlagen. Die Tab.1 gibt einen Überblick über die verschiedenen vorgeschlagenen Stoffgesetze (ohne Anspruch auf Vollständigkeit) und bringt einige als wahrscheinlich geltende Stoffkennwerte (Mittelwerte).

Die bereits abgeleitete Forderung, daß für exakte Modellversuche der Modellwerkstoff das gleiche rheologische Verhalten wie das Original mit maßstabsgerecht veränderten Stoffkonstanten zeigen muß, führt zu Tab.2 in der rheologische Stoffgleichungen und Kennwerte verschiedener üblicher Modellmaterialien in einer kleinen Auswahl zusammengefaßt sind.

Ein Vergleich mit Tab.1 zeigt, daß auch hier alle bisher angesprochenen Stoffgesetze vertreten sind:

Material/Bereich	Rheolog. Modell	Stoffgleichung	Bedingung	Mittlere Konstanten	Autor
Idealer allgem. rheolog. Gebirgskörper	Erweiterter BURGERS-K. m. Fließgrenze	$e(t) = e_{el} + e_{nel} + e_{pl}$ $= \frac{\sigma}{G} + \sigma \sum_{i=1}^{n} \frac{1}{G_i} \left[1 - \exp\left(-\frac{t}{T_{ret_i}}\right)\right] + \frac{\sigma - \tau_{Fl}}{\eta^*} t$			LANGER 1969 a
Gestein (Handstück)	Empirischer visko-elast. Körper	$e(t) = e_{el} + e_{nel}$ $= \frac{\sigma}{G} + \frac{\sigma}{G} \cdot q \cdot \log(1 + \alpha t)$	$T < 0{,}2\ T_m$	$\alpha = 6 \cdot 10^3\ sec^{-1}$	LOMNITZ 1956
		$e(t) = e_{nel} = \beta \cdot t^{1/3} \quad \beta \approx \sigma^2$	$T \approx 0{,}5\ T_m$	$\beta = 3 \cdot 10^{-5}$ cgs - Einh.	MURELL 1967
	MAXWELL-K.	$e(t) = e_{visk} = \frac{\sigma}{\eta} t$	$T \gg 0{,}5\ T_m$	$\eta = f(T)$	
Fels (Baubereich)	Erweiterter NAKAMURA-K.	$e(t) = e_{el} + e_{nel} \quad \Big\vert\ \frac{t_i}{T_{ret_i}} = const = h$ $= \frac{\sigma}{G} + \sigma \sum_{i=1}^{n} \frac{1}{G_i} \left[1 - \exp\left(-\frac{t}{T_{ret_i}}\right)\right]$	$e_{pl} \ll e_{el} + e_{nel}$	$G = 10^5\ kp/cm^2$ $G_i = 2 \cdot 10^4\ kp/cm^2$ $h = 10$	LANGER 1969 b
	BINGHAM-K.	$e(t) = e_{pl} = \frac{\sigma - \tau_{Fl}}{\eta^*} t$	$e_{el} + e_{nel} \ll e_{pl}$	$\eta^* = 5 \cdot 10^{12}\ kp\ sec/cm^2$ $\tau_{Fl} = 100\ kp/cm^2$	LANGER 1972
Gebirge (tekton. Großbereich)	BURGERS-K.	$e(t) = e_{el} + e_{nel} + e_{pl}$ $= \frac{\sigma}{G} + \frac{\sigma}{G_K} \left[1 - \exp\left(-\frac{G_K}{\eta_K}\right) t\right] + \frac{\sigma}{\eta^*} t$		$G = 5 \cdot 10^5\ kp/cm^2$ $G_K = 5 \cdot 10^5\ kp/cm^2$ $T_{ret} = 1h$ $\eta^* = 5 \cdot 10^{14}\ kp\ sec/cm^2$	GZOVSKY 1959
Erdkruste/ Erdmantel	KELVIN-K. m. Bruchfestigkeit	$e(t) = e_{nel} = \frac{\sigma}{G_K} \left[1 - \exp\left(-\frac{t}{T_{ret}}\right)\right]$	$4h < t < 15 \cdot 10^3$ Jhr.	$G_K = 2 \cdot 10^6\ kp/cm^2$ $T_{ret} = 2$ Tage	SCHEIDEGGER 1962
	BINGHAM-K.	$e(t) = e_{pl} = \frac{\sigma - c_{Fl}}{\eta^*} t$	$t > 15 \cdot 10^3$ Jhr.	$\eta^* = 10^{16}\ kp\ sec/cm^2$ $\tau_{Fl} = 4 \cdot 10^3\ kp/cm^2$	

Tab. 1: Rheologische Stoffgleichungen für Gebirgskörper verschiedener Bereiche
Rheological stress-strain relations for rock
Des équations rhéologiques pour des corps de roches

Material	Rheolog. Modell	Stoffgleichung	Kennwerte	Autor
Araldit/Aluminium	HOOKE-K.	$\varepsilon = \varepsilon_{el} = \frac{\sigma}{E}$	$E = 3 \cdot 10^5$ bis $1 \cdot 10^6\ kp/cm^2$	HOSSDORF, 1971
Epoxydharz /Quarz			$E = 3 \cdot 10^4$ bis $2 \cdot 10^5\ kp/cm^2$	WÜSTENHAGEN, 1967
Gips / Kieselgur			$E = 4 \cdot 10^3$ bis $4 \cdot 10^4\ kp/cm^2$	SERAFIM, 1963
Gelatine (25 %)	NAKAMURA-K.	$e(t) = e_{el} + e_{nel}$ $= \frac{\sigma}{G} + \frac{\sigma}{G_K} \left[1 - \exp\left(-\frac{t}{T_{ret}}\right)\right]$	$G = G_K = 0{,}1$ bis $1\ kp/cm^2$ $T_{ret} = 10^2$ bis 10^4 sec $\tau_{Br} = 10$ bis $100\ kp/cm^2$	GZOVSKY, 1959
Beton	BURGERS-K. m. Bruchfestigkeit	$e(t) = e_{el} + e_{nel} + e_{pl}$ $= \frac{\sigma}{G} + \frac{\sigma}{G_K} \left[1 - \exp\left(-\frac{t}{T_{ret}}\right)\right] + \frac{\sigma}{\eta^*} t$	$G = 2{,}5 \cdot 10^5$ bis $3 \cdot 10^5\ kp/cm^2$ $G_K = 2 \cdot 10^5$ bis $4 \cdot 10^5\ kp/cm^2$ $T_{ret} = 5 \cdot 10^5$ bis $1 \cdot 10^6$ sec $\eta^* = 3 \cdot 10^{12}$ bis $8 \cdot 10^{12}\ kp\ sec/cm^2$ $\tau_{Br} = 300$ bis $350\ kp/cm^2$	CUEVAS, 1971
BAKU - Petrolatum			$G = G_K \approx 1\ kp/cm^2$, $\tau \approx 0{,}1\ kp/cm^2$ $T_{ret} = 1$ bis 10 sec, $\eta^* = 1$ bis $10\ p\ sec/cm^2$	GZOVSKY, 1959
Asphalt/Petrowachs	BINGHAM-K.	$e(t) = e_{pl} = \frac{\sigma - \tau_{Fl}}{\eta^*} t$	$\eta^* \approx 100\ kp\ sec/cm^2$, $\tau_{Fl} = 0{,}2$ bis $0{,}5\ p/cm^2$	HAMILTON, 1962
Kolophonium / Äthylen - phthalat	NEWTON-K.	$e(t) = e_{visk} = \frac{\sigma}{\eta} t$	$\eta = 1$ bis $100\ kp\ sec/cm^2$	RAMBERG, 1967

Tab. 2: Rheologische Stoffgleichungen und Kennwerte üblicher Modellmaterialien (Auswahl)
Rheological constitutive equations and numerical characteristics of some model material (selection)
Des équations rhéologiques et des valeurs caractéristiques à l'égard des matériaux d'usage dans les expériences sur maquette (sélection)

elastisches Verhalten, z.B. Araldit oder Expoxydharz-Quarz-Gemische, elastisch-nachelastisches Verhalten, z.B. Gelatine, elastisch-nachelastisch-plastisches Verhalten, z.B. Beton, Petroleum, bis hin zum viskosen bzw. plastischen Verhalten, z.B. Asphalt, Kollophonium-Äthylenphthalat-Mischungen. Vom prinzipiellen rheologischen Verhalten her gesehen macht es also keine Schwierigkeit, ein passendes Modellmaterial zu finden. Die dazugehörigen Kennwerte sind allerdings nur in gewissen Grenzen zu verändern, und es ist im Einzelfall zu entscheiden, welche Materialien, auch hier nicht aufgeführte, zu wählen sind.

5. Schlußfolgerungen für die Ausführung von Modellversuchen

Zum Schluß seien einige Schlußfolgerungen für die Ausführung von Modellversuchen aus rheologischer Sicht mitgeteilt. Diese Schlußfolgerungen ergeben sich entweder direkt aus dem Ausgeführten oder folgen aus weiteren Ableitungen, auf die hier im einzelnen nicht eingegangen werden konnte:

1. Ein exaktes Modell muß geometrisch, kinematisch und dynamisch ähnlich sein. Es hat denselben physikalischen Bedingungen wie der Prototyp Natur zu unterliegen; dies sind die Bewegungsgleichungen bzw. bei genügend langsam ablaufenden Bewegungen die Gleichgewichtsbedingungen, die Bedingung der Kontinuität, das rheologische Stoffgesetz, die Ausgangs- und Randbedingungen. Ist das rheologische Verhalten der Natur und damit des Modellstoffes in erster Näherung nicht als rein elastisch (Hooke-Körper) oder rein plastisch (Bingham-Körper) anzunehmen, müssen diese Gleichungen in dimensionlose Form überführt werden, d.h. es müssen Referenzlängen, Referenzzeiten und Referenzmassen (bzw. Referenzdichten) angenommen werden(HAMILTON, 1962). Dies gilt auch, wenn illineares Spannungs-Verformungs-Verhalten simuliert werden soll.
2. Zwecks Vergleichbarkeit von Modellversuchen verschiedener Autoren sollten stets die rheologischen Kennwerte des benutzten Modellmaterials gemessen werden. Dies kann bei weichen Stoffen mit einem Viskosimeter, bei festen Stoffen durch Kriechversuche recht einfach geschehen. Das Verhalten gegen Volumenveränderung ist dabei (gegenüber der Verzerrung) gesondert zu bestimmen.
3. Ton-Wasser- bzw. Ton-Öl- oder Sand-Öl-Mischungen werden als besonders günstig für felsmechanische und tektonische Modellversuche erachtet, da sie denselben rheologischen Stoffgesetzen wie die Gebirgsverformung gehorchen und eine große Variation in den einzelnen Stoffparametern zulassen (vgl. Tab.3).
4. Die Tendenz der Entwicklung felsmechanischer und kleintektonischer Modellversuche geht hin zur Quantifizierung der Versuchsergebnisse mit Hilfe der Modellmechanik und Strukturrheologie. Eine Möglichkeit der rechnerischen Überprüfung einfacher Modellversuche mit theologischen Medien ergibt sich aus dem sog. Korrespondenzprinzip, mit dessen Hilfe viskoelastische Grenzprobleme gelöst werden können, wenn eine entsprechende elastizitätstheoretische Lösung bekannt ist.
5. Wegen der bekannten Schwierigkeiten, die felsmechanischen Ausgangsdaten exakt zu ermitteln, kann man jedoch bis heute nur von Quasi-Modellen sprechen, die für viele Fragen keine eindeutigen Antworten geben können, jedoch hilfreich sind in der Verifizierung bestimmter tektonischer Hypothesen oder theoretisch abgeleiteter Zusammenhänge oder umgekehrt für die Ablehnung bestimmter hypothetisch angenommener Verformungsmechanismen. Insbesondere beim Ansatz von felsmechanischen in-situ-Messungen und bei der Interpretation solcher Versuchsergebnisse können Modellversuche behilflich sein.Es liegt beim Experimentator, vorhandene Unsicherheiten in der Annahme der naturgegebenen Ausgangsbedingungen abzuschätzen und in ihrer Bedeutung für die Aussagekraft der Ergebnisse des Experimentes kritisch zu beurteilen.

Schrifttum

ALBRECHT,H.: 1972, Rheologische und gefügekundliche Untersuchungen beim Bau einer Krafthauskaverne.- Ein ingenieurgeologischer Beitrag zum Problem des Faktors "Zeit" im gebirgsmechanischen Modellversuch.- Diss.Uni Kiel, 67 S

CAREY,S.W.: 1954, The rheid concept in geotectonics.- J.Geol.Soc. Austral. Bd.1,1, S.67-117

CUEVAS,N.R.: 1971,Viscoelastic constants for a model representing the mechanical behaviour of materials.- Proc.Southampton 1969,Civil Eng.Mat.Conf.,Bd.1, S.533-543

Konsistenz	Rheolog. Modell	Stoffgleichung	Kennwerte
breiig bis flüssig $w_n > w_f$	Rheolog. Körper für Tonsuspensionen ($\hat{N}$IO)-N [LANGER] O = Orientierungskörper	$e(t) = e_{visk}$ $\frac{de}{dt} = \frac{\sigma}{\eta} + \frac{\sigma}{\hat{\eta}}\left[1 - \exp\left(-\frac{\hat{\eta}}{x}t\right)\right]$ $\sigma > \tau_{Fl}$, x = Orientierungsgröße	$\tau_{Fl} = 1$ bis 100 p/cm^2 $\eta = 0{,}01$ bis 1 $p\,sec/cm^2$ $\hat{\eta} = 0{,}01$ bis 1 $p\,sec/cm^2$ $x = 0{,}1$ bis 1 $p\,sec^2/cm^2$
weich, bildsam $w_n < w_f$ $w_n > w_a$	LETHERSICH - K. m. Fließgrenze bzw. Kohäsion	$e(t) = e_{nel} + e_{pl}$ $e(t) = \frac{\sigma}{G_K}\left[1 - \exp\left(-\frac{t}{T_{ret}}\right)\right] + \frac{\sigma - \tau_{Fl}}{\eta^x}t$	$c = \tau_{Fl} = 0{,}1$ bis 0,5 kp/cm^2 $G_K = 1$ bis 50 kp/cm^2 $T_{ret} = 10^3$ bis 10^4 sec $\eta^x = 0{,}1$ bis 10^2 $kp\,sec/cm^2$
halbfest bis fest $w_n < w_a$	NAKAMURA - K. m. Bruchgrenze	$e(t) = e_{el} + e_{nel}$ $e(t) = \frac{\sigma}{G} + \frac{\sigma}{G_K}\left[1 - \exp\left(-\frac{t}{T_{ret}}\right)\right]$	$\tau_{Br} = 1$ bis 10 kp/cm^2 $G = 10^3$ bis 10^4 kp/cm^2 $G_K = 5 \cdot 10^2$ bis $5 \cdot 10^3$ kp/cm^2 $T_{ret} = 10^2$ bis $5 \cdot 10^3$ sec

Tab.3: Rheologische Stoffgleichungen und Kennwerte von Ton-Wasser-Gemischen verschiedener Konsistenz

Rheological material laws and numerical characteristics of clay-water mixtures of different consistence

Des équations rhéologiques et des valeurs caractéristiques pour des mélanges d'argile et d'ean accusant des consistence diverses

GZOVSKY,M.V.: 1959, The use of scale models in tectonophysics.- Int.Geol.Rev., Bd.1,4, S.31-45

HAMILTON,W.S.: 1962, Structural model of large part of the earth.- Bull. Am. Ass. Petr. Geol., Bd.46,5, S.61o-639

HOSSDORF,H.: 1971, Modellstatik.- 258 S., Wiesbaden (Bauverlag)

HUBBERT,M.K.: 1937, Theory of scale models as applied to the study of geologic structures.- Bull.Geol. Soc. Am., Bd.48, 1o, S.1459-152o

LANGER,M.: 1966, Grundlagen einer theoretischen Gebirgskörpermechanik.- Proc. 1.Int.Congr.Rock Mech., Bd.1, S.277-282,Lissabon

-: 1969a, Rheologie der Gesteine.- Z.Dtsch.Geol.Ges., Bd.119, S.313-425

-: 1969b, Rheologische Probleme im Felsbau.- Z.dt. geol.Ges., Bd.119, S.71-95

-: 1969c, Grundbegriffe der Rheologie und ihre Anwendbarkeit bei der Verformung von Gebirgskörpern.- Felsmechan. u.Ingenieurgeol., Suppl.V, S.9-2o

-: 197o, Die Bestimmung rheologischer Stoffkonstanten in Gebirgskörpern.- Proc. 2.Int.Congr.Rock Mech., Belgrad, Bd.2,Arbeit Nr.19, 1o S.

-: 1972a, Ingenieurgeologische Probleme bei der Speicherung von Öl und Gas.- Geol.Jb., Bd.9o, S.315-358

-: 1972b, Rheologische und modellmechanische Grundlagen für tektonische Experimente.- Geol.Rundschau, Bd.61,3, S.8o6-823

LANGHAAR,H.L.: 1962, Dimensional analysis and theory of models.- New York (J.Wiley)

LOMNITZ,C.: 1956, Creep measurements in igneous rocks.- J.Geol., Bd.64, S.473-479

MURRELL,S.A.F.: 1967, An experimental study of the effect of temperature and stress on the creep of rocks, with a discussion of earth tide damping, isostasy and mantle convection.- Geophys.J.R.astr. Soc., Bd.14, S.51-55

RAMBERG,H.: 1967, Gravity, deformation and the earth's crust as studied by centrifuged models. 214 S., London (Academic Press)

SCHEIDEGGER,A.E.: 1963, Principles of geodynamics.- 362 S., Berlin

SERAFIM,J.L. & CRUZ AZEVEDO,M.: 1963, Methods in use at the LNEC for the stress analysis in models of dams.- LNEC Techn.Paper Nr. 2o1, Lissabon

WÜSTENHAGEN, K.: 1967, Der Einfluß der sedimentpetrographischen Ausbildung von Buntsandstein-Kernen auf den statischen Elastizitätsmodul und andere geomechanische Kennziffern.- Diss. Uni Hamburg, 11o S.

UNE MÉTHODE ANALYTIQUE DE LOCALISATION DES ACCIDENTS STRUCTURAUX DANS UN MASSIF ROCHEUX

AN ANALYTIC METHOD FOR LOCALIZING STRUCTURAL DISCONTINUITIES IN A ROCK MASS

EINE ANALYTISCHE METHODE FÜR DIE LOKALISIERUNG VON STRUKTURELLEN DISKONTINUITÄTEN EINER FELSMASSE

A. THOMAS

Ingénieur Ecole Nationale Supérieure de Géologie Nancy

J.L. MALLET F. DE BEAUCOURT

Ingénieurs Centre de Recherche Pétrographique et Géochmique Nancy

France

ABSTRACT

The autors present an analytic method for location of fractures and faults by tension or shear, with or without sliding, on a calcareous plane, in the case when these discontinuities are hiden by a recent covering.

By mean of a physic model, they show that the strains are related with spatial curvature of structural areas;

On an example of computing and mapping of curvatures they show the possibilities of the method for estimating the shape and the importance of invisible discontinuities. They recommend as a conclusion the use of such mapping to regional study of rippability and risks due, in Civil Engineering, to the discontinuities and their associated phenomenon such as sink-holes.

ZUSAMMENFASSUNG

Die Verfasser zeigen eine analytische Methode für die Lokalisierung von Störungen und Klüften, mit oder ohne Erdrutsch, auf einer kalksteinhaltigen Hochebene, wenn diese Brüche von einer neueren Decke verhüllt sind.

An Hand eines physischen Modells zeigen sie, dass die Verformungen an die räumlichen Krümmungen der struktorologischen Flächen gebunden sind.

Mittels eines Rechenbeispiels und einer automatischen Krümmungskartographie, zeigen sie die Möglichkeiten der Methode, für die Schätzung der Art und des Umfanges der nicht sichtbaren Diskontinuitäten. Als Schlussfolgerung schlagen sie die Anwendung solcher Karten vor, bei regionaler Prüfung der Anwendbarkeit von "Rippern" und bei der Untersuchung der Gefahren, die an solchen Bruchzonen in der Ingenieurgeologie sowie auch an die daran gebundenen Folgen, wie z. B. Verkarstung, gebunden sind.

RESUME

Les auteurs présentent une méthode analytique de localisation des zones de fractures ou failles d'extension et de cisaillement, avec ou sans glissement, sur un plateau calcaire, dans le cas où ces accidents sont masqués par une couverture récente.

A partir d'un modèle physique ils montrent que les déformations sont liées à la courbure spatiale de la surface structurale.

A partir d'un exemple de calcul et de cartographie automatique des courbures, ils montrent les possibilités de la méthode pour l'estimation du type et de l'importance des discontinuités non apparentes. Ils préconisent en conclusion l'application de telles cartes à l'étude régionale de la rippabilité et des risques liés en génie civil aux zones de fracturation et aux phénomènes associés tels que les karsts.

INTRODUCTION

Dans les terrains sédimentaires non métamorphisés, les grandes discontinuités, fractures et failles, affectant les massifs rocheux naissent de deux types d'états de contraintes d'origine tectonique :

- **des états de traction produisant des fissures d'extension**
- **des états déviatoires produisant des fractures de cisaillement.**

Dans des domaines de pressions et températures ne permettant pas les déformations visqueuses ou plastiques les efforts tectoniques conduisent à une rupture de type fragile, consécutive au dépassement local de la limite élastique.

Dans ces conditions, les grandes déformations des masses rocheuses ne sont possibles que par formation de discontinuités et déplacements le long de ces discontinuités.

Il existe donc nécessairement un lien entre la densité et l'importance des discontinuités et les grandes déformations des masses rocheuses, lien qui dépend, bien sûr, de la nature des roches.

Dans les régions fortement tectonisées, ce lien est fort complexe mais peut, par contre, être mis en évidence dans les massifs lithologiquement homogènes et faiblement tectonisés, c'est-à-dire dans les massifs où il est assez aisé de définir à la fois les conditions spatiales de déformation et la répartition spatiale des discontinuités. Le plateau de calcaires bajociens au voisinage de Nancy satisfait en première approximation à ces critères. C'est d'ailleurs une somme d'observations géologiques et structurales effectuées sur ce plateau qui nous a suggéré la méthode d'analyse exposée ici.

Mettre en évidence les corrélations entre discontinuités et déformations présente un intérêt économique certain dans la mesure où, s'il est relativement facile de mesurer ou d'évaluer les déformations, il est souvent très difficile de détacher les zones de fracturations le plus souvent masquées par une couverture limoneuse. Or les fractures ou les failles représentent des zones de faiblesse mécanique et des décalages dont la prévision est importante en Génie Civil. Elles sont, de plus, génératrices de réseaux de dissolutions karstiques dont il est inutile de souligner le danger lorsqu'ils sont superficiels et masqués.(THOMAS, 1973).

I. - CARACTERES GENERAUX DU SITE

Le plateau est formé d'une série calcaire d'environ 130 à 150 mètres de puissance, juxtaposition d'horizons mécaniquement différents d'une puissance de l'ordre de 10 à 20 mètres, que l'on peut considérer comme relativement constante dans la zone étudiée : environ 100 km^2.

L'ensemble repose sur l'épaisse série des marnes du Lias. Les caractères structuraux majeurs de ce plateau sont les suivants :

- un pendage général O-NO de l'ordre de 2 à 5 % ;
- des déformations tectoniques de faible amplitude, dépassant rarement 10 %, formant un assemblage complexe de flexures, d'anticlinaux, de synclinaux, de dômes et de cuvettes ; cette tectonique datant d'une époque post-jurassique est très probablement liée à des mouvements différentiels du socle primaire, considérablement atténués par les épaisses formations marneuses du Lias et du Trias ;
- des déformations structurales d'origine gravitaire sur le bord des cuestas découpant le plateau ;
- les cassures franches à rejet supérieur à quelques mètres sont exceptionnelles sur le plateau, les grandes failles ayant toutes favorisé le creusement par le réseau hydrographique de vallées qui ont traversé la série et atteint le substratum calcaire.

Manifestement, étant donné l'allure des déformations et l'orientation des grands plans de discontinuité, les efforts tectoniques responsables des déformations n'étaient pas horizontaux. La structure est ainsi liée à des mouvements différentiels essentiellement verticaux du substratum. Le phénomène dynamique majeur est donc la flexion. Les moments de flexion résultent de la répartition variable d'efforts antagonistes : les efforts tectoniques et la pesanteur.

L'examen des zones de fort gradient de déformation là où elles sont observables (carrières ou rocades) nous a conduit à distinguer deux types de grandes déformations, associées respectivement aux deux modes de rupture précités :

. la déformation par fissures d'extension radiales donne naissance à des plis "isopaques" selon la définition de MATTAUER (1973) ; Fig. 1a

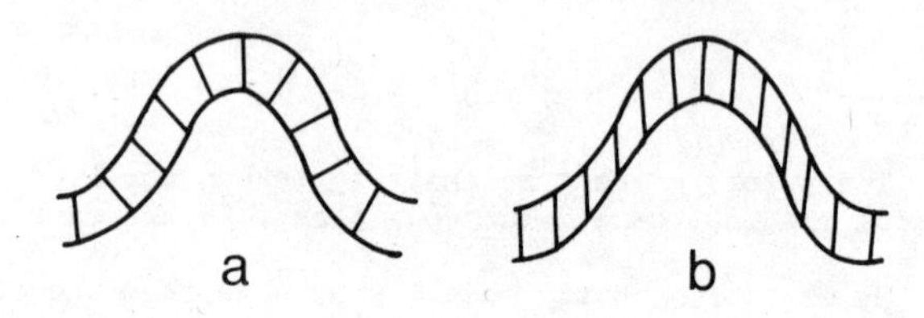

Fig. 1 - a) pli isopaque
b) pli semblable *(selon MATTAUER, 1973)*

. la déformation par glissements selon des "cascades" de discontinuités mineures (Fig. 1 b) qui donne naissance à des "pseudo-plis" de type "semblable" selon MATTAUER, c'est-à-dire dont l'épaisseur normale varie, bien que la puissance des couches reste constante.

Nous nous proposons de montrer brièvement, à l'aide d'un modèle mécanique simple, comment la flexion élastique d'une série rocheuse peut conduire à ces deux type de rupture.

II. - MODELE MECANIQUE

On ne connaît pas l'épaisseur des formations ayant recouvert le plateau avant l'érosion, mais on peut supposer que les contraintes normales étaient telles que le glissement sur les surfaces de séparation entre couches ou entre bancs à l'intérieur des couches était impossible, car nous n'avons jamais observé, sur le plateau, de traces de déplacements dans les plans de stratification.

On peut assimiler la flexion d'une portion de massif à celle d'une poutre élastique formée d'un empilement de lames minces de caractéristiques élastiques différentes, rivetée aux deux extrémités pour interdire le glissement lame sur lame (image des amortisseurs à lames).

On peut supposer la poutre non pesante et lui associer une charge uniformément répartie sur sa partie supérieure, représentant la pesanteur dans les conditions de similitude requises, une charge égale et opposée représentant sur la partie inférieure la réaction du substratum marneux.

Essayons de représenter les conditions de flexion de la série rocheuse subissant les effets du relèvement d'un compartiment du substratum (Fig. 2). La série marneuse sous-jacente ayant pour effet de diffuser la pression, nous pouvons supposer qu'il en résulte un diagramme de pression p sous la série rocheuse, du type représenté sur la figure 2. Dans notre modèle, on peut assimiler l'effet de la pesanteur, à l'extérieur du segment déformé AB, à un encastrement des deux extrémités, seule la partie centrale étant soumise à la pression p. Sur la figure 3, a été représenté le diagramme des efforts tranchants V correspondant (CRANDALL, et al, 1959) obtenu en négligeant les composantes horizontales des contraintes transmises par le support marneux.

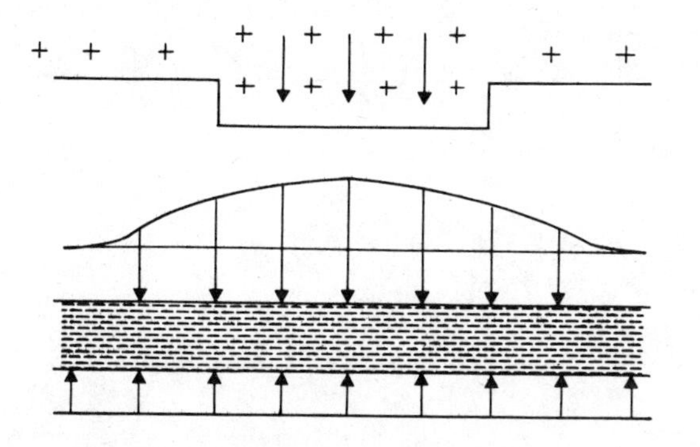

Fig. 2 - Contraintes dues au soulèvement d'un compartiment du substratum

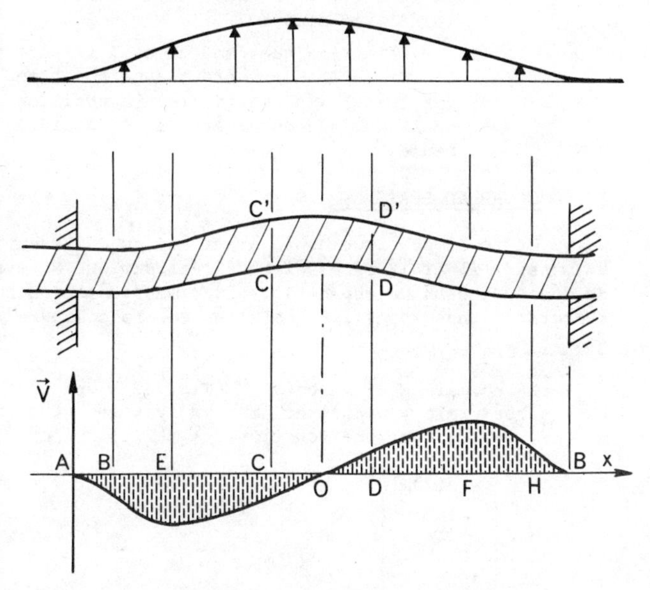

Fig. 3 - Déformation en flexion et effort tranchant dans une poutre encastrée

On constate qu'au voisinage de l'axe de flexure O et des points A et B, la faible valeur des efforts de cisaillement dans les sections planes normales à l'axe de la poutre permet d'assimiler la flexion à une flexion pure sur les segments CD, AG, et BH.

Dans la section CDC'D' (Fig. 4) de la poutre, existent donc une zone supérieure de traction, une zone inférieure de compression séparées par une surface neutre (non déformée).

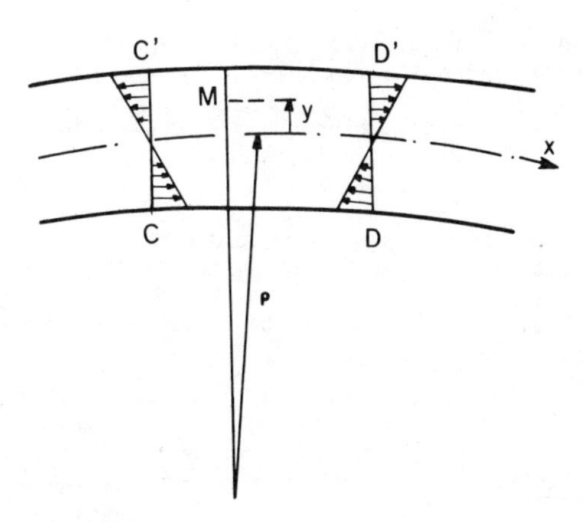

Fig. 4 - Déformation dans un état de flexion pure

Si l'on attribue au modèle une résistance à la traction relativement faible comme l'est celle des roches calcaires, on obtiendra dans cette zone une rupture par création d'un système de fissuration radiales.

Au voisinage des points d'encastrement A et B (Fig. 3), le sens de la flexion étant inverse, on aura inversion des zones de traction et compression.

Par contre, au voisinage des points d'inflexion E et F se développent d'importants efforts tranchants qui rendent probables dans ces zones, des ruptures par cisaillement. La rupture a le maximum de chances de se produire selon celle des directions conjuguées qui se rapproche le plus de la verticale, puisque rien, dans cette direction, ne s'oppose au déplacement.

Ce modèle nous permet de penser que les deux types de discontinuités sont liés au même phénomène tectonique de déformation par flexion. Ainsi, si l'on est en mesure de définir les conditions géométriques de déformation, il est possible d'en déduire l'existence et l'allure des discontinuités.

Ainsi, dans les zones où la densité d'informations ponctuelles permet d'estimer convenablement la géométrie d'une surface structurale, il sera possible de prévoir, avec une certaine probabilité, la présence de fractures de traction ou de cisaillement masquées par la couverture récente, à condition de connaître l'ordre de grandeur des déformations limites c'est-à-dire celles qui se produisent lors de la rupture en traction et en cisaillement.

III. - DEFORMATION ET COURBURE PLANE

Dans la zone étudiée, la structure présente des variations de grande amplitude auxquelles correspondent des déformations ponctuelles négligeables. Les zones de forte déformation sont les zones de variation rapide de la pente de la structure. Il était donc possible d'utiliser par exemple la norme du gradient de pente de la fonction structurale $\varphi\ (x,y)$.

Nous avons préféré user d'une quantité indépendante du repère, la courbure.

Dans le plan, la courbure C en un point d'une fonction $y = f(x)$ s'écrit :

$$C = \frac{1}{\rho}$$

où ρ est le rayon du cercle ausculateur de la fonction au point M. On notera que dans le système d'axe XY, constitué par la tangente et la normale en M, on peut écrire :

$$C = \left| Y''(X) \right|$$

. Dans le cas de la flexion pure, il existe d'ailleurs une relation simple entre déformation et courbure. En effet, dans le système d'axe constitué par la fibre neutre et sa normale, en un point M, la déformation en M a pour composantes (CRANDALL et al, 1953) (Fig. 4) :

$$\varepsilon x = -\frac{1}{\rho} y = -Cy$$

$$\varepsilon y = 0 \qquad \varepsilon xy = 0$$

Dans ce cas, on constate qu'il n'est pas indifférent, pour estimer les déformations, de mesurer la courbure au toit ou au mur de la série ou sur un niveau repère intermédiaire. Ceci présente un avantage pour l'analyse structurale. En effet, si l'on choisit comme surface de référence le toit de la formation supposé parallèle à la fibre neutre et si ce toit est une surface topographique, en tenant compte du signe algébrique de la courbure (positif si la concavité est tournée vers les z négatifs, négative dans le cas contraire) les zones présentant le maximum de déformation par extension, et donc présentant le maximum de risques de fracturation ouverte correspondront aux zones présentant un maximum de courbure positive et la courbure sera linéairement proportionnelle aux déformations de la surface de référence.

Les zones présentant les risques maximaux de fracturations ouvertes en profondeur (karstification profonde) correspondront inversement aux maxima de courbure négative, avec encore proportionnalité des courbures et des déformations.

Enfin, une étude de courbure effectuée sur ou à proximité de la ligne neutre permettra les mêmes localisations, mais les déformations superficielles ou profondes ne seront pas proportionnelles à la courbure calculée.

Il est de toute façon difficile d'estimer la position de la ligne neutre dans une série composite.

. Dans les zones en flexion avec contraintes de cisaillement, on ne peut plus écrire de relation de proportionnalité entre déformation et courbure. La courbure étant une fonction croissante de la déformation, il est néanmoins intéressant d'utiliser la fonction courbure pour la localisation des zones fissurées par cisaillement. La figure 5 représente le diagramme de courbure obtenu pour la couche déformée sur laquelle nous avons reporté la répartition des zones travaillant en extension ou en cisaillement.

On constate que l'on peut user de deux méthodes approximatives de localisation des zones cisaillées que l'on peut faire correspondre :

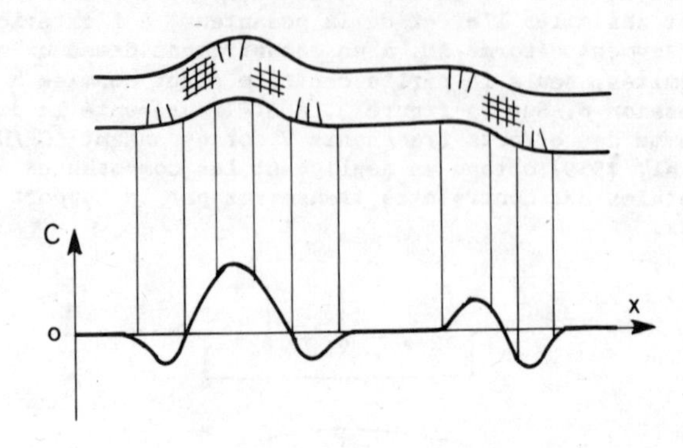

Fig. 5 - Diagramme de courbure plane d'une couche déformée

- soit aux zones de fort gradient de courbure ;
- soit plus précisément aux zones correspondant à la fois à un point d'inflexion, et à une pente forte de la fonction courbure, c'est-à-dire, les zones de maxima de la dérivée première et de minima de la dérivée seconde.

On notera que dans ce cas, le toit et le mur de la série étant superposables par translation verticale, la position de la surface de référence est indifférente.

IV. - COURBURE SPATIALE

Cette étude structurale ayant été conduite sur un massif, il était nécessaire de réaliser une analyse de courbure dans un espace à trois dimensions et donc recourir à une expression analytique de la courbure spatiale.

La normale $\vec{N}$ en un point M (Fig. 6) d'une surface structurale représentée dans un système orthonormé $(\vec{ox}, \vec{oy}, \vec{oz})$ par une fonction $z = \varphi(x,y)$, s'écrit :

$$\vec{N} = \begin{bmatrix} -\partial\varphi/\partial x \\ -\partial\varphi/\ y \\ 1 \end{bmatrix}$$

Dans un plan P passant par M et contenant $\vec{N}$, désignons par $\Gamma(S,P)$ la trace de $\varphi(x,y)$ et par $R(P)$ le rayon de courbure de $\Gamma(S,P)$ au point M. Le centre de courbure C_p de $\Gamma(S,P)$ en M satisfait à :

$$\vec{MC_p} = -R(P) \cdot \vec{N}$$

Pour deux plans Pi et Pj différents, on a en général $R(P_i) \neq R(P_j)$ et donc $C_{Pj} \neq C_{Pi}$ (Fig. 6).

On démontre, en géométrie différentielle des surfaces, que, parmi tous les plans passant par M et contenant $\vec{N}$, il en existe deux P_1 et P_2, orthogonaux tels que $R_1 = R(P_1)$ soit, en valeur algébrique, le rayon maximal et $R_2 = R(P_2)$ le rayon minimal de courbure de toutes les courbes $\Gamma(S,P)$. Par définition, R_1 et R_2 sont appelés "rayons de courbure (normale) principaux" de la surface $\Gamma(x,y)$ en M.

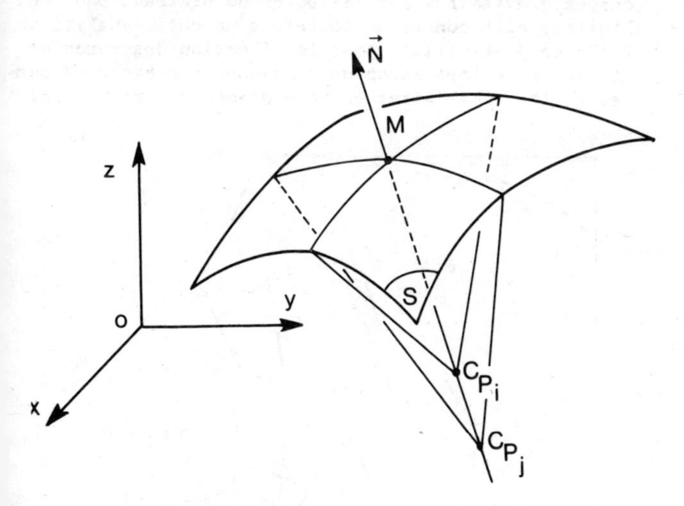

Fig. 6 - Courbures normales en un point M d'une surface S suivant 2 plans P_i et P_j

Schématiquement, la méthode de calcul de R_1 et R_2 est la suivante :

- soit $\|\vec{N}\|$ la somme du vecteur $\vec{N}$ qui s'écrit :

$$\|\vec{N}\| = \sqrt{\left(\frac{\partial\varphi}{\partial x}\right)^2 + \left(\frac{\partial\varphi}{\partial y}\right)^2 + 1}$$

- soient d'autre part [A] et [B] les matrices

$$[A] = \begin{bmatrix} 1 + \left(\frac{\partial\varphi}{\partial x}\right)^2 & \frac{\partial\varphi}{\partial x} \cdot \frac{\partial\varphi}{\partial y} \\ \frac{\partial\varphi}{\partial x} \frac{\partial\varphi}{\partial y} & 1 + \left(\frac{\partial\varphi}{\partial y}\right)^2 \end{bmatrix}$$

$$[B] = \frac{1}{\|\vec{N}\|} \begin{bmatrix} \frac{\partial^2\varphi}{\partial x^2} & \frac{\partial^2\varphi}{\partial x \partial y} \\ \frac{\partial^2\varphi}{\partial x \partial y} & \frac{\partial^2\varphi}{\partial y^2} \end{bmatrix}$$

dont les éléments a_{ij} et b_{ij} représentent respectivement les premier et second tenseur intrinsèque co-variant de la surface au point M considéré. En désignant par a^{ij} les éléments de la matrice $[A]^{-1}$, si l'on pose :

$$H = \frac{1}{2} \sum_i \sum_j a^{ij} \cdot b_{ij}$$

$$K = \frac{\text{dét } [B]}{\text{dét } [A]}$$

on montre en géométrie différentielle des surfaces que :

$$H = \frac{1}{2} \left(\frac{1}{R_1} + \frac{1}{R_2}\right)$$

$$K = \frac{1}{R_1 R_2}$$

H et K appelés respectivement "courbure moyenne" et "courbure totale" permettent de calculer R_1 et R_2 et les courbures maxima et minima

$$C_1 = \frac{1}{R_1}, \quad C_2 = \frac{1}{R_2}$$

V. - OBTENTION D'UNE CARTE DE COURBURE

La figure 7 représente une carte de la courbure principale majeure effectuée sur la surface structurale d'un horizon repère situé à la base de la série calcaire.

Cette carte a été réalisée sur table traçante d'un ordinateur à partir d'un calcul de courbure au noeud d'un réseau régulier dense, à partir d'une fonction représentant la surface structurale. Cette fonction a été calculée par la méthode des filtres autorégressifs, à l'aide d'un programme réalisé par J.L. MALLET (1972), à partir d'un ensemble de 96 points de mesure.

La figure 8 qui représente les failles et zones de fracturation connues ou observables sur le territoire étudié donne une idée globale des possibilités de cette méthode pour l'évaluation des possibilités de fracturations avec ou sans rejet, ouvertes ou non. Cette information est importante mais il semble que l'on puisse aller beaucoup plus loin dans l'interprétation.

VI. - POSSIBILITES ET LIMITATIONS DE LA METHODE

1 - Nous avons vu qu'il était possible de distinguer le risque de fracturation d'extension ou de cisaillement. Nous ne présentons pas ici, faute de place, de carte des gradients de courbure, significatifs des déformations de cisaillement. La densité des courbes en donne toutefois une visualisation satisfaisante.

2 - Une autre possibilité est offerte par la définition d'une courbure limite de rupture ou "seuil de courbure". S'il n'est pas envisageable de faire appel aux lois rhéologiques inconnues à grande échelle des différents faciès et donc de construire à partir de ces lois un modèle assez satisfaisant pour définir des seuils de courbures calculés relatifs à l'extension et au cisaillement, il est, par contre, possible de les définir statistiquement à partir de zones-étalons où la tectonique est connue.

Il est toutefois illusoire de prétendre définir deux seuils de courbure distincts relatifs à chaque type de déformation.

Si l'on se donne un seuil commun, on peut toutefois avoir une idée à postériori du type et de l'importance des déformations, d'après l'importance de la variation de courbure au-delà de ce seuil, seules les déformations de cisaillement pouvant dans ce contexte géologique produire, après rupture, d'importants gradients de courbure.

Il existe toutefois une méthode plus élégante d'estimation des déformations basée sur les propriétés des surfaces développables (déformées d'un plan sans étirement) qui, en tout point, possèdent une courbure principal mineure nulle et une courbure principale majeure finie non nulle.

Fig. 7 - Carte de la courbure principale majeure
- positive en hachures verticales
- négative en hachures obliques

Prenons comme surface de référence une limite de faciès qu'on peut estimer proche de surface neutre dans la partie centrale de la série ; si l'on réalise une carte de la courbure principale mineure de cette surface, on trouvera une courbure nulle ou presque, à l'aplomb des zones d'extension où la surface neutre est déformée sans étirement, non nulle dans les zones de cisaillement et de valeur absolue d'autant plus importante que les déplacements par glissement sont importants.

En dehors des hypothèses d'application, la principale limitation à cette méthode est liée à la valeur de la fonction représentant la surface structurale. Cette valeur dépend en effet de la densité des points de mesure au voisinage des variations structurales et de la stabilité de la fonction d'interpolation. Pour cette dernière condition, nous pensons disposer d'un outil analytique satisfaisant.

La première condition exige que l'analyse structurale soit effectuée par étape en ajoutant si possible à chaque étape, des points de mesure dans les zones jugées suspectes à l'étape précédente.

CONCLUSION

Il est certain que cette méthode est assujettie à des hypothèses géologiques restrictives, en particulier l'hypothèse d'isopuissance de la série, restriction qui peut toutefois être limitée aux unités de faciès constitutives dans la mesure où l'on peut découper le domaine en secteurs approximativement d'égale puissance, sur lesquels on peut définir des seuils de courbure différents, ce que nous avons fait pour l'étude des fauchages gravitaires sur les bords du plateau. Dans ces limites, elle constitue toutefois un outil analytique riche en possibilités pour la sélection des zones de risques et la prévision de campagnes géophysiques sur les plateaux calcaires en voie d'aménagement urbain.

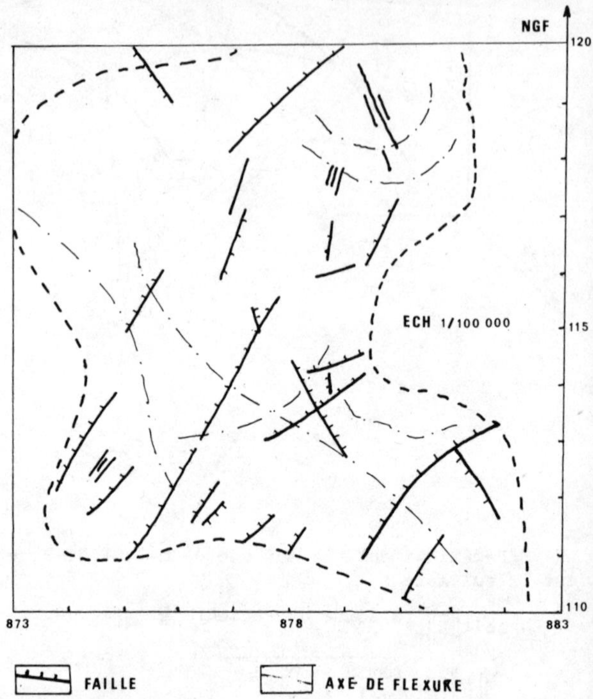

Fig. 8 - Failles et zones de flexure reconnues

BIBLIOGRAPHIE

CRANDALL S.H., DAHL N.C., LARDNER T.J., 1959 - An Introduction to the Mechanics of solids. Mac Graw Hill NEW-YORK.

MALLET J.L., 1972 - Méthodes et techniques de la cartographie automatique numérique. C.R.P.G. NANCY, (à paraître).

MATTAUER M., 1973 - Les déformations des Matériaux de l'Ecorce Terrestre - Hermann PARIS.

THOMAS A., 1973 - Détermination et cartographie des zones de risque en mécanique des sols. Symposium Sol et Sous-sol et Sécurité des Constructions - CANNES.

THOMAS A., 1973 - Détermination probabiliste des zones de karstification. Symposium de l'IAEG, HANOVRE.

THEME 2

THÈME 2

THEMA 2

D

Fluid Flow Effects

D

Effets de l'écoulement du liquide

D

Flüssigkeitsströmungseffekt

ACOUSTIC EMISSION IN ROCK DURING FLUID INJECTION

L'ÉMISSION ACOUSTIQUE EN ROCHE ENGENDIT PENDANT L'INJECTION DE FLUIDE

AKUSTISCHE AUSSENDUNG IM GESTEIN UNTER FLÜSSIGKEITSEINSPRITZUNG

James D. BYERLEE
Geophysicist
U.S. Geological Survey
Menlo Park, California

SUMMARY

A large scale field experiment at the Rangely oil field has been underway since 1969 to determine whether earthquakes can be controlled by controlling the fluid pressure in active fault zones. Concurrently, laboratory experiments have been carried out to study the acoustic emission generated during fluid injection into a fault zone in a sample of Weber Sandstone, the reservoir rock at the oil field. As in the field experiments, the laboratory experiments show that when the fluid injection pressure in increased, the elastic shock activity increases, and it decreases when the injection pressure is decreased. Also, the results from a number of cycles of fluid pressure increase and decrease have shown that the elastic shock activity decreases as the stress is relieved by movement on the fault. Thus, it is clear that earthquakes can be generated by fluid injection into active faults, and the earthquake hazard may be reduced as the tectonic stresses are relieved.

RÉSUMÉ

Depuis 1969, une expérience de champ a la grande échelle au champ de pétrole de Rangely a été en train pour déterminer soit que l'influence de la force de fluide peut contrôler les tremblements de terre dans une zone de faille. Des expériences de laboratoire a été accomplies pour étudier l'émission acoustique qui est engendrée pendant l'injection de fluide dans une zone de faille dans un exemple de "Weber Sandstone", la roche réservoir au champ de pétrole. Comme les expériences de champ, les expériences de laboratoire montrent que l'activité de choc élastique d'accroît quand la pression d'injection s'accroît, et elle décroît quand la pression décroît. Aussi, les conséquences de plusieurs cycles d'accroissement et décroissement de pression fluide ont montré que l'activité de choc élastique décroît quand la force est soulagée par mouvement sur la faille. Donc c'est évident que l'injection de fluide dans les failles actives peut engendrer les tremblements de terre, et l'hasard de ces tremblements peut être réduit pendant que les forces tectoniques soient soulagées.

ZUSAMMENFASSUNG

Seit 1969 wurde ein ausgedehntes Experiment im Rangely Ölgebiet durchgeführt um festzustellen, ob Erdbeben durch Kontrolle des Flüssigkeitsdruckes in aktiven Verwerfungszonen reguliert werden können. Gleichzeitig wurden Laboruntersuchungen an einer Probe des Webersandsteins, dem "reservoir rock" im Ölgebiet durchgeführt um das akustische Aussenden, hervorgerufen durch Flüssigkeitseinspritzung in eine Verwerfungszone, zu erforschen. Die Versuche im Ölgebiet wie auch im Labor zeigen, dass durch Erhöhen des Flüssigkeitseinspritzdruckes die elastische Erschütterungsaktivität zunimmt, und dass sie abnimmt, wenn der Einspritzdruck erniedrigt wird. Ausserdem zeigen die Ergebnisse einer Anzahl von abwechselnden Flüssigkeitsdruck Erhöhungen und Senkungen, dass die elastische Erschütterungsaktivität mit einer Druckentlastung durch Bewegung an der Verwerfung abnimmt. Daraus geht hervor, dass Erdbeben durch Flüssigkeitseinspritzungen in aktive Verwerfungszonen hervorgerufen werden können, und das die Erdbebengefahr durch Entlasten des tektonischen Druckes reduziert werden kann.

INTRODUCTION

It has been suggested (Scholz and others 1973) that changes in seismic velocity, electrical resistivity, radon emission, ground tilt, and seismic activity may precede large earthquakes. A vigorous program of research is currently underway in a number of institutions throughout the world to test whether it is possible to predict the time, location and size of an earthquake using any of the abovementioned phenomenon.

Another direction of earthquake research is in earthquake control. The basic idea is that it may be possible to release the tectonic stresses in a series of small earthquakes and thus reduce the risk of the stresses building up to a level high enough to trigger a catastrophic earthquake. This idea is not new; during an ad hoc panel discussion on earthquake prediction in 1965, David Griggs suggested that earthquakes might be controlled by injecting fluid into a fault zone. The idea gained nationwide attention when Evans (1966) suggested that a large number of earthquakes in the Denver region had been triggered by the injection of fluid into a waste-disposal well at the Rocky Mountain Arsenal. Healy and others (1968) have subsequently shown that there was a high correlation between the fluid pressure and the level of seismic activity.

The Rangely oil field in northwest Colorado is now seismically active. Since 1958, water has been injected into the reservoir rock in a program of secondary oil recovery. It has been assumed that as at Denver, the earthquakes in the region have been triggered by an increase of fluid pressure in a fault zone, which is under shear stress (Raleigh and others, 1972).

Since 1969, the U.S. Geological Survey, in cooperation with the Chevron Oil Company, has been carrying out a series of experiments at the Rangely oil field. The aim of the project has been to find out if it is possible to control earthquake activity by controlling the fluid pressure in the fault zone. Concurrently with this large-scale field experiment, laboratory experiments were carried out to study the acoustic emission generated in rock during fluid injection. The purpose of the laboratory experiments was to provide information that could be used to guide the direction of the costly and time-consuming field experiments.

In this paper we report the results of one of the laboratory experiments that is closely analogous to the field experiment.

EXPERIMENTAL METHOD

Specimens of Weber Sandstone, the reservoir rock at the oil field, were cylinders 7.6 cm diameter and 19 cm long. They were jacketed in a polyurethane tube with a wall thickness of 0.476 cm.

Lead zirconate piezoelectric transducers that had a resonant frequency of 600 Khz were attached to hardened steel plugs and fastened to the cylindrical surface of the rock with epoxy cement. Six transducers were used. The position of four of them is shown in Figure 1. The position of the other two is at the center line of the sample on the outer surface facing the viewer and on the opposite side away from the viewer. The electrical leads from the transducers passed through insulated leads in the hardened steel end plug to an electronic system which will be described below.

The confining pressure fluid was kerosene. Water could be injected into the sample through the hollow end plug. The confining pressure and the fluid injection pressure were measured with heise gauges.

The axial force on the sample was applied with a hydraulic ram through a hardened steel piston. The force on the piston was measured with a DCDT 1000 transducer. The output of the load cell and the displacement transducer were recorded with an xy recorder.

The electronic system for recording the acoustic emission was supplied by Nanodyne Corporation, Sudbury, Massachusetts. It consisted of six amplifiers, discriminators and counters. The frequency response of the amplifiers was from 20 Khz to 10 Mhz. The counters counted pulses of 0.1 microsecond interval. When any one of the channels received a signal from the transducers that was above the threshold level of the discriminators, all six channels would start counting. When each channel received a signal above the threhold level, its counter would stop. Thus, when an acoustic emission event occurred in the sample, six numbers would be recorded. One set of numbers would be zero because the start and stop signal on one channel would occur at the same time. The other channels would record to an accuracy of 0.1 microsecond the relative arrival time of the acoustic emission event at the transducers.

From this data, the coordinates of the source of the acoustic emission event could be calculated. After each event, the recorded data would be printed on paper tape and the system reset. During the experiment, minute time marks would also be recorded. From these data, a histogram of the number of events per minute that occurred during the experiment could be constructed.

EXPERIMENTAL RESULTS

In some of the experiments an initially intact sample would be subjected to a confining pressure and a differential stress. Fluid would then be injected at one end of the sample and the location of the shocks could be mapped as a function of time as the pressure front advanced. Probably the most significant experiment that we have done, as far as earthquake generation and control is concerned, is the one that we report here.

In this experiment a sample under a confining pressure of 1200 bars was subjected to a differential stress until failure occurred on a throughgoing fault inclined at an angle of approximately 18° to the axis of the cylinder. The differential stress on the sample was then increased to 3.0 Kb and the acoustic emission generated in the sample was recorded.

During this experiment, the piston was advanced until the axial stress reached the required value and then stopped. As movement occurred on the fault, the axial stress decreased slightly but no attempt was made to adjust for this because the threshold level of the electronic system was set to such a low level that the acoustic signals generated by injection of hydraulic fluid into the ram was sufficient to trigger the system. The exact decrease in load due to movement on the fault throughout the experiment could not be calculated because of the large friction at the O-ring through which the piston moved. The decrease in differential stress on the sample was probably of the order of 100 bars.

The shocks that were recorded in this experiment were very small and accurate locations of the source of the signals could not be calculated because by the time that the signals arrived at a remote transducer, they would be attenuated to such a low level that accurate timing of their arrival could not be obtained.

A histogram of the number of the small shocks could, however, be constructed. The results from this experiment are shown in Figure 2. The level of activity was initially about 15 acoustic emission events per minute. After fifteen minutes, water was ejected at one end of the sample at a pressure of 600 bars. The activity of shocks rapidly increased to a level of about 55 shocks per minute. After fifteen minutes, the injection pressure was decreased to zero. Following this, the acoustic emission activity decreased and after fifteen minutes, the level was about 20 shocks per minute.

The injection pressure was once more increased to 600 bars and as in the previous injection cycle, the activity of acoustic emission increased, but this time even after twenty minutes of fluid injection, the activity only reached a level of about 35 shocks per minute. Once more, the injection pressure was decreased to zero and after fifteen minutes, the number of shocks per minute had reached 10.

The injection pressure was increased to 600 bars again and held this time for forty minutes. During this injection cycle, the activity reached a level of only 25 shocks per minute, and when the injection pressure dropped to zero, the activity fell off to about 10 shocks per minute.

In this experiment it is clear that the acoustic emission increased when the fluid injection pressure was increased, and decreased when the injection pressure was decreased. It is also clear that the level of activity decreased with each successive injection cycle.

Scholz (1968) has shown that the acoustic emission generated during sliding on a saw cut in a rock sample under confining pressure increases as the differential stress is increased. In our experiments, the differential stress decreased as movement occurred on the fault surfaces; thus, the differential stress on the sample was lower with each successive injection cycle, and this is most probably the reason that the maximum number of events per minute during fluid injection decreased with each cycle.

DISCUSSION

Acoustic emission is the name given by material scientists to high frequency elastic radiation generated in material under stress. In our study the frequency of the radiation that could be detected was in the range of 20 Khz to 10 Mhz. In the earth, elastic radiation generated by an earthquake has a frequency of about 10 hz. It is similar to acoustic emission except that the frequency is much lower, and the amplitude of the signals is much greater.

Our laboratory experiments show that acoustic emission in rock can be triggered by injecting fluid into a fault zone which is under shear stress. It has also been demonstrated at Denver and at the Rangely oil field that earthquakes can be triggered by the injection of fluid into the earth.

At the Rangely oil field, it has been shown (Raleigh and others, 1972) that the earthquakes in the region are caused by movement on a pre-existing fault that is under shear stress. At Denver the subsurface structure and state of stress in the rocks is not well known, but the historical records reveal that a number of small earthquakes had occurred in the region prior to the injection of fluid (Hadsell, 1967). It therefore seems likely that as at Rangely, the subsurface rocks in the region are under tectonic stresses and that the earthquakes generated during fluid injection occurred on a pre-existing fault.

Thus, the laboratory experiment that we have reported here is closely analogous to the large-scale field experiments at Denver and at Rangely. In the field experiments, it is both time-consuming and costly to carry out a number of fluid injection and withdrawal cycles to find out whether it is possible to turn the earthquakes on and off at will. Nevertheless, with the financial support of the Advanced Research Project Agency, the U.S. Geological Survey commenced an earthquake control program at the Rangely oil field in 1969 (Healy and others, 1972; Healy and Pakiser, 1971).

Between October 1969 and May 1971, one cycle of fluid injection and withdrawal was completed (Healy and others, 1972; Handin and Raleigh, 1972). The results of this experiment are shown in Figure 3. As in the laboratory experiments, the earthquake activity increased during fluid injection and decreased during fluid withdrawal. A second cycle of fluid injection was commenced in May 1971, and the results, although not shown in Figure 3, reveal that as in the first injection cycle, the earthquake activity increased when the fluid pressure was increased, and it decreased when the fluid pressure was decreased. They also show that as in the laboratory experiments, the earthquake activity during the second cycle was lower than what it was during the first cycle (Healy, oral communication, 1973). The large-scale field experiments at Rangely have now been terminated, but our laboratory experiments would suggest that, if a third injection cycle was carried out, the earthquake activity would be even lower than what it was during the second cycle.

The reason for this decrease in earthquake activity during the second injection cycle at Rangely is most probably because the earthquakes are generated by sudden slip on a pre-existing fault, and as this occurs, the tectonic stresses are relieved. It seems likely that if fluid was injected for a long enough period of time, all the tectonic stresses would be relieved, and the earthquake activity would stop altogether regardless of the fluid pressure in the fault zone.

Both the laboratory experiments and the large-scale field experiments clearly show that shear stress on a fault can be relieved by injecting fluid into the fault zone, and that when this stress is relieved, the earthquake activity decreases.

REFERENCES

Evans, D. M., 1966, The Denver area earthquakes and the Rocky Mountain Arsenal disposal well: Mountain Geologist, v. 3, no. 1, p. 23-36.

Hadsell, F., 1968, History of earthquake activity in Colorado: Colorado School of Mines Quart. Rep., v. 63, no. 1, p. 57-72.

Handin, J., and Raleigh, C. B., 1972, Manmade earthquakes and earthquake control: Proc. Internat. Soc. for Rock Mech., Stuttgart, T2-D1-T2-D1-.

Healy, J. H., Rubey, W. W., Griggs, D. T., and Raleigh, C. B., 1968, The Denver earthquakes: Sci., v. 161, p. 1301-1310.

Healy, J. H., and Pakiser, L. C., 1971, Manmade earthquakes and earthquake prediction: Am. Geophys. Union Trans., v. 52, no. 5, p. 171-173.

Healy, J. H., Lee, W. H. K., Pakiser, L. C., Raleigh, C. B., and Wood., M. D., 1972, Prospects for earthquake prediction and control: Tectonophys., v. 14, p. 319-332.

Raleigh, C. B., Healy, J. H., and Bredehoeft, J. D., 1972, Faulting and crustal stress at Rangely Colorado: Flow and Fracture of Rocks, A.G.U. Monog. 16, p. 275-284.

Scholz, C. H., 1968, Microfracturing and the inelastic deformation of rock in compression: Jour. Geophys. Research, v. 73, no. 4, p. 1417-1432.

Scholz, C. H., Sykes, L. R., and Aggarwal, Y. P., 1973, Earthquake prediction: a physical basis: Sci., v. 181, p. 803-810.

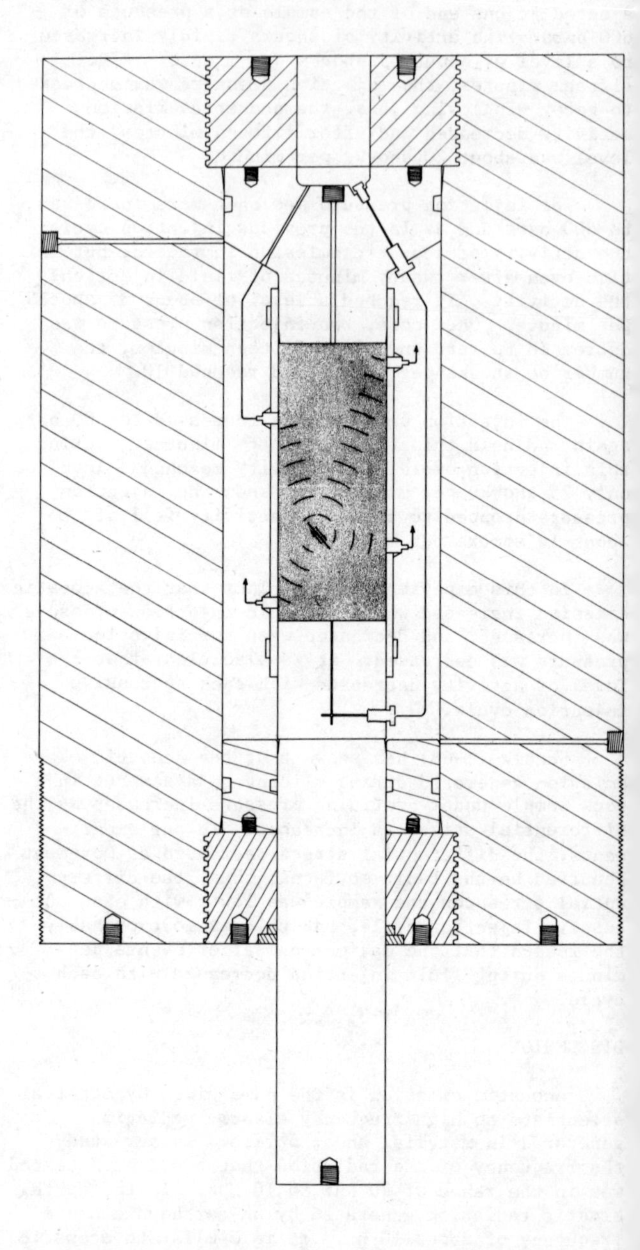

Fig. 1. Schematic diagram of loading system, the sample shown shaded is contained within a pressure vessel. Load is applied to the sample with a pisto[n] which moves through an O-ring seal.

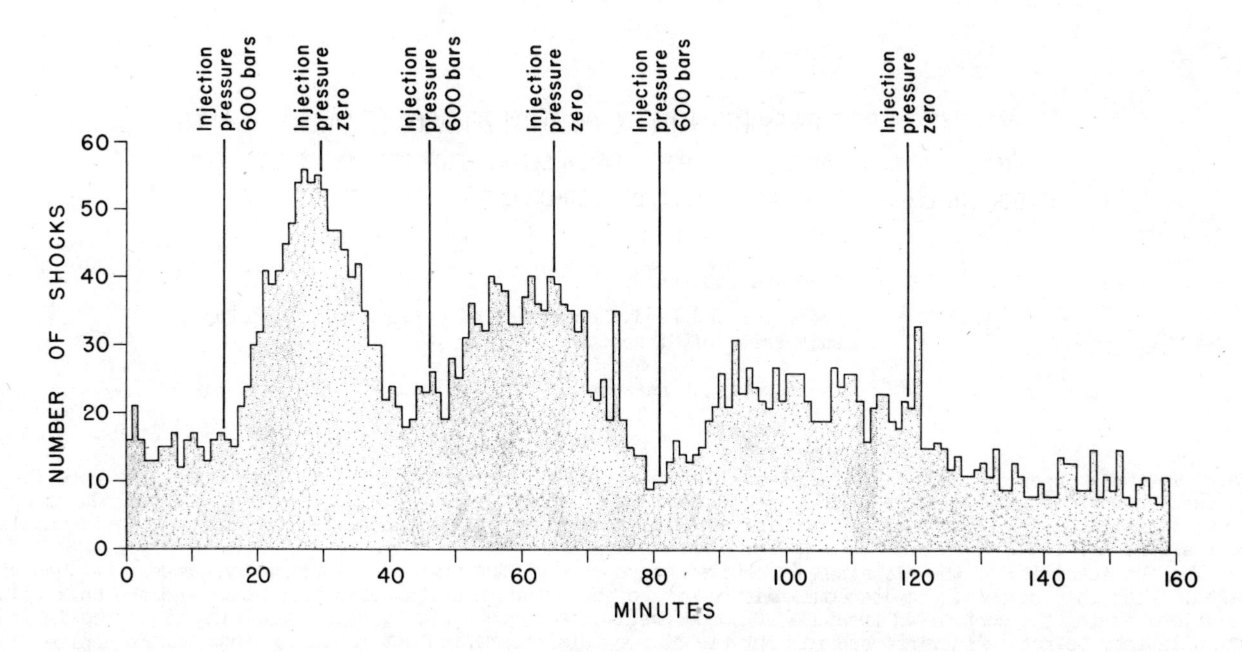

Fig. 2. Histogram of the number of acoustic emission events during fluid injection into a sample of Weber Sandstone containing a fault.

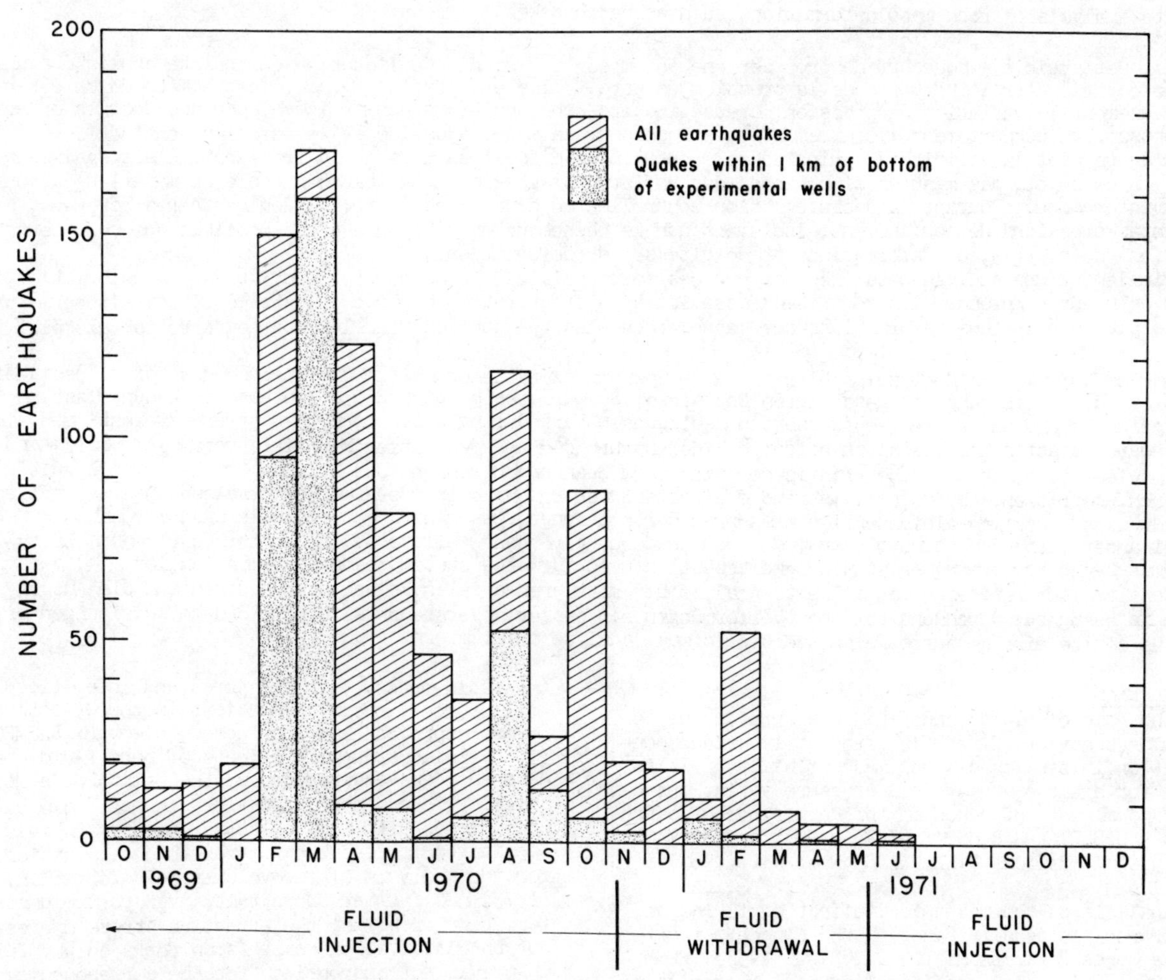

Fig. 3. Histogram of the number of earthquakes during fluid injection and withdrawal at the Rangely oil field (courtesy of J. H. Healy).

INFLUENCE OF PORE PRESSURE ON THE DEFORMATION BEHAVIOR OF SATURATED ROCKS

INFLUENCE DE LA PRESSION DE PORE SUR LA DÉFORMATION DES ROCHES SATURÉES

DER EINFLUSS DES PORENDRUCKS AUF DIE VERFORMUNG VON GESÄTTIGTEN GESTEINEN

F. H. CORNET Graduate student

C. FAIRHURST Professor and Head, Department of Civil and Mineral Eng., University of Minnesota

Minneapolis, Minnesota

ABSTRACT: This paper proposes a simple stress decomposition for the analysis of the influence of a pore fluid pressure on the deformation of saturated rocks. Using this approach, the change of pore pressure induced by external loads is derived for undrained conditions assuming a linear elastic behavior for both the solid matrix and the bulk material.

The applicability of the classical effective stress concept during the disintegration process is then discussed. With this respect, simultaneous measurements of both the interconnected pore space and the bulk volume variations during the controlled fracture of porous sedimentary rocks with various confining pressures indicate that dilatancy is not an intrinsic characteristic of rock disintegration but rather depends on the applied loads the deformations and the deformation rates for a constant temperature.

Finally a detailed analysis of the mean axial force-mean deformations curves obtained in laboratory conditions is shown to provide a better comprehension of rock fracture mechanisms which ultimately could allow a more accurate analysis of rock mass deformations such as earthquakes.

RESUME: Cet article a pour but de proposer une décomposition simple de l'état de contrainte appliqué à une roche saturée pour étudier l'influence de la pression de pore. Il a été possible grace à cette méthode de déterminer rigoureusement la variation de pression poreuse induite, en conditions non-drainées, par des charges exterieures en supposant un comportement linéairement élastique pour la matrice solide et le matériau considéré.

D'autre part la validité du principe des contraintes éffectives lors de la fracturation est également discutée. A ce sujet, des mesures simultanées des variations aussi bien du volume globale du materiau que du volume poreux interconnecté durant la désintegration controllée de deux types de roches sédimentaires poreuses, pour diférentes pressions de confinement, indiquent que le phénomène de dilatance n'est possible que pour certaines conditions de charges, de déformations et de vitesses de déformations.

Finalement une analyse detaillée des courbes force axiale moyenne par unité de surface - déformation moyenne permet de mieux comprendre les mécanismes associés à la fracturation des roches. Celle-ci devrait permettre une analyse plus précise des déformations des masses rocheuses tel que les tremblements de terre par example.

ZUSAMENFASSUNG: Dieses Heft zeigt eine einfache Spannungszergliederung für die Analyse des Porenflüssigkeitsdrucks auf die Verformung von gesättigten Gesteinen So wurde es möglich die durch äussere Ladungslasten herbeigeführte und unter nicht-entw sserten Bedingungen Veränderung des Porendrucks streng zu bestimmen, indem ein lineares elastisches Verhalten beider solider Naturböden und des ganzen Materials vorausgesetzt wird.

In wie weit das klassische Prinzip der wirksamen Spannungen während des Zusammenbruchsvorgangs gültig ist, wird auch umstritten. Daraufhin, während des gesteuerten Bruchs beider sedimentaren Felsen unter verschiedenen Manteldrücken, bezeigen gleichzeitige Messungen der Änderungen des ganzen Materialvolumens bezeichnungsweise untereinander verbunden Porenvolumens, das der Ausdehnungsvorgang (dilatancy) nur unter bestimmten Zasts-, Verformungs-und Verformungs-geschwindigkeitsbestimmungen für eine steten Temperatur möglich ist.

Schliesslich wird eine detaillierte Analyse der mittleren axialen Belastungen bezogen auf die Ausgangsquerfläche in Bezug zu durchschnittlichen Verformungen ein besseres Verständnis für die Brucherscheinungen ermöglichen; es sollte eine genauere Felsmassensverformung analyse erleichtern.

Introduction

The role of fluids and fluid pressure on the deformation behavior of rock is often an important consideration in studies of rock mass stability. It is known, for example, that fluid pressure variations can exert a dominant influence on the occurrence of earthquakes [HUBBERT and RUBEY (1959), HANDIN and RALEIGH (1972)] or landslides [TERMINASSIAN et al. (1967), LANE (1969)].

Analysis of the mechanical effect of fluids on soil or rock is usually based on the concept of "effective stress" [TERZAGHI (1923), BIOT (1955), SKEMPTON (1960)], in which the 'total stress' tensor usually employed in mechanics is replaced by a stress tensor dependent on both the applied (solid) forces and the fluid pressure in the pores and interstices of th soil or rock. Some limitations in the effective stress approach have been noted, however. SKEMPTON (1960), discussing the effects of pore fluid pressure on the stresses generated at the points of contact of soil particles, concluded that, for the same total applied load, different effective stresses should be considered for the shear strength determination and for the analysis of the volumetric deformation. ROB (1973) has further shown that, even for volumetric deformation problems, the effective stress expression is not unique, i.e. the expression for a bulk volumetric change is not appropriate for the corresponding pore volume variation. He concluded that, since the effective stress tensor is not uniquely defined, the concept is of no real help in a study of the influence of pore fluid pressure on rock.

This paper outlines a different stress decomposition that is seen to yield interesting results in the study of pore pressure effects, both for the elastic domain and during the disintegration process. Results of laboratory experiments involving disintegration of fluid filled specimens are included, together with a discussion of some possible implications concerning earthquake mechanisms.

1. Effective Stresses and a Proposed Alternative

SKEMPTON (1954) noted that, in various problems involving the undrained strength of soils, the change in pore pressure occurring under changes in total stresses must be known, and that, for this purpose it was convenient to express the pore pressure variation Δu, due to changes $\Delta\sigma_1$, $\Delta\sigma_3$, in the two principal stresses, as follows:

$$\Delta u = B[\Delta\sigma_3 + A(\Delta\sigma_1 - \Delta\sigma_3)]$$

where A and B are "pore pressure coefficients". Since these coefficients can be measured experimentally in the undrained triaxial test, where the change $\Delta\sigma_3$ is applied by the so-called 'confining pressure', he proposed that the application of the change in stresses $\Delta\sigma_1$ and $\Delta\sigma_3$ be considered as taking place in two stages: (1) an all-round increment $\Delta\sigma_3$ is applied and (2) the 'deviator stress" $(\Delta\sigma_1 - \Delta\sigma_3)$ is applied.

Accordingly, he derived expressions for A and B and discussed the influences of the degree of saturation and of the rheological characteristics of the soil on these two coefficients. This approach has been found very useful in solving problems of soils in undrained conditions.

However, it is important to note that the expressions for A and B were derived with the implicit assumption that the solid matrix compressibility is negligible. As will be shown in a subsequent paragraph, this assumption is not always permissible for rocks. In addition, it should be noted that SKEMPTON'S deviator stress $(\Delta\sigma_1 - \Delta\sigma_3)$ is not a deviator stress in the classical sense, since it does not correspond to a pure shear stress (a pure shear stress is a tensor in which the sum of the diagonal terms is identically 0).

Classically, the stress tensor $\underset{\sim}{\sigma}$ (the subscript $\sim$ is used to indicate a tensor, the unit tensor being denoted by $\underset{\sim}{1}$)can be decomposed into a mean normal stress and a deviator stress part, the latter corresponding to a pure shear stress.

Accordingly, the total state of stress acting on a saturated rock element [assumed to be large enough compared to the size of the pores that it is representative of the whole volume, but small enough so that it can be considered as infinitesimal in the mathematical analysis] may be decomposed analytically into three components as shown in Figure 1.

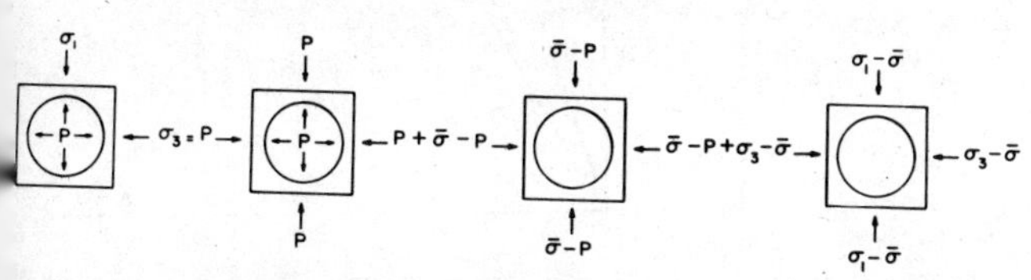

Figure 1 - Decomposition de l'état de contrainte proposé dans le texte

Abb. 1 - Spennungszergliederung die im text vorgeschlagen wird

Component I corresponds to an equal internal and external hydrostatic pressure $p\underset{\sim}{1}$ ('internal' refers to the interconnected pore space).

Component II corresponds to an external hydrostatic stress

$$\bar{\sigma}\underset{\sim}{1} - p\underset{\sim}{1} \text{ where } \bar{\sigma} = \sigma_{ii}/3$$

Component III corresponds to an external deviator stress tensor

$$\tilde{\underset{\sim}{\sigma}} = \underset{\sim}{\sigma} - \bar{\sigma}\underset{\sim}{1}, \ \tilde{\sigma}_{ij} = \sigma_{ij} - \bar{\sigma}\delta_{ij}$$

where δ_{ij} is the Kronecker delta symbol.

In such a stress decomposition component III corresponds to a pure shear. Its influence on rock deformation behavior is described more easily than in the usual "effective stress" decomposition, as is demonstrated below.

2. Elastic Behavior

Both the solid matrix and the bulk material are assumed to be linearly elastic. Following GEERTSMA (1957) and NUR and BYERLEE (1971) it can be shown that the bulk volumetric strain of a linear elastic body resulting from components I, II, and III is

$$\Delta V_b/V_b = (\bar{\sigma} - P)/K + P/K_i \quad (1)$$

where $\Delta V_b/V_b$ is the volumetric strain of the bulk material

$1/K$ is the compressibility of the bulk material

$1/K_i$ is the compressibility of the solid material.

For simplicity, the pore space is assumed to be fully interconnected; the validity of this assumption is discussed in a subsequent paragraph.

Applying Betti's reciprocal theorem it can be shown that the corresponding pore volume change is

$$\Delta V_p/V_p = 1/f(1/K - 1/K_i)(\bar{\sigma} - P) + P/K_i \quad (2)$$

where $f = V_p/V_b$ is the volume porosity

V_p is the initial pore volume.

The change of porosity is consequently easily obtained from Equations (1) and (2).

If ΔP is the pore pressure change under undrained conditions when a saturated rock element is submitted to the stress state $\underset{\sim}{\sigma}$, the pore volume change is:

$$\Delta V_p/V_p = \Delta P/K_i + (\bar{\sigma} - \Delta P)/k = \Delta P/K_e \quad (3)$$

where $1/K_e$ is the fluid compressibility

$1/k = 1/f(1/K - 1/K_i)$

Accordingly, the change of pore pressure in undrained conditions can be derived from Equation (3):

$$\Delta P = \frac{1/K - 1/K_i}{f(1/K_e - 1/K_i) + (1/K - 1/K_i)} \cdot \bar{\sigma} \quad (4)$$

and substituting Equation (4) in Equation (1) gives the bulk volumetric strain of a linearly-elastic saturated body deformed in undrained conditions.

The ratio $\Delta P/\bar{\sigma}$, which corresponds to SKEMPTON'S definition of his "B coefficient" can be derived from Equation (4), and is found to be dependent upon solid matrix compressibility $1/K_i$. This last quantity was neglected justifiably by SKEMPTON, since he was interested in the study of soils where pore pressures are relatively low and matrix compressibility of the soil is insignificant. However, it must be taken into account for certain rocks. Consider, for example, a fissured porous rock with a pore space in which the non-connected portion is significant while the interconnected part is filled by a fluid under pressure. The compressibility $1/K_i$ refers to that part of the body which is not occupied by fluid, and may have a value of the same order of magnitude as that of the fluid compressibility, so cannot be neglected. More generally, when the pore space is not fully interconnected, the complementary portion in the bulk volume of the interconnected pore space is considered as an 'equivalent homogeneous material'. Consequently, the volume porosity mentioned in Equations (2) and (3) refers only to the interconnected pore volume, and is called the 'interconnected volume porosity'. Similarly the 'solid matrix compressibility' becomes the "equivalent homogeneous material compressibility".

If the body does not behave elastically, the fluid pressure produced by a change in the stresses applied at the boundary must be determined by laboratory tests.

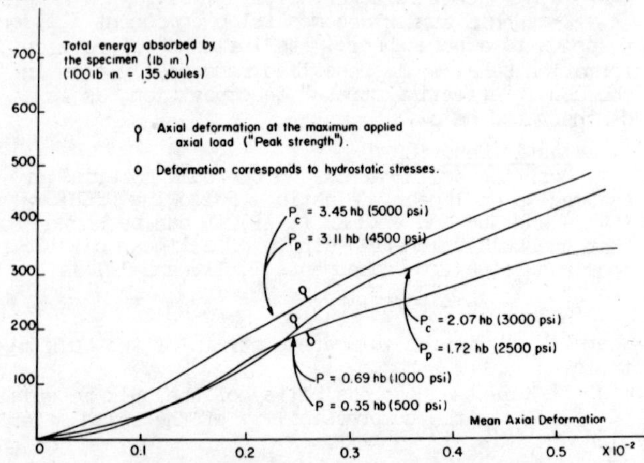

FIGURE 2 - TOTAL ENERGY ABSORBED VERSUS MEAN AXIAL DEFORMATION CURVES, FOR DIFFERENT COMBINATIONS OF PORE AND CONFINING PRESSURE, ON SATURATED CYLINDRICAL SPECIMENS OF INDIANA LIMESTONE. (50mm diam X 100mm long).

Figure 2 - Courbes déformation axiale moyenne - quantité d'énergie absorbée obtenues pour différentes combinaisons de pression de pore et pression de confinement avec des éprouvettes cylindinques (50mm x 100mm) de calcaire de l'Indiana.

3. The Disintegration Process

Here, disintegration has to be understood as post-elastic deformation. Since the mean axial force-mean deformations relations are no more linear, the stress decomposition is used, in this section, only to analyze the influence of each component during the fracture process. Its use to determine deformations should be considered with care.

3.1 The Classical Effective Stress Concept

While the classical effective stress concept is of little significance in analysis of the elastic behavior of rocks, it is a more fruitful approach when the disintegration process is considered.

HANDIN et al. (1963), and BRACE and MARTIN (1968 in triaxial tests on several rocks of different porosity, observed that the peak strength was constant for different combinations of pore and confining pres sures, provided the difference between the two values remained constant.

Similar results were observed by CORNET and FAIR HURST (1972) with respect to the elastic limit of Berea Sandstone specimens.

It is now generally recognized that no throughgoing shear plane exists in the rock specimen at the elastic limit [e.g. WAWERSIK (1968)], so that the con clusion that agreement between predicted and observed values of peak strength exists because the pore pressure is acting over the entire area of a throughgoing plane of fracture [LAUBSHER (1960), SERAFIM (1972)] must be rejected as incorrect.

An alternative explanation for such a good agree ment can be provided by considering the stress decomposition proposed in Figure 1.

Component I represents the application of the same hydrostatic pressure to the element and to the saturating fluid. Thus, the stress state in the soli matrix is hydrostatic and equal to the applied pressure. The effect of this pressure depends on both the magnitude of the pressure, and the constitutive equation of the solid. In most cases, and more especially in those considered by the previously mentioned authors, this effect (of the hydrostatic pressure) is negligible, and the behavior of rock is affected by the stress (σ - P1) only, i.e. the effectiv stress concept provides a satisfactory explanation.

However, this pressure (P) has been shown for certain rocks to have a significant influence [GRIGGS (1936), McHENRY (1948)]. It may modify the behavior of the matrix, where the rock material has a tendency to behave plastically under high principal minimum stresses; as is the case for potash or calcite, for example. In addition it must be noted that the hydro static pressure induces an hydrostatic stress state i the matrix only if the pore space is fully intercon-

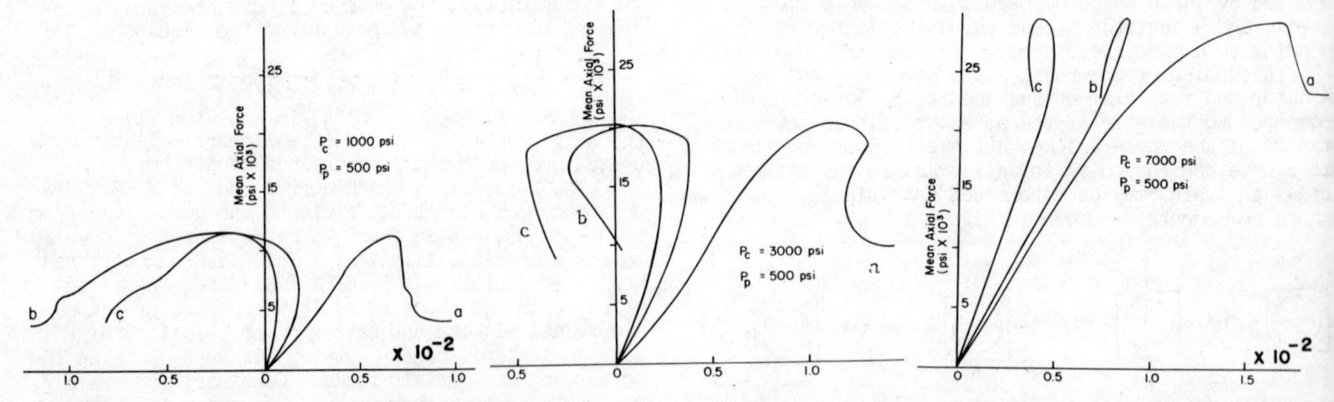

Curves a - x Axis = Mean Axial Deformation = $\Delta l/l$
Curves b - x Axis = Mean Volumetric Deformation = $\Delta V_b/V_b$
Curves c - x Axis = Mean Pore Volume Change = $\Delta V_p/V_b$
Average Lateral Deformation Rate: 10^{-5} sec^{-1}

Figure 3 - Drained Triaxial Tests on Saturated Cylindrical Specimens of Berea Sandstone [Specimens 50mm (2 in.) x 100mm (4 in.) long]

Figure 3 - Essais triaxiaux drainés effectués sur des éprouvettes saturées de gres de Berea (diamètre 50mm hauteur 100mm).

Abb. 3 - Dreiaxialversuchen an gesattigten Berea Sandstein Proben.

nected, i.e. so that the pressure is constant throughout the pore volume. For rocks in which a certain part of the pore space is not interconnected, the hydrostatic pressure P existing in the interconnected part may induce sufficiently high stresses in the matrix to provoke microfractures, which in turn will influence the overall behavior of the material. Experimental tests performed by the authors in triaxial conditions on unjacketed specimens of Indiana limestone, in which the pore and the confining pressure are equal, confirm this hypothesis. It was observed that, while the maximum load-bearing capacity was not affected significantly by an increase from 1.72hb* (2500 psi) to 3.45hb (5000 psi) in hydrostatic pressure, the post-peak slope of the ['mean axial force'/'mean axial deformation'] curve** was steeper for a 1.72hb (2500 psi) confining pressure than for that with 3.45hb (5000 psi).

In addition, drained triaxial tests were performed on the same rock with different combinations of pore and confining pressures, maintaining a constant difference between the two values. The strain rate ($0.8 \cdot 10^{-6}$/sec) was chosen to insure uniform pore pressure throughout the specimen. It was found (Fig. 3) that more energy was needed to deform axially the specimen up to a certain amount at high values of pore pressure than at low values. This result confirms the above mentioned proposition. A more detailed analysis of this possible effect is in progress. Already it appears that curves of 'total absorbed energy' versus 'volumetric deformation' may yield very promising results.

It is generally recognized that a hydrostatic pressure applied to the exterior of a specimen (Component II of Fig. 1) greatly influences the pre-peak force behavior of specimen of porous rocks [WALSH (1965), BRACE (1965), KING (1969), GARG and NUR (1973)]. Therefore, the same effect will occur with equal internal and external pressures for porous rocks in which part of the pore space is not interconnected.

3.2 Pore Volume Changes

It has been shown above that, for fracture problems involving a pore pressure (P), the influence of the pressure in the interconnected pore space must first be determined; the analysis then can be carried out by simply considering the classical effective stresses. To accomplish this, it is thus essential to determine the pore fluid pressure.

In drained conditions, the pore fluid pressure remains constant with deformation; its influence is thus the same throughout the disintegration process.

In undrained conditions, no fluid is allowed to flow in or out of the material and the fluid pressure changes in accordance with its compressibility (see Equation 3) and the interconnected pore volume variation. The latter quantity consequently must be determined if the pore pressure is to be computed.

Actual loading conditions usually lie somewhere between these limits, depending on such factors as fluid viscosity, permeability, deformation rate, temperature, etc. Thus, the analysis of the influence of the pore pressure usually involves considerations of these two extremes.

*1hb - 1 'hectobar' = 1,454 psi

**Stress conditions in a laboratory rock specimen tested in compression are quite inhomogeneous and become even more inhomogeneous in the post-elastic deformation range. Consequently, it is not meaningful to reduce the force deformation diagrams to stress-strain curves. In fact, reference to such diagrams as stress-strain curves is misleading and their use should be discouraged.

Drained Conditions

In addition to the mechanical effect of the fluid pressure in the interconnected pore space, it is well known that fluids can chemically affect the rock by dissolution of the matrix (BARON et al. 1963), change of the free surface energy of the rock (REHBINDER and LIKHTMAN 1957), and modification of the internal friction coefficient (HORN and DEER 1962, COULSON 1971). Thus, any test designed to determine the saturated rock properties must be performed on the saturated, and not on the dry material. On the other hand, the pore volume of the rock changes with deformation (ROBINSON 1959). In particular, it increases during disintegration (BRACE et al. 1966) under low minimum principal stress. If no pressure is applied to the internal fluid, the pore pressure will decrease and even may become negative due to dilatancy. Thus, wherever possible, tests designed to determine the characteristics of wet rocks should be performed in drained conditions because of the simplicity of the analysis.

Simultaneous measurements of the bulk volumetric change and the pore volume variations during the rock disintegration process under drained conditions facilitates:

The determination of the volumetric deformation for that part of the body which is not occupied by the internal fluid, and

The analysis of the behavior for the bulk material in undrained conditions, since the change of pore pressure can be determined.

Figure 3 shows some results of drained tests on Berea Sandstone. It is seen that the increase in volume of the pores at 0.7hb (1000 psi) confining pressure is slightly smaller than the measured increase in the bulk volume; this is due to less than complete penetration of the fluid into the newly created cracks.

Conversely, in tests on Indiana limestone (Fig. 4) it appears that the pore volume variations are slightly greater than those measured for the rock volume. In this case, it is expected that the pore volume initially was not fully interconnected and that fractures, developed during loading, created links between the isolated pores and the interconnected pore space.

In either case it is seen that computation of pore pressure variations for undrained conditions in the post-elastic range on the assumption that the fluid filled pore space changed in direct proportion to the change in bulk volume, would give an incorrect result.

Figures 3 and 4 also reveal the influence of confining pressure on pore volume variations during the disintegration process for highly porous rocks (Berea sandstone 18% porosity, Indiana limestone 15% porosity). It is evident from the results of the tests on Indiana limestone at 3.79hb (5500 psi) confining pressure, and at 0.34hb (500 psi) pore pressure (Fig. 3, Curve C), that the pore volume can decrease continuously during post-elastic deformations. However, these tests were stopped at 0.9% mean axial deformation. Tests performed on the same rock under dry conditions and 3.45hb (5000 psi) confining pressure revealed a continuous decrease of the mean volumetric deformation up to a mean axial deformation of 1%, beyond which the volume increased continuously although remaining smaller than the original value. These tests were stopped at 2% mean axial deformation.

No increase in the bulk volume probably would be observed in tests on saturated specimens at larger confining pressure. A recent publication [SCHOCK et al. (1973)] indicating such a continuous decrease in

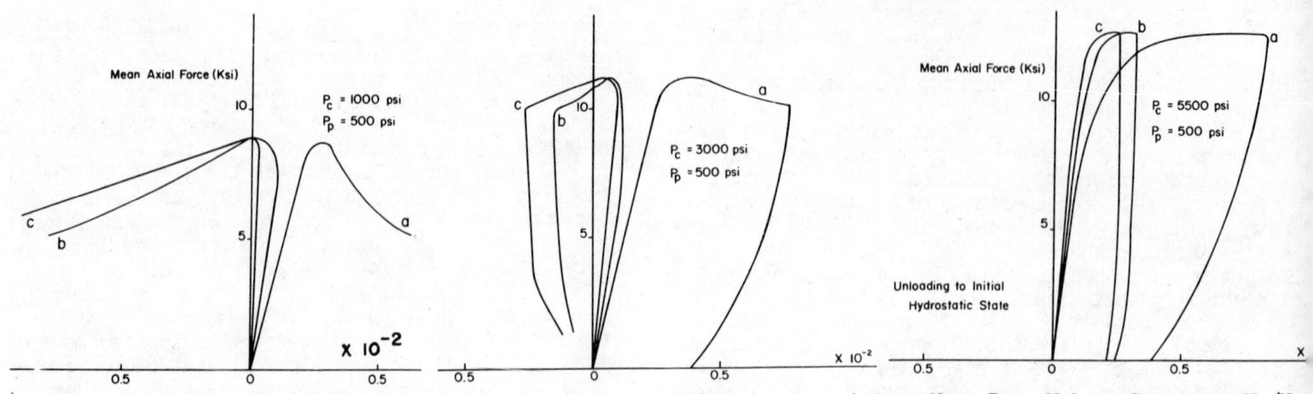

Curves a - x Axis = Mean Axial Deformation = $\Delta l/l$ Curves c - x Axis = Mean Pore Volume Change = $\Delta V_p/V_b$
Curves b - x Axis = Mean Volumetric Deformation = $\Delta V_b/V_b$ Average Lateral Deformation Rate: 5.10^{-5} min^{-1}

Figure 4 - Drained Triaxial Tests on Saturated Cylindrical Specimens of Indiana Limestone [Specimens 50mm (2 in x 100mm (4 in.) long].

Figure 4 - Essais triaxiaux drainés éffectués sur des éprouvettes saturées de calcaire de l'Indiana (diametre 5cm, hauteur 10cm).

Abb. 4 - Dreiaxialversuchen an gesattigten Indiana kalk stein Proben.

tests on dry sandstone at confining pressures up to 20 kb confirms this supposition. If high minimum principal stresses induce a behavior in the matrix that satisfies the Tresca criterion of plasticity, the material should flow with no volumetric change and it should then be possible to obtain large deformations with no pore volume change for such rocks.

In summary, the results shown in Figs. 3 and 4 indicate that for a certain domain of load, deformations, and deformation rates, under constant temperature conditions, the post-elastic behavior of rock is associated with pore volume decrease and that it is necessary to obtain a precise knowledge of this domain to explain pore pressure effects under load. Studies on the influence of the deformation rate are underway at the University of Minnesota.

Undrained Conditions

It was suggested in the previous section that, because of the simplicity of the analysis, pore volume changes during fracture should be determined experimentally by triaxial tests under drained conditions. Nevertheless, if in-situ conditions are known to be undrained, it might be simpler to perform, in the laboratory, triaxial tests in which the pore fluid is not allowed to flow, the variation of pore pressure being directly measured.

Also BRACE and MARTIN (1968) have observed that the pore pressure distribution in rocks is dependent on the deformation rate, due to the dilatancy phenomenon.

Consequently, since it is necessary, for the experimental study of the pore fluid influence on rock deformations, to use the saturated material - and since drained conditions cannot be achieved with deformation rates faster than a critical value, then for these higher rates, tests should be performed in undrained conditions. However, even this procedure is not fully satisfactory since local pressure gradients may still exist in the specimen at high deformation rates. Thus, although testing under undrained conditions enlarges the range of deformation rates over which direct experimentation is meaningful, a limit still is imposed by the rock permeability and the fluid viscosity.

Very little work has been carried out in the post-peak region with respect to the influence of dilatancy. In tests on a Berea sandstone specimen at 2.07hb (3000 psi) confining pressure, and 0.34hb (500 psi) pore pressure, CORNET and FAIRHURST observed that the development of a fault plane traversing the specimen w associated with a stress drop in the material, the e fect of which was to close cracks that previously we opening up in the bulk of the material prior to the development of the through-going plane. This reduct of pore volume exceeds the increase associated with formation of the fault plane. Thus fracture would have resulted in an overall pore-pressure increase, had undrained conditions been used.*

No such behavior was observed in similar tests Indiana limestone specimens (for the .8 $10^{-6}sec^{-1}$ de formation rate used in the experiment). In fact, no significant dilatancy was observed in the pre-peak force region, but became significant only after the maximum load bearing capacity had been reached, for effective confining pressures up to 1.72hb (2500 psi At higher confining pressures a continuous pore volu decrease was observed which, in undrained conditions would have been associated with a reduction of the e fective confining pressure ($P_c - P_p$) and thus would have yielded results opposite to those predicted by BRACE and MARTIN'S dilatancy-hardening theory.

4. Mean Force - Mean Deformation Curves Interpretat

From the above experimental results, dilatancy not a permanent feature of rock fracture but rather flects only one energy dissipation process observed low confining pressures and which corresponds simply to the creation and opening of microcracks. For intermediate confining pressure conditions, the develo ment of microcracks allows a relative movement of th grains of the matrix and consequently is associated with an overall volume decrease; this fracture mecha ism is described by EDMUND and PATERSON (1972) as ca clastic flow. Finally, at higher confining pressure once the cataclastic flow has reduced the pore volum to nearly zero, intracrystaline plasticity may take place with virtually no volume changes (SCHOLZ 1968)

When dilatancy does occur, tests in which fracture development is controlled indicate that the fra ture may develop in one of two ways: either the dil tancy monotonically increases (first mode) or, after

*This has been observed in tests for which fracture was not controlled. Since the collapse occurred ve suddenly, the pore pressure could not be monitored. However, it was found to be larger after fracture than before.

an initial increase, the stress-drop associated with the development of a single fracture plane is followed by an overall pore volume decrease (second mode). The latter requires that the solid behaves elastically, a feature which is indicated in the mean-axial force/mean-deformation curve [i.e. as obtained in experimental conditions] by a portion with a positive slope in the post-peak region (the first derivative of the function represented by the mean force-mean deformation curves is at first negative, then positive, and finally negative again for a continuous load decrease). In this case the elastic energy stored in the material is larger than that required for formation of the macro-fracture plane; laboratory control of the unstable development of this plane is achieved by reducing the elastic energy of the testing system, i.e. by relieving the applied load (reversing the platens).

In some testing situations and with certain rocks no such instability is observed and energy has to be continuously supplied to the rock for its progressive disintegration. However, two kinds of energy-absorbing processes are still possible. The first is associated with an elastic behavior of the matrix, the increase of energy necessary for fracture extension arising from the fact that microcracks propagate toward a more stable configuration, so that more energy is required for the continued extension. This behavior is characterized by a large dilatancy. The second is associated with local plastic deformations or any other energy absorption mechanism (such as friction), involving no volume changes but absorbing a significant amount of energy.

5. Possible Application to Earthquakes Mechanisms

NUR (1972) described an interesting variation of the ratio $\zeta = t_s/t_p$ of the arrival times t_s over t_p for the P and S seismic waves observed before several earthquakes.

He proposed that the observed decrease in the ratio was probably attributable to dilatancy, while an increase observed just prior to the earthquake was probably due to percolation of fluid through the newly created cracks, the pore pressure increasing until the earthquake was triggered.

However, it usually is observed that dilatancy, when it occurs, is largest just before macrofracture develops. At least this is true for laboratory specimens. On the other hand, newly created cracks can be filled by a fluid only if dilatancy ceases, or at least if the dilatancy rate is sufficiently slow to allow fluid pressure build-up to take place.

WAWERSIK (1968) and SCHOLZ (1968) observed that cracks induced by compressive loading are more or less randomly distributed throughout a specimen for applied loads up to 85% of the peak strength. Just prior to fracture, however, the new cracks tend to be localized in the immediate vicinity of the region in which the fracture surface is to appear. In addition, the dilatancy rate accelerates as the applied load approaches the maximum load-bearing capacity.

If this mechanism occurs also under field conditions, (i.e. slip along a fault) fluid from the surrounding saturated rock mass can fill up the cracks in that part of the rock in which dilatancy has ceased (i.e. outside the fault region). But since dilatancy is likely to be accelerating in the region of the fault, it seems improbable that fluid pressure can build up in this region. If this is true, then the observed increase of the ratio ζ would be an indication that dilatancy is becoming a local phenomenon, and that fracture will soon occur. In such a case the influence of the pore fluid is only secondary and does not trigger the earthquake.

An alternative explanation can be offered if slip along the fault is not assumed to occur as a single event. Indeed it is most probable that some regions along the fault are more highly stressed than others and, consequently, that local fracture develops before overall slip. [This hypothesis is strongly supported by the occurrence of foreshocks often described in the literature].

Now, let us assume that these local fractures occur in accordance with the second mode of fracture as this was previously defined.
In this case the stress drop in the masses on each side of the local slip will be accompanied by local pore pressure increases, forcing the saturating fluid into the regions of lowest pore pressure, i.e. along the fault where dilatancy is highest. The fact, as observed by NUR, that dilatancy takes place long before the earthquakes occur, and that the minimum principal stress is in the range of 1 to 2 kilobars, appear to be similar to the conditions necessary for the second mode as described in the previous paragraph.

This proposed mechanism seems to be in good agreement with most observed facts. It provides an explanation for the pore pressure increase that does not require dilatancy to cease.

In such a mechanism, (i.e. localized fracturing, inducing pore pressure increase, which consequently triggers the earthquake) the pore pressure acts merely as an added factor promoting instability. The question may arise as to whether it is desirable to increase this pressure so that the earthquake is triggered earlier, with possibly lower elastic strain energy release, or if complete cancellation of pore pressure would induce a more stable fracture process such as creep. The authors do not feel ready to answer such a question; but propose that such parameters as in-situ stress conditions, pore pressure magnitude, and influence of the minimum principal stress on the fracture process, will affect the situation and need to be considered.

Conclusion

The deformation behavior of saturated rocks can be analyzed in two steps:

1. Examine the influence of hydrostatice pressure on that part of the material not occupied by the interconnected pore space. This is achieved experimentally by performing tests on saturated, unjacketed specimens using a classical pressure vessel. The influence of the hydrostatic pressure on the elastic deformation now is generally recognized but usually is considered to be negligible for post-elastic deformations. The validity of such an assumption depends on the nature of the rock and the magnitude of the pressure.

2. Investigation of the influence of the classical "effective stresses" on the bulk material (fluids and solids) appears to be simpler, at least in the elastic domain, if the effective stress tensor is decomposed into the mean normal component, and its deviatoric component. Experimentally, investigation of the effective stress is achieved by performing drained triaxial tests (in which influence of the pore fluid remains, mechanically and physicochemically, constant throughout the experiment). However, for deformation rates faster than a critical value, drained conditions cannot be attained and undrained tests must be performed. For such conditions the pore pressure changes in accordance with its compressibility and the interconnected pore volume variations.

In the elastic domain variation of the interconnected pore volume has been shown to depend on (i) the compressibility of the fluid, (ii) the compressibility of that part of the bulk volume which is complementary to the interconnected pore space, (iii) the compressibility of the bulk material, and (iv) the interconnected volume porosity.

In the post-elastic domain the variation of the interconnected pore volume is dependent on the applied loads, the deformation, and the deformation rate. This variation, while following a similar trend to that of the dilatancy, is not always equal to this last quantity and, consequently, should be determined, if possible, independently of it (the dilatancy). Thus, the interconnected pore space has been shown to decrease during fracture for some values of the confining pressure, especially with very brittle materials. Such a variation has been proposed as a possible factor of instability during earthquakes.

REFERENCES

References in common in this text and in the General Report of Theme 2 will be referred to General Report: (see G.R.).

BARON, G., Y. CASTEL and P.HABIB (1963) "Influence de la pression interstitielle sur les caractéristiques mécaniques des roches en condition de fond" revue de l'I.F.P. vol. XVIII nº hors série décembre.

BIOT, M.A. (1955) "Theory of elasticity and consolidation for a porous anisotropic solid" J. App. Phy. vol. 26, p. 182.

BRACE, W.F. (1965) "Some new measurements of linear compressibility of rocks", Jour. Geoph. Res. vol. 70 nb 2, pps. 391-398.

BRACE, W.F., B.W. PAULDING and C. SCHOLZ (1966) (see G. R.).

BRACE, W.F. and R.J. MARTIN III (1968) "A test of effective stress law for crystalline rocks of low porosity", Int. J. Rock Mech. & Min. Sc. vol. 5, p. 415.

CORNET, F. H. and C. FAIRHURST (1972) "Variations of pore volume in disintegrating rocks" Percolation through fissured rocks - a symp., Int. Soc. Roch Mech. Stuttgart.

COULSON, J.H. (1971) "Shear strength of flat surfaces in rock" 13th Symp. Rock Mech. Urbana-Champaign, Ill. A.S.C.E.

EDMUND, J.M. and M.S. PATERSON (1972) "Volume change during the deformation of rocks at high pressure" Int. J. Rock Mech. vol. 9, p. 161.

GARG, S.K. and A. NUR (1973) "Effective stress law for fluid saturated porous rocks" J. Geophy. Res. vol. 78, no. 26, p. 5911.

GEERTSMA, J. (1957) (see G.R.).

GRIGGS, D.T. (1936) "Deformation of rock under high confining pressures" Journ. of Geol., vol. 44, pps. 541-577.

HANDIN, J., R.V. HAGER, M. FRIEDMAN and J.N. FEATHER (1963) (see G.R.).

HANDIN, J. and C.B. RALEIGH (1972) "Man-made earthquakes and earthquake control" Percolation through fissured rocks symp. Int. Soc. Rock Mech. Stuttgart, published by Deutsche Gesellscheft fur Erd und Grundbau, edited by Wittke.

HODGE, P.G. (1972) Plasticity lectures, U. of Minnesota Unpublished.

HORN, H.M. and D.H. DEER (1962) "Frictional characteristics of minerals" Geotechnique, vol. 12, p. 319.

HUBBERT, M.K. and M.W. RUBEY (1959) (see G.R.).

HUDSON, J.A., S.L. CROUCH, and C. FAIRHURST (1972) "Soft, stiff, and servo-controlled testing machines" Eng. Geol., vol. 6, no. 3.

KING, M.S. (1969) "Static and dynamic elastic moduli of rocks under pressure" 11th Symp. Rock Mech., Berkeley, p. 329, A.I.M.E.

LANE, K.S. (1969) "Engineering problems due to fluid pressure in rocks" 11th Symp. Rock Mech. Berkeley, p. 501, A.I.M.E.

LAUBSCHER, H. (1960) "Mechanics of fluid filled porou solids and its application to overthrust faulting: a discussion", Bul. Geol. Soc. Am., vol. 71, no. 5.

McHENRY, D. (1948) "The effect of uplift pressure on the shearing strength of concrete". Proc. 6th Congr. Large Dams. Paper 48.

NUR, A. and J.D. BYERLEE (1971) (see G.R.).

NUR, A. (1972) (See G.R.).

REHBINDER, D.A. and V. LICHTMAN (1957) "Effect of sur face active media on strains and ruptures in solids", Proc. Sec. Int. Con. Surface Activity, vol. III, p.56

ROBIN, P.Y.F. (1973) "Note on effective pressure", J. Geophy, Res., vol. 78, no. 4, p. 2434.

ROBINSON, L.A. (1959) "The effect of pore and confining pressure on the failure process in sedimentary rocks" Col. School Mines Quart., vol. 54, no. 3, p. 1

SCHOCK, R.N., H.C. HEARD and D.R. STEPHENS (1973) "Stress-strain behavior of a granodiorite and two graywackes on compression to 20 kilobars", J. Geophy. Res., vol. 78, no. 26, p. 5922.

SCHOLZ, C.M. (1968) "Experimental study of the fracturing process in brittle rock", J. Geophy. Res., Vol 73, no. 4, pps. 1447-1554.

SERAFIM, J.L. (1972) General report on theme 4, percolation through fissured rocks, Symp. Int. Soc. Rock Mech., Stuttgart.

SKEMPTON, A.W. (1954) "The pore pressure coefficients A and B", Geotechnique, Dec., p. 143.

SKEMPTON, A.W. (1960) (See G.R.).

TER MINASSIAN, W., F. SABARLY, P. LONDE (1967) "Comment proteger les barrage-voutes contre la pression de l'eau dans les appuis" 9th Cong. Large Dams, Q32, R12.

TERZAGHI, K. (1923) (See G.R.)

WALSH, J.B. (1965) "The effect of cracks on the compressibility of rocks", J. Geophy. Res., vol. 70, no 2, p. 381.

WAWERSIK, W. (1968) "Detailed analysis of rock failu in laboratory compression tests" Ph.D. thesis, University of Minnesota. (Unpublished).

IN-SITU TESTING FOR DETERMINING THE MODULUS OF COMPRESSIBILITY OF A ROCKMASS CONSISTING OF SHALES

MESURES IN SITU DE LA COMPRESSIBILITÉ D'UN MASSIF SCHISTEUX

MESSUNGEN IN SITU DER VERFORMUNGSEIGENSCHAFTEN EINES SCHIEFRIGEN GEBIRGES

E.E. DE BEER — Professor at Universities of Ghent and Leuven, general director of the Belgian Geotechnical Institute

J.M. GRAULICH — Chief geologist of the Belgian Geological Survey

M. WALLAYS — Director of the Geotechnical Office of Pieux Franki Ltd.

Belgium

UMMARY: In the case of rocks, it is not easy to predict the behavior of a rock mass under the nfluence of a ground-water lowering, as the result of such a prediction depends largely on the upposed structure of the rockmass.

On the other hand it is not always easy to obtain an exact figure of the modulus of ompressibility of a rockmass from plate loading tests, as these tests, even when plates of m^2 are used, do only interest a relatively small volume of the rockmass, which furthermore s located in the neighbourhood of the unloaded surface.

Although the method of the flat jacks (1) prevents certain of the imperfections of he plate bearing tests, it still interest only a limited volume, located in the neighbourhood f the surface.

For a special problem it has been possible to measure the movements of a rockmass of hale, caused by a ground-water lowering. This ground-water lowering was realized by pumping he water out of a gallery measured with reference to a point located at a depth of 150 m nder the soil surface.

The contribution describes the testing equipment used to insure an accuracy of the rder of 1/10th mm, and the conclusions drawn from the observations.

ÉSUMÉ: Dans le cas des roches, el n'est pas facile de prévoir le comportement d'une masse ocheuses soumise à l'influence d'un abaissement de la nappe phréatique car le résultat d'une elle prévision dépend avant tout de ce que l'on suppose être la structure de la masse rocheuse.

D'autre part, il n'est pas toujours facile de déterminer le chiffre exact du module e compression de la masse rocheuse à partir d'essais de chargement sur plaque d'appui, car, ême si l'on utilise des plaques d'l m^2, ces essais n'intéressent qu'un volume relativement imité de la masse rocheuse qui de plus est située au voisinage de la surface non chargée.

Bien que la méthode des vérins plats permette d'échapper à certaines des imperfections hérentes aux essais de chargement sur plaques d'appui, le volume de la masse rocheuse sur equel porte l'essai reste encore limité, cette masse étant d'ailleurs située au voisinage de a surface.

Lors de l'étude d'un problème particulier, il a été possible de mesurer les mouvements 'une roche schisteuse causés par un abaissement de la nappe phréatique. Cet abaissement a pu re réalisé en évacuant l'eau d'une gallerie par pompage, les mesures étant ensuite effectuées ar rapport à un point de réference situé à une profondeur de 150 m. au dessous de la surface a sol.

La présente communication décrit le matériel d'essai utilisé pour assurer une précision l'ordre de 1/10ème de mm et présente les conclusions tirées de ces observations.

SAMMENFASSUNG: Es ist schwierig, das Benehmen von Felsgesteinen, die unter dem Einfluss von undwassersenkungen stehen, vorauszusagen, da die Vorhersage zum grossen Teil auf den Ergeb- ssen einer angenommenen Felsstruktur beruht.

Andererseits ist es nicht immer leicht, anhand von Belastungsplattenversuche genaue ten über den Druckfestigkeitsmodul der Felsmasse feststellen zu können. Auch wenn Platten in in dem Masse 1 m^2 benutzt werden, so können diese nur ein geringes Volumen erfassen, welches sich wiederum in der Nähe der unbelasteten Oberfläche befindet.

Obgleich sich die Methode mit einer Flachhebewinde (1) bewährt hat, bei welcher eine Ungenauigkeit der Belastungstragplatten vermieden werden soll, so kann doch nur ein begrenztes sich in der Nähe der Oberfläche befindendes Volumen erfasst werden.

In einem besonders schwierigen Fall ist es möglich gewesen, aufgrund einer Grundwassersenkung Bewegungen in einer aus Schieferton bestehenden Felsmasse festzustellen. Diese Grundwassersenkung wurde beim Auspumpen von Wasser aus einem Stollen, welcher sich in einer Tiefe von 150 m unter der Erdoberfläche befand, festgestellt.

Dieser Beitrag enthält die bei dem Versuch ermittelten Ergebnisse und beschreibt weiter das Versuchsgerät, welches benutzt wurde, um die Genauigkeit im Rahmen von 1/10 mm zu gewährleisten.

PURPOSE OF THE TEST

As a possible site for the synchrotron of the C.E.R.N. the Belgian authorities presented the site of Focant. This site consits of shales of the Upper Devonian, the Frasnian and the Famennian. All these formations have been tectonized the Hercynian Orogenesis.

The rockmass shows stratification joints, and diaclases normal to the stratification. The mean percentage of voids is 4,6% and the mean volume wieght is 2,75 t/m^3. Thus the rockmass has much less voids than a soil.

As the gallery of the synchroton was to be provided at a depth of 30 m under the soil surface, and as the ground-water table was located near the soil surface, a lowering of the ground-waterlevel was to be expected. The first question was to predict the movements which could be caused by changes of the ground-waterlevel of about 25 m. To be able to give a quantitative answer to that question in situ measurements appeared necessary.

At the same time the results of these measurements should enable to give more precise information concerning the modulus of deformation of the rockmass.

PREVIOUS RESULTS

A more or less exact determination of the compressibility of a rockmass is not an easy problem, as the placement of the testing equipment causes some modifications of the rock properties in the neighbourhood of that equipment. Furthermore, as the deformations of rockmasses are rather small, the testing equipment must present a high degree of precision, which, is not always the case for an equipment used in field conditions.

For instance Focant the first determination of the compressibility of the rockmass of shale has been made with the pressiometer Ménard. The pressiometer readings have been made in borings, reaching a depth of 45 m under the soil surface. The mean values of the modulus of deformability obtained by rep-ated loadings and unloadings in the pressiometer over the range between 2 m and 45 m depth varied for all the performed borings between 7 100 and 18 200 kg/cm^2.

The modulus of deformability was also determined by careful loading tests on a plat of 1 m^2 placed in a gallery dug at a depth of 30 m under the soil surface (1). The loadi tests were performed in a zone of sound non fissured shale, with a subhorizontal stratification, and gave the following results:

modulus of compressibility normal to the stratification and
in the downward direction : $E_\perp$ = 85 000 kg/c
in the upward direction : $E_\perp$ = 40 à 55 000 kg/c

modulus of compressibility parallel to the stratification :

$E_{//}$ > 100 000 kg/c

The values obtained by the plate loadi tests of 1 m^2 are of much higher order of magnitude than those obtained by the pressiometer tests, indicating that, with the degree of precision of the normal pressiometer equipment, and with the normal precautions for making the holes, the pressiometer tests are likel- to give, in the shales tested, muc too pessimistic results.

---

x - Professor at Universities of Ghent and Leuven, general director of the Belgian Geotechnical Institute.

xx - Chief geologist of the Belgian Geological Survey

xxx - Director of the Geotechnical Office of Pieux Franki Ltd.

A third way of determining the mo-
ulus of compressibility consisted in the use
f flat jacks and of the dilatometers accor-
ing to the methods of Rocha (2),

The results obtained with that
ethod were the following:

ith flat jacks : mean modulus of deformability

ormal to the stratification : $E_{\perp} = 50\ 000\ kg/cm^2$

arallel to the stratification : $E_{//} = 110\ 000\ kg/cm^2$

ith the dilatometers the obtained values were
omewhat lower than those obtained with the
lat jacks.

The tests with the flat jacks and
ne dilatometers confirm the order of magni-
ude of the results obtained with the plate
oading tests.

EASUREMENT OF THE SOIL MOVEMENTS CAUSED BY RTIFICIAL CHANGES OF THE GROUND-WATERLEVEL

The circular gallery of the planned
ynchrotron should be located at a depth of
) m under the soil surface. As the natural
round-waterlevel is only a few meters under
nat surface, the digging of the gallery
nould cause a general ground-waterlowering.
ne question arised which should be the order
magnitude of the movements of the rockmass
aused by that lowering.

In order to answer that question a
est gallery with a length of 655 meters was
ug at a depth between 24 and 30 m, and by
umping the water out from that gallery a
round-water lowering was realized. By instal-
ing a check point of the vertical displace-
ents near the bottom of the gallery at a
epth of 24,37 m under the soil surface, and
nother at a depth of 151,16 meter, it became
ossible to measure the variation in thick-
ess of a rockmass with a total thickness of
26,79 m, this is much more than the thick-
ess involved in all previous tests.

The loadvariation of that rockmass is
btained by varying the waterlevel in the soil,
filling and emptying the test gallery and
s shafts, and waiting for the stabilization
the waterlevel in the surrounding rockmass.

On fig. 1 the curves (1) and (2)
epresent respectively the natural ground-
aterlevel, and that obtained after pumping
n the gallery G.

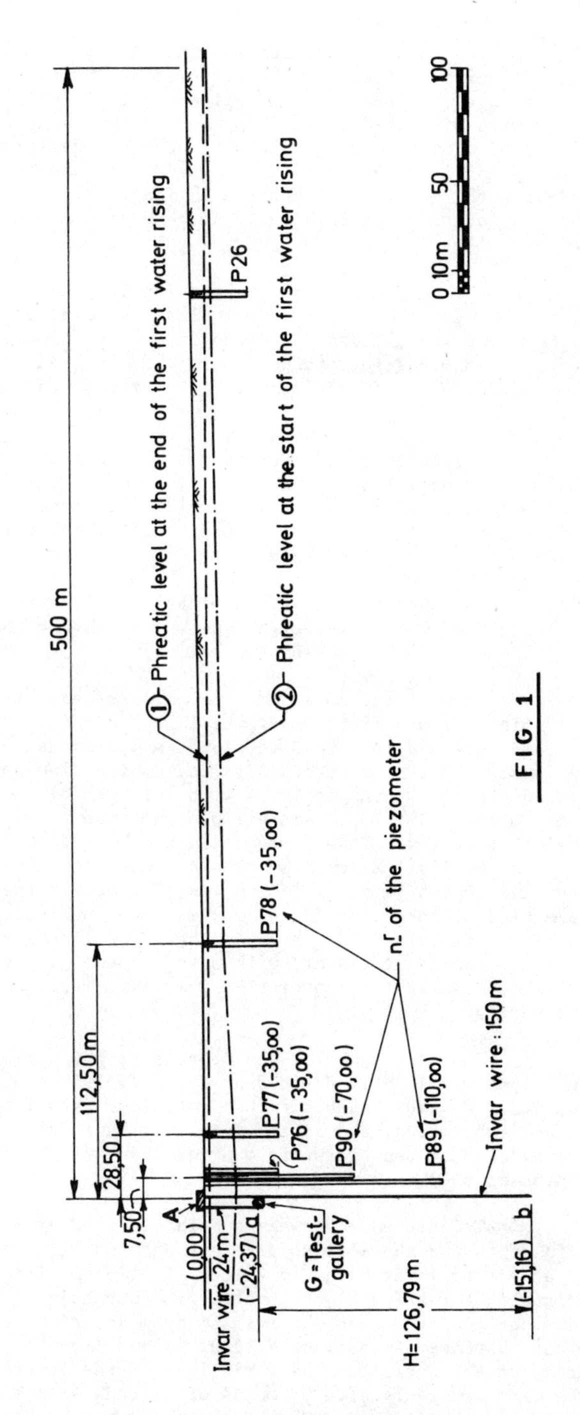

FIG. 1

The lowering of the ground-water from the situation (1) to the situation (2) causes an increase of the effective stresses in the underlaying rockmass. Because of the very small void percentage (n = 4,6 %) it can be assumed that the volume weight of the shales does practically not change by the ground-water lowering and remains practically constant at 2,75 t/m3. With that assumption a variation of the ground-waterlevel does not change the value of the total vertical stress, but causes only variations of the vertical stresses in the liquid phase and in the solid phase.

The movements connected with the changes in the effective stresses can be measured by installing, before any modification of the ground-waterlevel, a first wire of invar allowing to measure the changes in lenght between the point a located near the gallery G and a point A of the soil surface, and a second one allowing to measure the changes in length between the point b located at a relatively large depth and the point A (fig. 1).

During the filling or emptying of the gallery G, the changes in the ground-waterlevel were observed by means of 44 piezometers,placed in borings with a depth of 35 m and performed on verticals located at 7,50 m, 28,50 m and 112,50 m from the axis of the gallery.

Furthermore two piezometers were placed with their lower ends resp. at a depth of 70 m and 110 m of the soil surface, and at a distance of 7,50 m of the axis of the gallery. The filtered pat of these piezometers had an height of 25 m.

The observations showed that the fluctuations of the ground-waterlevel extended over a range of 400 till 800 m on both sides of the gallery.

Each of the 35 m long piezometers consists of a 1" pipe, with a filter over the last 2 meters. After thorough cleaning of the borehole, the piezometer pipe is lowered in the hole, and surrounded with fine calibrated gravel (0,3 mm to 1 mm) with a length of 15 meter. The upper 15 meters are plugged with a non shrinking cement. This disposition has been adopted in order to limit as much as possible the influence of the superficial water (rain and run-off) but at the same time to encounter in the lower part a sufficient number of fissures and seams, so that the piezometric readings should represent, with a sufficient probability, the phreatic level over the 20 m lower meters of the boring.

The equipment for the measure of the variation in length was jointly devised by Mr. Gervaise,expert of the C.E.R.N. and a specialist in metrology with international reputation, and by the Belgian technicians. Mr. Gervaise has given elsewhere a brief description of the equipment used [4].

The distance between a point located at a certain depth and the soil surface has been materialized by a wire of invar with a diameter of 1,75 mm, fixed to a weight resting on the bottom of a borehole, and tensioned under a constant stress, by means of a lever-arm L suspended on a frame F (fig. 2a and fig. 2b) located at the surface. The variations of the length of the wire are registered by means of a transducer T attached to the frame F. The borehole has been realized by means of a double diamant core drill with a diameter of 146 mm.

Over the upper 20 m, the borehole has been provided with a mantle tube in order to avoid pieces of schist falling at the bottom of the hole. After a thorough cleaning of the borehole, a ball B (fig. 2a) of rustless steel with a diameter of 100 mm was lowered at the bottom of the borehole and driven in this bottom by means of driving weight. The weight W (fig. 2a and 2b) of 37 kg, on which the invar wire is attached, is resting on the steelball. The steelball is inserted in order to insure that, whatever the position

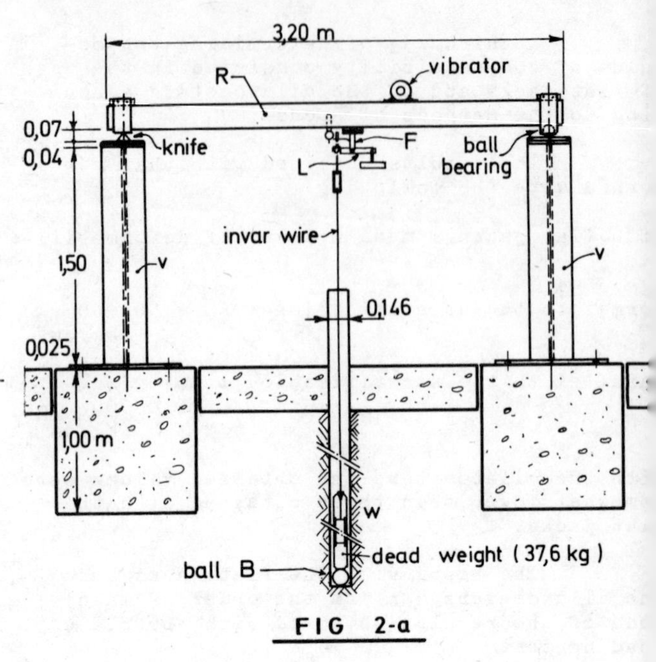

FIG 2-a

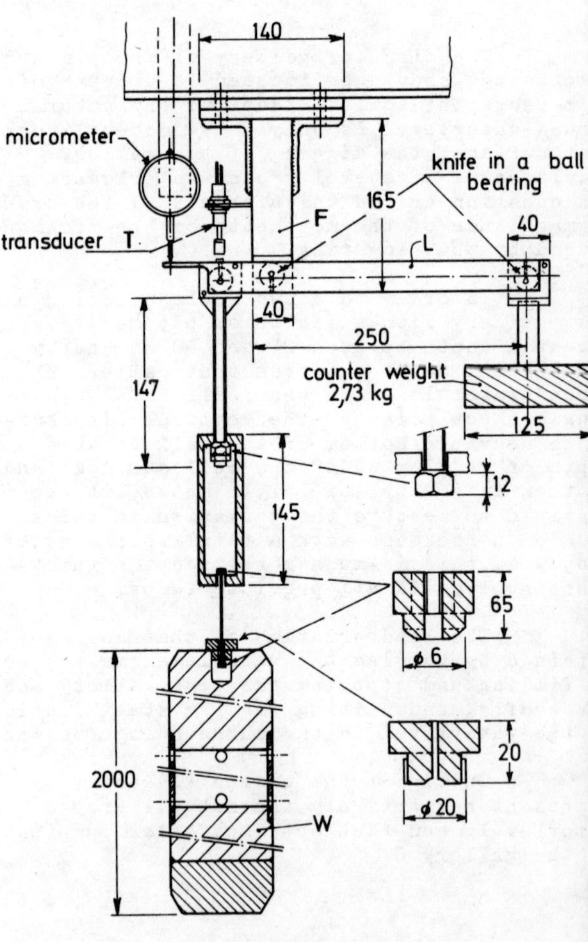

FIG. 2-b

: the weight W may be in the borehole, the weight is
›sting on the bottom of the borehole.

The ball is driven into the bottom in order to
›tain that it rests without any displacement on the
›ttom of the hole. The ball B and also the lower
art of the weight W are made of rustless steel in or-
er to avoid any relative movement of these two bodies
ıe to the progressive rusting of these elements.

The wire connecting the weight W with the le-
erarm is made of invar, in order to eliminate the in-
luence of temperature variations.

In the deep borehole of 150 m the water fil-
ing the hole has been replaced by a suspension of
›lykote C 20 %. Indeed, notwithstanding the systema-
ic use of a core drill with a length of 6 m, and the
imitation of the contact force of the drill on the
›ttom, a progressive deviation of the borehole from
ıe vertical, due to the progressive deviation of
ıe boretool has to be taken into consideration. In
ase of such a deviation, the possibility exists that
ıe wire rubs against the wall of the hole over a re-
atively important length, which should cause an error
ı the measures. A suspension of Molykote C has been
ıosen, for two reasons :
ıe suspension has a density which is lightly larger
ıan that of water, preventing it being displaced by
ıe water; the second reason is that the suspension
; seemingly stable with time. The percentage of 20 %
f the suspension has been determined in the laboratory
y the producer in order to lower the friction factor
› 0,12 under small pressures.

In order to insure a maximum sensitivity of
ıe leverarm L, the three bearings have been realized
y knives fixed in ball bearings (fig. 2b). The two
ixing points of the wire and the connexions transmit-
ing the effort in the wire to the leverarm have been
ealized in such a way that the rotation does not cau-
e any parasitical longitudinal movement.

The transducer used is of the type without
wn inertia.

The frame F on which the transducer T is fi-
ed, is connected to a beam R resting on one end
rough a ball bearing, and on the other end through
knife, on two vertical beams V, anchored on founda-
ion blocs with a thickness of 1 m (fig. 2a). The
all bearing and the knife have been provided in order
› eliminate any influence of possible small tempera-
ure variations of the horizontal beam R on the lectu-
e.

In order to eliminate temperature variations
f the vertical steel beams V on the lectures the whole
quipment has been placed in an insulated and clima-
ized provisory building (see photo 1).

The lectures of the displacements for both ap-
aratus were made directly in millivolts; furthermore
device was installed, registrating in fuction of
ime the difference of the measures between the two ex-
ensometers.

PHOTO 1.

Photo of the testing equipment in the insulated and climatized building.

During some preliminary testing, it was observed that by small vibrations the friction of the wire against the wall of the borehole could be eliminated, enabling to make a correct reading. Therefore on the horizontal beam R of the frame of the apparatus with the wore of 150 m length, a very small vibrator (fig. 2a) was installed. This vibrator (an ordinary boringtool with a small excentric weight) is actioned for about 10 seconds before the readings on the voltmeters are made.

TEST RESULTS

The readings of the deformeters and of the piezometers have been made during the following processes :

1°) a first rising of the water table, when the pumps installed for dewatering the gallery, were stopped.

2°) a subsequent lowering of the watertable, when the water was again pumped out of the gallery.

3°) a second rising of the watertable.

For each of these processes the obtained results are shown respectively on the figures 3, 4 and 5.

On each of these drawings, the curve Δ H gives in fuction of the time elapsed since the beginning of the considered process, the variation of the thickness of the rock mass located between the observation points a and b (fig. 1). The curves marked P give the variations in function of time of the piezometric levels in the piezometers 76, 77, 78, 89 and 90 (fig. 1). As the piezometers 89 and 90 were only placed after the first rising their curves are only shown on the figures 4 and 5.

The fig. 3, 4 and 5 show that the first rising, the subsequent sinking and the second rising of the watertable have caused resp. a swelling of 0,97 mm, a contraction of 1,76 mm, and a swelling of 1,79 mm of the soil mass located between the levels a and b (fig. 1).

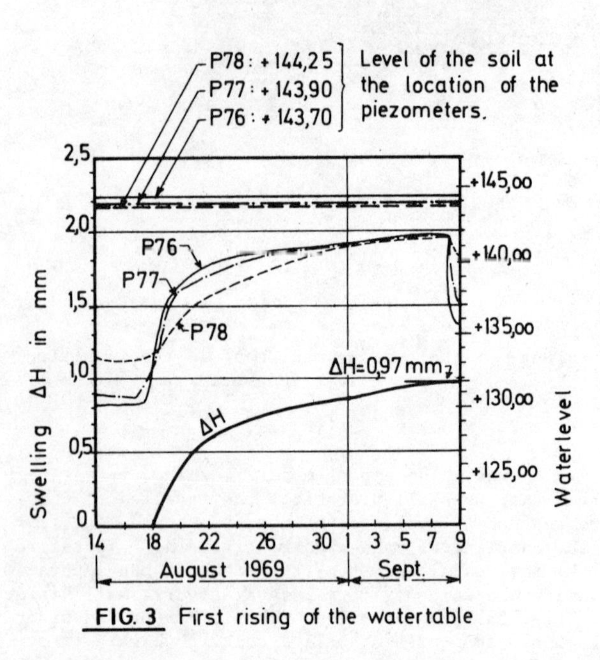

FIG. 3 First rising of the watertable

The curves Δ H of the fig. 3, 4 and 5 show that the piezometric levels and the compression, resp. swelling of the considered rockmass vary at first very rapidly after starting resp. stopping pumping , but that with elapsing time they tend to asymptotic values. There is a marked parallelism between the curves Δ H giving the swelling or the contraction of the considered rockmass, and the curves P showing the variations in the piezometric levels.

The piezometric curves also show that the delay in the rising or sinking of the waterlevel in the piezometers with respect to that in the entrance shaft to the gallery increases with the distance of the considered piezometer to the gallery.

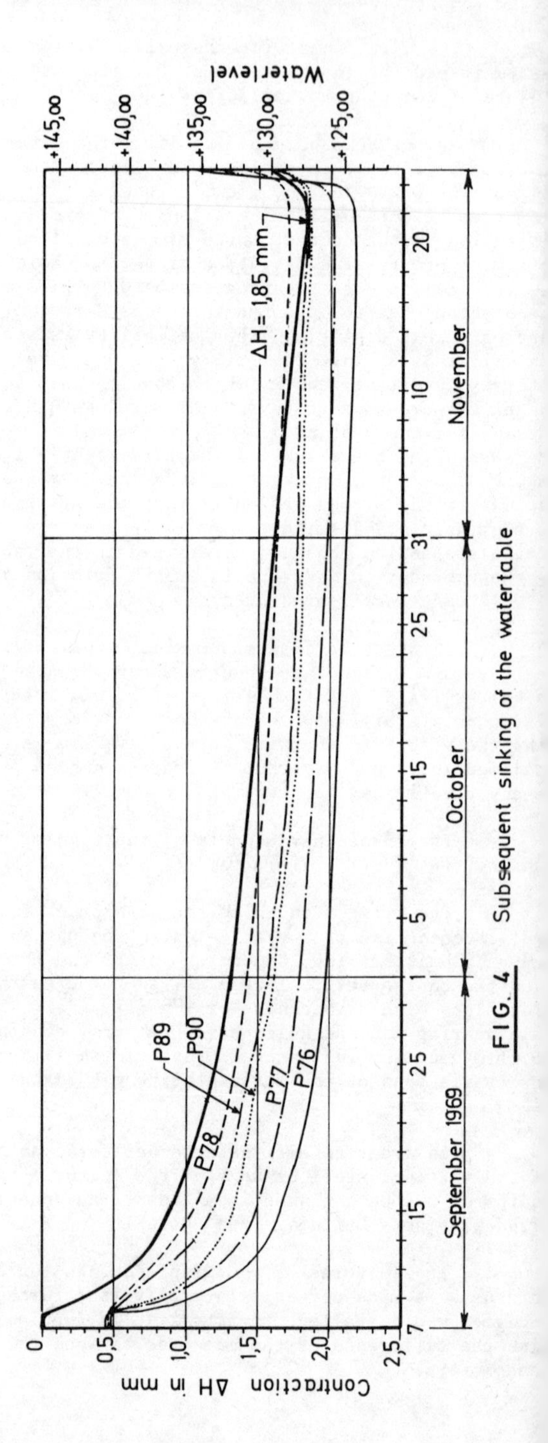

FIG. 4 Subsequent sinking of the watertable

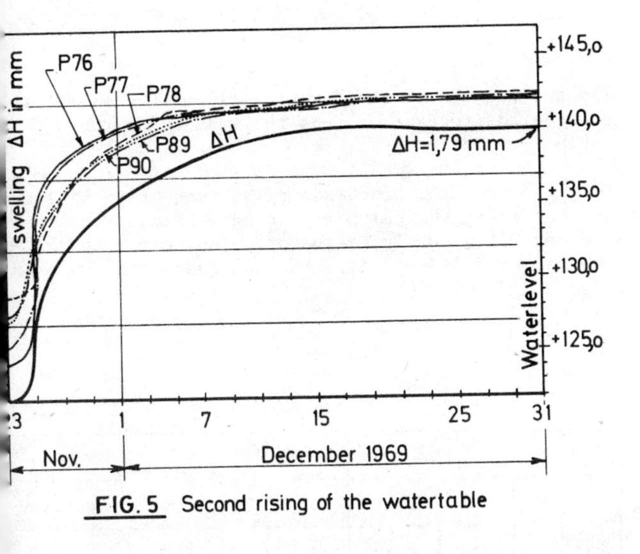

FIG. 5 Second rising of the watertable

EDUCTION OF THE MODULUS OF DEFORMABILITY FROM THE EFORMATION OF THE ROCKMASS, LOCATED BETWEEN THE DEPTH F 24,37 m AND 151,16 m UNDERNEATH THE SOIL SURFACE, ND WITH A TOTAL THICKNESS OF 126,79 m.

The completely exact calculation of the modulus of deformation from the obtained data, is not possible for the following reasons :

°) One should know the exact value of the change of water pressure at each point. Because the groundwater at the start or at the end of the observation period has an incurved shape (fig. 1), a large number of piezometers should be necessary in order to obtain sufficiently accurate data.

°) As the rockmass has a porosity of only 4,6 % (γ_d = 2,75 t/m3-, one cannot immediately assimilate the problem of the determination of the effective stresses to that in a soil; in the latter it is admitted that it is possible to conceive a large number of surfaces along which the surface of the contacts grain to grain is negligible. This assumption deviates the more from reality, the lower is the porosity. Furthermore in case of rocks the porosity is not homogeneously distributed, but is concentrated in the seams and the joints. Therefore it is quite possible to imagine, in case of a rockmass, with a given porosity, a mechanical model which is quite different from that of a soil mass. As this model is not know beforehand, this is again a reason why an exact calculation of the modulus of deformability from the obtained results is impossible.

In order to obtain an approximate or conventional value of the modulus of deformability, the following assumptions can be made.

1°) as the depth of 150 m is relatively small in comparison to the width of the zone influenced by the water movements (fig. 1), it is assumed that along a vertical there exists an hydrostatic law. This is of course a crude hypothesis. Furthermore it is assumed that at the site of the extensometers the waterlevels are those measured in the piezometer 76. Starting with this hypothesis the following changes in water pressure are to be considered :

1st rising of the watertable (fig. 3)
from + 130,2 to + 141,80

$$\Delta\sigma_w = (141,80 - 130,2)\,\delta_w = 11,60 \text{ t/m}^2$$

subsequent lowering of the watertable (fig. 4)
from + 141,60 to + 124,2

$$\Delta\sigma_w = (124,2 - 141,6)\,\delta_w = - 17,40 \text{ t/m}^2$$

2nd rising of the watertable (fig. 5)
from + 124,4 to + 142

$$\Delta\sigma_w = (142 - 124,4)\,\delta_w = + 17,6 \text{ t/m}^2$$

However, as for the subsequent sinking, and the second rising, we dispose of the lectures of the deep piezometers 89 and 90, we can in order to have a better approximation, make a mean between the waterpressures changes registered in the piezometers 76, 89 and 90.

For the subsequent lowering of the watertable we get (fig. 4)

P 76 : 124,2 - 141,60 = - 17,40
P 90   127,1 - 141,20 = - 14,20
P 89   127,6 - 141,30 = - 13,70

$$(\Delta\sigma_w)_m = - 15,10 \text{ t/m}^2$$

For the second rising we get (fig. 5)

P 76 : 142 - 124,4 = 17,6
P 90   142,4 - 127,1 = 15,3
P 89   142,3 - 127,6 = 14,7

$$(\Delta\sigma_w)_m = 15,87 \text{ t/m}^2$$

2°) It is assumed that in the rockmass in relation with the effective stresses, the same mechanical model as for the soil masses can be introduced, with the only difference that the own compressibility of the rock itself is no longer neglected against the deformability of the skeleton constituting the rockmass. This problem has been treated by Zienkiewicz [5] and by Mallet [6].

Supposing that the rockmass reacts as a purely linearly elastic, homogeneous and isotropic body, and denoting by

E = the modulus of deformability of the soil mass
μ = Poisson's ratio of the soil mass
E_k = the modulus of deformability of the rock itself
μ_k = Poisson's ratio of the rock itself.

One gets fot the deformations in the horizontal and vertical direction, under influence of a change $\Delta\sigma_w$ of the waterpressure, causing changes $\Delta\sigma'_v$ and $\Delta\sigma'_h$ in the effective stresses in vertical and horizontal directions

$$\varepsilon_h = \frac{1}{E}\left[\Delta\sigma'_h - \mu(\Delta\sigma'_h + \Delta\sigma'_v)\right] + \frac{1-2\mu_k}{E_k}\Delta\sigma_w \quad (1)$$

$$\varepsilon_v = \frac{1}{E}\left[\Delta\sigma'_v - 2\mu\Delta\sigma'_h\right] + \frac{1-2\mu_k}{E_k}\Delta\sigma_w \quad (2)$$

As any horizontal deformation of the rockmass is prevented, one has $\varepsilon_h = 0.$ (3)

As the variation $\Delta\sigma_v$ of the total stress is zero, one has

$$\Delta\sigma_v = \Delta\sigma'_v + \Delta\sigma_w = 0 \qquad \Delta\sigma'_v = -\Delta\sigma_w \quad (4)$$

From these 4 equations, one deduces :

$$\varepsilon_v = \frac{1+\mu}{1-\mu}\Delta\sigma_w\left[-\frac{1-2\mu}{E} + \frac{1-2\mu_k}{E_k}\right] \quad (5)$$

$$\frac{d\,(dh)}{dh} = \varepsilon_v \quad (6)$$

and when $\Delta\sigma_w$ is considered constant with depth, one gets

$$\Delta H = \frac{1+\mu}{1-\mu}\Delta\sigma_w\left[-\frac{1-2\mu}{E} + \frac{1-2\mu_k}{E_k}\right]H \quad (7)$$

which solved for E gives :

$$E = \frac{1-2\mu}{\frac{1-2\mu_k}{E_k} - \frac{\Delta H}{\Delta\sigma_w}\frac{1-\mu}{1+\mu}\frac{1}{H}} \quad (8)$$

Let us suppose for the rock itself

$$E_k = 400.000 \text{ kg/cm}^2 \qquad \mu_k = 0,3 \quad (9)$$

From laboratory tests one has found $= 0,28$ (10)

$$\frac{1-2\mu_k}{E_k} = \frac{1 - 2 \times 0,3}{4 \times 10^6} = 10^{-7} \text{ t/m}^2$$

$$1 - 2\mu = 1 - 2 \times 0,28 = 0,44 \qquad \frac{1-\mu}{1+\mu} = \frac{1-0,28}{1+0,28} = 0,563$$

$$H = 126,79 \text{ m}$$

$$E = \frac{0,44}{10^{-7} - \frac{\Delta H}{\Delta\sigma_w}\frac{0,563}{126,79}} = \frac{0,44}{10^{-7} - 4,44 \times 10^{-3}\frac{\Delta H}{\Delta\sigma_w}} \quad (11)$$

The application of the formula (11) at the end of the considered processes, gives the results of the table I.

For the processes of subsequent sinking and second rising the calculations have been performed for the case of a purely hydrostatic law, and with the mean of $\Delta\sigma_w$ deduced from the readings in the piezometers 76, 89 and 90.

TABLE I

Process	$\Delta\sigma_w$		ΔH	E	
		t/m²	m	t/m²	kg/cm²
First rising	hydr.	11,60	$-9,7 \times 10^{-4}$	$9,34 \times 10^5$	93400
Subsequent sinking	hydr.	$-17,40$	$1,85 \times 10^{-3}$	$7,69 \times 10^5$	76900
	mean	$-15,10$		$6,83 \times 10^5$	68300
Second rising	hydr.	$+17,6$	$-1,79 \times 10^{-3}$	$7,98 \times 10^5$	79800
	mean			$7,32 \times 10^5$	73200

The calculated values are of the order of 70.000 to 80.000 kg/cm2. Although based on rather arbitrary assumptions, the calculations based on the special extensometertests performed, give values located between those obtained with the flat jack tests for directions normal and parallel to the stratification. This result is logical as, due to the folding along a vertical, all directions of the stratification can be found.

SETTLEMENT DUE TO A GENERAL GROUND-WATER LOWERING OF

The question to be solved was to get an idea of the settlement which could occur under the influence of a general ground-water lowering extending over an area of several km2.

The shale rockmass has a thickness of several hundred meters. Of course the modulus of deformability is certainly not constant, but can be considered to depend on the ratio $\frac{\Delta\sigma'}{\sigma'}$ of the effective stress increase to natural effective stress at the considered point, and on the value $\frac{\sigma_c}{E_k}$.

However the performed extensometertests do not give any information about these relationships.

Therefore, in order to still get an idea about the settlement caused by a general ground-water lowering of 30 m, and assuming an affected thickness of the schistmass of H = 500 m, taking E = 70.000 kg/cm2 one gets a settlement given by the formula (7)

$$\Delta H = \frac{1}{0,563} \Delta\sigma_w \left[- \frac{0,44}{7 \times 10^5} + 10^{-7} \right] 500$$

$\Delta\sigma_w = -\ 30$ t/m2 $\qquad \Delta H = 1,41$ cm.

CONCLUSIONS.

1) The measurement of the deformations of a shale rockmass with a thickness of about 125 m under the influence of artificial groundwater lowerings and risings, has allowed to calculate an order of magnitude of the modulus of deformability of the shalebody of 70.000 to 80.000 kg/cm2, which lays in the range of the values found by flat jack tests.
2) The test results show that a ground-water lowering extending over a very large area, can in the case of shalebodies of great thickness, cause non negligible settlements.

LITERATURE.

[1] DE BEER, E., DELMER A. and WALLAYS, M., 1968, Essais de charge en galerie et en surface avec plaques de grandes dimensions, International Symposium on Rock Mechanics, Madrid.

[2] ROCHA, M. and Jorge Neves da Silva, 1970, A new method for the determination of deformability in rock masses, Laboratorio Nacional de Engenharia Civil, Lisboa, Memoria n° 361.

[3] ROCHA, M., 1970, A new method for the determination of the deformability in rock masses, Proceedings, 2nd Congress of the International Society for Rock Mechanics, Beograd, Volume I.

[4] GERVAISE, J., 1969, Extensomètre vertical pour la mesure des mouvements du sol lors de variations provoquées du niveau de la nappe aquifère, Proceedings, International Symposium on Large permanent underground openings, Oslo, pp. 346 - 353.

[5] STAGG, K.G. and ZIENKIEWICS O.C., 1968, Rock mechanics in engineering practice, J. Wiley & Sons, London, pp. 81 - 89.

[6] MALLET, Ch., 1967, Réflexions sur les mouvements d'un sol ou d'une roche dus aux variations de niveau d'une nappe aquifère, Internal Report of the CERN, August.

DYNAMISCHE WIRKUNGEN AUF FELS INFOLGE INSTATIONARER KLUFTWASSERSTRØMUNG

DYNAMIC FORCES APPLIED TO ROCK BY UNSTEADY FLOW OF WATER IN JOINTS

EFFETS DYNAMIQUES SUR LA ROCHE DUS À DES ÉCOULEMENTS INSTATIONNAIRES DAN LES FISSURES

Dieter KIRSCHKE

Austria

Zusammenfassung

Die Beeinflussung des Spannungszustandes im Fels durch Kluftwasser wird bisher, wenn überhaupt, nur unter der Annahme stationärer Verhältnisse, also konstanter hydraulischer Randbedingungen berücksichtigt. In der vorliegenden Arbeit wird untersucht, ob diese Annahme in allen Fällen ausreichend ist. Es wird gezeigt, daß dynamische Wasserdruckkräfte, die wesentlich höher liegen als im stationären Fall, nur bei sehr schnellem Anstieg des auf das Kluftwasser wirkenden Randdruckes auftreten können. Ist die Anstiegszeit länger, als eine Druckschwankung braucht, um in der wassergefüllten Kluft mit Schallgeschwindigkeit (1400 m/sec) zweimal hin- und herzulaufen, reicht die Annahme eines stationären Vorganges meistens schon aus. In Klüften mit sehr geringer Spaltweite ist die Druckkraft des Wassers wegen der starken Dämpfung sogar niemals größer als im stationären Fall.

Summary

All previous studies of the influence of joint water on the state of stress in a rock mass were carried out on the assumption of stationary water pressure i. e. constant hydraulic boundary conditions. This paper investigates the limitations placed on the validity of this assumption. It is shown, that forces due to dynamic water pressure, which are substantially larger than the forces due to stationary pressure conditions are to be expected as a consequence of a very rapid increase of boundary pressures acting on the water. If the rise time of the pressure is larger than the time needed by a pulse to travel four joint lengths at the velocity of sound in water, the assuption of stationary conditions yields sufficiently accurate results. Due to strong damping effects the water pressure in very narrow joints never exceeds the pressure expected under stationary conditions.

Résumé

Habituellement et dans les cas où l'on en tient compte, l'influence de l'eau circulant dans les fissures sur l'état des contraintes dans un massif rocheux est déterminée dans l'hypothèse d'écoulements stationnaires. Dans l'étude présentée on examine dans quelle mesure cette hypothèse est suffisante. On démontre que des pressions hydrauliques dynamiques, qui sont nettement plus élevées que pour un écoulement stationnaire, ne peuvent apparaître que dans le cas où la pression agissant aux limites croît très rapidement. Si le temps d'application de cet accroissement de pression est supérieur à celui d'un aller-retour d'une onde sonore dans la fissure remplie d'eau (1400 m/sec), l'hypothèse d'un écoulement stationnaire suffit dans la plupart des cas. En outre, dans le cas de fissures étroites, la pression de l'eau n'est jamais supérieure à celle existant dans le cas stationnaire, l'amortissement étant alors important.

Einleitung

Es ist seit längerem bekannt, daß bei Standsicherheitsuntersuchungen an Felsbauwerken auch die Kräfte berücksichtigt werden müssen, die evtl. vorhandenes Kluftwasser auf seine Umgebung ausübt (Müller, 1960). Kluftwasserkräfte haben vor allem zwei bemerkenswerte Eigenschaften:

- Ihr Richtung kann völlig vom sonstigen Kräfteverlauf im Fels abweichen,
- sie reduzieren die aktivierbaren Reibungskräfte auf möglichen Gleitflächen.

Bei stehendem Kluftwasser ergibt sich die Druckverteilung in einfachster Weise aus der jeweiligen Lage unterhalb des freien Wasserspiegels. Für strömendes Kluftwasser wird die Druckverteilung aus der Potentialverteilung ermittelt, die sich wie bei einem elektrischen Netzwerk aus den Längen und Fließwiderständen der einzelnen durchströmten Kluftabschnitte berechnen läßt (Louis, 1967). Dieses Verfahren geht aber von der Annahme einer stationären Strömung bei unveränderlichen hydraulischen Randbedingungen aus. Wieweit die Druckkräfte des Kluftwassers bei instationären Strömungsvorgängen hiervon abweichen, soll im folgenden untersucht werden.

Ursachen instationärer Kluftwasserströmung

Instationäre Strömungsvorgänge werden verursacht durch zeitlich veränderliche hydraulische Randbedingungen. Hierzu gehören Wasserspiegelschwankungen in Gewässern, die mit dem betreffenden wassergefüllten Kluftsystem in Verbindung stehen, Erdbebenwirkungen sowie die unmittelbare Kraftausübung auf das Kluftwasser durch den Gasdruck von Sprengladungen. In idealisierter Form läßt sich die Druckaufbringung durch einen linearen Druckanstieg in der Zeit t_s auf das Maximum max p_o und ein anschließendes Konstanthalten dieses Druckes beschreiben (Abb. 1).

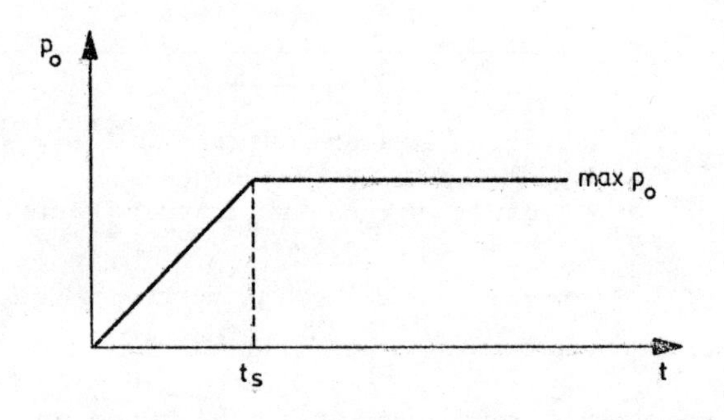

Abb. 1: Idealisierter zeitlicher Verlauf des auf eine Kluft wirkenden Randdruckes p_o

Geometrie und Eigenschaften der Klüfte

Eine Kluft ist in ihrer allgemeinsten Form gekennzeichnet durch ihre flächenhafte Ausdehnung, unregelmäßige Spaltweite und das Vorhandensein von Abzweigungen. Die Kluftwände sind als Teil des den Fels bildenden Gesteins elastisch, aber nicht trägheitslos verformbar, wenn der Druck des Kluftwassers sich ändert. Diese Verformbarkeit ist aber dadurch begrenzt, daß die Kluftwände an vielen Stellen der Kluft gegeneinander gepreßt sind. Eine grössere Verformung ist erst möglich, wenn die Druckkraft des Kluftwassers die Kontaktkräfte an den Berührungsstellen der Kluftwände überschreitet. Im Rahmen der vorliegenden Fragestellung, bei der eine obere Schranke für die mögliche Druckkraft in einer wassergefüllten Kluft gefunden werden soll, reicht es aus, die eindimensionale Ausbreitung einer Randdruckänderung in einer Kluft mit konstanter Spaltweite, unverschieblichen Kluftwänden und ohne Abzweigungen zu untersuchen (Abb. 2).

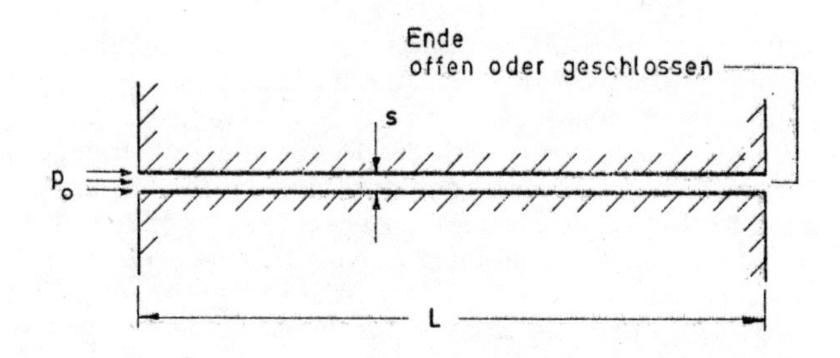

Abb. 2: Auf eine starre Kluft mit konstanter Spaltweite s wirkt der Randdruck p_o

Dies ergibt in jedem Fall die größtmögliche Druckkraft, da eine flächenhafte Druckausbreitung, nachgiebige Kluftwände, häufiger Spaltweitenwechsel und Abzweigungen eine starke Druckverminderung zur Folge haben.

Für die viskose Dämpfung einer Druckänderung bei ihrer Ausbreitung in einer Kluft wird das Widerstandsgesetz der laminaren Kluftströmung angesetzt. Der Druckverlust Δp längs einer Strecke l ist also proportional zu der mit der Druckänderung verbundenen Fließgeschwindigkeit des Kluftwassers:

$$\frac{\Delta p}{l} = v \cdot c$$

c hängt von der Spaltweite s (cm) der Kluft sowie der Wassertemperatur ab. Bei 5° C ergibt sich:

$$c = 1,86 \cdot 10^{-7} \frac{1}{s^2}$$

Diese Beziehung ist in Abb. 3 graphisch dargestellt.

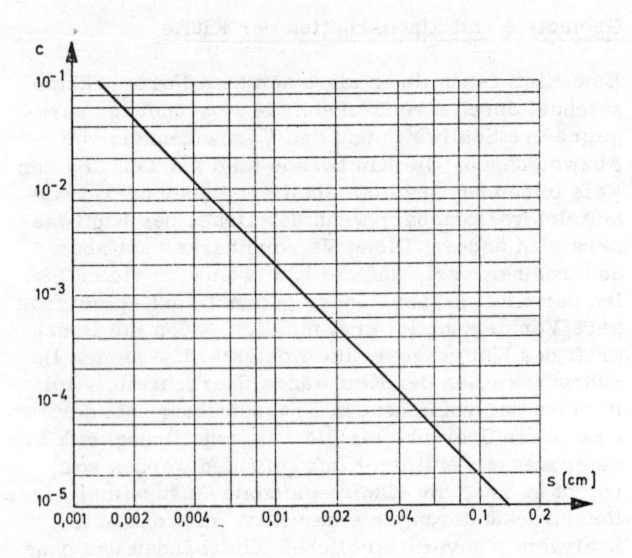

Abb. 3: Dämpfungsbeiwert c als Funktion der Kluftspaltweite s. Wassertemperatur 5° C.

Während c der für die Dämpfung eines Randdruckes p_o maßgebliche Wert ist, wird das Schwingungsverhalten des Kluftwassers durch die Kluftlänge L bestimmt. Daneben ist noch die Frage von Bedeutung, ob das Kluftende offen oder geschlossen ist. Diese zwei Fälle müssen immer unterschieden werden. c und L können dagegen zusammengefaßt werden zu einer Kenngröße $c \cdot L$. Für Klüfte mit gleichem $c \cdot L$-Wert ergeben sich bei dimensionsloser Darstellung identische Ergebnisse.

Das Berechnungsverfahren

Die Berechnung der Druckausbreitung im Kluftwasser erfolgt mit einem neuentwickelten numerischen Verfahren, welches sich am ehesten mit dem Charakteristikenverfahren vergleichen läßt. Es wurde jedoch ohne Verwendung der Navier-Stokes-Gleichungen unmittelbar mit Hilfe von Impulssatz, Energieerhaltungssatz und Kontinuitätsbedingung aus einer Betrachtung der Wechselwirkung zwischen "Wasserelementen" hergeleitet. Der Vorteil des Verfahrens ist insbesondere, daß die Dämpfung eine in jeden Rechenschritt einbezogene Eigenschaft der Wasserelemente ist, so daß jeglicher Iterationsprozeß entfällt. Damit ist auch die Erfassung der extrem starken Dämpfung in sehr engen Klüften ohne erhöhten Rechenaufwand möglich. Das Verfahren erlaubt eine durchgehende Berechnung der Druck- und Geschwindigkeitsverteilung in einer Kluft vom Augenblick der ersten Druckaufbringung bis zum Erreichen eines stationären Endzustandes (Kirschke, 1974).

Die Wirkung der Erdbeschleunigung wird bei der Berechnung nicht berücksichtigt, da diese keinen Einfluß auf das Ergebnis hat. Betrachtet wird nur die Änderung eines stationären Zustandes, wie er vor Aufbringung des neuen Randdruckes p_o geherrscht hatte. Um den neuen Gesamtzustand zu erhalten, müssen die Wasserdrücke des Ausgangszustandes und der Änderung gegebenenfalls addiert werden.

Ergebnisse der rechnerischen Untersuchung instationärer Strömungsvorgänge in Klüften

Die größten dynamischen Wirkungen sind zu erwarten, wenn der Randdruck p_o sofort in voller Höhe aufgebracht wird ($t_s = o$). Der Randdruck wandert mit der Schallgeschwindigkeit a_o in die wassergefüllte Kluft und wird hierbei je nach deren Spaltweite gedämpft (Abb. 4 und 5).

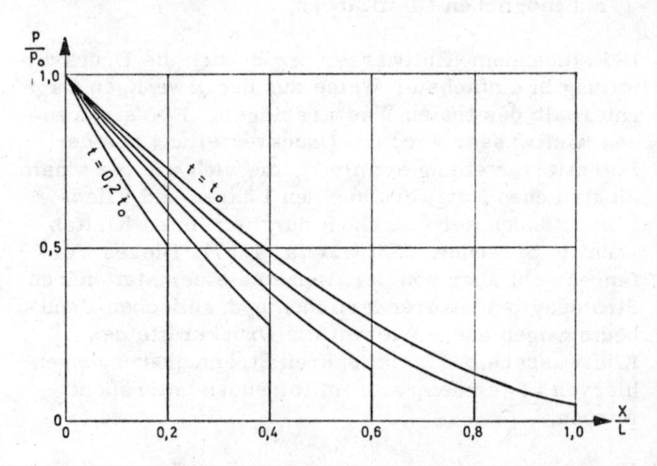

Abb. 4: Druckverlauf in einer engen Kluft zu verschiedenen Zeitpunkten nach Aufbringung des Randdruckes p_o = const. ($t_s = o$)

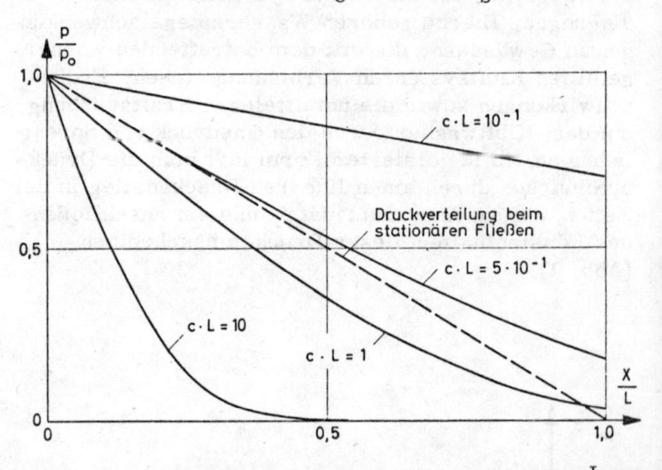

Abb. 5: Druckverlauf in einer Kluft zur Zeit $t_o = \frac{L}{a_o}$ nach Aufbringung des Randdruckes p_o = const bei verschieden starker Dämpfung

Zur Zeit $t_o = \frac{L}{a_o}$ hat die durch p_o hervorgerufene Druckänderung die Kluft zum erstenmal durchlaufen.

Nach mehreren Reflexionen am Kluftende und am Kluftanfang stellt sich ein Endzustand ein, der sich nicht mehr ändert, solange der auf den Kluftanfang wirkende Randdruck konstant bleibt. Bei Klüften mit offenem Ende bedeutet der Endzustand stationäres Fließen des Kluftwassers bei linearem Druckabfall in Fließrichtung. Bei Klüften mit geschlossenem Ende befindet sich das Kluftwasser dagegen schließlich in Ruhe und hat überall den gleichen Druck $p = p_o$. Abb. 6 und 7 zeigen diesen Einschwingvorgang anhand der zeitlichen Entwicklung des Mittelwertes p_m des in der Kluft herrschenden Druckes. p_m ist ein Maß für die vom Kluftwasser auf die Kluftwände insgesamt ausgeübte Druckkraft.

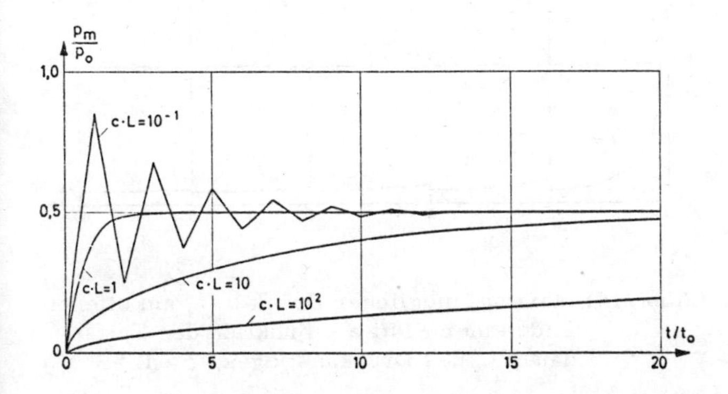

Abb. 6: Zeitliche Entwicklung des mittleren Druckes p_m in einer Kluft mit offenem Ende bei verschiedenen Werten von $c \cdot L$, p_o = const.

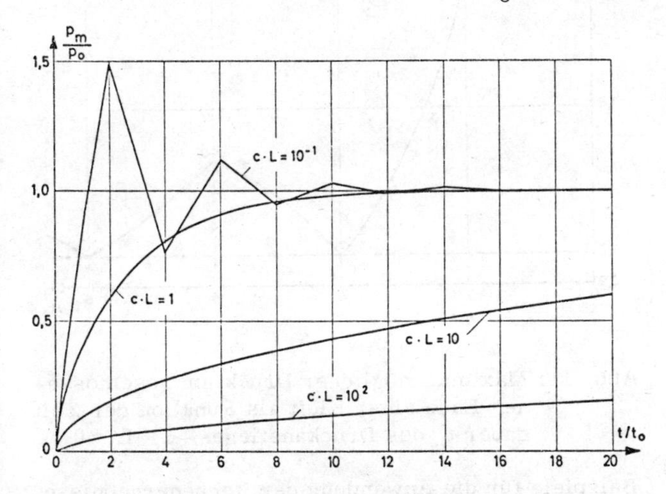

Abb. 7: Zeitliche Entwicklung des mittleren Druckes p_m in einer Kluft mit geschlossenem Ende bei verschiedenen Werten von $c \cdot L$, p_o = const.

Bei starker Dämpfung wird der Maximalwert von p_m erst im Endzustand erreicht. In diesem Fall reicht es aus, gleich die Wasserdrücke des stationären Zustandes zu ermitteln.

$t_s = 0$ ist ein nicht vorkommender Idealfall. Es soll daher untersucht werden, welche Wasserdrücke bei $t_s > 0$ zu erwarten sind:

Je länger es dauert, bis der auf das Kluftwasser wirkende Randdruck auf seinen Höchstwert max p_o gestiegen ist, desto mehr verringert sich das erreichbare Maximum von p_m gegenüber den Werten, die sich für $t_s = 0$ ergeben (Abb. 8 und 9). Es zeigt sich, daß Werte von max p_m, die diejenigen des

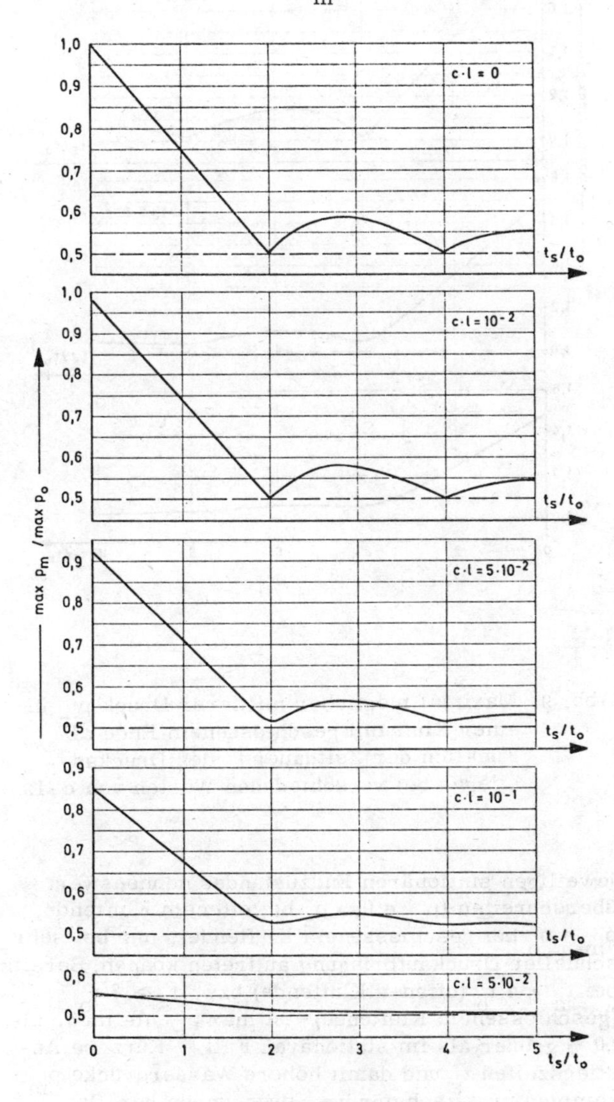

Abb. 8: Maximal möglicher mittlerer Druck p_m in einer Kluft mit offenem Ende als Funktion der Zeitdauer t_s des Druckanstieges bei verschiedenen Werten von $c \cdot L$

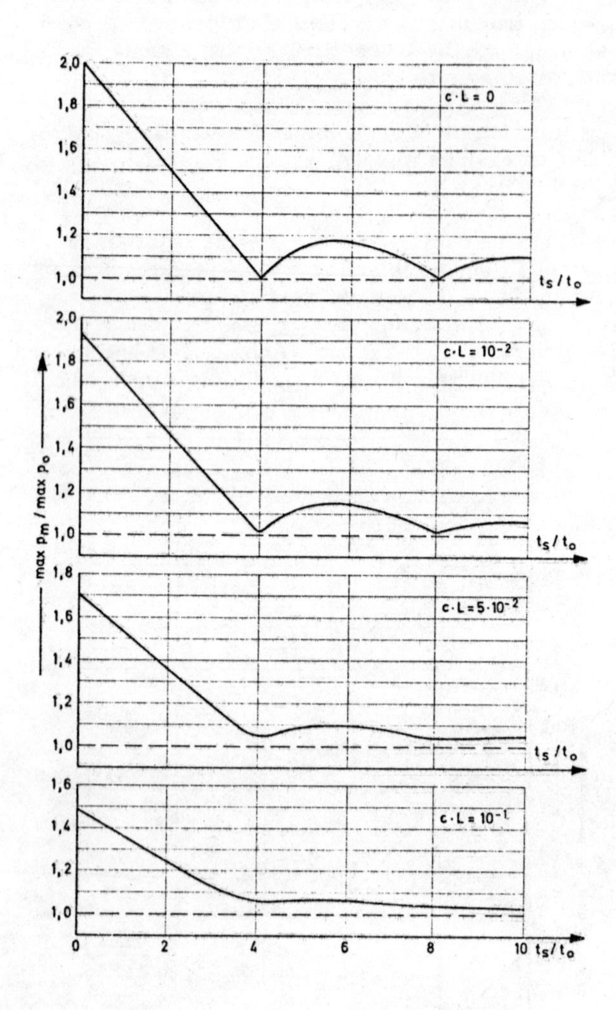

Abb. 9: Maximal möglicher mittlerer Druck p_m in einer Kluft mit geschlossenem Ende als Funktion der Zeitdauer t_s des Druckanstieges bei verschiedenen Werten von c·L

jeweiligen stationären Endzustandes nennenswert überschreiten ($p_m = 0,5\ p_o$ bei offenem Kluftende, $p_m = p_o$ bei geschlossenem Kluftende), nur bei sehr schneller Druckaufbringung auftreten können. Bereits bei $t_s > 4\ t_o$ (offenes Kluftende) bzw. $t_s > 8\ t_o$ (geschlossenem Kluftende) ist max p_m nie mehr als 10 % größer als im stationären Fall. Kürzere Anstiegszeiten t_s und damit höhere Wasserdrücke p_m kommen praktisch nur bei Sprengungen vor. In allen anderen Fällen mit veränderlichen hydraulischen Randbedingungen braucht nicht damit gerechnet zu werden, daß das Kluftwasser größere Kräfte ausübt als im stationären Fall.

Zur Beantwortung der Frage, welches örtliche Druckmaximum max p_{end} am Ende einer Kluft auftreten kann, dienen die Diagramme der Abb. 10 und 11. Sie geben max p_{end} für den Fall einer ungedämpften Druckausbreitung als Funktion von t_s an. Bei Klüften mit $c \cdot L > 0$ sind die Maxima entsprechend kleiner.

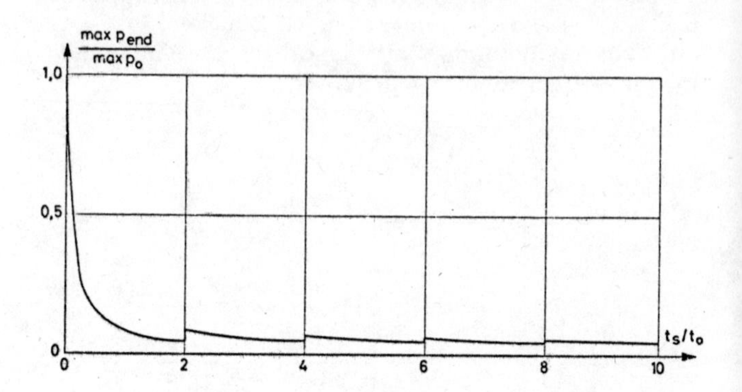

Abb. 10: Maximal möglicher Druck p_{end} am offenen Ende einer Kluft als Funktion der Zeitdauer t_s des Druckanstieges. $c \cdot L = 0$

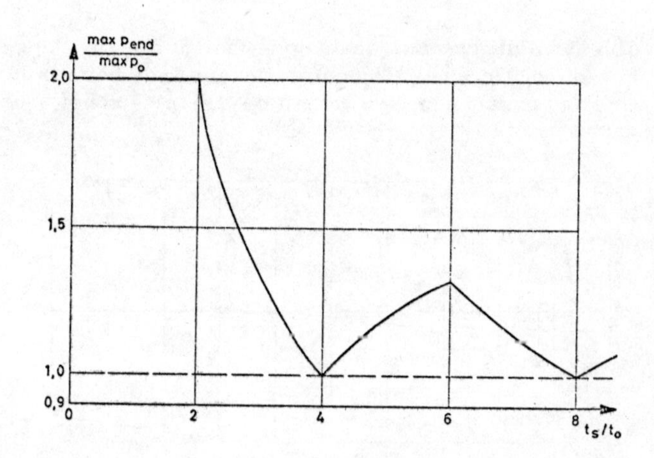

Abb. 11: Maximal möglicher Druck am geschlossenen Ende einer Kluft als Funktion der Zeitdauer t_s des Druckanstieges. $c \cdot L = 0$

Beispiele für die Anwendung der Rechenergebnisse

1. Beispiel

In einem gleitgefährdeten Hang, dessen potentielle Gleitflächen großräumig durchstreichende Klüfte mit vollkommener Durchtrennung sind, die von Kluftwasser durchströmt werden, soll ein nicht ausgekleidetes Wasserschloß gebaut werden. Die aktivierbare Reibungskraft auf den möglichen Gleitflächen wird durch den Kluftwasserdruck vermindert. Es ist zu prüfen, ob sich bei Berücksichtigung des instationären Strömungsvorganges infolge des rasch steigenden Wasserspiegels im Wasserschloß größere Wasserdruckkräfte auf den Gleitflächen ergeben können als bei Annahme stationären Fließens.

Länge der möglichen Gleitflächen: $L = 2000$ cm
mittlere Spaltweite der Klüfte $s = 0{,}20$ cm
Anstiegszeit bis zum höchsten Wasserspiegel im Wasserschloß $t_s = 50$ sec
Schallgeschwindigkeit im Wasser $a_o = 140000$ cm/sec

$$t_o = \frac{L}{a_o} = \frac{2000}{140000} = \frac{1}{70} \text{ sec}$$

$$\frac{t_s}{t_o} = 3500$$

In diesem Fall kann bereits aufgrund des hohen Wertes von t_s/t_o gesagt werden, daß keinerlei dynamische Wirkung zu erwarten ist.

2. Beispiel

In einem Steinbruch, dessen Gesteinsklüfte stark von Kluftwasser durchströmt sind, sind die Sprengladungen häufig unmittelbar von Wasser umgeben. Es soll festgestellt werden, ob durch die bei einer Sprengung auf das Kluftwasser aufgebrachte und von diesem weitergeleitete Energie eine höhere Gefährdung der Standsicherheit der Felswände verursacht werden kann.

Länge der für eine Gefährdung der Standsicherheit in Frage kommenden, wassergefüllten Klüfte $L = 700$ cm
mittlere Spaltweite der Klüfte $s = 0{,}05$ cm
Anstiegszeit des Gasdruckes bei der Sprengung $t_s = \frac{1}{200}$ sec

$c = 7{,}4 \cdot 10^{-5}$ (aus Abb. 3)
$c \cdot L = 5{,}2 \cdot 10^{-2}$

$$t_o = \frac{700}{140000} = \frac{1}{200}$$

$$\frac{t_s}{t_o} = 1$$

Aus Abb. 9 ist zu entnehmen, daß in den betrachteten Klüften ein mittlerer Druck auftreten kann, der den bei der Sprengung entstehenden Gasdruck noch um etwa 60 % (interpoliert aus den Diagrammen für $c \cdot L = 10^{-2}$ und $c \cdot L = 5 \cdot 10^{-2}$) übersteigt. Hierdurch dürfte die Stabilität der Felswand erheblich beeinflußt werden. Andererseits könnte dieser Effekt eine erwünschte Verstärkung der Sprengwirkung bedeuten.

Würde die Spaltbreite der Klüfte nur 0,001 cm betragen, wäre das Ergebnis völlig anders. Mit $c = 1{,}86 \cdot 10^{-1}$ ergibt sich aus Abb. 7, daß sich ein nennenswerter Kluftwasserdruck erst sehr spät aufbauen kann. Bis dahin ist der Gasdruck der Sprengung aber bereits wieder abgeklungen, da die Umgebung der Sprengladung völlig zerstört wird und der Druck entweichen kann.

Anmerkung

Die dargestellten Ergebnisse sind Teil eines Forschungsprojektes des Sonderforschungsbereiches 77 "Felsmechanik" an der Universität Karlsruhe.

Literatur

Müller, L., 1960, Der Einfluß des Bergwassers auf die Standsicherheit der Felswiderlager von Talsperren, Österreichische Wasserwirtschaft, Jg. 12, H. 8/9, Wien, Springer

Louis, C., 1967, Strömungsvorgänge in klüftigen Medien und ihre Wirkung auf die Standsicherheit von Bauwerken und Böschungen im Fels, Diss. Karlsruhe

Kirschke, D., 1974, Druckstoßvorgänge in wassergefüllten Felsklüften, Diss. Karlsruhe (im Druck)

RESULTS OF LABORATORY TESTS ON WATER PRESSURE AND FLOW IN JOINTS

RÉSULTATS D'ESSAIS EFFECTUÉS EN LABORATOIRE SUR LA PRESSION HYDROSTATIQUE ET L'ÉCOULEMENT DANS LES DIACLASES

ERGEBNISSE AUFGRUND LABORUNTERSUCHUNGEN ÜBER PORENWASSERSPANNUNG UND WASSERFLUSS IN KLÜFTEN

Yuzo OHNISHI
Dept. of Transportation Eng., Kyoto University, Kyoto, Japan

Richard E. GOODMAN
Dept. of Civil Eng., University of California, Berkeley, Calif.

Summary

This paper discusses the results of triaxial and direct shear tests on artificial joints in sandstone during which no drainage was allowed into or out of the rock sample. Pore pressure induced in the joints amounted to ten to fifteen percent of the deviator stress at peak load in triaxial experiments, meaning that the effective joint normal stress was significantly reduced during shear. Induced water pressures measured in direct shear experiments were ten to twenty percent of the peak shear stress. Joint permeability tests were conducted: by measuring axial water flow along a longitudinal joint in a triaxial specimen; and by measuring radially outward flow along a joint normal to a thick walled rock cylinder. All data show a rapid drop in fracture permeability as normal stress increases, with almost no flow in the joint above 600 psi (4 MN/m^2). Thus it seems likely that pore pressures induced in situ in initially confined joints may exist as transient precursors of slip.

Résumé

Cet article concerne les résultats d'essais triaxiaux et d'essais de cisaillement direct sur joints artificiels dans le grès, aucours desquels on interdit tout drainage à l'intérieur ou à l'extérieur de l'échantillon de la roche. La pression intersticielle induite dans les joints atteint dix à quinze pour cent du déviateur à la valeur maximale du chargement dans les essais triaxiaux c'est à dire que la contrainte normale effective du joint a diminué de façon significative pendant le cisaillement. Les pressions d'eau induites mesurées au cours des essais de cisaillement direct atteignent dix à vingt pour cent de la contrainte de cisaillement maximale. On a effectué des essais de perméabilité du joint: en mesurant l'écoulement d'eau axial le long d'un joint longitudinal dans un échantillon triaxial; et en mesurant l'écoulement radial dirigé vers l'extérieur le long d'un joint normal à un tube de roche de forte épaisseur. Toutes les données montrent une chute brutale de la perméabilité de la fracture au fur et à mesure que la contrainte normale augmente, avec pratiquement aucun écoulement dans le joint au dessus de 600 psi (4 MN/m^2). Ainsi, l'existence de pressions intersticielles induites in situ dans les joints, comprimés latéralement à l'état initial, semble constituer un phenoméne précurseur temporaire de glissement.

Zusammenfassung

Dieser Bericht beschreibt die Resultate von Triaxial - und Direktscherversuchen an künstlich hergestellten Klüften in Sandstein wobei eine Drainage in oder aus der Felsprobe verhindert war. In den Triaxialversuchen stieg die in den Klüften induzierte Porenwasserspannung auf 10 bis 15 Prozent der Deviatorspannung bei Maximallast. Dies bedeutet , dass die effektive Kluftnormalspannung während dem Versuch bedeutend herabgesetzt war. In Direktscherversuchen wurden induzierte Porenwasserspannungen von 10 bis 20 Prozent der maximalen Scherspannung gemessen. Kluftdurchlässigkeitsversuche wurden durchgeführt: Durch Messen des axialen Wasserflusses längs einer longitudinalen Kluft in einer Triaxialprobe, sowie durch Messen radial nach aussen fliessenden Wassers längs einer Kluft normal zu einem dickwandigen Felszylinder. Alle Daten zeigen eine schnelle Abnahme der Kluftdurchlässigkeit bei zunehmenden Normaldruck, wobei bei Drücken über 600 psi (4 MN/m^2) die Durchlässigkeit sehr gering ist. Somit scheint es wahrscheinlich, dass induzierte Porenwasserspannungen bei anfänglich unter Druck stehenden Klüften als vorübergehende Vorläufer eines Rutsches aufreten können.

INTRODUCTION

We tend to overlook the possibility that water inside joints in rocks may not be able to drain during a shearing event. One rationale for this is as follows: when the joint reaches its peak strength and begins to slide, it dilates and its aperture increases. The joint then drains the rock mass and the local pore pressures decline. Neglect of this phenomenon should be a conservative omission.

It is true, that rock dilates before fracture. Joints dilate too but not until near peak load and only at low normal pressure.* If the water pressure should increase as a result of sub-peak

*Rough joints dilated significantly during shear when the normal stress was less than about 20 percent of the unconfined compression strength of the wall rock in a test series by the authors. Granite, rhyolite and friable sandstone were tested in direct shear.

loading, the effective stress normal to the joint would decrease; this is not conservative.

An *undrained test,* i.e. with absolutely no drainage from the joint into the surrounding environment is impractical to arrange. But a *closed system test* can be conducted to evaluate pore water behavior in joints during shear. This is the subject of this paper, as well as discussion of flow characteristics of joints under changing stress. By a *closed system test* we refer to a shear test conducted in such a way that no water enters or leaves the specimen as it shears. There is nothing to impede the flow of the joint water into the interstices of the wall rock, except for its own inertia and the limited transmissibility of the rock. In our experiments, a sandstone with a permeability to water of 20 to 50 millidarcies (190 to 480 x $10^{-6}mm^2$) was sheared at a rate of 0.1 inches per minute. The experimental apparatus consists of a direct shear machine with a sealed water chamber around the specimen, and a triaxial test cell of a conventional design, Goodman and Ohnishi (1973). The shear machine provides a uniform rate of displacement in one direction to the bottom of a shear box while the top of the shear box is permitted to move only in the normal sense. All rotations are prohibited. The specimen is jacketed. Fluid pressure can be maintained outside the jacket and all around the specimen up to a practical working maximum of 700 psi. (4.8 MN/m^2). The inside of the shear box can receive an original water pressure up to but not exceeding the outside chamber pressure (the jacket will balloon and rupture if the inside pressure becomes greater). During shearing, all water lines into the specimen are closed. Apparatus stretch is small, but can be cancelled by manual adjustment of a regulator based upon a calibration run with sample ports closed. Specimens were four inch diameter circular cylinders, either intact, or with an artificial joint in the shear plane. The maximum load is such that average normal and shear stresses on the shear plane cannot exceed about 2,000 psi. Water pressure changes in the shear zone are reflected by the response of 2 transducers close to the base of the specimen and linked to it by two 3/16th inch diameter piezometer holes.

The triaxial cell accomodates a two inch diameter intact or jointed specimen encased in a rubber jacket. The joint was oriented at a steep angle so as to slip before the rock could break. The specimen ends were not perfectly smooth because porous stainless steel and discs were used with some specimens and in the others precision grinding of the ends was not accomplished. (There was no friction reducer on the ends). As the joint slipped, the top of the rock became eccentrically loaded and eventually it developed incipient flexural cracks, as discussed by Jaeger and Cook (1969). But the conditions up to and shortly after joint slip were acceptable so that the test is appropriate for a study of conditions and responses up to and slightly beyond the onset of joint slip. The water pressures were read by means of piezometer holes in the top and bottom drilled into the joint plane leading to transducers next to the triaxial cell.

TRIAXIAL COMPRESSION TEST RESULTS

Tests conducted in this paper were all performed on specimens drilled from a large block of Lyons sandstone, a friable sandstone with confined compressive strength equal to 4000 psi (28 MN/m^2) a table of properties was presented by Goodman and Ohnishi). This rock is weakened by wetting, as established by significantly lower flexural and Brazilian strength when wet. Figure 1 gives results of triaxial compression tests on wet samples of sandstone. The circles mark the summits of Mohr

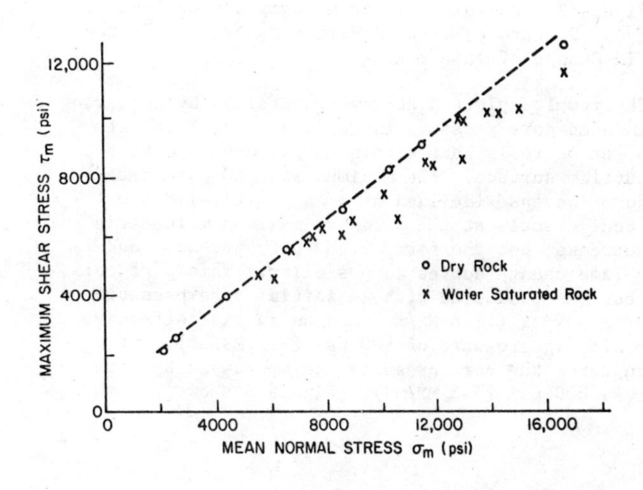

Figure 1: Failure Locus of Lyons Sandstone in Terms of Maximum Shear Stress (τ_m) and Mean Normal Stress (σ_m).

circles drawn for the stresses at peak load in drained tests. The points marked with x's are the summits of effective stress Mohr circles at failure in drained tests. The effective stress principle would tend to force all the points onto a line, but in fact the points are biased towards lower strength values in the undrained tests. The explanation of Robinson and Holland (1969) for a discrepancy in effective strength lines for triaxial tests at different pressures, based upon the concept of a boundary porosity value less than unity, works in the wrong direction here. The probable explanation lies in some chemical effect of the water on the cement; this was not explored. All tests described here were conducted with water in the pores. The rocks were saturated by a back pressure technique, described by Ohnishi (1973). Bruhn (1972), Deklotz et al (1968) and others have confirmed that pore pressure and volumetric change effects measured in undrained triaxial tests on sandstone agree in general principle with the relationships demonstrated by Bieniawski (1972). This is also the case for the Lyons sandstone, as shown in Figure 2.

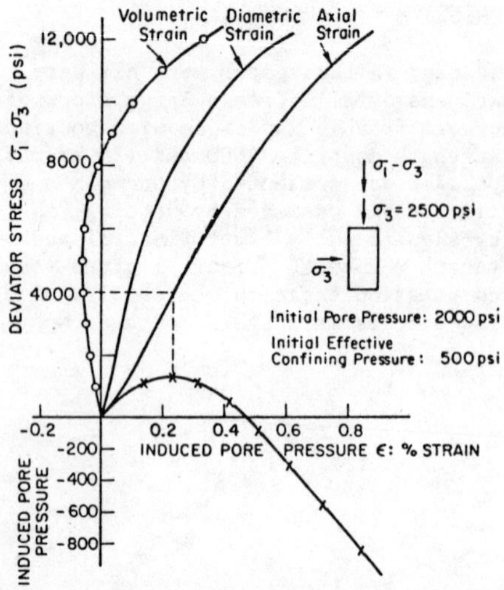

Figure 2: Undrained Triaxial Compression Test of Lyons Sandstone; Induced Pore Pressure and Volumetric Change of Intact Rock.

The results plotted here were obtained by measuring induced pore pressure in an intact specimen with a set of resistance strain gauges attached to the outside surface. The maximum induced pore pressure increase (defined here as positive) did not occur exactly at the point of maximum volumetric decrease, but the form of the pore pressure and volume change curves were similar. This particular test was conducted with an initial pore pressure of 2000 psi (13.8 MN/m^2) and an initial effective confining pressure of 500 psi (3.5 MN/m^2). At rupture, the pore pressure had decreased by more than 800 psi (5.5 MN/m^3). Figure 3 shows a number

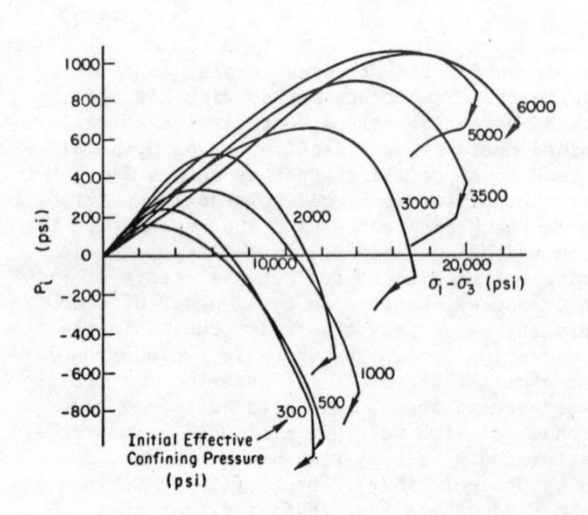

Figure 3: Induced Pore Pressure in Triaxial Tests on Intact Sandstone.

*This test was conducted by Mr. Andre Kolbrunner and Mr. Ohnishi.

of curves of induced pore pressure in tests with varying values of initial effective stress. A cross plot of these data, Figure 4 predicts that if a test is begun with an initial effective confining stress of 2,800 psi (18.5 MN/m^2), the pore pressure at rupture will have been restored precisely to its value at the start of the test after having risen from the initial value by about 500 psi (3.5 MN/m^2).

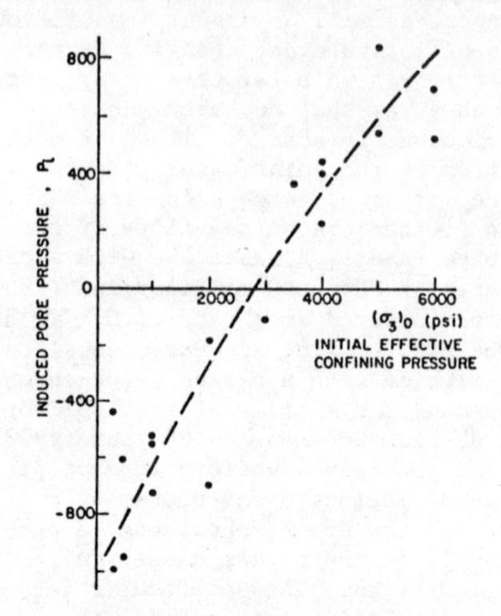

Figure 4: Induced Pore Pressure at Peak Stress in Undrained Triaxial Test for Intact Lyons Sandstone.

A number of parameters can be used to describe the results presented in these figures. The coefficient $\bar{A}$, (Skempton, 1954), expresses the rate of change of induced pore pressure P_i with deviatoric stress.** One can employ a secant $\bar{A}$ giving the correct induced pore pressure corresponding to a defined point, e.g. the point of maximum positive pore pressure, or the point of rupture. Figure 5 presents the variation of secant $\bar{A}$ values with deviator pressure for various initial confining pres-

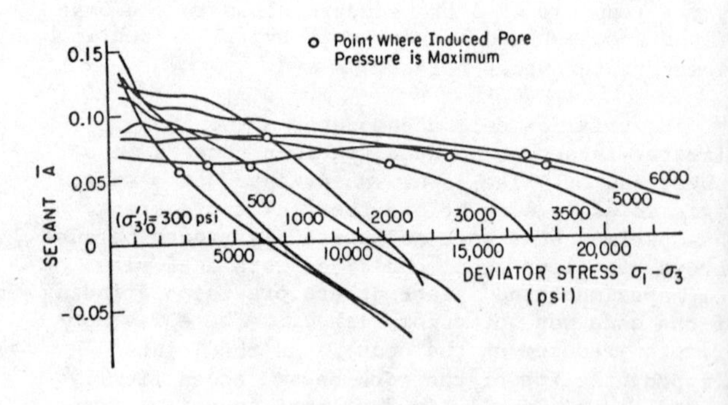

Figure 5: Secant $\bar{A}$ Coefficient of Intact Lyons Sandstone as a Function of Deviator Stress and Initial Effective Confining Pressure.

**$\bar{A}$ is defined by Skempton's equation:

$$\Delta P_i = \bar{A}\,(\Delta\ (\sigma_1-\sigma_3)\ ) + B\Delta\sigma_3$$

where $\Delta(\sigma_1-\sigma_3)$ is the change in deviator stress and $\Delta\sigma_3$ is the change in confining pressure for a triaxial test brought to an initial condition with $\Delta P_i = 0$.

sures. At confining pressures below 2800 psi (18.5 MN/m^2) the secant $\bar{A}$ decreases quickly with deviator stress. Thereafter, it is interesting to observe how $\bar{A}$ becomes approximately constant at between 0.06 and 0.08 over a vary wide deviatoric stress range.

Now consider the inclusion of a joint in a triaxial specimen. A series of tests were run in which the core was diamond sawed at an angle of 60 degrees, (all other aspects of the environmental conditions being identical to the tests with intact rock). The pore water pressure was monitored, as previously, through piezometer holes leading from the joint through the rock to a pair of stiff transducers. Figure 6 presents the observed variation of pore water pressure with the application of deviatoric stress. Unlike the intact rock, the the pore pressure continued to increase throughout the range of deviator stress shown. The graphs end at the peak stress, after which slip occurred and the record became unsatisfactory.

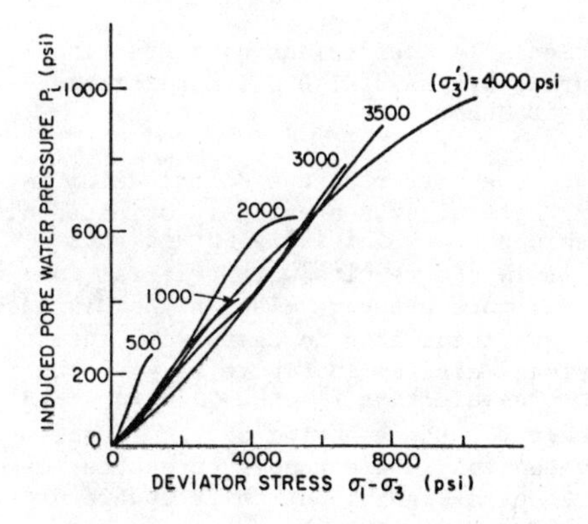

Figure 6: Induced Pore Pressure for Jointed Specimens of Sandstone in Triaxial Compression.

One way in which to compare the series of tests on intact and jointed triaxial samples is by means of the secant $\bar{A}$ parameters derived from the measured data (Figure 5 versus Figure 7). This shows

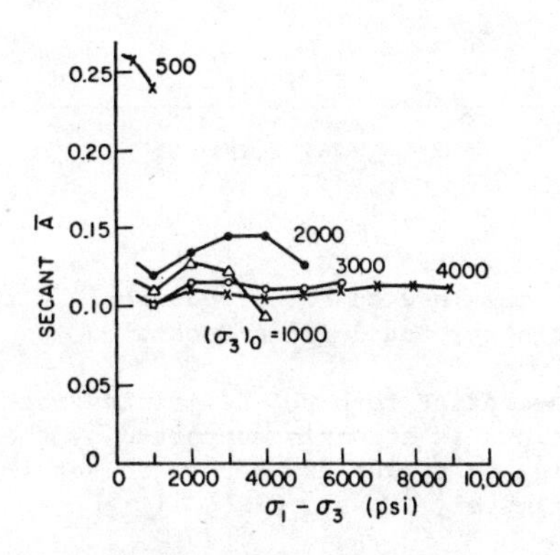

Figure 7: Secant $\bar{A}$ Coefficient of Jointed Rock as a Function of Deviator Stress and Initial Effective Confining Pressure.

the rate of change of pore pressure with deviator stress to be faster (i.e. $\bar{A}$ is higher) for the jointed specimens. At 4000 psi (27 MN/m^2) effective confining pressure for example, the intact rock $\bar{A}$ value remained around 0.08 while the jointed rock $\bar{A}$ stayed near 0.11. There appears to be a pore pressure source associated with the joint.

To further establish this result, Figure 8 is presented in which data from the tests with intact and jointed rock samples in triaxial compression are compared directly. The ordinate is the maximum pore

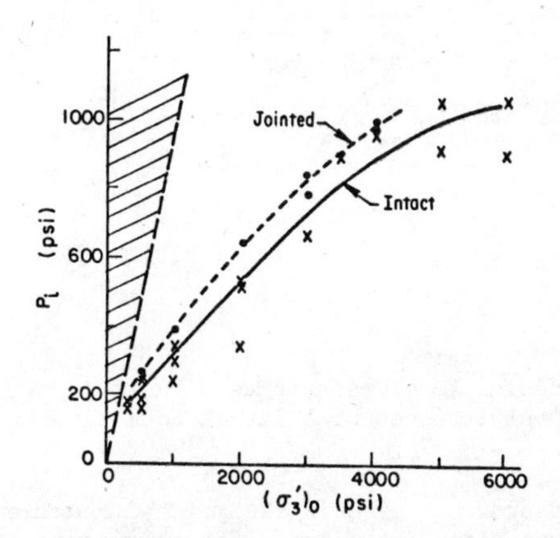

Figure 8: Maximum Induced Pore Pressure Under Triaxial Compression for Intact Rock (x's) and Jointed Rock (Open Circles).

pressure increase ever attained by the sample in the course of loading. This has been plotted against the effective initial confining pressure $(\sigma_3{}^1)_o$ as abscissa for both jointed rock samples (open circles) and intact rock samples (x's). The jointed rock consistently produced a higher excess pore pressure at the transducers, the departure reaching about 100 psi (.7 MN/m^2) at the maximum confining pressures used.

A joint can initiate pore pressure excess in its neighbourhood in two ways. Relative closure or opening of the joint accompanying shearing, (contractancy or dilatancy) would tend to compress or decompress the water between the joint walls; this might be termed a geometric effect. Then, the changing state of stress within surficial regions of the wall rock and filling material, if present, accompanying the development of the shear displacement and its intense local effects could engender pore pressure building up within and immediately adjacent to the joint. These ideas are examined by Ohnishi (1973).

RESULTS OF DIRECT SHEAR TESTS

Direct shear specimens were first saturated and subjected to an effective normal load which was then held constant during shearing. The pore pressure increase in intact specimens followed the same trend as in the triaxial tests with an initial pressure increase followed by a rapid drop in pore pressure until rupture. The jointed rock, on the other hand retained a pore pressure surplus throughout the test. As one would expect, the peak strength for specimens of intact rock was always considerably greater than for those specimens with joints. Pore pressure buildup in the intact rock tests has been plotted against shear stress τ in Figure 9.

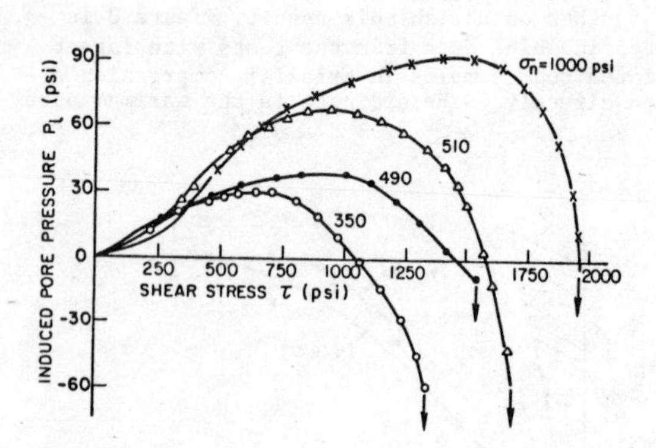

Figure 9: Induced Pore Pressure as a Function of Shear and Normal Stresses with Intact Rocks in the Direct Shear.

Pore pressures measured in the jointed specimen test series are plotted against τ for four representative test results in Figure 10. Significant

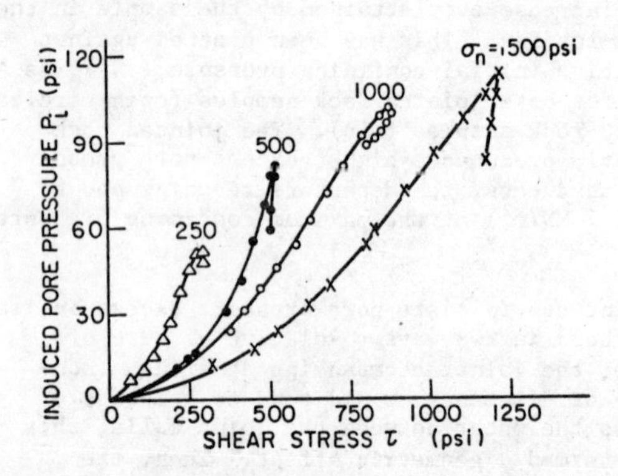

Figure 10: Induced Pore Pressure as a Function of Shear and Normal Stresses with Saw-cut Joint in Direct Shear Test.

pore pressure increase was recorded reaching a maximum of 120 psi (.83 MN/m^2) in the test with initial confining pressure of 1500 psi (10.3 MN/m^2). More importantly, as in the triaxial tests, the point when slip occurs is a positive pore pressure region. It seems that no one has performed undrained shear tests previously so we have no easy source upon which to base an evaluation of these results. The stress state within the shear box is quite different from that of the triaxial tests, therefore a new set of descriptive pore pressure parameters was introduced imitating Skempton as follows:

$$\Delta p_i = \bar{A}_1 \Delta\tau + B_1 \Delta\underline{\sigma} \qquad (1)$$

Secant $\bar{A}_1$ values derived from these four tests on jointed specimens (Figure 11) are more regular in their variation with shear stress than the corresponding curves for the intact rock; possibly,

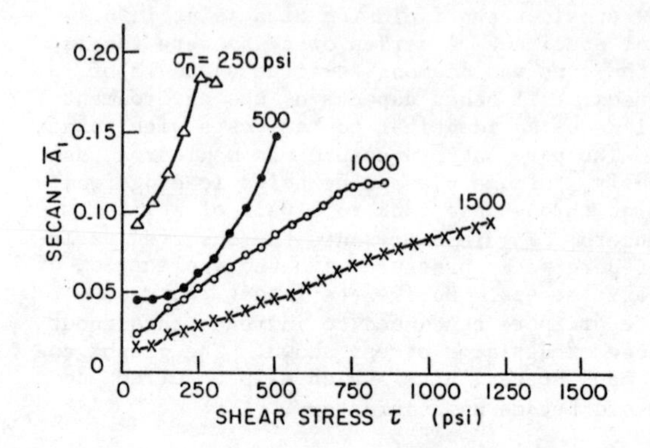

Figure 11: Secant $\bar{A}$ Coefficient as a Function of Shear and Normal Stresses with Saw-cut Jointed Rocks in Direct Shear Test.

this is due to the better stress distribution in direct shear tests along a previously oriented discontinuity than through initially intact rock specimens. As in the results with triaxial compression tests, pore pressure rises higher in tests with jointed specimens than in tests with intact ones. The closed circles in Figure 12 give the maximum pore pressure rise for the jointed tests; The x's account for the behavior of the intact rocks. Unfortunately a great deal of scatter was experienced. But a significant shift upward pro-

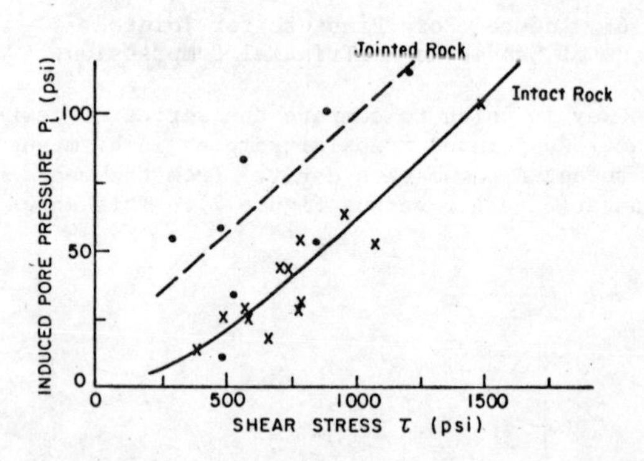

Figure 12: Maximum Induced Pore Pressure in Direct Shear Tests of Intact and Jointed Rocks.

ceeding from the intact rock to the jointed rock sets of data points is strongly supported by the data. The indicated curves are separated vertically by approximately 40 psi (0.27 MN/m^2).

PERMEABILITY TESTS ON JOINTS

Pore pressure generated during the buildup of

stress reduces the effective normal stress and, accordingly, the shear strength of joints. In a jacketed specimen, this increased joint water pressure can be maintained but in nature the joint would conduct water away, "bleeding" the excess pore pressure. The duration of any pore pressure transient depends upon the permeability of the joint, which in turn depends upon the normal stress. Snow (1965, 1968), Serafim and delCampo (1965), Maini (1971), Wittke et al (1972), Louis and Maini (1972) and others have considered water flow along joints. A parallel plate model leads to the non linear relationship between discharge q and aperture a

$$q = \text{const } a^n \tag{2}$$

For example, Sharp and Maini (1972) reported n = 3 for laminar flow between smooth parallel plates. In a Supplementary Report in the Proceedings of this Congress, Goodman suggested a simple hyperbolic relationship between normal stress σ and normal deformation ΔV

$$\Delta V = V_{mc} - \frac{\xi}{\sigma} V_{mc}$$

where V_{mc} is the maximum amount a joint can close from an initial condition $\Delta V = 0$ when $\sigma = \xi$. The joint aperture a at any compressive stress larger than ξ is

$$a = V_{mc} - \Delta V = \frac{\xi}{\sigma} V_{mc}$$

More generally,

$$a = \left(\frac{\xi}{\sigma}\right)^m V_{mc} \tag{3}$$

Substituting in (2) gives

$$q = \text{const } \sigma^{-nm} \tag{4}$$

Figure 13 gives the rate of discharge in cm^3/min of a saw-cut fracture parallel to the long axis of a

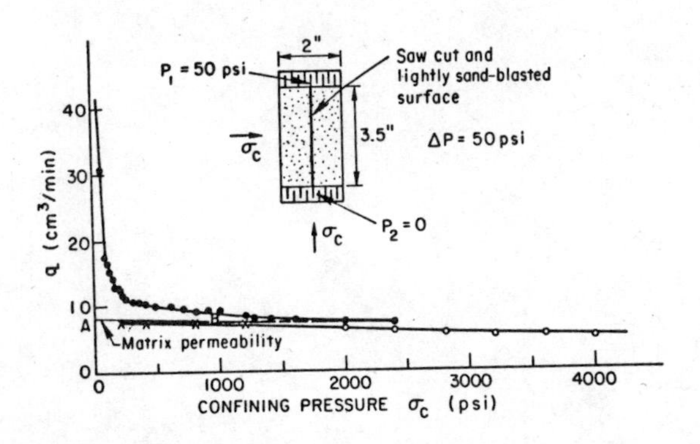

Figure 13: Permeability Test of Jointed Lyons Sandstone.

triaxial test specimen of sandstone. The water pressure in the fracture was 50 psi (0.35 MN/m^2) upstream and atmospheric pressure downstream, so that the normal effective stress increased slightly in the direction of flow. This test configuration is analogous to certain natural cases where water seeps from a reservoir into an open fracture to discharge on a rock face. (flow from a line source to a line sink). The discharge was measured simply by collecting the water in a flask. If the joint flow is assumed to be only that part of the total flow above the sloping asymptote on Figure 13 (line AB) the discharge is found to vary approximately with $\sigma^{-1.2}$. Since joint normal deformation is mainly unrecoverable the discharge-stress variation displays pronounced mysteresis, as previously reported by Jouanna (1972).

A thick-walled cylinder affords a better test configuration; with divergent radial flow along a joint oriented normal to the cylinder axis, both joint closure and steady flow rate can be measured on the outside surface at different normal stresses. Experiments were run on artificial fractures and saw-cut surfaces in coarse marble, which has some matrix permeability and fine-grained granite, which is impermeable. The cylinders were 5-5/8 inch (14.1 cm) outside and 7/8 inch (2.2 cm) inside. Figure 14 shows a typical result for a split surface in granite with 50 psi (.35 MN/m^2) inside and atmospheric pres-

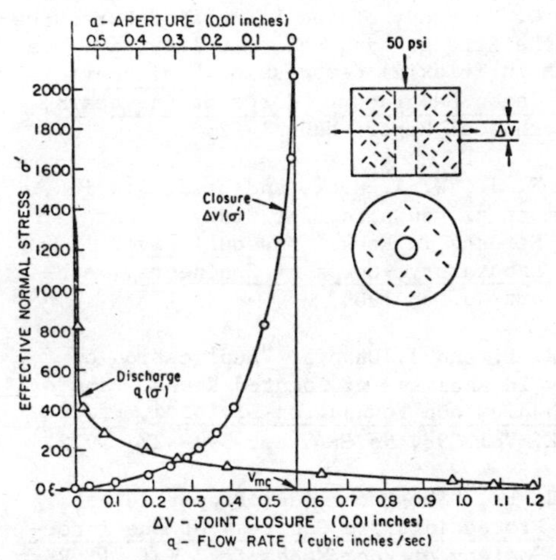

Figure 14: Radial Permeability Test on Rough Joint in Granite; Joint Compression and Discharge Under Changing Normal Stress.

sure outside. A logarithmic plot of q versus a defines a straight line for σ below 300 psi (2. MN/m^2) with slope n = 2.7. Between 70 psi (.5 MN/m^2) and 300 psi, a varies approximately with $\sigma^{-.53}$ and q varies approximately with $\sigma^{-1.4}$. The latter two exponents (m and mn) increase as σ grows larger than 300 psi.

CONCLUSION

It appears that significant induced pressures can be generated inside joints undergoing shear deformation at constant normal pressure, and presumably even higher pressures would be induced in shear at constant normal displacement. Rough joints under high initial normal stress are strong and impermeable; at low initial normal stress they are weak and quite permeable. The question of joint weakening as a result of pore pressure transients resulting from shear stress therefore concerns mainly the intermediate stress region, e.g. 100 to 1000 psi (0.7 to 7.0 MN/m^2). A pressure increase of as much as 150 psi (1. MN/m^2) could then presumably serve as a precursor to a shear movement. In our experiments with saw-cuts, no significant bleeding of induced pressure due to dilatancy occurred before slip. However, additional research with rough natural joints is necessary before this conclusion can be generalized. As far as we know, only Jouanna (1972) has studied the influence of shear stress on joint permeability.

ACKNOWLEDGEMENTS

We appreciate the assistance of Mr. K. Iwai in conducting laboratory permeability tests, and acknowledge with gratitude financial support received from the U.S. Geological Survey through its National Center for Earthquake Research.

REFERENCES

Bieniawski, Z. T. "Propagation of Brittle Fractures in Rock," Proceedings 10th Symposium on Rock Mechanics, pp. 409-427. (preprints issued May 1968). 1972.

Bruhn, R. W. "A Study of the Effects of Pore Pressure on the Strength and Deformability of Berea Sandstone in Triaxial Compression," Missouri River Division Laboratory, Corps of Engineers, Omaha, Technical Report MRDL 1-72.

De Klotz, F. J., W. J. Heck, and M. J. Aldrich, "Development of Equipment for Studying Pore Pressure Effects in Rock," Missouri River Division Laboratory, Corps of Engineers, Technical Report No. 3, 1968.

Goodman, R. E. and J. Dubois, "Duplication of Dilatancy in Analysis of Jointed Rocks," Journal Soil Mechanics and Foundation Division, Proceedings ASCE, Vol. 98, No. SM4 pp. 399-422, 1972.

Goodman, R. E., "The Mechanical Properties of Joints," Proceedings 3rd Congress of the International Society of Rock Mechanics, Vol. 1, Part 2, Supplementary Reports Volume (pre Congress volume), 1973.

Goodman, R. E., and Y. Ohnishi, "Undrained Shear Testing of Jointed Rock," Rock Mechanics, Vol. 5, pp. 129-149, 1973.

Jaeger, J. C. and N. G. W. Cook, "Fundamentals of Rock Mechanics," Methuen, 1969.

Jouanna, P., "Essais de percolation au laboratoire sur des echantillons de micaschiste soumis à des contraintes," Proceedings Symposium on Percolation through Fissured Rock, Stuttgart, International Society of Rock Mechanics, paper T2-F, 1972.

Louis, C., and Y.N.T. Maini, "The Determination of Hydraulic Parameters in Jointed Rock," Proceedings 2nd. Congress International Society of Rock Mechanics, Belgrade, Vol. I, paper 1-32, 1970.

Ohnishi, Y., "Laboratory Measurement of Induced Water Pressures in Jointed Rocks," Ph.D. Thesis University of California, College of Engineering, Berkeley, 1973.

Maini, Y. N. T., "In Situ Hydraulic Parameters in Jointed Rock - Their Measurement and Interpretation," Ph.D. Thesis, Imperial College, England, 1971.

Robinson, C. H., and W. E. Holland, "Some Interpretations of Pore Fluid Effects in Rock Failure," Proceedings 11th Symposium Rock Mechanics, AIME, p. 585, 1969.

Serafim, J. L., and A. del Campo, "Interstitial Pressures on Rock Foundations of Dams," Journal Soil Mechanics & Foundation Division, Proceedings ASCE, Vol. 91, No. SM5, p. 65, 1965.

Sharp, J. C., and Y. N. T. Maini, "Fundamental Considerations on the Hydraulic Character of Joints in Rock," Proceedings Symposium on Percolation through Fissured Rock, Stuttgart, 1972.

Skempton, A. W., "The Pore Pressure Coefficient A and B," Geotechnique Vol. 4, No. p. 143, 1954.

Snow, D. T., "A Parallel Plate Model of Permeable, Fractured Media," Ph.D. Thesis, University of California, College of Engineering, Berkeley, 1965.

Snow, D. T., "Fracture Deformation and Change of Permeability and Storage Upon Changes of Fluid Pressures," Quarterly Colorado School of Mines, Vol. 63, No. 1, 1968.

Wittke, W., P. Rissler, and S. Semprich, "Raumlich, Laminare und Turbulent Stromung in Kluftigen Fels Nach Zwei Verschiedenen Rechenmodellen," Proceedings Symposium on Percolation through Fissured Rock, Stuttgart, International Society of Rock Mechanics, paper T1-11, 1972.

INFLUENCE DES CONTRAINTES ET DE LA PRESSION DE FLUIDE SUR L'ÉCOULEMENT DANS LES ROCHES FISSURÉES

INFLUENCE OF EXTERNAL STRESSES AND FLUID PRESSURE ON THE FLOW IN FISSURED ROCKS

EINFLUSS DER ÄUSSEREN SPANNUNGEN UND DES FLÜSSIGKEITSDRUCKS AUF DIE STRÖMUNG IN ZERSPALTENEN GESTEINEN

J.P. SARDA Ingénieur Civil des Mines

P.LE TIRANT Ingénieur E.T.P.

G. BARON Docteur-Sciences Institut Francais du Pétrole

France

RESUME

La perméabilité des formations fissurées dépend fortement des contraintes normales à la direction des fissures. On observe généralement que l'évolution de la perméabilité en fonction de la contrainte effective est en partie irréversible dans les roches sédimentaires fissurées. Dans le grès et les calcaires que nous avons étudiés l'influence de la rhéologie du matériau sur ces propriétés est sensible.

Ces faits prennent une importance particulière en drainage et en injection dans le cas de gisements d'huile ou de gaz pour lesquels les contraintes effectives peuvent varier dans de larges limites au cours de l'exploitation. On discute par ailleurs le régime d'écoulement des fluides dans les fissures au laboratoire et sur le gisement.

SUMMARY

The permeability of fissured rocks depends on stresses, especially when their direction is normal to fissures plan. It is generally observed that the permeability decrease as a function of effective stress is partly non reversible for fissured sedimentary rocks. In the sandstones and limestones studied, these properties are strongly influenced by the rock material rheology.

These facts lead to important consequences concerning extraction and injection in oil and gas wells, because of the possible large variations of effective stresses. The flow regime in fissures in laboratory experiments as in field operations is discussed.

ZUSAMMENFASSUNG

Die Permeabilität der zerspaltenen Gesteine hängt viel von den Spannungen ab, hauptsächlich, wenn diese senkrecht zu den Spaltungsrichtungen sind. Man beobachtet meistens, dass für sedimentäre zerspaltene Gesteine, die Entwicklung der Permeabilität in Funktion der wirklichen Spannung zum Teile irreversibel ist. In den studierten Sand - und Kalksteinen hängen diese Eigenschaften viel von der Rheologie des Materials ab.

Diese Beobachtungen nehmen eine besondere Bedeutung in der Förderung und in der Injektion bei Öl - oder Gas - feldern, bei welchen die wirklichen Spannungen während der Ausbeutung sich viel ändern. Der Strömungszustand von Flüssigkeiten in den Spaltungen im Laboratorium und auf dem Felde wird ebenfalls erläutert.

Le comportement des fissures naturelles ou artificielles dans leur environnement physique et mécanique ("conditions de fond") peut conditionner la production d'un gisement pétrolier. Les problèmes apparaissent principalement pendant les phases successives ou simultanées de l'exploitation : en déplétion primaire, en injection et en récupération secondaire, enfin dans les opérations de stimulation.

Pendant la phase dite de déplétion primaire l'exploitant laisse opérer les mécanismes naturels de production. La pression des fluides en place diminue, la porosité et la perméabilité de la roche peuvent s'en trouver affectées si les propriétés mécaniques de la roche réservoir s'y prêtent. En particulier les fissures naturelles peuvent diminuer progressivement d'épaisseur.

Au cours de la phase de récupération dite "secondaire", on injecte dans le gisement un fluide judicieusement choisi à la fois pour maintenir la pression en place et pour obtenir un "balayage" des fluides qui intéressent le producteur. Nous n'aborderons pas ici l'étude difficile du balayage d'un gisement fissuré, nous nous intéresserons seulement aux puits d'injection. Dans ces puits l'injection établit un régime d'écoulement inverse de celui de la production : la pression au puits P_F est supérieure à la pression de couche P_C. La perméabilité des fissures au puits va-t-elle évoluer? peut-on même espérer, pour un puits d'injection antérieurement utilisé pour la production, une restauration de la perméabilité initiale?

Le contexte physique et mécanique de ce problème est, dans une certaine mesure, analogue à celui qui est rencontré dans le procédé de stimulation par fracturation hydraulique. Il s'agit, comme on sait, d'injecter un fluide sous pression de façon à fracturer artificiellement la couche. C'est une méthode comparable au "craquage" employé en géotechnique.

Drainage et injection dans les roches fissurées ont été beaucoup étudiés en géotechnique [1] [2] [3] [4]. Il nous a paru intéressant de comparer ces études à deux séries d'essais réalisés à l'I.F.P. sur des roches réservoir. Il s'agit d'un grès quartzitique cambro-ordovicien provenant d'un réservoir saharien et d'un calcaire du Dogger du Bassin Parisien.

L'objectif principal était de mesurer les variations des caractéristiques d'écoulement de ces roches fissurées, et d'analyser les résultats observés à partir :

- des contraintes extérieures appliquées, allant jusqu'à 200 bars.
- des conditions d'écoulement - linéaire, radial centripède, radial centrifuge - et des pressions de fluide aux limites du matériau.
- du comportement mécanique du matériau : élastique, viscoélastique, éventuellement plastique.

I. RELATIONS ENTRE LES CONTRAINTES, LA PRESSION ET L'ECOULEMENT D'UN FLUIDE DANS LES MILIEUX FISSURES

Considérons un massif fissuré naturellement ou artificiellement. Soit P_F la pression de fluide au puits, P_C la pression aux limites du massif (fig. 1), ΔP la différence $P_C - P_F$. Au régime de drainage, caractérisé par $\Delta P > 0$, correspondent un débit Q_D et un index de productivité IP :

$$IP = \frac{Q_D}{\Delta P}$$

Au régime d'injection, caractérisé par $\Delta P < 0$, correspondant un débit d'injection Q_I et un index d'injectivité II :

$$II = \frac{Q_I}{|\Delta P|}$$

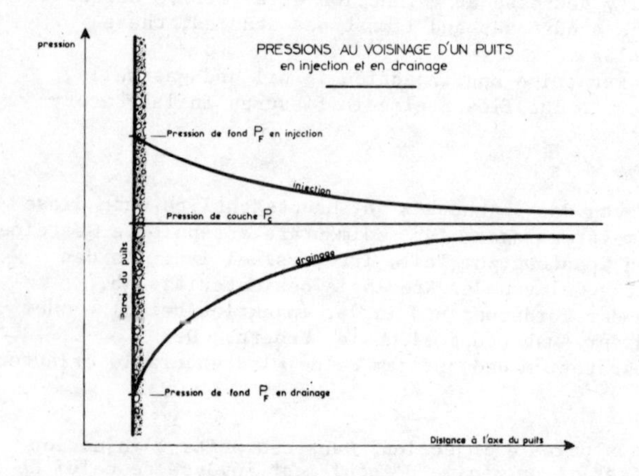

figure 1 : pressures near an oil-well; production and injection.

Connaissant les contraintes en place est-il possible, sinon de calculer, du moins de prévoir qualitativement les comportements en drainage ou en injection? Nous expliciterons d'abord la notion de contrainte effective, base actuelle de l'analyse de tels problèmes. Nous en montrerons ensuite l'application au cas de la fracturation hydraulique du solide élastique par un fluide en écoulement laminaire. Nous indiquerons enfin les corrections qu'il est possible d'apporter à un tel schéma : comportement rhéologique complexe de la roche, écoulement laminaire non linéaire ou écoulement turbulent.

1) Perméabilité en drainage et en injection, contrainte effective.

Dans l'interprétation mécanique habituelle des essais de drainage et d'injection, et depuis les expériences désormais classiques de BERNAIX [1] , le rôle principal est dévolu aux contraintes "effectives" qui s'exercent sur la roche c'est-à-dire à la différence entre les contraintes totales en place et la pression de fluide. Cette interprétation rend compte aisément du fait que l'index d'injectivité est communément supérieur à l'index de productivité : la pression d'injection étant nécessairement plus élevée que la pression de soutirage, les contraintes effectives s'exerçant sur la roche sont moindres et les fissures sont plus ouvertes.

Les améliorations possibles de l'interprétation jouent d'ailleurs dans le même sens : les forces capillaires qui freinent l'écoulement en drainage tendent à devenir du second ordre en injection puisque les fissures sont plus ouvertes; à l'ouverture des fissures lors de l'injection peut s'ajouter une érosion de la roche, signalée par BERNAIX.

Remarquons enfin qu'une telle interprétation suppose une parfaite reversibilité des phénomènes : à un tenseur donné des contraintes effectives correspond une perméabilité, quelle que soit l'histoire mécanique du matériau.

2) Relation contrainte effective - dimension des fissures dans l'hypothèse élastique et en écoulement laminaire.

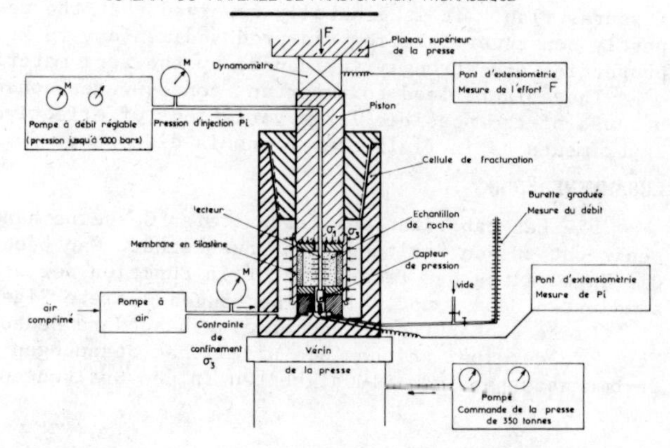

figure 2 : schematic drawing of the hydraulic fracturing cell

a) Injection : les études réalisées sur la fracturation hydraulique des réservoirs pétroliers ont permis d'expliciter complètement [5] la relation contrainte-dimension des fissures dans le cas où le solide est élastique et où l'écoulement du fluide de fracturation est laminaire.

Nous rappellerons la solution dans le cas d'une fissure plane de rayon R, dite "penny shaped crack" :

$$W_o = k \left(\frac{Q \eta R}{E}\right)^{1/4} \qquad \text{(PERKINS)} \quad (1)$$

$$W_o = \frac{8 (1 - \nu^2)(p - \gamma H)}{\pi E} \alpha^2 R \qquad (2)$$

W_o et R désignent respectivement l'épaisseur et le rayon de la fissure.

E et ν les paramètres élastiques du matériau.

P,Q et η la pression moyenne, le débit et la viscosité du fluide de fracturation.

γH contrainte due au "poids des terres".

k et α des coefficients sans dimension (α est voisin de 1).

Les formules (1) et (2) sont valables si la pression P du fluide est supérieure à la contrainte γH due au poids des terres, en d'autres termes si la contrainte effective sur la fracture est une traction. De (1) et (2) on déduit :

$$Q = \beta (P - \gamma H)^4 R^3 \quad (3)$$

Effectuant la même analyse, LONDE et SABARLY proposent une formulation plus simple [4] :

$$Q = C P^4 \quad (4)$$

En fait, ils considèrent un craquage pratiqué à faible profondeur, c'est-à-dire pour lequel le poids des terres est pratiquement nul. Nous nous autoriserons pour les besoins de la comparaison à transformer leur formulation en :

$$Q = C' (P - \gamma H)^4 \quad (5)$$

La comparaison de (5) et (3) montre que la formulation (5) revient à négliger les variations du rayon de la fracture devant celles de la pression. Il ressort des enregistrements débit-pression réalisés sur chantier [4] , que cette approximation est légitime. Dans la troisième partie nous essaierons de vérifier si elle peut aussi rendre compte de la pratique pétrolière.

b) Drainage : si la relation débit-pression a été explicitée dans le problème de l'ouverture des fissures, il n'en est pas de même en ce qui concerne leur fermeture, conséquence possible du drainage. Les seuls résultats expérimentaux interprétés quantitativement concernent des roches micro-fissurées [6] . Le problème des fractures nous paraît pouvoir être analysé de la façon suivante : les faces d'une fracture ne s'emboîtant pas parfaitement l'une dans l'autre, il faut analyser les contraintes et les déplacements comme résultant d'une multitude de contacts ponctuels (contrainte de HERTZ). Au-delà d'une certaine contrainte la résistance mécanique de ces contacts devient insuffisante. Nous verrons que les résultats exposés dans la deuxième partie permettent apparemment de repérer cette contrainte.

3) Rhéologie de la roche et réversibilité

La relation conductivité hydraulique-contrainte effective peut être bi-univoque. C'est par exemple ce qu'observe BERNAIX sur un échantillon de la roche du Malpasset soumis à un essai de drainage. Opérant sur un massif à fissuration horizontale sous des contraintes de compression croissantes JOUANNA montre au contraire une évolution irréversible de la perméabilité qui met nettement en valeur l'influence de l'histoire du matériau. BERNAIX a aussi montré que l'irréversibilité peut se manifester après une injection, il s'agirait alors de l'ouverture de nouvelles fissures.

4) Ecoulement dans les fissures

Si l'écoulement dans les fissures reste laminaire et linéaire, on peut définir une perméabilité de fissure au sens de DARCY et cette perméabilité est proportionnelle au carré de l'épaisseur.

Cependant MAINI et SHARP montrent que l'écoulement reste laminaire mais devient non linéaire au-delà d'un grandient hydraulique très faible (0,25). Les conslusions de JOUANA rejoignent cette observation : elles reviennent à dire que l'écoulement laminaire et linéaire n'existe pas dans un massif fissuré complexe. Il faut alors s'en remettre à un empirisme complet et étudier expérimentalement la loi pression-débit pour chaque matériau et pour chaque fluide. D'une façon générale le milieu fissuré serait représenté par une loi d'écoulement du type :

$$Q \propto \alpha e^n \quad \text{avec } n = 1,2 \text{ à } 1,5$$

où e est l'épaisseur de la fissure.

II. ETUDE EXPERIMENTALE DE L'ECOULEMENT DANS LES ROCHES SEDIMENTAIRES FISSUREES

1) Généralités

Les études présentées ici ont été menées sur des roches réservoir présentant une macrofissuration très apparente. Le but principal était de formuler un diagnostic sur la baisse de productivité possible en cours d'exploitation et consécutive à la baisse de pression dans le gisement. On prétendait donc reproduire au laboratoire sur des échantillons relativement volumineux (h = 10 cm, $\emptyset$ = 10 cm) les conductivités notées in situ, en se plaçant dans des conditions mécaniques voisines. Une telle entreprise se heurte à quelques difficultés qu'il nous paraît utile de signaler.

a) Echantillonnage : l'échantillonnage utilisé conduit nécessairement à une sous-estimation de la perméabilité en place. En effet lorsque les fissures sont réellement ouvertes au fond et se développent sur des longueurs importantes, le pourcentage de récupération est faible et, en somme, les "meilleures" fissures restent au fond.

b) Effet d'échelle : nous ferons dans ce paragraphe l'hypothèse que l'écoulement est laminaire.

On peut montrer aisément que tant que les fissures ne sont pas fermées les perméabilités mesurées dépendent de la dimension des échantillons.

Soit :

ΔP la différence de pression appliquée entre les faces planes et parallèles de l'échantillon.

l et S la longueur et la section droite de cet échantillon.

l_f la longueur des fissures recoupée par une section droite.

h leur épaisseur.

S_f leur section droite : $S_f = h\, l_f$

S_m la section droite de matrice.

Q le débit total.

Q_m le débit à travers la matrice.

Q_f le débit à travers les fissures.

K_m la perméabilité de matrice.

K_f la perméabilité des fissures.

Les équations du problème ainsi simplifié, sont :

$$\frac{\Delta P}{l} = \frac{\eta}{K_f} \frac{Q_f}{h\, l_f} \quad \text{écoulement à travers les fissures} \quad (6)$$

$$\frac{\Delta P}{l} = \frac{\eta}{K_m} \frac{Q_m}{S_m} \quad \text{écoulement à travers la matrice} \quad (7)$$

$$Q_f + Q_m = Q \quad \text{et} \quad S_f + S_m = S \quad (8)$$

Les sections droites S et S_m de la carotte et de la matrice sont très voisines, et :

$$Q = \frac{S\,\Delta P}{\eta\, l} \left(K_f \times \frac{h\, l_f}{S} + K_m\right) \quad (9)$$

C'est donc la grandeur $K_f \times \frac{h\, l_f}{S} + K_m$, homogène à une perméabilité, qui est accessible à l'expérience. Puisque l'écoulement est laminaire, la loi de POISEUILLE est applicable, et :

$$K_f \sim \frac{h^2}{12} \quad (10)$$

la grandeur mesurée expérimentalement serait donc $\frac{h^3\, l_f}{12\, S} + K_m$

Dans le cas d'une fissure unique traversant la carotte dans le sens de la longueur, rencontré fréquemment dans nos essais, on voit que l_f augmente linéairement avec le diamètre de l'échantillon alors que la surface S augmente, bien sûr, comme le carré de ce diamètre. Le rapport $\frac{h\, l_f}{S}$ diminue dans l'expression de la perméabilité totale. Il en résulte que la fermeture des fissures sera d'autant mieux mise en évidence que le diamètre de l'échantillon sera plus faible.

Ces inconvénients ne se présenteraient évidemment pas dans le cas, probablement rare, ou plusieurs "mailles" de fissuration recouperaient une carotte dont le volume serait alors représentatif de l'hétérogénéité du champ.

c) Réversibilité : Une hypothèse implicite dans ce genre d'expérience est que, les roches étant remises dans les"conditions de fond", les effets de la décompression et du remaniement sont annulés. C'est, en d'autres termes, supposer une réversibilité au moins partielle du comportement mécanique et des grandeurs qui lui sont liées - par exemple la conductivité hydraulique - dans le domaine des contraintes déjà supportées par la roche. Aussi, une diminution irréversible de perméabilité au premier chargement a-t-elle toujours une signification ambigüe : il se peut qu'elle soit normale et due au serrage de la roche, il se peut aussi que les contraintes appliquées et leur mode d'application soit inadéquats. Par contre l'observation d'un comportement réversible est très intéressante, car en somme, elle légitime la méthode et son application.

d) Contraintes effectives : pour des raisons évidentes de commodité expérimentale, nous avons admis le principe des "contraintes effectives" et remplacé le système des contraintes (Σ_V, Σ_H, P) par le système (Σ_V - P, Σ_H - P, p) où :

Σ_V et Σ_H sont la contrainte verticale et une contrainte horizontale totales.

On posera désormais :

$$\Sigma_V - P = \sigma_V, \quad \Sigma_H - P = \sigma_H$$

P est la pression du fluide en place.

p est une pression de quelques bars qui simule au laboratoire la pression du gisement.

2) Expérimentation sur des grès quartzitiques

Ces grès d'âge cambro-ordovicien provenaient d'un gisement d'huile situé vers 2600 mètres de profondeur et produisant essentiellement par fissures. La perméabilité du système de fissures naturelles était telle qu'une différence de quelques bars entre pression de couche P_C et pression de puits P_F suffisait à assurer des débits importants.

Chaque tronçon de carotte soumis à l'essai présentait une ou plusieurs fractures verticales partiellement recimentées ainsi que des fissures.

Les essais étaient effectués à l'aide du matériel construit à l'Institut Français du Pétrole pour l'étude de la fracturation hydraulique (voir schéma fig. 2). Une presse hydraulique et un piston permettent l'application de la contrainte verticale tandis que les contraintes horizontales sont exercées par l'intermédiaire d'une pression de fluide -- ($\sigma_H = \sigma_2 = \sigma_3$)

L'égalité ainsi réalisée des contraintes horizontales principales est évidemment une hypothèse.

Les mesures de densité étaient réalisées :

- en écoulement longitudinal parallèle à l'axe de la carotte.
- en écoulement radial centripète, un puits étant alors pratiqué dans l'axe de l'échantillon.
- sous une différence de pression Δ P de un bar entre face d'entrée et de sortie du fluide.
- avec une huile de viscosité 15 centipoises.

Pour pallier la méconnaissance du rapport $\frac{\sigma_V}{\sigma_H}$ des contraintes verticale et horizontale en place, deux états de contraintes particuliers ont été appliqués : $\sigma_V = \sigma_H$ et $\sigma_V = 3\,\sigma_H$. L'ensemble des résultats a montré que ces fissures verticales étaient essentiellement influencées par la contrainte horizontale σ_H. C'est donc cette contrainte qui est portée en abscisse sur les figures 3 à 5.

La perméabilité est déduite des mesures de débit par les formules classiques de l'écoulement linéaire ou radial circulaire, en admettant que le régime est laminaire.

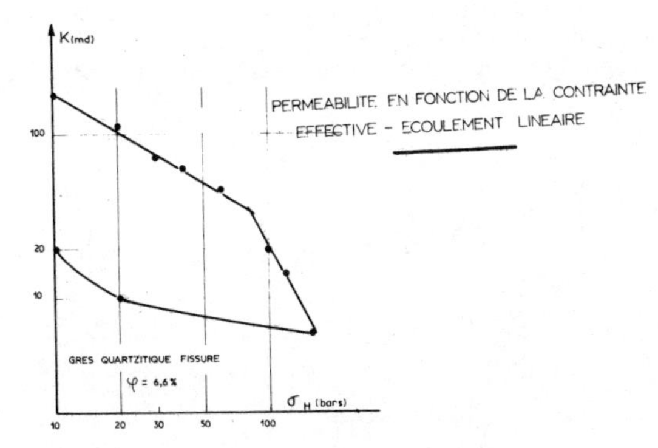

Figure 3 : Linear flow-permeability versus effective stress.

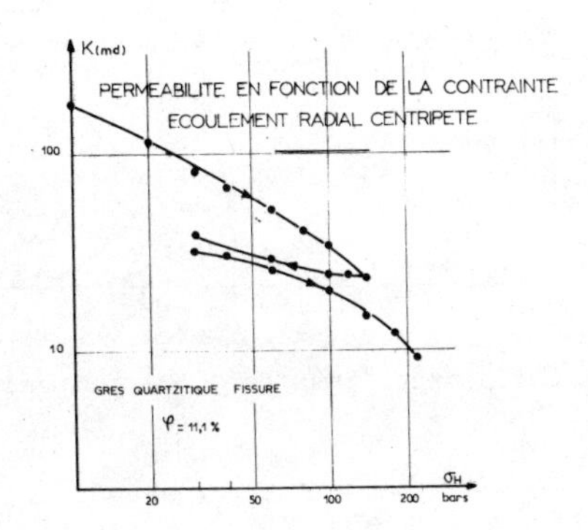

Figure 4 : permeability versus effective stress; centripetal flow.

a) Variation de perméabilité : une présentation bilogarithmique montre que la variation de perméabilité (ou de débit) peut être exprimée analytiquement en fonction de la contrainte horizontale par une loi du type :

$$K = m\sigma_H^{-n} \tag{11}$$

On distingue deux parties sur les courbes, et particulièrement sur la figure 3. Pour la première partie n est voisin de 0,7 et ceci quel que soit l'essai considéré :

b) Contrainte limite et irréversibilité :

On aurait n = 2,5 pour la deuxième partie : à partir d'une certaine contrainte la décroissance de la perméabilité est beaucoup plus accentuée. On est tenté de conclure par analogie avec les courbes oedométriques, que cette contrainte est la plus élevée subie par la roche en place. Au delà se produiraient des modifications mécaniques irréversibles (ruptures de grains?), comme en témoigne par exemple la courbe "retour" de la figure 2. Il ne faut pourtant pas perdre de vue qu'une diminution du débit peut aussi être due à un changement de régime d'écoulement.

On notera deux traits, à notre avis caractéristiques, de comportement de ces grès durs : l'amplitude faible des variations de perméabilité, le fait que cette perméabilité ne devient jamais nulle. Dans des roches aussi peu ductiles l'effet des contraintes sur la perméabilité reste en somme assez limité.

3) Expérimentation sur des calcaires

Ces calcaires durs et fissurés verticalement provenaient du DOGGER du Bassin de Paris (profondeur voisine de 1800 mètres). La fissuration ressemblait à celle des grès précédemment décrits et l'essentiel du débit était donc apparemment assuré par quelques fractures verticales.

Les débits ont été mesurés :

- en écoulement linéaire.
- en écoulement radial centripète,
- en écoulement radial centrifuge,
- le fluide saturant étant une huile de viscosité 3 centipoises.

Comme dans les expériences précédentes la différence de pression entre les faces d'entrée et de sortie du fluide était normalement de 1 bar. Toutefois il a fallu quelquefois augmenter cette valeur jusqu'à 15 bars en cours d'expérience pour que les débits restent mesurables. Le gradient de pression était donc considérable. Malgré cela des mesures répétées ont permis de conclure que la loi de Darcy était remarquablement vérifiée par l'expérience. Il était dès lors légitime de présenter les résultats sous la forme de diagrammes perméabilité-contrainte.

a) Variation de perméabilité en fonction des contraintes extérieures : ces résultats sont caractérisés par des variations de perméabilité beaucoup plus considérables que les précédentes. Sur la figure 5 on peut observer qu'une perméabilité de 3 Darcys sous 25 bars de contrainte extérieure tombe à 1 millidarcy sous 150 bars.

b) Variation de perméabilité en fonction du temps : une présentation bilogarithmique est sans intérêt car une fonction puissance est apparemment insuffisante pour exprimer la diminution de perméabilité en fonction de contraintes extérieures croissantes. En fait l'influence du temps s'ajoute à celle des contraintes. Un exemple est donné sur la figure 5 : la contrainte extérieure étant maintenue constante et égale à 100 bars, la perméabilité passe de 100 à 20 millidarcys en deux heures environ. L'expérimentateur [7] a pu écrire que pour certains échantillons " le temps allait plus vite que les contraintes ".

c) Ductilité et viscoélasticité : la réversibilité est en général médiocre, mais exceptionnellement bonne ou très bonne. Une mauvaise réversibilité et des perméabilités très basses montrent la ductilité de ces carbonates. Par contre la réversibilité quelquefois observée et l'influence du temps sont la manifestation d'un comportement viscoélastique. Il faudrait, pour aller plus loin, essayer de distinguer:

- la viscoélasticité propre du matériau
- la viscoélasticité due à la saturation en liquide, décrite notamment par BIOT.

d) Perméabilité en injection : on peut enfin apprécier sur la figure 6 l'amélioration de la perméabilité lorsque la pression d'injection augmente. La contrainte extérieure isotrope étant de 50 bars la perméabilité passe de 30 à 85 millidarcys lorsque la pression d'injection est portée de 3 à 10 bars. On a représenté dans l'encadré de la figure 5 et en coordonnées bilogarithmiques la perméabilité en fonction de la contrainte effective au puits ($\Sigma - \Delta P$). Trois points de mesure ne permettent pas de tirer des conclusions quantitatives, mais il est clair que la variation de perméabilité est très importante et qu'elle confirme qualitativement les résultats théoriques et expérimentaux obtenus en fracturation hydraulique.

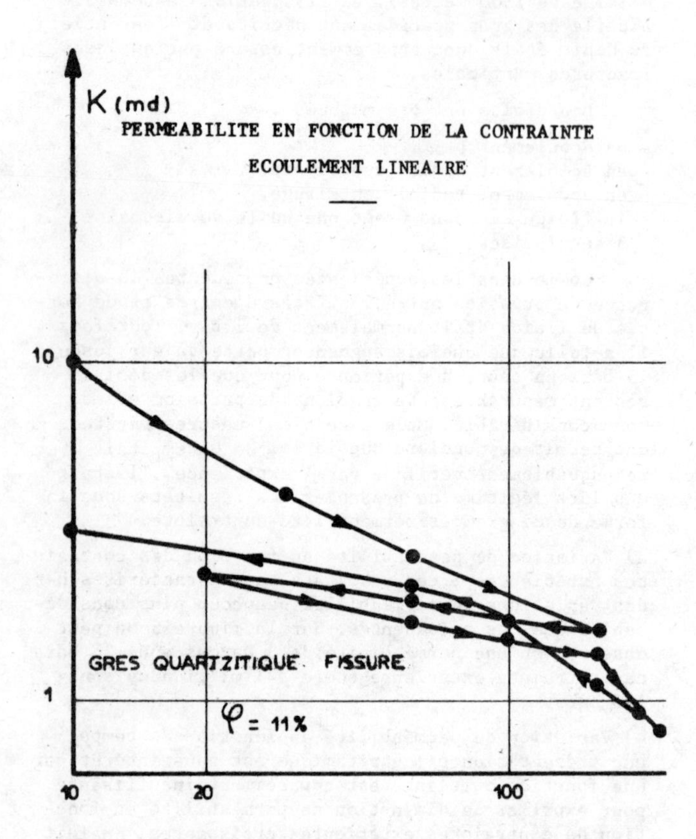

figure 5 : linear-flow. Permeability versus effective stress

III. COMPORTEMENT DES PUITS PRODUCTEURS EN DRAINAGE ET EN INJECTION

La connaissance du gisement pétrolier impose des mesures périodiques de son index de productivité. L'index d'injectivité est mesuré à l'occasion de travaux spéciaux sur les puits producteurs, ou dans des puits spécialement réservés à l'injection de fluides. Moyennant une hypothèse sur la hauteur de la courbe perméable et sur la géométrie de l'écoulement ces index permettent de remonter à la perméabilité. La pratique montre que cette perméabilité est plus grande en injection qu'en production.

La figure 7 représente dans le diagramme $(\dot{Q}, \Delta P)$ un essai d'injectivité suivi d'une fracturation de la roche. Le rapport $\frac{dQ}{d(\Delta P)}$ augmente avec ΔP; en d'autres termes la perméabilité de la roche augmente lorsque les contraintes effectives diminuent.

Dès qu'il y a fracture (point A) le phénomène s'accélère considérablement. On peut donc supposer que la différence entre les index d'injectivité et de productivité est plus importante dans les réservoirs fissurés que dans les autres.

A titre d'exemple, les courbes indicatrices d'u puits producteur (a) et d'un puits d'injection (b) sont établies sur champ produisant par fractures (fig. 8).

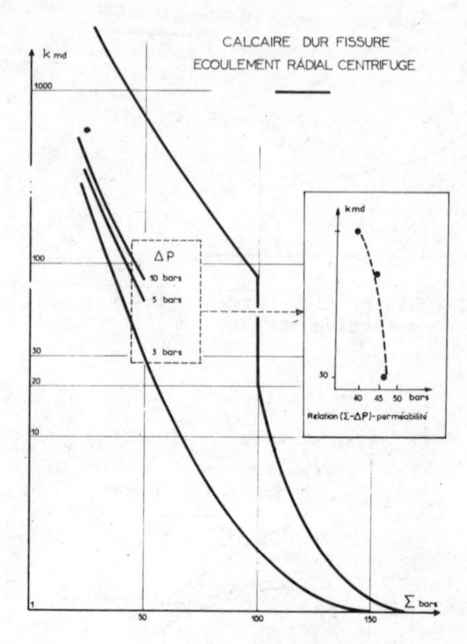

figure 6 : fissured limestone; centrifugal radial fl

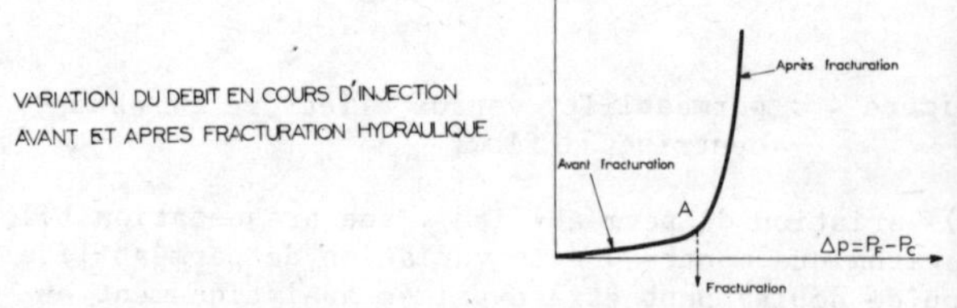

Q débit
VARIATION DU DEBIT EN COURS D'INJECTION
AVANT ET APRES FRACTURATION HYDRAULIQUE
Après fracturation
Avant fracturation
A
$\Delta p = P_f - P_c$
Fracturation

figure 7 : flow rate during hydraulic fracturing.

Si, l'écoulement restant laminaire, la perméabilité était constante pendant la production, la courbe indicatrice (a) serait une droite. Sa courbure - concavité tournée vers l'axe des pressions motrices - peu s'interpréter comme une fermeture progressive des fissures en place, toutefois le passage d'un écoulement laminaire à un écoulement turbulent conduirait à la même allure de courbe. Il est probable que les deux phénomènes se superposent.

Par contre l'augmentation de l'injectivité avec la pression d'injection - concavité tournée vers l'ax des débits - ne peut s'interpréter que par une ouverture des fissures en place. Le diagramme $(Q, \Delta P)$ représenté en (b) peut être correctement approché par une relation du type :

$$Q = A \Delta P + B \Delta P^2 \qquad (12)$$

PRODUCTION ET INJECTION DE DEUX PUITS D UN RESERVOIR
A FISSURES NATURELLES

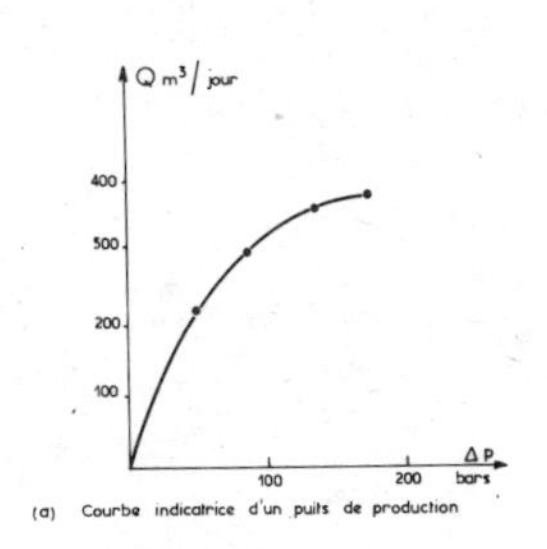

(a) Courbe indicatrice d'un puits de production

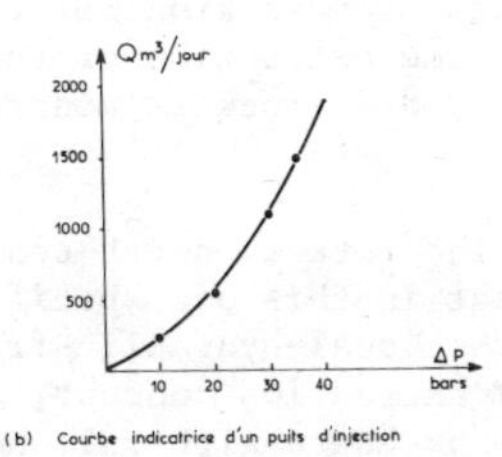

(b) Courbe indicatrice d'un puits d'injection

figure 8 : production and injection in two wells of a fissured reservoir.

IV. CONCLUSIONS

Les essais réalisés sur des grès quartzitiques et des calcaires durs et la comparaison avec quelques observations sur champ nous permettent d'avancer quelques conclusions concernant la perméabilité des roches fissurées au cours du drainage ou de l'injection :

1) dans les grès durs, et sous l'effet des contraintes de compression croissantes dues au drainage, la baisse des caractéristiques d'écoulement s'accélère à partir d'une contrainte critique.

2) cette limite pourrait être la contrainte plus élevée subie par la roche en place au cours de son histoire.

3) en injection l'expérimentation sur les calcaires montre que les caractéristiques d'écoulement s'améliorent fortement lorsque la pression de fluide augmente. Cette amélioration confirme la tendance prévue par la théorie du craquage ou de la fracturation hydraulique.

4) les variations de perméabilité sont plus importantes pour les calcaires que pour les grès fissurés. La différence paraît s'expliquer par le comportement viscoélastique et ductile des premiers, le comportement plus rigide des seconds.

5) le passage à des écoulements non linéaires ou turbulents pourrait être une base d'explication complémentaire. Ce phénomène a été noté par plusieurs expérimentateurs opérant sur des roches saturées d'eau mais nos essais, effectués sur des roches sédimentaires saturées d'huile, n'ont pas permis de mettre en évidence un écart à la loi de Darcy.

BIBLIOGRAPHIE

1. J. BERNAIX - Etude géotechnique de la roche de Malpasset, Dunod - Paris 1967.

2. J.C. SHARP, Y.N.T. MAINI - Fundamental considerations on the hydraulic characteristics of joints in rock.
Symposium percolation through fissured rocks. Stuttgart 1972.

3. P. JOUANNA - Essais in situ de percolation sous contrainte.
Symposium percolation through fissured rocks. Stuttgart 1972

4. P. LONDE, F. SABARLY - La distribution des perméabilités dans la fondation des barrages voûtes en fonction du champ de contraintes.
Comptes rendus du 1er Congrès de Mécanique des Roches - Lisbonne 1966 - Volume II.

5. P. LE TIRANT, L. GAY - Manuel de Fracturation Hydraulique. Technip 1972.

6. P. MORLIER - Spectre de fissuration et célérité des ondes.
Revue de l'Industrie Minérale - Juillet 1969 - pages 21-24.

7. P. NAHMIAS - Rapport de stage effectué à l'Institut Français du Pétrole (non publié).

GEOTHERMAL ENERGY: A NEW APPLICATION OF ROCK MECHANICS?

GÉOTHERMIQUE L'ÉNERGIE: NOUVELLE L'APPLICATION DE LA MÉCANIQUES DES ROCHES?

GEOTHERMISCHE ENERGIE: EINE NEUE ANWENDUNGSMETHODE AUF DEM GEBIETE DER FELS-MECHANIK?

J.C. ROEGIERS D.W. BROWN

Los Alamos Scientific Laboratory of the
University of California
Los Alamos, New Mexico

SUMMARY

A small group of scientists from the Los Alamos Scientific Laboratory has been working for the past 2 years in developing a new energy source based on the earth's heat. Their concept, the extraction of thermal energy from the numerous regions of the earth's crust containing hot--but essentially dry--rock at moderate depths, may offer a solution to the developing world energy crisis.

A deep exploratory hole has already been drilled into basement crystalline rock in north-central New Mexico and tested at various horizons. These experiments have demonstrated, at least in this one specific region, that a large vertical fracture system can be created in granitic rocks using conventional-hydraulic-fracturing techniques. Of more importance relative to the Los Alamos convective energy extraction concept, an open pressurized fracture system has been maintained in these crystalline rocks for many hours with only negligible fluid leak off. Further, an analysis of seismic signals resulting from the hydraulic fracturing process indicates tha a method may be available to determine both the orientation and vertical extent of the resulting fracture system

In conjunction with the <u>in situ</u> tests, theoretical and laboratory studies have been undertaken in order to fully understand the different features observed in the field fracturing experiments. Permeability tests under various stress conditions have revealed the importance of this factor, and have drastically changed the procedur for measuring stress at great depths using the hydraulic fracturing technique.

Geochemical problems associated with the dissolution of certain minerals are also being investigated. The variation in concentration of the materials contained in a closed-loop fracture circulation system could be an indicator of the fracture extension rate due to thermal contraction of the reservoir rock as energy is withdrawn from it. This concept, however, must be tested and will be investigated in a subsequent field experiment.

SOMMAIRE

Dans le cadre des travaux réalisés, depuis deux ans, au Laboratoire Scientifique de Los Alamos, une étude relative au développement d'une nouvelle source d'énergie - ayant comme origine la chaleur contenue à l'intérieur de l'écorce terrestre - a été entreprise par un groupe de chercheurs. Leur concept consiste à extraire de l'énergie thermique de régions contenant des roches chaudes, mais surtout sèches, se trouvant à des profondeurs modérées. Si cette technique s'avère efficace, elle présenterait une finalité pratique à la crise énergétique mondiale.

Un forage exploratoire atteignant la roche crystalline a déja été réalisé au Nord du Nouveau-Mexique et plusieurs expériences y furent conduites à diverses profondeurs. Elles démontrèrent que, dans une région au moin il fut possible de créer une fracture verticale dans la roche granitique en utilisant les techniques conventionnelles de fracturation hydraulique. Cette série de tests a aussi mis en évidence le fait que le système pouvait être maintenu sous pression pendant plusieurs heures, sans pour autant enregistrer des pertes de fluide considérables. Une analyse complémentaire des signaux séismiques, provenant de la fracturation hydraulique proprement dite, indiqua la possibilité d'utiliser cette technique afin de déterminer l'orientation et la géométrie spatiale du système de fractures.

Parallèlement aux essais sur champs, un programme d'études théoriques et d'expériences en laboratoire fut conduit afin de mieux justifier les résultats obtenus lors des essais in-situ. Des essais de perméabilité radiale sous contraintes révélèrent l'importance de ce facteur au point de modifier le procédé à suivre lors de la détermination des contraintes existant à grande profondeur au moyen de la fracturation hydraulique.

Des recherches ont également été entreprises concernant les problèmes géochimiques associés à la dissolution de certains minéraux contenus dans la formation rocheuse. On a observé que la variation en concentration de certains d'entre-eux pourrait indiquer, quantitativement, la vitesse d'extension du système de fracturations due à la contraction thermique du réservoir, au fur et à mesure que l'énergie en est extraite. Ce concept se doit toutefois d'être testé lors d'expériences futures sur champs.

ZUSAMMENFASSUNG

Wissenschaftler des Los Alamos Scientific Laboratory haben in den letzten zwei Jahren eine neue Energiequelle entwickelt, die die hohen inneren Temparaturen unserer Erde ausnuezt. Die Methode, die die Nutzung thermaler Energy in vielen Gebieten vorsieht, in denen die Erdkruste in geringer Tiefe aus heissem--hauptsaechlich trockenem --Gestein besteht, koennte die drohende Weltenergiekrise vermeiden.

Ein tiefes Bohrloch ist bereits zu Forschungszwecken in kristallinisches Grundgestein des noerdlichen, zentralen New Mexico gesenkt worden. Der Versuch hat erwiesen, dass, zumindest in diesem Gebiet, ein ausgedehntes System von Bruchrissen in Granit mit konventionellen hydraulischen Druckmethoden erzeugt werden kann. Von besonderer Bedeutung fuer das Los Alamos Konzept konvektieven Energieentzuges ist die Tatsache, dass das Bruchsystem in kristallinischem Gestein viele Stunden lang ohne nennenswerten Fluessigkeitsverlust unter Druck offen gehalten werden konnte. Auswertung der seismischen Signale, die von dem entstehendem Bruchsystem ausgingen, hat ausserdem ergeben, dass die Signale sowohl die Ausrichtung als auch die Tiefe der Bruchrisse anzeigen koennten.

Gleichzeitig mit dem in situ Test wurden theoretische und Laborversuche durchgefuehrt, um die verschiedentlichen waehrend des Tests beobachteten Merkmale zu erklaeren. Durchlaessigkeitsversuche unter verschiedenen Druckverhaeltnissen haben die Wichtigkeit dieses Faktors erwiesen und haben die Methode drastisch geaendert, mit der der hydraulisch erzeugte Druck in grosser Tiefe gemessen wird.

Geochemische Probleme, die mit der Loeslichkeit gewisser Minerale verbunden sind, werden auch untersucht. Die Konzentrationsschwankungen von Stoffen im geschlossenen Zirkulationssystem der Bruchrisse koennten anzeigen, wie rasch sich die Risse wegen thermaler Zusammenziehung ausweiten, wenn Energie aus dem Gesteinsreservoir entzogen wird. Diese Moeglichkeit wird in kommenden Gelaendeversuchen untersucht werden.

Introduction

Due to the energy crisis that the world is facing, the development of new resources--other than fossil fuel--is of great value and interest. Considering the amount of heat contained in the earth's crust, it is quite obvious that geothermal energy represents, theoretically, the largest energy reserve available to man. So far, this supply of usable energy has been generally ignored, except for a few natural hydrothermal regions, such as those located at Larderello, Italy; Cierro Prieto, Mexico; and The Geysers in California. Geothermal energy does not have the disadvantages associated with the use of the fossil resources. This energy already exists in the form of clean heat; and pollution--other than thermal--is avoided.

In nature, connecting water circulation channels in combination with overlying impermeable rock layers have produced natural steam reservoirs. However, this represents only a small portion of the very large energy resource available from "hot dry rock." The logical approach in developing a method to use this energy would be to create the circulation system in hot dry rocks that nature has failed to provide.

Technologically, it would appear that man-made geothermal systems are possible and that one could economically develop a method to extract this form of energy in the near future (Smith, 1973). Both the ideas and the tools to develop this resource are under active investigation at the Los Alamos Scientific Laboratory. If the system works, it will provide mankind with a significant new energy source, the extraction of which will not deteriorate our environment.

Potential of This Energy Resource

The largest part of the heat that is available underground is not yet accessible with today's existing technology. The magnitude of the usable geothermal resources will, consequently, increase with the degree to which any of these technological advancements can be achieved. Improvements need to be made in the following areas:

- Techniques of prospecting.
- Improvements in high temperature drilling technology.
- Detection of induced underground fracture systems from downhole measurements.
- Chemical and mechanical behavior of hot dry reservoirs.
- Heat transfer mechanisms in rock.

However, the relatively small amount of geothermal heat now available to man from hot dry rocks, and which could be extracted with present technology, is sufficient to satisfy the demand for several thousands of years.

If one considers, for example, a volume of granite of about 160 km^3, the amount of energy which could be extracted by cooling it by 200°C is of the order of 1.7×10^{19} calories, a number which corresponds to the total energy used in the United States in 1970. This volume of rock represents an infinitesimal quantity (5 km by 4 km by 8 km) of the total rock reservoir available for such purposes.

Site Selection

It was necessary that the dry hot rock geothermal demonstration be undertaken in a region where relatively impermeable rock at a usefully high temperature could be reached at reasonable cost. Somewhat arbitrarily, 200°C had been set as a minimum useful temperature and 10^{-17} m^2 was the permeability limit. In addition, the maximum depth to be considered, at least initially, was about 3500 m.

The site chosen for the project is situated in the Jemez Mountains in north-central New Mexico about 50 km from the Los Alamos Scientific Laboratory. The Jemez Mountains are part of the Southern Rockies and are located at the northern limit of the Rio Grande depression.

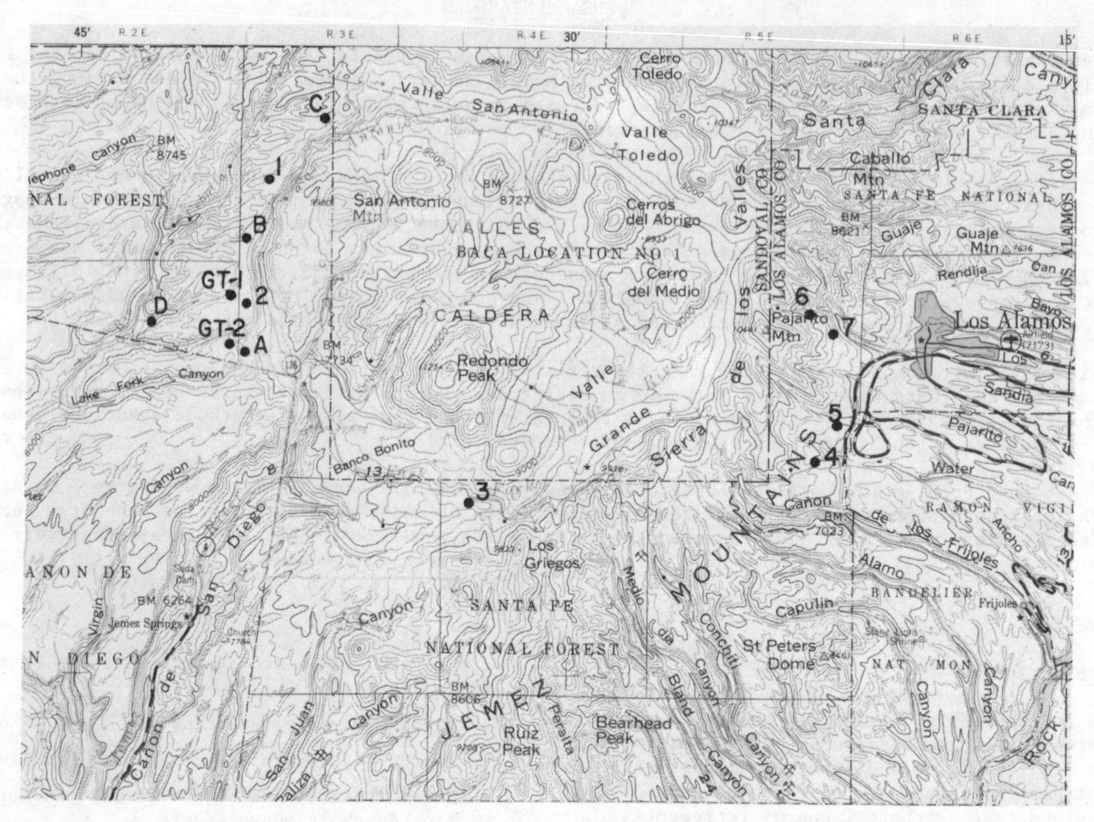

Figure 1 Regional map of the Valles Caldera (U.S.G.S. Map NI13-1; scale 1:250000; contour intervals: 200 ft).

This region had been tectonically active during most of geologic time and has, in recent time, been the site of large scale volcanic eruptions. As lavas and ashes accumulated, the eruptions were less frequent but more violent. The last one, the largest, produced a local tuff layer of about 300 m thick. The volcanic center later collapsed to form what is believed to be one of the largest calderas in the world (Purtymun, 1973; West, 1973). The Valle Grande, a valley nearly 12 km across, lies in this caldera.

The latest geothermal experimental site, referred to as GT-2, lies on the western outside slope of the caldera, at a distance of about 13 km from the center of it. Several exploratory boreholes were drilled around the edge of the caldera prior to this selection, and are indicated on the region map (Fig. 1).

In this particular locality, the heat flow measured *in situ* gives a value of about 5 cal/cm^2-sec (which is sufficient for the projected experiment) as compared to an average value of 1.5 cal/cm^2-sec for the total area of the earth's crust.

Extraction Techniques

The experiment involves drilling two holes of unequal depth (Fig. 2) into the hot basement rock, connecting them by means of a large crack that will furnish enough surface area to effectively transfer the heat from the rock to the circulation fluid (Brown et al, 1973; Smith, 1973a). The loop will be closed by means of a heat exchanger at the surface.

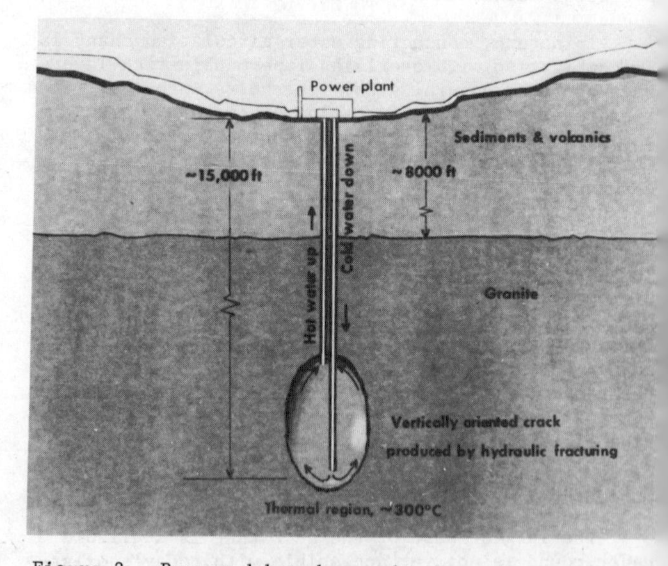

Figure 2 Proposed hot-dry rock extraction scheme.

The creation of the connecting fracture is based on the hydraulic fracturing technique that has been used for about 30 years in the oil industry. However, very few hydraulic fracture experiments have been carried out in crystalline formations, and the technique had to be adapted to the granitic basement rock in the experimental area (Roegiers et al, 1973; Roegiers, 1974).

Basically, the technique consists of drilling a borehole to the appropriate depth. A section of hole is then sealed off by means of packers and the pressure in the so-formed cavity is increased until a vertical fracture occurs. The breakdown of the borehole wall occurs as soon as the local stress concentration plus the tensile strength of the formation is overcome (Fairhurst, 1964). This is referred to as the intiation pressure, P_i. The fracture is then extended at a somewhat lower pressure, the propagating pressure, P_p; the value of which is very much dependent on the viscosity of the fluid and the pumping rate. At this stage, proppants may be added to keep the crack open after the pressure is released. Finally, when the fracture is sufficiently extended, pumping is stopped and the pressure rapidly drops to a lower value, the instantaneous shut-in pressure, P_{ISIP}, which is a very good approximation for the least *in situ* principal stress. It is worthwhile noting that the difference between the values of P_p and P_{ISIP} depends on the fracture extent--it is almost negligible for a very large fracture. (Experimental work has recently been done in the U.S.S.R. where a hydraulic fracture has been continuously pumped for 24 consecutive hours and has proven that statement.)

From the spatial geometry of an induced fracture, one can determine the orientation of the stress vector since the propagation of the crack occurs in a direction perpendicular to the least principal compressive stress.

We, consequently, propose to drill a borehole of 2750 m depth in order to attain a temperature of about 250°C in the basement granite rock. After having induced a fracture of more than a 500 m radius, a second shallower borehole will be drilled to intersect the fracture plane. The deepest borehole will be used to inject the fluid, which will travel through the fracture, absorb heat and be returned to the surface. Additional fluid will be added as required to make up for permeability losses and for rock shrinkage due to cooling.

Due to the density differences between the injected relatively cool fluid and the heat effluent, a spontaneous circulation may develop and no pumping facility will be needed. The system will be operated under pressure to avoid the production of steam.

The system described above is believed to be capable of producing about 100 MW of power (corresponding to 20 MW electrical). However, if the fracture network propagates further as the rock cools off, the lifetime of the system and the power generated could very well increase.

As will be seen, the development of the dry geothermal energy concept involves several rock mechanics problems which are at the present time under investigation, both in the field and on laboratory scale.

Field Testing

Prior to drilling the present test hole, several exploratory holes were drilled to determine the area of highest temperature gradient and the simplest geology. The holes had an average depth of 200 m and were located in an arc around the west side of the caldera. This preliminary investigation showed that the temperature gradient rapidly decreases as one goes away from the center of the caldera (Smith, 1973b).

A first deep borehole, designated as GT-1, was then drilled to a depth of 760 m, the last 120 m being in the Precambrian granite rock. The rock formation at that depth varied between a granitic gneiss and an amphibolite. Several vertical hydraulic fractures were then induced at surface pressures between 8.1 x 10^6 and 15.7 x 10^6 Pa. The general orientation of the fractures was NW/SE. The temperature at the bottom of the borehole stabilized at 100.4°C, which indicated that the heat gradient interpolations made from the previous exploratory holes were reasonable. The cores obtained from near the bottom of the hole indicated a very competent rock; *in situ* tests verified that fractures could be maintained open at fluid pressures of 6 x 10^6 Pa.

The following table summarizes the various hydraulic fracturing tests which were undertaken in GT-1. The pressures were measured at the surface; σ_3 referring to the smallest *in situ* principal compressive stress.

TABLE I

RESULTS OF HYDRAULIC FRACTURING TESTS PERFORMED ON GT-1

	Pressures			
Date	Depth (m)	Breakdown (10^6)	ISIP (Pa)	σ_3 (10^6 Pa)
7/3	761	9.10	7.94	15.55
14/3	730	15.66	13.38	20.67
21/3	751	9.52	8.05	15.56
23/3	776	9.10	--	--
24/3	740	8.07	6.99	14.39
27/3	748	11.74	8.96	16.44
28/3	745	10.41	7.41	14.86

Making the usual assumptions of elasticity would allow us to compute the value of the second horizontal principal stress, this can however be of very dubious value as we will see later.

Another approach to compute the stresses is to use energy considerations (Aamodt, 1974). By successively inducing a fracture, letting it collapse and repressurizing it, we were able to compare the energies involved. Knowing the specific fracturing energy (α), Young's modulus (E), and Poisson's ratio (ν), an equation of energy balance can be written as follows.

$$\left.\begin{array}{l}\text{Work to extend fracture}\\ \text{Work to reopen pre-existing fracture}\end{array}\right\} 2\pi\,\alpha R^2$$

Where R is the crack radius.

Introducing then Sneddon's and Sack's equations, we end up with a system of three equations between the three unknowns $(P - \sigma_3)$, α and R. The value of the least compressive stress, σ_3, is finally computed knowing that the work needed to reopen a pre-existing fracture of volume, V, is given by

$$U_r = \frac{(P + \sigma_3)V}{2} .$$

By applying this technique to the test performed in GT-1, we obtained

$$\sigma_3 = 14.7 \times 10^6 \text{ Pa}.$$

The value of σ_3 compares very well with the one obtained from the pressure curve.

Seismic Detection of Fracturing Events

One of the most significant results obtained from the recent series of rock mechanics experiments performed in GT-1 was the seismic detection, at the surface, of downhole fracturing events (Potter et al, 1974). Although no seismic signals were detected at the surface during the extensive series of small-scale (about 3 m high) hydraulic fracturing experiments, seismic signals were obtained both during and following the formation of the final large (about 34 m high) hydraulic fracture.

Of particular note was a large seismic event that occurred some 6 sec after the termination of pumping on the final large hydraulic fracture. This event, as shown in Fig. 3, was preceded by a large damped pressure oscillation with an initial peak-to-peak variation of 5×10^6 Pa. It is postulated that this seismic event was related to the preceding shut-in-induced large-scale pressure oscillation, which may have resulted in the broaching of the lower packer. The significant shear component recorded by the vertical seismometer channel would support this hypothesis, for a suddenly extending fracture in an inclined borehole.

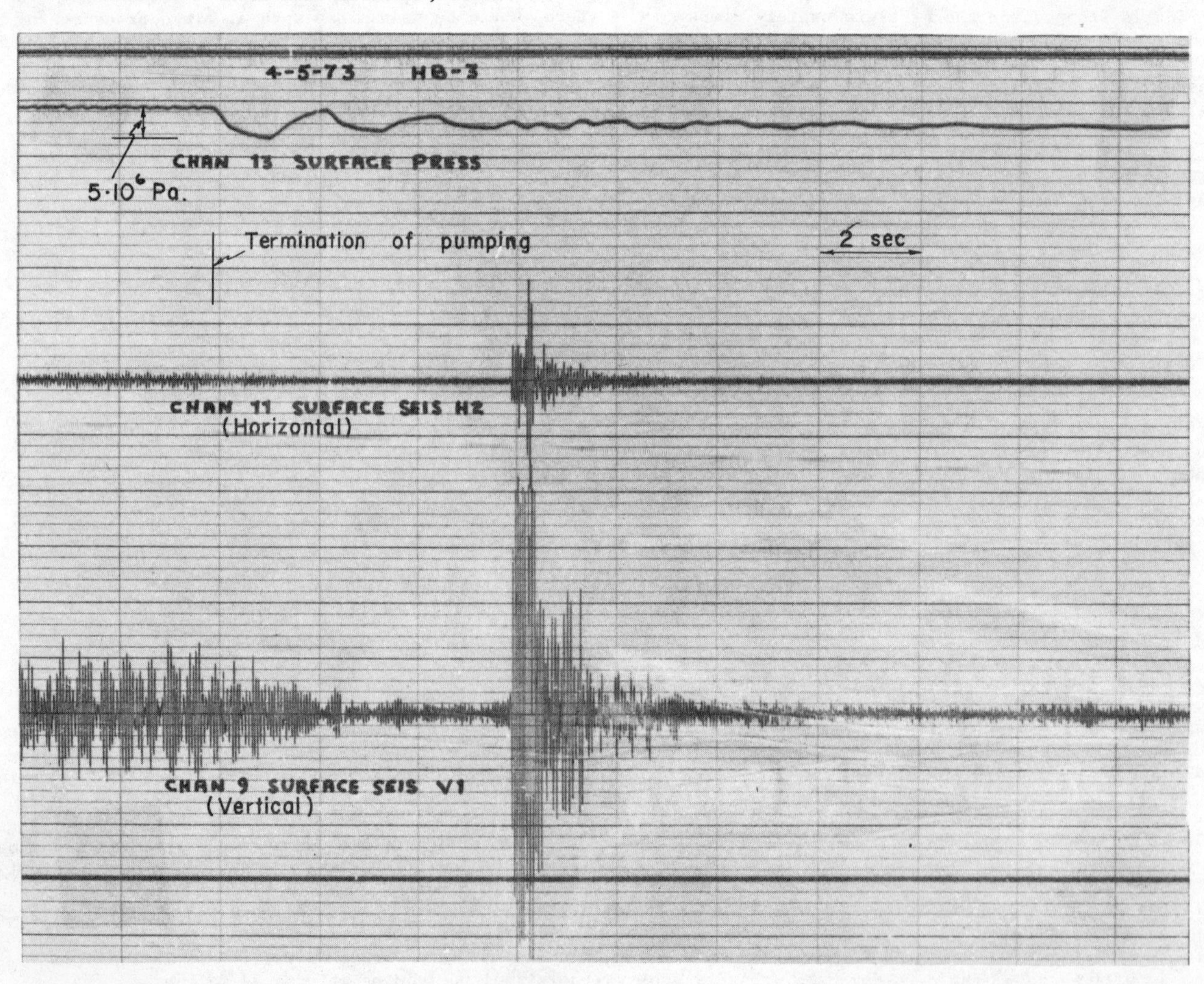

Figure 3 Seismic surface recordings during a typical hydraulic fracturing test in GT-1.

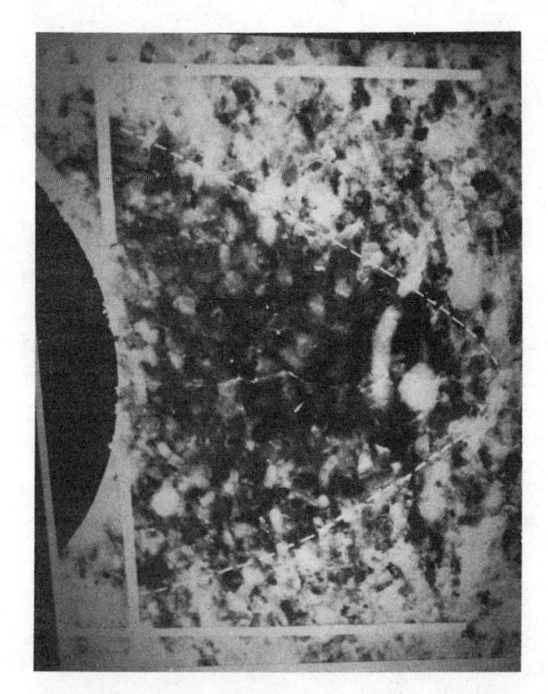

Figure 4 Close up of cross-section of granite specimen. (Note the arrowhead fluid penetration surrounding a fracture which has been propagated and stopped halfway through the specimen).

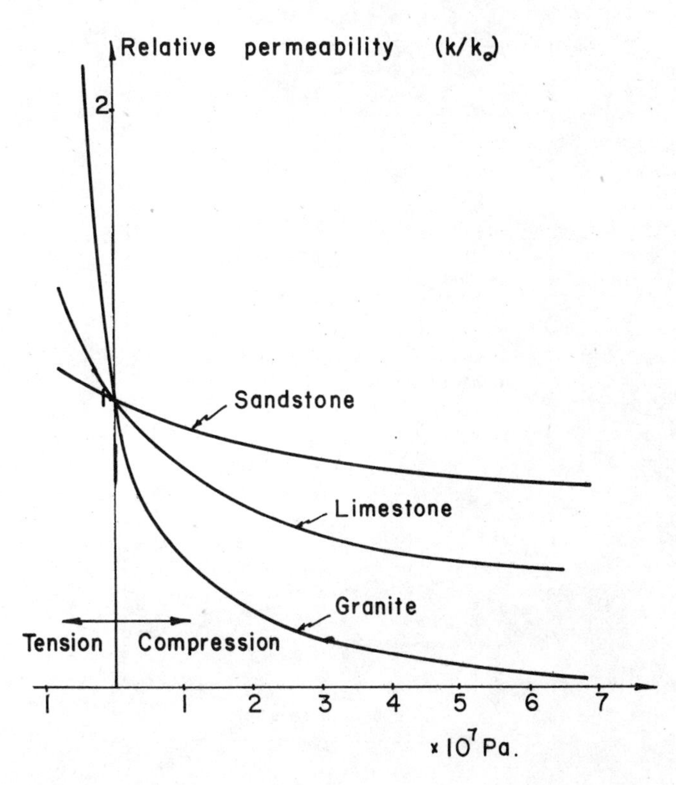

Figure 5 Schematic representation of relative permeability variations.

Laboratory Tests

Two laboratory research projects are in direct relationship with the Geothermal Energy Program. One concerns the effects of the stress field on the permeability coefficient and the other is associated with the induced fracture geometry.

In the Dry Hot Rock Geothermal Demonstration, a hydraulically induced fracture will provide the man-made circulation system. Although there seems to be no doubt that this fracture will propagate in a direction perpendicular to the least compressive stress (Haimson, 1968), many assumptions have to be made to compute the horizontal principal stress acting parallel to the plane of the crack. The accuracy of the usual analytical approach using elasticity theory is doubtful because laboratory tests have shown that various loading rates lead to different values of the breakdown pressure. The problem seems to be the unknown stress concentration around the borehole which has to be overcome if a fracture is to be created. This stress concentration is very dependent on the fluid percolation rate prior to fracture initiation. Consequently, the variation in permeability as a function of applied stress is a factor of major importance (Roegiers, 1974). If even a small amount of fluid percolates though microcracks, it will induce a body force which will influence the value of the breakdown pressure.

Up until now, granite has been generally considered impermeable (Fig. 4). Its permeability is probably very low indeed, but the relative change in permeability under compressive and tensile stresses is enormous compared to a limestone or a sandstone (Fig. 5). In a borehole, the granite is subjected to a circumferential tensile stress field prior to fracture initiation. Percolation occurs under these conditions and the breakdown pressure changes, which is contrary to what elasticity theory would predict. Nevertheless, the value of the breakdown pressure decreases as the permeability increases. For instance, on a saturated laboratory sample of granite, under tensile stress, the breakdown pressure can be decreased to as low as 5.10^6 Pa, as compared to the usual value of 1.5×10^7 Pa generally given in the literature (Fig. 6). The conclusion is that the assumed value of the breakdown pressure can only be used if preliminary laboratory tests have first been undertaken to determine if the percolation rate changes under the applied stress conditions.

An additional important problem is the detection of the fracture geometry at some distance from the borehole. The solution of this problem would have a tremendous impact in several ways. We would not only be able to detect variation in the orientation of the stress tensor from the side of the borehole, but the problem of trying to intersect the fracture by means of an additional borehole would be much easier.

Model studies using the first arrival refraction wave method have shown that acoustic detection can be used to determine the extent and the orientation of an induced fracture (Fig. 7). The compressional P waves refract at the tip of the crack and by placing an emitter and receiver on each side of the crack, the travel time to the tip of the crack and back can be determined. Two different measurements are sufficient

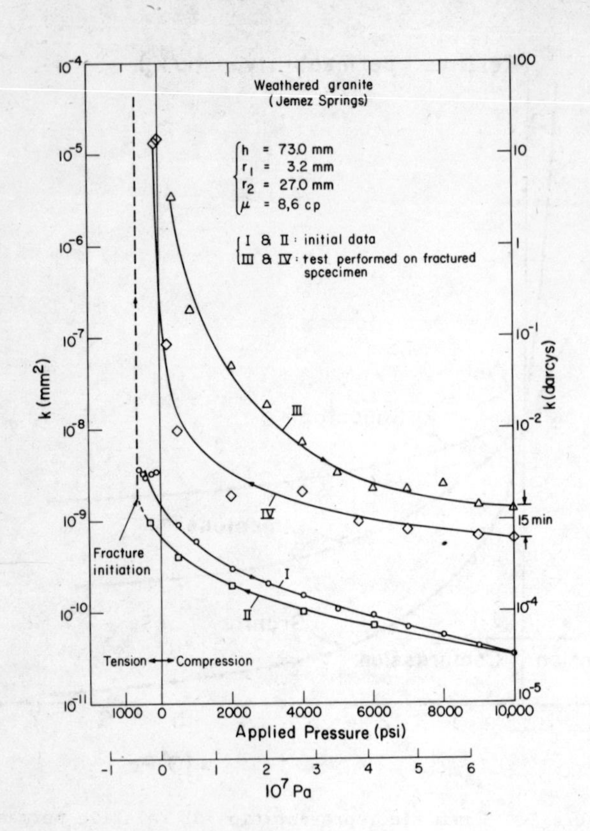

Figure 6 Permeability variation of granite specimen (intact and fractured).

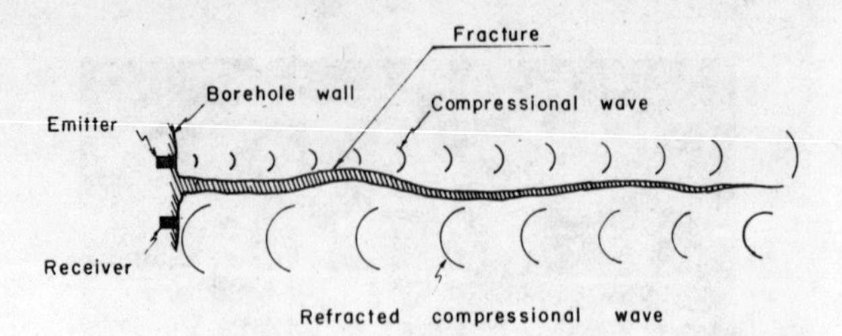

Figure 7 Schematic representation of the first refraction technique.

to locate the crack tip. Several tests were also conducted with a water-filled crack and the fluid seems not to alter the method.

Conclusions

Although hydraulic fracturing is a well known technique, many refinements in measuring and calculating rock stresses are needed for future geothermal energy extraction experiments. Several additional research topics in rock mechanics definitely need to be developed to better utilize the natural heat of the earth. Another important need is the development of more efficient air drilling methods operable at temperatures reaching 400°C. Also, downhole measuring instruments will have to be produced which are heat and corrosion resistant.

In order to break away from the conventional natural steam systems used in the past, a better understanding of dry hot rock reservoir behavior will be required for the successful formation of artificial hot water systems. These problems offer many new challenges to the science of rock mechanics.

Acknowledgments

The authors would like to thank Mr. Osamu Kudo from Tiekoku Oil Company for his help in setting up the active acoustic fracture detection method.

References

Smith, M. C., 1973, "The Potential for the Production of Power from Geothermal Resources," statement before the Subcommittee on Water and Power Resources, Committee on Interior and Insular Affairs, U. S. Senate.

Purtymun, W. D., 1973, "Geology of the Jemez Plateau West of Valles Caldera," Los Alamos Scientific Laboratory report LA-5124-MS.

West, F. G., 1973, "Regional Geology and Geophysics of the Jemez Mountains," Los Alamos Scientific Laboratory report LA-5362-MS.

Brown, D. W., Smith, M. C., and Potter, R. M., 1973, "A New Method for Extracting Energy from 'Dry' Geothermal Reservoirs," Los Alamos Scientific Laboratory internal report LA-DC-72-1157.

Smith, M. C., 1973, "The Los Alamos Geothermal Energy Project," Los Alamos Scientific Laboratory internal report LA-UR-73-1028.

Roegiers, J. C. and Fairhurst, C., 1973, "The D. S. P.- A New Instrument for Estimation of the In Situ Stress State at Depth," 6th Conference on Drilling of Rock Mechanics, Austin, Texas.

Roegiers, J. C., 1974, "The Development and Evaluation of a Field Method for In Situ Stress Determination Using Hydraulic Fracturing," Ph. D. Thesis, University of Minnesota.

Fairhurst, C., 1964, "Measurement of In Situ Rock Stresses with Particular Reference to Hydraulic Fracturing," Felsmechanik und Ingenienvsgeologic, Vol. II.

Smith, M. C., 1973, "Geothermal Energy," Los Alamos Scientific Laboratory report LA-5289-MS.

Potter, R. M. and Dennis, B. R., 1974, "Seismic and Fluid Pressure Response from a Series of Hydraulic Fractures in Granite," 55th Annual A.G.U. Meeting, Washington, D. C.

Haimson, B. C., 1968, "Hydraulic Fracturing in Porous and Nonporous Rock and Its Potential for Determining In Situ Stresses at Great Depths," Ph. D. Thesis, University of Minnesota.